THE MONEYCHANGERS

Novels by Arthur Hailey

Collected Plays

The Moneychangers

ARTHUR HAILEY

DOUBLEDAY & COMPANY, INC., GARDEN CITY, NEW YORK

FICTION

175257

> If thou art rich, thou'rt poor;
> For, like an ass whose back with ingots bows,
> Thou bear'st thy heavy riches but a journey,
> And death unloads thee.
>
> Shakespeare, *Measure for Measure*

> Foul-cank'ring rust the hidden treasure frets,
> But gold that's put to use more gold begets.
>
> *Venus and Adonis*

THE MONEYCHANGERS

PART ONE

1

Long afterward, many would remember those two days in the first week of October with vividness and anguish.

It was on Tuesday of that week that old Ben Rosselli, president of First Mercantile American Bank and grandson of the bank's founder, made an announcement—startling and somber—which reverberated through every segment of the bank and far beyond. And the next day, Wednesday, the bank's "flagship" downtown branch discovered the presence of a thief—beginning a series of events which few could have foreseen, and ending in financial wreckage, human tragedy, and death.

The bank president's announcement occurred without warning; remarkably, there were no advance leaks. Ben Rosselli had telephoned a few of his senior executives early in the morning, catching some at home at breakfast, others soon after their arrival at work. There were a few, too, who were not executives, simply longtime employees whom old Ben thought of as his friends.

To each, the message was the same: Please be in the Headquarters Tower boardroom at 11 A.M.

Now all except Ben were assembled in the boardroom, twenty or so, talking quietly in groups, waiting. All were standing; no one chose to be first to pull a chair back from the gleaming directors' table, longer than a squash court, which seated forty.

A voice cut sharply across the talk. "Who authorized that?"

Heads turned. Roscoe Heyward, executive vice-president and comptroller, had addressed a white-coated waiter from the senior officers' dining room. The man had come in with decanters of sherry which he was pouring into glasses.

Heyward, austere, Olympian in FMA, was a zealous teetotaler. He glanced pointedly at his watch in a gesture which said clearly: Not only drinking, but this *early*. Several who had been reaching out for the sherry withdrew their hands.

"Mr. Rosselli's instructions, sir," the waiter stated. "And he especially ordered the best sherry."

A stocky figure, fashionably dressed in light gray, turned and said easily, "Whatever time it is, no sense passing up the best."

Alex Vandervoort, blue-eyed and fair-haired with a touch of gray at the temples, was also an executive vice-president. Genial and informal, his easygoing, "with-it" ways belied the tough decisiveness beneath. The two men—Heyward and Vandervoort—represented the second management echelon immediately below the presidency and, while each was seasoned and capable of co-operation, they were, in many ways, rivals. Their rivalry, and differing viewpoints, permeated the bank, giving each a retinue of supporters at lower levels.

Now Alex took two glasses of sherry, passing one to Edwina D'Orsey, brunette and statuesque, FMA's ranking woman executive.

Edwina saw Heyward glance toward her, disapproving. Well, it made little difference, she thought. Roscoe knew she was a loyalist in the Vandervoort camp.

"Thank you, Alex," she said, and took the glass.

There was a moment's tension, then others followed the example.

Roscoe Heyward's face tightened angrily. He appeared about to say something more, then changed his mind.

At the boardroom doorway the vice-president for Security, Nolan Wainwright, a towering, Othello-like figure and one of two black executives present, raised his voice. "Mrs. D'Orsey and gentlemen—Mr. Rosselli."

The hum of conversation stopped.

Ben Rosselli stood there, smiling slightly, as his eyes passed over the group. As always, his appearance seemed to strike a median point between a benevolent father figure and the strong solidity of one to whom thousands of fellow citizens entrusted money for safekeeping. He looked both parts, and dressed them: in statesman-banker black, with the inevitable vest, across its front a thin gold chain and fob. And it was striking how closely this man resembled the first Rosselli—Giovanni —who had founded the bank in the basement of a grocery store a century ago. It was Giovanni's patrician head, with flowing silver hair and full mustache, which the bank reproduced on passbooks and travelers checks as a symbol of probity, and whose bust adorned Rosselli Plaza down below.

The here-and-now Rosselli had the silver hair and mustache, almost as luxuriant. Fashion across a century had revolved full circle. But what no reproduction showed was the family drive which all Rossellis had possessed and which, with ingenuity and boundless energy, raised First Mercantile American to its present eminence. Today, though, in Ben Rosselli the usual liveliness seemed missing. He was walking with the aid of a cane; no one present had seen him do so before.

Now he reached out, as if to pull one of the heavy directors' chairs toward him. But Nolan Wainwright, who was nearest, moved more quickly. The security chief swung the chair around, its high back to the boardroom table. With a murmur of thanks the president settled into it.

Ben Rosselli waved a hand to the others. "This is informal. Won't take long. If you like, pull chairs around. Ah, thank you." The last remark was to the waiter from whom he accepted a glass of sherry. The man went out, closing the boardroom doors behind him.

Someone moved a chair for Edwina D'Orsey, and a few others seated themselves, but most remained standing.

It was Alex Vandervoort who said, "We're obviously here to celebrate." He motioned with his sherry glass. "The question is—what?"

Ben Rosselli again smiled fleetingly. "I wish this were a celebration, Alex. It's simply an occasion when I thought a drink might help." He paused, and suddenly a new tension permeated the room. It was evident to everyone now that this was no ordinary meeting. Faces mirrored uncertainty, concern.

"I'm dying," Ben Rosselli said. "My doctors tell me I don't have long. I thought all of you should know." He raised his own glass, contemplated it, and took a sip of sherry.

Where the boardroom had been quiet before, now the silence was intense. No one moved or spoke. Exterior sounds intruded faintly; the muted tapping of a typewriter, an air-conditioning hum; somewhere outside a whining jet plane climbed above the city.

Old Ben leaned forward on his cane. "Come now, let's not be embarrassed. We're all old friends; it's why I called you here. And, oh yes, to save anyone asking, what I've told you is definite; if I thought there was a chance it wasn't, I'd have waited longer. The other thing you may be wondering—the trouble is lung cancer, well advanced I'm told. It's probable I won't see Christmas." He paused and suddenly all the frailty and fatigue showed. More softly he added, "So now that you know, and as and when you choose, you can pass the word to others."

Edwina D'Orsey thought: there would be no choosing the time. The moment the boardroom emptied, what they had just heard would spread through the bank, and beyond, like prairie fire. The news would affect many—some emotionally, others more prosaically. But mostly she was dazed and sensed the reaction of others was the same.

"Mr. Ben," one of the older men volunteered. Pop Monroe was a senior clerk in the trust department, and his voice was wavering. "Mr. Ben, I guess you floored us good. I reckon nobody knows what the hell to say."

There was a murmur, almost a groan, of assent and sympathy.

Above it, Roscoe Heyward injected smoothly, "What we can say, and must"—there was a hint of reproof in the comptroller's voice, as if others should have waited to allow him to speak first—"is that while this terrible news has shocked and saddened us, we pray there may be leeway and hope in the matter of time. Doctors' opinions, as most of us know, are seldom exact. And medical science can achieve a great deal in halting, even curing . . ."

"Roscoe, I said I'd been over all that," Ben Rosselli said, betraying his first trace of testiness. "And as to doctors, I've had the best. Wouldn't you expect me to?"

"Yes, I would," Heyward said. "But we should remember there is a higher power than doctors and it must be the duty of us all"—he glanced pointedly around the room—"to pray to God for mercy, or at least more time than you believe."

The older man said wryly, "I get the impression God has already made up his mind."

Alex Vandervoort observed, "Ben, we're all upset. I'm especially sorry for something I said earlier."

"About celebrating? Forget it!—you didn't know." The old man chuckled. "Besides, why not? I've had a good life; not everyone does, so surely that's a cause to celebrate." He patted his suit coat pockets, then looked around him. "Anybody have a cigarette? Those doctors cut me off."

Several packs appeared. Roscoe Heyward queried, "Are you sure you should?"

Ben Rosselli looked at him sardonically but failed to answer. It was no secret that while the older man respected Heyward's talents as a banker, the two had never achieved a personal closeness.

Alex Vandervoort lighted the cigarette which the bank president took. Alex's eyes, like others in the room, were moist.

"At a time like this there are some things to be glad of," Ben said. "Being given a little warning is one, the chance to tie loose ends." Smoke from his cigarette curled around him. "Of course, on the other side, there're regrets for the way a few things went. You sit and think about those, too."

No one had to be told of one regret—Ben Rosselli had no heir. An only son had been killed in action in World War II; more recently a promising grandson had died amid the senseless waste of Vietnam.

A fit of coughing seized the old man. Nolan Wainwright, who was nearest, reached over, accepted the cigarette from shaking fingers and stubbed it out. Now it became evident how weakened Ben Rosselli really was, how much the effort of today had tired him.

Though no one knew it, it was the last time he would be present at the bank.

They went to him individually, shaking his hand gently, groping for words to say. When Edwina D'Orsey's turn came, she kissed him lightly on the cheek and he winked.

2

Roscoe Heyward was one of the first to leave the boardroom. The executive vice-president-comptroller had two urgent objectives, resulting from what he had just learned.

One was to ensure a smooth transition of authority after Ben Rosselli's death. The second objective was to ensure his own appointment as president and chief executive.

Heyward was already a strong candidate. So was Alex Vandervoort and possibly, within the bank itself, Alex had the larger following. However, on the board of directors, where it counted most, Heyward believed his own support was greater.

Wise in the ways of bank politics and with a disciplined, steely mind, Heyward had begun planning his campaign, even while this morning's boardroom session was in progress. Now he headed for his office suite, paneled rooms with deep beige broadloom and a breathtaking view of the city far below. Seated at his desk, he summoned the senior of his two secretaries, Mrs. Callaghan, and gave her rapid-fire instructions.

The first was to reach by telephone all outside directors, whom Roscoe Heyward would talk to, one by one. He had a list of directors on the desk before him. Apart from the special phone calls, he was not to be disturbed.

Another instruction was to close the outer office door as she left—in itself unusual since FMA executives observed an open-door tradition, begun a century ago and stolidly upheld by Ben Rosselli. That was one tradition which had to go. Privacy, at this moment, was essential.

Heyward had been quick to observe at this morning's session that only two members of First Mercantile American's board, other than the senior management officers, were present. Both directors were personal friends of Ben Rosselli—obviously the reason they had been called in. But it meant that fifteen members of the board were uninformed, so far, of the impending death. Heyward would make sure that all fifteen received the news personally from him.

He calculated two probabilities: First, the facts were so sudden and shattering that there would be an instinctive alliance between anyone receiving the news and whoever conveyed it. Second, some directors might resent not having been informed in advance, particularly before some of FMA's rank and file who heard the announcement in the boardroom. Roscoe Heyward intended to capitalize on this resentment.

A buzzer sounded. He took the first call and began to talk. Another call followed, and another. Several directors were out of the city but Dora Callaghan, an experienced, loyal aide, was tracking them down.

A half hour after he began phoning, Roscoe Heyward was informing the Honorable Harold Austin earnestly, "Here at the bank, of course, we're overwhelmingly emotional and distressed. What Ben told us simply does not seem possible or real."

"Dear God!" The other voice on the telephone still reflected the dismay expressed moments earlier. "And to have to let people know personally!" Harold Austin was one of the city's pillars, third generation old family, and long ago he served a single term in Congress—hence the title "honorable," a usage he encouraged. Now he owned the state's largest advertising agency and was a veteran director of the bank with strong influence on the board.

The comment about a personal announcement gave Heyward the opening he needed. "I understand exactly what you mean about the method of letting this be known, and frankly it did seem unusual. What concerned me most is that the directors were not informed first. I felt they should have been. But since they weren't, I considered it my duty to advise you and the others immediately." Heyward's aquiline, austere face showed concentration; behind rimless glasses his gray eyes were cool.

"I agree with you, Roscoe," the voice on the telephone said. "I believe we should have been told, and I appreciate your thinking."

"Thank you, Harold. At a time like this, one is never sure exactly what is best. The only thing certain is that someone must exercise leadership."

The use of first names came easily to Heyward. He was old family himself, knew his way around most of the power bases in the state, and was a member in good standing of what the British call the old boy network. His personal connections extended far beyond state boundaries, to Washington and elsewhere. Heyward was proud of his social status and friendships in high places. He also liked to remind people of his own direct descent from one of the signers of the Declaration of Independence.

Now he suggested, "Another reason for keeping board members informed is that this sad news about Ben is going to have tremendous impact. And it will travel quickly."

"No doubt of it," the Honorable Harold concurred. "Chances are, by tomorrow, the press will have heard and will be asking questions."

"Exactly. And the wrong kind of publicity could make depositors uneasy as well as depress the price of our stock."

"Um."

Roscoe Heyward could sense wheels turning in his fellow director's mind. The Austin Family Trust, which the Honorable Harold represented, held a big block of FMA shares.

Heyward prompted, "Of course, if the board takes energetic action to reassure shareholders and depositors, also the public generally, the entire effect could be negligible."

"Except for the friends of Ben Rosselli," Harold Austin reminded him drily.

"I was speaking entirely outside the framework of personal loss. My grief, I assure you, is as profound as anyone's."

"Just what do you have in mind, Roscoe?"

"In general, Harold—a continuity of authority. Specifically, there should be no vacancy in the office of chief executive, even for a day." Heyward continued, "With the greatest of respect to Ben, and notwithstanding all our deep affection for him, this bank has been regarded for too long as a one-man institution. Of course, it hasn't been that way for many years; no bank can achieve a place among the nation's top twenty and still be individually run. But there are those, outside, who think it is. That's why, sad as this time is, the directors have an opportunity to act to dissipate that legend."

Heyward sensed the other man thinking cagily before answering. He could visualize Austin, too—a handsome, aging playboy type, flamboyant dresser and with styled and flowing iron-gray hair. Probably, as usual, he was smoking a large cigar. Yet the Honorable Harold was nobody's fool and had a reputation as a shrewd, successful businessman. At length he declared, "I think your point about continuity is valid. And I agree with you that Ben Rosselli's successor needs to be decided on, and probably his name announced before Ben's death."

Heyward listened intently as the other went on.

"I happen to think you are that man, Roscoe. I have for a long time. You've the qualities, experience, the toughness, too. So I'm willing to pledge you my support and there are others on the board whom I can persuade to go the same route with me. I assume you'd wish that."

"I'm certainly grateful . . ."

"Of course, in return I may ask an occasional *quid pro quo.*"

"That's reasonable."

"Good! Then we understand each other."

The conversation, Roscoe Heyward decided as he hung up the phone, had been eminently satisfactory. Harold Austin was a man of consistent loyalties who kept his word.

The preceding phone calls had been equally successful.

Speaking with another director soon after—Philip Johannsen, president of MidContinent Rubber—another opportunity arose. Johannsen volunteered that frankly he didn't get along with Alex Vandervoort whose ideas he found unorthodox.

"Alex *is* unorthodox," Heyward said. "Of course he has some personal problems. I'm not sure how much the two things go together."

"What kind of problems?"

"It's women actually. One doesn't like to . . ."

"This is important, Roscoe. It's also confidential. Go ahead."

"Well, first, Alex has marital difficulties. Second, he's involved with another woman, as well. Third, she's a left-wing activist, frequently in the news, and not in the kind of context which would be helpful to the bank. I sometimes wonder how much influence she has on Alex. As I said, one doesn't like to . . ."

"You were right to tell me, Roscoe," Johannsen said. "It's something the directors ought to know. Left-wing, eh?"

"Yes. Her name is Margot Bracken."

"I think I've heard of her. And what I've heard I haven't liked."

Heyward smiled.

He was less pleased, however, two telephone calls later, when he reached an out-of-town director, Leonard L. Kingswood, chairman of the board of Northam Steel.

Kingswood, who began his working life as a furnace melder in a steel plant, said, "Don't hand me that line of bullshit, Roscoe," when Heyward suggested that the bank's directors should have had advance warning of Ben Rosselli's statement. "The way Ben handled it is the way I'd have done myself. Tell the people you're closest to first, directors and other stuffed shirts later."

As to the possibility of a price decline in First Mercantile American stock, Len Kingswood's reaction was, "So what?"

"Sure," he added, "FMA will dip a point or two on the Big Board when this news gets out. It'll happen because most stock transactions are on behalf of nervous nellies who can't distinguish between hysteria and fact. But just as surely the stock will go back up within a week because the value's there, the bank is sound, and all of us on the inside know it."

And later in the conversation: "Roscoe, this lobbying job of yours is as transparent as a fresh washed window, so I'll make my position just as plain, which should save us both some time.

"You're a topflight comptroller, the best numbers and money man I know anywhere. And any day you get an urge to move over here with Northam, with a fatter paycheck and a stock option, I'll shuffle my own people and put you at the top of our financial pile. That's an offer and a promise. I mean it."

The steel company chairman brushed aside Heyward's murmured thanks as he went on.

"But good as you are, Roscoe, the point I'm making is—you're not an over-all leader. At least, that's the way I see it, also the way I'll call it when the board convenes to decide on who's to follow Ben. The other thing I may as well tell you is that my choice is Vandervoort. I think you ought to know that."

Heyward answered evenly, "I'm grateful for your frankness, Leonard."

"Right. And if ever you think seriously about that other, call me anytime."

Roscoe Heyward had no intention of working for Northam Steel. Though money was important to him, his pride would not permit it after Leonard Kingswood's biting verdict of a moment earlier. Besides, he was still fully confident of obtaining the top role at FMA.

Again the telephone buzzed. When he answered, Dora Callaghan announced that one more director was on the line. "It's Mr. Floyd LeBerre."

"Floyd," Heyward began, his voice pitched low and serious, "I'm deeply sorry to be the one to convey some sad and tragic news."

3

Not all who had been at the momentous boardroom session left as speedily as Roscoe Heyward. A few lingered outside, still with a sense of shock, conversing quietly.

The old-timer from the trust department, Pop Monroe, said softly to Edwina D'Orsey, "This is a sad, sad day."

Edwina nodded, not ready yet to speak. Ben Rosselli had been important to her as a friend and he had taken pride in her rise to authority in the bank.

Alex Vandervoort stopped beside Edwina, then motioned to his office several doors away. "Do you want to take a few minutes out?"

She said gratefully, "Yes, please."

The offices of the bank's top echelon executives were on the same floor as the boardroom—the 36th, high in FMA Headquarters Tower. Alex Vandervoort's suite, like others here, had an informal conference area and there Edwina poured herself coffee from a Silex. Vandervoort produced a pipe and lit it. She observed his fingers moving efficiently, with no waste motion. His hands were like his body, short and broad, the fingers ending abruptly with stubby but well-manicured nails.

The camaraderie between the two was of long standing. Although Edwina, who managed First Mercantile American's main downtown branch, was several levels lower than Alex in the bank's hierarchy, he had always treated her as an equal and often, in matters affecting her branch, dealt with her directly, bypassing the layers of organization between them.

"Alex," Edwina said, "I meant to tell you you're looking like a skeleton."

A warm smile lit up his smooth, round face. "Shows, eh?"

Alex Vandervoort was a committed partygoer, and loved gourmet food and wine. Unfortunately he put on weight easily. Periodically, as now, he went on diets.

By unspoken consent they avoided, for the moment, the subject closest to their minds.

He asked, "How's business at the branch this month?"

"Excellent. And I'm optimistic about next year."

"Speaking of next year, how does Lewis view it?" Lewis D'Orsey, Edwina's husband, was owner-publisher of a widely read investors newsletter.

"Gloomily. He foresees another big drop in the value of the dollar."

"I agree with him." Alex mused, "You know, Edwina, one of the failures of American banking is that we've never encouraged our clients to hold accounts in foreign currencies—Swiss francs, Deutsche marks, others—as European bankers do. Oh, we accommodate the big corporations because they know enough to insist; and American banks make generous profits from other currencies for themselves. But rarely, if ever, for the small or medium depositors. If we'd promoted European currency accounts ten or even five years ago, some of our customers would have gained from dollar devaluations instead of lost."

"Wouldn't the U. S. Treasury object?"

"Probably. But they'd back down under public pressure. They always do."

Edwina asked, "Have you ever broached the idea—of more people having foreign currency accounts?"

"I tried once. I was shot down. Among us American bankers the dollar—no matter how weak—is sacred. It's a head-in-sand concept we've forced upon the public and it's cost them money. Only a sophisticated few had the sense to open Swiss bank accounts before the dollar devaluations came."

"I've often thought about that," Edwina said. "Each time it happened, bankers knew in advance that devaluation was inevitable. Yet we gave our customers—except for a favored few—no warning, no suggestion to sell dollars."

"It was supposed to be unpatriotic. Even Ben . . ."

Alex stopped. They sat for several moments without speaking.

Through the wall of windows which made up the east side of Alex's office suite they could see the robust Midwest city spread before them. Closest to hand were the business canyons of downtown, the larger buildings only a little lower than First Mercantile American's Headquarters Tower. Beyond the downtown district, coiled in a double-S, was the wide, traffic-crowded river, its color—today as usual—pollution gray. A tangled latticework of river bridges, rail lines, and freeways ran outward like unspooled ribbons to industrial complexes and suburbs in the distance, the latter sensed rather than seen in an all-pervading haze. But nearer than the industry and suburbs, though beyond the river, was the inner residential city, a labyrinth of predominantly substandard housing, labeled by some the city's shame.

In the center of this last area, a new large building and the steelwork of a second stood out against the skyline.

Edwina pointed to the building and high steel. "If I were the way Ben is now," she said, "and wanted to be remembered by something, I think I'd like it to be Forum East."

"I suppose so." Alex's gaze swung to follow Edwina's. "For sure, without him it would have stayed an idea, and not much more."

Forum East was an ambitious local urban development, its objective to rehabilitate the city's core. Ben Rosselli had committed First Mercantile American financially to the project and Alex Vandervoort was directly in charge of the bank's involvement. The big main downtown branch, run by Edwina, handled construction loans and mortgage details.

"I was thinking," Edwina said, "about changes which will happen here." She was going to add, *after Ben is dead . . .*

"There'll be changes, of course—perhaps big ones. I hope none will affect Forum East."

She sighed. "It isn't an hour since Ben told us . . ."

"And we're discussing future bank business before his grave is dug. Well, we have to, Edwina. Ben would expect it. Some important decisions must be made soon."

"Including who's to succeed as president."

"That's one."

"A good many of us in the bank have been hoping it would be you."

"Frankly, so was I."

What both left unsaid was that Alex Vandervoort had been viewed, until today, as Ben Rosselli's chosen heir. But not this soon. Alex had been at First Mercantile American only two years. Before that he was an officer of the Federal Reserve and Ben Rosselli had personally persuaded him to move over, holding out the prospect of eventual advancement to the top.

"Five years or so from now," old Ben had told Alex at the time, "I want to hand over to someone who can cope efficiently with big numbers, and show a profitable bottom line, because that's the only way a banker deals from strength. But he must be more than just a top technician. The kind of man I want to run this bank won't ever forget that small depositors—individuals—have always been our strong foundation. The trouble with bankers nowadays is that they get too remote."

He was making no firm promise, Ben Rosselli made clear, but added, "My impression, Alex, is you are the kind of man we need. Let's work together for a while and see."

So Alex moved in, bringing his experience and a flair for new technology, and with both had quickly made his mark. As to philosophy, he found he shared many of Ben's views.

Long before, Alex had also gained insights into banking from his father—a Dutch immigrant who became a Minnesota farmer.

Pieter Vandervoort, Sr. had burdened himself with a bank loan and, to pay interest on it, labored from pre-dawn until after darkness, usually seven days a week. In the end he died of overwork, impoverished, after which the bank sold his land, recovering not only arrears of interest but its original investment. His father's experience showed Alex —through his grief—that the other side of a bank counter was the place to be.

Eventually the route to banking for young Alex was a Harvard scholarship and an honors degree in economics.

"Everything may still work out," Edwina D'Orsey said. "I presume the board will make the choice of president."

"Yes," Alex answered almost absently. He had been thinking of Ben Rosselli and his father; his memories of the two were strangely intertwined.

"Length of service isn't everything."

"It counts."

Mentally, Alex weighed the probabilities. He knew he had the talent and experience to head First Mercantile American but chances were, the directors would favor someone who had been around here longer. Roscoe Heyward, for example, had worked for the bank for almost twenty years and despite his occasional lack of rapport with Ben Rosselli, Heyward had a significant following on the board.

Yesterday the odds favored Alex. Today, they had been switched.

He stood up and knocked out his pipe. "I must get back to work."

"Me, too."

But Alex, when he was alone, sat silent, thoughtful.

Edwina took an express elevator from the directors' floor to the main floor foyer of FMA Headquarters Tower—an architectural mix of Lincoln Center and the Sistine Chapel. The foyer surged with people—hurrying bank staff, messengers, visitors, sightseers. She acknowledged a security guard's friendly salute.

Through the curving glass front Edwina could see Rosselli Plaza outside with its trees, benches, a sculpture court, and gushing fountain. In summer the plaza was a meeting place and downtown office workers ate their lunches there, but now it appeared bleak and inhospitable. A raw fall wind swirled leaves and dust in small tornadoes and sent pedestrians scurrying for indoor warmth.

It was the time of year, Edwina thought, she liked least of all. It spoke of melancholy, winter soon to come, and death.

Involuntarily she shuddered, then headed for the "tunnel," carpeted and softly lighted, which connected the bank's headquarters with the main downtown branch—a palatial, single-story structure.

This was her domain.

4

Wednesday, at the main downtown branch, began routinely.

Edwina D'Orsey was branch duty officer for the week and arrived promptly at 8:30, a half hour before the bank's ponderous bronze doors would swing open to the public.

As manager of FMA's flagship branch, as well as a corporate vice-president, she really didn't have to do the duty officer chore. But Edwina preferred to take her turn. Also it demonstrated that she expected no special privileges because of being a woman—something she had always been careful about during her fifteen years at First Mercantile American. Besides, the duty only came around once in ten weeks.

At the building's side door she fumbled in her brown Gucci handbag for her key; she found it beneath an assortment of lipstick, wallet, credit cards, compact, comb, a shopping list, and other items—her handbag was always uncharacteristically disorganized. Then, before using the key, she checked for a "no ambush" signal. The signal was where it should be—a small yellow card, placed inconspicuously in a window. The card would have been put there, minutes earlier, by a porter whose job was to be first in the big branch each day. If all was in order inside, he placed the signal where arriving staff would see it. But if robbers had broken in during the night and were waiting to seize hostages—the porter first—no signal would be placed, so its absence became a warning. Then, later arriving staff not only would not enter, but instantly would summon aid.

Because of increasing robberies of all types, most banks used a "no ambush" signal nowadays, its type and location changing frequently.

On entering, Edwina went immediately to a hinged panel in the wall

and swung it open. In sight was a bell push which she pressed in code
—two long, three short, one long. The Central Security operations room
over in Headquarters Tower now knew that the door alarm, which Edwina's entry had triggered a moment ago, could be ignored and that
an authorized officer was in the bank. The porter, also on entering,
would have tapped out his own code.

The ops room, receiving similar signals from other FMA branch banks,
would switch the building's alarm system from "alert" to "stand by."

Had either Edwina, as duty officer, or the porter failed to tap out their
correct code, the ops room would have alerted police. Minutes later
the branch bank would have been surrounded.

As with other systems, codes were changed often.

Banks everywhere were finding security in positive signals when all
was well, an absence of signals if trouble erupted. That way, a bank employee held hostage could convey a warning by merely doing nothing.

By now other officers and staff were coming in, checked by the uniformed porter who had taken command at the side door.

"Good morning, Mrs. D'Orsey." A white-haired bank veteran named
Tottenhoe joined Edwina. He was operations officer, in charge of staff
and routine running of the branch, and his long, lugubrious face made
him seem like an ancient kangaroo. His normal moodiness and pessimism had increased as compulsory retirement neared; he resented his
age and seemed to blame others for it. Edwina and Tottenhoe walked
together across the bank's main floor, then down a wide, carpeted stairway to the vault. Supervising the vault's opening and closing was the
duty officer's responsibility.

While they waited by the vault door for the time lock to switch off,
Tottenhoe said gloomily, "There's a rumor that Mr. Rosselli's dying. Is
it true?"

"I'm afraid it is." She told him briefly of the meeting yesterday.

Last night at home Edwina had thought of little else, but this morning she was determined to concentrate on bank business. Ben would
expect it.

Tottenhoe mumbled something dismal which she didn't catch.

Edwina checked her watch. 8:40. Seconds later, a faint click within
the massive chrome steel door announced that the overnight time lock,
set before the bank closed the night before, had switched itself off. Now
the vault combination locks could be actuated. Until this moment
they could not.

Using another concealed pushbutton, Edwina signaled Central Security ops room that the vault was about to be opened—a normal opening, not under duress.

Standing side by side at the door, Edwina and Tottenhoe spun separate combinations. Neither knew the combination setting of the other; thus neither could open the vault alone.

An assistant operations officer, Miles Eastin, had now arrived. A young, handsome, well-groomed man, he was invariably cheerful—in pleasant contrast to Tottenhoe's dependable glumness. Edwina liked Eastin. With him was a senior vault teller who would supervise transference of money in and out of the vault through the remainder of the day. In cash alone, nearly a million dollars in currency and coinage would be under his control through the next six operating hours.

Checks passing through the big branch bank during the same period would represent another twenty million.

As Edwina stood back, the senior teller and Miles Eastin together swung open the huge, precision-engineered vault door. It would remain open until the close of business tonight.

"Just took a phone message," Eastin informed the operations officer. "Scratch two more tellers for today."

Tottenhoe's look of melancholy deepened.

"Is it flu?" Edwina asked.

An epidemic had swept the city for the past ten days, leaving the bank short of staff, especially tellers.

"Yes, it is," Miles Eastin answered.

Tottenhoe complained, "If I could just catch it myself, I could go home to bed and leave someone else to worry about manning the counters." He asked Edwina, "Do you insist we open today?"

"It seems to be expected of us."

"Then we'll empty an executive chair or two. You're the first elected," he said to Miles Eastin, "so get a cash box and be ready for the public. Do you remember how to count?"

"Up to twenty," Eastin said. "As long as I can work with my socks off."

Edwina smiled. She had no fears about young Eastin; everything he touched he did well. When Tottenhoe retired next year, Miles Eastin would almost certainly be her choice as operations officer.

He returned the smile. "Not to worry, Mrs. D'Orsey. I'm a pretty good utility outfielder. Besides, I played handball for three hours last night and managed to keep score."

"But did you win?"

"When I keep score? Of course."

Edwina was aware, too, of Eastin's other hobby, one which had proved useful to the bank—the study and collection of currencies and coin. It was Miles Eastin who gave orientation talks to new employees at the branch, and he liked to toss in historical nuggets such as the fact that paper money and inflation were both invented in China. The first recorded instance of inflation, he would explain, was during the thirteenth century when the Mongol emperor, Kublai Khan, was unable to pay his soldiers in coin, so used a wood printing block to produce military money. Unfortunately so much was printed that it quickly became worthless. "Some people," young Eastin would quip, "believe the dollar is being Mongolized right now." Because of his studies, Eastin had also become the resident expert on counterfeit money, and doubtful bills which turned up were referred to him for his opinion.

The three of them—Edwina, Eastin, Tottenhoe—ascended the stairs from the vault to the main banking area.

Canvas sacks containing cash were being delivered from an armored truck outside, the money accompanied by two armed guards.

Cash arriving in large volume always came early in the morning, having been transferred earlier still from the Federal Reserve to First Mercantile American's own Central Cash Vault. From there it was distributed to branch banks in the FMA system. Reason for the same-day schedule was simple. Excess cash in vaults earned nothing; there were dangers, too, of loss or robbery.

The trick, for any branch bank manager, was never to run short of cash, but not to hold too much.

A large branch bank like FMA's downtown kept a working cash float of half a million dollars. The money now arriving—another quarter million—was the difference required on an average banking day.

Tottenhoe grumbled to the delivery guards, "I hope you've brought us some cleaner money than we've been getting lately."

"I told them guys over at Central Cash about your beef, Mr. Tottenhoe," one guard said. He was youngish, with long black hair overflowing his uniform cap and collar. Edwina looked downward, wondering if he were wearing shoes. He was.

"They said you'd phoned in, too," the guard added. "Now me, I'll take money clean or dirty."

"Unfortunately," the operations officer said, "some of our customers won't."

New currency, arriving from the Bureau of Printing and Engraving via the Federal Reserve, was keenly competed for by banks. A surprising number of customers, referred to as "the carriage trade," rejected dirty bills and demanded new, or at least clean notes which bankers called "fit." Fortunately there were others who simply didn't care and tellers had instructions to pass out the worst soiled money where they could get away with it, saving their fresh, crisp bills for those who asked for them.

"Hear there's lots of high-grade counterfeit stuff around. Maybe we could get you a bundle." The second guard winked at his companion.

Edwina told him, "That kind of help we can do without. We've been getting too much of it."

Only last week the bank had discovered nearly a thousand dollars in counterfeit bills—money paid in, though the source was unknown. More than likely it had come through numerous depositors—some who had been defrauded themselves and were passing their loss along to the bank; others who had no idea the bills were counterfeit, which was not surprising since the quality was remarkably high.

Agents of the U. S. Secret Service, who had discussed the matter with Edwina and Miles Eastin, were frankly worried. "The counterfeit money we're seeing has never been as good, and there's never been as much in circulation," one of them admitted. A conservative estimate was that thirty million dollars of bogus money had been produced the previous year. "And a lot more never gets detected."

England and Canada were major supply sources of spurious U.S. currency. The agents also reported that an incredible amount was circulating in Europe. "It's not so easily detected there, so warn your friends who go to Europe never to accept American bills. There's a strong chance they could be worthless."

The first armed guard shifted the sacks on his shoulders. "Don't worry, folks! These are genuine greenbacks. All part of the service!"

Both guards went down the stairway to the vault.

Edwina walked to her desk on the platform. Throughout the bank, activity was increasing. The main front doors were open, early customers streaming in.

The platform where, by tradition, the senior officers worked, was raised slightly above the main-floor level and carpeted in crimson. Edwina's desk, the largest and most imposing, was flanked by two flags—behind her and to the right the Stars and Stripes, and on her left the state burgee. Sometimes, seated there, she felt as if she were on TV, ready to make a solemn announcement while cameras dollied in.

The big downtown branch itself was modern. Rebuilt a year or two ago when FMA's adjoining Headquarters Tower was erected, the structure had had design expertise and a fortune lavished on it. The result, in which crimson and mahogany predominated with an appropriate sprinkling of gold, was a combination of customer convenience, excellent working conditions and just plain opulence. Occasionally, Edwina admitted to herself, the opulence seemed to have an edge.

As she settled down, her tall, lithe figure slipping familiarly into a high-backed swivel chair, she smoothed her short hair—needlessly, since as usual it was impeccably in place.

Edwina reached for a group of files containing loan applications for amounts higher than other officers in the branch had authority to approve.

Her own authorization to lend money extended to a million dollars in any single instance, providing two other officers in the branch concurred. They invariably did. Amounts in excess were referred to the bank's credit policy unit over in Headquarters.

In First Mercantile American, as in any banking system, an acknowledged status symbol was the size of a loan which a bank official had power to sanction. It also determined his—or her—position on the organization totem pole and was spoken of as "the quality of initial," because an individual's initial put final approval on any loan proposal.

As a manager, the quality of Edwina's initial was unusually high, though it reflected her responsibility in running FMA's important downtown branch. A manager of a lesser branch might approve loans from ten thousand to half a million dollars, depending on the manager's ability and seniority. It always amused Edwina that quality of initial supported a caste system with attendant perks and privileges. In the Headquarters credit policy unit, an assistant loan inspector, whose authority was limited to a mere fifty thousand dollars, worked at an unimpressive desk alongside others in a large open office. Next in the pecking order, a loan inspector whose initial was good for a quarter million dollars rated a larger desk in a glass-paneled cubicle.

An honest-to-goodness office with door and window was the perquisite of an assistant loan supervisor whose quality of initial extended higher, to a half million dollars. He also rated a capacious desk, an oil painting on the wall and printed memo pads with his name, a free daily copy of *The Wall Street Journal* and a complimentary shoeshine every morning. He shared a secretary with another assistant supervisor.

Finally, a loan officer–vice-president whose initial was good for a million dollars, worked in a corner office with *two* windows, *two* oil paintings, and a secretary of his own. His name memos were *engraved*. He, too, had a free shoeshine and newspaper, plus magazines and journals, the use of a company car when required for business, and access to the senior officers' dining room for lunch.

Edwina qualified for almost all the quality of initial perks. She had never used the shoeshine.

This morning, she studied two loan requests, approved one and penciled some queries on another. A third proposal stopped her short.

Startled, and conscious of a bizarre coincidence after yesterday's experience, she read through the file again.

The loan officer who had prepared the file answered Edwina's intercom buzz.

"Castleman here."

"Cliff, please come over."

"Sure." The loan officer, only half a dozen desks away, looked directly at Edwina. "And I'll bet I know why you want me."

Moments later, as he seated himself beside her desk, he glanced at the open file. "I was right. We get some lulus, don't we?"

Cliff Castleman was small and precise with a round pink face and soft smile. Borrowers liked him because he was a good listener and sympathetic. But he was also a seasoned loan man with sound judgment.

"I was hoping," Edwina said, "that this application is some kind of sick joke, even if a ghastly one."

"Ghoulish would be more apt, Mrs. D'Orsey. And while the whole thing may be sick, I assure you it's real." Castleman motioned to the file. "I included all the facts because I knew you'd want them. Obviously you've read the report. And my recommendation."

"Are you serious in proposing to lend this much money for *this* purpose?"

"I'm deadly serious." The loan officer stopped abruptly. "Sorry!—that wasn't intended to be gallows humor. But I believe you should approve the loan."

It was all there in the file. A forty-three-year-old pharmaceutical salesman named Gosburne, locally employed, was applying for a loan of twenty-five thousand dollars. He was married—a first marriage which had lasted seventeen years, and the Gosburnes owned their suburban home except for a small mortgage. They had had a joint account with FMA for eight years—no problems. An earlier, though smaller, bank loan had been repaid. Gosburne's employment record and other financial history were good.

The intended purpose of the new loan was to buy a large stainless steel capsule in which would be placed the body of the Gosburnes' child, Andrea. She had died six days ago, at age fifteen, from a kidney malignancy. At present Andrea's body was at a funeral home, stored in dry ice. Her blood had been drawn off immediately after death and replaced with a blood-like "anti-freeze" solution called dimethylsulfoxide.

The steel capsule was specially designed to contain liquid nitrogen at a subzero temperature. The body, wrapped in aluminum foil, would be immersed in this solution.

A capsule of the type sought—a giant bottle, really, and known as a "cryo-crypt"—was available in Los Angeles and would be flown from there if the bank loan was approved. About a third of the intended loan was for prepayment of vault storage rent for the capsule, and replacement of the liquid nitrogen every four months.

Castleman asked Edwina, "You've heard of cryonics societies?"

"Vaguely. It's pseudo-scientific. Not very reputable."

"Not very. And pseudo indeed. But the fact is, cryonics groups have a big following and they've convinced Gosburne and his wife that when medical science is more advanced—say fifty or a hundred years from now —Andrea can be thawed out, brought back to life and cured. Incidentally, the cryonics people have a motto: *Freeze—wait—reanimate.*"

"Horrible," Edwina said.

The loan officer conceded, "Mostly I agree with you. But look at it their way. They believe. Also they're adult, reasonably intelligent people, deeply religious. So who are we, as bankers, to be judge and jury? As I see it, the only question is: Can Gosburne repay the loan? I've gone over the figures, and I say he can and will. The guy may be a nut. But the record shows he's a nut who pays his bills."

Reluctantly Edwina studied the income and expenses figures. "It will be a terrible financial strain."

"The guy knows that but insists he can handle it. He's taking on some spare-time work. And his wife is looking for a job."

Edwina said, "They have four younger children."

"Yes."

"Has anyone pointed out that the other children—the living—will need money soon for college, other things, and that twenty-five thousand dollars could be put to better use for them?"

"I did," Castleman said. "I've had two long interviews with Gosburne. But according to him, the whole family talked that over and they made their decision. They believe the sacrifices they'll have to make will be worth the chance of bringing Andrea back to life some day. The children also say that when they're older they'll take over responsibility for her body."

"Oh God!" Again Edwina's thoughts went back to yesterday. Ben Rosselli's death, whenever it came, would be dignified. This made death ugly and a mockery. Should the bank's money—in part, Ben's—be used for such a purpose?

"Mrs. D'Orsey," the loan officer said, "I've had this on my desk for two days. My first feeling was the same as yours—the whole thing's sick. But I've thought about it and I've come around. In my opinion, it's an acceptable risk."

Acceptable risk. Essentially, Edwina realized, Cliff Castleman was right because acceptable risks were what banking was all about. He was also right in asserting that in most personal matters a bank should not be judge and jury.

Of course, this particular risk might not work out, though even if it failed to, Castleman would not be blamed. His record was good, his "wins" far greater than his losses. In fact, a perfect win record was frowned on, a busy retail loan officer was expected, almost obligated, to have a few of his loans turn sour. If he didn't, he could be in trouble in reverse when a computer printout warned management he was losing business through excessive caution.

"All right," Edwina said. "The idea appalls me but I'll back your judgment."

She scribbled an initial. Castleman returned to his desk.

Thus—apart from a loan for a frozen daughter—this day had begun like any other.

It stayed that way until early afternoon.

On days when she lunched alone, Edwina used the basement cafeteria over at FMA Headquarters. The cafeteria was noisy, the food only so-so, but service was brisk and she could be in and out in fifteen minutes.

Today, however, she had a client as a guest and exercised her vice-president's privilege by taking him to the senior officers' private dining room, high in the executive tower. He was the treasurer of the city's largest department store and needed a three-million-dollar short-term loan to cover a cash deficit resulting from light fall sales plus costlier-than-usual purchases of Christmas merchandise.

"This goddamned inflation!" the treasurer complained over a spinach soufflé. Then, licking his lips, he added, "But we'll get our money back this next two months, and then some. Santa Claus is always good to us."

The department store account was an important one; nevertheless

Edwina drove a tough bargain, with terms favorable to the bank. After some grumbling by the customer, these were agreed by the time they reached Peach Melba for dessert. The three million dollars exceeded Edwina's personal authority, though she anticipated no trouble getting approval from Headquarters. If necessary, for speed's sake, she would talk with Alex Vandervoort who had backed up her judgments in the past.

It was while they were having coffee that a waitress brought a message to their table.

"Mrs. D'Orsey," the girl said, "a Mr. Tottenhoe is on the phone for you. He says it's urgent."

Edwina excused herself and went to a telephone in an annex.

The voice of her branch operations officer complained, "I've been trying to locate you."

"Now you have. What is it?"

"We have a serious cash shortage." He went on to explain: A teller had reported the loss a half hour ago. Checking had been going on continuously since. Edwina sensed panic as well as gloom in Tottenhoe's voice and asked how much money was involved.

She heard him swallow. "Six thousand dollars."

"I'll be down right away."

Within less than a minute, after apologizing to her guest, she was in the express elevator en route to the main floor.

5

"As far as I can see," Tottenhoe said morosely, "the only thing all of us know for certain is that six thousand dollars in cash is not where it should be."

The operations officer was one of four people seated around Edwina D'Orsey's desk. The others were Edwina; young Miles Eastin, Tottenhoe's assistant; and a teller named Juanita Núñez.

It was from Juanita Núñez's cash drawer that the money was missing.

A half hour had elapsed since Edwina's return to the main branch. Now, as the others faced her across the desk, Edwina answered Tottenhoe. "What you say is true, but we can do better. I want us to go over everything again, slowly and carefully."

The time was shortly after 3 P.M. Customers had gone. The outer doors were closed.

Activity, as usual, was continuing in the branch, though Edwina was conscious of covert glances toward the platform from other employees who knew by now that something serious was wrong.

She reminded herself that it was essential to remain calm, analytical, to consider every fragment of information. She wanted to listen carefully to nuances of speech and attitude, particularly those of Mrs. Núñez.

Edwina was aware, too, that very soon she must notify head office of the apparent heavy cash loss, after which Headquarters Security would become involved, and probably the FBI. But while there was still a chance of finding a solution quietly, without bringing up the heavy artillery, she intended to try.

"If you like, Mrs. D'Orsey," Miles Eastin said, "I'll start because I was the first one Juanita reported to." He had shed his usual breeziness.

Edwina nodded approval.

The possibility of a cash shortage, Eastin informed the group, first came to his attention a few minutes before 2 P.M. At that time Juanita Núñez approached him and stated her belief that six thousand dollars was missing from her cash drawer.

Miles Eastin was working a teller's position himself, filling in as he had through most of the day because of the shortage of tellers. In fact, Eastin was only two stations away from Juanita Núñez, and she reported to him there, locking her cash box before she did so.

Eastin had then locked his own cash box and gone to Tottenhoe.

Gloomier than usual, Tottenhoe took up the story.

He had gone to Mrs. Núñez at once and talked with her. At first he hadn't believed that as much as six thousand dollars could be missing because even if she suspected *some* money had gone, it was virtually impossible at that point to know how much.

The operations officer pointed out: Juanita Núñez had been working all day, having started with slightly more than ten thousand dollars cash-from-vault in the morning, and she had been taking in and paying out money since 9 A.M. when the bank opened. That meant she had been working for almost five hours, except for a forty-five-minute lunch break, and during that time the bank was crowded, with all tellers busy. Furthermore, cash deposits today had been heavier than usual; therefore the amount of money in her drawer—not including checks—could have increased to twenty or twenty-five thousand dollars. So how, Tottenhoe reasoned, could Mrs. Núñez be certain not only that money was missing but know the amount so specifically?

Edwina nodded. The same question had already occurred to her.

Without being obvious, Edwina studied the young woman. She was small, slight, dark, not really pretty but provocative in an elfin way. She looked Puerto Rican, which she was, and had a pronounced accent. She had said little so far, responding only briefly when spoken to.

It was hard to be sure just what Juanita Núñez's attitude was. It was certainly not co-operative, at least outwardly, Edwina thought, and the girl had volunteered no information other than her original statement. Since they started, the teller's facial expression had seemed either sulky or hostile. Occasionally her attention wandered, as if she were bored and regarded the proceedings as a waste of time. But she was nervous, too, and betrayed it by her clasped hands and continuous turning of a thin gold wedding band.

Edwina D'Orsey knew, because she had glanced at an employment record on her desk, that Juanita Núñez was twenty-five, married but separated, with a three-year-old child. She had worked for First Mercantile American for almost two years, all of that time in her present job. What wasn't in the employment record, but Edwina remembered hearing, was that the Núñez girl supported her child alone and had been, perhaps still was, in financial difficulties because of debts left by the husband who deserted her.

Despite his doubts that Mrs. Núñez could possibly know how much money was missing, Tottenhoe continued, he had relieved her from duty at the counter, after which she was immediately "locked up with her cash."

Being "locked up" was actually a protection for the employee concerned and was also standard procedure in a problem of this kind. It simply meant that the teller was placed alone in a small, closed office, along with her cash box and a calculator, and told to balance all transactions for the day.

Tottenhoe waited outside.

Soon afterward she called the operations officer in. Her cash did not balance, she informed him. It was six thousand dollars short.

Tottenhoe summoned Miles Eastin and together they ran a second check while Juanita Núñez watched. They found her report to be correct. Without doubt there was cash missing, and precisely the amount she had stated all along.

It was then that Tottenhoe had telephoned Edwina.

"That brings us back," Edwina said, "to where we started. Have any fresh ideas occurred to anyone?"

Miles Eastin volunteered, "I'd like to ask Juanita some more questions if she doesn't mind."

Edwina nodded.

"Think carefully about this, Juanita," Eastin said. "At any time today did you make a TX with any other teller?"

As all of them knew, a TX was a teller's exchange. A teller on duty would often run short of bills or coins of one denomination and if it happened at a busy time, rather than make a trip to the cash vault, tellers helped each other by "buying" or "selling" cash. A TX form was used to keep a record. But occasionally, through haste or carelessness, mistakes were made, so that at the end of the business day one teller would be short on cash, the other long. It would be hard to believe, though, that such a difference could be as large as six thousand dollars.

"No," the teller said. "No exchanges. Not today."

Miles Eastin persisted, "Were you aware of anyone else on the staff, at any time today, being near your cash so they could have taken some?"

"No."

"When you first came to me, Juanita," Eastin said, "and told me you thought there was some money gone, how long before that had you known about it?"

"A few minutes."

Edwina interjected, "How long was that after your lunch break, Mrs. Núñez?"

The girl hesitated, seeming less sure of herself. "Maybe twenty minutes."

"Let's talk about *before* you went to lunch," Edwina said. "Do you think the money was missing then?"

Juanita Núñez shook her head negatively.

"How can you be sure?"

"I know."

The unhelpful, monosyllabic answers were becoming irritating to Edwina. And the sulky hostility which she sensed earlier seemed more pronounced.

Tottenhoe repeated the crucial question. "After lunch, why were you certain not only that money was missing, but exactly how much?"

The young woman's small face set defiantly. "I knew."

There was a disbelieving silence.

"Do you think that some time during the day you could have paid six thousand dollars out to a customer in error?"

"No."

Miles Eastin asked, "When you left your teller's position before you went to lunch, Juanita, you took your cash drawer to the cash vault, closed the combination lock and left it there. Right?"

"Yes."

"Are you sure you locked it?"

The girl nodded positively.

"Was the operations officer's lock closed?"

"No, left open."

That, too, was normal. Once the operations officer's combination had been set to "open" each morning, it was usual to leave it that way through the remainder of the day.

"But when you came back from lunch your cash drawer was still in the vault, still locked?"

"Yes."

"Does anyone else know your combination? Have you ever given it to anyone?"

"No."

For a moment the questioning stopped. The others around the desk, Edwina suspected, were reviewing mentally the branch's cash vault procedures.

The cash drawer which Miles Eastin had referred to was actually a portable strongbox on an elevated stand with wheels, light enough to be pushed around easily. Some banks called it a cash truck. Every teller had one assigned and the same cash drawer or truck, conspicuously numbered, was used normally by the same individual. A few spares were available for special use. Miles Eastin had been using one today.

All tellers' cash trucks were checked in and out of the cash vault by a senior vault teller who kept a record of their removal and return. It was impossible to take a cash unit in or out without the vault teller's scrutiny or to remove someone else's, deliberately or in error. During nights and weekends the massive cash vault was sealed tighter than a Pharaoh's tomb.

Each cash truck had two tamperproof combination locks. One of these was set by the teller personally, the other by the operations officer or assistant. Thus, when a cash unit was opened each morning it was in the presence of two people—the teller and an operations officer.

Tellers were told to memorize their combinations and not to confide them to anyone else, though a combination could be changed any time a teller wished. The only written record of a teller's combination was in a sealed and double-signed envelope which was kept with others—again in double custody—in a safe deposit box. The seal on the envelope was only broken in event of a teller's death, illness, or leaving the bank's employ.

By all these means, only the active user of any cash drawer knew the combination which would open it and tellers, as well as the bank, were protected against theft.

A further feature of the sophisticated cash drawer was a built-in alarm system. When rolled into place at any teller's position at a counter, an electrical connection linked each cash unit with an interbank communications network. A warning trigger was hidden within the drawer beneath an innocuous appearing pile of bills, known as "bait money."

Tellers had instructions never to use the bait money for normal transactions, but in event of a holdup to hand over this money first. Simply removing the bills released a silent plunger switch. This, in turn, alerted bank security staff and police, who were usually on the scene in minutes; it also activated hidden cameras overhead. Serial numbers of the bait money were on record for use as evidence later.

Edwina asked Tottenhoe, "Was the bait money among the missing six thousand dollars?"

"No," the operations officer said. "The bait money was intact. I checked."

She reflected: So there was no hope of tracing anything that way.

Once more Miles Eastin addressed the teller. "Juanita, is there any way you can think of that anyone, *anyone at all,* could have taken the money out of your cash drawer?"

"No," Juanita Núñez said.

Watching closely as the girl answered, Edwina thought she detected fear. Well, if so, there was good reason because no bank would give up easily where a loss of this magnitude was involved.

Edwina no longer had doubts about what had happened to the missing money. The Núñez girl had stolen it. No other explanation was possible. The difficulty was to find out—how?

One likely way was for Juanita Núñez to have passed it over the counter to an accomplice. No one would have noticed. During an ordinarily busy day it would have seemed like any routine cash withdrawal. Alternatively, the girl could have concealed the money and carried it from the bank during her lunch break, though in that case the risk would have been greater.

One thing Núñez must have been aware of was that she would lose her job, whether it was proven she had stolen the money or not. True, bank tellers were allowed occasional cash discrepancies; such errors were normal and expected. In the course of a year, eight "overs" or "unders" was average for most tellers and, provided each error was no larger than twenty-five dollars, usually nothing was said. But no one who experienced a major cash shortage kept her job, and tellers knew it.

Of course, Juanita Núñez could have taken this into account, deciding that an immediate six thousand dollars was worth the loss of her job, even though she might have difficulty getting another. Either way, Edwina was sorry for the girl. Obviously she must have been desperate. Perhaps her need had to do with her child.

"I don't believe there's any more we can do at this point," Edwina told the group. "I'll have to advise head office. They'll take over the investigation."

As the three got up, she added, "Mrs. Núñez, please stay." The girl resumed her seat.

When the others were out of hearing, Edwina said with deliberate informality, "Juanita, I thought this might be a moment for us to talk frankly to each other, perhaps as friends." Edwina had banished her earlier impatience. She was aware of the girl's dark eyes fixed intently on her own.

"I'm sure that two things must have occurred to you. First, there's going to be a thorough investigation into this and the FBI will be involved because we're a federally insured bank. Second, there is no way that suspicion cannot fall on you." Edwina paused. "I'm being open with you about this. You understand?"

"I understand. But I did not take any money."

Edwina observed that the young woman was still turning her wedding ring nervously.

Now Edwina chose her words carefully, aware she must be cautious in avoiding a direct accusation which might rebound in legal trouble for the bank later.

"However long the investigation takes, Juanita, it's almost certain the truth will come out, if for no other reason than that it usually does. Investigators are thorough. They're also experienced. They do not give up."

The girl repeated, more emphatically, "I did not take the money."

"I haven't said you did. But I do want to say that if by any chance you know something more than you have said already, now is the time to speak out, to tell me while we're talking quietly here. After this there will be no other chances. It will be too late."

Juanita Núñez seemed about to speak again. Edwina raised a hand. "No, hear me out. I'll make this promise. If the money were returned to the bank, let's say no later than tomorrow, there would be no legal action, no prosecution. In fairness, I'll have to say that whoever took the money could no longer work here. But nothing else would happen. I guarantee it. Juanita, do you have *anything* to tell me?"

"No, no, no! *¡Te lo juro por mi hija!*" The girl's eyes blazed, her face came alive in anger. "I tell you I did not take any money, now or ever."

Edwina sighed.

"All right, that's all for now. But please do not leave the bank without checking with me first."

Juanita Núñez appeared on the verge of another heated reply. Instead, with a slight shrug, she rose and turned away.

From her elevated desk, Edwina surveyed the activity around her; it was her own small world, her personal responsibility. The day's branch transactions were still being balanced and recorded, though a preliminary check had shown that no teller—as was originally hoped—had a six-thousand-dollar overage.

Sounds were muted in the modern building: in low key, voices buzzed, papers rustled, coinage jingled, calculators clicked. She watched it all briefly, reminding herself that for two reasons this was a week she would remember. Then, knowing what must be done, she lifted a telephone and dialed an internal number.

A woman's voice answered. "Security department."

"Mr. Wainwright, please," Edwina said.

6

Nolan Wainwright had found it hard, since yesterday, to concentrate on normal work within the bank.

The chief of security had been deeply affected by Tuesday morning's session in the boardroom, not least because, over a decade, he and Ben Rosselli had achieved both friendship and mutual respect.

It had not always been that way.

Yesterday, returning from the tower executive floor to his own more modest office which looked out onto a light well, Wainwright had told his secretary not to disturb him for a while. Then he had sat at his desk, sad, brooding, reaching back in memory to the time of his own first clash with Ben Rosselli's will.

It was ten years earlier. Nolan Wainwright was the newly appointed police chief of a small upstate town. Before that he had been a lieutenant of detectives on a big city force, with an outstanding record. He had the ability for a chief's job and, in the climate of the times, it probably helped his candidacy that he was black.

Soon after the new chief's appointment, Ben Rosselli drove through the outskirts of the little town and was clocked at 80 mph. A police patrolman of the local force handed him a ticket with a summons to traffic court.

Perhaps because his life was conservative in other ways, Ben Rosselli always loved fast cars and drove them as their designers intended—with his right foot near the floor.

A speeding summons was routine. Back at First Mercantile American Headquarters he sent it, as usual, to the bank's security department with instructions to have it fixed. For the state's most powerful man of money, many things could be fixed and often were.

The summons was dispatched by courier next day to the FMA branch manager in the town where it was issued. It so happened that the branch manager was also a local councilman and he had been influential in Nolan Wainwright's appointment as chief of police.

The bank manager-councilman dropped over to police headquarters to have the traffic summons withdrawn. He was amiable. Nolan Wainwright was adamant.

Less amiably, the councilman pointed out to Wainwright that he was new to the community, needed friends, and that non-co-operation was not the way to recruit them. Wainwright still declined to do anything about the summons.

The councilman put on his banker's hat and reminded the police chief of his personal application to First Mercantile American Bank for a home mortgage loan which would make it possible to bring Wainwright's wife and family to the town. Mr. Rosselli, the branch manager added somewhat needlessly, was president of FMA.

Nolan Wainwright said he could see no relationship between a loan application and a traffic summons.

In due course Mr. Rosselli, for whom counsel appeared in court, was fined heavily for reckless driving and awarded three demerit points, to be recorded on his license. He was exceedingly angry.

Also in due course the mortgage application of Nolan Wainwright was turned down by First Mercantile American Bank.

Less than a week later Wainwright presented himself in Rosselli's office on the 36th floor of FMA Headquarters Tower, taking advantage of the accessibility on which the bank president prided himself.

When he learned who his visitor was, Ben Rosselli was surprised that he was black. No one had mentioned that. Not that it made any difference to the banker's still simmering wrath at the ignominious notation on his driving record—the first of a lifetime.

Wainwright spoke coolly. To his credit, Ben Rosselli had known nothing of the police chief's mortgage loan application or its rejection; such matters were conducted at a lower level than his own. But he smelled the odor of injustice and sent, there and then, for the loan file which he reviewed while Nolan Wainwright waited.

"As a matter of interest," Ben Rosselli said when he had finished reading, "if we don't make this loan what do you intend to do?"

Wainwright's answer now was cold. "Fight. I'll hire a lawyer and we'll go to the Civil Rights Commission for a start. If we don't succeed there, whatever else can be done to cause you trouble, that I'll do."

It was obvious he meant it and the banker snapped, "I don't respond to threats."

"I'm not making threats. You asked me a question and I answered it."

Ben Rosselli hesitated, then scribbled a signature in the file. He said, unsmiling, "The application is approved."

Before Wainwright left, the banker asked him, "What happens now if I get caught speeding in your town?"

"We'll throw the book at you. If it's another reckless driving charge, you'll probably be in jail."

Watching the policeman go, Ben Rosselli had the thought, which he would confide to Wainwright years later: *You self-righteous s.o.b.! One day I'll get you.*

He never had—in that sense. But in another, he did.

Two years later when the bank was seeking a top security executive who would be—as the head of Personnel expressed it—"tenaciously strong and totally incorruptible," Ben Rosselli stated, "I know of such a man."

Soon after, an offer was made to Nolan Wainwright, a contract signed, and Wainwright came to work for FMA.

From then on, Ben Rosselli and Wainwright had never clashed. The new head of Security did his job efficiently and added to his understanding of it by taking night school courses in banking theory. Rosselli, for his part, never asked Wainwright to breach his rigid code of ethics and the banker got his speeding tickets fixed elsewhere rather than through Security, believing Wainwright never knew, though usually he did. All the while the friendship between the two grew until, after the death of Ben Rosselli's wife, Wainwright frequently would eat dinner with the old man and afterwards they would play chess into the night.

In a way it had been a consolation for Wainwright, too, for his own marriage had ended in divorce soon after he went to work for FMA. His new responsibilities, and the sessions with old Ben, helped fill the gap.

They talked at such times about personal beliefs, influencing each other in ways they realized and in others of which neither was aware. And it was Wainwright—though only the two of them ever knew it—who helped persuade the bank president to employ his personal prestige and FMA's money in helping the Forum East development in that neglected city area where Wainwright had been born and spent his adolescent years.

Thus, like many others in the bank, Nolan Wainwright had his private memories of Ben Rosselli and his private sorrow.

Today, his mood of depression had persisted, and after a morning during which he had stayed mostly at his desk, avoiding people whom he did not need to see, Wainwright left for lunch alone. He went to a small cafe on the other side of town which he favored sometimes when he wanted to feel briefly free from FMA and its affairs. He returned in time to keep an appointment with Vandervoort.

The locale of their meeting was the bank's Keycharge credit-card division, housed in the Headquarters Tower.

The Keycharge bank-card system had been pioneered by First Mercantile American and now was operated jointly with a strong group of other banks in the U.S., Canada, and overseas. In size, Keycharge ranked immediately after BankAmericard and MasterCharge. Alex Vandervoort, within FMA, had over-all responsibility for the division.

Vandervoort was early and, when Nolan Wainwright arrived, was already in the Keycharge authorization center watching operations. The bank security chief joined him.

"I always like to see this," Alex said. "Best free show in town."

In a large, auditorium-like room, dimly lighted and with acoustic walls and ceilings to deaden sound, some fifty operators—predominantly women—were seated at a battery of consoles. Each console comprised a cathode ray tube, similar to a TV screen, with a keyboard beneath.

It was here that Keycharge cardholders were given or refused credit.

When a Keycharge card was presented anywhere in payment for goods or services, the place of business could accept the card without question if the amount involved was below an agreed floor limit. The limit varied, but was usually between twenty-five and fifty dollars. For a larger purchase, authorization was needed, though it took only seconds to obtain.

Calls poured into the authorization center twenty-four hours a day, seven days a week. They came from every U.S. state and Canadian province, while a row of chattering Telex machines brought queries from thirty foreign countries including some in the Russian-Communist orbit. Whereas builders of the British Empire once cheered proudly for the "red, white, and blue," creators of the Keycharge economic empire rooted with equal fervor for the "blue, green, and gold"—international colors of the Keycharge card.

The approval procedures moved at jet speed.

Wherever they were, merchants and others dialed directly through WATS lines to the Keycharge nerve center in FMA Headquarters

Tower. Automatically, each call was routed to a free operator whose first words were, "What is your merchant number?"

As the answer was given, the operator typed the figures, which appeared simultaneously on the cathode ray screen. Next was the card number and amount of credit being sought, this too typed and displayed.

The operator pressed a key, feeding the information to a computer which instantly signaled "ACCEPTED" or "DECLINED." The first meant that credit was good and the purchase approved, the second that the cardholder was delinquent and credit had been cut off. Since credit rules were lenient, with banks in the system wanting to lend money, acceptances by far outnumbered turndowns. The operator informed the merchant, the computer meanwhile recording the transaction. On a normal day fifteen thousand calls came in.

Both Alex Vandervoort and Nolan Wainwright had accepted headsets so they could listen to exchanges between callers and operators.

The security chief touched Alex's arm and pointed, then changed headset plugs for both of them. The console Wainwright indicated was carrying a flashing message from the computer—"STOLEN CARD."

The operator, speaking calmly and as trained, answered, "The card presented to you has been reported as stolen. If possible, detain the person presenting it and call your local police. Retain the card. Keycharge will pay you thirty dollars reward for its return."

They could hear a whispered colloquy, then a voice announced, "The bastard just ran out of my store. But I grabbed the mother's plastic. I'll mail it in."

The storekeeper sounded pleased at the prospect of an easy thirty dollars. For the Keycharge system it was also a good deal since the card, left in circulation, could have been used fraudulently for a much greater total amount.

Wainwright removed his headset; so did Alex Vandervoort. "It works well," Wainwright said, "when we get the information and can program the computer. Unfortunately most of the defrauding happens before a missing card's reported."

"But we still get a warning of excessive purchasing?"

"Right. Ten purchases in a day and the computer alerts us."

Few cardholders, as both men were aware, ever made more than six or eight purchases during a single day. Thus a card could be listed as "PROBABLY FRAUDULENT" even though the true owner might be unaware of its loss.

Despite all warning systems, however, a lost or stolen Keycharge card, if used cagily, was still good for twenty thousand dollars' worth of fraudulent purchasing in the week or so during which most stolen cards stayed unreported. Airline tickets for long-distance flights were favorite buys by credit-card thieves; so were cases of liquor. Both were then re-sold at bargain prices. Another ploy was to rent a car—preferably an expensive one—using a stolen or counterfeit credit card. The car was driven to another city where it received new license plates and forged registration papers, and was then sold or exported. The rental agency never saw car or customer again. One more gimmick was to buy jewelry in Europe on a fraudulent credit card backed up by a forged passport, then smuggle the jewelry into the U.S. for resale. In all such instances the credit-card company bore the eventual loss.

As both Vandervoort and Wainwright knew, there were devices used by criminals to decide whether a credit card in their possession could be used again, or if it was "hot." A favorite was to pay a headwaiter twenty-five dollars to check a card out. He could get the answer easily by consulting a weekly confidential "warning list" issued by the credit-card company to merchants and restaurants. If the card was unreported as hot, it was used for a further round of buying.

"We've been losing a helluva lot of money through fraud lately," Nolan Wainwright said. "Much more than usual. It's one of the reasons I wanted to talk."

They moved into a Keycharge security office which Wainwright had arranged to use this afternoon. He closed the door. The two men were much in contrast physically—Vandervoort, fair, chunky, non-athletic, with a touch of flab; Wainwright, black, tall, trim, hard, and muscular. Their personalities differed, too, though their relationship was good.

"This is a contest without a prize," Nolan Wainwright told the executive vice-president. He placed on the office desk eight plastic Key-charge credit cards, snapping them down like a poker dealer, one by one.

"Four of those credit cards are counterfeit," the security chief announced. "Can you separate the good ones from the bad?"

"Certainly. It's easy. The counterfeits always use different typefaces for embossing the cardholder's name and . . ." Vandervoort stopped, peering down at the group of cards. "By God! These don't. The type-face is the same on every card."

"Almost the same. If you know what to look for, you can detect slight divergences with a magnifier." Wainwright produced one. Dividing the cards into two groups, he pointed to variations between the embossing on the four genuine cards and the others.

Vandervoort said, "I see the difference, though I wouldn't have without the glass. How do the counterfeits look under ultraviolet?"

"Exactly the same as real ones."

"That's bad."

Several months earlier, following an example set by American Express, a hidden insignia had been imprinted on the face of all authentic Keycharge credit cards. It became visible only under ultraviolet light. The intention was to provide a quick, simple check of any card's genuineness. Now that safeguard, too, had been outflanked.

"It's bad, all right," Nolan Wainwright agreed. "And these are only samples. I've four dozen more, intercepted *after* they'd been used successfully in retail outlets, restaurants, for airline tickets, liquor, other things. And all of them are the best counterfeits which have ever shown up."

"Arrests?"

"None so far. When people sense a phony card is being queried they walk out of a store, away from an airline counter, or whatever, just as happened a few minutes ago." He motioned toward the authorization room. "Besides, even when we do arrest some users it doesn't follow we'll be near the source of the cards; usually they're sold and resold carefully enough to cover a trail."

Alex Vandervoort picked up one of the fraudulent blue, green, and gold cards and turned it over. "The plastic seems an exact match too."

"They're made from authentic plastic blanks that are stolen. They have to be, to be that good." The security chief went on, "We think we've traced the source of the cards themselves. Four months ago one of our suppliers had a break-in. The thieves got into the strong room where finished plastic sheets are stored. Three hundred sheets were missing."

Vandervoort whistled softly. A single plastic sheet would produce sixty-six Keycharge credit cards. That meant, potentially, almost twenty thousand fraudulent cards.

Wainwright said, "I did the arithmetic too." He motioned to the counterfeits on the desk. "This is the tip of an iceberg. Okay, so the phony cards we know about, or think we do, can mean ten million dollars' loss in charges before we pull them out of circulation. But what about others we haven't heard of yet? There could be ten times as many more."

"I get the picture."

Alex Vandervoort paced the small office as his thoughts took shape. He reflected: Ever since bank credit cards were introduced, all banks issuing them had been plagued by heavy loss through fraud. At first, entire mailbags of cards were stolen, their contents used for spending sprees by thieves—at bank expense. Some mail shipments were hijacked and held for ransom. Banks paid the ransom money, knowing the cost would be far greater if cards were distributed through the underworld, and used. Ironically, in 1974 Pan American Airways was castigated by press and public after admitting it paid money to criminals for the return of large quantities of stolen ticket blanks. The airline's objective was to avoid enormous losses through misuse of the tickets. Yet unknown to Pan Am's critics, some of the nation's biggest banks had quietly been doing the same thing for years.

Eventually, mail theft of credit cards was reduced, but by then criminals had moved on to other, more ingenious schemes. Counterfeiting was one. The early counterfeit cards were crude and easily recognizable, but quality improved until now—as Wainwright had shown—it took an expert to detect the difference.

As fast as any credit-card security measure was devised, criminal cleverness would circumvent it or attack a vulnerability elsewhere. As an example, a new type credit card now being marketed used a "scrambled" photograph of the cardholder. To ordinary eyes the photo was an indistinguishable blur, but placed in a descrambling device it could be viewed clearly and the cardholder identified. At the moment the scheme looked promising, but Alex had not the least doubt that organized crime would soon find a way to duplicate the scrambled photos.

Periodically, arrests and convictions of those using stolen or bogus credit cards were made, but these represented a small portion only of the total traffic. The main problem, so far as banks were concerned, was a lack of investigative and enforcement people. There simply were not enough.

Alex ceased his pacing.

"These latest counterfeits," he queried, "is it likely that there's some kind of ring behind them?"

"It's not only likely, it's a certainty. For the end product to be this good there has to be an organization. And it's got money behind it, machinery, specialist know-how, a distribution system. Besides, there are other signs pointing the same way."

"Such as?"

"As you know," Wainwright said, "I keep in touch with law agencies. Recently there's been a big increase through the whole Midwest in counterfeit currency, travelers checks, credit cards—other cards as well as our own. There's also a lot more traffic than usual in stolen and counterfeit securities, stolen and forged checks."

"And you believe all this, and our Keycharge fraud losses, are linked?"

"Let's say it's possible."

"What's Security doing?"

"As much as we can. Every lost or missing Keycharge card that turns fraudulent is being checked out and, where possible, tracked down. Recovered cards and fraud prosecutions have increased every month this year; you've had the figures in reports. But something like this needs a full-scale investigation and I don't have either staff or budget to handle it."

Alex Vandervoort smiled ruefully. "I thought we'd get around to budget."

He surmised what was coming next. He knew of the problems under which Nolan Wainwright labored.

Wainwright, as a vice-president of First Mercantile American, was in charge of all security matters in the Headquarters Tower and at branches. The credit-card security division was only one of his responsibilities. In recent years the status of Security within the bank had been advanced, its operating funds increased, though the amount of money allotted was still inadequate. Everyone in management knew it. Yet because Security was a non-revenue producing function, its position on the priority list for additional funds was low.

"You've got proposals and figures, I presume. You always have, Nolan."

Wainwright produced a manila folder which he had brought with him. "It's all there. The most urgent need is two more full-time investigators for the credit-card division. I'm also asking for funds for an undercover agent whose assignment would be to locate the source of these counterfeit cards, also to find out where the leakage is occurring inside the bank."

Vandervoort looked surprised. "You think you can get someone?"

This time Wainwright smiled. "Well, you don't begin by advertising in 'help wanted' columns. But I'm willing to try."

"I'll look carefully at what you've suggested and do my best. That's all I can promise. May I keep these cards?"

The security chief nodded.

"Anything else on your mind?"

"Only this: I don't think anyone around here, including you, Alex, is taking this whole credit-card fraud problem seriously. Okay, so we congratulate ourselves that we've held losses down to three quarters of one percent of total business, but business has grown enormously while the percentage has stayed steady, even increased. As I understand it, Keycharge billings next year are expected to be three billion dollars."

"That's what we're hoping for."

"Then—at the same percentage—fraud losses could be more than twenty-two million."

Vandervoort said drily, "We prefer to speak of it in percentages. That way it doesn't sound as much, and the directors don't get alarmed."

"That's pretty cynical."

"Yes, I suppose it is."

And yet, Alex reasoned, it was an attitude which banks—all banks—took. They played down, deliberately, credit-card crime, accepting such losses as a cost of doing business. If any other bank department showed a seven-and-a-half-million-dollar loss in a single year, all hell would erupt before the board. But where credit cards were concerned, "three quarters of one percent" for criminality was accepted or conveniently ignored. The alternative—an all-out fight against crime—would be more costly by far. It could be said, of course, that the bankers' attitude was indefensible because in the end it was customers—credit-card holders—who paid for fraud through increased charges. But, from a financial point of view, the attitude made business sense.

"There are times," Alex said, "when the credit-card system sticks in my gullet, or rather parts of it do. But I live within the limits of what I think I can accomplish in the way of change, and what I know I can't. The same goes for budget priorities." He touched the manila folder which Wainwright had put down. "Leave it with me. I've already promised I'll do what I can."

"If I don't hear, I'll be along to pound the desk."

Alex Vandervoort left but Nolan Wainwright was delayed by a message. It asked the security chief to contact Mrs. D'Orsey, manager of the main downtown branch, at once.

7

"I've spoken to the FBI," Nolan Wainwright informed Edwina D'Orsey. "They'll have two special agents here tomorrow."

"Why not today?"

He grinned. "We've no dead body; there wasn't even any shooting. Besides, they have a problem over there. A thing called manpower shortage."

"Don't we all?"

"Then can I let the staff go home?" asked Miles Eastin.

Wainwright answered, "All except the girl. I'd like to talk with her again."

It was early evening, two hours since Wainwright had responded to Edwina's summons and taken over investigation of the cash loss. In the meantime he had covered the same ground the branch officers had gone over earlier, interviewing the teller, Juanita Núñez, Edwina D'Orsey, Tottenhoe, the operations officer, and young Miles Eastin, the operations assistant.

He had also spoken with other tellers who had been working near the Núñez girl.

Not wanting to be a focus of attention on the platform, Wainwright had taken over a conference room at the rear of the bank. He was there now with Edwina D'Orsey and Miles Eastin.

Nothing new had emerged except that theft appeared likely; therefore, under federal law the FBI must be called in. The law, on such occasions, was not always applied painstakingly, as Wainwright was well aware. First Mercantile American and other banks often labeled thefts of money as "mysterious disappearances" and, that way, such incidents could be handled internally, avoiding prosecution and publicity. Thus a member of the bank's staff suspected of theft might suffer dismissal only—ostensibly for some other reason. And since the guilty individuals were not inclined to talk, a surprisingly large number of theft cases were kept secret, even within the bank itself.

But the present loss—assuming it to be theft—was too large and flagrant to be concealed.

Nor was it a good idea to wait, hoping for more information. Wainwright knew the FBI would be angry if called in several days after the event to investigate a cold trail. Until the Bureau agents arrived, he intended to do what he could himself.

As Edwina and Miles Eastin left the small office, the operations assistant said helpfully, "I'll send Mrs. Núñez in."

A moment later the small, slight figure of Juanita Núñez appeared at the office doorway. "Come in," Nolan Wainwright instructed. "Shut the door. Sit down."

He made his tone official and businesslike. Instinct told him that phony friendliness would not deceive this girl.

"I want to hear your whole story again. We'll take it step by step."

Juanita Núñez looked sulky and defiant, as she had earlier, but now there were traces of fatigue. With a sudden flash of spirit, though, she objected, "Three times I have already done that. Everything!"

"Perhaps you forgot something the other times."

"I forgot nothing!"

"Then this time will make a fourth, and when the FBI arrive there'll be a fifth, and maybe after that a sixth." He held her eyes with his own and kept authority in his voice but didn't raise it. If he were a police officer, Wainwright thought, he'd have had to caution her about her rights. But he wasn't, and wouldn't. Sometimes, in a situation like this, private security forces had advantages which police were not allowed.

"I know what you are thinking," the girl said. "You think I will say something different this time, so you can prove that I was lying."

"*Are* you lying?"

"No!"

"Then why worry about that?"

Her voice quavered. "Because I am tired. I would like to go."

"I would, too. And if it wasn't for a missing six thousand dollars—which you admit you had in your possession earlier—I'd be finished work for the day and driving home. But the money *is* gone and we'd like to find it. So tell me about this afternoon again—when you say you first saw something wrong."

"It was like I told you—twenty minutes after lunch."

He read contempt in her eyes. Earlier, when he began asking questions, he had sensed the girl's attitude as being easier toward him than the others. No doubt because he was black and she was Puerto Rican, she assumed they might be allies or, if not that, that he would be a softer touch. What she didn't know was that where investigative work was concerned he was color-blind. Nor could he concern himself about any personal problems the girl might have. Edwina D'Orsey had mentioned these, but no personal circumstance, in Wainwright's view, ever justified stealing or dishonesty.

The Núñez girl had been right, of course, about his wanting to catch her out in some variation of her story. And it could happen, despite her obvious caution. She had complained of being tired. As an experienced investigator, Wainwright knew that guilty people, when tired, were apt to make mistakes during interrogation, a small one first, then another and another, until they became trapped in a web of lies and inconsistency.

Wondering if it would happen now, he pressed on.

It took three quarters of an hour, during which Juanita Núñez's version of events remained identical with what she had stated earlier. While disappointed at having uncovered nothing new, Wainwright was not overly impressed with the girl's consistency. His police background made him realize that such exactitude could have two interpretations: Either she was speaking the truth or she had rehearsed her story so carefully that she was perfect in it. The latter seemed a probability because innocent people usually had a few slight variations between one recounting and the next. It was a symptom which detectives learned to look for.

At the end, Wainwright said, "All right, that's everything for now. Tomorrow you can take a lie detector test. The bank will arrange it."

He made the announcement casually, though watching for a reaction. What he had not expected was one as sudden or as fierce.

The girl's small dark face flushed red. She shot upright in her chair.

"No, I will not! I will not take such a test!"

"Why not?"

"Because it is an insult!"

"It's no insult. Lots of people take the test. If you're innocent, the machine will prove it."

"I do not trust such a machine. Or you. *¡Basta con mi palabra!*"

He ignored the Spanish, suspecting it was abusive. "You've no reason not to trust me. All I'm interested in is getting to the truth."

"You have heard truth! You do not recognize it! You, like the others, believe I took the money. It is useless to tell you I did not."

Wainwright stood up. He opened the door of the tiny office for the girl to go. "Between now and tomorrow," he advised, "I suggest you reconsider your attitude about that test. If you refuse to take it, it will look bad for you."

She looked him fully in the face. "I do not have to take such a test, do I?"

"No."

"Then I will not."

She marched from the office with short, quick steps. After a moment, unhurriedly, Wainwright followed.

Within the bank's main working area, though a few people were still at desks, the majority of staff had gone and overhead lights were dimmed. Outside, darkness had descended on the raw fall day.

Juanita Núñez went to a locker room for her street clothes, and returned. She ignored Wainwright. Miles Eastin, who had been waiting with a key, let her out through the main street door.

"Juanita," Eastin said, "is there anything I can do? Shall I drive you home?"

She shook her head without speaking and went out.

Nolan Wainwright, watching from a window, saw her walk to a bus stop across the street. If he had had a larger security force, he thought, he might have had her followed, though he doubted it would do any good. Mrs. Núñez was clever and she would not give herself away, either by handing the money to someone else in public or even storing it in a predictable place.

He was convinced the girl did not have the money on her. She was too astute to run that risk; also, the amount of cash would be too bulky to conceal. He had looked at her closely during their talk and afterward, observing that her clothes clung tightly to her small body and there were no suspicious bulges. The purse she carried from the bank was tiny. She had no packages.

Wainwright felt certain that an accomplice was involved.

He had little remaining doubt, if any, that Juanita Núñez was guilty. Her refusal to submit to a lie detector test, considered with all other facts and indications, had convinced him. Remembering her emotional outburst of a few minutes ago, he suspected it was planned, perhaps rehearsed. Bank employees were well aware that in cases of suspected theft a lie detector was employed; the Núñez girl was likely to have known that, too. Therefore she could have guessed the subject would come up and been ready for it.

Remembering how she had looked at him with contempt and, before that, her unspoken assumption of alliance, Wainwright felt a surge of anger. With an unusual intensity he found himself hoping that tomorrow the FBI team would give her a hard time and shake her down. But it would not be easy. She was tough.

Miles Eastin had relocked the main street door and now returned.

"Well," he said cheerfully, "time to head for the showers."

The security chief nodded. "It's been quite a day."

Eastin seemed about to say something else, then apparently decided otherwise.

Wainwright asked him, "Something on your mind?"

Again Eastin hesitated, then admitted, "Well, yes, there is. It's a thing I haven't mentioned to anyone because it could be just a wild pitch."

"Does it relate in any way to the missing money?"

"I suppose it could."

Wainwright said sternly, "Then whether you're sure or not, you have to tell me."

The assistant operations officer nodded. "All right."

Wainwright waited.

"It was mentioned to you—by Mrs. D'Orsey, I think—that Juanita Núñez is married. Her husband deserted her. He left her with their child."

"I remember."

"When the husband was living with Juanita he used to come in here occasionally. To meet her, I guess. I spoke to him a couple of times. I'm pretty sure his name is Carlos."

"What about him?"

"I believe he was in the bank today."

Wainwright asked sharply, "Are you sure?"

"Fairly sure, though not enough so I could swear to it in court. I just noticed someone, thought it was him, then put it out of mind. I was busy. There was no reason for me to think about it—at least not until a long time later."

"What time of day was it when you saw him?"

"About midmorning."

"This man you thought was the Núñez girl's husband—did you see him go to the counter where she was working?"

"No, I didn't." Eastin's handsome young face was troubled. "As I say,

I didn't think about it much. The only thing is, if I saw him, he couldn't have been far away from Juanita."

"And that's everything?"

"That's it." Miles Eastin added apologetically, "I'm sorry it isn't more."

"You were right to tell me. It could be important."

If Eastin were right, Wainwright reasoned, the presence of the husband could tie in with Wainwright's own theory of an outside accomplice. Possibly the girl and her husband were together again or, if not, had some arrangement. Perhaps she had passed the money over the counter to him, and he had taken it from the bank, to divide it with her later. The possibility was certainly something for the FBI to work on.

"Quite apart from the missing money," Eastin said, "everybody in the bank is talking about Mr. Rosselli—we heard about the announcement yesterday, his illness. Most of us are pretty sad."

It was a sudden, painful reminder as Wainwright regarded the younger man, usually so full of banter and joviality. At this moment, the security chief saw, there was distress in Eastin's eyes.

Wainwright realized that the investigation had driven all thought of Ben Rosselli from his mind. Now, remembering, he experienced new anger that thievery should leave its ugly mark at such a time.

With a murmured acknowledgment and a good night to Eastin, he walked through the tunnel from the branch bank, using his passkey to re-enter the FMA Headquarters Tower.

8

Across the street, Juanita Núñez—a tiny figure against the soaring city block complex of First Mercantile American Bank and Rosselli Plaza —was still waiting for her bus.

She had seen the security officer's face watching her from a window of the bank, and had a sense of relief when the face disappeared, though commonsense told her the relief was only temporary, and the wretchedness of today would resume and be as bad, or even worse, tomorrow.

A cold wind, knifing through downtown streets, penetrated the thin coat she had on, and she shivered as she waited. Her regular bus had gone. She hoped another would come soon.

The shivering, Juanita knew, was partly from fear because, at this moment, she was more frightened, more terror-stricken, than ever before in all her life.

Frightened and perplexed.

Perplexed because she had no idea how the money had been lost.

Juanita knew that she had neither stolen the money, nor handed it across the counter in error, or disposed of it in any other way.

The trouble was: no one would believe her.

In other circumstances, she realized, she might not have believed herself.

How *could* six thousand dollars have vanished? It was impossible, *impossible*. And yet it had.

Time after time this afternoon she had searched her recollection of every single moment of the day to find some explanation. There was none. She had thought back over cash transactions at the counter during the morning and early afternoon, using the remarkable memory she knew she had, but no solution came to her. Not even the wildest possibility made any sense.

She was positive, too, that she had locked her cash drawer securely before taking it to the vault while she had lunch, and it was still locked when she returned. As to the combination, which Juanita had chosen and set herself, she had never discussed it with anyone else or even written it down, relying as usual on her memory.

In one way it was her memory which had added to her troubles.

Juanita knew she had not been believed, either by Mrs. D'Orsey, Mr. Tottenhoe, or Miles, who at least had been friendlier than the others, when she claimed to know, at two o'clock, the exact amount of money which was gone. They said it was impossible she could know.

But she *had* known. Just as she *always* knew how much cash she had when she was working as a teller, although she found it impossible to explain to others how or why.

She was not even sure herself how she kept the running tally in her head. It was simply there. It happened without effort, so that she was scarcely aware of the arithmetic involved. For almost as long as Juanita could remember, adding, subtracting, multiplying, and dividing seemed as easy as breathing, and as natural.

She did it automatically at the bank counter as she took money in from customers or paid it out. And she had learned to glance at her cash drawer, checking that the cash she had on hand was what it should be, that various denominations of notes were in their right order, and in sufficient numbers. Even with coins, while not knowing the total so precisely, she could estimate the amount closely at any time. Occasionally, at the end of a busy day when she balanced her cash, her mental figure might prove to be in error by a few dollars, but never more.

Where had the ability come from? She had no idea.

She had never excelled in school. During her sketchy high school education in New York, she seldom achieved more than a low average in most subjects. Even in mathematics she had no real grasp of principles, merely an ability to calculate with lightning speed and carry figures in her head.

At last the bus arrived with an uneven roar and diesel stink. With others who were waiting, Juanita climbed aboard. No seats were available and standing space was crowded. She managed to grab a handhold and continued thinking, straining to remember as the bus swayed through the city streets.

What would happen tomorrow? Miles had told her that FBI men were coming. The thought filled her with fresh dread and her face set

tensely in a bleakness of anxiety—the same expression which Edwina
D'Orsey and Nolan Wainwright had mistaken for hostility.

She would say as little as possible, just as she had done today after
she found that no one was believing.

As to the machine, the lie detector, she would refuse. She knew nothing of how such a machine worked, but when no one else would understand, believe, or help her, why would a machine—the bank's machine
—be different?

It was a three-block walk from the bus to the nursery school where
she had left Estela this morning on her way to work. Juanita hurried,
knowing she was late.

The little girl ran toward her as she entered the small school play-
room in the basement of a private house. Though the house, like others
in the area, was old and dilapidated, the school rooms were clean and
cheerful—the reason Juanita had chosen the school in preference to others, though the cost was higher and a strain for her to pay.

Estela was excited, as full of joy as always.

"Mommy! Mommy! See my painting. It's a train." She pointed with
a paint-covered finger. "There's a bagoose. That's a *man* inside."

She was a small child, even for three, dark like Juanita, with large
liquid eyes reflecting her wonder at each new interest, at the fresh discoveries she made every day.

Juanita hugged her and corrected her gently. "Caboose, *amorcito*."

It was obvious from the stillness that the other children were all gone.

Miss Ferroe, who owned and ran the school, came in primly, frowning. She looked pointedly at her watch.

"Mrs. Núñez, as a special favor I agreed that Estela could stay after
the others, but this is far too late . . ."

"I really am sorry, Miss Ferroe. Something happened at the bank."

"I have private responsibilities also. And other parents observe the
school's closing time."

"It won't happen again. I promise."

"Very well. But since you are here, Mrs. Núñez, may I remind you
that last month's bill for Estela has not been paid."

"It will be on Friday. I'll have my paycheck then."

"I'm sorry to have to mention it, you understand. Estela is a sweet
little girl and we're glad to have her. But I have bills to pay . . ."

"I do understand. It will be Friday for sure. I promise."

"That's two promises, Mrs. Núñez."

"Yes, I know."

"Good night then. Good night, Estela dear."

Despite her starchiness, the Ferroe woman ran an excellent nursery school and Estela was happy there. The money owing to the school, Juanita decided, would have to come out of her pay this week, as she had said, and somehow she must manage until the payday after that. She wasn't sure how. Her wage as a teller was $98 weekly; after taxes and Social Security deductions, her take-home pay was $83. Out of that there was food to buy for the two of them, Estela's school fees, plus rent of the tiny walk-up flat they lived in at Forum East; also the finance company would demand a payment since she had missed the last.

Before Carlos left her, simply walking out and disappearing a year ago, Juanita had been naive enough to sign finance papers jointly with her husband. He had bought suits, a used car, a color TV, all of which he took with him. Juanita, however, was still paying, the installments seeming to stretch on into a limitless future.

She would have to visit the finance company office, she thought, and offer them less. They would undoubtedly be nasty, as they were before, but it would have to be endured.

On the way home, Estela skipped happily along, one small hand in Juanita's. In her other hand Juanita carried Estela's painting, carefully rolled up. In a little while, in the apartment, they would have their evening meal and afterward they usually played and laughed together. But Juanita would find it difficult to laugh tonight.

Her earlier terror deepened as she considered for the first time what might happen if she lost her job. The probability, she realized, was strong.

She knew, too, that it would be hard to find work elsewhere. No other bank would hire her and other employers would want to know where she had worked before, then would find out about the missing money and reject her.

Without a job, what would she do? How could she support Estela?

Abruptly, stopping on the street, Juanita reached down and clasped her daughter to her.

She prayed that tomorrow someone would believe her, would recognize the truth.

Someone, *someone*.

But who?

9

Alex Vandervoort, also, was abroad in the city.

Earlier in the afternoon, returning from the session with Nolan Wainwright, Alex had paced his office suite, seeking to place recent events in true perspective. Yesterday's announcement by Ben Rosselli was a major cause for reflection. So was the resultant situation in the bank. So, too, were developments, within recent months, in Alex's personal life.

Pacing back and forth—twelve strides one way, twelve the other—was an old established habit. Once or twice he had stopped, re-examining the counterfeit Keycharge credit cards which the security chief had allowed Alex to bring away. Credit and credit cards were additionally a part of his preoccupation—not only fraudulent cards, but genuine ones, too.

The genuine variety was represented by a series of advertising proofs, also on the desk, and now spread out. They had been prepared by the Austin Advertising Agency and the purpose was to encourage Keycharge holders to use their credit and their cards increasingly.

One announcement urged:

WHY WORRY ABOUT MONEY?
USE YOUR KEYCHARGE CARD
AND
LET *US* WORRY FOR YOU!

Another claimed:

BILLS ARE PAINLESS
WHEN YOU SAY
"PUT IT ON MY KEYCHARGE!"

A third advised:

WHY WAIT?
YOU CAN AFFORD TOMORROW'S DREAM
TODAY!
USE YOUR KEYCHARGE
—NOW!

A half dozen others were on similar themes.

Alex Vandervoort was uneasy about them all.

His unease did not have to be translated into action. The advertising, already approved by the bank's Keycharge division, had merely been sent to Alex for general information. Also, the over-all approach had been agreed on several weeks ago by the bank's board of directors as a means to increase the profitability of Keycharge which—like all credit-card programs—sustained losses in its initial, launching years.

But Alex wondered: Had the board envisaged a promotional campaign quite so blatantly aggressive?

He shuffled the advertising proofs together and returned them to the folder they had arrived in. At home tonight he would reconsider them and he would hear a second opinion, he realized—probably a strong one —from Margot.

Margot.

The thought of her melded with the memory of Ben Rosselli's disclosure yesterday. What had been said then was a reminder to Alex of life's fragility, the brevity of time remaining, the inevitability of endings, a pointer to the unexpected always close at hand. He had been moved and saddened for Ben himself; but also, without intending to, the old man had revived once more an oft-recurring question: Should Alex make a fresh life for himself and Margot? Or should he wait? And wait for what?

For Celia?

That question, too, he had asked himself a thousand times.

Alex looked out across the city toward where he knew Celia to be. He wondered what she was doing, how she was.

There was a simple way to find out.

He returned to his desk and dialed a number which he knew by heart.

A woman's voice answered, "Remedial Center."

He identified himself and said, "I'd like to talk with Dr. McCartney."

After a moment or two a male voice, quietly firm, inquired, "Where are you, Alex?"

"In my office. I was sitting here wondering about my wife."

"I asked because I intended to call you today and suggest you come in to visit Celia."

"The last time we talked you said you didn't want me to."

The psychiatrist corrected him gently. "I said I thought any more visits inadvisable for a while. The previous few, you'll remember, seemed to unsettle your wife rather than help."

"I remember." Alex hesitated, then asked, "There's been some change?"

"Yes, there is a change. I wish I could say it was for the better."

There had been so many changes, he had become dulled to them. "What kind of change?"

"Your wife is becoming even more withdrawn. Her escape from reality is almost total. It's why I think a visit from you might do some good." The psychiatrist corrected himself, "At least it should do no harm."

"All right. I'll come this evening."

"Any time, Alex; and drop in to see me when you do. As you know, we've no set visiting hours here and a minimum of rules."

"Yes, I know."

The absence of formality, he reflected, as he replaced the telephone, was a reason he had chosen the Remedial Center when faced with his despairing decision about Celia nearly four years ago. The atmosphere was deliberately non-institutional. The nurses did not wear uniforms. As far as was practical, patients moved around freely and were encouraged to make decisions of their own. With occasional exceptions, friends and families were welcome at any time. Even the name Remedial Center had been chosen intentionally in preference to the more forbidding "mental hospital." Another reason was that Dr. Timothy McCartney, young, brilliant, and innovative, headed a specialist team which achieved cures of mental illnesses where more conventional treatments failed.

The Center was small. Patients never exceeded a hundred and fifty though, by comparison, the staff was large. In a way, it was like a school with small classes where students received personal attention they could not have gained elsewhere.

A modern building and spacious gardens were as pleasing as money and imagination could make them.

The clinic was private. It was also horrendously expensive but Alex had been determined, and still was, that whatever else happened, Celia would have the best of care. It was, he reasoned, the very least that he could do.

Through the remainder of the afternoon he occupied himself with bank business. Soon after 6 P.M. he left FMA Headquarters, giving his driver the Remedial Center address, and read the evening paper while they crawled through traffic. A limousine and chauffeur, available at any time from the bank's pool of cars, were perquisites of the executive vice-president's job and Alex enjoyed them.

Typically, the Remedial Center had the façade of a large private home with nothing outside, other than a street number, to identify it.

An attractive blonde, wearing a colorful print dress, let him in. He recognized her as a nurse from a small insignia pin near her left shoulder. It was the only permitted dress distinction between staff and patients.

"Doctor told us you'd be coming, Mr. Vandervoort. I'll take you to your wife."

He walked with her along a pleasant corridor. Yellows and greens predominated. Fresh flowers were in niches along the walls.

"I understand," he said, "that my wife has been no better."

"Not really, I'm afraid." The nurse shot him a sideways glance; he sensed pity in her eyes. But for whom? As always, when he came here, he felt his natural ebullience desert him.

They were in a wing, one of three running outward from the central reception area. The nurse stopped at a door.

"Your wife is in her room, Mr. Vandervoort. She had a bad day today. Try to remember that, if she shouldn't . . ." She left the sentence unfinished, touched his arm lightly, then preceded him in.

The Remedial Center placed patients in shared or single rooms according to the effect which the company of others had on their condition. When Celia first came she was in a double room, but it hadn't worked; now she was in a private one. Though small, Celia's room was cozily comfortable and individual. It contained a studio couch, a deep armchair and ottoman, a games table and bookshelves. Impressionist prints adorned the walls.

"Mrs. Vandervoort," the nurse said gently, "your husband is here to visit you."

There was no acknowledgment, neither movement nor spoken response, from the figure in the room.

It had been a month and a half since Alex had seen Celia and, though he had been expecting some deterioration, her present appearance chilled him.

She was seated—if her posture could be called that—on the studio couch. She had positioned herself sideways, facing away from the outer door. Her shoulders were hunched down, her head lowered, arms crossed in front, with each hand clasping the opposite shoulder. Her body, too, was curled upon itself and her legs drawn up with knees together. She was absolutely still.

He went to her and put a hand gently on one shoulder. "Hullo, Celia. It's me—Alex. I've been thinking about you, so I came to see you."

She said, low-voiced, without expression, "Yes." She did not move.

He increased the pressure on the shoulder. "Won't you turn around to look at me? Then we can sit together and talk."

The only response was a perceptible rigidity, a tightening of the position in which Celia was huddled.

Her skin texture, Alex saw, was mottled and her fair hair only roughly combed. Even now her gentle, fragile beauty had not entirely vanished, though clearly it would not be long before it did.

"Has she been like this long?" he asked the nurse quietly.

"All of today and part of yesterday; some other days as well." The girl added matter-of-factly, "She feels more comfortable that way, so it's best if you take no notice, just sit down and talk."

Alex nodded. As he went to the single armchair and settled himself, the nurse tiptoed out, closing the door gently.

"I went to the ballet last week, Celia," Alex said. "It was *Coppélia*. Natalia Makarova danced the lead and Ivan Nagy was Frantz. They were magnificent together and, of course, the music was wonderful. It reminded me of how you loved *Coppélia*, that it was one of your favorites. Do you remember that night, soon after we were married, when you and I . . ."

He could call back in memory clearly, even now, the way Celia had looked that evening—in a long, pale green chiffon gown, tiny sequins glittering with reflected light. As usual, she had been ethereally beautiful, slim and gossamer-like, as if a breeze might steal her if he looked away. In those days he seldom did. They had been married six months and she was still shy at meeting Alex's friends, so that sometimes in a group she clung tightly to his arm. Because she was ten years younger than himself, he hadn't minded. Celia's shyness, at the beginning, had been one of the reasons why he fell in love with her, and he was proud of her reliance on him. Only long after, when she continued to be diffident and unsure—foolishly, it seemed to him—had his impatience surfaced, and eventually anger.

How little, how tragically little, he had understood! With more perception he would have realized that Celia's background before they met was so totally different from his own that nothing had prepared her for

*the active social and domestic life he accepted matter-of-factly. It was
all new and bewildering to Celia, at times alarming. She was the only
child of reclusive parents of modest means, had attended convent
schools, had never known the leavening propinquity of college living.
Before Celia met Alex she had had no responsibilities, her social experience was nil. Marriage increased her natural nervousness; at the same
time, self-doubts and tensions grew until eventually—as psychiatrists
explained it—a burden of guilt at failing snapped something in her
mind. With hindsight, Alex blamed himself. He could, he afterwards
believed, have helped Celia so easily, could have given advice, eased
tensions, offered reassurance. But when it mattered most he never had.
He had been too thoughtless, busy, ambitious.*

". . . so last week's performance, Celia, made me sorry we weren't
seeing it together . . ."

*In fact, he had been to Coppélia with Margot, whom Alex had known
now for a year and a half, and who zestfully filled a gap in his life which
had been empty for so long. Margot, or someone else, had been necessary if Alex—a flesh and blood man—were not to become a mental case,
too, he sometimes told himself. Or was that a self-delusion, conveniently assuaging guilt?*

Either way, this was no time or place to introduce Margot's name.

"Oh, yes, and not long ago, Celia, I saw the Harringtons. You remember John and Elise. Anyway, they told me they had been to Scandinavia to see Elise's parents."

"Yes," Celia said tonelessly.

She had still not stirred from the huddled position, but evidently was
listening, so he continued talking, using only half his mind while the
other half asked: *How did it happen? Why?*

"We've been busy at the bank lately, Celia."

*One reason, he assumed, had been his preoccupation with his work,
the long hours during which—as their marriage deteriorated—he had
left Celia alone. That, as he now saw it, was when she had needed him
most. As it was, Celia accepted his absences without complaint but
grew increasingly reserved and timid, burying herself in books or looking interminably at plants and flowers, appearing to watch them grow,
though occasionally—in contrast and without apparent reason—she became animated, talking incessantly and sometimes incoherently. Those
were periods in which Celia seemed to have exceptional energy. Then,
with equal suddenness, the energy would disappear, leaving her depressed and withdraw once more. And all the while their communication and companionship diminished.*

It was during that time—the thought of it shamed him now—he had suggested they divorce. Celia had seemed shattered and he let the subject drop, hoping things would get better, but they hadn't.

Only at length, when the thought occurred to him almost casually that Celia might need psychiatric help, and he had sought it, had the truth of her malady become clear. For a while, anguish and concern revived his love. But, by then, it was too late.

At times he speculated: *Perhaps it had always been too late. Perhaps not even greater kindness, understanding, would have helped.* But he would never know. He could never nurture the conviction he had done his best and, because of it, could never shed the guilt which haunted him.

"Everybody seems to be thinking about money—spending it, borrowing it, lending it, though I guess that's not unusual and what banks are for. A sad thing happened yesterday, though. Ben Rosselli, our president, told us he was dying. He called a meeting and . . ."

Alex went on, describing the scene in the boardroom and reactions afterward, then abruptly stopped.

Celia had begun to tremble. Her body was rocking back and forth. A wail, half moan, escaped her.

Had his mention of the bank upset her?—*the bank into which he had thrown his energies, widening the gulf between them.* It was another bank then, the Federal Reserve, but to Celia one bank was like another. Or was it his reference to Ben Rosselli?

Ben would die soon. *How many years before Celia died? Many, perhaps.*

Alex thought: she could easily outlive him, could live on like this.

She looked like an animal!

His pity evaporated. Anger seized him; the angry impatience which had marred their marriage. "For Christ's sake, Celia, control yourself!"

Her trembling and the moans continued.

He hated her! She wasn't human any more, yet she remained the barrier between himself and a full life.

Getting up, Alex savagely punched a bell push on the wall, knowing it would summon help. In the same motion he strode to the door to leave.

And looked back. At Celia—his wife whom once he had loved; at what she had become; at the gulf between them they would never bridge. He paused, and wept.

Wept with pity, sadness, guilt, his momentary anger spent, the hatred washed away.

He returned to the studio couch and, on his knees before her, begged, "Celia, forgive me! Oh, God, forgive me!"

He felt a gentle hand on his shoulder, heard the young nurse's voice. "Mr. Vandervoort, I think you should go now."

"Water or soda, Alex?"

"Soda."

Dr. McCartney took a bottle from the small refrigerator in his consulting room and used an opener to flip the top. He poured into a glass which already contained a generous slug of scotch and added ice. He brought the glass to Alex, then poured the rest of the soda, without liquor, for himself.

For a big man—Tim McCartney was six feet five with a football player's chest and shoulders, and enormous hands—his movements were remarkably deft. Though the clinic director was young, in his mid-thirties Alex guessed, his manner and voice seemed older and his brushed-back brown hair was graying at the temples. Probably because of a lot of sessions like this, Alex thought. He sipped the scotch gratefully.

The paneled room was softly lighted, its color tones more muted than the corridors and other rooms outside. Bookshelves and racks for journals filled one wall, the works of Freud, Adler, Jung, and Rogers prominent.

Alex was still shaken as the result of his meeting with Celia, yet in a way the horror of it seemed unreal.

Dr. McCartney returned to a chair at his desk and swung it to face the sofa where Alex sat.

"I should report to you first that your wife's general diagnosis remains the same—schizophrenia, catatonic type. You'll remember we've discussed this in the past."

"I remember all the jargon, yes."

"I'll try to spare you any more."

Alex swirled the ice in his glass and drank again; the scotch had warmed him. "Tell me about Celia's condition now."

"You may find this hard to accept, but your wife, despite the way she seems, is relatively happy."

"Yes," Alex said. "I find that hard to believe."

The psychiatrist insisted quietly, "Happiness is relative, for all of us. What Celia has is security of a kind, a total absence of responsibility or the need to relate to others. She can withdraw into herself as much as she wants or needs to. The physical posture she's been taking lately, which you saw, is the classic fetal position. It comforts her to assume it, though for her physical good, we try to dissuade her when we can."

"Comforting or not," Alex said, "the essence is that after having had the best possible treatment for four years, my wife's condition is still deteriorating." He eyed the other man directly. "Is that right or wrong?"

"Unfortunately it's right."

"Is there any reasonable chance of a recovery, ever, so that Celia could lead a normal or near-normal life?"

"In medicine there are always possibilities . . ."

"I said *reasonable chance*."

Dr. McCartney sighed and shook his head. "No."

"Thank you for a plain answer." Alex paused, then went on, "As I understand it, Celia has become—I believe the word is 'institutionalized.' She's withdrawn from the human race. She neither knows nor cares about anything outside herself."

"You're right about being institutionalized," the psychiatrist said, "but you're wrong about the rest. Your wife has not totally withdrawn, at least not yet. She still knows a little about what's going on outside. She also is aware she has a husband, and we've talked about you. But she believes you're entirely capable of taking care of yourself without her help."

"So she doesn't worry about me?"

"On the whole, no."

"How would she feel if she learned her husband had divorced her and remarried?"

Dr. McCartney hesitated, then said, "It would represent a total break from the little outside contact she has remaining. It might drive her over the brink into a totally demented state."

In the ensuing silence Alex leaned forward, covering his face with his hands. Then he removed them. His head came up. With a trace of irony, he said, "I guess if you ask for plain answers you're apt to get them."

The psychiatrist nodded, his expression serious. "I paid you a compliment, Alex, in assuming you meant what you said. I would not have been as frank with everyone. Also, I should add, I could be wrong."

"Tim, *what the hell does a man do?*"

"Is that rhetoric or a question?"

"It's a question. You can put it on my bill."

"There'll be no bill tonight." The younger man smiled briefly, then considered. "You ask me: *What does a man do in a circumstance like yours?* Well, to begin, he finds out all he can—just as you have done.

Then he makes decisions based on what he thinks is fair and best for everyone, including himself. But while he's making up his mind he ought to remember two things. One is, if he's a decent man, his own guilt feelings are probably exaggerated because a well-developed conscience has a habit of punishing itself more harshly than it need. The other is that few people are qualified for sainthood; the majority of us aren't born with the equipment."

Alex asked, "And you won't go further? You won't be more specific?"

Dr. McCartney shook his head. "Only you can make the decision. Those last few paces each of us walks alone."

The psychiatrist glanced at his watch and got up from his chair. Moments later they shook hands and said good night.

Outside the Remedial Center, Alex's limousine and driver—the car's motor running, its interior warm and comfortable—were waiting.

10

"Without doubt," Margot Bracken declared, "that is one crappy collection of chicanery and damn lies."

She was looking down, elbows aggressively out, hands on slender waist, her small but resolute head thrust forward. She was provocative physically, Alex Vandervoort thought—a "slip of a girl" with pleasingly sharp features, chin jutting and aggressive, thinnish lips, though the mouth was sensual over-all. Margot's eyes were her strongest feature; they were large, green, flecked with gold, the lashes thick and long. At this moment those eyes were glaring. Her anger and forcefulness stirred him sexually.

The object of Margot's censure was the assortment of advertising proofs for Keycharge credit cards which Alex had brought home from FMA, and which now were spread out on the living-room rug of his apartment. Margot's presence and vitality were providing, also, a needed contrast to Alex's ordeal of several hours ago.

He told her, "I had an idea, Bracken, you might not like those advertising themes."

"Not like them! I *despise* them."

"Why?"

She pushed back her long chestnut hair in a familiar though unconscious gesture. An hour ago Margot had kicked off her shoes and now stood, all five-foot-two of her, in stockinged feet.

"All right, look at that!" She pointed to the announcement which began: WHY WAIT? YOU CAN AFFORD TOMORROW'S DREAM TODAY! "What it is, is dishonest bullshit—high-powered, aggressive selling of debt—concocted to entrap the gullible. Tomorrow's dream, for anyone, is sure to be expensive. That's why it's a dream. And *no one* can afford it unless they have the money now or are certain of it soon."

"Shouldn't people make their own judgments about that?"

"No!—not the people who'll be influenced by that perverted advertising, the ones you're *trying* to influence. They're the unsophisticated, the easily persuadable, those who believe that what they see in print is true. I know. I get plenty of them as clients in my law practice. My unprofitable law practice."

"Maybe those aren't the kind of people who have our Keycharge cards."

"Dammit, Alex, you know that isn't true! The most unlikely people nowadays have credit cards because you all have pushed them so hard. The only thing you haven't done is hand cards out at street corners, and it wouldn't surprise me if you started that soon."

Alex grinned. He enjoyed these debating sessions with Margot and liked to keep them fueled. "I'll tell our people to think about it, Bracken."

"What I wish other people would think about is that Shylocking eighteen percent interest all bank credit cards charge."

"We've been over that before."

"Yes, we have. And I've never heard an explanation which satisfied me."

He countered sharply, "Maybe you don't listen." Enjoyable in debate or not, Margot had a knack of getting under his skin. Occasionally their debates developed into fights.

"I've told you that credit cards are a packaged commodity, offering a range of services," Alex insisted. "If you add those services together, our interest rate is not excessive."

"It's as excessive as hell if you're the one who's paying."

"Nobody *has* to pay. Because nobody *has* to borrow."

"I can hear you. You don't have to shout."

"All right."

He took a breath, determined not to let *this* discussion get out of hand. Besides, while disputing some of Margot's views, which in economics, politics, and everything else were left of center, he found his own thinking aided by her forthrightness and keen lawyer's mind. Margot's practice, too, brought her contacts which he lacked directly—among the city's poor and underprivileged for whom the bulk of her legal work was done.

He asked, "Another cognac?"

"Yes, please."

It was close to midnight. A log fire, blazing earlier, had burned low in the hearth of the snug room in the small, sumptuous bachelor suite.

An hour and a half ago they had had a late dinner here, delivered from a service restaurant on the apartment block's main floor. An excellent Bordeaux—Alex's choice, Château Gruaud-Larose '66—accompanied the meal.

Apart from the area where the Keycharge advertising had been spread out, the apartment lights were low.

When he had replenished their brandy glasses, Alex returned to the argument. "If people pay their credit-card bills when they get them, there *is* no interest charge."

"You mean pay their bills in full."

"Right."

"But how many do? Don't most credit-card users pay that convenient 'minimum balance' that the statements show?"

"A good many pay the minimum, yes."

"And carry the rest forward as debt—which is what you bankers really want them to do. Isn't that so?"

Alex conceded, "Yes, it's true. But banks have to make a profit somewhere."

"I lay awake nights," Margot said, "worrying if banks are making enough profit."

As he laughed, she went on seriously, "Look, Alex, thousands of people who shouldn't are piling up long-term debts by using credit cards. Often it's to buy trivia—drugstore items, phonograph records, bits of hardware, books, meals, other minor things; and they do it partly through unawareness, partly because small amounts of credit are ridiculously easy to obtain. And those small amounts, which ought to be paid by cash, add up to crippling debts, burdening imprudent people for years ahead."

Alex cradled his brandy glass in both hands to warm it, sipped, then rose and tossed a fresh log on the fire. He protested, "You're worrying too much, and the problem isn't that big."

And yet, he admitted to himself, some of what Margot had said made sense. Where once—as an old song put it—miners "owed their souls to the company store," a new breed of chronic debtor had arisen, naively mortgaging future life and income to a "friendly neighborhood bank." One reason was that credit cards had replaced, to a large extent, small loans. Where individuals used to be dissuaded from excessive borrowing, now they made their own loan decisions—often unwisely. Some observers, Alex knew, believed the system had down-graded American morality.

Of course, doing it the credit-card way was much cheaper for a bank; also, a small loan customer, borrowing through the credit-card route, paid substantially higher interest than on a conventional loan. The *total* interest the bank received, in fact, was often as high as twenty-four percent since merchants who honored credit cards paid their own additional bank levy, ranging from two to six percent.

These were reasons why banks such as First Mercantile American were relying on credit-card business to swell their profits, and they would increasingly in future years. True, initial losses with all credit-card schemes had been substantial; as bankers were apt to put it, "we took a bath." But the same bankers were convinced that a bonanza was close at hand which would outstrip in profitability most other kinds of bank business.

Another thing bankers realized was that credit cards were a necessary way station on the route to EFTS—the Electronic Funds Transfer System which, within a decade and a half, would replace the present avalanche of banking paper and make existing checks and passbooks as obsolete as the Model T.

"That's enough," Margot said. "The two of us are beginning to sound like a shareholders meeting." She came to him and kissed him fully on the lips.

The heat of their argument earlier had already aroused him, as skirmishes with Margot so often did. Their first encounter had begun that way. Sometimes, it seemed, the angrier both became, the larger their physical passion for each other grew. After a while he murmured, "I declare the shareholders meeting closed."

"Well . . ." Margot eased away and regarded him mischievously. "There *is* some unfinished business—that advertising, darling. You're not really going to let it go out to the public the way it is?"

"No," he said, "I don't believe I am."

The Keycharge advertising was a strong sell—too strong—and he would use his authority to exercise a veto in the morning. He realized he had intended to, anyway. Margot had merely confirmed his own opinion of this afternoon.

The fresh log he had added to the fire was alight and crackling. They sat on the rug before the fireplace, savoring its warmth, watching the rising tongues of flame.

Margot leaned her head against Alex's shoulder. She said softly, "For a stuffy old moneychanger, you're really not too bad."

He put his arm around her. "I love you, too, Bracken."

"Really and truly? Banker's honor?"

"I swear by the prime rate."

"Then love me now." She began to take off her clothes.

He whispered with amusement, "Here?"

"Why not?"

Alex sighed happily. "Why not indeed?"

Soon after, he had a sense of release and joy in contrast to the anguish of the day.

And later still, they held each other, sharing the warmth from their bodies and the fire. At last Margot stirred. "I've said it before and I say it again: You're a delicious lover."

"And you're okay, Bracken." He asked her, "Will you stay the night?"

She often did, just as Alex frequently stayed at Margot's apartment. At times it seemed foolish to maintain their two establishments, but he had delayed the step of merging them, wanting first to marry Margot if he could.

"I'll stay for a while," she said, "but not all night. Tomorrow I have to be in court early."

Margot's court appearances were frequent and in the aftermath of such a case they had met a year and a half ago. Shortly before that first encounter Margot had defended a half dozen demonstrators who clashed with police during a rally urging total amnesty for Vietnam deserters. Her spirited defense, not only of the demonstrators but of their cause, attracted wide attention. So did her victory—dismissal of all charges—at the trial's end.

A few days later, at a milling cocktail party given by Edwina D'Orsey and her husband Lewis, Margot was surrounded by admirers and critics. She had come to the party alone. So had Alex, who had heard of Margot, though only later did he discover she was a first cousin to Edwina. Sipping the D'Orseys' excellent Schramsberg, he had listened for a while, then joined forces with the critics. Soon after, others stood back, leaving debate to Alex and Margot, squared off like verbal gladiators.

At one point Margot had demanded, "Who the hell are you?"

"An ordinary American who believes that, in the military, discipline is necessary."

"Even in an immoral war like Vietnam?"

"A soldier can't decide morality. He operates under orders. The alternative is chaos."

"Whoever you are, you sound like a Nazi. After World War II, we executed Germans who offered that defense."

"The situation was entirely different."

"No different at all. At the Nuremberg trials the Allies insisted Germans should have heeded conscience and refused orders. That's exactly what Vietnam draft defectors and deserters did."

"The American Army wasn't exterminating Jews."

"No, just villagers. As in My Lai and elsewhere."

"No war is clean."

"But Vietnam was dirtier than most. From the Commander-in-Chief down. Which is why so many young Americans, with a special courage, obeyed their consciences and refused to take part in it."

"They won't get unconditional amnesty."

"They should. In time, when decency wins out, they will."

They were still arguing fiercely when Edwina separated them and performed introductions. Later they resumed the argument, and continued it while Alex drove Margot home to her apartment. There, at one point, they came close to blows but instead found suddenly that physical desire eclipsed all else and they made love excitedly, heatedly, until exhausted, knowing already that something new and vital had entered both their lives.

As a footnote to that occasion, Alex later reversed his once-strong views, observing, as other disillusioned moderates did, the hollow mockery of Nixon's "peace with honor." And later still, while Watergate and related infamies unfolded, it became clear that those at the highest level of government—who had decreed: "No amnesty"—were guilty of more villainy by far than any Vietnam deserter.

There had been other occasions, since that first one, when Margot's arguments had changed or widened his ideas.

Now, in the apartment's single bedroom, she selected a nightgown from a drawer which Alex left for her exclusive use. When she had it on, Margot turned out the lights.

They lay silently, in comforting companionship in the darkened room. Then Margot said, "You saw Celia today, didn't you?"

Surprised, he turned to her. "How did you know?"

"It always shows. It's hard on you." She asked, "Do you want to talk about it?"

"Yes," he said, "I think so."

"You still blame yourself, don't you?"

"Yes." He told her about his meeting with Celia, the conversation afterward with Dr. McCartney, and the psychiatrist's opinion about the probable effect on Celia of a divorce and his own remarriage.

Margot said emphatically, "Then you mustn't divorce her."

"If I don't," Alex said, "there can be nothing permanent for you and me."

"Of course there can! I told you long ago, it can be as permanent as we both want to make it. Marriage isn't permanent any more. Who really believes in marriage nowadays, except a few old bishops?"

"I believe," Alex said. "Enough to want it for us."

"Then let's have it—on our terms. What I don't need, darling, is a piece of legal stationery saying I'm married, because I'm too used to legal papers for them to impress me overmuch. I've already said I'll live with you—gladly and lovingly. But what I won't have on my conscience, or burden you with either, is shoving what's left of Celia's sanity into a bottomless pit."

"I know, I know. Everything you say makes sense." His answer lacked conviction.

She assured him softly, "I'm happier with what we have than I've ever been before in all my life. It's you, not me, who wants more."

Alex sighed and, soon after, was asleep.

When she was sure that he was sleeping soundly, Margot dressed, kissed Alex lightly, and let herself out of the apartment.

While Alex Vandervoort slept part of that night alone, Roscoe Heyward would sleep in solitude the whole night through.

Though not yet.

Heyward was at home, in his rambling, three-story house in the suburb of Shaker Heights. He was seated at a leather-topped desk, with papers spread out before him, in the small, sedately furnished room he used as a study.

His wife Beatrice had gone upstairs to bed almost two hours ago, locking her bedroom door as she had for the past twelve years since—by mutual consent—they moved into separate sleeping quarters.

Beatrice's locking of her door, though characteristically imperious, had never offended Heyward. Long before the separate arrangement, their sexual exercises had grown fewer and fewer, then tapered into nothingness.

Mostly, Heyward supposed, when occasionally he thought about it, their sexual shutdown had been Beatrice's choice. Even in the early years of marriage she made plain her mental distaste for their gropings and heavings, though her body at times demanded them. Sooner or later, she implied, her strong mind would conquer that rather disgusting need, and eventually it had.

Once or twice, in rare whimsical moments, it had occurred to Heyward that their only son, Elmer, mirrored Beatrice's attitude to the method of his conception and birth—an offending, unwarranted invasion of her bodily privacy. Elmer, now nearing thirty, and a certified public accountant, radiated disapproval about almost everything, stalking through life as with a thumb and finger over his nose to protect him from the stench. Even Roscoe Heyward at times found Elmer a bit much.

As to Heyward himself, he had accepted sexual deprivation uncomplainingly, partly because twelve years ago he was at a point where sex was something he could take or leave; partly because ambition at the bank had, by then, become his central driving force. So, like a machine which slips into disuse, his sexual urgings dwindled. Nowadays they revived only rarely—even then, mildly—to remind him with a certain sadness of a portion of his life on which the curtain fell too soon.

But in other ways, Heyward admitted, Beatrice had been good for him. She was descended from an impeccable Boston family and, in her youth, had "come out" properly as a debutante. It was at the debutante ball, with young Roscoe in tails and white gloves, and standing yardstick straight, that they were formally introduced. Later they had dates on which chaperones accompanied them and, following a suitable period of engagement, were married two years after meeting. The wedding, which Heyward still remembered with pride, was attended by a Who's Who of Boston society.

Then, as now, Beatrice shared Roscoe's notions about the importance of social position and respectability. She had followed through on both by long service to the Daughters of the American Revolution and was now National Recording Secretary General. Roscoe was proud of this and delighted with the prestigious social contacts which it brought. There had been only one thing Beatrice and her illustrious family lacked—money. At this moment, as he had many times before, Roscoe Heyward wished fervently that his wife had been an heiress.

Roscoe and Beatrice's biggest problem was, and always had been, managing to live on his bank salary.

This year, as the figures he had been working on tonight showed, the Heywards' expenses would substantially exceed their income. Next April he would have to borrow to pay the income tax he owed, as had been necessary last year and the year before. There would have been other years, too, except that during some he had been lucky with investments.

Many people with much smaller incomes would have scoffed at the idea that an executive vice-president's $65,000 a year salary was not ample to live on, and perhaps to save. In fact, for the Heywards, it was not.

To begin with, income taxes cut the gross amount by more than a third. After that, first and second mortgages on the house required payments of another $16,000 yearly, while municipal taxes ate up a further $2,500. That left $23,000—or roughly $450 a week—for all other expenses including repairs, insurance, food, clothes, a car for Beatrice (the bank supplied Roscoe with a chauffeur-driven pool car when he needed it), a housekeeper-cook, charitable donations, and an incredible array of smaller items adding up to a depressingly large sum.

The house, Heyward always realized at times like this, was a serious extravagance. From the beginning it had proved larger than they needed, even when Elmer lived at home, which now he didn't. Vandervoort, whose salary was identical, was wiser by far to live in an apartment and pay rent, but Beatrice, who loved their house for its size and prestige, would never hear of that, nor would Roscoe favor it.

As a result they had to scrimp elsewhere, a process which Beatrice sometimes refused to acknowledge, taking the view she *ought* to have money; therefore to worry about it herself was lèse majesté. Her attitude was reflected in countless ways around the house. She would never use a linen napkin twice; soiled or not, it must be laundered after every use. The same applied to towels, so that linen and laundry bills were high. She made long-distance phone calls casually and rarely deigned to turn off switches. Moments earlier, Heyward had gone to the kitchen for a glass of milk and, though Beatrice had been in bed for two hours, every downstairs light was on. He had irritatedly snapped them off.

Yet, for all Beatrice's attitude, fact was fact and there were things they simply could not afford. An example was holidays—the Heywards had had none for the past two years. Last summer Roscoe told colleagues at the bank, "We considered a Mediterranean cruise, but decided after all we'd prefer to stay home."

Another uncomfortable reality was that they had virtually no savings —only a few shares of FMA stock which might have to be sold soon, though the proceeds would not be enough to offset this year's deficit.

Tonight, the only conclusion Heyward had reached was that after borrowing they must hold the line on expenses as best they could, hoping for a financial upturn before too long.

And there would be one—satisfyingly generous—if he became president of FMA.

In First Mercantile American, as with most banks, a wide salary gap existed between the presidency and the next rank downward. As president, Ben Rosselli had been paid $130,000 annually. It was a virtual certainty his successor would receive the same.

If it happened to Roscoe Heyward, it would mean *immediate doubling* of his present salary. Even with higher taxes, what was left would eliminate every present problem.

Putting his papers away, he began to dream about it, a dream which extended through the night.

12

Friday morning.

In their penthouse atop fashionable Cayman Manor, a residential high-rise a mile or so outside the city, Edwina and Lewis D'Orsey were at breakfast.

It was three days since Ben Rosselli's dramatic announcement of his impending death, and two days since discovery of the heavy cash loss at First Mercantile American's main downtown branch. Of the two events, the cash loss—at this moment—weighed more heavily on Edwina.

Since Wednesday afternoon, nothing new had been discovered. Through all of yesterday, with low-key thoroughness, two FBI special agents had intensively questioned members of the branch staff, but without tangible result. The teller directly involved, Juanita Núñez, remained the prime suspect, but she would admit nothing, continued to insist that she was innocent, and refused to submit to a lie detector test.

Although her refusal increased the general suspicion of her guilt, as one of the FBI men put it to Edwina, "We can suspect her strongly, and we do, but there isn't a pinhead of proof. As to the money, even if it's hidden where she lives, we need some solid evidence before we can get a search warrant. And we don't have any. Naturally, we'll keep an eye on her, though it isn't the kind of case where the Bureau can maintain a full surveillance."

The FBI agents would be in the branch again today, yet there seemed little more that they could do.

But what the bank could do, and would, was end Juanita Núñez's employment. Edwina knew she must dismiss the girl today.

But it would be a frustrating, unsatisfactory ending.

Edwina returned her attention to breakfast—lightly scrambled eggs and toasted English muffins—which their maid had served a moment earlier.

Across the table, Lewis, hidden behind *The Wall Street Journal,* was growling as usual over the latest lunacy from Washington where an Under Secretary of the Treasury had declared before a Senate committee that the U.S. would never again return to a gold standard. The secretary used a Keynesian quotation in describing gold as "this barbarous yellow relic." Gold, he claimed, was finished as an international exchange medium.

"My God! That leprous ignoramus!" Glaring over his steel-rimmed half-moon glasses, Lewis D'Orsey flung his newspaper to the floor to join *The New York Times, Chicago Tribune,* and a day-old *Financial Times* from London, all of which he had skimmed through already. He stormed on about the Treasury official, "Five centuries after dimwits like him have rotted into dust, gold will still be the world's only sound basis for money and value. With the morons we have in power, there's no hope for us, absolutely none!"

Lewis seized a coffee cup, raised it to his lean, grim face and gulped, then wiped his lips with a linen napkin.

Edwina had been leafing through *The Christian Science Monitor.* She looked up. "What a pity you won't be around five centuries from now to say, 'I told you so.' "

Lewis was a small man with a body like a twig, making him seem frail and half starved, though in fact he was neither. His face matched his body and was lean, almost cadaverous. His movements were quick, his voice more often than not impatient. Occasionally Lewis would joke about his unimpressive physique. Tapping his forehead he asserted, "What nature omitted on the bodywork it made up behind here."

And it was true, even those who detested him conceded, he had a remarkably agile brain, particularly when applied to money and finance.

His morning tantrums seldom bothered Edwina. For one thing, over their fourteen years of marriage she had learned they were rarely directed at herself; and for another, she realized Lewis was girding himself for a morning session at his typewriter where he would roar like the righteously angry Jeremiah that readers of his twice-a-month financial newsletter expected him to be.

The high-priced, private newsletter containing Lewis D'Orsey's investment advice to an exclusive list of international subscribers provided him with both a rich livelihood and a personal spear on which to impale governments, presidents, prime ministers, and assorted politicians when any of their fiscal acts displeased him. Most did.

Many financial men attuned to modern theories, including some at First Mercantile American Bank, abhorred Lewis D'Orsey's independent, acidly biting, ultraconservative newsletter. Not so, however, most of Lewis's enthusiastic subscribers who regarded him as a combination of Moses and Midas in a generation of financial fools.

And with good reason, Edwina admitted. If making money was your objective in life, Lewis was a sound man to follow. He had proved it many times, uncannily, with advice which paid off handsomely for those who followed it.

Gold was one example. Long before it happened, and while others scoffed, Lewis D'Orsey predicted a dramatic upsurge in the free market price. He also urged heavy buying of South African gold mining shares, at that time low-priced. Since then, several subscribers to *The D'Orsey Newsletter* had written to say they were millionaires, solely as a result of taking this advice.

With equal prescience he had foreseen the series of U.S. dollar devaluations and advised his readers to put all the cash they could raise into other currencies, notably Swiss francs and Deutsche marks, which many did—to their great profit.

In the most recent edition of *The D'Orsey Newsletter* he had written:

> The U.S. dollar, a once-proud and honest currency, is moribund, like the nation it represents. Financially, America has passed the point of no return. Thanks to insane fiscal policies, misconceived by incompetent and corrupt politicians who care solely about themselves and re-election, we are living amid financial disaster which can only worsen.
>
> Since our rulers are knaves and imbeciles and the docile public stands vacuously indifferent, it's time for the financial lifeboats! Every man (or woman) for himself!
>
> If you have dollars, keep only enough for cab fare, food, and postage stamps. Plus sufficient for an airline ticket to some happier land.
>
> For the wise investor is the investor who is departing these United States, living abroad and shedding U.S. nationality. Officially, Internal Revenue Code section 877 says that if U.S. citizens renounce their citizenship to avoid income taxes, and the IRS can

prove it, their tax liability remains. But for those who know, there are legal ways to thwart the IRS. (See *The D'Orsey Newsletter* of July last year on how to become an ex-American citizen. *Single copies available for $12 or Swiss fr.40 each.*)

The reason for a change of allegiance and scene: The value of the U.S. dollar will continue to diminish, along with Americans' fiscal freedom.

And even if you can't leave personally, send your money overseas. Convert your U.S. dollars while you can (it may not be for long!) into Deutsche marks, Swiss francs, Dutch guilders, Austrian schillings, Lebanese pounds, almost *anything!*

Then place them, out of reach of U.S. bureaucrats, in a European bank, preferably Swiss . . .

Lewis D'Orsey had trumpeted variations on that theme for several years. His latest newsletter continued with more of the same and concluded with specific advice on recommended investments. Naturally, all were in non-U.S. currencies.

At the breakfast table Edwina continued to read the *Monitor*. There was a report of a House of Representatives bill proposing tax law changes which would reduce depreciation allowances on real property. It could affect mortgage lending at the bank and she asked Lewis his opinion about the likelihood of the bill becoming law.

He answered crisply, "Nil. Even if it gets through the House, it will never pass the Senate. I phoned a couple of senators yesterday. They don't take it seriously."

Lewis had an extraordinary range of friends and contacts—one of several reasons for his success. He kept abreast, too, of anything affecting taxes, advising his newsletter readers on situations they could exploit to their advantage.

Lewis himself paid only a token amount of income tax each year—never more than a few hundred dollars, he boasted proudly, yet his real income was in seven figures. He achieved this by utilizing tax shelters of all kinds—oil investments, real estate, timber exploitation, farming, limited partnerships, and tax-free bonds. Such devices enabled him to spend freely, live splendidly, yet—on paper—sustain a personal loss each year.

Yet all these tax devices were totally legal. "Only a fool conceals income, or cheats on taxes in some other way," Edwina had heard Lewis declare often. "Why take that risk when there are more legitimate escape hatches from taxes than holes in a Swiss cheese? All that's needed is the work to understand, and enterprise to use them."

So far, Lewis had not taken his own advice to live overseas and shed his U.S. citizenship. However, he detested New York where he had once lived and worked and now called it "a decaying, complacent, bankrupt bandit lair existing on solipsism and with bad breath." It was also an illusion, he maintained, "fostered by arrogant New Yorkers, that the best brains are to be found in that city. They aren't." He preferred the Midwest where he had moved, and met Edwina a decade and a half ago.

Despite her husband's example in avoiding taxes, Edwina went her own way on that subject, filing her individual return and paying far more than Lewis, even on her more modest income. But it was Lewis who took care of their bills—for this penthouse and staff, their twin Mercedes cars, and other luxuries.

Edwina admitted honestly to herself that the high style of living, which she enjoyed, had been a factor in her decision to marry Lewis and her adaptation to their marriage. And the arrangement, as well as their independence and dual careers, worked well.

"I wish," she said, "your insight extended to knowing where all that cash of ours went on Wednesday."

Lewis looked up from his breakfast which he had attacked fiercely, as if the eggs were enemies. "The bank's cash is still missing? Once more the gallant, fumble-fisted FBI has discovered nothing?"

"I suppose you could put it that way." She told him of the impasse they had reached, and of her own decision that the teller would have to be let go today.

"And after that, no one else will employ her, I suppose."

"Certainly no other bank."

"She has a child, I think you said."

"Unfortunately, yes."

Lewis said gloomily, "Two more recruits for the already swollen welfare rolls."

"Oh, really! Save all that Birchism for your Texas readers."

Her husband's face cracked into one of his rare smiles. "Forgive me. But I'm not used to your needing advice. It's not often that you do."

It was a compliment, Edwina realized. One of the things she appreciated about their marriage was that Lewis treated her, and always had, as an intellectual equal. And although he had never said so directly, she knew he was proud of her senior management status at FMA—unusual even nowadays for a woman in the male chauvinist world of banking.

"Naturally I can't tell you where the missing money is," Lewis said; he appeared to have been thinking. "But I'll give you a piece of advice I've found useful sometimes in conundrum situations."

"Yes, go on."

"It's this: Mistrust the obvious."

Edwina felt disappointed. Illogically, she supposed, she had expected some kind of miracle solution. Instead, Lewis had delivered a hoary old bromide.

She glanced at her watch. It was almost eight o'clock. "Thank you," she said. "I must go."

"Oh, by the way, I'm leaving for Europe tonight," he informed her. "I'll be back Wednesday."

"Have a good trip." Edwina kissed him as she left. The sudden announcement did not surprise her. Lewis had offices in Zurich and London, and his comings and goings were casual.

She went down in the private elevator which connected their penthouse with an indoor parking garage.

As she drove to the bank, and despite her dismissal of Lewis's advice, the words *mistrust the obvious* stayed annoyingly, persistently in her mind.

A discussion at midmorning with the two FBI agents was brief and inconclusive.

The meeting took place in the conference room at the rear of the bank where, over the preceding two days, the FBI men had interviewed members of the staff. Edwina was present. So was Nolan Wainwright.

The senior of the two agents, whose name was Innes and who spoke with a New England twang, told Edwina and the bank's security chief, "We've gone as far as we can with our investigation here. The case will stay open and we'll be in touch if new facts come to light. Of course, if anything more develops here you'll inform the Bureau at once."

"Of course," Edwina said.

"Oh, there is an item of negative news." The FBI man consulted a notebook. "The Núñez girl's husband—Carlos. One of your people thought they saw him in the bank the day the money was missing."

Wainwright said, "Miles Eastin. He reported it to me. I passed the information on."

"Yes, we questioned Eastin about that; he admitted he could have been mistaken. Well, we've traced Carlos Núñez. He's in Phoenix, Arizona; has a job there as a motor mechanic. Our Bureau agents in Phoenix have interviewed him. They're satisfied he was at work on

Wednesday, in fact every day this week, which rules him out as an accomplice."

Nolan Wainwright escorted the FBI agents out. Edwina returned to her desk on the platform. She had reported the cash loss—as she was required to do—to her immediate superior in Headquarters Administration and word, it seemed, had filtered upward to Alex Vandervoort. Late yesterday, Alex had telephoned, sympathetic, and asking if there was anything he could do to help. She had thanked him, but said no, realizing that she was responsible and must do whatever had to be done herself.

This morning, nothing had changed.

Shortly before noon Edwina instructed Tottenhoe to advise the payroll department that Juanita Núñez's employment would be terminated at the end of the day, and to have her severance paycheck sent down to the branch. The check, delivered by messenger, was on Edwina's desk when she returned from lunch.

Uneasy, hesitating, Edwina turned the check over in her hand.

At this moment Juanita Núñez was still working. Edwina's decision about that yesterday had brought grouchy objections from Tottenhoe who protested, "The sooner we're rid of her, the surer we'll be of no repetition." Even Miles Eastin, back at his regular operations assistant's desk, had raised his eyebrows, but Edwina overruled them both.

She wondered why on earth she was worrying so much, when obviously the time had come to end the incident and put it out of mind.

Obviously out of mind. The *obvious* solution. Again Lewis's phrase occurred to her—*mistrust the obvious.*

But how? In what way?

Edwina told herself: Think just once more. Go back to the beginning.

What were the *obvious* facets of the incident as they occurred? The first obvious thing was that money was missing. *No room for dispute there.* The second obvious thing was that the amount was six thousand dollars. That had been agreed by four people: Juanita Núñez herself, Tottenhoe, Miles Eastin, and, eventually, the vault teller. *No argument.*

The third obvious feature concerned the Núñez girl's assertion that she knew the exact amount of money missing from her cash drawer at 1:50 P.M., after almost five hours of busy transactions at the counter, and *before* she had balanced out her cash. All others in the branch who knew about the loss, including Edwina, agreed that was obviously impossible; from the start, the knowledge had been a cornerstone of their joint belief that Juanita Núñez was a thief.

Knowledge . . . *obvious* knowledge . . . *obviously* impossible.

And yet was it impossible? . . . An idea occurred to Edwina.

A wall clock showed 2:10 P.M. She noted that the operations officer was at his desk nearby. Edwina got up. "Mr. Tottenhoe, will you come with me, please?"

With Tottenhoe glumly trailing, she crossed the floor, briefly greeting several customers en route. The branch was crowded and busy, as usual in the closing hours of business before a weekend. Juanita Núñez was accepting a deposit.

Edwina said quietly, "Mrs. Núñez, when you've dealt with this customer, please put up your 'position closed' sign and lock your cash box."

Juanita Núñez made no response, nor did she speak when she had completed the transaction, or while transferring a small metal plaque to the counter as instructed. When she turned to close the cash box, Edwina saw why. The girl was crying silently, tears coursing down her cheeks.

The reason was not hard to guess. She had expected to be fired today and Edwina's sudden appearance confirmed that belief.

Edwina ignored the tears. "Mr. Tottenhoe," she said, "I believe Mrs. Núñez has been working on cash since we opened this morning. Is that correct?"

He acknowledged, "Yes."

The time period was roughly the same as on Wednesday, Edwina thought, though the branch had been busier today.

She pointed to the cash box. "Mrs. Núñez, you've been insisting that you always know the amount of cash you have. Do you know how much is in there now?"

The young woman hesitated. Then she nodded, still unable to speak through tears.

Edwina took a slip of paper from the counter and held it out. "Write down the amount."

Again, visible hesitation. Then Juanita Núñez took a pencil and scribbled $23,765.

Edwina passed the slip to Tottenhoe. "Please go with Mrs. Núñez and stay with her while she balances out today's cash. Check the result. Compare it with this figure."

Tottenhoe looked at the paper skeptically. "I'm busy, and if I stayed with every teller . . ."

"Stay with this one," Edwina said. Recrossing the bank floor, she returned to her desk.

Three quarters of an hour later Tottenhoe reappeared.

He looked nervous. Edwina saw his hand was shaking. He had the slip of paper and put it on her desk. The figure which Juanita Núñez had written had a single penciled tick beside it.

"If I hadn't seen it myself," the operations officer said, "I might not have believed." For once his gloom was gone, surprise replacing it.

"The figure was right?"

"*Exactly* right."

Edwina sat tensely, marshaling her thoughts. Abruptly and dramatically, she knew, almost everything concerning the investigation had changed. Until this moment, all assumptions had been based upon the Núñez girl's inability to do what she had now demonstrated conclusively that she could.

"I remembered something while I was walking over just now," Tottenhoe said. "I did know somebody once; it was in a little country branch upstate—must be twenty years or more ago—who had that knack of keeping track of cash. And I remember, then, hearing there are other people like that. It's as if they had a calculating machine right inside their heads."

Edwina snapped, "I wish your memory had been working better on Wednesday."

As Tottenhoe returned to his own desk, she drew a notepad toward her and scribbled summations of her thoughts.

Núñez not yet cleared, but more believable. Possibly innocent victim? If not Núñez, who?

Someone who knows procedures, could somehow watch for opportunity.

Staff? Inside job?

But how?

"How" later. *Find motive first, then person.*

Motive? Someone who needs money badly?

She repeated in capitals, *NEEDS MONEY.* And added: *Examine personal checking/savings accounts, all branch personnel—TONIGHT!*

Edwina began leafing quickly through an FMA Headquarters phone book, looking for "Chief of Audit Service."

13

On Friday afternoons all branches of First Mercantile American Bank
stayed open an extra three hours.

Thus, at the main downtown branch this Friday, the outer street
doors were closed and locked by a security guard at 6 P.M. A few customers, still in the bank at closing time, were let out by the same guard,
one by one, through a single plate-glass door.

At 6:05 precisely, a series of sharp, peremptory taps sounded on the
outside of the glass door. When the guard turned his head in response,
he observed a young male figure dressed in a dark topcoat and business
suit, carrying a briefcase. To attract attention inside, the figure had
tapped with a fifty-cent piece wrapped in a handkerchief.

As the guard approached, the man with the briefcase held an identity document flat against the glass. The guard inspected it, unlocked
the door, and the young man stepped inside.

Then, before the guard could close the door, a proliferation occurred,
as unexpected and remarkable as a magician's trick. Where there had
been one individual with briefcase and proffered credentials, suddenly
there were six, behind them six more, with still another phalanx at the
rear. Swiftly, like an inundation, they streamed into the bank.

A man, older than most of the others and emanating authority, announced curtly, "Headquarters Audit Staff."

"Yessir," the security guard said; he was a veteran at the bank who
had been through this before, and he continued checking the other
credentials holders in. There were twenty, mostly men, four women.
All went immediately to various locations in the bank.

The older man who had made the announcement headed for the

platform and Edwina's desk. As she rose to greet him, she regarded the continuing influx into the bank with unconcealed surprise.

"Mr. Burnside, is this a full-dress audit?"

"It certainly is, Mrs. D'Orsey." The audit department head removed his overcoat and hung it near the platform.

Elsewhere in the bank other staff members wore disconcerted expressions, while some groaned and voiced aggrieved comments. "Oh, jeez! A Friday, of all times to pick!" . . . "Dammit, I had a dinner date!" . . . "Who says auditors are human?"

Most were aware of what the visit by a headquarters audit group entailed. Tellers knew there would be an extra counting of their cash before they left tonight, and vault reserve cash would be checked out too. Accountants would be required to stay until their records were listed and balanced. Senior management staff would be lucky to be away by midnight.

The newcomers had already, quickly and politely, taken over all ledgers. From this moment any additions or changes would be under scrutiny.

Edwina said, "When I asked for an examination of staff accounts I didn't expect *this*." Normally a branch bank audit took place every eighteen months to two years and tonight's was doubly unexpected since a full audit of the main downtown branch had occurred only eight months earlier.

"We decide the how, where, and when of audit, Mrs. D'Orsey." As always, Hal Burnside maintained a cool aloofness, the hallmark of a bank examiner. Within any major bank an audit department was an independent, watchdog unit with authority and prerogatives like the Inspectorate General of an army. Its members were never intimidated by rank, and even senior managers were candidates for reproof about irregularities which a thoroughgoing inspection of a branch revealed— and there were invariably some.

"I know about that," Edwina acknowledged. "I'm just surprised you could arrange all this so quickly."

The audit chief smiled, a trifle smugly. "We have our methods and resources."

What he did not reveal was that a surprise audit of another FMA branch had been planned for this evening. Following Edwina's phone call three hours ago, the earlier plan was canceled, arrangements hastily revised, and additional staff called in for the present expedition.

Such cloak-and-dagger tactics were not unusual. An essential part of the audit function was to descend, irregularly and without warning, on any of the bank's branches. Elaborate precautions were taken to preserve secrecy and any audit staff member who violated it was in serious trouble. Few did, even inadvertently.

For today's maneuver, the score of auditors involved had assembled an hour ago in a salon of a downtown hotel, though even that destination had not been revealed until the latest possible moment. There they were briefed, duties allocated, then inconspicuously, in twos and threes, they had walked toward the main downtown branch of FMA. Until the last few crucial minutes they loitered in lobbies of nearby buildings, strolled casually, or browsed store windows. Then, traditionally, the most junior member of the group had rapped on the bank door to demand admission. As soon as it was gained, the others, like an assembling regiment, fell in behind him.

Now, within the bank, audit team members were at every key position.

A convicted bank embezzler of the 1970s, who successfully concealed his massive defalcations for some twenty years, observed while eventually en route to prison, "The auditors used to come in and do nothing but shoot the breeze for forty minutes. Give me half of that time and I can cover up anything."

The audit department of First Mercantile American, and other large North American banks, took no such chance. Not even five minutes passed after the surprise of the auditors' arrival until they were all in preassigned positions, observing everything.

Resigned, regular staff members of the branch went on to complete their day's work, then to assist the auditors as needed.

Once started, the process would continue through the following week and part of the next. But the most critical portion of the examination would take place within the next few hours.

"Let's you and me get to work, Mrs. D'Orsey," Burnside said. "We'll start with the deposit accounts, both time and demand." He opened his briefcase on Edwina's desk.

By 8 P.M. the initial surprise attending the audit team's arrival had worn off, a notable amount of work had been accomplished, and ranks of the regular branch staff were thinning. All tellers had left; so had some of the accountants. Cash had been counted, inspection of other records was well advanced. The visitors had been courteous and, in some cases, helpful in pointing out mild errors, all of which was part of their job.

Among the senior management staff still remaining were Edwina, Tottenhoe, and Miles Eastin. The two men had been kept busy locating information and responding to queries. Now, however, Tottenhoe appeared tired. But young Eastin, who had responded helpfully and cheerfully to every demand so far, was as fresh and energetic as when the evening had begun. It was Miles Eastin who arranged for sandwiches and coffee to be sent in for auditors and staff.

Of the several audit task forces, a small group was concentrating on savings and checking accounts and, from time to time, one among their number would bring a written note to the Chief of Audit Service at Edwina's desk. In every case he glanced over the information, nodded, and added the note to other papers in his briefcase.

At ten minutes to nine he received what appeared to be a lengthier note with several other papers clipped to it. This Burnside studied carefully, then announced, "I think Mrs. D'Orsey and I will take a break. We'll go out for our coffee and supper."

A few minutes later he escorted Edwina through the same street door by which the auditors had entered nearly three hours earlier.

Outside the building the audit chief apologized. "I'm sorry, but that was a small theatrical performance. I'm afraid our supper, if any, will have to wait." As Edwina looked puzzled he added, "You and I are on our way to a meeting, but I didn't want it known."

With Burnside leading, they turned right, walking half a block from the still brightly lighted bank, then used a pedestrian mall to double back to Rosselli Plaza and the FMA Headquarters Tower. The night was cold and Edwina pulled her coat tightly around her, reflecting that the tunnel route would have been both shorter and warmer. Why all the mystery?

Inside the bank headquarters building, Hal Burnside signed a night visitors book, after which a guard accompanied them in an elevator to the eleventh floor. A sign and arrow indicated SECURITY DEPARTMENT. Nolan Wainwright and the two FBI men who had dealt with the cash loss were waiting for them there.

Almost at once they were joined by another member of the audit team who clearly had followed Edwina and Burnside from the bank.

Introductions were accomplished quickly. The latest arrival was a youngish man named Gayne, with cool alert eyes behind heavy-rimmed glasses which made him look severe. It was Gayne who had delivered the several notes and documents to Burnside while the latter worked at Edwina's desk.

Now, at Nolan Wainwright's suggestion, they moved into a conference room and seated themselves around a circular table.

Hal Burnside told the FBI agents, "I hope what we've discovered will justify calling you gentlemen out at this time of night."

This meeting, Edwina realized, must have been planned several hours ago. She asked, "Then you *have* discovered something?"

"Unfortunately, a good deal more than anyone expected, Mrs. D'Orsey."

At a nod from Burnside, the audit assistant, Gayne, began to spread out papers.

"As the result of your suggestion," Burnside stated in a lecturer's tone, "an examination has been made of personal bank accounts—savings and checking—of all personnel employed at the main downtown branch. What we were seeking was some evidence of individual financial difficulty. Fairly conclusively, we found it."

He sounds like a pompous schoolmaster, Edwina thought. But she continued listening intently.

"I should perhaps explain," the audit chief told the two FBI men, "that most bank employees maintain their personal accounts at the branch where they work. One reason is that the accounts are 'free'—that is, without service charges. Another reason—the more important—is that employees receive a special low interest rate on loans, usually one percent below prime rate."

Innes, the senior FBI agent, nodded. "Yes, we knew that."

"You'll also realize, then, that an employee who has taken advantage of his or her special bank credit—has borrowed to the limit, in fact—and then borrows other sums from an outside source such as a finance company, where interest rates are notoriously high, has placed himself or herself in a tenuous financial position."

Innes, with a trace of impatience, said, "Of course."

"It appears we have a bank employee to whom exactly that has happened." He motioned to the assistant, Gayne, who turned over several canceled checks which until now had been face down.

"As you'll observe, these checks are made out to three separate finance companies. Incidentally, we've already been in touch by telephone with two of the companies, and notwithstanding the payments that you see, both accounts are seriously delinquent. It's a reasonable guess that, in the morning, the third company will tell us the same story."

Gayne interjected, "And these checks are for the current month only. Tomorrow we'll look at microfilm records for several months back."

"One other fact is relevant," the audit chief proceeded. "The individual concerned could not possibly have made these payments"—he gestured toward the canceled checks—"on the basis of a bank salary, the

amount of which we know. Therefore during the past several hours we
have searched for evidence of theft from the bank, and this has now been
found."

Once again the assistant, Gayne, began placing papers on the conference table.

. . . *evidence of theft from the bank . . . this has now been found.*
Edwina, scarcely listening any more, had her eyes riveted on the signature on each of the canceled checks—a signature she saw each day, familiar to her, bold and clear. The sight of it, here and now, appalled and
saddened her.

The signature was Eastin's—young Miles whom she liked so well, who
was so efficient as assistant operations officer, so helpful and tireless,
even tonight, and whom only this week she had decided to promote
when Tottenhoe retired.

The Chief of Audit Service had now moved on. "What our sneak thief
has been doing is milking dormant accounts. Once we detected a single
fraudulent pattern earlier this evening, others were not hard to find."

Still in his lecturer's manner, and for the benefit of the FBI men, he
defined a dormant account. It was an account—savings or checking,
Burnside explained—which had little or no activity. All banks had customers who for varied reasons left such accounts untouched over long
periods, sometimes for many years, and with surprisingly large sums remaining in them. Modest interest did accumulate in savings accounts, of
course, and some people undoubtedly had that in mind, though others
—incredible but true—abandoned their accounts entirely.

When a checking account was observed to be inactive, with no deposits or withdrawals, banks ceased mailing monthly statements and
substituted an annual one. Even those, at times, were returned marked:
"Moved—address unknown."

Standard precautions were taken to prevent fraudulent use of dormant accounts, the audit chief continued. The account records were
segregated; then, if a transaction suddenly occurred it was scrutinized
by an operations officer to make sure it was legitimate. Normally such
precautions were effective. *As assistant operations officer, Miles Eastin
had authority to scrutinize and approve dormant account transactions.
He had used the authority to cover up his own dishonesty—the fact that
he had been stealing from such accounts himself.*

"Eastin has been rather clever, selecting those accounts least likely
to cause trouble. We have here a series of forged withdrawal slips, though
not forged very skillfully because there are obvious traces of his handwriting, after which the amounts have been transferred into what ap-

pears to be a dummy account of his own under an assumed name. There's an obvious similarity of handwriting there also, though naturally experts will be needed to give evidence."

One by one they examined the withdrawal slips, comparing the handwriting with the checks they had looked at earlier. Although an attempt had been made at disguise, a resemblance was unmistakable.

The second FBI agent, Dalrymple, had been writing careful notes. Looking up, he asked, "Is there a total figure on the money involved?"

Gayne answered, "So far we've pinpointed close to eight thousand dollars. Tomorrow, though, we'll have access to older records through microfilm and the computer, which may show more."

Burnside added, "When we confront Eastin with what we know already, it could be he'll decide to make things easier by admitting the rest. That's sometimes a pattern when we catch embezzlers."

He's enjoying this, Edwina thought; really enjoying it. She felt irrationally defensive about Miles Eastin, then asked, "Have you any idea how long this has been going on?"

"From what's been uncovered so far," Gayne informed them, "it looks like at least a year, possibly longer."

Edwina turned to face Hal Burnside. "So you missed it completely at the last audit. Isn't an inspection of dormant accounts part of your job?"

It was like pricking a bubble. The audit chief flushed crimson as he admitted, "Yes, it is. But even we miss things occasionally when a thief has covered his tracks well."

"Obviously. Though you did say a moment ago the handwriting was a giveaway."

Burnside said sourly, "Well, we've caught it now."

She reminded him, "After I called you in."

The FBI agent Innes broke the ensuing silence. "None of this puts us any further ahead so far as Wednesday's missing cash goes."

"Except it makes Eastin the prime suspect," Burnside said. He seemed relieved to redirect the conversation. "And he may admit that, too."

"He won't," Nolan Wainwright growled. "That cat is too damn smart. Besides, why should he? We still don't know how he did it."

Until now the bank security head had said little, though he had shown surprise, then his face had hardened as the auditors produced their succession of documents and the evidence of guilt. Edwina wondered if Wainwright was remembering how both of them had put pressure on the teller, Juanita Núñez, disbelieving the girl's protested innocence. Even now, Edwina supposed, there was a possibility the Núñez girl had been in league with Eastin, but it seemed unlikely.

Hal Burnside stood up to go, refastening his briefcase. "Here's where Audit leaves off and the law takes over."

"We'll require these papers and a signed statement," Innes said.

"Mr. Gayne will stay, and be at your disposal."

"One more question. Do you think that Eastin has any idea he's been found out?"

"I doubt it." Burnside glanced toward his assistant who shook his head.

"I'm certain he doesn't. We were careful not to show what we were looking for and, to cover up, we asked for many things we didn't need."

"I don't think so either," Edwina said. She remembered sadly how busy and cheerful Miles Eastin had been immediately before she had left the branch with Burnside. *Why had he done it? Why, oh why?*

Innes nodded his approval. "Then let's keep it that way. We'll pick Eastin up for questioning as soon as we've finished here, but he mustn't be warned. He's still at the bank?"

"Yes," Edwina said. "He'll stay at least until we get back, and normally he'd be among the last to leave."

Nolan Wainwright cut in, his voice unusually harsh, "*Amend* those instructions. Keep him there as late as possible. After that, let him go home thinking he hasn't been found out."

The others glanced at the bank security chief, puzzled and startled. In particular the eyes of the two FBI men searched Wainwright's face. A message seemed to pass between them.

Innes hesitated, then conceded, "All right. Do it that way."

A few minutes later, Edwina and Burnside took the elevator down.

Innes said politely to the remaining auditor, "Before we take your statement, I wonder if you'd leave us alone a moment."

"Certainly." Gayne left the conference room.

The second FBI agent closed his notebook and put down his pencil. Innes faced Nolan Wainwright. "You've something in mind?"

"I have." Wainwright hesitated, wrestling mentally with choices and his conscience. Experience told him that the evidence against Eastin had gaps which needed to be filled. Yet to fill them the law would have to be bent in a way running counter to his own beliefs. He asked the FBI man, "Are you sure you want to know?"

The two eyed each other. They had known each other for years and shared a mutual respect.

"Getting evidence nowadays is sensitive," Innes said. "We can't take some of the liberties we used to, and if we do it's liable to bounce back."

There was a silence, then the second FBI agent said, "Tell us as much as you think you should."

Wainwright interlaced his fingers and considered them. His body transmitted tension, as his voice had earlier. "Okay, we've enough to nail Eastin on a larceny rap. Let's say the amount stolen is eight thousand dollars, more or less. What do you think a judge will give him?"

"For a first offense he'll draw a suspended sentence," Innes said. "The court won't worry about the money involved. They'll figure banks have lots and it's insured anyway."

"Check!" Wainwright's fingers tightened visibly. "But if we can prove he took that other cash—the six thousand last Tuesday; if we can show he aimed to throw the blame on the girl, and damn near did . . ."

Innes grunted understanding. "*If* you could show that, any reasonable judge would send him straight to jail. But can you?"

"I intend to. Because I personally want that son of a bitch behind bars."

"I know what you mean," the FBI man said thoughtfully. "I'd like to see it happen too."

"In that case do it my way. Don't pick up Eastin tonight. Give me until morning."

"I'm not sure," Innes mused. "I'm not sure I can."

The three of them waited, conscious of knowledge, duty, and a pull and tug within themselves. The other two guessed roughly what Wainwright had in mind. But when, and to what extent, did an end justify the means? Equally to the point: How much liberty nowadays could a law-enforcement officer take and get away with?

Yet the FBI men had become involved in the case and shared Wainwright's view about objectives.

"If we do wait till morning," the second agent cautioned, "we don't want Eastin to run. That could cause everybody trouble."

"And I don't want a bruised potato either," Innes said.

"He won't run. He won't be bruised. I guarantee it."

Innes glanced toward his colleague who shrugged.

"Okay, then," Innes said. "Until morning. But understand one thing, Nolan—this conversation never took place." He crossed to the conference room door and opened it. "You can come in, Mr. Gayne. Mr. Wainwright's leaving and we'll take your statement now."

14

A list of branch bank officers, maintained in the security department for emergency use, revealed Miles Eastin's home address and telephone number. Nolan Wainwright copied down both.

He recognized the address. A medium income residential area about two miles from downtown. It included the information "Apartment 2G."

Leaving FMA Headquarters Building, the security chief used a pay phone on Rosselli Plaza to dial the telephone number and heard the ringing continue unanswered. He already knew Miles Eastin was a bachelor. Wainwright was hoping he also lived alone.

If the phone had been answered, Wainwright would have made an excuse about a wrong number and revised his plans. As it was, he now headed for his car, parked in the headquarters basement garage.

Before leaving the garage he opened the trunk of the car and removed a slim chamois case, placing it in an inside pocket. He then drove across town.

He walked toward the apartment building casually but taking in details. A three-story structure, probably forty years old and showing signs of disrepair. He guessed it contained two dozen or so apartments. No doorman was visible. Inside a vestibule Nolan Wainwright could see an array of mail boxes and call buttons. Dual glass doors opened from the street to the vestibule; beyond them was a more solid door, undoubtedly locked.

The time was 10:30. Traffic on the street was light. No other pedestrians were near the apartment house. He went in.

Next to the mail boxes were three rows of buzzers and a speakerphone. Wainwright saw the name EASTIN and depressed the button beside it. As he expected, there was no response.

Guessing that 2G indicated the second floor, he chose a bell button at random with the prefix 3 and pressed it. A man's voice on the speakerphone rasped, "Yeah, who is it?"

The name beside the button was Appleby.

"Western Union," Wainwright said. "Telegram for Appleby."

"Okay, bring it up."

Behind the heavy interior door a buzzer sounded and a lock clicked open. Wainwright opened the door and went in quickly.

Immediately ahead was an elevator which he ignored. He saw a stairway to the right and went up it, two stairs at a time, to the second floor.

On his way Wainwright reflected on the astounding innocence of people generally. He hoped that Appleby, whoever he was, would not wait too long for his telegram. This night Mr. Appleby would suffer no harm beyond minor puzzlement, perhaps frustration, though he might have fared far worse. Yet apartment tenants everywhere, despite repeated warnings, continued to do exactly the same. Of course, Appleby might grow suspicious and alert the police, though Wainwright doubted it. In any case, a few minutes from now it would make no difference.

Apartment 2G was near the end of the second-floor corridor and the lock proved uncomplicated. Wainwright tried a succession of slim blades from the chamois case he had pocketed, and on the fourth attempt the lock cylinder turned. The door swung open and he went in, closing the door behind him.

He waited, letting his eyes adjust to the darkness, then crossed to a window and drew drapes. He found a light switch and turned it on.

The apartment was small, designed for use by one person; it was a single room divided into areas. A living-dining space contained a sofa, armchair, portable TV, and meal table. A bed was located behind a partition; the kitchenette had folding louvered doors. Two other doors which Wainwright checked revealed a bathroom and a storage closet. The place was orderly and clean. Several shelves of books and a few framed prints added a touch of personality.

Without wasting time, Wainwright began a systematic, thorough search.

He tried to suppress, as he worked, gnawing self-criticism for the illegal acts he was committing tonight. He did not wholly succeed. Nolan Wainwright was aware that everything he had done so far represented a reversal of his moral standards, a negation of his belief in law and order. Yet anger drove him. Anger and the knowledge of failure, four days ago, within himself.

He remembered with excruciating clarity, even now, the mute appeal in the eyes of the young Puerto Rican girl, Juanita Núñez, when he encountered her for the first time last Tuesday and began the interrogation. It was an appeal which said unmistakably: *You and I . . . you are black, I am brown. Therefore you, of all people, should realize I am alone here, at a disadvantage, and desperately need help and fairness.* But while recognizing the appeal, he had brushed it aside harshly, so that afterwards contempt replaced it, and he remembered that in the girl's eyes too.

This memory, coupled with chagrin at having been duped by Miles Eastin, made Wainwright determined to beat Eastin at his game, no matter if the law was bent in doing it.

Therefore, methodically, as his police training had taught him, Wainwright went on searching, determined that if evidence existed he would find it.

Half an hour later he knew that few places remained where anything could be hidden. He had examined cupboards, drawers and contents, had probed furniture, opened suitcases, inspected pictures on the walls, and removed the back of the TV. He also riffled through books, noting that an entire shelf was devoted to what someone had told him was Eastin's hobby—the study of money through the ages. Along with the books, a portfolio contained sketches and photographs of ancient coins and banknotes. But of anything incriminating there was no trace. Finally he piled furniture in one corner and rolled up the living area rug. Then, with a flashlight, he went over every inch of floorboard.

Without the flashlight's aid he would have missed the carefully sawn board, but two lines, lighter colored than the wood elsewhere, betrayed where cuts had been made. He gently pried up the foot or so of board between the lines and in the space beneath were a small black ledger and cash in twenty-dollar bills.

Working quickly, he replaced the board, the rug, the furniture.

He counted the cash; it totaled six thousand dollars. Then he studied the small black ledger briefly, realized it was a betting record and he whistled softly at the size and number of amounts involved.

He put the book down—it could be examined in detail later—on an occasional table in front of the sofa, with the money beside it.

Finding the money surprised him. He had no doubt it was the six thousand dollars missing from the bank on Wednesday, but he would have expected Eastin to have exchanged it by now, or have deposited it elsewhere. Police work had taught him that criminals did foolish, unexpected things, and this was one.

What still had to be learned was how Eastin had taken the money and brought it here.

Wainwright glanced around the apartment, after which he turned out the lights. He reopened the drapes and, settling comfortably on the sofa, waited.

In the semidarkness, with the small apartment lighted by reflections from the street outside, his thoughts drifted. He thought again of Juanita Núñez and wished somehow he could make amends. Then he remembered the FBI report about her missing husband, Carlos, who had been traced to Phoenix, Arizona, and it occurred to Wainwright that this information might be used to help the girl.

Of course, Miles Eastin's story about having seen Carlos Núñez in the bank the same day as the cash loss was a fabrication intended to throw even more suspicion on Juanita.

That despicable *bastard!* What kind of man was he, first to direct blame toward the girl, and later to add to it? The security chief felt his fists tighten, then warned himself not to allow his feelings to become too strong.

The warning was necessary, and he knew why. It was because of an incident long buried in his mind and which he seldom disinterred. Without really wanting to, he began remembering it.

Nolan Wainwright, now nearly fifty, had been spawned in the city's slums and, from birth, had found life's odds stacked against him. He grew up with survival as a daily challenge and with crime—petty and otherwise—a surrounding norm. In his teens he had run with a ghetto gang to whom brushes with the law were proof of manhood.

Like others, before and since, from the same slum background, he was driven by an urge to be somebody, to be noticed in whatever way, to release an inner rage against obscurity. He had no experience or philosophy to weigh alternatives, so participation in street crime appeared the only, the inevitable route. It seemed likely he would graduate, as many of his contemporaries did, to a police and prison record.

That he did not was due, in part, to chance; in part, to Bufflehead Kelly.

Bufflehead was a not-too-bright, lazy, amiable elderly neighborhood cop who had learned that a policeman's survival in the ghetto could be lengthened by adroitly being somewhere else when trouble erupted, and by taking action only when a problem loomed directly under his nose. Superiors complained that his arrest record was the worst in the precinct, but against this—in Bufflehead's view—his retirement and pension moved satisfyingly closer every year.

But the teenage Nolan Wainwright *had* loomed under Bufflehead's nose the night of an attempted gang-bust into a warehouse which the beat cop unwittingly disturbed, so everyone had run, escaping, except Wainwright who tripped and fell at Bufflehead's feet.

"Y' stupid, clumsy monkey," Bufflehead complained. "Now it's all kinds of paper and court work you'll be causin' me this night."

Kelly detested paperwork and court appearances which cut annoyingly into a policeman's off-duty time.

In the end he compromised. Instead of arresting and charging Wainwright he took him, the same night, to the police gym and, in Bufflehead's own words, "beat the b'jesus out of him" in a boxing ring.

Nolan Wainwright, bruised, sore, and with one eye badly swollen—though still with no arrest record—reacted with hatred. As soon as possible he would smash Bufflehead Kelly to a pulp, an objective which brought him back to the police gym—and Bufflehead—for lessons in how to do it. It was, Wainwright realized long afterward, the needed outlet for his rage. He learned quickly. When the time arrived to reduce the slightly stupid, lazy cop to a punished punching bag, he found the desire to do so had evaporated. Instead he had become fond of the old man, an emotion surprising to the youth himself.

A year went by during which Wainwright continued boxing, stayed in school, and managed to keep out of trouble. Then one night Bufflehead, while on duty, accidentally interrupted a holdup of a grocery store. Undoubtedly the cop was more startled than the two small-time hoodlums involved and would certainly not have impeded them since both were armed. As investigation afterward brought out, Bufflehead did not even try to draw his gun.

But one robber panicked and, before running, fired a sawed-off shotgun into Bufflehead's gut.

News of the shooting spread quickly and a crowd gathered. It included young Nolan Wainwright.

He would always remember—as he did now—the sight and sound of harmless, lazy Bufflehead, conscious, writhing, wailing, screaming in demented agony as blood and entrails gushed from his capacious, mortal wound.

An ambulance was a long time coming. Moments before it arrived, Bufflehead, still screaming, died.

The incident left its mark forever on Nolan Wainwright, though it was not Bufflehead's death itself which affected him most. Nor did the arrest and later execution of the thief who fired the shot, and his companion, seem more than anticlimactic.

What shocked and influenced him above all else was the appalling, senseless waste. The original crime was mean, foolish, foredoomed to failure; yet, in failing, its devastation was outrageously immense. Within young Wainwright's mind that single thought, that reasoning, persisted. It proved a catharsis through which he came to see all crime as equally negative, equally destructive—and, later still, as an evil to be fought. Perhaps, from the beginning, a streak of puritanism had been latent, deep inside him. If so, it surfaced.

He progressed from youth to manhood as an individual with uncompromising standards and, because of this, became something of a loner, among his friends and eventually when he became a cop. But he was an efficient cop who learned and rose fast, and was incorruptible, as Ben Rosselli and his aides once learned.

And later still, within First Mercantile American Bank, Wainwright's strong feelings stayed with him.

It was possible that the security chief dozed off, but a key inserted in the apartment lock alerted him. Cautiously he sat up. His illuminated watch dial showed it was shortly after midnight.

A shadowy figure came in; a shaft of outside light revealed it as Eastin. Then the door closed and Wainwright heard Eastin fumble for a switch. The light came on.

Eastin saw Wainwright at once and his surprise was total. His mouth dropped open, blood drained from his face. He tried to speak, but gulped, and no words came.

Wainwright stood up, glaring. His voice cut like a knife. "How much did you steal today?"

Before Eastin could answer or recover, Wainwright seized him by the coat lapels, turned him and pushed. He fell sprawling on the sofa.

As surprise turned to indignation, the young man spluttered, "Who let you in? What the hell do you . . ." His eyes moved to the money and the small black ledger, and he stopped.

"That's right," Wainwright said harshly, "I came for the bank's money, or what little is left." He motioned to the bills stacked on the table. "We know what's there, is what you took on Wednesday. And in case you're wondering, we know about the milked accounts and all the rest."

Miles Eastin stared, his expression frozen, stupefied. A convulsive shudder went through him. In fresh shock his head came down, his hands went to his face.

"Cut that out!" Wainwright reached over, pulled Eastin's hands free and pushed his head up, though not roughly, remembering his promise to the FBI man. No bruised potato.

He added, "You've got some talking to do, so let's start."

"Hey, time out, huh?" Eastin pleaded. "Give me a minute to think."

"Forget it!" The last thing Wainwright wanted was to give Eastin time to reflect. He was a bright young man who might reason, correctly, that his wisest course was silence. The security chief knew that at this moment he had two advantages. One was having Miles Eastin off balance, the other being unrestricted by rules.

If the FBI agents were here they would have to inform Eastin of his legal rights—the right not to answer questions, and to have a lawyer present. Wainwright, not a policeman any more, had no such obligation.

What the security chief wanted was hard evidence pinning the six-thousand-dollar cash theft on Miles Eastin. A signed confession would do it.

He sat down facing Eastin, his eyes impaling the younger man. "We can do this the long, hard way or we can move fast."

When there was no response, Wainwright picked up the small black ledger and opened it. "Let's start with this." He put his finger on the list of sums and dates; beside each entry were other figures in a code. "These are bets. Right?"

Through a muddled dullness Eastin nodded.

"Explain this one."

It was a two-hundred-and-fifty-dollar bet, Miles Eastin mumbled, on the outcome of a football game between Texas and Notre Dame. He explained the odds. The bet had been on Notre Dame. Texas had won.

"And this?"

Another mumbled answer: Another football game. Another loss.

"Go on." Wainwright persisted, keeping his finger on the page, maintaining pressure.

Responses came slowly. Some of the entries covered basketball games. A few bets were on the winning side, though losses outnumbered them. The minimum bet was one hundred dollars, the highest three hundred.

"Did you bet alone or with a group?"

"A group."

"Who was in it?"

"Four other guys. Working. Like me."

"Working at the bank?"

Eastin shook his head. "Other places."

"Did they lose, too?"

"Some. But their batting average was better than mine."

"What are the names of the other four?"

No answer. Wainwright let it go.

"You made no bets on horses. Why?"

"We got together. Everybody knows horse racing is crooked, races fixed. Football and basketball are on the level. We worked out a system. With honest games, we figured we could beat the odds."

The total of losses showed how wrong that figuring had been.

"Did you bet with one bookie, or more?"

"One."

"His name?"

Eastin stayed mute.

"The rest of the money you've been stealing from the bank—where is it?"

The young man's mouth turned down. He answered miserably, "Gone."

"And more besides?"

An affirmative, dismal nod.

"We'll get to that later. Right now let's talk about *this* money." Wainwright touched the six thousand dollars which lay between them. "We know you took it on Wednesday. How?"

Eastin hesitated, then shrugged. "I guess you may as well know."

Wainwright said sharply, "You're guessing right but wasting time."

"Last Wednesday," Eastin said, "we had people away with flu. That day I filled in as a teller."

"I know that. Get to what happened."

"Before the bank opened for business I went to the vault to get a cash truck—one of the spares. Juanita Núñez was there. She unlocked her regular cash truck. I was right alongside. Without Juanita knowing, I watched to see her combination."

"And?"

"I memorized it. As soon as I could, I wrote it down."

With Wainwright prompting, the damning facts multiplied.

The main downtown branch vault was large. During daytime a vault teller worked in a cage-like enclosure just inside, near the heavy, time-lock controlled door. The vault teller was invariably busy, counting currency, handing out packages of bills or receiving them, checking tellers and cash trucks in or out. While no one could pass the vault teller without being seen, once they were inside he took little notice of them.

That morning, while outwardly cheerful, Miles Eastin was desperate for cash. There had been betting losses the week before and he was being pressed for payment of accumulated debts.

Wainwright interrupted, "You already had an employee bank loan. You owed finance companies. Also the bookie. Right?"

"Right."

"Did you owe anyone else?"

Eastin nodded affirmatively.

"A loan shark?"

The younger man hesitated, then admitted, "Yes."

"Was the loan shark threatening you?"

Miles Eastin moistened his lips. "Yes; so was the bookie. They both are, still." His eyes went to the six thousand dollars.

The jigsaw was fitting together. Wainwright motioned to the money. "You promised to pay the shark and the bookie that?"

"Yes."

"How much to each?"

"Three thousand."

"When?"

"Tomorrow." Eastin looked nervously at a wall clock and corrected himself. "Today."

Wainwright prompted, "Go back to Wednesday. So you knew the combination of the Núñez girl's cash box. How did you use it?"

As Miles Eastin revealed the details now, it was all incredibly simple. After working through the morning, he took his lunch break at the same time as Juanita Núñez. Before going to lunch they wheeled their cash trucks into the vault. The two cash units were left side by side, both locked.

Eastin returned from lunch early and went into the vault. The vault teller checked Eastin in, then went on working. No one else was in the vault.

Miles Eastin went directly to Juanita Núñez's cash truck and opened it, using the combination he had written down. It took seconds only to remove three packages of bills totaling six thousand dollars, then close and relock the box. He slipped the currency packages into inside pockets; the bulges scarcely showed. He then checked out his own cash truck from the vault and returned to work.

There was a silence, then Wainwright said, "So while questioning was going on Wednesday afternoon—some of it by you, and while you and I were talking later that same day—all that time you had the money on you?"

"Yes," Miles Eastin said. As he remembered how easy it had been, a faint smile creased his face.

Wainwright saw the smile. Without hesitating, and in a single movement, he leaned forward and hit Eastin hard on both sides of the face. He used his open palm for the first blow, the back of his hand for the second. The double blow was so forceful that Wainwright's hand stung. Miles Eastin's face showed two bright weals. He shrunk backward on the sofa and blinked as tears formed in his eyes.

The security chief said grimly, "That's to let you know I see nothing funny in what you did to the bank or to Mrs. Núñez. Nothing at all." Something else he had just learned was that Miles Eastin was afraid of physical violence.

He observed that it was 1 A.M.

"The next order of business," Nolan Wainwright announced, "is a written statement. In your own handwriting and with everything in it that you've told me."

"No! I won't do that!" Eastin was wary now.

Wainwright shrugged. "In that case there's no point in my staying longer." He reached for the six thousand dollars and began stowing it in his pockets.

"You can't do that!"

"Can't I? Try stopping me. I'm taking it back to the bank—the night depository."

"Listen!—you can't prove . . ." The younger man hesitated. He was thinking now, remembering too late that the serial numbers of the bills had never been recorded.

"Maybe I can prove it's the same money that was taken Wednesday; maybe not. If not, you can always try suing the bank to get it back."

Eastin pleaded, "I need it now! Today!"

"Oh, sure, some for the bookie and some for the loan shark. Or the strong-arm guys they'll send. Well, you can try explaining how you lost it, though I doubt if they'll listen." The security chief eyed Eastin for the first time with sardonic amusement. "You really *are* in trouble. Maybe they'll both come together, then they'll break one of your arms and one leg each. They're apt to do that sort of thing. Or didn't you know?"

Fear, real fear, showed in Eastin's eyes. "Yes, I do know. You've got to help me! Please!"

From the apartment doorway Wainwright said coldly, "I'll consider it. *After* you've written that statement."

The bank security chief dictated while Eastin wrote the words down obediently.

I, Miles Broderick Eastin, make this statement voluntarily. I have

been offered no inducement to make it. No violence or threat of vio-
lence has been used . . .

I confess to stealing from First Mercantile American Bank the sum
of six thousand dollars in cash at approximately 1:30 P.M. on Wednes-
day, October . . .

I obtained and concealed this money by the following means . . .

A quarter of an hour ago, after Wainwright's threat to walk out, Miles
Eastin had collapsed entirely, co-operative and cowed.

Now, while Eastin continued writing his confession, Wainwright telephoned Innes, the FBI man, at his home.

15

During the first week of November, Ben Rosselli's physical condition worsened. Since the bank president's disclosure of his terminal illness four weaks earlier, his strength had ebbed, his body wasted as proliferating and invading cancerous cells tightened their stranglehold on his remaining life.

Those who visited old Ben at home—including Roscoe Heyward, Alex Vandervoort, Edwina D'Orsey, Nolan Wainwright, and various directors of the bank—were shocked at the extent and speed of his deterioration. It was obvious he had very little time to live.

Then, in mid-November, while a savage storm with gale force winds beset the city, Ben Rosselli was moved by ambulance to the private pavilion of Mount Adams Hospital, a short journey which was to be his last alive. By then he was under almost continuous sedation, so that his moments of awareness and coherence became fewer day by day.

The last vestiges of any control of First Mercantile American Bank had now slipped from him, and a group of the bank's senior directors, meeting privately, agreed the full board must be summoned, a successor to the presidency named.

The decisive board meeting was set for December 4.

Directors began arriving shortly before 10 A.M. They greeted one another cordially, each with an easy confidence—the patina of a successful businessman in the company of his peers.

The cordiality was slightly more restrained than usual in deference to the dying Ben Rosselli, still clutching feebly to life a mile or so away. Yet the directors now assembling were admirals and field marshals of commerce, as Ben had been himself, who knew that whatever else obtruded, business, which kept civilization lubricated, must go on. Their mood appeared to say: *The reason behind decisions we must make today is regrettable, but our solemn duty to the system shall be done.*

Thus they moved resolutely into the walnut paneled boardroom, hung with paintings and photographs of selected predecessors, once important themselves, now long departed.

A board of directors of any major corporation resembles an exclusive club. Apart from three or four top management executives who are employed full time, the board comprises a score or so of outstanding businessmen—often board chairmen or presidents themselves—from other, diverse fields.

Usually such outside directors are invited to join the board for one or more of several reasons—their own achievements elsewhere, the prestige of the institution they represent, or a strong connection—usually financial—with the company on whose board they sit.

Among businessmen it is considered a high honor to be a company director, and the more prestigious the company the greater the glory. This is why some individuals collect directorships the way some Indians once collected scalps. Another reason is that directors are treated with ego-satisfying reverence and also generously—major companies pay each director between one and two thousand dollars for every meeting attended, normally ten a year.

Particularly high in prestige is a directorship of any major bank. For a businessman to be invited to serve on a topflight bank board is roughly equivalent to being knighted by the British Queen; therefore the accolade is widely sought. First Mercantile American, as befitting a bank among the nation's top twenty, possessed a board of directors appropriately impressive.

Or so they thought.

Alex Vandervoort, surveying the other directors as they took seats around the long, elliptical boardroom table, decided there was a high percentage of deadwood. There were also conflicts of interest since some directors, or their companies, were major borrowers of bank money. Among his long-term objectives if he became president would be to make the FMA board more representative and less like a cozy club.

But would he be president? Or would Heyward?

Both of them were candidates today. Both, in a short time, like any seeker after office, would expound their views. Jerome Patterton, vice-chairman of the board, who would preside at today's meeting, had approached Alex two days earlier. "You know as well as the rest of us, our decision's between you and Roscoe. You're both good men; making a choice isn't easy. So help us. Tell us your feelings about FMA, in any way you like; the what and how, I leave to you."

Roscoe Heyward, Alex was aware, had been similarly briefed.

Heyward, typically, had armed himself with a prepared text. Seated directly across from Alex, he was studying it now, his aquiline face set seriously, the gray eyes behind rimless glasses unwaveringly focused on the typewritten words. Among Heyward's abilities was intense concentration of his scalpel-sharp mind, especially on figures. A colleague once observed, "Roscoe can read a profit and loss statement the way a symphony conductor reads a score—sensing nuances, awkward notes, incomplete passages, crescendos, and potentialities which others miss." Without doubt, figures would be included in whatever Heyward had to say today.

Alex was unsure whether he would use numbers in his own remarks or not. If they were used, they would have to be from memory since he had brought no materials. He had deliberated far into last night and decided eventually to wait until the moment came, then speak instinctively, as seemed appropriate, letting thoughts and words fall into place themselves.

He reminded himself that in this same room, so short a time ago, Ben had announced, *"I'm dying. My doctors tell me I don't have long."* The words had been, still were, an affirmation that all in life was finite. They mocked ambition—his own, Roscoe Heyward's, others'.

Yet whether ambition was futile in the end or not, he wanted very much the presidency of this bank. He longed for an opportunity—just as Ben in his time had—to determine directions, decide philosophy, allot priorities and, through the sum of all decisions, leave behind a worthwhile contribution. And whether, viewed across a larger span of years, whatever was accomplished mattered much or little, the zest itself would be rewarding—the doing, leading, striving, and competing, here and now.

Across the boardroom table to the right, the Honorable Harold Austin slipped into his accustomed seat. He wore a windowpane check Cerruti suit, with a classic button-down shirt and houndstooth pattern tie, and looked like a pacesetting model from the pages of *Playboy*. He held a fat cigar, ready to be lighted. Alex saw Austin and nodded. The nod was returned, but with noticeable coolness.

A week ago the Honorable Harold had dropped by to protest Alex's veto of Keycharge credit-card advertising prepared by the Austin agency. "Keycharge marketing expansion was approved by the board of directors," the Honorable Harold had objected. "What's more, the department heads at Keycharge had already okayed that particular ad campaign before it got to you. I'm of two minds whether to bring your high-handed action to the attention of the board or not."

Alex was blunt, "To begin with, I know exactly what the directors decided about Keycharge because I was there. What they did *not* agree to was that marketing expansion would include advertising which is sleazy, misleading, half-truthful and discreditable to the bank. Your creative people can do better than that, Harold. In fact, they already have—I've seen and approved the revised versions. As for being high-handed, I made an executive management decision well within my authority, and any time necessary I'll do the same again. So if you choose to bring the subject before the board, you can. If you want my opinion, they won't thank you for it—they're more likely to thank me."

Harold Austin had glowered, but apparently decided to drop the subject, perhaps wisely because Austin Advertising was going to do just as well financially with the revised Keycharge campaign. But Alex knew he had created an antagonist. He doubted, though, if it would make any difference today since the Honorable Harold obviously preferred Roscoe Heyward and was likely to support him anyway.

One of his own strong supporters, Alex knew, was Leonard L. Kingswood, outspoken, energetic chairman of Northam Steel, now seated near the head of the table, conversing intently with his neighbor. It was Len Kingswood who had telephoned Alex several weeks ago to advise him that Roscoe Heyward was actively canvassing directors for support as president. "I'm not saying you should do the same, Alex. That's for you to decide. But I'm warning you that what Roscoe's doing can be effective. He doesn't fool me. He's not a leader and I've told him so. But he has a persuasive way which is a hook that some may swallow."

Alex had thanked Len Kingswood for the information but made no attempt to copy Heyward's tactics. Solicitation might help in some cases but could antagonize others who objected to personal pressure in such matters. Besides, Alex had an aversion to campaigning actively for Ben's job while the old man remained alive.

But Alex accepted the necessity for today's meeting and decisions to be made here.

A hum of conversation in the boardroom quietened. Two late arrivals who had just come in were settling down. Jerome Patterton, at the table's head, tapped lightly with a gavel and announced, "Gentlemen, the board will come to order."

Patterton, projected into prominence today, was normally self-effacing and, in the management echelon of the bank, something of a timeserver. Now in his sixties and near retirement, he had been acquired as part of a merger with another, smaller bank several years ago; since then his responsibilities had quietly, and by mutual agreement, diminished. Currently he concerned himself almost equally with trust department matters and playing golf with clients. The golf took priority, to the extent that on any working day Jerome Patterton was seldom in his office after 2:30 P.M. His title of vice-chairman of the board was largely honorary.

In appearance he resembled a gentleman farmer. Mostly bald, except for a white, halo-fringe of hair, he had a pointed pink head uncannily like the narrow end of an egg. Paradoxically, his eyebrows were matted and fiercely sprouting; the eyes beneath were gray, bulbous, and becoming rheumy. Adding to the farmer image, he dressed tweedily. Alex Vandervoort's assessment of Patterton was that the vice-chairman had an excellent brain which in recent years he had used minimally, like an idling motor.

Predictably, Jerome Patterton began by paying tribute to Ben Rosselli, after which he read aloud the latest hospital bulletin which reported "diminishing strength and eroding consciousness." Among the directors, lips were pursed, heads shaken. "But the life of our community goes on." The vice-chairman enumerated reasons for the present meeting, principally the need to name, speedily, a new chief executive for First Mercantile American Bank.

"Most of you gentlemen are aware of procedures which have been agreed on." He then announced what everyone knew—that Roscoe Heyward and Alex Vandervoort would address the board, after which both would leave the meeting while their candidacies were discussed.

"As to the order of speaking, we'll employ that ancient chance which all of us were born under—alphabetical precedence." Jerome Patterton's eyes twinkled toward Alex. "I've paid a penalty sometimes for being a 'P.' I hope that 'V' of yours hasn't been too burdensome."

"Not often, Mr. Chairman," Alex said. "On some occasions it gives me the last word."

A ripple of laughter, the first today, ran around the table. Roscoe Heyward shared in it, though his smile seemed forced.

"Roscoe," Jerome Patterton instructed, "at your convenience, please begin."

"Thank you, Mr. Chairman." Heyward rose to his feet, moved his chair well back and calmly surveyed the nineteen other men around the table. He took a sip of water from a glass in front of him, cleared his throat perfunctorily, and began speaking in a precise and even voice.

"Members of the board, since this is a closed and private meeting, not to be reported in the press or even to other shareholders, I shall be forthright today in emphasizing what I conceive to be my first responsibility, and this board's—the profitability of First Mercantile American Bank." He repeated with emphasis, "Profitability, gentlemen —our priority number one."

Heyward glanced briefly at his text. "Allow me to elaborate on that.

"In my view, too many decisions in banking, and in business generally, are being excessively influenced nowadays by social issues and other controversies of our times. As a banker I believe this to be wrong. Let me emphasize that I do not in any way diminish the importance of an individual's social conscience; my own, I hope, is well developed. I accept, too, that each of us must re-examine his personal values from time to time, making adjustments in the light of new ideas and offering such private contributions as he can. But corporate policies are something else. They should not be subject to every changing social wind or whim. If they were, if that kind of thinking is allowed to rule our business actions, it would be dangerous for American free enterprise and disastrous for this bank by lessening our strength, retarding growth, and reducing profits. In short, like other institutions, we should once again stay aloof from the socio-political scene which is none of our concern other than how that scene affects our clients' financial affairs."

The speaker intruded a thin smile into his seriousness. "I concede that if these words were spoken publicly they would be undiplomatic and unpopular. I will go further and say that I would never utter them in any public place. But between us here, where real decisions and policy are made, I conceive them to be wholly realistic."

Several of the directors gave approving nods. One enthusiastically thumped his fist upon the tabletop. Others, including the steelman Leonard Kingswood, remained expressionless.

Alex Vandervoort reflected: So Roscoe Heyward had decided on a direct confrontation, a total clash of views. As Heyward was undoubtedly aware, everything he had just said ran contrary to Alex's own convictions, as well as Ben Rosselli's, as demonstrated by Ben's increasing liberalization of the bank in recent years. It was Ben who had involved FMA in civic affairs, both city and statewide, including projects like Forum East. But Alex had no delusions. A substantial segment of the board had been uneasy, at times unhappy, about Ben's policies and would welcome Heyward's hard, all-business line. The question was: How strong was the hard line segment?

With one statement made by Roscoe Heyward, Alex was in full agreement. Heyward had said: *This is a closed and private meeting . . . where real decisions and policy are made.*

The operative word was "real."

While shareholders and public might later be fed a soporific, sugarcoated version of bank policy through elaborately printed annual reports and other means, here, behind closed boardroom doors, was where true objectives were decided in uncompromising terms. It was a reason why discretion and a certain silence were requirements of any company director.

"There is a close-to-home parallel," Heyward was explaining, "between what I have spoken of and what has happened in the church which I attend, through which I make some social contributions of my own.

"In the 1960s our church diverted money, time, and effort to social causes, notably those of black advancement. Partly this was because of outside pressures; also certain members of our congregation saw it as 'the thing to do.' In sundry ways our church became a social agency. More recently, however, some of us have regained control, and decided such activism is inappropriate, and we should return to the basics of religious worship. Therefore we have increased religious ceremonies —our church's primary function as we see it—and are leaving active social involvement to government and other agencies where, in our opinion, it belongs."

Alex wondered if other directors found it hard, as he did, to think of social causes as "inappropriate" to a church.

"I spoke of profit as our principal objective," Roscoe Heyward was continuing. "There are some, I am aware, who will object to that. They will argue that the predominant pursuit of profit is a crass endeavor, shortsighted, selfish, ugly, and without redeeming social value." The speaker smiled tolerantly. "You gentlemen are familiar with arguments along those lines.

"Well, as a banker I profoundly disagree. The search for profit is not shortsighted. And, where this bank or any other is concerned, the social value of profitability is high.

"Let me enlarge on that.

"All banks measure profit in terms of earnings per share. Such earnings—which are a matter of public record—are widely studied by shareholders, depositors, investors, and the business community nationally and internationally. A rise or fall in bank earnings is taken as a sign of strength or weakness.

"While earnings are strong, confidence in banking continues high. But let a few big banks show decreased earnings per share and what would happen? General disquiet, increasing swiftly to alarm—a situation in which depositors would withdraw funds and shareholders their investments, so that bank stocks tumbled with the banks themselves imperiled. In short, a public crisis of the gravest kind."

Roscoe Heyward removed his glasses and polished them with a white linen handkerchief.

"Let no one say: this cannot happen. It happened before in the depression which began in 1929, though today, with banks larger by far, the effect would be cataclysmic by comparison.

"This is why a bank like ours must remain vigilant in its duty to make money for itself and its shareholders."

Again there were murmurings of approval around the boardroom. Heyward turned another page of his text.

"How, as a bank, do we achieve maximum profit? I will tell you first how we do *not* achieve it.

"We do not achieve it by becoming involved with projects which, while admirable in intent, are either financially unsound or tie up bank funds at low rates of yield for many years. I refer, of course, to funding of low-income housing. We should not, in any case, place more than a minimal portion of bank funds in housing mortgages of any kind, which are notorious for their low return of profit.

"Another way not to achieve profitability is by making concessions and lowering lending standards as, for example, with so-called minority business loans. This is an area nowadays where banks are subjected to enormous pressures and we should resist them, not with racial motives but with business shrewdness. By all means let us make minority loans when possible, but let terms and standards be as strict as those for any other borrower.

"Nor, as a bank should we concern ourselves unduly with vague matters of environment. It is not *our* business to pass judgment on the way our customers conduct *their* business vis-à-vis ecology; all we ask is that they be in good financial health.

"In short, we do *not* achieve profitability by becoming our brother's keeper—or his judge or jailer.

"Oh, at times we may support these public objectives with our voice —low-cost housing, civic rehabilitation, improvement of environment, energy, conservation, and other issues which arise. After all, this bank has influence and prestige which we can lend without financial loss. We can even allocate token amounts of money, and we have a public relations department to make our contributions known—even," he chuckled, "to exaggerate them on occasions. But for real profitability we should direct our major thrust elsewhere."

Alex Vandervoort thought: Whatever criticism might be leveled at Heyward, no one could complain later that he had failed to make his viewpoints clear. In a way his statement was an honest declaration. Yet it was also shrewdly, even cynically, calculated.

Many leaders in business and finance—including a good proportion of the directors in the room—chafed at restrictions on their freedom to make money. They resented, too, the need to be circumspect in public utterances lest they draw fire from consumer groups or other business critics. Thus it was a relief to hear their inner convictions spoken aloud and unequivocally.

Clearly, Roscoe Heyward had considered this. He had also, Alex was certain, counted heads around the boardroom table, calculating who would vote which way, before committing himself.

But Alex had made his own calculations. He still believed a middle group of directors existed, sufficiently strong to swing this meeting from Heyward toward himself. But they would have to be persuaded.

"Specifically," Heyward declared, "this bank should depend, as it has traditionally, on its business with American industry. By that I mean the type of industry with a proven record of high profits which will, in turn, enhance our own.

"Expressed another way, I am convinced that First Mercantile American Bank has, at present, an insufficient proportion of its funds available for large loans to industry, and we should embark immediately on a program of increasing such lending . . ."

It was a familiar script which Roscoe Heyward, Alex Vandervoort, and Ben Rosselli had debated often in the past. The arguments which Heyward now advanced were not new, though he presented them convincingly, using figures and charts. Alex sensed the directors were impressed.

Heyward talked for another thirty minutes on his theme of expanded industrial lending against a contraction in community commitments. He ended with—as he put it—"an appeal to reason."

"What is needed most today in banking is pragmatic leadership. The kind of leadership which will not be swayed by emotion or pressured into 'soft' uses of money because of public clamor. As bankers, we must insist on saying 'no' when our fiscal view is negative, 'yes' when we foresee a profit. We must never buy easy popularity at stockholders' expense. Instead we should lend our own and our depositors' money solely on the basis of the best return and if, as a result of such policies, we are described as 'hard-nosed bankers,' so be it. I am one who will be glad to be counted among that number."

Heyward sat down amid applause.

"Mr. Chairman!" The steelman, Leonard Kingswood, leaned forward with a hand raised. "I've several questions and some disagreement."

From lower down the table the Honorable Harold Austin riposted, "For the record, Mr. Chairman, I have *no* questions and total *agreement* with everything presented so far."

Laughter erupted and a fresh voice—that of Philip Johannsen, president of MidContinent Rubber—added, "I'm with you, Harold. I agree it's time we took a harder line." Someone else injected, "Me, too."

"Gentlemen, gentlemen." Jerome Patterton rapped lightly with his gavel. "Only part of our business is concluded. I'll allow time for questions later; as for disagreement, I suggest we save that until our discussion when Roscoe and Alex have withdrawn. First, though, let's hear Alex."

"Most of you know me well, as a man and as a banker," Alex began. He stood at the boardroom table casually, shoulders slightly hunched as usual, leaning forward momentarily to catch sight of those directors on his right and left as well as others facing him. He let his tone stay conversational.

"You also know, or should, that as a banker I am tough—hard-nosed, if anyone prefers that word. Proof of this exists in financing I've conducted for FMA, all of it profitable, none involving loss. Obviously in banking like any other business, when you deal from profitability you deal from strength. That applies to people in banking, too.

"I'm glad, though, that Roscoe brought up this subject because it gives me an opportunity to declare my own belief in profitability. Ditto for freedom, democracy, love, and motherhood."

Someone chuckled. Alex responded with an easy smile. He pushed the chair behind him farther back to give himself a few paces of free movement.

"Something else about our profitability here at FMA is that it should be drastically improved. More about that later.

"For the moment I'd like to stay with beliefs.

"A belief of my own is that civilization in this decade is changing more meaningfully and quickly than at any other time since the Industrial Revolution. What we are seeing and sharing is a social revolution of conscience and behavior.

"A few don't like this revolution; personally I do. But like it or not, it's here; it exists; it will not reverse itself or go away.

"For the driving force behind what's happening is the determination of a majority of people to improve the quality of life, to stop spoliation of our environment and to preserve what's left of resources of all kinds. Because of this, new standards are being demanded of industry and business so that the name of the game is 'corporate social responsibility.' What's more, higher standards of responsibility *are* being achieved and without significant loss of profits."

Alex moved restlessly in the limited space behind the boardroom table. He wondered if he should meet another of Heyward's challenges head on, then decided, *yes*.

"In the matter of responsibility and involvement, Roscoe introduced the subject of his church. He told us that those who have—as he puts it —'regained control' are opting out and favoring a policy of non-involvement. Well, in my opinion, Roscoe and his churchmen are marching resolutely backwards. Their attitude is neither good for Christianity nor banking."

Heyward shot up straight. He protested, "That's unpleasantly personal and a misinterpretation."

Alex said calmly, "I don't believe it's either."

Harold Austin rapped sharply with his knuckles. "Mr. Chairman, I object to Alex's descent to personalities."

"Roscoe dragged in his church," Alex argued. "I'm simply commenting."

"Maybe you'd better not." The voice of Philip Johannsen cut sharply, unpleasantly, across the table. "Otherwise we might judge the two of you by the company you keep, which would put Roscoe and his church way out ahead."

Alex flushed. "May I ask exactly what that means?"

Johannsen shrugged. "The way I hear it, your closest lady friend, in your wife's absence, is a left-wing activist. Maybe that's why you like involvement."

Jerome Patterton pounded with his gavel, this time forcefully. "That's sufficient, gentlemen. The Chair instructs there will be no more references of this kind, either way."

Johannsen was smiling. Despite the ruling, he had made his point.

Alex Vandervoort, seething, considered a firm statement that his private life was his own affair, then he rejected the idea. Some other time it might be necessary. Not now. He realized he had made a bad mistake by returning to Heyward's church analogy.

"I'd like to get back," he said, "to my original contention: How, as bankers, can we afford to ignore this changing scene? To attempt to do so is like standing in a gale, pretending the wind does not exist.

"On pragmatic, financial grounds alone we cannot opt out. As those around this table know from personal experience, business success is never achieved by ignoring change, but by anticipating and adapting to it. Thus, as custodians of money, sensitive to the changing climates of investment, we shall profit most by listening, heeding, and adapting now."

He sensed that, apart from his lapse of judgment moments earlier, his opening gambit, with its practical emphasis, had captured attention. Almost every outside board member had had experience with legislation affecting pollution control, consumer protection, truth in advertising, minority hiring, or equal rights for women. Often, such laws were enacted over angry opposition from companies which these bank directors headed. But once the laws were passed, the same companies learned to live with new standards and proudly touted their contributions to the public weal. Some, like Leonard Kingswood, concluded that corporate responsibility was good for business and espoused it strongly.

"There are fourteen thousand banks in the United States," Alex reminded the FMA directors, "with enormous fiscal power in extending loans. Surely, when the loans are to industry and business, that power should involve responsibility on our part, too! Surely among criteria for lending should be the standards of public conduct of our borrowers! If a factory is to be financed, will it pollute? When a new product is to be developed, is it safe? How truthful is a company's advertising? As between companies A and B, to one of which we have funds to lend, which has the better record of non-discrimination?"

He leaned forward, glancing around the elliptical table to meet, in turn, the eyes of each board member.

"It is true these questions are not always asked, or acted on, at present. But they are beginning to be asked by major banks as matters of sound business—an example which FMA will be wise to emulate. For just as leadership in any enterprise can produce strong dividends, so leadership in banking will prove rewarding, too.

"Equally important: It is better to do this freely now than have it forced on us by regulation later."

Alex paused, took a pace from the table, then swung back. Now he asked, "In which other areas should this bank accept corporate responsibility?

"I believe, with Ben Rosselli, that we should share in improving the life of this city and state. An immediate means is through financing of low-rental housing, a commitment this board has already accepted with the early stages of Forum East. As time goes on I believe our contribution should be greater."

He glanced toward Roscoe Heyward. "Of course, I realize that housing mortgages are not a notably high profit area. Yet there are ways to achieve that involvement with excellent profits, too."

One means, he told the listening directors, was through a determined, large-scale expansion of the bank's savings department.

"Traditionally, funds for home mortgages are channeled from savings deposits because mortgages are long-term investments while savings are similarly stable and long-term. The profitability we shall gain by volume—far greater than our savings volume now. Thus we will attain a threefold objective—profit, fiscal stability, and a major social contribution.

"Only a few years ago large commercial banks like ourselves spurned consumer business, including small savings, as being unimportant. Then, while we dozed, savings and loan associations astutely seized the opportunity we ignored and forged ahead of us, so now they are a main competitor. But still, in personal savings, gigantic opportunities remain. It's likely that, within a decade, consumer business will exceed commercial deposits everywhere and thus become the most important money force existing."

Savings, Alex argued, was only one of several areas where FMA interests could be dramatically advanced.

Still moving restlessly as he spoke, he ranged through other bank departments, describing changes he proposed. Most had been in a report, prepared by Alex Vandervoort at Ben's request a few weeks before the bank president's announcement of his impending death. In the pressure of events it had remained, so far as Alex knew, unread.

One recommendation was to open nine new branches in suburban areas through the state. Another was for a drastic overhaul of FMA organization. Alex proposed to hire a specialist consulting firm to advise on needed changes and he advised the board, "Our efficiency is lower than it should be. The machinery is creaking."

Near the end he returned to his original theme. "Our banking relationship with industry should, of course, continue to be close. Industrial loans and commercial business will remain pillars of our activity.

But not the only pillars. Nor should they be overwhelmingly the larg
est. Nor should we be so preoccupied with bigness that the importance
of small accounts, including those of individuals, becomes diminished
in our minds.

"The founder of this bank established it to serve those of modest
means to whom other banking facilities were denied. Inevitably, the
bank's purpose and operations have broadened across a century, yet
neither the founder's son nor grandson ever lost sight of those origins
or ignored the precept that smallness multiplied can represent the great
est strength of all.

"A massive and immediate growth in small savings, which I urge the
board to set as an objective, will honor those origins, enhance our fisca
strength and—in the climate of the times—advance the public good
which is our own."

As they had for Heyward, board members applauded as Alex sat
down. Some of the applause was merely polite, Alex realized; perhaps
half of the directors seemed more enthusiastic. He guessed that the
choice between Heyward and himself could still go either way.

"Thank you, Alex." Jerome Patterton glanced around the table
"Questions, gentlemen?"

The questioning occupied another half hour, after which Roscoe
Heyward and Alex Vandervoort left the boardroom together. Each
returned to his office to await the board's decision.

The directors debated through the remainder of the morning but
failed to reach agreement. They then adjourned to a private dining
room for lunch, their discussion continuing over the meal. The out
come of the meeting was still inconclusive when a dining-room steward
quietly approached Jerome Patterton, carrying a small silver tray. On
it was a single sheet of paper, folded.

The vice-chairman accepted the paper, unfolded and read it. After
a pause he rose to his feet and waited while conversation around the
luncheon table quietened.

"Gentlemen." Patterton's voice quavered. "I grieve to inform you
that our beloved president, Ben Rosselli, died a few minutes ago."

Soon after, by mutual consent and without further discussion, the
board meeting was abandoned.

16

The death of Ben Rosselli attracted international press coverage and some news writers, reaching for the nearest cliché, labeled it "an era's end."

Whether it was, or wasn't, his departure signaled that the last major American bank to be identified with a single entrepreneur had moved into mid-twentieth century conformation, with committee and hired management control. As to who would head the hired management, that decision had been postponed until after the Rosselli funeral when the bank's board of directors would convene again.

The funeral took place on Wednesday in the second week of December.

Both the funeral and a lying-in-state which preceded it were garnished with the full rites and panoply of the Catholic Church, suitable to a papal knight and large cash benefactor which Ben Rosselli was.

The two-day lying-in-state was at St. Matthew's Cathedral, appropriate since Matthew—once Levi the tax collector—is considered by bankers as a patron saint. Some two thousand people, including a presidential representative, the state governor, ambassadors, civic leaders, bank employees and many humbler souls, filed past the bier and open casket.

On the morning of burial—taking no chances—an archbishop, a bishop, and a monsignor concelebrated a Mass of the Resurrection. A full choir intoned responses to prayers with reassuring volume. Within the cathedral, which was filled, a section near the altar had been reserved for Rosselli relatives and friends. Immediately behind were directors and senior officers of First Mercantile American Bank.

Roscoe Heyward, dressed somberly in black, was in the first row of bank mourners, accompanied by his wife Beatrice, an imperious, sturdy woman, and their son, Elmer. Heyward, an Episcopalian, had studied the correct Catholic procedures in advance and genuflected elegantly, both before seating himself and on departure later—the last a piece of punctilio which many Catholics ignored. The Heywards also knew the Mass responses so that their voices dominated others nearby who didn't.

Alex Vandervoort, wearing charcoal gray and seated two rows behind the Heywards, was among the non-responders. An agnostic, he felt out of place in these surroundings. He wondered how Ben, essentially a simple man, would have regarded this ornate ceremony.

Beside Alex, Margot Bracken looked around her with curiosity. Originally Margot had planned to attend the funeral with a group from Forum East, but last night she had stayed at Alex's apartment and he persuaded her to accompany him today. The Forum East delegation —a large one—was somewhere behind them in the church.

Next to Margot were Edwina and Lewis D'Orsey, the latter looking gaunt and starved as usual and frankly bored. Probably, Alex thought, Lewis was mentally drafting the next edition of his investment newsletter. The D'Orseys had ridden here with Margot and Alex—the four of them were often together, not just because Edwina and Margot were cousins, but because they found each other's company agreeable. After the Mass of the Resurrection they would all go to the graveside service.

In the row ahead of Alex were Jerome Patterton, the vice-chairman, and his wife.

Despite his detachment from the liturgy, Alex found tears spring to his eyes as the coffin passed by and was carried from the church. His feeling for Ben, he had realized over the past few days, was close to love. In some ways the old man had been a father figure; his death left a gap in Alex's life which would not be filled.

Margot reached gently for his hand and held it.

As mourners began filing out he saw Roscoe and Beatrice Heyward glance their way. Alex nodded and the greeting was returned. Heyward's face softened in an acknowledgment of mutual grief, their feud—in recognition of their own, as well as Ben's mortality—for this brief moment put aside.

Outside the cathedral, regular traffic had been diverted. The coffin was already in a flower-laden hearse. Now, relatives and bank officials were getting into limousines being brought up under police direction. A police motorcycle escort, engines running noisily, was at the head of the assembling cortege.

The day was gray and cold with eddies of wind raising dust whorls in the street. High above, the cathedral towers loomed, the whole façade immense and blackened by the grime of years. Snow had been forecast earlier but so far had not appeared.

While Alex signaled for his car, Lewis D'Orsey peered over his half-moon glasses at TV and still cameramen, shooting pictures of the emerging mourners. He observed, "If I find all this depressing, and I do, the reports should depress FMA stock even more tomorrow."

Alex murmured uneasy agreement. Like Lewis, he was aware that First Mercantile American shares, listed on the New York Stock Exchange, had fallen five and a half points since news of Ben's illness. The death of the last Rosselli—a name which for generations had been synonymous with the bank—coupled with uncertainty about the course of future management, had caused the most recent drop. Now, even though illogically, publicity about the funeral could depress the stock still further.

"Our stock will go up again," Alex said. "Earnings are good and nothing's really changed."

"Oh, I know that," Lewis agreed. "It's why I'll cover my short position tomorrow afternoon."

Edwina looked shocked. "You shorted FMA?"

"Sure did. Advised a few clients to do the same. As of right now there's a tidy profit."

She protested, "You and I know I never discuss anything confidential with you, Lewis. Others don't. Because of my connection with the bank you could be accused of insider trading."

Alex shook his head. "Not in this case, Edwina. Ben's illness was public knowledge."

"When we eventually make over the capitalist system," Margot said, "selling short on the stock market will be one of the first things to go."

Lewis raised his eyebrows. "Why?"

"Because it's *totally* negative. Short selling is disruptive speculation that requires someone else to lose. It's ghoulish and a non-contribution. It creates nothing."

"It creates a handy-dandy capital gain." Lewis grinned broadly; he had crossed arguments with Margot many times before. "And that isn't easy to come by nowadays, at least with American investments."

"I still don't like you doing it with FMA stock," Edwina said. "It's too close to home."

Lewis D'Orsey looked at his wife gravely. "In that case, my dear, after I've covered my shorts tomorrow I will never trade in FMA again."

Margot glanced over sharply.

"You know he means it," Alex said.

Alex wondered sometimes about the relationship between Edwina and her husband. Outwardly they seemed ill-matched—Edwina elegantly attractive and self-possessed; Lewis, scrawny, unimpressive physically, an introvert except with those he knew well, though the personal reticence never showed in his roaring-lion financial newsletter. But their marriage appeared to work well, and each showed respect and affection for the other, as Lewis had just now. Perhaps, Alex thought, it proved that not only did opposites attract; they tended to stay married.

Alex's Cadillac from the bank car pool moved into the lengthening line outside the cathedral and the four of them walked toward it.

"It would have been a more civilized promise," Margot said, "if Lewis agreed not to sell *anything* short."

"Alex," Lewis said, "what the hell do you have in common with this socialist broad?"

"We're great in the sack," Margot told him. "Isn't that enough?"

Alex said, "And I'd like to marry her soon."

Edwina responded warmly, "Then I hope you will." She and Margot had been close since childhood, despite occasional clashes of temperament and outlook. Something they had in common was that in both branches of their family women were strong, with a tradition of involvement in public life. Edwina asked Alex quietly, "Anything new with Celia?"

He shook his head. "Nothing's changed. If anything, Celia's worse."

They were at the car. Alex motioned the chauffeur to remain seated, then opened a rear door for the others and followed them in. Inside, the glass panel separating the driver from the passenger seats was closed. They settled down while the still assembling cortege inched forward.

For Alex, the mention of Celia sharpened the sadness of this moment; it also reminded him guiltily that he should visit her again soon. Since the session at the Remedial Center in early October which had so depressed him, he had paid one other call, but Celia had been even more withdrawn, gave not the slightest sign of recognition, and wept silently the entire time. He remained dejected for days afterward and dreaded a repeat performance.

The thought occurred now that Ben Rosselli, in the coffin up ahead, was better off than Celia because his life had ended conclusively. *If only Celia would die* . . . Alex quelled the thought with shame.

Nor had anything new developed between himself and Margot, who remained adamantly opposed to a divorce, at least until it became clear that Celia would be unaffected. Margot seemed willing to go on indefinitely with the arrangement they had. Alex was less resigned.

Lewis addressed Edwina. "I've been meaning to ask what the latest is about that young assistant of yours. The one who got caught with his arm in the cash drawer. What was his name?"

"Miles Eastin," Edwina answered. "He appears in criminal court next week and I have to be a witness. I'm not looking forward to it."

"At least you got the blame where it should be," Alex said. He had read the audit chief's report about the embezzlement and cash loss; also that of Nolan Wainwright. "What about the teller who was involved— Mrs. Núñez? Is she okay?"

"She seems to be. I'm afraid we gave Juanita a hard time. Unjustly, as it turned out."

Margot, only half listening, now sharpened her attention. "I know a Juanita Núñez. Nice young woman who lives at Forum East. I believe her husband left her. She has a child."

"That sounds like our Mrs. Núñez," Edwina said. "Yes, I remember now. She does live at Forum East."

Though Margot was curious, she sensed it was not a time for further questions.

As they sat, briefly silent, Edwina pursued her thoughts. The two recent events—Ben Rosselli's death and Miles Eastin's foolish wrecking of his life—had come too close together. Both, involving people whom she liked, had saddened her.

She supposed she should care more about Ben; she owed him most. Her own rapid rise within the bank had been due to ability; however, Ben had never hesitated—as many employers did—to allow a woman the same opportunity as men. Nowadays Edwina resented the parrot cries of women's lib. As she saw it, women in business were being favored *because* of their sex, giving them an advantage Edwina had never sought or needed. Just the same, across the years she had known Ben, his presence was a guarantee of equal treatment.

Like Alex, Edwina had been moved to tears in the cathedral as Ben's body passed by on its outward journey.

Her thoughts returned to Miles. He was young enough, she supposed, to build another kind of life, though it would not be easy. No bank would ever employ him; nor would anyone else, in a position of trust. Despite what he had done, she hoped he would not be sent to prison.

Aloud, Edwina said, "I always get a guilty feeling about ordinary conversation at a funeral."

"No reason to," Lewis said. "Personally, at mine I'd like to think there was something solid being said, not just small talk."

"You could make certain of that," Margot suggested, "by publishing a farewell edition of *The D'Orsey Newsletter*. Pallbearers could hand out copies."

Lewis beamed. "I might just do that."

Now the cortege began to move onward more purposefully. Up ahead the motorcycle escort had revved up and was rolling; two outriders shot forward to halt traffic at intersections. The other vehicles following increased their speed and moments later the procession left St. Matthew's Cathedral behind and was passing through city streets.

The snow which had been forecast was beginning to fall lightly.

"I like that idea of Margot's," Lewis mused. "A 'Bon Voyage Bulletin.' And I have a headline for it. *'Bury the U. S. Dollar with Me! You Might as Well—It's Dead and Done For.'* Then, in what follows, I shall urge creation of a new unit of currency to replace the dollar—the 'U. S. D'Orsey.' Based, of course, on gold. Later, when it's happened, the rest of the world will hopefully have the sense to follow suit."

"Then you'd be a monument to retrogression," Margot said, "and any picture of you should have the head facing backwards. On a gold standard, even fewer people than now would own most of the world's wealth, with the rest of mankind left bare-assed."

Lewis grimaced. "A distasteful prospect—at least, the last one. But even that price might be worth a stable money system."

Alex, on a jump seat ahead of the other three, half turned to join the conversation. "Lewis, I try to be objective and sometimes your gloom about dollars and the money system makes sense. But I can't share your total pessimism. I believe the dollar can recover. I can't believe everything monetary is falling apart."

"That's because you don't want to believe it," Lewis retorted. "You're a banker. If the money system collapses, you and your bank are out of business. All you could do would be to sell off the worthless paper currency as wallpaper or toilet rolls."

Margot said, "Oh, *come on!*"

Edwina sighed. "You know this always happens when you provoke him, so why do it?"

"No, no!" her husband insisted. "With all respect, my dear, I demand to be taken seriously. I neither need nor want tolerance."

Margot asked, "What *do* you want?"

"I want the truth to be accepted that America has ruined its own and the world's money system because of politics, greed, and debt. I want it clearly understood that bankruptcy can happen to nations as well as to individuals and corporations. I want a realization that the United States *is* close to bankruptcy because, God knows!, there's enough precedent and history to show us how and why it happens. The collapse of currencies isn't new. Our own century is littered with examples, each one traceable to the selfsame cause—a government which began the syphilis of inflation by printing fiat money unbacked by gold or any other value. For the past fifteen years the United States has done precisely that."

"There are more dollars in circulation than there should be," Alex admitted. "No one with any sense doubts it."

Lewis nodded dourly. "There's also more debt than can ever be repaid; debt that's expanding like a monstrous bubble. American governments have spent billions wildly, borrowed insanely, piled up debits beyond believing, then used the printing presses to create more paper money and inflation. And people, individuals, have followed that example." Lewis motioned in the direction of the hearse ahead. "Bankers like Ben Rosselli have done their damnedest, piling crazy debts on debts. You too, Alex, with your inflationary credit cards and easy borrowing. When will people relearn the lesson that there *isn't* any easy debt? I tell you, as a nation and as individuals, Americans have lost what they once had—financial sanity."

"In case you're wondering, Margot," Edwina said, "Lewis and I don't discuss banking much. It's more peaceful at home that way."

Margot smiled. "Lewis, you sounded exactly like your newsletter."

"Or," he said, "like the beating of wings in an empty room where no one hears."

Edwina said suddenly, "It's going to be a white funeral." She leaned forward, looking through the car's steamy windows at the snow outside, now falling heavily. The suburban streets which they had reached were smooth with freshly fallen snow and the cortege slowed as the police motorcycle escort up ahead reduced its speed for safety.

The cemetery, Alex realized, was barely half a mile away.

Lewis D'Orsey was adding a postscript. "So, for the bulk of people, all hope is gone, the money game is over. Savings, pensions and fixed interest investments are becoming worthless; the clock's at five past midnight. Right now it's every man for himself, a time to survive, for individuals to scramble for financial life belts. And there *are* ways to profit from general misfortune. In case you're interested, Margot, you'll find descriptions in my latest book, *Depressions and Disasters: How to Make Money from Them*. Incidentally, it's selling very well."

"If you don't mind," Margot said, "I'll pass. It seems a bit like corner
ing vaccine in an outbreak of bubonic plague."

Alex had turned his back to the others and was peering through the
windshield. Sometimes, he reflected, Lewis became theatrical and went
too far. Usually, though, an undercurrent of sense and solid reasoning
ran through everything he said. It had today. And Lewis *could* be right
about a financial crash ahead. If it happened, it would be the most dis
astrous in history.

Nor was Lewis D'Orsey alone. A few financial pundits shared his
views, though they were unpopular and frequently derided, perhaps be
cause no one wanted to believe an apocalypse of doom—bankers least
of all.

But it was coincidental that Alex's own thoughts had been turning of
late in two of Lewis's directions. One was a need for greater thrift and
saving—a reason Alex had urged emphasis on savings deposits in his
presentation to the board a week ago. The second was unease about
the swelling debts of individuals resulting from proliferating credit, in
cluding, especially, those plastic cards.

He swung around once more, confronting Lewis. "Believing the way
you do—that a crash is coming soon—and assuming you were an ordi
nary saver or depositor with U.S. dollars, what kind of bank would you
want to have your money in?"

Lewis said unhesitatingly, "A big bank. When a crash comes, small
banks are the first to fail. It happened in the 1920s when small banks
went down like tenpins, and it will happen again because small banks
don't have sufficient cash to survive a panic and a run. Incidentally, for
get federal deposit insurance! The money available is less than one per
cent of all bank deposits, nowhere near enough to cover a countrywide
chain of bank failures."

Lewis considered, then went on. "But small banks won't be the only
ones to fail next time. A few of the big ones will go under, too—those
with too many millions locked into big industrial loans; with too high
a proportion of international deposits—hot money which can vanish
overnight; with too little liquidity when scared depositors want cash.
So if I were your mythical depositor, Alex, I'd study the balance sheets
of the big banks, then choose one with a low loan-to-deposit ratio and
a broad base of domestic depositors."

"Well, that's nice," Edwina said. "It just so happens that FMA fills
all of those conditions."

Alex nodded. "At the moment." But the picture could change, he reasoned, if Roscoe Heyward's plans for new and massive loans to industry were agreed to by the board.

The thought was a reminder that the bank's directors would meet again, two days from now, to resume their interrupted meeting of a week ago.

Now the car slowed and stopped, inched forward, stopped again. They had come to the cemetery and traveled through its roads.

Doors of other cars were opening, figures emerging, carrying umbrellas or holding coat collars tightly, hunched up against the cold and falling snow. The coffin was being lifted from the hearse. Soon it, too, was snow covered.

Margot took Alex's arm and, with the D'Orseys, joined others in the quiet procession following Ben Rosselli to his grave.

17

By prior agreement, Roscoe Heyward and Alex Vandervoort did not attend the reconvened meeting of the board. Each waited in his office until summoned.

The summons came shortly before noon, two hours after the board had begun discussion. Also called to the boardroom was the bank's vice-president of public relations, Dick French, who would release an announcement to the press concerning the new FMA president.

Already the p.r. chief had had two news releases prepared with accompanying photographs.

Their respective headings read:

ROSCOE D. HEYWARD
IS FIRST MERCANTILE AMERICAN BANK PRESIDENT

ALEXANDER VANDERVOORT
IS FIRST MERCANTILE AMERICAN BANK PRESIDENT

Envelopes were addressed. Messengers had been alerted. Priority copies of one release or the other were to be delivered this afternoon to wire services, newspaper city desks, TV and radio stations. Several hundred more would go out by first-class mail tonight.

Heyward and Alex arrived at the boardroom together. They slipped into their regular, vacant seats at the long elliptical table.

The p.r. vice-president hovered behind the meeting chairman, Jerome Patterton.

It was the director with the longest service, the Honorable Harold Austin, who announced the board's decision.

Jerome Patterton, he stated, until now vice-chairman of the board, would become president of First Mercantile American Bank immediately.

While the announcement was being made, the appointee himself seemed somewhat dazed.

The p.r. vice-president mouthed inaudibly, "Oh, shit!"

Later the same day Jerome Patterton had separate talks with Heyward and Vandervoort.

"I'm an interim Pope," he informed each of them. "I didn't seek this job, as you're aware. You also know, and so do the directors, that I'm only thirteen months from mandatory retirement.

"But the board was deadlocked over you two, and choosing me allows that length of time before they need make up their minds.

"Your guess about what happens then is as good as mine. In the meantime, though, I intend to do my best and I need the help of both of you. I know I shall get it because that's to your best advantage.

"Apart from that, the only thing I can promise is an interesting year."

18

Even before excavation, Margot Bracken was actively involved with Forum East. First she was legal counsel for a citizens group which campaigned to get the project going and later she filled the same role in a Tenants Association. She also gave legal aid to families in the development who needed it—at little cost to them, or none. Margot went to Forum East often and, in doing so, she came to know many of those living there, including Juanita Núñez.

Three days after the Rosselli funeral—on a Saturday morning—Margot encountered Juanita in a delicatessen, part of a Forum East shopping mall.

The Forum East complex had been planned as a homogeneous community with low-cost living accommodation—attractive apartments, townhouses and remodeled older buildings. There were sports facilities, a movie theater, an auditorium, as well as stores and cafes. The buildings completed so far were linked by tree-lined malls and overhead walkways—many of the ideas adapted from San Francisco's Golden Gateway and London's Barbican. Other portions of the project were under construction, with still further additions at the planning stage, awaiting financing.

"Hello, Mrs. Núñez," Margot said. "Will you join me for coffee?"

On a terrace adjoining the delicatessen they sipped espresso and chatted—about Juanita, her daughter Estela who this morning was at a community-sponsored ballet class, and progress at Forum East. Juanita and her husband Carlos had been among the early tenants in the development, occupying a tiny walk-up apartment in one of the rehabilitated older buildings, though it was shortly after moving in that

Carlos had departed for parts unknown. So far Juanita had kept the same accommodations.

But managing was very difficult, she confided. "Everyone here has the same problem. Each month our money will buy less. This inflation! Where will it end?"

According to Lewis D'Orsey, Margot reflected, it would end in disaster and anarchy. She kept the thought to herself, but was reminded of the conversation three days ago between Lewis, Edwina, and Alex.

"I heard," she said, "that you had some kind of problem at the bank where you work."

Juanita's face clouded. For a moment she seemed close to tears and Margot said hastily, "I'm sorry. Perhaps I shouldn't have asked."

"No, no! It was just that remembering suddenly . . . Anyway, it is over now. But I will tell you if you wish."

"One thing you should know about us lawyers," Margot said, "is that we're always nosy."

Juanita smiled, then was serious as she described the six-thousand-dollar cash loss and the forty-eight-hour nightmare of suspicion and interrogation. As Margot listened, her anger, never far below the surface, rose.

"The bank had no right to keep on pressuring you without your having legal advice. Why didn't you call me?"

"I never thought of it," Juanita said.

"That's the whole trouble. Most innocent people don't." Margot considered, then added, "Edwina D'Orsey is my cousin. I'm going to talk to her about this."

Juanita looked startled. "I didn't know. But please don't! After all, it was Mrs. D'Orsey who found the truth."

"All right," Margot conceded, "if you don't want me to, I won't. But I'll talk to someone else you don't know. And remember this: If you're in trouble again, about *anything*, call me. I'll be there to help."

"Thank you," Juanita said. "If it happens, I will. I really will."

"If the bank had actually fired Juanita Núñez," Margot told Alex Vandervoort that night, "I'd have advised her to sue you, and we'd have collected—heavily."

"You might well have," Alex agreed. They were on their way to a supper dance and he was driving Margot's Volkswagen. "Especially when the truth about our thieving operations man, Eastin, came out—as it was bound to eventually. Fortunately, Edwina's womanly instincts functioned, saving us from yours."

"You're being flip."

His tone changed. "You're right, and I shouldn't be. The fact is, we behaved shabbily to the Núñez girl, and everybody concerned knows it. I do, because I've read everything to do with the case. So does Edwina. So does Nolan Wainwright. But fortunately, in the end nothing really bad happened. Mrs. Núñez still has her job, and our bank has learned something which will help us do better in the future."

"That's more like it," Margot said.

They left it there, which, given their mutual love of argument, was an accomplishment.

19

During the week preceding Christmas, Miles Eastin appeared in Federal Court charged with embezzlement on five separate counts. Four of the charges involved fraudulent transactions at the bank from which he had benefited; these totaled thirteen thousand dollars. The fifth charge related to the six-thousand-dollar cash theft.

Trial was before the Honorable Judge Winslow Underwood, sitting with a jury.

On advice of counsel, a well-meaning but inexperienced young man appointed by the court after Eastin's personal resources had proven to be nil, a not guilty plea was entered on all counts. As it turned out, the advice was bad. A more seasoned lawyer, assessing the evidence, would have urged a guilty plea and perhaps a deal with the prosecutor, rather than have certain details—principally Eastin's attempt to incriminate Juanita Núñez—revealed in court.

As it was, everything came out.

Edwina D'Orsey testified, as did Tottenhoe, Gayne of central audit staff, and another audit colleague. FBI Special Agent Innes introduced as evidence Miles Eastin's signed admission of guilt concerning the cash theft, made at FBI local headquarters subsequent to the confession which Nolan Wainwright extracted from Eastin at the latter's apartment.

Two weeks before the trial, at discovery proceedings, defendant's counsel had objected to the FBI document and made a pre-trial motion to have it barred from evidence. The motion was denied. Judge Underwood pointed out that before Eastin made his statement he had been properly cautioned about his legal rights in the presence of witnesses.

The earlier confession obtained by Nolan Wainwright, the legality of which might have been challenged more effectively, was not needed and therefore was not introduced.

The sight of Miles Eastin in court depressed Edwina. He appeared pale and haggard with dark rings beneath his eyes. All of his accustomed buoyancy had gone and, in contrast to the immaculate grooming she remembered, his hair was untidy and his suit rumpled. He seemed to have aged since the night of the branch audit.

Edwina's own evidence was brief and circumstantial and she gave it straightforwardly. While being mildly cross-examined by counsel for the defense, she glanced several times toward Miles Eastin, but his head was down and he declined to meet her eyes.

Also a witness for the prosecution—albeit a reluctant one—was Juanita Núñez. She was nervous and the court had difficulty hearing her. On two occasions the judge intervened, asking Juanita to raise her voice, though his approach was coaxing and gentle, since by then her injured innocence in the whole affair had been made clear.

Juanita demonstrated no antagonism toward Eastin in her evidence, and kept her answers brief, so that the prosecutor pressed her constantly to amplify them. Plainly all she wanted was to have the ordeal over.

Defense counsel, making a belated wise decision, waived his right to question her.

It was immediately following Juanita's testimony that defense counsel, after a whispered consultation with his client, asked leave to approach the bench. Permission was granted. The prosecutor, judge, and defense counsel thereupon engaged in a low-toned colloquy during which the latter requested leave to change Miles Eastin's original "not guilty" plea to "guilty."

Judge Underwood, a quiet-spoken patriarch, with steel not far below the surface, surveyed both lawyers. He matched their lowered voices so the jury could not hear. "Very well, the change of plea will be permitted if the defendant so wishes. But I advise counsel that at this point it makes little, if any, difference."

Sending the jury from the courtroom, the judge then questioned Eastin, confirming that he wished to change his plea and realized the consequences. To all the questions the prisoner answered dully, "Yes, your honor."

The judge recalled the jury to the courtroom and dismissed it.

After an earnest entreaty by the young defense lawyer for clemency, including a reminder that his client had no previous criminal record,

Miles Eastin was remanded into custody for sentencing the following week.

Nolan Wainwright, though not required to testify, had been present throughout the court proceedings. Now, as the court clerk called another case and the contingent of bank witnesses filed out from the courtroom, the bank security chief moved alongside Juanita.

"Mrs. Núñez, may I talk with you for a few minutes?"

She glanced at him with a mixture of indifference and hostility, then shook her head. "It is all finished. Besides, I am going back to work."

When they were outside the Federal Courts Building, only a few blocks from FMA Headquarters Tower and the downtown branch, he persisted, "You're walking to the bank? Right now?"

She nodded.

"Please. I'd like to walk with you."

Juanita shrugged. "If you must."

Wainwright watched as Edwina D'Orsey, Tottenhoe, and the two audit staff men, also heading for the bank, crossed a nearby intersection. He deliberately held back, missing a green pedestrian light so the others would remain ahead.

"Look," Wainwright said, "I've never found it easy to say I'm sorry."

Juanita said tartly, "Why should you bother? It is only a word, not meaning much."

"Because I want to say it. So I do—to you. I'm sorry. For the trouble I caused you, for not believing you were telling the truth when you were and needed somebody to help."

"So now you feel better? You have swallowed your little aspirin? The tiny pain is gone?"

"You don't make it easy."

She stopped. "Did you?" The small elfin face was tilted upward, her dark eyes met his own steadily and for the first time he was aware of an underlying strength and independence. He was also, to his own surprise, conscious of her strong sexuality.

"No, I didn't. Which is why I'd like to help now if I can."

"Help about what?"

"About getting maintenance and child support from your husband." He told her of the FBI inquiries concerning her absent husband Carlos, and tracing him to Phoenix, Arizona. "He has a job there as a motor mechanic and obviously is earning money."

"Then I am pleased for Carlos."

"What I had in mind," Wainwright said, "is that you should consult one of our lawyers at the bank. I could arrange that. He would advise you how to take action against your husband and afterwards I'd see to it you weren't charged any legal fees."

"Why would you do that?"

"We owe it to you."

She shook her head. "No."

He wondered if she had properly understood.

"It would mean," Wainwright said, "there would be a court order and your husband would have to send you money to help take care of your little girl."

"And will that make Carlos a man?"

"Does it matter?"

"It matters that he should not be forced. He knows that I am here and that Estela is with me. If Carlos wanted us to have his money he would send it. *¿Si no, para qué?*" she added softly.

It was like a fencing match with shadows. He said in exasperation, "I'll never understand you."

Unexpectedly Juanita smiled. "It is not necessary that you should."

They walked the remaining short distance to the bank in silence, Wainwright nursing his frustration. He wished she had thanked him for his offer; if she had, it would have meant, at least, she took it seriously. He tried to guess at her reasoning and values. She obviously rated independence high. After that he imagined she accepted life as it came, fortune or misfortune, hopes raised or yearnings shattered. In a way he envied her and, for that reason and the sexual attraction he had been aware of earlier, he wished he knew her better.

"Mrs. Núñez," Nolan Wainwright said, "I'd like to ask you something."

"Yes."

"If you have a problem, a real problem, something I might help with, will you call me?"

It was the second such offer she had had in the past few days. "Maybe."

That—until much later—was the last conversation between Wainwright and Juanita. He felt he had done all he could, and had other things on his mind. One was a subject he had raised with Alex Vandervoort two months ago—planting an undercover informer in an attempt to track down the source of counterfeit credit cards, still gouging deep financial wounds in the Keycharge card system.

Wainwright had located an ex-convict, known to him only as "Vic," who was prepared to take the considerable risk in return for money.

They had had one secret meeting, with elaborate precautions. Another was expected.

Wainwright's fervent hope was to bring the credit-card swindlers to justice, as he had Miles Eastin.

The following week, when Eastin appeared once more before Judge Underwood—this time for sentencing—Nolan Wainwright was the sole representative of First Mercantile American Bank in court.

With the prisoner standing, facing the bench on the court clerk's orders, the judge took his time about selecting several papers and spreading them before him, then regarded Eastin coldly.

"Do you have anything to say?"

"No, your honor." The voice was barely audible.

"I have received a report from the probation officer"—Judge Underwood paused, scanning one of the papers he had selected earlier—"whom you appear to have convinced that you are genuinely penitent for the criminal offenses to which you have pleaded guilty." The judge articulated the words "genuinely penitent" as if holding them distastefully between thumb and forefinger, making clear that he was not so naive as to share the opinion.

He continued, "Penitence, however, whether genuine or otherwise, is not only belated but cannot mitigate your vicious, despicable attempt to thrust blame for your own malfeasance onto an innocent and unsuspecting person—a young woman—one, moreover, for whom you were responsible as a bank officer and who trusted you as her superior.

"On the basis of the evidence it is clear you would have persisted in that course, even to having your innocent victim accused, found guilty, and sentenced in your place. Fortunately, because of the vigilance of others, that did not occur. But it was not through any second thoughts or 'penitence' of yours."

From his seat in the body of the court, Nolan Wainwright had a partial view of Eastin's face which had suffused deep red.

Judge Underwood referred again to his papers, then looked up. His eyes, once more, impaled the prisoner.

"So far I have dealt with what I regard as the most contemptible part of your conduct. There is, additionally, the basic offense—your betrayal of trust as a bank officer, not merely once but on five occasions, widely separated. One such instance of dishonesty might be argued to be the result of reckless impulse. No such argument can be advanced for five carefully planned thefts, executed with perverted cleverness.

"A bank, as a commercial undertaking, is entitled to expect probity in those whom it selects—as you were selected—for exceptional trust. But a bank is more than a commercial institution. It is a place of public trust, and therefore the public is entitled to protection from those who abuse that trust—individuals such as you."

The judge's gaze shifted to include the young defense counsel, waiting dutifully beside his client. Now the tone of voice from the bench became more brisk and formalized.

"Had this been a more ordinary case, and in view of the absence of a previous criminal record, I would have imposed probation as defense counsel eloquently urged last week. But this is no ordinary case. It is an exceptional one for the reasons I have stated. Therefore, Eastin, you will go to prison where you will have time to reflect on your own activities which brought you there.

"The sentence of the Court is that you be committed to the custody of the Attorney General for a period of two years."

At a nod from the court clerk, a jailer moved forward.

A brief conference took place, a few minutes after sentencing, in a small locked and guarded cubicle behind the courtroom, one of several reserved for prisoners and their legal counsel.

"The first thing to remember," the young lawyer told Miles Eastin, "is that a two-year prison term doesn't mean two years. You'll be eligible for parole after a third of the sentence is served. That's in less than a year."

Miles Eastin, wrapped in misery and a sense of unreality, nodded dully.

"You can, of course, appeal the sentence, and you don't have to make a decision about that now. But I'll tell you frankly, I don't advise it. For one thing I don't believe you'd be released pending an appeal. For another, since you pleaded guilty, the grounds for appeal are limited. Also, by the time any appeal was heard, you might have served your sentence."

"The ball game's over. No appeal."

"I'll be in touch with you anyway, in case you change your mind. And while I think of it, I'm sorry how things came out."

Eastin acknowledged wryly, "So am I."

"It was your confession, of course, that did us in. Without that I don't believe the prosecution would have proved its case—at least the six-thousand-dollar cash theft, which weighed heaviest with the judge. I know, of course, why you signed that second statement—the FBI one; you thought the first was valid so another wouldn't make any difference.

Well, it did. I'm afraid that security man, Wainwright, tricked you all the way."

The prisoner nodded. "Yes, I know that now."

The lawyer looked at his watch. "Well, I have to go. I've a heavy date tonight. You know how it is."

A jailer let him out.

Next day Miles Eastin was transferred to a federal prison, out of state.

At First Mercantile American Bank, when news of Miles Eastin's sentencing was received among those who knew him, some felt regret, others held the view that the retribution was what he had deserved. One opinion was unanimous: No more would be heard of Eastin at the bank again.

Only time would prove how much in error that last assumption was.

PART TWO

1

Like a bubble surfacing from underwater, the first hint of trouble appeared in mid-January. It was an item in a gossip column, "Ear to the Ground," published in a city newspaper's Sunday edition.

The columnist wrote:

> . . . Whispers around downtown predict major cutbacks soon at Forum East. 'Tis said the big-big rehab project has bankroll problems. Nowadays who hasn't? . . .

Alex Vandervoort was unaware of the item until Monday morning when his secretary placed it, ringed in red, on his desk with other papers.

During Monday afternoon Edwina D'Orsey telephoned to inquire if Alex had read the rumor and if he knew of anything behind it. Edwina's concern was not surprising. Since the beginning of Forum East, her downtown branch bank had handled construction loans, many of the mortgages involved, and accompanying paperwork. By now the project represented an important segment of branch business.

"If there's something in the wind," Edwina insisted, "I want to be told."

"So far as I know," Alex reassured her, "nothing's changed."

Moments later he returned his hand to the telephone intending to check with Jerome Patterton, then changed his mind. Misinformation about Forum East was nothing new. The project had generated much publicity; inevitably some was inaccurate.

It was pointless, Alex decided, to bother the bank's new president with needless trivia, particularly when he wanted Patterton's support on a major issue—a large-scale expansion of FMA savings activity, now being planned for consideration by the board.

However, Alex was more concerned a few days later when a longer item appeared, this time in the regular news column of the daily *Times-Register*.

The report read:

> Anxiety about the future of Forum East persists amid growing rumors that financial backing may shortly be reduced severely or withdrawn.
>
> The Forum East project, which has as its long-term goal a total rehabilitation of the city's downtown core both business and residential, has been underwritten by a consortium of financial interests spearheaded by First Mercantile American Bank.
>
> A spokesman for First Mercantile American today acknowledged the rumors but would make no comment except to say, "An announcement will be forthcoming in due course."
>
> Under the Forum East plan, some inner city residential areas have already been modernized or rebuilt. A highrise, low-rental community development has been completed. Another is in progress.
>
> A ten-year master plan includes programs to improve schools, assist minority businesses, provide job training and employment as well as cultural opportunities and recreation. Major construction, begun two and a half years ago, has so far remained on schedule.

Alex read the morning news story at his apartment over breakfast. He was alone; Margot had been out of town on legal business for the past week.

On arrival at FMA Headquarters Tower he summoned Dick French. As vice-president of public relations, French, a burly, blunt-speaking ex-financial editor, ran his department knowledgeably.

"In the first place," Alex demanded, "who was the bank spokesman?"

"That was me," French said. "And I'll tell you right now I wasn't happy about that 'statement in due course' crap. But Mr. Patterton told me to use those words. He also insisted I shouldn't say more."

"What more is there?"

"You tell me, Alex. Obviously something's going on and, good or bad, the sooner we put it on the line, the better."

Alex curbed a rising anger. "Is there a reason I wasn't consulted about any of this?"

The p.r. head appeared surprised. "I thought you were. When I talked on the phone to Mr. Patterton yesterday I know Roscoe was with him because I could hear them talking. I assumed you were in there, too."

"Next time," Alex said, "don't assume anything."

He dismissed French, then instructed his secretary to inquire if Jerome Patterton were free. He was informed that the president had not yet arrived at the bank, but was on his way, and Alex could see him at 11 A.M. He grunted impatiently and went back to work on the savings expansion program.

At eleven Alex walked the few yards to the presidential suite—two corner rooms, each with a view of the city. Since the new president had taken over, the second room usually had the door closed and visitors were not invited in. Word had leaked out through secretaries that Patterton used it to practice putting on the rug.

Today, bright sunshine from a cloudless winter sky shone through the wall-wide windows onto Jerome Patterton's pink, near-hairless head. Seated behind a desk, he wore a light patterned suit, a switch from his usual tweeds. A newspaper in front of him was folded open to the news story which had brought Alex here.

On a sofa, in shadow, was Roscoe Heyward.

The three exchanged good mornings.

Patterton said, "I asked Roscoe to stay because I'd a notion what the subject might be." He touched the paper. "You've seen this, of course."

"I've seen it," Alex said. "I've also had Dick French in. He tells me that you and Roscoe discussed the press queries yesterday. So my first question is, why wasn't I informed? I'm as involved as anyone with Forum East."

"You should have been informed, Alex." Jerome Patterton seemed embarrassed. "The truth is, I guess, we got a little rattled when the press calls showed there had been a leak."

"A leak of what?"

It was Heyward who answered. "Of a proposal I'll be bringing before the money policy committee next Monday. I'm suggesting a reduction of the bank's present commitment to Forum East by approximately fifty percent."

In view of the rumors which had surfaced, the confirmation was not surprising. What astounded Alex was the extent of the proposed incision.

He addressed Patterton. "Jerome, do I understand that you are in favor of this incredible piece of folly?"

A flush suffused the president's face and egg-like head. "It's neither true nor untrue. I've reserved judgment until Monday. What Roscoe has been doing here—yesterday and today—is some advance lobbying."

"Right." Heyward added blandly, "An entirely legitimate tactic, Alex. And in case you object, let me remind you that on plenty of occasions you took your own ideas to Ben in advance of money policy meetings."

"If I did," Alex said, "they made a damn sight better sense than this one."

"That, of course, is solely your opinion."

"Not solely. Others share it."

Heyward was unruffled. "My own opinion is that we can put the bank's money to substantially better use." He turned toward Patterton. "Incidentally, Jerome, those rumors now circulating could be helpful to us if the proposal for a cutback is agreed to. At least the decision won't come as a sudden shock."

"If you see it that way," Alex said, "maybe it was you who leaked the rumors."

"I assure you it was not."

"Then how do you explain them?"

Heyward shrugged. "Coincidence, I suppose."

Alex wondered: Was it coincidence? Or had someone close to Roscoe Heyward floated a trial balloon on his behalf? Yes. It might well be Harold Austin, the Honorable Harold, who, as head of an advertising agency, would have plenty of contacts with the press. It seemed unlikely, though, that anyone would ever find out.

Jerome Patterton raised his hands. "Both of you save any more arguments until Monday. We'll go over all of them then."

"Let's not fool ourselves," Alex Vandervoort insisted. "The point we are deciding today is how much profit is reasonable and how much is excessive."

Roscoe Heyward smiled. "Frankly, Alex, I've never considered *any* profit excessive."

"Nor have I," Tom Straughan put in. "I recognize, though, that making an exceptionally high profit is sometimes indiscreet and asking for trouble. It becomes known and criticized. At the end of the financial year we have to publish it."

"Which is another reason," Alex added, "why we should strike a balance between achieving profit and giving service."

"Profit is giving service to our shareholders," Heyward said. "That's the kind of service I put first."

The bank's money policy committee was in session in an executive conference room. The committee, which had four members, met every other Monday morning with Roscoe Heyward as chairman. The other members were Alex and two senior vice-presidents—Straughan and Orville Young.

The committee's purpose was to decide the uses to which bank funds would be put. Major decisions were referred afterward to the board of directors for confirmation, though the board rarely changed what the committee recommended.

Individual sums discussed here were seldom less than in the tens of millions.

The president of the bank sat in, ex-officio, at the committee's more important meetings, voting only if it became necessary to break a tie. Jerome Patterton was here today, though so far he had not contributed to the discussion.

Being debated now was Roscoe Heyward's proposal for a drastic cut in Forum East financing.

Within the next few months, if Forum East was to continue as programmed, new construction loans and mortgage funds would be required. First Mercantile American's expected share of this financing was fifty million dollars. Heyward had proposed a reduction of that amount by half.

He had pointed out already, "We will make clear to all concerned that we are not opting out of Forum East, nor do we intend to. The explanation we will give is simply that in light of other commitments, we have adjusted the flow of funds. The project will not be halted. It will simply proceed more slowly than was planned."

"If you look at it in terms of need," Alex had protested, "progress is already slower than it should be. Retarding it still further is the worst thing we can do in every way."

"I am looking at it in terms of need," Heyward said. "The bank's need."

The riposte was uncharacteristically flip, perhaps, Alex thought, because Heyward was confident that today's decision would go the way he wanted. Alex was sure that Tom Straughan would join him in opposing Heyward. Straughan was the bank's chief economist—young, studious, but with a broad spectrum of interests—whom Alex had personally promoted over the heads of others.

But Orville Young, treasurer of First Mercantile American, was Heyward's man and would undoubtedly vote with him.

In FMA, as in any major bank, the true lines of power were seldom reflected in organizational charts. Real authority flowed sideways or in detours, depending on loyalties of individuals to other individuals, so that those who chose not to join in power struggles were bypassed or marooned in backwaters.

The power struggle between Alex Vandervoort and Roscoe Heyward was already well known. Because of it, some FMA executives had chosen sides, pinning their hopes for advancement on the victory of one adversary or the other. The split was also evident in the lineup of the money policy committee.

Alex argued, "Our profit last year was thirteen percent. That's damned good for any business, as all of us know. This year the prospect's even better—a fifteen percent return on investment, maybe sixteen. But should we strain for more?"

The treasurer, Orville Young, asked, "Why not?"

"I already answered that," Straughan shot back. "It's shortsighted."

"Let's remind ourselves of one thing," Alex urged. "In banking it's not hard to make large profits, and any bank that doesn't is manned by simpletons. In plenty of ways the cards are stacked in our favor. We've opportunities, our own experience, and reasonable banking laws. The last is probably the most important. But the laws won't always be as reasonable—that is, if we go on abusing the situation and abdicating community responsibility."

"I fail to see how staying in Forum East is abdicating," Roscoe Heyward said. "Even after the reduction I'm proposing, we'd still be committed substantially."

"Substantially, my foot! It would be minimal, just as the social contribution of American banks has always been minimal. In financing of low-income housing alone the record of this bank and every other is dismal. Why fool ourselves? For generations banking has ignored public problems. Even now we do the minimum we can get away with."

The chief economist, Straughan, shuffling papers, consulted some handwritten notes. "I intended to bring up the subject of home mortgages, Roscoe. Now Alex has, I'd like to point out that only twenty-five percent of our savings deposits are currently in mortgage loans. That's low. We could increase it to fifty percent of deposits without harming our liquidity position. I believe we should."

"I'll second that," Alex said. "Our branch managers are pleading for mortgage money. The return on investment is fair. We know from experience the downside risk on mortgages is negligible."

Orville Young objected, "It ties up money for long term, money on which we can earn substantially higher rates elsewhere."

Alex slammed the flat of his hand impatiently on the conference table. "Once in a while we've a public obligation to accept lower rates. That's the point I'm making. It's why I object to weaseling out of Forum East."

"There's one more reason," Tom Straughan added. "Alex touched on it—legislation. Already there are rumblings in Congress. A good many there would like to see a law similar to Mexico's—requiring a fixed percentage of bank deposits to be used for financing low-income housing."

Heyward scoffed, "We'd never let it happen. The banking lobby is the strongest in Washington."

The chief economist shook his head. "I wouldn't count on that."

"Tom," Roscoe Heyward said, "I'll make a promise. A year from now we'll take a fresh look at mortgages; maybe we'll do what you advocate; maybe we'll reopen Forum East. But not this year. I want this to be a bumper profit year." He glanced toward the bank president who had still not joined in the discussion. "And so does Jerome."

For the first time Alex perceived the shape of Heyward's strategy. A year of exceptional profit for the bank would make Jerome Patterton, as president, a hero to its shareholders and directors. All Patterton had was a one-year reign at the end of a so-so career, but he would go into retirement with glory and the sound of trumpets. And Patterton was human. Therefore it was understandable the idea would appeal to him.

The scenario afterward was equally easy to guess. Jerome Patterton, grateful to Roscoe Heyward, would promote the idea of Heyward as his successor. And, because of the profitable year, Patterton would be in a strong position to make his wishes work.

It was a neatly ingenious sequence, devised by Heyward, which Alex would find hard to break.

"There's something else I haven't mentioned," Heyward said. "Not even to you, Jerome. It could have a bearing on our decision today."

The others regarded him with fresh curiosity.

"I'm hopeful, in fact the probability is strong, that we shall shortly enjoy substantial business with Supranational Corporation. It's another reason I'm reluctant to commit funds elsewhere."

"That's fantastic news," Orville Young said.

Even Tom Straughan reacted with surprised approval.

Supranational—or SuNatCo, as identified by its familiar worldwide logo—was a multinational giant, the General Motors of global communications. As well, SuNatCo owned or controlled dozens of other companies, related and unrelated to its main purpose. Its prodigious influence with governments of all stripes, from democracies through dictatorships, was reportedly greater than that of any other business complex in history. Observers sometimes said that SuNatCo had more real power than most of the sovereign states in which it operated.

Until now SuNatCo had confined its U.S. banking activity to the big three—Bank of America, First National City, and Chase Manhattan. To be added to this exclusive trio would boost immeasurably the status of First Mercantile American.

"That's an exciting prospect, Roscoe," Patterton said.

"I expect to have more details for our next money policy meeting," Heyward added. "It appears likely that Supranational will want us to open a substantial line of credit."

It was Tom Straughan who reminded them, "We still need a vote on Forum East."

"So we do," Heyward acknowledged. He was smiling confidently, pleased at the reaction to his announcement and certain of the way the Forum East decision would go.

Predictably, they divided two by two—Alex Vandervoort and Tom Straughan opposed to the cutback of funds, Roscoe Heyward and Orville Young in favor of it.

Heads swung to Jerome Patterton who had the decisive vote.

The bank president hesitated only briefly, then announced, "Alex, on this one I'll go with Roscoe."

2

"Sitting around here feeling sorry won't do one damn bit of good," Margot declared. "What we need is to rise off our collective asses and initiate some action."

"Like dynamiting the goddam bank?" someone asked.

"Nix on that! I've friends in there. Besides, blowing up banks isn't legal."

"Who says we have to stay legal?"

"I do," Margot snapped. "And if any smart cats think otherwise, you can find yourselves some other mouthpiece and another pad."

Margot Bracken's law office, on a Thursday evening, was the scene of an executive committee meeting of the Forum East Tenants Association. The association was one of many groups in the inner city for which Margot was legal counsel and which utilized her office for meetings, a convenience for which she was occasionally paid, but mostly wasn't.

Fortunately her office was a modest affair—two rooms in what had once been a neighborhood grocery store and some of the ancient merchandise shelves now housed her law books. The remainder of the furnishings, mostly ill-assorted, comprised bits and pieces she had acquired cheaply.

Typical of the general location, two other former stores, on either side, were abandoned and boarded up. Someday, with luck and enterprise, the rehabilitating tide of Forum East might lap this particular area. It hadn't yet.

But developments at Forum East had brought them here.

The day before yesterday, in a public announcement, First Mercan-

tile American Bank had changed rumor into fact. Financing of future
Forum East projects was to be cut in half, effective at once.

The bank's statement was couched in officialese with euphemistic
phrases like "temporary shortage of long-term funding" and "periodic
reconsideration will be given," but no one believed the last and everyone, inside and outside the bank, knew exactly what the statement
meant—the ax.

The meeting now was to determine what, if anything, could be done.

The word "tenants" in the association's name was a loose one. A
large segment of members were Forum East tenants; many others were
not, but hoped to be. As Deacon Euphrates, a towering steelworker
who had spoken earlier, put it, "There's plenty of us, expectin' to be in,
who ain't gonna make it if the big bread doan' come through."

Margot knew that Deacon, his wife and five children lived in a tiny,
crowded walk-up, part of a rat-infested tenement that should have
been torn down years ago. She had made several attempts to help them
find other rental quarters, without success. A hope that Deacon Euphrates lived with was that he would move his family into one of the
new Forum East housing units, but the Euphrates' name was only midway on a long waiting list and a slowdown in construction was likely
to keep it there for a long time to come.

The FMA announcement had been a shock to Margot, too. Alex, she
was sure, would have resisted any cutback proposal within the bank,
but obviously he had been overruled. For that reason she had not discussed the subject with him yet. Also, the less Alex knew about some
simmering plans of Margot's, the better for them both.

"The way I see the ball game," Seth Orinda, another committee
member, said, "whatever we do, and legal or not, there's no way, but
no way, we can squeeze that money out of those banks. That is, if
they've their minds set on clamming up."

Seth Orinda was a black high school teacher, already "in" at Forum
East. But he possessed a keen civic sense and cared greatly about the
thousands of others still waiting hopefully on the outside. Margot relied
a good deal on his stability and help.

"Don't be so sure, Seth," she responded. "Banks have soft under-
bellies. Stick a harpoon in a tender place and surprising things could
happen."

"What kind of harpoon?" Orinda asked. "A parade? A sit-in? A demonstration?"

"No," Margot said. "Forget all that stuff. It's old hat. Nobody's impressed by conventional demonstrations any more. They're just a nuisance. They achieve nothing."

She surveyed the group facing her in the crowded, cluttered, smoky office. They were a dozen or so, mixed blacks and whites, in assorted shapes, sizes, and demeanors. Some were perched precariously on rickety chairs and boxes, others squatted on the floor. "Listen carefully, all of you. I said we need some action, and there *is* a kind of action which I believe will work."

"Miss Bracken." A small figure near the back of the room stood up. It was Juanita Núñez, whom Margot had greeted when she came in.

"Yes, Mrs. Núñez?"

"I want to help. But you know, I think, that I work for the FMA Bank. Perhaps I should not hear what you will tell the others . . ."

Margot said appreciatively, "No, and I should have thought of that instead of embarrassing you."

There was a general murmur of understanding. Amid it, Juanita made her way to the door.

"What you heard awready," Deacon Euphrates said, "that's a secret, ain't it?"

As Juanita nodded, Margot said quickly, "We can all trust Mrs. Núñez. I hope her employers are as ethical as she is."

When the meeting had settled down again, Margot faced the remaining members. Her stance was characteristic: hands on small waist, elbows aggressively out. A moment earlier she had pushed her long chestnut hair back—a gesture of habit before action, like the raising of a curtain. As she talked, interest heightened. A smile or two appeared. At one point Seth Orinda chuckled deeply. Near the end, Deacon Euphrates and others were grinning broadly.

"Man, oh man!" Deacon said.

"That's goddam clever," someone else put in.

Margot reminded them, "To make the whole scheme work, we need a lot of people—at least a thousand to begin with, and more as time goes on."

A fresh voice asked, "How long we need 'em?"

"We'll plan on a week. A banking week, that is—five days. If that doesn't work we should consider going longer and extending our scope of operations. Frankly, though, I don't believe it will be necessary. Another thing: Everyone involved must be carefully briefed."

"I'll help with that," Seth Orinda volunteered.

There was an immediate chorus of, "So will I."

Deacon Euphrates's voice rose above others. "I got time comin' to me. Goddam, I'll use it; take a week off work, an' I can pull in others."

"Good!" Margot said. She went on decisively, "We'll need a master plan. I'll have that ready by tomorrow night. The rest of you should begin recruiting right away. And remember, secrecy is important."

Half an hour later the meeting broke up, the committee members far more cheerful and optimistic than when they had assembled.

At Margot's request, Seth Orinda stayed behind. She told him, "Seth, in a special way I need your help."

"You know I'll give it if I can, Miss Bracken."

"When any action starts," Margot said, "I'm usually at the front of it. You know that."

"I sure do." The high school teacher beamed.

"This time I want to stay out of sight. Also, I don't want my name involved when newspapers, TV, and radio start their coverage. If that happened it could embarrass two special friends of mine—the ones I spoke about at the bank. I want to prevent that."

Orinda nodded sagely. "So far as I can see, no problem."

"What I'm really asking," Margot insisted, "is that you and the others front this one for me. I'll be behind scenes, of course. And if there's need to, you can call me, though I hope you won't."

"That's silly," Seth Orinda said. "How could we call you when none of us ever heard your name?"

On Saturday evening, two days after the Forum East Tenants Association meeting, Margot and Alex were guests at a small dinner party given by friends, and afterward went together to Margot's apartment. It was in a less fashionable part of the city than Alex's elegant suite, and was smaller, but Margot had furnished it pleasingly with period pieces she had collected at modest prices in the course of years. Alex loved to be there.

The apartment was greatly in contrast to Margot's law office.

"I missed you, Bracken," Alex said. He had changed into pajamas and a robe which he kept at Margot's and was relaxed in a Queen Anne wing chair, Margot curled on a rug before him, her head tilted back against his knees while he stroked her long hair gently. Occasionally his fingers strayed—gentle and sexually skillful, beginning to arouse her as he always did, and in the way she loved. Margot sighed with gratification. Soon they would go to bed. Yet, while mutual desire mounted, there was exquisite pleasure in self-imposed delay.

It was a week and a half since they had last been together, conflicting schedules having kept them apart.

"We'll make up for those lost days," Margot said.

Alex was silent. Then, "You know, I've been waiting all evening for you to fry me on a griddle about Forum East. Instead, you haven't said a word."

Margot tilted her head farther back, looking at him upside down. She asked innocently, "Why should I fry you, darling? The bank's money cutback wasn't your idea." Her small brow furrowed. "Or was it?"

"You know darn well it wasn't."

"Of course I knew. Just as I was equally sure that you'd opposed it."

"Yes, I opposed it." He added ruefully, "For all the good it did."

"You tried your best. That's all anyone can ask."

Alex regarded her suspiciously. "None of this is like you."

"Not like me in what way?"

"You're a fighter. It's one of the things I love about you. You don't give up. You won't accept defeat calmly."

"Perhaps some defeats are total. In that case nothing can be done."

Alex sat up straight. "You're up to something, Bracken! I know it. Now tell me what it is."

Margot considered, then said slowly, "I'm not admitting anything. But even if what you just said is true, it could be there are certain things it's better you don't know. Something I'd never want to do, Alex, is embarrass you."

He smiled affectionately. "You *have* told me something after all. All right, if you don't want any probing, I won't do it. But I'll ask one assurance: that whatever you have in mind is legal."

Momentarily, Margot's temper flared. "I'm the lawyer around here. I'll decide what's legal and what isn't."

"Even clever lady lawyers make mistakes."

"Not this time." She seemed about to argue further, then relented. Her voice softened. "You know I always operate inside the law. Also you know why."

"Yes, I do," Alex said. Relaxed once more, he went back to stroking her hair.

She had confided in him once, after they knew each other well, about her reasoning, reached years before, the result of tragedy and loss.

At law school, where Margot was an honors student, she had joined, like others at the time, in activism and protest. It was the period of increasing American involvement in Vietnam and bitter divisions in the nation. It was the beginning, too, of restlessness and change within the legal profession, a rebellion of youth against the law's elders and establishment, a time for a new breed of belligerent lawyer of whom Ralph Nader was the publicized, lauded symbol.

Earlier at college, and later at law school, Margot had shared her avant-garde views, her activism, and herself with a male fellow student —the only name Alex ever heard was Gregory—and Gregory and Margot cohabited, as was customary too.

For several months there had been student-administration confrontations and one of the worst began over the official appearance on campus of U. S. Army, and Navy recruiters. A student body majority, including Gregory and Margot, wanted the recruiters ordered off. The school authorities took an opposite, strong view.

In protest, militant students occupied the Administration Building, barricading themselves in and others out. Gregory and Margot, caught up in the general fervor, were among them.

Negotiations began but failed, not least because the students presented "non-negotiable demands." After two days the administration summoned state police, later unwisely supplemented by the National Guard. An assault was launched upon the now beleaguered building. During the fighting, shots were fired and heads were cracked. By a miracle, the shots hit no one. But, by tragic misfortune, one of the cracked heads—Gregory's—suffered a brain hemorrhage, resulting in death a few hours later.

Eventually, because of public indignation, an inexperienced, young, and frightened policeman who had struck the mortal blow, was arraigned in court. Charges against him were dismissed.

Margot, though in deep grief and shock, was enough of an objective law student to understand the dismissal. Her law training helped her also, amid later calmness, to evaluate and codify her own convictions. It was a belated process which the pressures of excitement and emotion had prevented far too long.

None of Margot's political and social views were diminished, either then or since. But she had the honest perception to recognize that the student body faction had withheld from others those same freedoms of which they claimed to be defenders. They had also, in their zeal, transgressed the law, a system to which their scholarship was dedicated, and presumably their lives.

It was only one step further in reasoning, which Margot took, to acknowledge that no less would have been achieved, and probably far more, by staying within legal limits.

As she confided to Alex during the only time they ever talked about that portion of the past, it had become her guiding principle, in all her activism, ever since.

Still curled comfortingly close to him, she asked, "How are things at the bank?"

"Some days I feel like Sisyphus. Remember him?"

"Wasn't he the Greek who pushed a rock uphill? Every time he got near the top it rolled back down again."

"That's the one. He should have been a bank executive trying to make changes. You know something about us bankers, Bracken?"

"Tell me."

"We succeed despite our lack of foresight and imagination."

"May I quote you?"

"If you do, I'll swear I never said it." He mused. "But between us privately, banking always reacts to social change, never anticipates it. All the problems which affect us now—environment, ecology, energy, minorities—have been with us a long time. What's happened in those areas to affect us could have been foreseen. We bankers could be leaders. Instead we're following, moving forward only when we have to, when we're pushed."

"Why stay a banker then?"

"Because it's important. What we do is worthwhile and whether we move forward voluntarily or not, we're professionals who are needed. The money system has become so huge, so complicated and sophisticated that only banks can handle it."

"So your greatest need is a shove now and then. Right?"

He looked at her intently, his curiosity reviving. "You're planning *something* in that convoluted pixie mind of yours."

"I admit nothing."

"Whatever it is, I hope it doesn't involve pay toilets."

"Oh God, no!"

At the year-old memory, both laughed aloud. It had been one of Margot's combat victories and created wide attention.

Her battle had been with the city's airport commission which, at the time, was paying its several hundred janitors and cleaners substantially lower wages than were normal in the area. The workers' union was corrupt, had a "sweetheart contract" with the commission, and had done nothing to help. In desperation a group of airport employees sought help from Margot who was beginning to build a reputation in such matters.

A frontal approach by Margot to the commission produced merely a rebuff. She therefore decided that public attention must be gained and one way to obtain it was by ridiculing the airport and its rulers. In preparation, and working with several other sympathizers who had aided her before, she made an intelligence study of the big, busy airport during a heavy traffic night.

A factor noted by the study was that when evening flights, on which dinner and drinks had been served, disgorged their passengers, the bulk of the arrivals headed promptly for airport toilets, thus creating maximum demand for those facilities over a period of several hours.

The following Friday night, when incoming and departing air traffic was heaviest of all, several hundred volunteers, principally off-duty janitors and cleaners, arrived at the airport under Margot's direction. From then until they left much later, all were quiet, orderly, and law-abiding.

Their purpose was to occupy, continuously throughout the evening, every public toilet in the airport. And they did. Margot and assistants had prepared a detailed plan and the volunteers went to assigned locations where they paid a dime and settled down, solaced by reading material, portable radios, and even food which many brought. Some of the women had their needlepoint or knitting. It was the ultimate in legal sit-ins.

In the men's toilets, more volunteers formed long lines in front of urinals, each dilatory line moving with stunning slowness. If a male not in the plot joined any lineup it took him an hour to reach the front. Few, if any, waited that long.

A floating contingent explained quietly to anyone who would listen what was happening, and why.

The airport became a shambles with hundreds of angry, anguished passengers complaining bitterly and heatedly to airlines who, in turn, assailed airport management. The latter found themselves frustrated and helpless to do anything. Other observers, not involved or in need, found the situation hilarious. No one was indifferent.

News media representatives, tipped off by Margot in advance, were present in force. Reporters vied with each other to write stories which were carried nationwide by wire services, then repeated internationally and used by such differing journals as *Izvestia*, Johannesburg *Star*, and *The Times* of London. Next day, as a result, the entire world was laughing.

In most news reports the name Margot Bracken figured prominently. There were intimations that more "sit-ins" would follow.

As Margot had calculated, ridicule is one of the stronger weapons in any arsenal. Over the weekend the airport commission conceded that discussions would be held on janitors' and cleaners' wages, which resulted in increases soon after. A further development was that the corrupt union was voted out, a more honest one replacing it.

Now Margot stirred, moving closer to Alex, then said softly, "What kind of a mind was it that you said I had?"

"Convoluted-pixie."

"That's bad? Or good?"

"It's good for me. Refreshing. And most of the time I like the causes that you work for."

"But not all the time?"

"No, not always."

"Sometimes the things I do create antagonism. Lots of it. Suppose the antagonism was about something you didn't believe in, or disliked? Suppose our names were linked together at a time like that, when you wouldn't want to be associated with me?"

"I'd learn to live with it. Besides, I'm entitled to a private life, and so are you."

"So is any woman," Margot said. "But I wonder sometimes if you really could live with it. That's if we were together all the time. I wouldn't change, you know; you have to understand that, Alex darling. I couldn't surrender independence, nor ever stop being myself and taking initiatives."

He thought of Celia who had taken no initiatives, ever, and how he had wished she would. And he remembered, as always with remorse, what Celia had become. He had learned something from her though: That no man is whole unless the woman he loves is free, and knows the use of freedom, exploiting it in fulfillment of herself.

Alex dropped his hands to Margot's shoulders. Through a thin silk nightgown he could sense the fragrant warmth of her, feel the softness of her flesh. He said gently, "It's the way you are that's the way I love and want you. If you changed, I'd hire some other lady lawyer and sue for breach of loving."

His hands left her shoulders, moving slowly, caressingly lower. He heard her breathing quicken; a moment later she turned to him, urgent and gasping. "What the hell are we waiting for?"

"God knows," he said. "Let's go to bed."

3

The sight was so unusual that one of the branch's loan officers, Cliff Castleman, strolled over to the platform.

"Mrs. D'Orsey, have you looked out of a window yet, by any chance?"

"No," Edwina said. She had been concentrating on the morning mail. "Why should I?"

It was 8:55 A.M., Wednesday, at First Mercantile American's main downtown branch.

"Well," Castleman said, "I thought you might be interested. There's a lineup outside such as I've never seen ahead of opening time before."

Edwina looked up. Several staff members were craning to look out of windows. There was a buzz of conversation among the employees generally, unusual this early in the day. She sensed an undercurrent of concern.

Leaving her desk, Edwina walked a few paces to one of the large plate-glass windows, part of the street frontage of the building. What she saw amazed her. A long queue of people, four or five abreast, extended from the main front door past the entire length of the building and out of sight beyond. It appeared as if all were waiting for the bank to open.

She stared incredulously. "What on earth . . . ?"

"Someone went outside just now," Castleman informed her. "They say the line extends halfway across Rosselli Plaza and more people are joining it all the time."

"Has anyone asked what they all want?"

"One of the security guards did, I understand. The answer was, they've come to open accounts."

"That's ridiculous! *All* of those people? There must be three hundred I can see from here. We've never had that many new accounts in a single day."

The loan officer shrugged. "I'm simply passing on what I heard."

Tottenhoe, the operations officer, joined them at the window, his face transmitting his normal grumpiness. "I've notified Central Security," he informed Edwina. "They say they'll send more guards and Mr. Wainwright's coming over. Also, they're advising the city police."

Edwina commented, "There's no outward sign of trouble. Those people all seem peaceful."

It was a mixed group, she could see, about two thirds women, with a preponderance of blacks. Many of the women were accompanied by children. Among the men, some were in coveralls, appearing as if they had left their jobs or were on the way to them. Others were in casual clothing, a few well dressed.

People in the lineup were talking to each other, some animatedly, but no one appeared antagonistic. A few, seeing themselves observed, smiled and nodded to the bank officials.

"Look at that!" Cliff Castleman pointed. A TV crew with camera had appeared. While Edwina and the others watched, it began filming.

"Peaceful or not," the loan officer said, "there has to be a motive behind all these people coming here at once."

A flash of insight struck Edwina. "It's Forum East," she said. "I'll bet it's Forum East."

Several others whose desks were nearby had approached and were listening.

Tottenhoe said, "We should delay opening until the extra guards get here."

All eyes swung to a wall clock which showed a minute to nine.

"No," Edwina instructed. She raised her voice so that others could hear. "We'll open as usual, on time. Everyone go back to their work, please."

Tottenhoe hurried away, Edwina returning to the platform and her desk.

From her vantage point she watched the main doors swing open and the first arrivals pour in. Those who had been at the head of the line paused momentarily on entry, looked around curiously, then quickly moved forward as others behind pressed in. Within moments the central public area of the big branch bank was filled with a chattering, noisy crowd. The building, relatively quiet less than a minute earlier, had become a Babel. Edwina saw a tall heavyset black man wave some dollar bills and declare loudly, "Ah want to put ma money in th' bank."

A security guard directed him, "Over there for new accounts."

The guard pointed to a desk where a clerk—a young girl—sat waiting. She appeared nervous. The big man walked toward her, smiled reassuringly, and sat down. Immediately a press of others moved into a ragged line behind him, waiting for their turns.

It seemed as if the report about everyone having come to open an account had been accurate after all.

Edwina could see the big man leaning back expansively, still holding his dollar bills. His voice cut across the noise of other conversations and she heard him proclaim, "Ah'm in no hurry. There's some things Ah'd like yo' to explain."

Two other desks were quickly manned by other clerks. With equal speed, long wide lines of people formed in front of them.

Normally, three members of staff were ample to handle new account business, but obviously were inadequate now. Edwina could see Tottenhoe on the far side of the bank and called him on the intercom. She instructed, "Use more desks for new accounts and take all the staff you can spare to man them."

Even leaning close to the intercom, it was hard to hear above the noise.

Tottenhoe grumbled in reply, "You realize we can't possibly process all these people today, and however many we do will tie us up completely."

"I've an idea," Edwina said, "that's what someone has in mind. Just hurry the processing all you can."

Yet she knew however much they hurried it would still take ten to fifteen minutes to open any single new account. It always did. The paperwork required that time.

First, an application form called for details of residence, employment, social security, and family matters. A specimen signature was obtained. Then proof of identity was needed. After that, the new accounts clerk would take all documents to an officer of the bank for approval and initialing. Finally, a savings passbook was made out or a temporary checkbook issued.

Therefore the most new accounts that any bank employee could open in an hour were five, so the three clerks presently working might handle a total of ninety in one business day, *if* they kept going at top speed, which was unlikely.

Even tripling the present complement of clerks would permit very few more than two hundred and fifty accounts to be opened in a day, yet already, in the first few minutes of business, the bank was crammed with at least four hundred people, with still more flooding in, and the line outside, which Edwina rose to check, appeared as long as ever.

Still the noise within the bank increased. It had become an uproar.

A further problem was that the growing mass of arrivals in the central public area of the bank was preventing access to tellers' counters by other customers. Edwina could see a few of them outside, regarding the milling scene with consternation. While she watched, several gave up and walked away.

Inside the bank some of the newcomers were engaging tellers in conversation and the tellers, having nothing else to do because of the melee, chatted back.

Two assistant managers had gone to the central floor area and were trying to regulate the flood of people so as to clear some space at counters. They were having small success.

But still no hostility was evident. Everyone in the now jam-packed bank who was spoken to by members of the staff answered politely and with a smile. It seemed, Edwina thought, as if all who were here had been briefed to be on best behavior.

She decided it was time for her own intervention.

Edwina left the platform and a railed-off staff area and, with difficulty, made her way through the milling crowd to the main front door. Signaling two security guards who elbowed their way toward her, she instructed, "That's enough people in the bank. Hold everyone else outside, letting a few in as the others leave. Except, of course, allow our regular customers to enter as they arrive."

The older of the two guards put his head close to Edwina's to make himself heard. "That won't be so easy, Mrs. D'Orsey. Some customers we'll recognize but a good many we won't. We get too many here each day to know 'em all."

"Another thing," the other guard put in, "when anybody arrives, those outside are shouting, 'Back of the line!' If we play favorites it could start a riot."

Edwina assured him, "There won't be any riot. Just do your best."

Turning back, Edwina spoke to several of those waiting. The surrounding constant conversations made it difficult to be heard and she raised her voice. "I'm the manager. Would some of you please tell me why you've all come here today?"

"We're opening accounts," a woman with a child beside her said. She giggled. "Nothing wrong with that, is there?"

"An' you guys put out them ads," another voice injected. "Ain't no amount too small to start one, is what they say."

"That's true," Edwina said, "and the bank means it. But there has to be some reason why you all chose to come together."

"You could say," an elderly cadaverous man chimed in, "we're all from Forum East."

A younger voice added, "Or want to be."

"That still doesn't tell me . . ." Edwina began.

"Perhaps I can explain, ma'am." A middle-aged, distinguished-looking black man was being shoved forward through the press of people.

"Please do."

At the same moment Edwina was aware of a new figure beside her. Turning, she saw it was Nolan Wainwright. And at the main doorway several more security guards had arrived and were assisting the original two. She glanced interrogatively at the security chief who advised, "Go ahead. You're doing okay."

The man who had been thrust forward said, "Good morning, ma'am. I didn't know there were lady bank managers."

"Well, there are," Edwina told him. "And getting to be more of us all the time. I hope you believe in the equality of women, Mr. . . . ?"

"Orinda. Seth Orinda, ma'am. And I sure do believe in that, and lots of other things besides."

"Is it one of the other things that brings you here today?"

"In a way, you could say that."

"Exactly what way?"

"I think you know we're all from Forum East."

She acknowledged, "I've been told that."

"What we're doing might be called an act of hope." The well-dressed spokesman mouthed his words carefully. They had been scripted and rehearsed. More people drew close, conversation stilling as they listened.

Orinda went on, "This bank, so it says, doesn't have enough money to go on helping Forum East get built. Anyway, the bank has cut its lending cash in half and some of us think that other half will get chopped too, that's if someone doesn't beat a drum or take some action."

Edwina said sharply, "And taking action, I suppose, means bringing the business of this entire branch bank to a standstill." As she spoke, she was aware of several new faces in the crowd and of open notebooks with racing pencils. She realized that reporters had arrived.

Obviously someone had alerted the press in advance, which explained the presence of the TV camera crew outside. Edwina wondered who had done it.

Seth Orinda looked pained. "What we're doing, ma'am, is bringing all the money we poor folks can raise to help this bank through its time of trouble."

"Yep," another voice threw in, "ain't that good neighborin' for sure?"

Nolan Wainwright snapped, "That's nonsense! This bank is not in trouble."

"If it ain't in trouble," a woman asked, "why'd it do what it done to Forum East?"

"The bank's position was made perfectly clear in its announcement," Edwina answered. "It's a question of priorities. Furthermore, the bank has said it hopes to resume the full financing later." Even to herself the words sounded hollow. Others evidently thought so too because a chorus of jeers erupted.

It was the first note of antagonism and ugliness. The distinguished-looking man, Seth Orinda, turned sharply, raising a hand in caution. The jeering ceased.

"Whichever way it looks to you folks here," he asserted to Edwina, "the fact is, we've all come to put some money in your bank. That's what I mean by an act of hope. We figure that when you see us all, and realize the way we feel, you'll maybe change your minds."

"And if we don't?"

"Then I reckon we'll go on finding more people and more bits of money. And we can do it. We've a lot more good souls coming here today, and tomorrow, and the day after. Then, by the weekend, word will have got around"—he swung toward the press reporters—"so there'll be others, and not just from Forum East, who'll join with us next week. Just to open an account, of course. To help out this poor bank. Nothing else."

More voices added cheerfully, "Yeah man, a whole lot more people" . . . "We ain't got much bread, but we sure got numbers" . . . "Tell your friends to come an' support us."

"Of course," Orinda said, his expression innocent, "some of the folks who are putting money in the bank today may have to come and take it out tomorrow, or the next day, or next week. Most haven't got so much that they can leave it in long. But then, soon as we can we'll be back to put it in again." His eyes glittered mischievously. "We aim to keep you busy."

"Yes," Edwina said, "I understand your aim."

One of the reporters, a slim blond girl, asked, "Mr. Orinda, how much will all of you be depositing in the bank?"

"Not much," he told her cheerfully. "Most have come with just five dollars. That's the smallest amount this bank will take. Isn't that right?" He looked at Edwina who nodded.

Some banks, as Edwina and those listening were aware, required a minimum of fifty dollars to open a savings account, a hundred for checking. A few had no minimums at all. First Mercantile American—seeking to encourage small savers—compromised at five dollars.

Another thing—once an account was accepted, most of the original five dollars could be withdrawn, with any credit balance sufficient to keep the account open. Seth Orinda and others had clearly realized this and proposed to drown the downtown branch bank with in-and-out transactions. Edwina thought: they might well succeed.

Yet nothing illegal or provably obstructionist was being done.

Despite her responsibilities and annoyance of a few moments earlier, Edwina was tempted to laugh, though realized she mustn't. She glanced again at Nolan Wainwright who shrugged and said quietly, "While there's no obvious disturbance there's nothing we can do except regulate the traffic."

The bank security chief swung toward Orinda and said firmly, "We'll expect all of you to help us keep this place orderly, inside and out. Our guards will give directions about how many people can come in at once, and where the waiting line should stay."

The other nodded agreement. "Naturally, sir, my friends and I will do everything possible to help. We don't want any disturbance either. But we shall expect you to be fair."

"What's that mean?"

"Those of us in here," Orinda declared, "and those outside, are customers just like anybody else who comes to this bank. And while we're willing to wait our turn and be patient, we don't expect others to get specially favored treatment or to be allowed in here ahead of us who've waited. What I mean is, anybody arriving—no matter who—must go to the back of the line."

"We'll see about that."

"So will we, sir. Because if you do it some other way, it'll be a clear case of discrimination. Then you'll hear us holler."

The reporters, Edwina saw, were still making notes.

She eased her way through the press of people, to the three new account desks, already supplemented by two more, while a further two were being set up.

One of the auxiliary desks, Edwina noted, was occupied by Juanita Núñez. She caught Edwina's eye, and they exchanged smiles. Edwina was suddenly reminded that the Núñez girl lived at Forum East. Had she known in advance of today's invasion? Then she reasoned: Either way, it made no difference.

Two of the bank's junior officers were supervising the new account activity and it was clear that all other work today would fall seriously behind.

The heavyset black man, who had been among the earliest arrivals, was getting up as Edwina arrived. The girl who had dealt with him, no longer nervous, said, "This is Mr. Euphrates. He just opened an account."

"Deacon Euphrates. Least, that's what most call me." Edwina was offered an enormous hand which she took.

"Welcome to First Mercantile American, Mr. Euphrates."

"Thank you, that's real nice. In fact, so nice that I think maybe after all I'll pop a little more bread in this here account." He examined a handful of small change, selected a quarter and two dimes, then strolled over to a teller.

Edwina asked the new accounts clerk, "What was the initial deposit?"

"Five dollars."

"Very well. Just try to keep going as fast as you can."

"I'll do that, Mrs. D'Orsey, but that one took a long time because he asked a lot of questions about withdrawals and interest rates. He had them written out on paper."

"Did you get the paper?"

"No."

"Others will probably have the same thing. Try to get one and show it to me."

It might provide a clue, Edwina thought, as to who had planned and executed this expert invasion. She did not believe that anyone she had spoken to so far was the key organizing figure.

Something else emerging: The attempt to inundate the bank would not be limited to merely opening new accounts. Those who had already opened accounts were now forming lines at tellers' counters, paying in or withdrawing tiny amounts at a glacial pace, asking questions or engaging tellers in conversation.

So not only would regular customers have difficulty getting into the building but, once inside, they would be further impeded.

She told Nolan Wainwright about the written lists of questions and her instructions to the girl clerk.

The security chief approved. "I'd like to see them, too."

"Mr. Wainwright," a secretary called over, "telephone."

He took the call and Edwina heard him say, "It *is* a demonstration, even if not in the legal sense. But it's peaceful and we could make trouble for ourselves by hasty decisions. The last thing we want is an ugly confrontation."

It was comforting, Edwina reasoned, to have Wainwright's sane solidity available. As he replaced the phone a thought occurred to her. "Someone mentioned calling the city police," she said.

"They came when I first got here and I sent them away. They'll haul back fast if we need them. I hope we won't." He motioned to the telephone, then in the direction of FMA Headquarters Tower. "Word has got to the brass. They're pressing panic buttons over there."

"One thing they could try is restoring funds to Forum East."

For the first time since his arrival, a brief smile crossed Wainwright's face. "I'd like to see that, too. But this isn't the way and, where the bank's money is on the line, outside pressure won't alter a thing."

Edwina was about to say, "I wonder," then changed her mind, remaining silent.

While they watched, the crowd monopolizing the bank's central floor area remained as great; the uproar, if anything, a little louder than before.

Outside, the lengthening line stayed fixedly in place.

It was now 9:45.

4

Also at 9:45 A.M., three blocks from First Mercantile American Head-quarters Tower, Margot Bracken was operating a command post from an inconspicuously parked Volkswagen.

Margot had intended to remain remote from the execution of her pressure ploy, but in the end she hadn't been able to. Like a war horse which paws the ground at the scent of battle, her resolve had weakened then dissolved.

Margot's concern about embarrassing Alex or Edwina remained, however, and was the reason for her absence from the front line of action on Rosselli Plaza.

If she appeared she would be quickly identified by members of the press, whose presence Margot knew about since she had arranged advance tip-offs to newspapers, TV, and radio.

Therefore, messengers were discreetly bringing news of developments to her car and carrying instructions back.

Since Thursday night a sizable feat of organization had been carried through.

On Friday, while Margot worked on the master plan, Seth, Deacon, and several committee members recruited block captains in and around Forum East. They described what was to be done only in general terms, but the response was overwhelming. Almost everyone wanted a piece of the action and knew others who could be counted on.

By late Sunday when lists were totaled, there were fifteen hundred names. More were coming in fast. According to Margot's plan it would be possible to maintain action for at least a week, longer if enthusiasm could be sustained.

Among the men with regular jobs who volunteered help, some like Deacon Euphrates had vacation time due which they declared they would use. Others simply said they would absent themselves as needed. Regrettably, many who volunteered were unemployed, their numbers swelled recently by a seasonal work shortage.

But women predominated, in part because of their greater availability in daytime, but also because—even more than with the men— Forum East had become a cherished, hopeful beacon in their lives.

Margot was aware of this, both from her advance staff work and this morning's reports.

The reports she was getting so far were highly satisfactory.

It had been Margot's insistence that at all times, and particularly during direct contacts with bank representatives, everyone in the Forum East contingent should be friendly, courteous, and ostensibly helpful. This was the reason for the phrase, "Act of Hope," which Margot coined, and the projected image that a group of interested individuals —though with limited means—was coming to the "help" of an FMA "in trouble."

She suspected, shrewdly, that any suggestion that First Mercantile American Bank was in trouble would touch a sensitive nerve.

And while there would be no concealment of the Forum East connection, at no point would outright threats be made, as—for example —that paralysis of the big bank would continue unless construction funds were reinstated. As Margot told Seth Orinda and the others, "Let the bank come to that conclusion."

At briefing sessions she had underlined the need to avoid any appearance of menace or intimidation. Those who attended the sessions made notes, then passed the instructions on.

Something else passed on were lists of questions to be asked by individuals while accounts were being opened. Margot had prepared those, too. There were hundreds of legitimate questions which anyone dealing with a bank could reasonably ask, though for the most part people didn't. Their ancillary effect would be to slow the bank to a near halt.

Seth Orinda would act as spokesman if an opportunity occurred. Margot's script needed little rehearsal. Orinda was a quick study.

Deacon Euphrates had been assigned to be early in line and the first to open an account.

It was Deacon—no one knew whether Deacon was a given name or a title from one of the offbeat religions in the area—who headed the staff work in advising volunteers where to go and when. He had worked with an army of lieutenants, fanning out like radii of a spider web.

Initially, for Wednesday morning, it had been essential there should be a large attendance at the bank to create a strong impression. But some of the attendees must be relieved periodically. Others who had not yet appeared were to be held in reserve for later that day, or other days.

To accomplish all this, a patchwork communications system had been set up with heavy use of local pay phones, monitored by more helpers stationed on the streets. Already, allowing for weaknesses in a short-notice, improvised scheme, communication was functioning well.

All these and other reports were being funneled to Margot in the back seat of her Volkswagen. Her information included the number of people in line, the length of time it was taking the bank to open each account, and the number of new account desks in operation. She had heard, too, about the jam-packed scene inside the bank; also the exchanges between Seth Orinda and bank officials.

Margot made a calculation, then instructed the latest messenger, a gangling youth now waiting in the car's front passenger seat, "Tell Deacon not to call any more volunteers for the time being; it looks as if we've enough for the rest of today. Let some of those standing outside be relieved for a while, though not more than fifty at a time, and warn them to be back to collect their lunches. And about the lunches, caution everyone again there's to be no litter on Rosselli Plaza, and no food or drinks taken into the bank."

The talk of lunch reminded Margot of money which, earlier in the week, had been a problem.

On Monday, reports filtering in through Deacon Euphrates made it clear that many of the willing volunteers lacked a spare five dollars—the minimum required to open an account at FMA. The Forum East Tenants Association had virtually no money. For a while it looked as if their scheme would founder.

Then Margot made a telephone call. It was to the union—the American Federation of Clerks, Cashiers & Office Workers—which now represented the airport janitors and cleaners whom she had aided a year ago.

Would the union help by lending money—enough to provide a five-dollar stake for each volunteer who could not afford it? Union leaders summoned a hasty meeting. The union said yes.

On Tuesday, employees from union headquarters helped Deacon Euphrates and Seth Orinda distribute the cash. All concerned knew that part of it would never be repaid and some of the five-dollar floats would be spent by Tuesday night, their original purpose forgotten or ignored.

But most of the money, they believed, would be used as intended. Judging by this morning's showing, they were right.

It was the union which had offered to supply and pay for lunches. The offer was accepted. Margot suspected a self-interest angle somewhere on the union's part but concluded it would not affect the Forum East objective, so was none of her business.

She continued to instruct the latest messenger. "We must maintain a lineup until the bank closes at three o'clock."

It was possible, she thought, that the news media might do some closing time photography so a show of strength for the remainder of today was important.

Tomorrow's plans could be co-ordinated late tonight. Mostly, they would be a repetition of today's.

Fortunately the weather—a spell of mildness with mainly clear skies —was helping, and forecasts for the next few days seemed good.

"Keep on emphasizing," Margot told another messenger a half hour later, "that everyone must stay friendly, friendly, friendly. Even if the bank people get tough or impatient, the thing to do is smile back."

At 11:45 A.M. Seth reported personally to Margot. He was grinning broadly and held out an early edition of the city's afternoon newspaper.

"Wow!" Margot spread the front page wide.

The activity at the bank commanded most of the available space. It was more, far more, attention than she had dared to hope for.

The main headline read:

BIG BANK IMMOBILIZED
BY FORUM EASTERS

And below:

First Merc American In Trouble?
Many Come To "Help"
With Small Deposits

Pictures and a two-column by-line story followed.

"Oh brother!" Margot breathed. "How FMA will hate *that!*"

They did.

Shortly after midday a hastily called conference took place on the 36th floor of First Mercantile American Headquarters Tower in the presidential suite.

Jerome Patterton and Roscoe Heyward were there, grim faced. Alex

Vandervoort joined them. He, too, was serious, though as discussion progressed Alex seemed less involved than the others, his expression mostly thoughtful, with once or twice a flicker of amusement. The fourth attendee was Tom Straughan, the bank's young and studious chief economist; the fifth, Dick French, vice-president of public relations.

French, burly and scowling, strode in chewing an unlighted cigar and carrying a bundle of afternoon newspapers which he slapped down one by one in front of the others.

Jerome Patterton, seated behind his desk, spread out a paper. When he read the words, "First Merc American In Trouble?" he spluttered, "That's a filthy lie! That paper should be sued."

"There's nothing to sue about," French said with his customary bluntness. "The newspaper hasn't stated it as fact. It's put as a question and in any case is quoting someone else. And the original statement was not malicious." He stood with a take-it-or-leave-it attitude, hands behind his back, cigar projecting like an accusatory torpedo.

Patterton flushed with anger.

"Of course it's malicious," Roscoe Heyward snapped. He had been standing, aloof, by a window and swung back toward the other four. "The entire exercise is malicious. Any fool can see that."

French sighed. "All right, I'll spell it out. Whoever is behind this is good at law *and* public relations. The exercise, as you call it, is cleverly set up to be friendly and helpful to this bank. Okay, we know it's neither. But you'll never prove that and I suggest we stop wasting time with talk about trying to."

He picked up one of the newspapers and spread the front page open. "One reason I earn my princely salary is because I'm an expert about news and media. Right now my expertise tells me that this same story —which is written and presented fairly, like it or not—is spewing out through every news wire service in the country *and will be used*. Why? Because it's a David and Goliath piece which reeks of human interest."

Tom Straughan, seated beside Vandervoort, said quietly, "I can confirm part of that. It *has* been on the Dow Jones news service and right afterward our stock dropped one more point."

"Another thing," Dick French went on as though he had not been interrupted, "we may as well brace ourselves now for the TV news tonight. There'll be plenty on local stations for sure, and my educated guess is we'll be on network, all three majors. Also, if any scripter can resist that 'bank in trouble' phrase I'll swallow my picture tube."

Heyward asked coldly, "Have you finished?"

"Not quite. I'd just like to say that if I'd blown this entire year's p.r.

budget on one thing, *just one thing,* to try to make this bank look *bad,* I couldn't have improved on the damage you guys have done unaided."

Dick French had a personal theory. It was that a good public relations man should go to work each day prepared to put his job on the line. If knowledge and experience required him to tell his superiors unpleasant facts they would prefer not to hear, and to be brutally frank while doing so, so be it. The frankness was part of p.r. too—a ploy to gain attention. To do less, or to court favor through silence or pussyfooting, would be to fail in his responsibilities.

Some days required more bluntness than usual. This was one.

Scowling, Roscoe Heyward asked, "Do we know yet who the organizers are?"

"Not specifically," French said. "I talked with Nolan who says he's working on that. Not that it makes much difference."

"And if you're interested in the latest from the downtown branch," Tom Straughan contributed, "I went in through the tunnel just before coming here. The place is still packed with demonstrators. Almost no one can get in to do regular banking business."

"They're not demonstrators," Dick French corrected him. "Let's get that clear, too, while we're about it. There's not a placard or a slogan among the lot, except maybe 'Act of Hope.' They're customers, and that's our problem."

"All right," Jerome Patterton said, "since you know so much about it, what do you suggest?"

The p.r. vice-president shrugged. "You guys pulled the rug from under Forum East. You're the ones who could put it back."

Roscoe Heyward's features tightened.

Patterton turned to Vandervoort. "Alex?"

"You know my feelings," Alex said; it was the first time he had spoken. "I was against the cut in funds to begin with. I still am."

Heyward said sarcastically, "Then you're probably delighted about what's going on. And I suppose you'd give in gladly to those louts and their intimidation."

"No, I'm not in the least delighted." Alex's eyes flashed angrily. "What I am is embarrassed and offended to see the bank in the position it's been placed. I believe what's happening could have been foreseen—that is, some response, some opposition. What matters most at the moment, though, is to set the situation right."

Heyward sneered, "So you *would* give in to intimidation. Just as I said."

"Giving in or not giving in is immaterial," Alex answered coldly.

"The real question is: Were we right or wrong in cutting off funds from Forum East? If we were wrong, we should have second thoughts, along with courage to admit our error."

Jerome Patterton observed, "Second thoughts or not, if we back down now we'll all look pretty foolish."

"Jerome," Alex said, "in the first place, I don't believe so. In the second, does it matter?"

Dick French interposed, "The financial end of this is none of my business. I know that. But I'll tell you one thing: If we decided now to change bank policy about Forum East, we'd look good, not bad."

Roscoe Heyward said acidly to Alex, "If courage is a factor here, I'd say that you are devoid of any. What you're doing is refusing to stand up to a mob."

Alex shook his head impatiently. "Stop sounding like a small-town sheriff, Roscoe. Sometimes, unwillingness to change a wrong decision is plain pigheadedness, nothing more. Besides, those people at the downtown branch are not a mob. Every report we've had has made that clear."

Heyward said suspiciously, "You seem to have a special affinity for them. Do you know something the rest of us don't?"

"No."

"Just the same, Alex," Jerome Patterton ruminated, "I don't like the idea of meekly giving in."

Tom Straughan had been following both arguments. Now he said, "I was opposed to cutting off Forum East funds, as everybody knows. But I don't like being pushed around by outsiders either."

Alex sighed. "If you all feel like that, we'd better accept that the downtown branch won't be much use to us for a while."

"That rabble can't possible keep up what they're doing," Heyward declared. "I predict that if we maintain our stand, refusing to be bluffed or stampeded, the entire exercise will fizzle out tomorrow."

"And I," Alex said, "predict it will continue through next week."

In the end, both predictions proved erroneous.

In the absence of any softening of attitude by the bank, inundation of the downtown branch by Forum East supporters continued through all of Thursday and Friday, until the close of business late Friday afternoon.

The big branch was almost helpless. And, as Dick French predicted, nationwide attention was focused on its plight.

Much of the attention was humorous. However, investors were less amused, and on the New York Stock Exchange on Friday, First Mercantile American Bank shares closed a further two and a half points lower.

Meanwhile, Margot Bracken, Seth Orinda, Deacon Euphrates, and others went on planning and recruiting.

On Monday morning the bank capitulated.

At a hastily called press conference at 10 A.M., Dick French announced that full Forum East financing would be restored at once. On behalf of the bank, French expressed the good-natured hope that the many from Forum East, and their friends, who had opened accounts at FMA over the past several days, would remain bank customers.

Behind the capitulation were several cogent reasons. One was: Prior to the downtown branch opening on Monday morning, the lineup outside the bank and on Rosselli Plaza was even larger than on previous days, so it became plain that the preceding week's performance would be repeated.

More disconcerting, a second long lineup appeared at another FMA branch bank, this in suburban Indian Hill. The development was not wholly unexpected. Extension of the Forum East activity to additional First Mercantile American branches had been forecast in Sunday's newspapers. When the line at Indian Hill began to form, an alarmed branch manager telephoned FMA Headquarters, asking for help.

But it was a final factor which clinched the outcome.

Over the weekend, the union which had loaned money to the Forum East Tenants committee and provided free lunches for those in line—the American Federation of Clerks, Cashiers & Office Workers—publicly announced its involvement. They pledged additional support. A union spokesman castigated FMA as a "selfish and gargantuan profit machine, geared to further enrich the wealthy at the expense of the have-nots." A campaign to unionize the bank's employees, he added, would soon begin.

The union thus tilted the scale, not with a straw, but a bale of bricks.

Banks—all banks—feared, even hated, unions. Banking's leaders and executives eyed unions the way a snake might view a mongoose. What bankers foresaw if unions became entrenched was a lessening of banks' financial freedom. At times their fear was irrational, but it existed.

Though unions had tried often, few had made the slightest headway where bank employees were concerned. Time after time, bankers adroitly outwitted union organizers and intended to keep on doing so. If the Forum East situation afforded leverage to a union, ipso facto, the leverage must be removed. Jerome Patterton, in his office early and movng with unusual speed, made the final decision authorizing the restitution of funds to Forum East. At the same time he approved the bank's announcement which Dick French rushed to release.

Afterward, to steady his nerves, Patterton cut off all communication and practiced chip shots on the inner office rug.

Later the same morning, at a mainly informal session of the money policy committee, the reinstatement was recorded, though Roscoe Heyward grumbled, "It's created a precedent and is a surrender we'll regret."

Alex Vandervoort was silent.

When the FMA announcement was read to Forum East supporters at both branch banks, there was some cheering, after which the assembled groups quietly dispersed. Within half an hour, business at the two branches returned to normal.

The matter might have ended there except for an information leak which, viewed in retrospect, was perhaps inevitable. The leak resulted in a newspaper commentary two days later—an item in the same column, "Ear to the Ground," which first brought the issue out into the open.

> Were you wondering who was really behind those Forum Easters who this week brought the proud and mighty First Mercantile American Bank to heel? The Shadow knows. It's Civil Rights Lawyer-Feminist Margot Bracken—she of "airport toilet sit-in" fame and other battles for the humble and stepped-on.
>
> This time, despite the "bank-in" being her idea, on which she labored, Ms. Bracken kept her activity tip-top secret. While others fronted, she stayed out of sight, avoiding the press, her normal allies. Are you wondering about that, too?
>
> Stop wondering! Margot's great and good friend, most often seen with her around town, is Swinging Banker Alexander Vandervoort, exec veep of First Merc Am. If *you* were Margot and had that connection cooking, wouldn't *you* stay out of sight?
>
> Only thing we're wondering: Did Alex know and approve the siege of his own home plate?

5

"Goddamit, Alex," Margot said, "I'm sorry!"

"The way it happened, so am I."

"I could skin that louse of a columnist alive. The only good thing is that he didn't mention I'm related to Edwina."

"Not many know that," Alex said, "even in the bank. Anyway, lovers make livelier news than cousins."

It was close to midnight. They were in Alex's apartment, their first meeting since the siege of FMA's downtown branch began. The item in "Ear to the Ground" had appeared the day before.

Margot had come in a few minutes ago after representing a client in night court—a well-to-do habitual drunk, whose habit of assaulting any one in sight when he was boozed made him one of her few steady sources of income.

"The newspaper writer was doing his job, I suppose," Alex said. "And almost certainly your name would have come out anyway."

She said contritely, "I tried to make sure it didn't. Only a few people knew what I was doing, and I wanted it to stay like that."

He shook his head. "No way. Nolan Wainwright told me early this morning—these were his words—'the whole caper had Margot Bracken's handwriting on it.' And Nolan had started to quiz people. He used to be a police detective, you know. Someone would have talked if the news item hadn't appeared first."

"But they didn't have to use *your* name."

"If you want the truth"—Alex smiled—"I rather liked that 'swinging banker' bit."

But the smile was false and he sensed that Margot knew it. The real truth was that the column item had jolted and depressed him. He was still depressed tonight, though he had been pleased when Margot telephoned earlier to say that she was coming.

He asked, "Have you talked to Edwina today?"

"Yes, I phoned her. She didn't seem upset. I suppose we're used to each other. Besides, she's pleased that Forum East is back on the rails again—all of it. You must be glad about that, too."

"You always knew my feelings on that subject. But it doesn't mean I approve your shady methods, Bracken."

He had spoken more sharply than he intended. Margot reacted promptly. "There was nothing shady in what I did, *or* my people. Which is more than I can say for your goddam bank."

He raised his hands defensively. "Let's not quarrel. Not tonight."

"Then don't say things like that."

"All right, I won't."

Their momentary anger disappeared.

Margot said thoughtfully, "Tell me—when it all started, didn't you have *some* idea I was involved?"

"Yes. Partly because I know you very well. Also, I remembered you clammed up about Forum East when I expected you to tear me—and FMA—to shreds."

"Did it make things difficult for you—while the bank-in was going on, I mean?"

He answered bluntly, "Yes, it did. I wasn't sure whether to share what I'd guessed or to keep quiet. Since bringing in your name wouldn't have made any difference to what was happening, I kept quiet. As it turned out, it was the wrong decision."

"So now some of the others believe you knew all the time."

"Roscoe does. Maybe Jerome. I'm not sure about the rest."

There was an uncertain silence before Margot asked, "Do you care? Does it matter terribly?" For the first time in their relationship her voice was anxious. Concern clouded her face.

Alex shrugged, then decided to reassure her. "Not really, I guess. Don't worry. I'll survive."

But it did matter. It mattered very much at FMA, despite what he had just said, and the incident had been doubly unfortunate at this time.

Alex was sure that most of the bank's directors would have seen the newspaper item which included his name and the pertinent question: *Did Alex know and approve the siege of his own home plate?* And if there were a few who hadn't seen it, Roscoe Heyward would make certain that they did.

Heyward had made his attitude plain.

This morning, Alex had gone directly to Jerome Patterton when the bank president arrived at 10 A.M. But Heyward, whose office was nearer had got there first.

"Come in, Alex," Patterton had said. "We might just as well have a threesome as two meetings of deuces."

"Before we talk, Jerome," Alex told him, "I want to be the first to bring up a subject. You've seen this?" He put a clipping of the previous day's "Ear to the Ground" on the desk between them.

Without waiting, Heyward said unpleasantly, "Do you imagine there' anyone in the bank who hasn't?"

Patterton sighed. "Yes, Alex, I've seen it. I've also had a dozen people direct my attention to it, and no doubt there'll be others."

Alex said firmly, "Then you're entitled to know that what was printed is mischief-making and nothing more. You have my word that I knew absolutely nothing in advance about what happened at the downtown branch, and no more than the rest of us while it was going on."

"A good many people," Roscoe Heyward commented, "might consider that with your connections"—he put sardonic emphasis on the word *connections*—"such ignorance would be unlikely."

"Any explanations I'm making," Alex snapped, "are directed at Jerome."

Heyward declined to be put off. "When the bank's reputation is demeaned in public, all of us are concerned. As to your so-called explanation, do you seriously expect anyone to believe that through Wednesday, Thursday, Friday, over a weekend and into Monday, you had no idea, no idea at all, your girl friend was involved?"

Patterton said, "Yes, Alex; how about that?"

Alex felt his face flush red. He felt resentful, as he had several times since yesterday, that Margot had placed him in this absurd position.

As calmly as he could, he told Patterton of his guess last week that Margot might be involved, his decision that nothing would be gained by discussing the possibility with others. Alex explained that he still had not seen Margot since more than a week ago.

"Nolan Wainwright had the same idea," Alex added. "He told me earlier this morning. But Nolan kept quiet, too, because for both of us it was no more than an impression, a hunch, until the news item appeared."

"Someone will believe you, Alex," Roscoe Heyward said. His tone and expression declared: *I don't*.

"Now, now, Roscoe!" Patterton remonstrated mildly. "All right, Alex, I accept your explanation. Though I trust you'll use your influence with Miss Bracken to see that in future she directs her artillery elsewhere."

Heyward added, "Or better still, not at all."

Ignoring the last remark, Alex told the bank president with a tight, grim smile, "You can count on that."

"Thank you."

Alex was certain he had heard Patterton's last word on the subject and that their relationship could revert to normal, at least on the surface. As to what went on beneath the surface, he was less sure. Probably in the minds of Patterton and others—including some members of the board—Alex's loyalty would, from now on, have an asterisk of doubt beside it. If not that, there could be reservations about Alex's discretion in the company he kept.

Either way, those doubts and reservations would be in the directors' minds near the end of this year, as Jerome Patterton's retirement neared, and the board reopened the subject of the bank presidency. And while directors were big men in some ways, in others, as Alex knew, they could be petty and prejudiced.

Why? Why did it all have to happen *now?*

His dark mood deepened while Margot regarded him, her eyes questioning, her expression still anxious and uncertain.

She said more seriously than before, "I've caused you trouble. Quite a lot, I think. So let's both stop pretending that I didn't."

He was about to reassure her again, then changed his mind, knowing this was a time for honesty between them.

"Another thing that has to be said," Margot went on, "is we talked about this, knowing it might happen, wondering whether we could remain the kind of people we are—independent—yet stay together."

"Yes," he told her, "I remember."

"The only thing is," she said wryly, "I didn't expect it all to come to a head so soon."

He reached for her, as he had done so often before, but she moved away from him and shook her head. "No, let's settle this."

Without warning, he realized, and without either of them intending it, their relationship had reached a crisis.

"It will happen again, Alex. Let's not fool ourselves it won't. Oh, not with the bank, but with other related things. And I want to be sure we

can handle it whenever it does, and not just for one time only, hopi
it will be the last."

He knew that what she had said was true. Margot's life was one
confrontations; there would be many more. And while some would
remote from his own interests, others would not.

It was equally true, as Margot had pointed out, that they had spoke
of this before—just a week and a half ago. But then the discussion h:
been in abstract, the choice less clear, not sharply defined as events
the past week had made it.

"One thing you and I could do," Margot said, "is call it quits no
while we've had fun, while we're still ahead. No hard feelings eith
side; just a sensible conclusion. If we did that, stopped seeing each oth
and being seen together, word would travel quickly. It always does. Ar
while it wouldn't wipe out what happened at the bank, it could mal
things easier for you there."

That, too, was true, Alex knew. He had a swift temptation to acce]
the offer, to exorcise—cleanly and swiftly—a complication from his lif
a complication likely to become greater, not less, as years went b
Again he wondered: Why did so many problems, pressures, come t
gether—Celia worsening; Ben Rosselli's death; the struggle at the ban
the undeserved harassment today. And now Margot and a choic
Why?

The question reminded him of something which happened years b
fore when he once visited the Canadian city of Vancouver. A your
woman had jumped to her death from a 24th floor hotel room and, b
fore jumping, scrawled in lipstick on the window glass, *Why, oh wh
Alex had never known her, or even learned later what were her pro
lems which she believed beyond solution. But he had been staying c
the same floor of the hotel and a talkative assistant manager had shov
him the sad, lipsticked window. The memory always stayed with hi

Why, oh why, do we make choices that we do? Or why does life mal
them? Why had he married Celia? Why had she become insane? Wl
did he still hold back from the catharsis of divorce? Why did Marg
need to be an activist? Why would he consider losing Margot now? Ho
much did he want to be president of FMA?

Not that much!

He made a forceful, self-controlled decision and thrust his gloo
away. *The hell with it all!* Not for FMA, nor boards of directors, or pe
sonal ambition, would he surrender, *ever*, his private freedom of actic
and independence. Or give up Margot.

"The most important thing is," he told her, "do *you* want it to be the way you said just now—a 'sensible conclusion'?"

Margot spoke through tears. "Of course not."

"Then I don't either, Bracken. Or am I ever likely to. So let's be glad this happened, that we've proved something, and that neither of us has to prove it any more."

This time, when he put out his arms, she did not hold back.

6

"Roscoe, my boy," the Honorable Harold Austin said on the telephone, sounding pleased with himself. "I've been talking with Big George. He's invited you and me to play golf in the Bahamas next Friday."

Roscoe Heyward pursed his lips doubtfully. He was at home, in the study of his Shaker Heights house, on a Saturday afternoon in March. Before taking the phone call he had been examining a portfolio of financial statements, with other papers spread on the floor around his leather armchair.

"I'm not certain I can get away that soon or go that far," he told the Honorable Harold. "Couldn't we try for a conference in New York?"

"Sure we could try. Except we'd be stupid, because Big George prefers Nassau; and because Big George likes doing business on a golf course—*our* kind of business that he attends to personally."

It was unnecessary for either of them to identify "Big George." For that matter, few others in industry, banking, or public life would have needed to.

G. G. Quartermain, board chairman and chief executive of Supranational Corporation—SuNatCo—was a bravura bull of a man who possessed more power than many heads of state and exercised it like a king. His interests and influence extended worldwide, like those of the corporation whose destiny he directed. Inside SuNatCo and out he was variously admired, hated, courted, lionized, and feared.

His strength lay in his record. Eight years earlier—on the basis of some previous financial wizardry—G. G. Quartermain had been summoned to the rescue of Supranational, then ailing and debt ridden. Between then and now he had restored the company's fortune, enlarged it to spectacular conglomerate, thrice split its shares and quadrupled its dividend. Shareholders, whom Big George had made wealthy, adored him; they also allowed him all the freedom of action he desired. True, a few Cassandras argued he had built an empire of cardboard. But financial statements of SuNatCo and its many subsidiaries—which Roscoe Heyward had been studying when the Honorable Harold telephoned—resoundingly contradicted them.

Heyward had met the SuNatCo chairman twice: once briefly in a crowd, the second occasion in a Washington, D.C., hotel suite with Harold Austin.

The Washington meeting came about when the Honorable Harold reported to Quartermain on the subject of a mission he had carried out for Supranational. Heyward had no idea what the assignment was—the other two had completed the main part of their conversation when he joined them—except that in some way it involved government.

The Austin Agency handled national advertising for Hepplewhite Distillers, a large SuNatCo subsidiary, although the Honorable Harold's personal relationship with G. G. Quartermain appeared to extend beyond this.

Whatever the report was, it appeared to have put Big George in a jovial humor. On being introduced to Heyward, he observed, "Harold tells me he's a director of your little bank and you'd both like a spoonful of our gravy. Well, sometime soon we'll see about it."

The Supranational chieftain had then clapped Heyward across the shoulders and talked of other things.

It was his Washington conversation with G. G. Quartermain which prompted Heyward in mid-January—two months ago—to inform the FMA money policy committee that doing business with SuNatCo was a probability. Later, he realized he had been premature. Now it seemed the prospect was revived.

"Well," Heyward conceded on the telephone, "perhaps I could get away next Thursday for a day or two."

"That's more like it," he heard the Honorable Harold say. "Whatever you might have planned can't be more important to the bank than this. And, oh yes, one thing I haven't mentioned—Big George is sending his personal airplane for us."

Heyward brightened. "Is he now? Is it big enough for a fast trip?"

"It's a 707. I thought that would please you." Harold Austin chuckled. "So we'll fly from here Thursday at noon, have all of Friday in the Bahamas, and be back on Saturday. By the way, how do the new SuNatCo statements look?"

"I've been studying them." Heyward glanced at the mess of financia data spread around his chair. "The patient appears healthy; very health indeed."

"If you say so," Austin said, "that's good enough for me."

As he replaced the telephone, Heyward permitted himself a slight sly smile. The impending trip, its purpose, and the fact of traveling to the Bahamas by private plane, would make a pleasant item to droy casually in conversation next week. Also, if anything came of it, it would enhance his own status with the board—something he never lost sigh of nowadays, remembering the interim nature of Jerome Patterton' appointment as FMA president.

He was pleased, too, about the scheduled return by air next Satur day. It meant he would not have to miss an appearance in his church —St. Athanasius's—where he was a lay reader and delivered the lesson clearly and solemnly, every Sunday.

The thought reminded him of tomorrow's reading which he had planned to go over in advance, as he usually did. Now he lifted a heavy family Bible from a bookshelf and turned to a page already flagged. The page was in *Proverbs* where tomorrow's reading included a verse which was a Heyward favorite: *Righteousness exalteth a nation: but sin is reproach to any people.*

To Roscoe Heyward, the Bahamas excursion was an education.

He was not unfamiliar with high living. Like most senior bankers, Hey ward had mingled socially with customers and others who used money freely, even aggressively, in achieving princely comforts and amuse ments. Almost always, he envied their financial freedom.

But G. G. Quartermain outdid them all.

The 707 jet, identified by a large *Q* on fuselage and tail, landed a the city's international airport precisely as scheduled, to the minute It taxied to a private terminal where the Honorable Harold and Hey ward left the limousine which had brought them from downtown and were whisked aboard, entering at the rear.

In a foyer like a miniature hotel lobby, a quartet greeted them—a middle-aged man, graying and with the mix of authority and deference which stamped him a majordomo, and three young women.

"Welcome aboard, gentlemen," the majordomo said. Heyward nod ded, but scarcely noticed the man, his attention being distracted by the women—breathtakingly beautiful girls in their twenties—who were smil ing agreeably. It occurred to Roscoe Heyward that the Quartermain organization must have assembled the most comely stewardesses from

TWA, United, and American, then skimmed off these three, like cream from richest milk. One girl was honey-blonde, another a striking brunette, the third a long-haired redhead. They were long-legged, willowy, healthily suntanned. The tans contrasted against their stylish but abbreviated pale beige uniforms.

The majordomo's uniform was of the same smart material as the girls'. All four had an embroidered Q on the left breast pocket.

"Good afternoon, Mr. Heyward," the redhead said. Her voice, pleasantly modulated, had a soft, almost seductive quality. She went on, "I'm Avril. If you'll come this way, I'll show you to your room."

As Heyward followed her, surprised at the reference to a "room," the Honorable Harold was being greeted by the blonde.

The elegant Avril preceded Heyward down a corridor extending part way along the aircraft on one side. Several doors opened from it.

Over her shoulder, she announced, "Mr. Quartermain is having a sauna and massage. He'll join you later in the lounge."

"A sauna? Aboard *here?*"

"Oh, yes. There's one directly behind the flight deck. A steam room, too. Mr. Quartermain likes either a sauna or a Russian bath wherever he is, and he has his own masseur always with him." Avril flashed a dazzling smile. "If you'd like a bath and massage there'll be plenty of time on the flight. I'll be glad to attend to it."

"No, thank you."

The girl stopped at a doorway. "This is your room, Mr. Heyward." As she spoke, the aircraft moved forward, beginning to taxi. At the unexpected movement, Heyward stumbled.

"Oops!" Avril put out her arm, steadying him, and for a moment they were close. He was conscious of long slim fingers, bronze-orange polished nails, a light firm touch and a waft of perfume.

She kept her hand on his arm. "I'd better strap you in for takeoff. The captain always goes quickly. Mr. Quartermain doesn't like lingering at airports."

He had a quick impression of a small, sumptuous parlor into which the girl led him, then he was seated on a softly comfortable settee while the fingers he had already become aware of deftly fastened a strap around his waist. Even through the strap he could feel the fingers moving. The sensation was not disagreeable.

"There!" The aircraft was taxiing fast now. Avril said, "If you don't mind, I'll stay until we're airborne."

She sat beside him on the settee and fastened a strap herself.

"No," Roscoe Heyward said. He felt absurdly dazed. "I don't mind at all."

Looking around, he took in more details. The parlor or cabin, such as he had seen on no aircraft before, had been designed to make efficient but luxurious use of space. Three of the walls were paneled in teak with carved Q motifs embellished in gold leaf. The fourth wall was almost entirely mirror, ingeniously making the compartment seem larger than it was. Recessed into the wall on his left was a compactly organized office bureau, including a telephone console and glass-shielded teletype. Nearby a small bar was stocked with an array of miniature bottles. Built into the mirror wall, which faced Heyward and Avril, was a TV screen with duplicate sets of controls, reachable from either side of the settee. A folding door behind was presumably to a bathroom.

"Would you like to watch our takeoff?" Avril asked. Without waiting for an answer, she touched the TV controls nearest her and a picture clear and in color, sprang to life. Obviously a camera was in the aircraft nose and, on the screen, they could see a taxiway leading to a wide runway, the latter coming fully into view as the 707 swung onto it. With no time wasted, the aircraft moved forward, simultaneously the runway began to rush beneath them, then the remainder of it tilted downward as the big jet angled up and they were airborne. Roscoe Heyward had a sense of soaring, not merely because of the TV image. With only sky and clouds ahead, Avril snapped it off.

"The regular TV channels are there if you need them," she informed him, then motioned to the teleprinter. "Over there you can get the Dow Jones, AP, UPI, or Telex. Just phone the flight deck and they'll feed in whichever you say."

Heyward observed cautiously, "All this is a little beyond my normal experience."

"I know. It has that effect on people sometimes, though it's surprising how quickly everyone adapts." Again the direct look and dazzling smile. "We have four of these private cabins and each one converts to a bedroom quite easily. You just push some buttons. I'll show you if you like."

He shook his head. "It seems unnecessary now."

"Whatever you wish, Mr. Heyward."

She released her seat belt and stood up. "If you want Mr. Austin, he's in the cabin immediately behind. Up forward is the main lounge you're invited to when you're ready. Then there's a dining room, offices, and beyond that Mr. Quartermain's private apartment."

"Thank you for the geography." Heyward removed his rimless glasses and took out a handkerchief to wipe them.

"Oh, please let me do that!" Gently but firmly Avril took the glasses from his hand, produced a square of silk and polished them. Then she replaced the glasses on his face, her fingers traveling lightly behind his ears in doing so. Heyward had a feeling he should protest, but didn't.

"My job on this trip, Mr. Heyward, is to take care of you exclusively and make sure you have everything you want."

Was it imagination, he wondered, or had the girl placed subtle emphasis on the word "everything"? He reminded himself sharply that he hoped not. If she had, the implication would be shocking.

"Two other things," Avril said. Gorgeous and slender, she had moved to the doorway, preparing to leave. "If you want me for anything at all, please press button number seven on the telephone."

Heyward answered gruffly, "Thank you, young lady, but I doubt if I'll do that."

She seemed unperturbed. "And the other thing: On the way to the Bahamas we'll be landing in Washington briefly. The Vice-President is joining us there."

"A vice-president from Supranational?"

Her eyes were mocking. "No, silly. The Vice-President of the United States."

Some fifteen minutes later, Big George Quartermain demanded of Roscoe Heyward, "For Chrissakes! Whatinhellzat you're drinking? Mother's milk?"

"It's lemonade." Heyward held up his glass, inspecting the insipid liquid. "I rather enjoy it."

The Supranational chairman shrugged his massive shoulders. "Every addict to his own poison. Girls taking care of you both?"

"No complaints from this quarter," the Honorable Harold Austin offered with a chuckle. Like the others, he was reclining comfortably in the 707's splendidly appointed main lounge with the blonde, who had revealed her name as Rhetta, curled on the rug at his feet.

Avril said sweetly, "We're trying our best." She was standing behind Heyward's chair and let a hand travel lightly across his back. He felt her fingers touch the base of his neck, linger momentarily, then move on.

Moments earlier, G. G. Quartermain had come into the lounge, resplendent in a crimson towel robe with white piping, the inevitable Q embroidered largely. Like a Roman senator, he was attended by acolytes —a hard-faced, silent man in gym whites, presumably the masseur, and still another hostess in trim beige uniform, her features delicately Japanese. The masseur and the girl supervised Big George's entry into broad, throne-like chair, clearly reserved for him. Then a third figure—the original majordomo—as if by magic produced a chilled martini an eased it into G. G. Quartermain's awaiting hand.

Even more than on previous occasions they had met, Heyward de cided, the name "Big George" seemed apposite in every way. Physicall their host was a mountain of a man—at least six and a half feet in heigh his chest, arms, and torso like a village blacksmith's. His head was ha the size again of most other men's and his facial features matched—prominent, large eyes, swift-moving and darkly shrewd, the mouth wide lipped and strong, as accustomed to issuing commands as a Marine dri sergeant's, though on larger issues. Equally clearly, surface joviality coul be banished instantly by powerful displeasure.

Yet he stopped short of coarseness, nor was there any sign of ove weight or flab. Through the enfolding towel robe, muscles bulged. Hey ward observed, too, that Big George's face betrayed no fat layers, hi massive chin no jowls. His belly appeared flat and taut.

As to other bigness, his corporate reach and appetite were reporte daily in the business press. And his living style aboard this twelve million-dollar airplane was unabashedly royal.

The masseur and majordomo quietly disappeared. Replacing then like one more character emerging on stage, was a chef—a pale, worrie pencil of a man, immaculate in kitchen whites with a high chef's ha which brushed the cabin ceiling. Heyward wondered just how big th on-board staff was. Later, he learned it totaled sixteen.

The chef stood stiffly beside Big George's chair, proffering an outsiz black leather folder embossed with a golden Q. Big George ignore him.

"That trouble at your bank." Quartermain addressed Roscoe Hey ward. "Demonstrations. All the rest. Is everything settled? Are yo solid?"

"We were always solid," Heyward answered. "That was never in ques tion."

"The market didn't think so."

"Since when was the stock market an accurate barometer of any thing?"

Big George smiled fleetingly, then swung to the petite Japanese host ess. "Moonbeam, get me the latest quote on FMA."

"Yes, Misto Q," the girl said. She went out by a forward door.

Big George nodded in the direction she had gone. "Still can't get tha

ongue of hers around Quartermain. Always calls me 'Misto Q.'" He
grinned at the others. "Manages nicely elsewhere, though."

Roscoe Heyward said quickly, "The reports you heard about our bank
concerned a trifling incident, magnified beyond importance. It happened also at a time of management transition."

"But you people didn't stand firm," Big George insisted. "You let outside agitators have their way. You went soft and surrendered."

"Yes, we did. And I'll be frank to say I didn't like the decision. In
fact, I opposed it."

"Stand up to 'em! Always clobber the bastards one way or another!
Never back down!" The Supranational chairman drained his martini
and the majordomo appeared from nowhere, removed the original glass
and placed a fresh one in Big George's hand. The drink's perfect chill
was apparent from its outside frosting.

The chef was still standing, waiting. Quartermain continued to ignore him.

He rumbled reminiscently, "Had a sub-assembly manufacturing plant
near Denver. Lots of labor trouble. Wage demands beyond all reason.
Early this year, union called a strike, the last of many. I told our people
—the subsidiary which ran it—warn the sons of bitches we'll close the
plant down. Nobody believed us. So we made studies, planned arrangements. Shipped tools and dies to one of our other companies. They took
up the manufacturing slack. At Denver we closed. Suddenly no plant,
no jobs, no payroll. Now, the lot of 'em—employees, union, Denver city,
state government, you name it—are down on their knees pleading with
us to reopen." He considered his martini, then said magnanimously,
'Well, we may. Doing other manufacturing, and on our terms. But we
didn't back down."

"Good for you, George!" the Honorable Harold said. "We need more
people to take that kind of stand. The problem at our bank, though,
has been somewhat different. In some ways we're still in an interim situation which began, as you know, with Ben Rosselli's death. But by
spring next year a good many of us on the board hope to see Roscoe here
firmly at the helm."

"Glad to hear it. Don't like dealing with people not at the top. Those
I do business with must be able to decide, then make decisions stick."

"I assure you, George," Heyward said, "that any decisions you and I
arrive at will be adhered to by the bank."

In an adroit way, Heyward realized, their host had maneuvered Harold Austin and himself into the stance of supplicants—a reversal of a
banker's usual role. But the fact was, any loan to Supranational would

be worry-free, as well as prestigious for FMA. Equally important, i could be a precursor of other new industrial accounts since Supran: tional Corporation was a pacesetter whose example others followed

Big George snapped abruptly at the chef. "Well, what is it?"

The figure in white was galvanized to action. He thrust forward th black leather folder he had been holding since his entry. "The luncheo. menu, monsieur. For your approval."

Big George made no attempt to take the folder but scanned its con tents held before him. He stabbed with a finger. "Change that Waldor salad to a Caesar."

"Oui, monsieur."

"And dessert. Not Glacé Martinique. A Soufflé Grand Marnier."

"Certainly, monsieur."

A nod of dismissal. Then, as the chef turned away, Big George glared "And when I order a steak, how do I like it?"

"Monsieur"—the chef gestured imploringly with his free hand—" 'ave already apologize twice for the unfortunate last night."

"Never mind that. The question was: *How do I like it?*"

With a Gallic shrug, repeating a lesson learned, the chef intoned, "On the slightly well-done side of medium-rare."

"Just remember that."

The chef asked despairingly, "'Ow can I forget, monsieur?" Crest fallen, he went out.

"Something else that's important," Big George informed his guests "is not to let people get away with things. I pay that frog a fortune to know *exactly* how I like my food. He slipped last night—not much, bu enough to ream him out so next time he'll remember. What's the quote?" Moonbeam had returned with a slip of paper.

She read out in accented English, "FMA trading now at forty-five and three quarters."

"There we are," Roscoe Heyward said, "we're up another point."

"But still not as high as before Rosselli bit the bullet," Big George said. He grinned. "Though when word gets out that you're helping fi nance Supranational, your stock'll soar."

It could happen, Heyward thought. In the tangled world of finance and stock prices, inexplicable things occurred. That someone would lend money to someone else might not seem to mean much—yet the market would respond.

More importantly, though, Big George had now declared positively that some kind of business *was* to be transacted between First Mercan

ile American Bank and SuNatCo. No doubt they would thrash out de-
ails through the next two days. He felt his excitement rising.

Above their heads a chime sounded softly. Outside, the jet thrum
hanged to lower tempo.

"Washington, ho!" Avril said. She and the other girls began fastening
he men to their seats with heavy belts and light fingers.

The time on the ground in Washington was even briefer than at the
previous stop. With a 14-carat-VIP passenger, it seemed, top priorities
or landing, taxiing, and takeoff were axiomatic.

Thus, in less than twenty minutes they had returned to cruising alti-
ude en route to the Bahamas.

The Vice-President was installed, with the brunette, Krista, taking
are of him, an arrangement which he patently approved.

Secret Service men, guarding the Vice-President, had been accommo-
lated somewhere at the rear.

Soon after, Big George Quartermain, now attired in a striking cream
ilk one-piece suit, jovially led the way forward from the lounge into the
airliner's dining room—a richly decorated apartment, predominantly silver and royal blue. There, the four men, seated at a carved oak table beneath a crystal chandelier, and with Moonbeam, Avril, Rhetta, and
Krista hovering deliciously behind, lunched in a style and on cuisine
which any of the world's great restaurants would have found it hard to
equal.

Roscoe Heyward, while relishing the meal, did not share in the several wines or a thirty-year-old Cognac brandy at the end. But he did
observe that the heavy, gold-rimmed brandy goblets omitted the tradi-
ional decorative N of Napoleon in favor of a Q.

7

Warm sunshine from an unbroken azure sky shone on the lush green fairway of the long par-5 fifth hole at the Bahamas' Fordly Cay Club golf course. The course and its adjoining luxury club were among the half-dozen most exclusive in the world.

Beyond the green, a white sand beach, palm-fringed, deserted, extended like a strip of Paradise into the distance. At the edge of the beach a pellucid turquoise sea lapped gently in tiny wavelets. A half mile out from shore a line of breakers creamed on coral reefs.

Nearer to hand, beside the fairway, an exotic crazy-quilt of flowers —hibiscus, bougainvillea, poinsettia, frangipani—competed in belief defying colors. The fresh, clear air, moved agreeably by a zephyr breeze held a scent of jasmine.

"I imagine," the Vice-President of the United States observed, "that this is as close to heaven as any politician gets."

"My idea of heaven," the Honorable Harold Austin told him, "would not include slicing." He grimaced and swung his four iron viciously "There must be some way to get better at this game."

The four were playing a best-ball match—Big George and Roscoe Heyward against Harold Austin and the Vice-President.

"What you should do, Harold," the Vice-President, Byron Stonebridge, said, "is get back into Congress, then work your way to the job I have. Once there, you'd have nothing else to do but golf; you could take all the time you wanted to improve your game. It's an accepted historical fact that almost every Vice-President in the past half century left office a better golfer than when he entered it."

As if to confirm his words, moments later he lofted his third shot— a beautiful eight iron—straight at the flagstick.

Stonebridge, lean and lithe, his movements fluid, was playing a spectacular game today. He had begun life as a farmer's son, working long
hours on a family small holding, and across the years had kept his body
sinewy. Now his homely plainsman's features beamed as his ball
dropped, then rolled to within a foot of the cup.

"Not bad," Big George acknowledged as his cart drew even. "Washington not keeping you too busy, eh, By?"

"Oh, I suppose I shouldn't complain. I ran an inventory of Administration paper clips last month. And there's been a news leak from the
White House—it seems there's a chance I'll sharpen pencils over there
quite soon."

The others chuckled dutifully. It was no secret that Stonebridge, ex-
State governor, ex-Minority Leader in the Senate, was fretful and restless in his present role. Before the election which had thrust him there,
his running mate, the presidential candidate, declared that *his* Vice-
President would—in a new post-Watergate era—play a meaningful, busy
part in government. As always after inauguration, the promise stayed
unfulfilled.

Heyward and Quartermain chipped onto the green, then waited with
Stonebridge as the Honorable Harold, who had been playing erratically,
hanked, laughed, flubbed, laughed, and finally chipped on.

The four men made a diverse foursome. G. G. Quartermain, towering above the others, was expensively immaculate in tartan slacks, a
Lacoste cardigan, and navy suede Foot-Joys. He wore a red golf cap, its
badge proclaiming the coveted status of a member of Fordly Cay Club.

The Vice-President portrayed stylish neatness—double knit slacks, a
mildly colorful shirt, his golfing footwear an ambivalent black and white.
In dramatic contrast was Harold Austin, the most flamboyant dresser
and a study in shocking pink and lavender. Roscoe Heyward was efficiently practical in dark gray slacks, a white, short-sleeved "dress"
shirt and soft black shoes. Even on a golf course he looked like a banker.

Their progress since the first tee had been something of a cavalcade.
Big George and Heyward shared one electric golf cart; Stonebridge and
the Honorable Harold occupied another. Six more electric carts had
been requisitioned by the Vice-President's Secret Service escort and now
surrounded them—on both sides and fore and aft—like a destroyer
squadron.

"If you had free choice, By," Roscoe Heyward said, "free choice to set
some government priorities, what would they be?"

Yesterday, Heyward had addressed Stonebridge formally as "Mr.
Vice-President," but was quickly assured, "Forget the formality; I get

weary of it. You'll find I answer best to 'By.'" Heyward, who cherishe first name friendships with important people, was delighted.

Stonebridge answered, "If I had my choice I'd concentrate on ec nomics—restoring fiscal sanity, some balanced national bookkeeping

G. G. Quartermain, who had overheard, remarked, "A brave few trie it, By. They failed. And you're too late."

"It's late, George, but not *too* late."

"I'll debate that with you." Big George squatted, considering the lin of his putt. "After nine. Right now the priority is sinking this."

Since the game started, Quartermain had been quieter than th others, and intense. He had his handicap down to three and alway played to win. Winning or turning in a sub-par score pleased him (s he said) as much as acquiring a new company for Supranational.

Heyward was playing with consistent competence, his performanc neither flashily spectacular nor anything to be ashamed of.

As all four walked from their carts at the sixth tee, Big George cat tioned: "Keep your banker's eye on the scores of those two, Roscoe To a politician and an advertising man, accuracy's not a natural habit.

"My exalted status requires that I win," the Vice-President said. "B any means."

"Oh, I have the scores." Roscoe Heyward tapped his forehea "They're all in here. On 1, George and By had fours, Harold a six, an I had a bogey. We all had pars on 2 except for By with that incredib birdie. Of course, Harold and I had net birds there, too. Everyone hel par on 3 except Harold; he had another six. The fourth hole was ou good one, fours for George and me (and I had a stroke there), a fiv for By, a seven for Harold. And, of course, this last hole was a real dis aster for Harold but then his partner comes through with another bir So as far as the match is concerned, right now we're even."

Byron Stonebridge stared at him. "That's uncanny! I'll be damned.

"You have me wrong for that first hole," the Honorable Harold said "I had a five, not a six."

Heyward said firmly, "Not so, Harold. Remember, you drove int that palm grove, punched out, hit your fairway wood short of the green chipped long and two-putted."

"He's right," Stonebridge confirmed. "I remember."

"Goddamit, Roscoe," Harold Austin grumbled, "whose friend ar you?"

"Mine, by God!" Big George exclaimed. He draped a friendly arm over Heyward's shoulders. "I'm beginning to like you, Roscoe, especiall our handicap!" As Heyward glowed, Big George lowered his voice to a confidential level. "Was everything satisfactory last night?"

"Perfectly satisfactory, thank you. I enjoyed the journey, the evening, and I slept extremely well."

He had not slept well at first. In the course of the previous evening at G. G. Quartermain's Bahamas mansion it had become evident that Avril, the slim and lovely redhead, was available to Roscoe Heyward on any terms he chose. That was made plain both by innuendo from the others and Avril's increasing nearness as the day, then night, progressed. She lost no opportunity to lean toward Heyward so that sometimes her soft hair brushed his face, or to make physical contact with him on the slightest pretext. And while he did not encourage her, neither did he object.

Equally clear was that the gorgeous Krista was available to Byron Stonebridge and the glamorous blonde Rhetta to Harold Austin.

The exquisitely beautiful Japanese girl Moonbeam was seldom more than a few feet away from G. G. Quartermain.

The Quartermain ménage, one of a half dozen owned by the Supranational chairman in various countries, was on Prospero Ridge, high above Nassau city and with a panoramic view of land and sea. The house was in landscaped grounds behind high stone walls. Heyward's room on the second floor, to which Avril escorted him on arrival, commanded the view. It also afforded a glimpse, through trees, of the house of a near-neighbor—the prime minister, his privacy protected by patrolling Royal Bahamas Police.

In late afternoon they had drinks beside a colonnaded swimming pool. Dinner followed, served on a terrace out of doors, by candlelight. This time the girls, who had shed their uniforms and were superbly gowned, joined the men at table. Hovering white-gloved waiters served while two strolling players added music. Companionship and conversation flowed.

After dinner, while Vice-President Stonebridge and Krista elected to stay on at the house, the others entered a trio of Rolls-Royces—cars which had met them at Nassau Airport earlier—and were driven to the Paradise Island gambling casino. There Big George played heavily and appeared to win. Austin participated mildly, Roscoe Heyward not at all. Heyward disapproved of gambling but was interested in Avril's description of the finer points of chemin de fer, roulette, and blackjack, which were new to him. Because of the hum of other conversations, Avril kept her face close to Heyward's while she talked and, as on the airplane earlier, he found the sensation not unpleasing.

But then, with disconcerting suddenness, his body began taking greater cognizance of Avril so that ideas and inclinations which he knew to be reprehensible were increasingly hard to banish. He sensed Avril's amused awareness of his struggle, which failed to help. Finally, at his bedroom door to which she escorted him at 2 A.M., it was with the greatest effort of will—particularly when she showed a willingness to linger—that he did not invite her in.

Before Avril left for wherever her own room was, she swirled her red hair and told him, smiling, "There's an intercom beside the bed. If there's *anything* you want, press button number seven and I'll come." This time there was no doubt of what "anything" meant. And the number seven, it seemed, was a code for Avril wherever she might be.

Inexplicably his voice had thickened and his tongue seemed oversized as he informed her, "Thank you, no. Good night."

Even then his inner conflict was not over. Undressing, his thoughts returned to Avril and he saw to his chagrin that his body was undermining his will's resolve. It had been a long time since, unbidden, it had happened.

It was then that he had fallen on his knees and prayed to God to protect him from sin and relieve him of temptation. And after a while, it seemed, the prayer was answered. His body drooped with tiredness. Later still, he slept.

Now, as they drove down the sixth fairway, Big George volunteered, "Look, fella, tonight if you like I'll send Moonbeam to you. A man wouldn't believe the tricks that little lotus blossom knows."

Heyward's face flushed. He decided to be firm. "George, I'm enjoying your company and I'd like to have your friendship. But I must tell you that in certain areas our ideas differ."

The big man's features stiffened. "In just what areas?"

"I imagine, moral ones."

Big George considered, his face a mask. Then suddenly he guffawed. "Morals—what are they?" He stopped the cart as the Honorable Harold prepared to hit from a fairway bunker on their left. "Okay, Roscoe, cut it your way. Just tell me if you change your mind."

Despite the firmness of his resolution, over the next two hours Heyward found his imagination turning to the fragile and seductive Japanese girl.

At the end of nine holes, on the course refreshment lanai, Big George resumed his fifth hole argument with Byron Stonebridge.

"The U.S. government and other governments," Big George declared, "are being run by those who don't, or won't understand economic prin-

:iples. It's a reason—the only reason—we have runaway inflation. It's why the world's money system is breaking down. It's why everything moneywise can only get worse."

"I'll go part way with you on that," Stonebridge told him. "The way Congress is spending money, you'd think the supply is inexhaustible. We've supposedly sane people in the House and Senate who believe that for every dollar coming in you can safely put out four or five."

Big George said impatiently, "Every businessman knows that. Known it for a generation. The question is not if, but when, will the American economy collapse?"

"I'm not convinced it has to. We could still avert it."

"Could, but won't. Socialism—which is spending money you don't have and never will—is too deep-rooted. So there comes a point when government runs out of credit. Fools think it can't happen. But it will."

The Vice-President sighed. "In public I'd deny the truth of that. Here, among us privately, I can't."

"The sequence which is coming," Big George said, "is easy to predict. It'll be much the way things went in Chile. A good many think that Chile was different and remote. It wasn't. It was a small-scale model of the U.S.A.—and Canada and Britain."

The Honorable Harold ventured thoughtfully, "I agree with your point about sequence. First a democracy—solid, world-acknowledged, and effective. Then socialism, mild at first but soon increasing. Money spent wildly until nothing's left. After that, financial ruin, anarchy, dictatorship."

"No matter how much in a hole we get," Byron Stonebridge said, "I'll not believe we'd go that far."

"We wouldn't need to," Big George told him. "Not if some of us with intelligence and power think ahead, and plan. When financial collapse comes, in the U.S. we've two strong arms to stop us short of anarchy. One is big business. By that I mean a cartel of multi-national companies like mine, and big banks like yours and others, Roscoe—which could run the country financially, exerting fiscal discipline. We would be solvent because of worldwide operation; we'd have put our own resources where inflation didn't swallow them. The other strong arm is the military and police. In partnership with big business, they'd keep order."

The Vice-President said drily, "In other words, a police state. You might encounter opposition."

Big George shrugged. "Some maybe; not much. People will accept the inevitable. Especially when democracy, so-called, has split apart, the money system shattered, individual purchasing power nil. Besides

that, Americans don't believe in democratic institutions any more. You
politicians undermined them."

Roscoe Heyward had kept silent, listening. Now he said, "What you
foresee, George, is an extension of the present military-industrial complex into an elitist government."

"Exactly! And industrial-military—I prefer it that way—is becoming
stronger as American economics weaken. And we've organization. It's
loose, but tightening fast."

"Eisenhower was first to recognize the military-industrial structure,"
Heyward said.

"And warn against it," Byron Stonebridge added.

"Hell, yes!" Big George agreed. "And more fool him! Ike, of all people, should have seen the possibilities for strength. Don't you?"

The Vice-President sipped his Planter's Punch. "This is off the record.
But yes, I do."

"I'll say this," Big George assured him, "*you're* one who should be
joining *us*."

The Honorable Harold asked, "How much time, George, do you believe we have?"

"My own experts tell me eight to nine years. By then, collapse of the
money system is inevitable."

"What appeals to me as a banker," Roscoe Heyward said, "is the idea
of discipline at last in money and government."

G. G. Quartermain signed the bar chit and stood up. "And you'll see
it. That I promise you."

They drove to the tenth tee.

Big George called over to the Vice-President, "By, you've been playing 'way over your head and it's your honor. Tee it up and let's see some
disciplined and *economic* golf. You're only one-up and there are nine
tough holes to go."

Big George and Roscoe Heyward waited on the cart path while
Harold Austin looked over his lie on the fourteenth hole; after general
searching, a Secret Service man had located his ball beneath a hibiscus
bush. Big George had relaxed since he and Heyward had taken two
holes and were now one-up. As they sat in the cart, the subject which
Heyward had been hoping for was raised. It happened with surprising
casualness.

"So your bank would like some Supranational business."

"The thought had occurred to us." Heyward tried to match the
other's casualness.

"I'm extending Supranational's foreign communications holdings by buying control of small, key telephone and broadcast companies. Some owned by governments, others private. We do it quietly, paying off local politicians where we have to; that way we avoid nationalistic fuss. Supranational provides advanced technology, efficient service, which small countries can't afford, and standardization for global linkage. There's good profitability for ourselves. In three more years we'll control, through subsidiaries, forty-five percent of communications linkages, worldwide. No one else comes close. It's important to America; it'll be vital in the kind of industrial-military liaison we were talking about."

"Yes," Heyward agreed, "I can see the significance of that."

"From your bank I'd want a credit line of fifty million dollars. Of course, at prime."

"Naturally, whatever we arranged would be at prime." Heyward had known that any loan to Supranational would be at the bank's best interest rate. In banking it was axiomatic that the richest customers paid least for borrowed money; highest interest rates were for the poor. "What we would have to review," he pointed out, "is our bank's legal limitation under Federal law."

"Legal limit, hell! There are ways around that, methods used every day. You know it as well as I do."

"Yes, I'm aware that there are ways and means."

What both men were speaking of, and fully understood, was a U.S. banking regulation forbidding any bank to loan more than ten percent of its capital and paid-in surplus to a single debtor. The purpose was to guard against bank failure and protect depositors from loss. In the case of First Mercantile American, a fifty-million-dollar loan to Supranational would substantially exceed that limit.

"The way to beat the regulation," Big George said, "is for you to split the loan among our subsidiary companies. Then we'll reallocate it as and where we need."

Roscoe Heyward mused, "It could be done that way." He was aware that the proposal violated the spirit of the law while remaining technically within it. But he also knew that what Big George had said was true: Such methods were in everyday use by the biggest, most prestigious banks.

Yet even with that problem handled, the size of the proposed commitment staggered him. He had envisaged twenty or twenty-five million as a starting point, with the sum increasing perhaps as relationships between Supranational and the bank developed.

As if reading his mind, Big George said flatly, "I never deal in small amounts. If fifty million is bigger than you people can handle, let's forget the whole thing. I'll give it to Chase."

The elusive, important business which Heyward had come here hoping to capture seemed suddenly to be slipping away.

He said emphatically, "No, no. It's not too large."

Mentally he reviewed other FMA commitments. No one knew them better. Yes, fifty million to SuNatCo *could* be managed. It would necessitate turning off taps within the bank—cutting back drastically on smaller loans and mortgages, but this could be handled. A large single loan to a client like Supranational would be immensely more profitable than a host of small loans, costly to process and collect.

"I intend to recommend the line of credit strongly to our board," Heyward said decisively, "and I'm certain they'll agree."

His golfing partner acknowledged curtly, "Good."

"Of course, it would strengthen my position if I could inform our directors that we would have some bank representation on the Supranational board."

Big George drove the golf cart up to his ball, which he studied before replying. "That might be arranged. If it was, I'd expect your trust department to invest heavily in our stock. It's time some fresh buying pushed the price up."

With growing confidence, Heyward said, "The subject could be explored, along with other matters. Obviously Supranational will have an active account with us now, and there's the question of a compensating balance . . ."

They were, Heyward knew, going through a banker-client ritualistic dance. What it symbolized was a fact of banking-corporate life: *You scratch my back, I'll scratch yours.*

G. G. Quartermain, jerking an iron from his alligator bag, said irritably, "Don't bother me with details. My financial man, Inchbeck, will be here today. He'll fly back with us tomorrow. You two can get together then."

Plainly, the brief business session was concluded.

By this time the Honorable Harold's erratic game seemed to have affected his partner. "You're psyching me," Byron Stonebridge complained at one point. At another: "Dammit, Harold, that slice of yours is contagious as smallpox. Anyone you play with should be vaccinated." And for whatever reason, the Vice-President's swing, shots and poise began to go awry for costly strokes.

Since Austin did not improve, even with the chiding, by the seventeenth hole Big George and short-but-straight Roscoe remained one-up in the lead. This suited G. G. Quartermain and he crunched his tee shot on eighteen about two hundred and seventy yards, straight down the middle, then proceeded to birdie the hole, giving his side the match.

Big George was jovial at his victory and clasped Byron Stonebridge around the shoulders. "I guess that makes my credit balance in Washington even better than before."

"Depends on what you want," the Vice-President said. He added pointedly, "And how discreet you are."

Over drinks in the men's locker room, the Honorable Harold and Stonebridge each paid G. G. Quartermain a hundred dollars—a bet they had agreed on before the game began. Heyward had demurred from betting, so was not included in the payoff.

It was Big George who said magnanimously, "I like the way you played, partner." He appealed to the others. "I think Roscoe ought to get some recognition. Don't you two?"

As they nodded, Big George slapped his knee. "I got it! A seat on the Supranational board. Howzat for a prize?"

Heyward smiled. "I'm sure you're joking."

Momentarily, the smile left the SuNatCo chairman's face. "About Supranational I never joke."

It was then Heyward realized that this was Big George's way of implementing their earlier conversation. If he agreed, of course, it would mean accepting the other obligations . . .

His hesitation lasted seconds only. "If you do mean it, I'll be delighted to accept."

"It will be announced next week."

The offer was so swift and staggering that Heyward still had difficulty believing. He had expected that someone else from among the directors of First Mercantile American Bank would be invited to join the board of Supranational. To be chosen himself, and personally by G. G. Quartermain, was an accolade of accolades. The SuNatCo board, as composed now, read like a blue ribboned Who's Who of business and finance.

As if reading his mind, Big George chuckled. "Among other things, you can keep an eye on your bank's money."

Heyward saw the Honorable Harold glance his way questioningly. As Heyward gave a small slight nod, his fellow FMA director beamed.

8

The second evening at G. G. Quartermain's Bahamas mansion held a subtly different quality from the first. It was as if all eight of them—the men and girls—shared a relaxed intimacy, lacking the night before. Roscoe Heyward, aware of the contrast, suspected he knew the reason for it.

Intuition told him that Rhetta had spent the previous night with Harold Austin, Krista with Byron Stonebridge. He hoped the two men did not believe the same was true of himself and Avril. He was sure that his host did not; his remarks of this morning indicated it, probably because Big George was kept informed about what went on, or didn't, within this house.

Meanwhile, the evening gathering—again around the pool and on the terrace at dinnertime—was delectable for its own sake. Roscoe Heyward allowed himself to be an untautened, cheerful part of it.

He was enjoying, quite frankly, the continued attentions of Avril who showed no sign of resenting his rejection of her last night. Since he had proven to himself that he could resist her ultimate temptations, he saw no reason to deny himself Avril's pleasant companionship now. Two other reasons for his euphoric state were the pledge of Supranational business for First Mercantile American Bank and the unexpected, dazzling trophy of a seat for himself on the SuNatCo board. He had no doubt whatever that both would enhance his own prestige importantly at FMA. Already his succession to the bank's presidency seemed nearer.

Earlier, he had had a short meeting with the Supranational comptroller, Stanley Inchbeck, who had arrived, as Big George said. Inchbeck was a balding, bustling New Yorker and he and Heyward arranged to work out details of the SuNatCo loan on the flight northward tomorrow. Apart from his meeting with Heyward, Inchbeck had been closeted through most of the afternoon with G. G. Quartermain. Although he was apparently staying somewhere in the house, Inchbeck did not appear for drinks or dinner.

Something else Roscoe Heyward had noticed earlier, from the window of his second-floor room, was G. G. Quartermain and Byron Stonebridge strolling in the grounds for almost an hour in the early evening, deep in conversation. They were too far from the house for anything they said to be overheard but Big George appeared to be talking persuasively, with the Vice-President interrupting occasionally with what probably were questions. Heyward remembered this morning's remark on the golf course about "a credit balance in Washington," then wondered which of Supranational's many interests were being discussed. He decided he would never know.

Now, after dinner, in the cool, sweet-scented darkness out of doors, Big George was once more the genial host. Cupping his hands around a *Q* emblazoned brandy glass, he announced, "No excursions tonight. We'll keep the party here."

The majordomo, waiters, and musicians had discreetly slipped away.

Rhetta and Avril, who were drinking champagne, chorused, "A party here!"

By Stonebridge raised his voice to match the girls'. "What kind of party?"

"A swinging party!" Krista declared, then corrected herself, her speech slurred slightly from dinner wine and champagne. "No, a swimming party! I want to swim."

Stonebridge challenged her, "What's stopping you?"

"Nothing, By, darling! Absolutely nothing!" In a series of swift movements, Krista set down her champagne glass, kicked off her shoes, unfastened straps on her dress and wiggled. The long green dinner gown she had been wearing cascaded to her feet. Beneath it was a slip. She pulled that over her head and tossed it away. She had been wearing nothing else.

Naked, smiling, her exquisitely proportioned body with high firm breasts and jet black hair making her like a Maillol sculpture in motion, Krista walked with dignity from the terrace, down steps to the lighted swimming pool, and dived in. She swam the length of the pool, turned and called to the others, "It's glorious! Come in!"

"By God!" Stonebridge said, "I reckon I will." He tossed off his sport shirt, slacks and shoes, and naked as Krista, though less alluring, padded over and dived.

Moonbeam, with a small high giggle, and Rhetta were already taking off their clothes.

"Hold on!" Harold Austin called. "This sport's coming, too."

Roscoe Heyward, who had watched Krista with a mixture of shock and fascination, found Avril close beside him. "Rossie, sweetie, undo my zipper." She presented him her back.

Uncertainly, he tried to reach the zipper from his chair.

"Stand up, you old silly," Avril said. As he did, with her head half turned she leaned against him, her warmth and fragrance overpowering.

"Have you done it yet?"

He was having difficulty concentrating. "No, it seems to be . . ."

Adroitly, Avril reached behind her. "Here, let me." Finishing what he had begun, she tugged the zipper down. With a shrug of her shoulders, her dress fell away.

She swirled her red hair in the gesture he had come to know. "Well, what are you waiting for? Undo my bra."

His hands were trembling, his eyes riveted on her, as he did as he was told. The bra dropped. His hands did not.

With a minimal, graceful movement, Avril pivoted. She leaned forward and kissed him fully on the lips. His hands, remaining where they were, touched the forward thrusting nipples of her breasts. Involuntarily, it seemed, his fingers curled and tightened. Electric, sensual waves shot through him.

"Um," Avril purred. "That's nice. Coming swimming?"

He shook his head.

"See you later, then." She turned, walking away like a Grecian goddess in her nudity, and joined the other five cavorting in the pool.

G. G. Quartermain had remained seated, his chair pushed back from the dinner table. He sipped his brandy, eying Heyward shrewdly. "I'm not much for swimming either. Though once in a while, if he's sure he's among friends, it's good for a man to let himself go."

"I suppose I should concede that. And I certainly do feel among friends." Heyward sank down into his chair again; removing his glasses, he began to polish them. He had control of himself now. The instant of mad weakness was behind him. He went on, "The problem is, of course: one occasionally goes slightly further than intended. However, if one maintains over-all control, that's really the important thing."

Big George yawned.

While they talked, the others, by this time out of the water, were toweling themselves and slipping on robes from a pile beside the pool.

Two hours or so later, as she had the night before, Avril escorted Roscoe Heyward to his bedroom doorway. At first, downstairs he had decided to insist that she not accompany him, then changed his mind, confident of his reasserted strength of will and positive now he would not succumb to wild, erotic impulses. He even felt assured enough to say cheerfully, "Good night, young lady. And, yes, before you tell me, I know your intercom number is seven, but I assure you there is nothing that I'll need."

Avril had looked at him with an enigmatic half smile, then turned away. He immediately closed and locked the bedroom door, afterward humming softly to himself as he prepared for bed.

But, in bed, sleep eluded him.

He lay awake for nearly an hour, the bedclothes thrown back, the bedding soft beneath him. Through an open window he could hear a drowsy hum of insects and, distantly, the sound of breakers on the shore.

Despite his best intentions, the focus of his thoughts was Avril.

Avril . . . as he had seen and touched her . . . breathtakingly beauteous, naked and desirable. Instinctively he moved his fingers, reliving the sensation of those full, firm breasts, their nipples extended, as he had cupped them in his hands.

And all the while his body . . . striving, burgeoning . . . made mock of his intended righteousness.

He tried to move his thoughts away—to banking affairs, to the Supranational loan, to the directorship which G. G. Quartermain had promised. But thoughts of Avril returned, stronger than ever, impossible to eclipse. He remembered her legs, her thighs, her lips, her soft smile, her warmth and perfume . . . her availability.

He got up and began pacing, seeking to redirect his energy elsewhere. It would not be redirected.

Stopping at the window, he observed that a bright three-quarter moon had risen. It bathed the garden, beaches, and the sea in white ethereal light. Watching, a long-forgotten phrase returned to him: *The night was made for loving . . . by the moon.*

He paced again, then returned to the window, standing there, erect.

Twice he made a move toward the bedside table with its intercom. Twice, resolve and sternness turned him back.

The third time he did not turn back. Grasping the instrument in his hand, he groaned—a mixture of anguish, self-reproach, heady excitement, heavenly anticipation.

Decisively and firmly, he pressed button number seven.

9

Nothing in Miles Eastin's experience or imagination, before entering Drummonburg Penitentiary, had prepared him for the merciless, degrading hell of prison.

It was now six months since his exposure as an embezzler, and four months since his trial and sentencing.

In rare moments, when his objectivity prevailed over physical misery and mental anguish, Miles Eastin reasoned that if society had sought to impose savage, barbaric vengeance on someone like himself, it had succeeded far beyond the knowing of any who had not endured, themselves, the brutish purgatory of prison. And if the object of such punishment, he further reasoned, was to push a human being out of his humanity, and make of him an animal of lowest instincts, then the prison system was the way to do it.

What prison did not do, and never would—Miles Eastin told himself —was make a man a better member of society than when he entered it. Given any time at all, prison could only degrade and worsen him; could only increase his hatred of "the system" which had sent him there; could only reduce the possibility of his becoming, ever, a useful, law-abiding citizen. And the longer his sentence, the less likelihood there was of any moral salvage.

Thus, most of all, it was time which eroded and eventually destroyed any potential for reform which a prisoner might have when he arrived.

Even if an individual hung on to some shards of moral values, like a drowning swimmer to a life preserver, it was because of forces within himself, and not because of prison but despite it.

Miles was striving to hang on, straining to retain some semblance of the best of what he had been before, trying not to become totally brutalized, entirely unfeeling, utterly despairing, savagely embittered. It was so easy to slip into a garment of all four, a hair shirt which a man would wear forever. Most prisoners did. They were those either brutalized before they came here and made worse since, or others whom time in prison had worn down; time and the cold-hearted inhumanity of a citizenry outside, indifferent to what horrors were perpetrated or decencies neglected—all in society's name—behind these walls.

In Miles's favor, and in his mind while he clung on, was one dominant possibility. He had been sentenced to two years. It made him eligible for parole in four more months.

The contingency that he might not receive parole was one he did not dare consider. The implications were too awful. He did not believe he could go through two years of prison and fail to emerge totally, irreparably, debased in brain and body.

Hold on! he told himself each day and in the nights. *Hold on* for the hope, the deliverance, of parole!

At first, after arrest and detention while awaiting trial, he had thought that being locked into a cage would send him mad. He remembered reading once that freedom, until lost, was seldom valued. And it was true that no one realized how much their physical freedom of movement meant—even going from one room to another or briefly out of doors—until such choices were denied them totally.

Just the same, compared with conditions in this penitentiary, the pre-trial period was a luxury.

The cage at Drummonburg in which he was confined was a six-by-eight-foot cell, part of a four-tiered, X-shaped cell house. When the prison was built more than half a century ago, each cell was intended for one person; today, because of prison overpopulation, most cells, including Miles's, housed four. On most days prisoners were locked into the tiny spaces for eighteen hours out of twenty-four.

Soon after Miles had come here, and because of trouble elsewhere in the prison, they had remained locked in—"lock-in, feed-in," the authorities called it—for seventeen whole days and nights. After the first week, the desperate cries of twelve hundred near-demented men made one more agony piled upon the others.

The cell to which Miles Eastin was allotted had four bunks clamped to walls, one sink and a single, seatless toilet which all four inmates shared. Because water pressure through ancient, corroded pipes was poor, water supply—cold only—to the sink was usually a trickle; occasionally it stopped entirely. For the same reason, the toilet often wouldn't flush. It was bad enough to be confined in the same close quarters where four men defecated with a total lack of privacy, but staying with the stench long after, while waiting for sufficient water to remove it, was a disgusting, stomach-heaving horror.

Toilet paper and soap, even when used sparingly, were never enough. A brief shower was allowed once weekly; in between showers, bodies grew rancid, adding to close quarters misery.

It was in the showers, during his second week in prison, that Miles was gang raped. Bad as other experiences were, this had been the worst.

He had become aware, soon after his arrival, that other prisoners were attracted to him sexually. His good looks and youthfulness, he soon found out, were to be a liability. Marching to meals or at exercise in the yard, the more aggressive homosexuals managed to crowd around and rub against him. Some reached out to fondle him; others, from a distance, pursed their lips and blew him kisses. The first he squirmed away from, the second he ignored, but as both became more difficult his nervousness, then fear, increased. It became plain that inmates not involved would never help him. He sensed that guards who looked his way knew what was happening. They merely seemed amused.

Though the inmate population was predominantly black, the approaches came equally from blacks and whites.

He was in the shower house, a single-story corrugated structure to which prisoners were marched in groups of fifty, escorted by guards. The prisoners undressed, leaving their clothing in wire baskets, then trooped naked and shivering through the unheated building. They stood under shower heads, waiting for a guard to turn on the water.

The shower-room guard was high above them on a platform, and control of the showers and water temperature was under the guard's whim. If the prisoners were slow in moving, or seemed noisy, the guard could send down an icy blast of water, raising screams of rage and protest while prisoners jumped around like wild men, trying to escape. Because of the shower-house design, they couldn't. Or sometimes the guard would maliciously bring the hot water close to scalding, to the same effect.

On a morning when a group of fifty which included Miles was emerging from the showers, and another fifty, already undressed, were waiting to go in, Miles felt himself surrounded closely by several bodies. Suddenly his arms were gripped tightly by a half dozen hands and he was being hustled forward. A voice behind him urged, "Move your ass, pretty boy. We ain't got long." Several others laughed.

Miles looked up toward the elevated platform. Seeking to draw the guard's attention, he shouted, "Sir! sir!"

The guard, who was picking his nose and looking elsewhere, appeared not to hear.

A fist slammed hard into Miles's ribs. A voice behind him snarled, "Shaddup!"

He cried out again from pain and fear and either the same fist or another thudded home once more. The breath went out of him. A fiery hurt shot through his side. His arms were being twisted savagely. Whimpering now, his feet barely touching the floor, he was hustled along.

The guard still took no notice. Afterward, Miles guessed the man had been tipped off in advance and bribed. Since guards were abysmally underpaid, bribery in the prison was a way of life.

Near the exit from the showers, where others were beginning to dress, was a narrow open doorway. Still surrounded, Miles was shoved through. He was conscious of black and white bodies. Behind them, the door slammed shut.

The room inside was small and used for storage. Brooms, mops, cleaning materials were in screened and padlocked cupboards. Near the room's center was a trestle table. Miles was slammed face downward on it; his mouth and nose hit the wooden surface hard. He felt teeth loosen. His eyes filled with tears. His nose began to bleed.

While his feet stayed on the floor, his legs were roughly pulled apart. He fought desperately, despairingly, trying to move. The many hands restrained him.

"Hold still, pretty boy." Miles heard grunting and felt a thrust. A second later he screamed in pain, disgust, and horror. Whoever was holding his head seized it by the hair, raised and slammed it down. "Shaddup!"

Now pain, in waves, was everywhere.

"Ain't she lovely?" The voice seemed in the distance, echoing and dreamlike.

The penetration ended. Before his body could know relief, another began. Despite himself, knowing the consequences, he screamed again. Once more his head was banged.

During the next few minutes and the monstrous repetition, Miles's mind began to drift, his awareness waned. As strength left him, his struggles lessened. But the physical agony intensified—a searing of membrane, the fiery abrasion of a thousand sensory nerve ends.

Consciousness must have left him totally, then returned. From outside he heard a guard's whistle being blown. It was a signal to hurry with the dressing and assemble in the yard. He was aware of restraining hands withdrawn. Behind him a door opened. The others in the room were running out.

Bleeding, bruised, and barely conscious, Miles staggered out. The merest movement of his body caused him suffering.

"Hey, you!" the guard bawled from the platform. "Move ass, you goddam pansy!"

Groping, only half aware of what he was doing, Miles took the wire basket with his clothes and began to pull them on. Most of the others in his group of fifty were already outside in the yard. Another fifty men who had been under the showers were ready to transfer to the dressing area.

The guard shouted fiercely for the second time, "Shithead! I said move!"

Stepping into his rough drill prison pants, Miles stumbled and would have fallen, but for an arm which reached out, holding him.

"Take it easy, kid," a deep voice said. "Here, I'll help." The first hand continued to hold him steady while a second aided in putting the pants on.

The guard's whistle blasted shrilly. "Nigger, you hear me! You an' that pansy get the hell outside, or be on report."

"Yassir, yassir, big boss. Right away, now. Let's go, kid."

Miles was aware, hazily, that the man beside him was huge and black. Later, he would learn the other's name was Karl and that he was serving a life sentence for murder. Miles would wonder, too, if Karl had been among the gang which raped him. He suspected that he was, but never asked, and never knew for sure.

What Miles did discover was that the black giant, despite his size and uncouthness, had a gentleness of manner and a sensitive consideration almost feminine.

From the shower house, supported by Karl, Miles walked unsteadily outdoors.

There were some smirks from other prisoners but on the faces of most Miles read contempt. A wizened old-timer spat disgustedly and turned away.

Miles made it through the remainder of the day—back to his cell, later to the mess hall where he couldn't eat the slop he usually forced down from hunger, and finally to his cell again, with help along the way from Karl. His other three cell companions ignored him as if he were a leper. Racked by pain and misery he slept, tossed, woke, lay fitfully awake for hours suffering the fetid air, slept briefly, woke again. With daybreak, and the clangor of cell doors opening, came renewed fear: When would it happen again? He suspected soon.

In the yard during "exercise"—two hours during which most of the prison population stood around aimlessly—Karl sought him out.

"How y' feel, kid?"

Miles shook his head dejectedly. "Awful." He added, "Thanks for what you did." He was aware that the big black had saved him from being on report, as the shower-room guard had threatened. That would have meant punishment—probably time in the hole—and an adverse mark on his record for parole.

"It's okay, kid. One thing, though, you gotta figure. One time, like yesterday, ain't gonna satisfy them guys. They like dogs now, with you a bitch in heat. They'll be after you again."

"What can I do?" The confirmation of Miles's fears made his voice quaver and his body tremble. The other watched him shrewdly.

"What you need, kid, is a protector. Some stud t' look out for you. How'd you like me for yours?"

"Why should you do that?"

"You start bein' my reg'lar boy friend, I take care o' you. Them others know you 'n me's steady, they ain't gonna lay no hand on you. They know they do, there's me to reckon with." Karl curled one hand into a fist; it was the size of a small ham.

Though he already knew the answer, Miles asked, "What would *you* want?"

"Your sweet white ass, baby." The big man closed his eyes and went on dreamily. "Your body just for me. Any time I need it. I'll take care of where."

Miles Eastin wanted to be sick.

"How 'bout it, baby? Waddya say?"

As he had so many times already, Miles thought despairingly: *Whatever was done before, does anyone deserve this?*

Yet he was here. And had learned that prison was a jungle—debased and savage, lacking justice—where a man was stripped of human rights the day he came. He said bitterly, "Do I have a choice?"

"Put it that way, no I guess you ain't." A pause, then impatiently, "Well, we on?"

Miles said miserably, "I suppose so."

Looking pleased, Karl draped an arm proprietorially around the other's shoulders. Miles, shriveling inside, willed himself not to draw away.

"We gotta git you moved some, baby. To my tier. Maybe my pad." Karl's cell was in a lower tier than Miles's, in an opposite wing of the

X-shaped cell house. The big man licked his lips. "Yeah, man." The hand on Miles was already wandering.

Karl asked, "You got bread?"

"No." Miles knew that if he had had money it could have eased his way already. Prisoners with financial resources on the outside, and who used them, suffered less than prisoners with none.

"Ain't got none neither," Karl confided. "Guess I'll hafta figure sumpum."

Miles nodded dully. Already, he realized, he had begun to accept the ignominious "girl friend" role. But he knew, too, the way things worked here, that while the arrangement with Karl lasted he was safe. There would be no further gang rape.

The belief proved correct.

There were no more attacks, or attempted fondlings, or kisses blown. Karl had a reputation for knowing how to use his mighty fists. It was rumored that a year ago he had used a shiv to kill a fellow prisoner who angered him, though officially the murder was unsolved.

Miles also was transferred, not only to Karl's tier, but to his cell. Obviously the transfer was a result of money changing hands. Miles asked Karl how he had managed it.

The big black chuckled. "Them guys in Mafia Row put up the bread. Over there they like you, baby."

"Like *me?*"

In common with other prisoners, Miles was aware of Mafia Row, otherwise known as the Italian Colony. It was a segment of cells housing the big wheels of organized crime whose outside contacts and influence made them respected and feared even, some said, by the prison governor. Inside Drummonburg their privileges were legendary.

Such privileges included key prison jobs, extra freedom of movement, and superior food, the latter either smuggled in by guards or pilfered from the general ration system. The Mafia Row inhabitants, Miles had heard, frequently enjoyed steaks and other delicacies, cooked on forbidden grills in workshop hideaways. They also managed extra comforts in their cells—among them, television and sun lamps. But Miles himself had had no contact with Mafia Row, nor been aware that anyone in it knew of his existence.

"They say you're a stand-up guy," Karl told him.

Part of the mystery was resolved a few days later when a weasel-faced, pot-bellied prisoner named LaRocca sidled alongside Miles in the prison yard. LaRocca, while not part of Mafia Row, was known to be on its fringes and acted as a courier.

He nodded to Karl, acknowledging the big black's proprietorial interest, then told Miles, "Gotta message f' ya from Russian Ominsky."

Miles was startled and uneasy. Igor (the Russian) Ominsky was the loan shark to whom he had owed—and still owed—fifteen thousand dollars. He realized, too, there must also be enormous accrued interest on the debt.

Six months ago it was Ominsky's threats which prompted Miles's six-thousand-dollar cash theft from the bank, following which his earlier thefts had been exposed.

"Ominsky knows ya kept ya trap shut," LaRocca said. "He likes the way ya did, 'n figures ya for a stand-up guy."

It was true that during interrogation prior to his trial, Miles had not divulged the names, either of his bookmaker or the loan shark, both of whom he feared at the time of his arrest. There had seemed nothing to be gained by doing so, perhaps much to lose. In any event he had not been pressed hard on the point either by the bank security chief, Wainwright, or the FBI.

"Because ya buttoned up," LaRocca now informed him, "Ominsky says to tell ya he stopped the clock while you're inside."

What that meant, Miles knew, was the interest on what he owed was no longer accumulating during his time in prison. He had learned enough of loan sharks to know the concession was a large one. The message also explained how Mafia Row, with its outside connections, knew of Miles's existence.

"Tell Mr. Ominsky thanks," Miles said. He had no idea, though, how he would repay the capital sum when he left prison, or even earn enough to live on.

LaRocca acknowledged, "Someone'll be in touch before ya get sprung. Maybe we can work a deal." With a nod which included Karl, he slipped away.

In the weeks which followed, Miles saw more of the weasel-faced La-Rocca who several times sought out his company, along with Karl's, in the prison yard. Something which appeared to fascinate LaRocca and other prisoners was Miles's knowledge about the history of money. In a way, what had once been an interest and hobby achieved for Miles the kind of respect which prison inmates have for those whose background and crimes are cerebral, as opposed to the merely violent. Under the system a mugger is at the bottom of the prison social scale, an embezzler or con artist near the top.

What intrigued LaRocca, in particular, was Miles's description of massive counterfeiting, by governments, of other countries' money.

"Those have always been the biggest counterfeit jobs of all," Miles told an interested audience of half a dozen one day.

He described how the British government sanctioned forgery of great quantities of French assignats in an attempt to undermine the French Revolution. This, despite the fact that the same crime by individuals was punishable by hanging, a penalty which continued in Britain until 1821. The American Revolution began with official forgery of British banknotes. But the greatest counterfeit venture of all, Miles reported, was during World War II when Germany forged £140 million in British money and unknown amounts of U.S. dollars, all of highest quality. The British also printed German money and so, rumor said, did most of the other Allies.

"Wouncha know it!" LaRocca declared. "Them's the kinda bastards put us in here. Betcha they're doing some o' the same right now."

LaRocca was appreciative of the cachet which attached to himself as a result of Miles's knowledge. He also made it clear that he was relaying some of the information to Mafia Row.

"Me and my people'll take care of ya outside," he announced one day, amplifying his earlier promise. Miles already knew that his own release from prison, and LaRocca's, could occur about the same time.

Talking money was a form of mental suspension for Miles, pushing away, however briefly, the horror of the present. He supposed, too, he should feel relief about the stopping of the loan clock. Yet neither talking nor thinking of other things was sufficient to exclude, except momentarily, his general wretchedness and self-disgust. Because of it, he began to consider suicide.

The self-loathing focused on his relationship with Karl. The big man had declared he wanted, "*Your sweet white ass, baby. Your body just for me. Any time I need it.*" Since their agreement, he had made the promise come true with an appetite which seemed insatiable.

At the beginning Miles tried to anesthetize his mind, telling himself that what was happening was preferable to gang rape, which—because of Karl's instinctive gentleness—it was. Yet disgust and consciousness remained.

But what had developed since was worse.

Even in his own mind Miles found it hard to accept, but the fact was: he was beginning to *enjoy* what was occurring between himself and Karl. Furthermore, Miles was regarding his protector with new feelings . . . Affection? *Yes* . . . Love? *No!* He *dared* not, for the moment, go that far.

The realizations shattered him. Yet he followed new suggestions which Karl made, even when these caused Miles's homosexual role to become more positive.

After each occasion questions haunted him. Was he a man any longer? He knew he had been before, but now could not be sure. Had he become perverted totally? Was this a way it happened? Could there ever be a turnabout, a reversion to normalcy later, canceling out the tasting, savoring, here and now? If not, was life worth living? He doubted it.

It was then that despair enveloped him and that suicide seemed logical—a panacea, an ending, a release. Though difficult in the crowded prison, it could be done—by hanging. Five times since Miles's arrival there had been cries of "hang-up!"—usually in the night—when guards would rush like storm troopers, cursing, pulling levers to unlock tiers, "cracking" a cell open, racing to cut down a would-be suicide before he died. On three of the five occasions, cheered on by prisoners' raucous cries and laughter, they were too late. Immediately after, because suicides were an embarrassment to the prison, night guard patrols were increased, but the effort seldom lasted.

Miles knew how it was done. You soaked a length of sheet or blanket so it wouldn't tear—urinating on it would be quieter—then secured it to an overhead beam which could be reached from a top bunk. It would have to be done silently while others in the cell were sleeping . . .

In the end one thing, and one thing only, stopped him. No other factor swayed Miles's decision to hang on.

He wanted, when his time in prison was done, to tell Juanita Núñez he was sorry.

Miles Eastin's penitence at his time of sentencing had been genuine. He had felt remorse at having stolen from First Mercantile American Bank where he had been treated honorably, and had given dishonor in return. In retrospect he wondered how he could have stifled his conscience as he did.

Sometimes, when he thought about it now, it seemed as if a fever had possessed him. The betting, socializing, sporting events, living beyond his means, the insanity of borrowing from a loan shark, and the stealing, appeared in hindsight like crazily mismated parts of a distemper. He had lost touch with reality and, as with a fever in advanced stages, his mind had been distorted until decency and moral values disappeared.

How else, he had asked himself a thousand times, could he have stooped so despicably, have been guilty of such vileness, as to cast blame for his own offense on Juanita Núñez?

At the trial, so great had been his shame, he could not bear to look Juanita's way.

Now, six months later, Miles's concern about the bank was less. He had wronged FMA but in prison would have paid his debt in full. *By God, he had paid!*

But not even Drummonburg in all its awfulness made up for what he owed Juanita. Nothing ever would. It was why he must seek her out and beg forgiveness.

Thus, since he needed life to do it, he endured.

10

"This is First Mercantile American Bank," the FMA money trader snapped crisply into the telephone; he had it cradled expertly between his shoulder and left ear so his hands were free. "I want six million dollars overnight. What's your rate?"

From the California West Coast the voice of a money trader in the giant Bank of America drawled, "Thirteen and five eighths."

"That's high," the FMA man said.

"Tough titty."

The FMA trader hesitated, trying to outguess the other, wondering which way the rate would go. From habit he filtered out the persistent drone of voices around him in First Mercantile American's Money Trading Center—a sensitive, security-guarded nerve core in FMA Headquarters Tower, which few of the bank's customers knew about and only a privileged handful ever saw. But it was in centers like this that much of a big bank's profit was made—or could be lost.

Reserve requirements made it necessary for a bank to hold specific amounts of cash against possible demand, but no bank wanted too much idle money or too little. Bank money traders kept amounts in balance.

"Hold, please," the FMA trader said to San Francisco. He pressed a "hold" button on his phone console, then another button near it.

A new voice announced, "Manufacturers Hanover Trust, New York."

"I need six million overnight. What's your rate?"

"Thirteen and three quarters."

On the East Coast the rate was rising.

"Thanks, no thanks." The FMA trader broke the connection with New York and released the "hold" button where San Francisco was waiting. He said, "I guess I'll take it."

"Six million sold to you at thirteen and five eighths," Bank of America said.

"Right."

The trade had taken twenty seconds. It was one of thousands daily between rival banks in a contest of nerve and wits, with stakes in seven figures. Bank money traders were invariably young men in their thirties —bright and ambitious, quick-minded, unflustered under pressure. Yet, since a record of success in trading could advance a young man's career and mistakes blight it, tension was constant so that three years on a money-trading desk was considered a maximum. After that, the strain began to show.

At this moment, in San Francisco and at First Mercantile American Bank the latest transaction was being recorded, fed to a computer, then transmitted to the Federal Reserve System. At the "Fed," for the next twenty-four hours, reserves of Bank of America would be debited by six million dollars, the reserves of FMA credited with the same amount. FMA would pay Bank of America for the use of its money for that time.

All over the country similar transactions between other banks were taking place.

It was a Wednesday, in mid-April.

Alex Vandervoort, visiting the Money Trading Center, a part of his domain within the bank, nodded a greeting to the trader who was seated on an elevated platform surrounded by assistants, the latter funneling information and completing paper work. The young man, already immersed in another trade, returned the greeting with a wave and cheerful smile.

Elsewhere in the room—the size of an auditorium and with similarities to the control center of a busy airport—were other traders in securities and bonds, flanked by aides, accountants, secretaries. All were engaged in deploying the bank's money—lending, borrowing, investing, selling, reinvesting.

Beyond the traders, a half-dozen financial supervisors worked at larger, plusher desks.

Traders and supervisors alike faced a huge board, running the trading center's length and giving quotations, interest rates and other information. The remote-controlled figures on the board changed constantly.

A bond trader at a desk not far from where Alex was standing rose to his feet and announced loudly, "Ford and United Auto Workers just announced a two-year contract." Several other traders reached for telephones. Important industrial and political news, because of its instant effect on securities prices, was always shared this way by the first in the room to hear of it.

Seconds later, a green light above the information board winked off and was replaced by flashing amber. It was a signal to traders not to commit themselves because new quotations, presumably resulting from the auto industry settlement, were coming in. A flashing red light, used rarely, was a warning of more cataclysmic change.

Yet the money-trading desk, whose operation Alex had been watching, remained a pivot point.

Federal regulations required banks to have seventeen and a half percent of their demand deposits available in liquid cash. Penalties for noncompliance were severe. Yet it was equally poor banking to leave large sums uninvested, even for a day.

Therefore banks maintained a continual tally of all money moving in and out. A central cashier's department kept a finger on the flow like a physician on a pulse. If deposits within a banking system such as First Mercantile American's were heavier than anticipated, the bank—through its money trader—promptly loaned surplus funds to other banks who might be short of their reserve requirements. Conversely, if customer withdrawals were unusually heavy, FMA would borrow.

A bank's position changed from hour to hour, so that a bank which was a lender in the morning could be a borrower at midday and a lender again before the close of business. This way, a large bank might trade better than a billion dollars in a day.

Two other things could be said—and often were—about the system. First, banks were usually faster in pursuing earnings for themselves than for their clients. Second, banks did far, far better in the way of profit for themselves than they achieved for outsiders who entrusted money to them.

Alex Vandervoort's presence in the Money Trading Center had been partly to keep in touch with money flow, which he often did, partly to discuss bank developments in recent weeks which had distressed him.

He was with Tom Straughan, a senior vice-president and fellow member of FMA's money policy committee. Straughan's office was immediately outside. He had walked into the Money Trading Center with Alex. It was young Straughan who, back in January, had opposed a cutback of Forum East funds but now welcomed the proposed loan to Supranational Corporation.

They were discussing Supranational now.

"You're worrying too much, Alex," Tom Straughan insisted. "Besides being a nil-risk situation, SuNatCo will be good for us. I'm convinced of it."

Alex said impatiently, "There's no such thing as nil-risk. Even so, I'm less concerned about Supranational than I am about the taps we'll have to turn off elsewhere."

Both men knew which taps, within First Mercantile American, Alex was referring to. A memorandum of proposals, drafted by Roscoe Heyward and approved by the bank's president, Jerome Patterton, had been circulated to members of the money policy committee a few days earlier. To make possible the fifty-million-dollar Supranational line of credit, it was proposed to cut back drastically on small loans, home mortgages and municipal bond financing.

"If the loan goes through and we make those cutbacks," Tom Straughan argued, "they'll be only temporary. In three months, maybe less, our funding can revert to what it was before."

"You may believe that, Tom. I don't."

Alex was dispirited before he came here. His conversation with young Straughan now depressed him further.

The Heyward-Patterton proposals ran counter, not only to Alex's beliefs, but also his financial instincts. It was wrong, he believed, to channel the bank's funds so substantially into one industrial loan at the expense of public service, even though the industrial financing would be far more profitable. But even from a solely business viewpoint, the extent of the bank's commitment to Supranational—through SuNatCo subsidiaries—made him uneasy.

On the last point, he realized, he was a minority of one. Everyone else in the bank's top management was delighted with the new Supranational connection and Roscoe Heyward had been congratulated effusively for achieving it. Yet Alex's uneasiness persisted, though he was unable to say why. Certainly Supranational seemed to be sound financially; its balance sheets showed the giant conglomerate radiating fiscal health. And in prestige, SuNatCo rated alongside companies like General Motors, IBM, Exxon, Du Pont, and U. S. Steel.

Perhaps, Alex thought, his doubts and depression stemmed from his own declining influence within the bank. And it *was* declining. That had become evident in recent weeks.

In contrast, Roscoe Heyward's star was high in the ascendant. He had the ear and confidence of Patterton, a confidence expanded by the dazzling success of Heyward's two-day sojourn in the Bahamas with G. G. Quartermain. Alex's own reservations about that success were, he knew, regarded as sour grapes.

Alex sensed, too, that he had lost his personal influence with Straughan and others who formerly considered themselves on the Vandervoort bandwagon.

"You have to admit," Straughan was saying, "that the Supranational deal is sweet. You've heard that Roscoe made them agree to a compensating balance of ten percent?"

A compensating balance was an arrangement, arrived at after tough bargaining between banks and borrowers. A bank insisted that a predetermined portion of any loan be kept on deposit in current account, where it earned no interest for the depositor yet was available to the bank for its own use and investment. Thus a borrower failed to have full use of all of his loan, making the real rate of interest substantially higher than the apparent rate. In the case of Supranational, as Tom Straughan had pointed out, five million dollars would remain in new SuNatCo checking accounts—very much to FMA's advantage.

"I presume," Alex said tautly, "you're aware of the other side of that cozy deal."

Tom Straughan appeared uncomfortable. "Well, I've been advised there was an understanding. I'm not sure we should call it 'the other side.'"

"Dammit, that's what it is! We both know that SuNatCo insisted, and Roscoe agreed, our trust department would invest heavily in Supranational common stock."

"If they did, there's nothing down on paper."

"Of course not. No one would be that foolish." Alex eyed the younger man. "You've access to the figures. How much *have* we bought so far?"

Straughan hesitated, then walked to the desk of one of the Trading Center supervisors. He returned with a penciled notation on a slip of paper.

"As of today, ninety-seven thousand shares." Straughan added, "The latest quote was at fifty-two."

Alex said dourly, "There'll be a rubbing of hands at Supranational. Our buying has already pushed up their price five dollars a share." He calculated mentally. "So in the past week we've bulldozed nearly five million dollars of trust clients' money into Supranational. Why?"

"It's an excellent investment." Straughan tried a light touch. "We'll make capital gains for all those widows and orphans and educational foundations whose money we take care of."

"Or erode it—while abusing our trust. What do we know about SuNatCo, Tom—any of us—that we didn't two weeks ago? Why, until this week, has the trust department never bought a single Supranational share?"

The younger man was silent, then said defensively, "I suppose Roscoe feels that now he'll be on the board he can watch the company more closely."

"I'm disappointed in you, Tom. You never used to be dishonest with yourself, especially when you know the real reasons as well as I do." As Straughan flushed, Alex persisted, "Have you any idea what kind of scandal would blow up if SEC stumbled onto this? There's conflict of interest; abuse of lending limitation law; the use of trust funds to influence the bank's own business; and I've not the least doubt there's agreement to vote the Supranational stock with management at the next SuNatCo annual meeting."

Straughan said sharply, "If it's so, it wouldn't be the first time—even here."

"Unfortunately that's true. But it doesn't make this smell any sweeter."

The question of trust department ethics was an old one. Supposedly, banks maintained an internal barrier—sometimes called a Chinese Wall —between their own commercial interests and trust investments. In fact, they didn't.

When a bank had billions of dollars in clients' trust funds to invest, it was inevitable that the "clout" this gave should be employed commercially. Companies in which a bank invested heavily were expected to respond with reciprocal banking business. Often, too, they were pressured into having a bank director on their board. If they did neither, other investments would speedily replace their own in trust portfolios, with their stock nudged downward as the result of a bank sell-off.

As well, brokerage houses which handled the huge volume of trust department buying and selling were expected to maintain large bank balances themselves. They usually did. If not, the coveted brokerage business went elsewhere.

Despite banks' public relations propaganda, the interests of trust department clients, including proverbial widows and orphans, often rated second to a bank's own interests. It was one reason why trust department results were generally so poor.

Thus, Alex knew, the Supranational-FMA situation was not unique. Just the same, the knowledge did not make him like it any more.

"Alex," Tom Straughan volunteered, "I may as well tell you that at the money committee tomorrow I intend to support the Supranational loan."

"I'm sorry to hear that."

But the news was not unexpected. And Alex wondered how much longer it would be before he would stand so alone and isolated that his position in the bank would be untenable. It could happen soon.

After tomorrow's money policy committee meeting, where the proposals concerning Supranational were certain to be approved by a majority, the full board of directors would meet next Wednesday with Supranational on its agenda too. At both meetings, Alex was sure, his would be a lone, dissenting voice.

He surveyed, once more, the ever-busy Money Trading Center, dedicated to wealth and profit, unchanged in principle from the ancient money temples of Babylon and Greece. Not, he thought, that money, commerce, and profit were in themselves unworthy. Alex was dedicated to all three, though not blindly, and with reservations involving moral scruples, the reasonable distribution of wealth, and banking ethics. Yet, when exceptional profit was in prospect, as all history showed, those with such reservations were shouted down or swept aside.

Facing the powerhouse forces of big money and big business—exemplified now by Supranational and a majority in FMA—what could one individual, alone in opposition, hope to do?

Little, Alex Vandervoort concluded dismally. Maybe nothing.

11

The meeting of the Board of Directors of First Mercantile American Bank, in the third week of April, was memorable on several counts.

Two major items of bank policy were the subject of intense discussion —one, the Supranational line of credit, the other a proposed expanding of the bank's savings activity and the opening of many new suburban branches.

Even before proceedings began, the meeting's tone was evident. Heyward, unusually jovial and relaxed, and wearing a smart new light gray suit, was on hand early. He greeted other directors at the boardroom door as they arrived. From the cordial responses it was clear that most members of the board had not only heard of the Supranational agreement through the financial grapevine but were heartily in favor of it.

"Congratulations, Roscoe," Philip Johannsen, president of Mid-Continent Rubber, said, "you've really moved this bank into the big league. More power to you, fella!"

A beaming Heyward acknowledged, "I appreciate your support, Phil. I'd like you to know I've other targets in mind."

"You'll hit them, never fear."

A beetle-browed director from upstate, Floyd LeBerre, board chairman of General Cable and Switchgear Corporation, came in. In the past LeBerre had never been especially cordial to Heyward, but now he shook the other's hand warmly. "Delighted to hear you're going on the Supranational board, Roscoe." The General Cable chairman lowered his voice. "My switchgear sales division is putting in some bids for SuNatCo business. Sometime soon I'd like to talk about them."

"Let's make it next week," Heyward said agreeably. "You can be sure I'll help all I can."

LeBerre moved on, his expression pleased.

Harold Austin, who had heard the exchange, winked knowingly. "Our little trip paid off. You're riding high."

Today, the Honorable Harold looked more than ever the aging playboy: a colorful plaid jacket, brown bell-bottom trousers, his gaily patterned shirt sporting a cerulean blue bow tie. The white flowing hair was newly trimmed and styled.

"Harold," Heyward said, "if there's anything at all I can do in return . . ."

"There will be," the Honorable Harold assured him, then strolled to his seat at the boardroom table.

Even Leonard L. Kingswood, the energetic chairman of Northam Steel and Alex Vandervoort's most fervent supporter on the board, had a good word as he passed by. "Hear you corralled Supranational, Roscoe. That's first-class business."

Other directors were equally complimentary.

Among the last arrivals were Jerome Patterton and Alex Vandervoort. The bank president, his white-fringed, bald head gleaming, and looking as usual like a gentleman farmer, went at once to the head of the long, elliptical boardroom table. Alex, carrying a file folder of papers, took his regular seat midway on the left-hand side.

Patterton gaveled for attention and speedily disposed of several routine matters. Then he announced, "The first main item of business is: *Loans submitted for board approval.*"

Around the table a flurry of turning pages signaled the opening of FMA's traditional blue, confidential loan folders, prepared for directors' use.

"As usual, gentlemen, you have in front of you details of management's proposals. What's of special interest today, as most of you know already, is our new account with Supranational Corporation. Personally, I'm delighted with the terms negotiated and strongly recommend approval. I'll leave it to Roscoe, who's responsible for bringing this new, important business to the bank, to fill in background and answer any questions."

"Thank you, Jerome." Roscoe Heyward eased on his rimless glasses which he had been polishing out of habit and leaned forward in his chair. When he spoke his manner seemed less austere than usual, his voice pleasant and assured.

"Gentlemen, in embarking on any large loan commitment, it is prudent to seek assurance of the borrower's financial soundness, even when that borrower has a triple-A credit rating, as Supranational does.

In appendix 'B' of your blue folders"—around the table there was again a riffling of pages—"you will find a summary I have personally prepared of assets and projected profits of the SuNatCo group, including all subsidiaries. This is based on audited financial statements plus additional data supplied at my request by Supranational's comptroller, Mr. Stanley Inchbeck. As you can see, the figures are excellent. Our risk is minimal."

"I don't know Inchbeck's reputation," a director interjected; he was Wallace Sperrie, owner of a scientific instrument company. "But I know yours, Roscoe, and if you approve these figures then they're quadruple-A for me."

Several others chimed in their assent.

Alex Vandervoort doodled with a pencil on a pad in front of him.

"Thank you, Wally, and gentlemen." Heyward permitted himself a slight smile. "I'm hopeful your confidence will extend to the concomitant action I have recommended."

Although the recommendations were listed in the blue folder, he described them anyway—the fifty-million-dollar line of credit to be granted in full to Supranational and subsidiaries immediately, with financial cutbacks in other areas of the bank to become effective at the same time. The cutbacks, Heyward assured the listening directors, would be restored "as soon as possible and wise," though he preferred not to specify when. He concluded, "I recommend this package to the board and I promise that, in light of it, our own profit figures will look very good indeed."

As Heyward leaned back in his chair, Jerome Patterton announced, "The meeting is open for questions and discussion."

"Frankly," Walter Sperrie said, "I see no need for either. Everything's clear. I think we're witnesses to a masterstroke of business for the bank and I propose approval."

Several voices together called out, "Second!"

"Proposed and seconded," Jerome Patterton intoned. "Are we ready to vote?" He obviously hoped so. His gavel was poised.

"No," Alex Vandervoort said quietly. He pushed his pencil and doodling away. "Nor do I think anyone else should vote without a great deal more discussion."

Patterton sighed. He set the gavel down. Alex had already warned him, as a courtesy, of his intentions, but Patterton had hoped that Alex, sensing the near-unanimous mood of the board, would change his mind.

"I genuinely regret," Alex Vandervoort was saying now, "to find myself before the board in conflict with my fellow officers, Jerome and Roscoe. But I cannot, as a matter of duty and conscience, conceal my anxiety about this loan and my opposition to it."

"What's the trouble? Doesn't your girl friend like Supranational?" The barbed question came from Forrest Richardson, a longtime FMA director; he was brusque-mannered, had a reputation as a martinet, and was a crown prince of meat-packing.

Alex flushed with anger. No doubt directors remembered the public linking of his name with Margot's "bank-in" campaign three months earlier; just the same, he was not prepared to have his personal life dissected here. But he withheld a strong retort and answered, "Miss Bracken and I rarely discuss banking nowadays. I assure you we haven't this."

Another director asked, "Just what is it you don't like about the deal, Alex?"

"Everything."

Around the table there was a restless stirring and exclamations of annoyed surprise. Faces which had turned toward Alex betrayed a lack of friendliness.

Jerome Patterton advised curtly, "You'd better lay the whole thing out."

"Yes, I will." Alex reached into the file folder he had brought and extracted a single page of notes.

"To begin with, I object to the *extent* of the commitment to a single account. And not only is it an ill-advised concentration of risk, in my opinion it is fraudulent under Section 23A of the Federal Reserve Act."

Roscoe Heyward leaped to his feet. "I object to that word 'fraudulent.'"

"Objecting doesn't change the truth," Alex said calmly.

"It is not the truth! We have made plain that the full commitment is not to Supranational Corporation itself, but to its subsidiaries. They are Hepplewhite Distillers, Horizon Land, Atlas Jet Leasing, Caribbean Finance, and International Bakeries." Heyward snatched up a blue folder. "The allocations are spelled out specifically in here."

"All those companies are controlled subsidiaries of Supranational."

"But also long-established, viable companies in their own right."

"Then why, today and all other times, have we been speaking solely of Supranational?"

"For simplicity and convenience." Heyward glowered.

"You know as well as I do," Alex insisted, "that once the bank's money is in *any* of those subsidiaries, G. G. Quartermain can, and will, move it around any way he chooses."

"Now *hold everything!*" The interruption came from Harold Austin who had leaned forward, slapping a hand on the table for attention. "Big George Quartermain is a good friend of mine. I won't sit quietly hearing an accusation of bad faith."

"There was no accusation of bad faith," Alex responded. "What I'm talking about is a fact of conglomerate life. Large sums of money are transferred frequently between Supranational subsidiaries; their balance sheets show it. And what that confirms is—we'll be lending to a single entity."

"Well," Austin said; he turned from Alex, addressing other members of the board, "I'll simply repeat that I know Quartermain well, and Supranational too. As most of you here are aware, I was responsible for the Bahamas meeting between Roscoe and Big George where this line of credit was arranged. In view of everything, I say it's an exceptionally good deal for the bank."

There was a momentary silence which Philip Johannsen broke.

"Could it be, Alex," the MidContinent Rubber president inquired, "that you're just a little sore because Roscoe, and not you, was invited to that Bahamas golf game?"

"No. The point I'm making has nothing to do with personalities."

Someone else said skeptically, "It sure doesn't look that way."

"Gentlemen, gentlemen!" Jerome Patterton rapped sharply with his gavel.

Alex had expected something of this kind. Keeping his cool, he persisted, "I repeat, the loan is too big a commitment to one borrower. Furthermore, pretending it isn't to a single borrower is an artful attempt to circumvent the law, and all of us in this room know it." He threw a challenging glance around the table.

"I don't know it," Roscoe Heyward said, "and I say your interpretation is biased and in error."

By now it was obvious this had become an extraordinary occasion. Board meetings normally were either rubber-stamp affairs or, in event of mild disagreement, directors exchanged polite, gentlemanly comments. Angry, acerbic argument was virtually unknown.

For the first time Leonard L. Kingswood spoke. His voice was conciliatory. "Alex, I'll admit there's some substance to what you say, but the fact is, what's being suggested here is done all the time between big banks and large corporations."

Intervention by the Northam Steel chairman was significant. At last

December's board meeting Kingswood had been a leader in urging Alex's appointment as chief executive officer of FMA. Now he went on, "Frankly, if there's anything to be guilty of with that kind of financing, my own company has been guilty of it too."

Regretfully, knowing it was costing him a friend, Alex shook his head. "I'm sorry, Len. I still don't believe that it's right, any more than I think we should leave ourselves open to a conflict-of-interest charge by Roscoe going on the Supranational board."

Leonard Kingswood's mouth tightened. He said nothing more.

But Philip Johannsen did. He told Alex sourly, "If, after that last remark, you expect us to believe there is nothing personal here, you're crazy."

Roscoe Heyward tried, but failed, to conceal a smile.

Alex's face was set grimly. He wondered if this was the last FMA board meeting he would attend, though whether it was or wasn't he would complete what he had begun. Ignoring Johannsen's remark, he declared, "As bankers we just don't learn. From all sides—Congress, consumers, our own customers, the press—we're accused of perpetuating conflict of interest through interlocking directorates. If we're honest with ourselves, most accusations are on target. Everyone here knows how the big oil companies liaise with each other by working closely on bank boards, and that's only one example. Yet we continue and continue with this same kind of inbreeding: *You be on my board, I'll be on yours.* When Roscoe is a director of Supranational, whose interests will be put first? Supranational's? Or First Mercantile American's? And on our board here will he favor SuNatCo over other companies because of his directorship over there? The shareholders of both companies are entitled to answers to those questions; so are legislators and the public. What's more, if we don't provide some convincing answers soon, if we don't cease being as high-handed as we are, all of banking will be faced with tough, restrictive laws. And we'll deserve them."

"If you followed through logically on all that," Forrest Richardson objected, "half the members of this board could be accused of conflict of interest."

"Precisely. And the time is close when the bank will have to face that situation and amend it."

Richardson growled, "There may be other opinions on that score." His own meat-packing company, as they all knew, was a large borrower from FMA and Forrest Richardson had participated in board meetings where loans to his company were approved.

Disregarding the growing hostility, Alex plowed on. "Other aspects of the Supranational loan disturb me equally. To make the money available we're to cut back mortgage lending and small loans. In these two areas alone the bank will be defective in its public service."

Jerome Patterton said huffily, "It's been clearly stated that those cutbacks are temporary."

"Yes," Alex acknowledged. "Except no one will say just how temporary, or what happens to the business and goodwill the bank will lose while the ban is on. And then there's the third area of cutback which we haven't touched on yet—municipal bonds." Opening his file folder, he consulted a second sheet of notes. "In the next six weeks, eleven issues of county and school district bonds within the state will be up for bid. If our bank fails to participate, at least half those bonds are certain to remain unsold." Alex's voice sharpened. "Is it the board's intention to dispense, *so quickly after Ben Rosselli's death*, with a tradition spanning three Rosselli generations?"

For the first time since the meeting began directors exchanged uneasy glances. A policy established long ago by the bank's founder, Giovanni Rosselli, had First Mercantile American Bank taking the lead in underwriting and selling bond issues of small municipalities in the state. Without such aid from the state's largest bank, such bond issues—never large, important, or well known—might go unmarketed, leaving financial needs of their communities unmet. The tradition had been faithfully adhered to by Giovanni's son, Lorenzo, and grandson Ben. The business was not especially profitable, though neither did it represent a loss. But it was a significant public service and also returned to small communities some of the money their own citizenry deposited in FMA.

"Jerome," Leonard Kingswood suggested, "maybe you should take another look at that situation."

There were murmurs of assent.

Roscoe Heyward made a swift assessment. "Jerome . . . if I may."

The bank president nodded.

"In view of what seems a sentiment of the board," Heyward offered smoothly, "I'm certain we can make a fresh appraisal and perhaps restore a portion of municipal bond funding without impeding any of the Supranational arrangements. May I suggest that the board, having made its feelings clear, leaves details to the discretion of Jerome and myself." Notably, he did not include Alex.

Nods and voices signified agreement.

Alex objected, "That's not a full commitment, nor does it do any thing to restore home mortgages and small loans."

The other board members were pointedly silent.

"I believe we've heard all viewpoints," Jerome Patterton suggested "Perhaps we can now vote on the proposal as a whole."

"No," Alex said, "there's still one other matter."

Patterton and Heyward exchanged glances of half-amused resig nation.

"I've already pointed to a conflict of interest," Alex stated somberly. "Now I warn the board of an even larger one. Since negotiation of the Supranational loan, and up to yesterday afternoon, our own trust de partment has bought"—he consulted his notes—"one hundred and twenty-three thousand Supranational shares. In that time, and almost certainly because of the substantial buying with our trust clients' money, the SuNatCo share price has risen seven and a half points which I'm sure was intended and agreed to as a condition . . ."

He was drowned out by protesting voices—Roscoe Heyward's, Jerome Patterton's, and those of other directors.

Heyward was on his feet again, eyes blazing. "That's a deliberate distortion!"

Alex slammed back, "The purchasing is no distortion."

"But your interpretation *is*. SuNatCo is an excellent investment for our trust accounts."

"What makes it *suddenly* so good?"

Patterton protested heatedly, "Alex, specific transactions of the trust department are not a matter for discussion here."

Philip Johannsen snapped, "I agree with that."

Harold Austin and several others called out loudly, "So do I!"

"Whether they are or aren't," Alex persisted, "I warn you all that what is happening may be in contravention of the Glass-Steagall Act of 1933, and that directors can be held responsible . . ."

A half dozen more voices erupted angrily at once. Alex knew he had touched a sensitive nerve. While board members were undoubtedly aware that the kind of duplicity he had described went on, they pre ferred not to know of it specifically. Knowledge implied involvement and responsibility. They wanted neither.

Well, Alex thought, like it or not, they knew now. Above the other voices he continued firmly, "I advise the board that if it ratifies the Supranational loan with all its ramifications, we'll regret it." He leaned back in his chair. "That's all."

As Jerome Patterton pounded with his gavel, the hubbub quietened.

Patterton, paler than before, announced, "If there is no further discussion we will record a vote."

Moments later the Supranational proposals were approved, with Alex Vandervoort the sole dissenter.

12

A coolness toward Vandervoort was evident when the directors resumed their meeting after lunch. Normally a two-hour morning session disposed of all board business. Today, however, extra time had been allotted.

Aware of the board's antagonism, Alex had suggested to Jerome Patterton during lunch that his presentation be deferred until next month's meeting. But Patterton told him curtly, "Nothing doing. If the directors are in a surly mood, you made them that way and you can damn well take your chances."

It was an extraordinarily strong statement for the mild-mannered Patterton, but illustrated the tide of disfavor now running against Alex. It also convinced him that the next hour or so would be an exercise in futility. His proposals seemed certain to be rejected out of perversity, if for no other reason.

As directors settled down, Philip Johannsen set the mood by pointedly consulting his watch. "I've already had to cancel one appointment this afternoon," the MidContinent Rubber chief grumbled, "and I've other things to do, so let's keep it short." Several others nodded agreement.

"I'll be as brief as possible, gentlemen," Alex promised when Jerome Patterton had introduced him formally. "My intention is to make four points." He ticked them off on his fingers as he spoke.

"One, our bank is losing important, profitable business by failing to make the most of opportunities for savings growth. Two, an expansion of savings deposits will improve the bank's stability. Third, the longer we delay, the harder it will be to catch up with our many competitors.

Fourth, there is scope for leadership—which we and other banks should exercise—in a return to habits of personal, corporate, and national thrift, neglected far too long."

He described methods by which First Mercantile American could gain an edge over competitors—a higher savings interest rate, to the top legal limit; more attractive terms for one-to-five-year certificates of deposit; checking facilities for savings depositors as far as banking law allowed; gifts for those opening new accounts; a massive advertising campaign embodying the savings program and the nine new branches.

For his presentation Alex had left his usual seat to stand at the head of the boardroom table. Patterton had moved his own chair to one side. Alex had brought in, also, the bank's chief economist, Tom Straughan, who had prepared charts displayed on easels for the board to view.

Roscoe Heyward had eased forward in his seat and was listening, his face expressionless.

As Alex paused, Floyd LeBerre interjected, "I have one observation right away."

Patterton, his habit of politeness back in place, inquired, "Do you want to take questions as we go, Alex, or leave them to the end?"

"I'll take Floyd's now."

"This isn't a question," the General Cable chairman said unsmilingly. "It's a matter of record. I'm against a major savings expansion because if we do it we'll be ripping our own gut. Right now we've big deposits from correspondent banks . . ."

"Eighteen million dollars from the savings and loan institutions," Alex said. He had expected LeBerre's objection, and it was valid. Few banks existed alone; most had financial ties with others and First Mercantile American was no exception. Several local savings and loan institutions maintained large deposits with FMA and fear that these sums would be withdrawn had deterred other proposed savings activity in the past. · ·

Alex stated, "I've taken that into account."

LeBerre was unsatisfied. "Have you taken into account that if we compete intensively with our own customers we'll lose every bit of that business?"

"Some of it. I don't believe all. In any case, new business we'll generate should far exceed what's lost."

"So you say."

Alex insisted, "I see it as an acceptable risk."

Leonard Kingswood said quietly, "You were against any risk with Supranational, Alex."

"I'm not against risks. This is a far smaller risk. The two have no relation."

Faces around the table mirrored skepticism.

LeBerre said, "I'd like to hear Roscoe's view."

Two others echoed, "Yes, let's hear Roscoe."

Heads turned to Heyward who had been studying his folded hands. He said blandly, "One doesn't like to torpedo a colleague."

"Why not?" someone asked. "It's what he tried to do to you."

Heyward smiled faintly. "I prefer to rise above that." His face went serious. "I do, however, agree with Floyd. Intensive savings activity on our part would lose us important correspondent business. I do not believe any theoretical potential gain is worth it." He pointed to one of Straughan's charts indicating the geography of proposed new branches. "Board members will observe that five of the suggested branches would be in locations close to savings and loan associations who are large depositors with FMA. We can be sure that that will not escape their attention either."

"Those locations," Alex said, "have been carefully chosen as a result of population studies. They're where the *people* are. Sure the S&Ls got there first; in many ways they've been more farsighted than banks like ours. But it doesn't mean we should stay away forever."

Heyward shrugged. "I've already given my opinion. I'll say one thing, though—I dislike the entire idea of storefront branches."

Alex snapped, "They'll be money shops—the branch banks of the future." Everything, he realized, was coming out contrary to the way he had intended. The subject of the branches themselves he had planned to get to later. Well, he supposed it made no difference now.

"From their description," Floyd LeBerre said—he was reading an information sheet Tom Straughan had circulated—"those branches sound like laundromats."

Heyward, also reading, shook his head. "Not in keeping with our style. No dignity."

"We'd do better to shed some dignity and add more business," Alex declared. "Yes, storefront banks resemble laundromats; just the same, they're the kind of branch banks which are coming in. I'll make a prediction to the board: Neither we nor our competitors can go on affording the gilded sepulchers we have as branch banks now. The cost of land and construction make it senseless. In ten years, half—at least—of our present branch banks will have ceased to exist as we know them. We'll retain a few key ones. The rest will be in less expensive premises, totally automated, with machine tellers, TV monitors to answer queries,

nd all linked to a computer center. In planning new branches—including the nine I'm advocating here—it's that transition we should be
anticipating."

"Alex is right about automation," Leonard Kingswood said. "Most of
us see it in our own businesses, moving in faster than we ever expected."

"What's equally important," Alex asserted, "is that we've a chance
to jump ahead profitably—that is, if we do it dramatically, with flair
and fanfare. The advertising and promotion campaign would be massive, saturation coverage. Gentlemen, look at the figures. First, our
present savings deposits—substantially lower than they should be . . ."

He moved on, aided by the charts and an occasional amplification
by Tom Straughan. Alex knew that the figures and proposals, which
he and Straughan had toiled over, were solid and logical. Yet he sensed
flat opposition from some board members, a lack of interest by others.
Lower down the table a director put a hand over his mouth, stifling
a yawn.

Obviously he had lost. The savings and branch expansion plan
would be rejected—and would be, in effect, a vote of "no confidence"
in him as well. As he had earlier, Alex wondered how long his own
tenure with FMA could continue. There seemed little future for him,
nor could he see himself as a participant in a Heyward-dominated
regime.

He decided not to waste more time. "Okay, I'll leave it there, gentlemen. Unless there are further questions."

He had not expected any. Least of all did he anticipate support from
the source from which suddenly, amazingly, it came.

"Alex," Harold Austin said with a smile and friendly tone, "I'd like
to say thank you. Frankly, I'm impressed. I hadn't expected to be, but
your presentation was convincing. What's more, I like the idea of those
new branch banks."

A few seats away Heyward looked startled, then glared at Austin.
The Honorable Harold ignored him and appealed to others at the table. "I think we should look at this with an open mind, putting aside
our disagreements of this morning."

Leonard Kingswood nodded, as did several others. Still more directors shed post-lunch drowsiness, their attention returning. Not for nothing was Austin the FMA board member with longest service. His
influence was pervasive. He also was adept at swinging others to his
points of view.

"Near the beginning of your remarks, Alex," he said, "you spoke of a return to personal thrift, and leadership which banks like ours might give."

"Yes, I did."

"Could you expand that thought?"

Alex hesitated. "I suppose so."

Should he? Alex weighed choices. He was no longer surprised at the interjection. He knew exactly why Austin had switched sides.

Advertising. Earlier, when Alex had suggested a "massive advertising campaign" with "saturation coverage," he had seen Austin's head come up, his interest clearly quicken. From that point it was not hard to see inside that head. The Austin Advertising Agency, by reason of the Honorable Harold's directorship and influence at FMA, had a monopoly of the bank's advertising business. A campaign such as Alex envisaged would bring substantial profit to the Austin Agency.

Austin's action was conflict of interest in its grossest form—the same conflict of interest which Alex had attacked this morning over Roscoe Heyward's appointment to the board of Supranational. Alex had asked then: *Whose interests would Roscoe put first? Supranational's or those of First Mercantile American shareholders?* Now, a parallel question should be asked of Austin.

The answer was obvious. Austin was looking out for his own interests; FMA came second. Never mind that Alex believed in the plan. The support—for selfish reasons—was unethical, an abuse of trust.

Should Alex say so? If he did, it would touch off an uproar even greater than this morning's, and he would lose again. Directors clung together like lodge brothers. Furthermore, such a confrontation would end, for sure, Alex's own effectiveness at FMA. So was it worth it? Was it necessary? Did his duties require him to be keeper of the board's conscience? Alex wasn't sure. Meanwhile the directors were watching him and waiting.

"Yes," he said, "I did refer—as Harold has reminded me—to thrift and a need for leadership." Alex glanced at notes which, a few minutes ago, he had decided to discard.

"It is often said," he told the listening directors, "that government, industry, and commerce of all kinds are founded upon credit. Without credit, without borrowing, without loans—small, medium, and massive —business would disintegrate and civilization wither. Bankers know this best.

"Yet, increasingly, there are those who believe that borrowing and deficit financing have gone mad, and have eclipsed all reason. Especially is this true of governments. The United States Government has amassed an appalling mountain range of debt, far beyond our ability ever to repay. Other governments are in as bad, or worse, condition. This is the real reason for inflation and the undermining of currencies at home and internationally.

"To a remarkable extent," Alex continued, "overwhelming government debt is matched by gargantuan corporate debt. And, at a lower financial level, millions of people—individuals following examples nationally set—have assumed debt burdens which they cannot pay. Total U.S. indebtedness is two and a half *trillion* dollars. National consumer debt is now approaching two hundred billion dollars. In the past six years more than a million Americans have gone bankrupt.

"Somewhere along the way—nationally, corporately, individually—we have lost the ancient verity of thrift and husbandry, of balancing what we spend against what we earn, and of keeping what we owe within honest limitations."

Suddenly the mood of the board had become sober. Responding to it, Alex said quietly, "I wish I could say there is a trend away from what I have described. I am not convinced there is. But trends begin with resolute action somewhere. Why not here?

"In the nature of our times, savings deposits—more than any other type of monetary activity—represent financial prudence. Nationally and individually we need more prudence. A way to achieve it is through enormous increases in savings.

"There *can* be tremendous increases—if we commit ourselves, and if we work. And while personal savings alone will not restore fiscal sanity everywhere, it is at least one major move toward that end.

"This is why there is an opportunity for leadership and also why—here and now—I believe this bank should exercise it."

Alex sat down. Seconds later he realized he had said nothing about his doubts concerning Austin's intervention.

Leonard Kingswood broke the brief, ensuing silence. "Sense and truth don't always make palatable listening. But I think we all just heard some."

Philip Johannsen grunted, then said grudgingly, "I'll buy part of that."

"I buy it all," the Honorable Harold said. "In my opinion the board should approve the savings and branch expansion plan as presented. I intend to vote for it. I urge the rest of you to do the same."

This time Roscoe Heyward did not display his outrage, though his face was tightly set. Alex figured that Heyward, too, had guessed Harold Austin's motivation.

For another fifteen minutes discussion swirled until Jerome Patter ton rapped with his gavel and called for a vote. By an overwhelmin majority Alex Vandervoort's proposals were approved. Floyd LeBerr and Roscoe Heyward were the only dissenters.

On his way out of the boardroom Alex was aware that the earlie hostility had not vanished. Some directors made it plain that they stil resented his strong stance of this morning on Supranational. But th latest, unexpected outcome had made him more buoyant, less pess mistic about his continuing role at FMA.

Harold Austin intercepted him. "Alex, when will you move on th savings plan?"

"Immediately." Not wishing to seem ungracious, he added, "Than you for your support."

Austin nodded. "What I'd like to do now is come in with two or thre of my agency people to discuss the campaign."

"Very well. Next week."

So Austin had confirmed—without delay or embarrassment—wha Alex had deduced. Though to be fair, Alex thought, the Austin Adver tising Agency did good work and could be selected to handle the sav ings campaign on merit.

But he was rationalizing and knew it. By keeping silent a few mi utes ago he had sacrificed principle to achieve an end. He wondere what Margot would think of his defection.

The Honorable Harold said affably, "Then I'll be seeing you."

Roscoe Heyward, leaving the boardroom just ahead of Alex, was ac costed by a uniformed bank messenger who handed him a sealed er velope. Heyward ripped it open and took out a folded message sli Reading it, he brightened visibly, glanced at his watch, and smilec Alex wondered why.

13

The note was a simple one. Typed by Roscoe's trusted senior secretary, Dora Callaghan, it informed him that Miss Deveraux had telephoned, leaving word she was in town and would like him to call as soon as possible. The note supplied a phone number and extension.

Heyward recognized the number: the Columbia Hilton Hotel. Miss Deveraux was Avril.

They had met twice since the trip to the Bahamas a month and a half ago. Both times it had been at the Columbia Hilton. And on each occasion, as well as during that night in Nassau when he had pressed button number seven to bring Avril to his room, she had taken him to a kind of paradise, a place of sexual ecstasy such as he had never dreamed existed. Avril knew incredible things to do to a man which—during that original night—had at first shocked and then delighted him. Later, her skill aroused wave after wave of sensual pleasure until he had cried out in sheer joy, using words which he did not know he knew. Afterward Avril had been gentle, caressing, loving, and patient, until, to his surprise and exultation, he was aroused once more.

It was then he began to realize, with an awareness which had heightened since, how much of life's passion and glory—the mutual exploring, uplifting, sharing, giving, and receiving—he and Beatrice had never known.

For Roscoe and Beatrice his discovery had come too late, though perhaps for Beatrice it was a discovery she never would have wanted. But there was time still for Roscoe and Avril; on the occasions since Nassau they had proved it. He glanced at his watch, smiling—the smile which Vandervoort had seen.

He'd go to Avril as soon as possible, of course. It would mean rearranging his schedule for this afternoon and evening, but no matter. Even now, the thought of seeing her once more excited him, so that his body was stirring and reacting like a youth's.

On a few occasions since the affair with Avril began, conscience had troubled him. During recent Sundays in church, the text he had read aloud before going to the Bahamas came back to haunt him: *Righteousness exalteth a nation: but sin is a reproach to any people.* At such moments he consoled himself with the words of Christ in the Gospel of St. John: *He that is without sin among you, let him first cast a stone . . .* And: *Ye judge after the flesh; I judge no man.* Heyward even permitted himself to reflect—with a levity which not long ago would have appalled him—that the Bible, like statistics, could be used to prove anything.

In any case, debate was immaterial. The intoxication with Avril was stronger than any stab of conscience.

Walking from the boardroom to his office suite on the same floor, he reflected, glowing: A session with Avril would consummate a triumphal day, with his Supranational proposals approved and his professional prestige at a zenith with the board. He had, of course, been disappointed at this afternoon's outcome and downright angry at what he saw as Harold Austin's betrayal, though he had deduced at once the selfish reasoning behind it. However, Heyward had little fear that Vandervoort's ideas would produce much real success. The plus-effect on bank profits this year of his own Supranational arrangements would be far, far greater.

Which reminded him—he must make a decision about the additional half million dollars requested by Big George Quartermain as a further loan to Q-Investments.

Roscoe Heyward frowned slightly. He supposed in the whole matter of Q-Investments there was some mild irregularity, though in view of the bank's commitment to Supranational, and vice versa, it didn't seem too serious.

He had raised the matter in a confidential memo to Jerome Patterton a month or so ago.

> G. G. Quartermain of Supranational phoned me twice yesterday from New York about a personal project of his called Q-Investments. This is a small private group of which Quartermain (Big George) is the principal, and our own director, Harold Austin, is a member. The group

has already bought large blocks of common stock of various Supranational enterprises at advantageous terms. More purchases are planned.

What Big George wants from us is a loan to Q-Investments of $1½ million—at the same low rate as the Supranational loan, though without any requirement of a compensating balance. He points out that the SuNatCo compensating balance will be ample to offset this personal loan—which is true, though of course there is no cross guarantee.

I might mention that Harold Austin also telephoned me to urge that the loan be made.

The Honorable Harold, in fact, had bluntly reminded Heyward of a *quid pro quo*—a debt for Austin's strong support at the time of Ben Rosselli's death. It was a support which Heyward would continue to need when Patterton—the interim Pope—retired in eight months' time.

The memo to Patterton continued:

Frankly, the interest rate on this proposed loan is too low, and waiving a compensating balance would be a large concession. But in view of the Supranational business which Big George has given us, I think we would be wise to go along.

I recommend the loan. Do you agree?

Jerome Patterton had sent the memo back with a laconic penciled *Yes* against the final question. Knowing Patterton, Heyward doubted if he had given the whole thing more than a cursory glance.

Heyward had seen no reason why Alex Vandervoort need be involved, nor was the loan large enough to require approval by the money policy committee. Therefore, a few days later, Roscoe Heyward had initialed approval himself, which he had authority to do.

What he did *not* have authority for—and had reported to no one—was a personal transaction between himself and G. G. Quartermain.

During their second telephone conversation about Q-Investments, Big George—calling from a SuNatCo offshoot in Chicago—had said, "Been talking to Harold Austin about you, Roscoe. We both think it's time you got involved in our investment group. Like to have you with us. So what I've done is allot two thousand shares which we'll regard

as fully paid for. They're nominee certificates endorsed in blank—more
discreet that way. I'll have 'em put in the mail."

Heyward had demurred. "Thank you, George, but I don't believe I
should accept."

"For Chrissakes, why not?"

"It would be unethical."

Big George had guffawed. "This is the real world, Roscoe. Same
kind of thing happens between clients and bankers all the time. You
know it. I know it."

Yes, Heyward knew, it did happen, though not "all the time," as
Big George claimed, and Heyward had never let it happen to himself.

Before he could answer, Quartermain persisted, "Listen, fella, don't
be a damn fool. If it makes you feel better we'll say the shares are in
return for your investment advice."

But Heyward knew he had given no investment advice, either then
or subsequently.

A day or two later, the Q-Investments share certificates arrived by
registered airmail, in an envelope with elaborate seals, and marked
STRICTLY PERSONAL AND CONFIDENTIAL. Even Dora Callaghan hadn't
opened that one.

At home that evening, studying the Q-Investments financial statement which Big George had also supplied, Heyward realized his two
thousand shares had a net asset value of twenty thousand dollars. Later
if Q-Investments prospered or went public, their worth would be much
greater.

At that point he had every intention of returning the shares to G. G.
Quartermain; then, reassessing his own precarious finances—no better
than they had been several months ago—he hesitated. Finally he
yielded to temptation and later that week put the certificates in his safe
deposit box at FMA's main downtown branch. It was not, Heyward
rationalized, as if he had deprived the bank of money. He hadn't. In
fact, because of Supranational, the reverse was true. So if Big George
chose to make a friendly gift, why be churlish and refuse it?

But his acceptance still worried him a little, especially since Big
George had telephoned at the end of last week—this time from Amster-
dam—seeking an additional half million dollars for Q-Investments.

"There's a unique chance for our Q group to pick up a block of stock
over here in Guilderland that's certain to be high flying. Can't say too
much on an open line, Roscoe, so trust me."

"I do, of course, George," Heyward had said, "but the bank will need
details."

"You'll get 'em—by courier tomorrow." To which Big George had added pointedly, "Don't forget you're one of us now."

Briefly, Heyward had a second uneasy feeling: G. G. Quartermain might be paying more attention to his private investments than to management of Supranational. But the next day's news had reassured him. *The Wall Street Journal* and other papers carried prominent stories about a major, Quartermain-engineered industrial takeover by SuNatCo in Europe. It was a commercial coup d'etat which sent Supranational shares soaring on the New York and London markets and made FMA's loan to the corporate giant seem even sounder.

As Heyward entered his outer office, Mrs. Callaghan offered him her usual matronly smile. "The other messages are on your desk, sir."

He nodded, but inside pushed the pile aside. He hesitated over papers which had been prepared, but were not yet approved, concerning the additional Q-Investments loan. Then he dismissed that too, and, using a phone which was a direct outside line, dialed the number of paradise.

"Rossie, sweetie," Avril whispered as the tip of her tongue explored his ear, "you're hurrying too much. *Wait! Lie still! Still! Hold back!*" She stroked his naked shoulder, then his spine, her fingernails hovering, sharp but gossamer light.

Heyward moaned—a mixture of savored, sweetest pleasure, pain, and postponed fulfillment—as he obeyed.

She whispered again, "It'll be worth waiting, I promise."

He knew it would be. It always was. He wondered again how someone so young and beautiful could have learned so much, be so emancipated . . . uninhibited . . . gloriously wise.

"*Not yet*, Rossie! Darling, *not yet! There! That's good.* Be patient!"

Her hands, skilled and knowing, went on exploring. He let his mind and body float, knowing from experience it was best to do everything . . . exactly as . . . she said.

"Oh, *that's good*, Rossie. Isn't it lovely?"

He breathed, "Yes. *Yes!*"

"Soon, Rossie. *Very soon.*"

Beside him, over the bed's two pillows, close together, Avril's red hair tumbled. Her kisses had devoured him. The ambrosial, heady fragrance of her filled his nostrils. Her marvelous, willowy, willing body was beneath him. This, his senses shouted, was the *best* of life, of earth and heaven, here and now.

The only bittersweet sadness was that he had waited so many years to find it.

Again Avril's lips searched for his and found them.

She urged him, "*Now*, Rossie! *Now*, sweetie! *Now!*"

The bedroom, as Heyward had observed when he arrived, was stand ard Hilton—clean, efficiently comfortable, and a characterless box. A compact sitting room of the same genre was outside; on this occasion as on the others, Avril had taken a suite.

They had been here since late afternoon. After the lovemaking they had dozed, awakened, made love again—though not with entire success —then slept for an hour more. Now both were dressing. Heyward's watch showed eight o'clock.

He was exhausted, physically drained. More than anything else he wanted to go home and go to bed—alone. He wondered how soon he could decently slip away.

Avril had been outside in the sitting room, telephoning. When she returned, she said: "I ordered dinner for us, sweetie. It'll be up soon."

"That's wonderful, my dear."

Avril had put on a filmy slip and pantyhose. No bra. She began brush ing her long hair which had become disordered. He sat on the bed watch ing her, despite his tiredness aware that every movement she made was lithe and sensuous. Compared with Beatrice, whom he was used to see ing daily, Avril was so *young*. Suddenly he felt depressingly old.

They went into the sitting room where Avril said, "Let's open the champagne."

It was on a sideboard in an ice bucket. Heyward had noticed it earlier. By this time most of the ice had melted but the bottle was still cold. He fumbled inexpertly with wire and cork.

"Don't try to move the cork," Avril told him. "Tilt the bottle to forty five degrees, then hold the cork and twist the bottle."

It worked easily. She knew *so much*.

Taking the bottle from him, Avril poured into two glasses. He shook his head. "You know I don't drink, my dear."

"It'll make you feel younger." She held out a glass. As he surrendered and took it, he wondered if she had read his mind.

Two refills later, when their room service meal arrived, he *did* feel younger.

When the waiter had gone, Heyward said, "You should have let me pay for that." A few minutes earlier he had brought out his wallet but Avril waved it away and signed the check.

"Why, Rossie?"

"Because you must allow me to give you back some of your expenses —the hotel bills, the cost of flying here from New York." He had learned that Avril had an apartment in Greenwich Village. "It's too much for you to spend yourself."

She looked at him curiously, then gave a silvery laugh. "You didn't think *I* was paying for all this?" She gestured around the suite. "Using *my* money? Rossie, baby, you have to be crazy!"

"Then who *is* paying?"

"Supranational of course, you old silly! Everything's charged to them —this suite, the meal, my air fare, my time." She crossed to his chair and kissed him; her lips were full and moist. "Just don't worry about it!"

He sat still, crushed and silent, absorbing the impact of what had just been said. The mellowing potency of the champagne still coursed through his body, yet his mind was sharp.

"*My time.*" That hurt most of all. Until now he had assumed the reason Avril telephoned him after the Bahamas, suggesting that they meet, was because she liked him and had enjoyed—as much as he did—what happened between them.

How *could* he have been so naive? *Of course* the entire exercise had been arranged by Quartermain and was at Supranational's expense. Shouldn't commonsense have told him? Or had he shielded himself by not inquiring sooner because he hadn't wanted to know? Something else: If Avril were being paid for "my time," what did that make her? A whore? If so, what then was Roscoe Heyward? He closed his eyes. *St. Luke* 18:13, he thought: *God be merciful to me a sinner.*

There was one thing he could do, of course. Immediately. That was find out how much had been expended until now, and afterwards send his personal check for that amount to Supranational. He began calculating, then realized he had no idea of the cost of Avril. Instinct told him it would not be small.

In any case he doubted the wisdom of such a move. His comptroller's mind reasoned: How would Supranational show the payment on its books? Even more to the point, he didn't have that much money to spare. And besides, what would happen when he wanted Avril again? He knew, already, that he would.

The telephone rang, filling the small sitting room with sound. Avril answered it, spoke briefly, then announced, "It's for you."

"For *me?*"

As he took the receiver, the voice boomed, "Hi there, Roscoe!"

Heyward asked sharply, "Where are you, George?"

"Washington. What's the difference? Got some real good news about SuNatCo. Quarterly earnings statement. You'll read about it in tomorrow's papers."

"You called me here to tell me that?"

"Interrupted you, did I?"

"No."

Big George chuckled. "Just a friendly phone call, fella. Checking that all arrangements were okay."

If he wanted to protest, Heyward realized, this was the moment. But protest what? The generous availability of Avril? Or his own acute embarrassment?

The booming telephone voice cut through his dilemma. "That Q-Investments credit okayed yet?"

"Not quite."

"Taking your time, aren't you?"

"Not really. There are formalities."

"Let's move 'em, or I'll have to give some other bank that business, and maybe shift some of Supranational's over, too."

The threat was clear. It did not surprise Heyward because pressures and concessions were a normal part of banking.

"I'll do my best, George."

A grunt. "Avril still there?"

"Yes."

"Lemme talk to her."

Heyward passed the phone to Avril. She listened briefly, said, "Yes, I will," smiled, and hung up.

She went into the bedroom where he heard a suitcase snap open and a moment later she emerged with a large manila envelope. "Georgie said I was to give you this."

It was the same kind of envelope, and with similar seals, as the one which had contained the Q-Investments share certificates.

"Georgie told me to say it's a reminder of our good time in Nassau."

More share certificates? He doubted it. He considered refusing to accept, but curiosity was strong.

Avril said, "You're not to open it here. Wait till you're away."

He seized the opportunity and checked his watch. "I shall have to go anyway, my dear."

"Me, too. I'm flying back to New York tonight."

They said goodbye in the suite. There could have been an awkwardness at parting. Because of Avril's practiced savoir-faire there wasn't. She draped her arms around him and they held each other closely while she whispered, "You're a sugarplum, Rossie. We'll see each other soon."

Notwithstanding what he had learned, or his present tiredness, his passion for her hadn't changed. And whatever the cost of "my time," he thought, one thing was sure: Avril delivered value in return.

Roscoe Heyward took a taxi from the hotel to First Mercantile American Headquarters Tower. In the main floor foyer of the bank building he left word that in fifteen minutes he would require a car and driver to take him home. Then he rode an elevator to the 36th floor and walked through silent corridors, past deserted desks, to his office suite.

At his desk he opened the sealed envelope which Avril had given him. In a second package inside, interleaved with tissue, were a dozen enlarged photographs.

That second night in the Bahamas, when the girls and men had bathed naked in Big George's pool, the photographer had remained discreetly invisible. Perhaps he employed a telephoto lens, possibly was screened from view by shrubbery in the lush garden. He had certainly used a fast film because there had been no betraying flash. It scarcely mattered. He—or she—had been there just the same.

The photos showed Krista, Rhetta, Moonbeam, Avril, and Harold Austin undressing and unclothed. Roscoe Heyward appeared with the naked girls around him, his face a study in fascination. There was a view of Heyward unfastening Avril's dress and bra; another of her kissing him, his fingers curled around her breasts. Whether by accident or design, only the back of Vice-President Stonebridge could be seen.

Technically and artistically the quality of all photographs was high and obviously the photographer had been no amateur. But then, Heyward thought, G. G. Quartermain was accustomed to paying for the best.

Notably, in none of the photographs did Big George appear.

The photos appalled Heyward by their existence. And why had they been sent? Were they some kind of threat? Or a heavy-handed joke? Where were the negatives and other copies? He was beginning to realize that Quartermain was a complex, capricious, perhaps even dangerous, man.

On the other hand, despite the shock, Heyward found himself fascinated. As he studied the photographs, unconsciously he moistened his lips with his tongue. His first impulse had been to destroy them. Now he couldn't do it.

He was startled to find he had been at his desk for nearly half an hour.

Obviously he couldn't take the photos home. What then? Carefully repacking them, he locked the envelope in a desk drawer where he kept several personal, private files.

Out of habit, he checked another drawer where Mrs. Callaghan was apt to leave current papers when she cleared his desk at night. On top of the pile inside were those concerning the additional Q-Investments loan. He reasoned: Why delay? Why vacillate? Was there really any need to consult Patterton a second time? The loan was sound, as were G. G. Quartermain and Supranational. Removing the papers, Heyward scribbled an *approved* and added his initials.

A few minutes later he came down to the foyer. His driver was waiting, the limousine outside.

14

Only rarely, nowadays, did Nolan Wainwright have occasion to visit the city morgue. The last time, he recalled, was three years before when he identified the body of a bank guard killed in a robbery shoot-out. When Wainwright was a police detective, visiting morgues and viewing the victims of violent crime was a necessary and frequent part of his job. But even then he had never grown used to it. A morgue, any morgue, with its aura of death and charnel house smell, depressed him and sometimes turned his stomach. It did now.

The sergeant of city detectives, who had met him by arrangement, walked stolidly beside Wainwright down a gloomy passageway, their footsteps echoing sharply off the ancient, cracked tile floor. The morgue attendant preceding them, who looked as if he would soon be a customer here himself, was wearing rubber-soled shoes and shambled ahead silently.

The detective, whose name was Timberwell, was young, overweight, had unkempt hair and needed a shave. Many things had changed, Nolan Wainwright ruminated, in the twelve years since he had been a city police lieutenant.

Timberwell said, "If the dead guy *is* your man, when was the last time you saw him?"

"Seven weeks ago. Beginning of March."

"Where?"

"A little bar across town. The Easy Over."

"I know the place. Did you hear from him after that?"

"No."

"Any idea where he lived?"

Wainwright shook his head. "He didn't want me to know. So I played it his way."

Nolan Wainwright hadn't been sure of the man's name either. He had been given one, but almost certainly it was false. As a matter of fairness he hadn't tried to discover the real one. All he knew was that "Vic" was an ex-con who needed money and was prepared to be an undercover informer.

Last October, on Wainwright's urging, Alex Vandervoort had authorized him to employ an informer to seek out the source of counterfeit Keycharge bank credit cards, then appearing in disquieting numbers. Wainwright put out feelers, using contacts in the inner city, and later, through more intermediaries, a meeting between himself and Vic had been arranged and a deal agreed on. That was in December. The security chief remembered it well because Miles Eastin's trial had taken place the same week.

There were two other encounters between Vic and Wainwright in the months which followed, each in a different out-of-the-way bar, and on all three occasions Wainwright had handed over money, gambling on receiving value for it later. Their communications scheme was one-sided. Vic could telephone him, setting up a meeting at a place of Vic's choosing, though Wainwright had no means of contact in return. But he saw the reasoning behind the arrangement and accepted it.

Wainwright hadn't liked Vic, but then had not expected to. The ex-con was shifty, evasive, with the perpetually drippy nose and other outward signs of a narcotics user. He exhibited contempt for everything, including Wainwright; his lip was permanently curled. But at their third meeting, in March, it seemed as if he might have stumbled on a lead.

He reported a rumor: A big supply of bogus twenty-dollar bills of high quality was ready to be spread out through distributors and passers. According to still more scuttlebutt, somewhere back in the shadows—behind the distributors—was a high-powered, competent organization into other lines of action, including credit cards. This last information was vague, and Wainwright suspected Vic might have made it up to please him. On the other hand he might not.

More specifically, Vic claimed he had been promised a small piece of the action with the counterfeit money. He figured that if he got it, and became trusted, he could work his way deeper into the organization. One or two details which, in Wainwright's opinion, Vic would not have had the knowledge or wit to invent, convinced the bank security chief that the main thrust of the information was authentic. The proposed plan also made sense.

Wainwright had always assumed that whoever was producing the fraudulent Keycharge bank cards was likely to be involved with other forms of counterfeiting. He had told Alex Vandervoort so last October. One thing he knew for certain: It would be highly dangerous to try to penetrate the organization and an informer—if discovered—was dead. He had felt obliged to warn Vic of this and was rewarded for his trouble by a sneer.

After that meeting, Wainwright had not heard from Vic again.

Yesterday a small news item in the *Times-Register*, about a body found floating in the river, caught his attention.

"I should warn you," Detective Sergeant Timberwell said, "that what's left of this guy isn't pretty. The medics figure he was in the water for a week. Also, there's a lot of traffic on that river and it looks as if some boat propeller cut him up."

Still trailing the elderly attendant, they entered a brightly lighted, long, low-ceilinged room. The air was chill. It smelled of disinfectant. Occupying one wall, facing them, was what looked like a giant file cabinet with stainless steel drawers, each identified by a number. A hum of refrigeration equipment came from behind the cabinet.

The attendant peered shortsightedly at a clipboard he was carrying, then went to a drawer midway down the room. He pulled and the drawer slid out silently on nylon bearings. Inside was the lumpy shape of a body, covered by a paper sheet.

"These are the remains you wanted, officers," the old man said. As casually as if uncovering cucumbers, he folded back the sheet.

Wainwright wished he hadn't come. He felt sick.

Once, the body they were looking at had had a face. It didn't have any more. Immersion, putrefaction and something else—probably a boat propeller, as Timberwell said—had left flesh layers exposed and lacerated. From the mess, white bones protruded.

They studied the corpse in silence, then the detective asked, "You see anything you can identify?"

"Yes," Wainwright said. He had been peering at the side of the face where what remained of the hairline met the neck. The apple-shaped red scar—undoubtedly a birthmark—was still clearly visible. Wainwright's trained eye had observed it on each of the three occasions that he and Vic had met. Though the lips that had sneered so frequently were gone, without doubt the body was that of his undercover agent. He told Timberwell, who nodded.

"We identified him ourselves from fingerprints. They weren't the clearest, but good enough." The detective took out a notebook and opened it. "His real name, if you'll believe it, was Clarence Hugo Levinson. He had several other names he used, and a long record, mostly petty stuff."

"The news report said he died of stab wounds, not drowning."

"It's what the autopsy showed. Before that he was tortured."

"How do you know?"

"His balls were crushed. The pathologist's report said they must have been put in some kind of vise which was tightened until they burst. You want to see?"

Without waiting to be told, the attendant pulled back the remainder of the paper sheet.

Despite shrinkage of the genitals during immersion, autopsy had exposed enough to show the truth of Timberwell's statement. Wainwright gulped. "Oh, Christ!" He motioned to the old man. "Cover him up."

Then he urged Timberwell, "Let's get out of here."

Over strong black coffee in a tiny restaurant a half block from the morgue, Detective Sergeant Timberwell soliloquized, "Poor bastard! Whatever he'd done, no one deserves that." He produced a cigarette, lit it, and offered the pack. Wainwright shook his head.

"I guess I know how you're feeling," Timberwell said. "You get hardened to some things. But there sure are others that make you think."

"Yes." Wainwright was remembering his own responsibility for what had happened to Clarence Hugo Levinson, alias Vic.

"I'll need a statement from you, Mr. Wainwright. Summarizing those things you told me about your arrangement with the deceased. If it's all the same to you, I'd like to go to the precinct house and take it after we're finished here."

"All right."

The policeman blew a smoke ring and sipped his coffee. "What's the score about counterfeit credit cards—right now?"

"More and more are being used. Some days it's like an epidemic. It's costing banks like ours a lot of money."

Timberwell said skeptically, "You mean it's costing the public money. Banks like yours pass those losses on. It's why your top management people don't care as much as they should."

"I can't argue with you there." Wainwright remembered his own lost arguments about bigger budgets to fight bank-related crime.

"Is the quality of the cards good?"

"Excellent."

The detective ruminated. "That's exactly what the Secret Service tell us about the phony money that's circulating in the city. There's a lot of it. I guess you know."

"Yes, I do."

"So maybe that dead guy was right in figuring both things came from the same source."

Neither man spoke, then the detective said abruptly, "There's something I should warn you about. Maybe you've thought of it already."

Wainwright waited.

"When he was tortured, whoever did it made him talk. You saw him. There's no way he wouldn't have. So you can figure he sang about everything, including the deal he had with you."

"Yes, I'd thought of it."

Timberwell nodded. "I don't think you're in any danger yourself, but as far as the people who killed Levinson are concerned, you're poison. If anyone *they* deal with as much as breathes the same air as you, and they find out, he's dead—nastily."

Wainwright was about to speak when the other silenced him.

"Listen, I'm not saying you shouldn't send some other guy underground. That's your business and I don't want to know about it—at least, not now. But I'll say this: If you do, be super-careful and stay away from him yourself. You owe him that much."

"Thanks for the warning," Wainwright said. He was still thinking about the body of Vic as he had seen it with the covering removed. "I doubt very much if there'll be anyone else."

PART THREE

1

Though it continued to be difficult on her $98 weekly bank teller's wage ($83 take-home after deductions), somehow Juanita managed, week by week, to support herself and Estela and to pay the fees for Estela's nursery school. Juanita had even—by August—slightly reduced the debt to the finance company which her husband, Carlos, had burdened her with before abandoning her. The finance firm had obligingly rewritten the contract, making the monthly installments smaller, though they now stretched on—with heavier interest payments—three years into the future.

At the bank, while Juanita had been treated considerately after the false accusations against her last October, and staff members had gone out of their way to be cordial, she had established no close friendships. Intimacy did not come easily to her. She had a natural wariness of people, partly inbred, partly conditioned by experience. The center of her life, the apogee to which each working day progressed, were the evening hours which she and Estela spent together.

They were together now.

In the kitchen of their tiny but comfortable Forum East apartment, Juanita was preparing dinner, assisted—and at times hindered—by the three-year-old. They had both been rolling and shaping Bisquick baking mix, Juanita to provide a top for the meat pie, Estela manipulating a purloined piece of the dough with her tiny fingers as imagination prompted.

"Mommy! Look, I made a magic castle!"

They laughed together. "*¡Qué lindo, mi cielo!*" Juanita said affectionately. "We will put the castle in the oven with the pie. Then both will become magic."

For the pie Juanita had used stewing beef, mixing in onions, a potato, fresh carrots, and a can of peas. The vegetables made up in volume for the small quantity of meat, which was all Juanita could afford. But she was an instinctively inventive cook and the pie would be tasty and nutritious.

It had been in the oven for twenty minutes, with another ten to go, and Juanita was reading to Estela from a Spanish translation of Hans Andersen, when a knock sounded on the apartment door. Juanita stopped reading, listening uncertainly. Visitors at any time were rare; it was especially unusual for anyone to call this late. After a few moments the knock was repeated. With some nervousness, motioning Estela to remain where she was, Juanita got up and went slowly to the door.

Her apartment was on a floor by itself at the top of what had once been a single dwelling, but which long ago was divided into separately rented living quarters. The Forum East developers retained the divisions in the building, while modernizing and repairing. But redevelopment alone did not amend the fact that Forum East generally was in an area notorious for a high crime rate, especially muggings and break-ins. Thus, although the apartment complexes were fully populated, at night most occupants locked and bolted themselves in. There was a stout outer door, useful for protection, on the main floor of Juanita's building, except that other tenants often left it open.

Immediately outside Juanita's apartment was a narrow landing at the head of a flight of stairs. With her ear pressed against the door, she called out, "Who is there?" There was no answer, but once more the knock—soft but insistent—was repeated.

She made certain that the inside protective chain was in place, then unlocked the door and opened it a few inches—all the chain allowed.

At first, because of dim lighting, she could see nothing, then a face came into view and a voice asked, "Juanita, may I talk to you? I have to—please! Will you let me come in?"

She was startled. Miles Eastin. But neither the voice nor the face were those of the Eastin she had known. Instead, the figure which she could see better now was pale and emaciated, his speech unsure and pleading.

She stalled for time to think. "I thought you were in prison."

"I got out. Today." He corrected himself. "I was released on parole."

"Why have you come here?"

"I remembered where you lived."

She shook her head, keeping the door chain fastened. "It was not what I asked. Why come to *me?*"

"Because all I've thought about for months, all through that time inside, was seeing you, talking to you, explaining . . ."

"There is nothing to explain."

"But there *is!* Juanita, I'm begging you. Don't turn me away! Please!"

From behind her, Estela's bright voice asked, "Mommy, who is it?"

"Juanita," Miles Eastin said, "there's nothing to be frightened about —for you or your little girl. I've nothing with me except this." He held up a small battered suitcase. "It's just the things they gave me back when I came out."

"Well . . ." Juanita wavered. Despite her misgivings, her curiosity was strong. Why *did* Miles want to see her? Wondering if she would regret it, she closed the door slightly and released the chain.

"Thank you." He came in tentatively, as if even now he feared Juanita might change her mind.

"Hullo," Estela said, "are you my mommy's friend?"

For a moment Eastin seemed disconcerted, then he answered, "I wasn't always. I wish I had been."

The small, dark-haired child regarded him. "What's your name?"

"Miles."

Estela giggled. "You're a thin man."

"Yes, I know."

Now that he was fully in view, Juanita was even more startled by the change in Miles. In the eight months since she had seen him, he had lost so much weight that his cheeks were sunken, his neck and body scrawny. His crumpled suit hung loosely, as if tailored for someone twice his size. He looked tired and weak. "May I sit down?"

"Yes." Juanita motioned to a wicker chair, though she continued to stand, facing him. She said, illogically accusing, "You did not eat well in prison."

He shook his head, for the first time smiling slightly. "It isn't exactly gourmet living. I suppose it shows."

"*Sí, me dí cuenta.* It shows."

Estela asked, "Have you come for dinner? It's a pie Mommy made." He hesitated. "No."

Juanita said sharply, "Did you eat today?"

"This morning. I had something at the bus station." The aroma of the almost-cooked pie was wafting from the kitchen. Instinctively Miles turned his head.

"Then you will join us." She began setting another place at the small table where she and Estela took their meals. The action came naturally.

In any Puerto Rican home—even the poorest—tradition demanded that whatever food was available be shared.

As they ate, Estela chattered, and Miles responded to her questions; some of the earlier tension began visibly to leave him. Several times he looked around at the simply furnished but pleasant apartment. Juanita had a flair for homemaking. She loved to sew and decorate. In the modest living room was an old, used sofa bed she had slip-covered with a cotton material, brightly patterned in white, red, and yellow. The wicker chair which Miles had sat in earlier was one of two she had bought cheaply and repainted in Chinese red. For the windows she had created simple, inexpensive draperies of bright yellow bark cloth. A primitive painting and some travel posters adorned the walls.

Juanita listened to the other two but said little, within herself still doubtful and suspicious. Why had Miles really come? Would he cause her as much trouble as he had before? Experience warned her that he might. Yet at the moment he seemed harmless—certainly weak physically, a little frightened, possibly defeated. Juanita had the practical wisdom to recognize those symptoms.

What she did *not* feel was antagonism. Though Miles had tried to have her blamed for the theft of money he himself had stolen, time had made his treachery remote. Even originally, when he was exposed, her principal feeling had been relief, not hate. Now, all Juanita wanted for herself and Estela was to be left alone.

Miles Eastin sighed as he pushed away his plate. He had left nothing on it. "Thank you. That was the best meal in quite some time."

Juanita asked, "What are you going to do?"

"I don't know. Tomorrow I'll start looking for a job." He took a deep breath and seemed about to say something else, but she motioned him to wait.

"*Estelita, vamos, amorcito.* Bedtime!"

Soon after, washed, her hair brushed, and wearing tiny pink pajamas, Estela came to say good night. Large liquid eyes regarded Miles gravely. "My daddy went away. Are you going away?"

"Yes, very soon."

"That's what I thought." She put up her face to be kissed.

When she had tucked in Estela, Juanita came out of the apartment's single bedroom, closing the door behind her. She sat down facing Miles, hands folded in her lap. "So. You may talk."

He hesitated, moistening his lips. Now that the moment had arrived he seemed irresolute, bereft of words. Then he said, "All this time since I was . . . put away . . . I've been wanting to say I'm sorry. Sorry for everything I did, but mostly for what I did to you. I'm ashamed. In one way I don't know how it happened. In another I think I do."

Juanita shrugged. "What happened is gone. Does it matter now?"

"It matters to me. Please, Juanita—let me tell you the rest, the way it was."

Then, like a gusher uncapped, words flooded out. He spoke of his awakened conscience, and remorse, of last year's insanity of gambling and debts, and how they had possessed him like a fever which distorted moral values and perception. Looking back, he told Juanita, it seemed as if someone else had inhabited his mind and body. He proclaimed his guilt at stealing from the bank. But worst of all, he avowed, was what he had done to her, or tried to. His shame about that, he declared emotionally, had haunted him through every day in prison and would never leave him.

When Miles began speaking, Juanita's strongest instinct was suspicion. As he continued, not all of it left her; life had fooled and shortchanged her too often to permit total belief in anything. Yet her judgment inclined her to accept what Miles had said as genuine, and a sense of pity overwhelmed her.

She found herself comparing Miles with Carlos, her absentee husband. Carlos had been weak; so had Miles. Yet, in a way, Miles's willingness to return and face her penitently argued a strength and manhood which Carlos never had.

Suddenly she saw the humor in it all: The men in her life—for one reason or another—were flawed and unimpressive. They were also losers, like herself. She almost laughed, then decided not to because Miles would never understand.

He said earnestly, "Juanita, I want to ask you something. Will you forgive me?"

She looked at him.

"And if you do, will you say it to me?"

The silent laughter died; tears filled her eyes. *That* she could understand. She had been born a Catholic, and though nowadays she rarely bothered with church, she knew the solace of confession and absolution. She rose to her feet.

"Miles," Juanita said. "Stand up. Look at me."

He obeyed her, and she said gently, "*Has sufrido bastante.* Yes, I forgive you."

The muscles of his face twisted and worked. Then she held him as he wept.

* * *

When Miles had composed himself, and they were seated again, Juanita spoke practically. "Where will you spend the night?"

"I'm not sure. I'll find somewhere."

She considered, then told him, "You may stay here if you wish." As she saw his surprise, she added quickly, "You can sleep in this room for tonight only. I will be in the bedroom with Estela. Our door will be locked." She wanted no misunderstandings.

"If you really don't mind," he said, "I'd like to do that. And you'll have nothing to worry about."

He did not tell her the real reason she had no cause to worry: That there were other problems within himself—psychological and sexual—which he had not yet faced. All that Miles knew, so far, was that because of repeated homosexual acts between himself and Karl, his protector in prison, his desire for women had evaporated. He wondered if he would be a man—in any sexual way—again.

Shortly after, as tiredness overcame them both, Juanita went to join Estela.

In the morning, through the closed bedroom door, she heard Miles stirring early. A half hour later, when she emerged from the bedroom, he had left.

A note was propped up on the living-room table.

> Juanita—
> With all my heart, thank you!
> Miles

While she prepared breakfast for herself and Estela, she was surprised to find herself regretting he had gone.

2

In the four and a half months since approval of his savings and branch bank expansion plan by FMA's board of directors, Alex Vandervoort had moved swiftly. Planning and progress sessions between the bank's own staff and outside consultants and contractors had been held almost daily. Work continued during nights, weekends, and holidays, spurred on by Alex's insistence that the program be operating before the end of summer and in high gear by mid-fall.

The savings reorganization was easiest to accomplish in the time. Most of what Alex wanted done—including launching four new types of savings accounts, with increased interest rates and geared to varying needs—had been the subject of earlier studies at his behest. It was merely necessary to translate these into reality. Some fresh ground to be covered involved a strong program of advertising to attract new depositors and this—conflict of interest or not—the Austin Agency produced with speed and competence. The theme of the savings campaign was:

WE'LL PAY YOU TO BE THRIFTY
AT FIRST MERCANTILE AMERICAN

Now, in early August, double-page spreads in newspapers proclaimed the virtues of savings à la FMA. They also showed locations of eighty bank branches in the state where gifts, coffee, and "friendly financial counseling" were available to anyone opening a new account. The value of a gift depended on the size of an initial deposit, along with agreement not to disturb it for a stated time. Spot announcements on TV and radio hammered home a parallel campaign.

As to the nine new branches—"our money shops," as Alex called them —two were opened in the last week of July, three more in the first few days of August, and the remaining four would be in business before September. Since all were in rented premises, which involved conversion rather than construction, speed had been possible here, too.

It was the money shops—a name that caught on quickly—which attracted most attention to begin with. They also produced far greater publicity than either Alex Vandervoort, the bank's p.r. department, or the Austin Advertising Agency had foreseen. And the spokesman for it all—soaring to prominence like an ascending comet—was Alex.

He had not intended it to be that way. It simply happened.

A reporter from the morning *Times-Register*, assigned to cover the new branch openings, dipped into that newspaper's morgue in search of background and discovered Alex's tenuous connection with the previous February's pro-Forum East "bank-in." Discussion with the features editor hatched the notion that Alex would make good copy for an expanded story. This proved true.

> When you think of modern bankers [the reporter later wrote] don't think of solemn, cautious functionaries in traditional double-breasted, dark blue suits, pursing their lips and saying "no." Think, instead, of Alexander Vandervoort.
>
> Mr. Vandervoort, who's an executive veep at our own First Mercantile American Bank, to begin with doesn't look like a banker. His suits are from the fashion section of *Esquire*, his mannerisms à la Johnny Carson, and when it comes to loans, especially small loans, he's conditioned—with rare exceptions —to pronouncing "yes." But he also believes in thrift and says most of us aren't being as wise about money as our parents and grandparents.
>
> Another thing about Alexander Vandervoort is that he's a leader in modern bank technology, some of which arrived in our city's suburbs just this week.
>
> The new look in banking is embodied in branch banks not having the appearance of banks at all—which seems appropriate because Mr. Vandervoort (who doesn't look like a banker, as we said) is the local driving force behind them.
>
> This reporter went along with Alexander Vandervoort this week for a glimpse of what he calls "consumer banking of the future that's here right now."

* * *

The bank's public relations chief, Dick French, had set up the arrangements. The reporter was a middle-aged, floppy blonde called Jill Peacock, no Pulitzer journalist, but the story interested her and she was friendly.

Alex and Ms. Peacock stood together in one of the new branch banks, located in a suburban shopping plaza. It was about equal in size to a neighborhood drugstore, brightly lighted, and pleasantly designed. The principal furnishings were two stainless-steel Ducotel automatic tellers, which customers operated themselves, and a closed-circuit television console in a booth. The auto-tellers, Alex explained, were linked directly to computers at FMA Headquarters.

"Nowadays," he went on, "the public is conditioned to expect service, which is why there's a demand for banks to stay open longer, and at more convenient hours. Money shops like this one will be open twenty-four hours a day, seven days a week."

"With staff here all that time?" Ms. Peacock asked.

"No. In daytime we'll have a clerk on hand to handle queries. The rest of the time there'll be no one except customers."

"Aren't you afraid of robberies?"

Alex smiled. "The auto-teller machines are built like fortresses, with every alarm system known to man. And TV scanners—one in each money shop—are monitored at a control center downtown. Our immediate problem isn't security—it's getting our customers to adapt to new ideas."

"It looks," Ms. Peacock pointed out, "as if some have adapted already."

Though it was early—9:30 A.M.—the small bank already had a dozen people in it and others were arriving. Most were women.

"Studies we've made," Alex volunteered, "show that women accept merchandising changes faster, which is probably why retail stores have always been so innovative. Men are slower, but eventually women persuade them."

Short lines had formed in front of the automatic tellers, but there was virtually no delay. Transactions were completed quickly after each customer had inserted a plastic identifying card and pressed a simple selection of buttons. Some were depositing cash or checks, others withdrawing money. One or two had come to pay bank card or utilities bills. Whatever the purpose, the machine swallowed paper and cash or spat them out at lightning speed.

Ms. Peacock pointed to the auto-tellers. "Have people learned to use these faster or slower than you expected?"

"Much, much faster. It's an effort to persuade people to try the machines the first time. But once they have, they become fascinated, and love them."

"You always hear that humans prefer dealing with other humans, rather than machines. Why should banking be different?"

"Those studies I mentioned tell us it's because of privacy."

There really *is* privacy [Jill Peacock acknowledged in her by-lined, Sunday edition feature story], and not just with those Frankenstein-monster tellers.

Sitting alone in a booth in the same money shop, facing a combination TV camera and screen, I opened an account and then negotiated a loan.

Other times I've borrowed money from a bank I felt embarrassed. This time I didn't because the face in front of me on the screen was impersonal. The owner of it—a disembodied male whose name I didn't know—was miles away.

"Seventeen miles, to be exact," Alex had said. "The bank officer you were talking with is in a control room of our downtown Headquarters Tower. From there he, and others, can contact any branch bank equipped with closed-circuit TV."

Ms. Peacock considered. "How fast, really, is banking changing?"

"Technologically, we're developing more swiftly than aerospace. What you're seeing here is the most important development since introduction of the checking account and, within ten years or less, most banking will be done this way."

"Will there still be *some* human tellers?"

"For a while, but the breed will disappear quickly. Quite soon, the notion of having an individual count out cash by hand, then pass it over a counter will be antediluvian—as outmoded as the old-fashioned grocer who used to weigh out sugar, peas, and butter, then put them into paper bags himself."

"It's all rather sad," Ms. Peacock said.

"Progress often is."

Afterward I asked a dozen people at random how they liked the new money shops. Without exception they were enthusiastic.

Judging by the large numbers using them, the view is wide-

spread and their popularity, Mr. Vandervoort told me, is
helping a current savings drive . . .

Whether the money shops were helping the savings drive, or vice
versa, was never entirely clear. What did become clear was that FMA's
most optimistic savings targets were being reached and exceeded with
phenomenal speed. It seemed—as Alex expressed it to Margot Bracken
—as if the public mood and First Mercantile American's timing had
uncannily coincided.

"Stop preening yourself and drink your orange juice," Margot told
him. Sunday morning in Margot's apartment was a pleasure. Still in
pajamas and a robe, he had been reading, for the first time, Jill Peacock's feature story in the *Sunday Times-Register* while Margot prepared a breakfast of Eggs Benedict.

Alex was still glowing while they ate. Margot read the *Times-
Register* story herself and conceded, "It's not a bad piece." She leaned
over and kissed him. "I'm glad for you."

"It's better publicity than the last you got me, Bracken."

She said cheerfully, "Can never tell how it'll go. The press giveth
and the press taketh away. Tomorrow you and your bank may be attacked."

He sighed. "You're so often right."

But this time she was wrong.

A condensed version of the original news feature was syndicated and
used by papers in forty other cities. AP, observing the wide, general
interest, did its own report for the national wire; so did UPI. *The Wall
Street Journal* dispatched a staff reporter and several days later fea-
tured First Mercantile American Bank and Alex Vandervoort in a front-
page review of automated banking. An NBC affiliate sent a TV crew
to interview Alex at a money shop and the videotaped result was aired
on the network's NBC Nightly News.

With each burst of publicity the savings campaign gained fresh mo-
mentum and money shop business boomed.

Unhurriedly, from its lofty eminence, *The New York Times* brooded
and took note. Then, in mid-August, its Sunday Business and Finance
section proclaimed: A *Banking Radical We May Hear More About.*

The Times interview with Alex consisted of questions and answers.
It began with automation, then moved to broader terrain.

QUESTION: What's mostly wrong with banking nowadays?
VANDERVOORT: We bankers have had things our own way too long.

We're so preoccupied with our own welfare, we give too little thought to the interests of our customers.

QUESTION: Can you quote an example?

VANDERVOORT: Yes. Customers of banks—particularly individuals—ought to receive much more money in interest than they do.

QUESTION: In what way?

VANDERVOORT: In several ways—in their savings accounts; also with certificates of deposit; and we should be paying interest on demand deposits—that is, checking accounts.

QUESTION: Let's take savings first. Surely there's a federal law that places a ceiling on savings interest rates at commercial banks.

VANDERVOORT: Yes, and the purpose of it is to protect savings and loan banks. Incidentally, there's another law which prevents savings and loan banks from letting their customers use checks. That's to protect commercial banks. What ought to happen is that laws should stop protecting banks and protect people instead.

QUESTION: By "protecting people" you mean letting those with savings enjoy the maximum interest rate and other services which any bank will give?

VANDERVOORT: Yes, I do.

QUESTION: You mentioned certificates of deposit.

VANDERVOORT: The U. S. Federal Reserve has prohibited large banks, like the one I work for, advertising long-term certificates of deposit at high interest rates. These kinds of CDs are especially good for anyone looking ahead to retirement and wanting to defer income tax until later, low income, years. The Fed hands out phony excuses for this ban. But the real reason is to protect small banks against big ones, the big banks being more efficient and able to give better deals. As usual, it's the public which is last to be considered and individuals who lose out.

QUESTION: Let's be clear about this. You're suggesting that our central bank—the Federal Reserve—cares more about small banks than the general populace?

VANDERVOORT: Damn right.

QUESTION: Let's move on to demand deposits—checking accounts. Some bankers are on record as saying they would like to pay interest on checking accounts, but federal law prohibits it.

VANDERVOORT: Next time a banker tells you that, ask him when our powerful banking lobby in Washington last did anything about getting the law changed. If there's ever been an effort in that direction, I've not heard of it.

QUESTION: You're suggesting, then, that most bankers really don't want that law changed?

VANDERVOORT: I'm not suggesting it. I know it. The law preventing payment of interest on checking accounts is very convenient if you happen to own a bank. It was introduced in 1933, right after the Depression, with the object of strengthening banks because so many had failed in the previous few years.

QUESTION: And that was more than forty years ago.

VANDERVOORT: Exactly. The need for such a law has long passed. Let me tell you something. Right at this moment, if all the checking account balances in this country were added together, they'd total more than $200 billion. You can bet your life the banks are earning interest on this money, but the depositors—the bank's customers—aren't getting a cent.

QUESTION: Since you yourself are a banker, and your own bank profits from the law we are talking about, why do you advocate change?

VANDERVOORT: For one thing, I believe in fairness. For another, banking doesn't need all those crutches in the way of protective laws. In my opinion we can do better—by that I mean render improved public service and be more profitable—without them.

QUESTION: Haven't there been recommendations in Washington about some of those changes you've spoken of?

VANDERVOORT: Yes. The Hunt Commission report of 1971, and proposed legislation resulting from it, which would benefit consumers. But the whole deal is stalled in Congress, with special interests—including our own banking lobby—holding up progress.

QUESTION: Do you anticipate antagonism from other bankers because of your frankness here?

VANDERVOORT: I really hadn't thought about it.

QUESTION: Apart from banking, do you have any over-all view on the current economic scene?

VANDERVOORT: Yes, but an over-all view should not be limited to economics.

QUESTION: Please state your view—and don't limit it.

VANDERVOORT: Our greatest problem, and our big shortcoming as a nation, is that almost everything nowadays is geared *against* the individual and in favor of the big institutions—big corporations, big business, big unions, big banking, big government. So not only does an individual have trouble getting ahead and staying there, he often has difficulty merely in surviving. And whenever bad things happen—inflation, devaluation, depression, shortages, higher taxes, even wars—it isn't the big institutions which get hurt, at least not much; it's the individual, all the time.

QUESTION: Do you see historical parallels to this?

VANDERVOORT: I do indeed. It may seem strange to say this, but the closest one, I think, is France immediately before the Revolution. At that time, despite unrest and a bad economy, everyone assumed there'd be business as usual. Instead, the mob—composed of individuals who rebelled—overthrew the tyrants who oppressed them. I'm not suggesting our conditions now are precisely the same, but in many ways we're remarkably close to tyranny, once more, against the individual. And telling people who can't feed their families because of inflation that, "You never had it so good," is uncomfortably like, "Let them eat cake." So I say, if we want to preserve our so-called way of life and individual freedom which we claim to value, we'd better start thinking and acting about the interests of individuals again.

QUESTION: And in your own case, you'd begin by making banks serve individuals more.

VANDERVOORT: Yes.

"Darling, it's magnificent! I'm proud of you, and I love you more than ever," Margot assured Alex when she read an advance copy a day before the interview was published. "It's the most honest thing I've ever read. But other bankers will hate you. They'll want your balls for breakfast."

"Some will," Alex said. "Others won't."

But now that he had seen the questions and replies in print, and despite the wave of success on which he had been riding, he was slightly worried himself.

3

"What saved you from being crucified, Alex," Lewis D'Orsey declaimed, "was that it happened to be *The New York Times*. If you'd said what you did for any other paper in the country, your bank's directors would have disowned you and cast you out like a pariah. But not with the *Times*. It clothed you in respectability, though never ask me why."

"Lewis, dear," Edwina D'Orsey said, "could you interrupt your speech to pour more wine?"

"I'm not making a speech." Her husband rose from the dinner table and reached for a second decanter of Clos de Vougeot '62. Tonight Lewis looked as puny and as underfed as ever. He continued, "I'm talking calmly and lucidly about *The New York Times* which, in my opinion, is an effete pinko rag, its unwarranted prestige a monument to American imbecility."

"It has a bigger circulation than your newsletter," Margot Bracken said. "Is that a reason you don't like it?"

She and Alex Vandervoort were guests of Lewis and Edwina in the D'Orseys' elegant Cayman Manor penthouse. At the table, in soft candlelight, napery, crystal, and polished silver gleamed. Along one side of the spacious dining room a wide, deep window framed the shimmering lights of the city far below. Through the lights a sinuous blackness marked the river's course.

It was a week since the controversial interview with Alex had appeared in print.

Lewis picked at a medallion of beef and answered Margot disdainfully. "My twice-a-month newsletter represents high quality and superior intellect. Most daily newspapers, including the *Times*, are vulgar quantity."

"Stop sparring, you two!" Edwina turned to Alex. "At least a dozen people who came into the downtown branch this week told me they'd read what you said and admired your outspokenness. What was the reaction in the Tower?"

"Mixed."

"I'll bet I know someone who didn't approve."

"You're right." Alex chuckled. "Roscoe did not lead the cheering section."

Heyward's attitude had recently become even icier than before. Alex suspected that Heyward was resentful, not only of the attention Alex was receiving, but also because of successes with the savings drive and money shops, both of which Roscoe Heyward had opposed.

Another downbeat prediction of Heyward and his supporters on the board had concerned the eighteen million dollars in deposits from savings and loan institutions. Though the S&Ls' managements had huffed and puffed, they had not withdrawn their deposits from First Mercantile American. Nor, it now seemed, did they intend to.

"Apart from Roscoe and any others," Edwina said, "I hear you've a big following these days among the staff."

"Maybe I'm a swiftly passing fad. Like streaking."

"Or an addiction," Margot said. "I've found you habit-forming."

He smiled. It had been heartening over the past week to receive congratulations from people whom Alex respected, like Tom Straughan, Orville Young, Dick French, and Edwina, and from others, including junior executives he had not previously known by name. Several directors had telephoned with words of praise. "You're doing the bank's image a power of good," Leonard L. Kingswood had called to say. And Alex's progress through the FMA Tower had, at times, been near triumphant, with clerks and secretaries greeting him and smiling warmly.

"Talking of your staff, Alex," Lewis D'Orsey said, "reminds me you've something missing over in that Headquarters Tower of yours—Edwina. It's time she moved higher. While she doesn't, you people are losing out."

"Really, Lewis, how *could* you?" Even in the candlelight it could be seen that Edwina had flushed deep red. She protested, "This is a social occasion. Even if it weren't, that kind of remark is quite improper. Alex, I apologize."

Lewis, unperturbed, regarded his wife over his half-moon glasses. "You may apologize, my dear. I won't. I'm aware of your ability and value; who's closer to it? Furthermore, it's my custom to draw attention to anything outstanding which I see."

"Well, three cheers for you, Lewis!" Margot said. "Alex, how about it? When does my esteemed cousin move over to the Tower?"

Edwina was becoming angry. "Stop it, please! You're embarrassing me acutely."

"No one need be embarrassed." Alex sipped his wine appreciatively. "Um! '62 was a fine year for Burgundy. Every bit as good as '61, don't you think?"

"Yes," his host acknowledged. "Fortunately I put down plenty of both."

"We're all four of us friends," Alex said, "so we can speak frankly, knowing it's in confidence. I don't mind telling you I've already been thinking about a promotion for Edwina, and I've a particular job in mind. How soon I can swing that, and some other changes, depends on what happens in the next few months, as Edwina is well aware."

"Yes," she said, "I am." Edwina knew, too, that her personal allegiance to Alex was well known within the bank. Since Ben Rosselli's death, and even before, she realized that Alex's promotion to the presidency would almost certainly advance her own career. But if Roscoe Heyward succeeded instead, it was unlikely she would go any higher at First Mercantile American.

"Something else I'd like to see," Alex said, "is Edwina on the board of directors."

Margot brightened. "Now you're talking! That would be an onward-up for women's lib."

"No!" Edwina reacted sharply. "Don't equate me with women's lib —ever! Anything I've achieved has been on my own, competing honestly with men. Women's lib—its catchwords, asking for favoritism and preference *because* you're a woman—has set sex equality back, not forward."

"That's nonsense!" Margot seemed shocked. "You can say that now because you've been unusual and lucky."

"There was no luck," Edwina said. "I've worked."

"No luck?"

"Well, not much."

Margot argued. "There has to have been luck involved because you're a woman. For as long as anybody can remember, banking's been an exclusive men's club—yet without the slightest reason."

"Hasn't experience been a reason?" Alex asked.

"No. Experience is a smokescreen, blown up by men, to keep women out. There's nothing masculine about banking. All it requires is brains —which women have, sometimes more abundantly than men. And everything else is either on paper, in the head, or in talk, so the only physical labor is hoisting money in and out of armored cars, which women guards could undoubtedly do, too."

"I won't dispute any of that," Edwina said. "Except you're out of date. The male exclusivity has already been broken—by people like me —and is being penetrated more and more. Who needs women's libbers? I don't."

"You haven't penetrated all that far," Margot shot back. "Otherwise you'd be in the Headquarters Tower already, and not just talking about it, as we are tonight."

Lewis D'Orsey chortled. "Touché, my dear."

"Others in banking need women's lib," Margot concluded, "and will for a long time."

Alex leaned back—as always, enjoying an argument when Margot was involved. "Whatever else might be said about our dinners together," he observed, "they're never dull."

Lewis nodded agreement. "Let me say—as the one who started all this—I'm glad about your intentions for Edwina."

"All right," his wife said firmly, "and I thank you too, Alex. But that's enough. Let's leave it there."

They did.

Margot told them about a legal class action she had brought against a department store which had been systematically cheating charge account customers. The printed totals on monthly bills, Margot explained, were always a few dollars larger than they should have been. If anyone complained, the difference was explained away as an error but hardly anyone did. "When people see a machine printed total they assume it has to be right. What they forget, or don't know, is that machines can be programmed to *include* an error. In this case, one was." Margot added that the store had profited by tens of thousands of dollars, as she intended to prove in court.

"We don't program errors at the bank," Edwina said, "but they happen, machines or not. It's why I urge people to check their statements."

In her department store investigation, Margot told the others, she had been helped by a private detective named Vernon Jax. He had been diligent and resourceful. She was strong in her praise of him.

"I know of him," Lewis D'Orsey said. "He's done investigative work for the SEC—something I put them on to once. A good man."

As they left the dining room, Lewis said to Alex, "Let's get liberated. How about joining me for a cigar and cognac? We'll go to my study. Edwina doesn't like cigar smoke."

Excusing themselves, the men went one floor down—the D'Orseys' penthouse occupied two levels—to Lewis's sanctum sanctorum. Inside, Alex looked around curiously.

The room was spacious, with bookcases on two sides and, on another, racks for magazines and newspapers. The shelves and racks were over-flowing. There were three desks, one with an electric typewriter, and all with papers, books, and files piled high. "When one desk becomes impossible to work at," Lewis explained, "I simply move to the next."

An open door revealed what, in daytime, was a secretary's office and file room. Stepping inside, Lewis returned with two brandy goblets and a bottle of Courvoisier from which he poured.

"I've often wondered," Alex mused, "about the background of a suc-cessful financial newsletter."

"I can only speak personally for mine, which is regarded by compe-tent judges as the best there is." Lewis gave Alex a cognac, then mo-tioned to an open box of cigars. "Help yourself—they're Macanudos, none better. Also tax deductible."

"How do you manage that?"

Lewis chuckled. "Take a look at the band around each cigar. At trifling cost I have the original bands removed and a special one put on which reads *The D'Orsey Newsletter*. That's advertising—a business expense, so every time I smoke a cigar I've the satisfaction of knowing it's on Uncle Sam."

Without comment, Alex took a cigar which he sniffed appreciatively. He had long since ceased to make moral judgments about tax loop-holes. Congress made them the law of the land, and who could blame an individual for using them?

"Answering your question," Lewis said, "I make no secret of the pur-pose of *The D'Orsey Newsletter*." He lit Alex's cigar, then his own, and inhaled luxuriously. "It's to help the rich get richer."

"So I've noticed."

Each newsletter, as Alex was aware, contained moneymaking advice —securities to buy or sell, currencies to switch into or out of, commodi-ties to deal in, foreign stock markets to favor or avoid, tax loopholes for the wealthy and freewheeling, how to deal through Swiss accounts, political background likely to affect money, impending disasters which those with inside knowledge could turn to profit. The list was always

long, the tone of the newsletter authoritative and absolute. There was
seldom any hedging.

"Unfortunately," Lewis added, "there are lots of phonies and charlatans in the financial newsletter business, which do the serious, honest
letters harm. Some so-called newsletters are skims of newspapers, and
therefore valueless; others tout stocks and take payoffs from brokers
and promoters, though in the end that kind of chicanery shows. There
are maybe half a dozen worthwhile newsletters, with mine at the apex."

In anyone else, Alex thought, the continual ego-thumping would be
offensive. Somehow, with Lewis, it wasn't, perhaps because he had the
track record to sustain it. And as to Lewis's extreme right-wing politics,
Alex found he could screen them out, leaving a clear financial distillate
—like tea passed through a strainer.

"I believe you're one of my subscribers," Lewis said.

"Yes—through the bank."

"Here's a copy of my new issue. Take it, even though you'll get yours
in the mail on Monday."

"Thank you." Alex accepted the pale blue lithographed sheet—four
quarto-size pages when folded, and unimpressive in appearance. The
original had been closely typewritten, then photographed and reduced.
But what the newsletter lacked in visual style, it make up in monetary
value. It was Lewis's boast that those who followed his advice could
increase whatever capital they had by a quarter to a half in any given
year, and in some years double or triple it.

"What's your secret?" Alex said. "How is it you're so often right?"

"I've a mind like a computer with thirty years of input." Lewis puffed
at his cigar, then tapped his forehead with a bony finger. "Every morsel
of financial knowledge that I've ever learned is stored in there. I also
can relate one item to another, and the future to the past. In addition
I've something a computer hasn't—instinctive genius."

"Why bother with a newsletter then? Why not just make a fortune for
yourself?"

"No satisfaction in it. No competition. Besides," Lewis grinned, "I'm
not doing badly."

"As I recall, your subscription rate . . ."

"Is three hundred dollars a year for the newsletter. A thousand dollars
an hour for personal consultations."

"I've sometimes wondered how many subscribers you have."

"So do others. It's a secret I guard carefully."

"Sorry. I didn't mean to pry."

"No reason not to. In your place, I'd be curious."

Tonight, Alex thought, Lewis seemed more relaxed than at any time before.

"Maybe I'll share that secret with you," Lewis said. "Any man likes to boast a little. I've more than five thousand newsletter subscribers."

Alex did mental arithmetic and whistled softly. It meant an annual income of more than a million and a half dollars.

"As well as that," Lewis confided, "I publish a book each year and do about twenty consultations every month. The fees and book royalties cover all my costs, so the newsletter is entirely profit."

"That's amazing!" And yet, Alex reflected, perhaps it really wasn't. Anyone who heeded Lewis's counsel could recoup their outlay hundreds of times over. Besides which, both the newsletter subscription and consultation fee were tax deductible.

"Is there any one piece of over-all guidance," Alex asked, "that you'd give to people with money to invest or save?"

"Absolutely, yes!—take care of it yourself."

"Supposing it's someone who doesn't know . . ."

"Then find out. Learning isn't all that hard, and looking after your own money can be fun. Listen to advice, of course, though be skeptical and wary, and selective about which advice you take. After a while you'll learn whom to trust, and not. Read widely, including newsletters like mine. But never give anyone else the right to make decisions for you. Especially that means stockbrokers, who represent the fastest way to lose what you already have, and bank trust departments."

"You don't like trust departments?"

"Dammit, Alex, you know perfectly well the record of yours and other banks is awful. Big trust accounts get individual service—of a sort. Medium and small ones are either in a general pot or are handled by low-salaried incompetents who can't tell a bull market from bearshit."

Alex grimaced, but didn't protest. He knew too well that—with a few honorable exceptions—what Lewis had said was true.

Sipping their cognac in the smoke-filled room, both men were silent. Alex turned the pages of the latest *Newsletter*, skimming its contents, which he would read in detail later. As usual, some material was technical.

> Chartwise we appear to be off on the 3rd leg of the bear mkt. The 200 day mvg avg has been broken in all 3 DJ averages which are in perfect downside synchronization. The AD line is crashing.

More simple was:

Recommended mix of currencies:

Currency	%
Swiss Francs	40%
Dutch Guilders	25%
Deutsche marks	20%
Canadian Dollars	10%
Austrian Schillings	5%
U.S. Dollars	0%

A regular column listed international securities to trade or hold. Alex's eye ran down the "buy" and "hold" lists, then the "sell." He stopped sharply at: "*Supranational*—sell immediately at market."

"Lewis, this Supranational item—why sell Supranational? And 'immediately at market'? You've had it for years as a 'long-term hold.'"

His host considered before answering. "I'm uneasy about SuNatCo. I'm getting too many fragments of negative information from unrelated sources. Some rumors about big losses which haven't been reported. Also stories of sharp accounting practices among subsidiaries. An unconfirmed story out of Washington that Big George Quartermain is shopping for a Lockheed-type subsidy. What it amounts to is—maybe —maybe not . . . shoal waters ahead. As a precaution, I prefer my people out."

"But everything you've said is rumor and shadow. You can hear it about any company. Where's the substance?"

"There is none. My 'sell' recommendation is on instinct. There are times I act on it. This is one." Lewis D'Orsey placed his cigar stub in an ashtray and put down his empty glass. "Shall we rejoin the ladies?"

"Yes," Alex said, and followed Lewis. But his mind was still on Supranational.

4

"I wouldn't have believed," Nolan Wainwright said harshly, "that you'd have the nerve to come here."

"I didn't think I would either." Miles Eastin's voice betrayed his nervousness. "I thought of coming yesterday, then decided I just couldn't. Today I hung around outside for half an hour, getting up courage to come in."

"You may call it courage. I call it gall. Now you're here, what do you want?"

The two men faced each other, both standing, in Nolan Wainwright's private office. They were sharply in contrast: the stern, black, handsome bank vice-president of security, and Eastin, the ex-convict—shrunken, pale, unsure, a long way from the bright and affable assistant operations manager who had worked at FMA only eleven months ago.

Their surroundings at this moment were spartan, compared with most other departments in the bank. Here were plain painted walls and gray metal furniture, including Wainwright's desk. The floor was carpeted, but thinly and economically. The bank lavished money and artistry on revenue-producing areas. Security was not among them.

"Well," Wainwright repeated, "what do you want?"

"I came to see if you'll help me."

"Why should I?"

The younger man hesitated before answering, then said, still nervously, "I know you tricked me with that first confession. The night I was arrested. My lawyer said it was illegal, it could never have been used in court. You knew that. But you let me go on thinking it was a legit confession, so I signed that second one for the FBI, not knowing there was any difference . . ."

Wainwright's eyes narrowed suspiciously. "Before I answer that, I want to know something. Are you carrying a recording device?"

"No."

"Why should I believe you?"

Miles shrugged, then held his hands above his head in the way he had learned from law-enforcement friskings and in prison.

For a moment it seemed as if Wainwright would refuse to search him, then quickly and professionally he patted down the other man. Miles lowered his arms.

"I'm an old fox," Wainwright said. "Guys like you think they can get smart and catch someone out, then start a legal suit. So you got to be a jailhouse lawyer?"

"No. All I found out about was the confession."

"All right, you've brought it up, so I'll tell you about that. Sure I knew it might not hold water legally. Sure I tricked you. And something else: In the same circumstances, I'd do the same again. You were guilty, weren't you? You were about to send the Núñez girl to jail. What difference do the niceties make?"

"I only thought . . ."

"I know what you thought. You thought you'd come back here, and my conscience would be bleeding, and I'd be a pushover for some scheme you have or whatever else you want. Well, it isn't and I'm not."

Miles Eastin mumbled, "I had no scheme. I'm sorry I came."

"What *do* you want?"

There was a pause while they appraised each other. Then Miles said, "A job."

"Here? You must be mad."

"Why? I'd be the most honest employee the bank ever had."

"Until somebody put pressure on you to steal again."

"It wouldn't happen!" Briefly, a flash of Miles Eastin's former spirit surfaced. "Can't you, can't anybody, believe I've learned something? Learned about what happens when you steal. Learned never, ever, to do the same again. Don't you think there's not a temptation in the world I wouldn't resist now, rather than take a chance of going back to prison?"

Wainwright said gruffly, "What I believe or disbelieve is immaterial. The bank has policies. One is not to employ anyone with a criminal record. Even if I wanted to, I couldn't change that."

"But you could try. There are jobs, even here, where a criminal record would make no difference, where there's *no way* to be dishonest. Couldn't I get some kind of work like that?"

"No." Then curiosity intruded. "Why are you so keen to come back, anyway?"

"Because I can't get any kind of work, not *anything*, not a look-in, not a chance, anywhere else." Miles's voice faltered. "And because I'm hungry."

"You're what?"

"Mr. Wainwright, it's been three weeks since I came out on parole. I've been out of money for more than a week. I haven't eaten in three days. I guess I'm desperate." The voice which had faltered cracked and broke. "Coming here . . . having to see you, guessing what you'd say . . it was the last . . ."

While Wainwright listened, some of the hardness left his face. Now he motioned to a chair across the room. "Sit down."

He went outside and gave his secretary five dollars. "Go to the cafeteria," he instructed. "Get two roast beef sandwiches and a pint of milk."

When he returned, Miles Eastin was still sitting where he had been told, his body slumped, his expression listless.

"Has your parole officer helped?"

Miles said bitterly, "He has a case load—so he told me—of a hundred and seventy-five parolees. He has to see everybody once a month, and what can he do for one? There are no jobs. All he gives is warnings."

From experience, Wainwright knew what the warnings would be: Not to associate with other criminals whom Eastin might have met in prison; not to frequent known haunts of criminals. To do either, and be officially observed, would ensure a prompt return to prison. But in practice the rules were as unrealistic as they were archaic. A prisoner without financial means had the dice loaded against him so that association with others like himself was frequently his only method of survival. It was also a reason why the rate of recidivism among ex-convicts was so high.

Wainwright asked, "You've really looked for work?"

"Everywhere I could think of. And I haven't been fussy either."

The closest Miles had been to a job in three weeks of searching had been as a kitchen helper in a third-rate, crowded Italian restaurant. The job was vacant and the proprietor, a sad whippet of a man, had been inclined to hire him. But when Miles revealed his prison record, as he knew he had to, he had seen the other glance at the cash register nearby. Even then the restaurateur had hesitated but his wife, a female drill sergeant, ruled, "No! We can't afford to take a chance." Pleading with them both had done no good.

Elsewhere, his parolee status had eliminated possibilities even faster

"If I could do something for you, maybe I would." Wainwright's tone had softened since the beginning of the interview. "But I can't. There's nothing here. Believe me."

Miles nodded glumly. "I guess I knew anyway."

"So what will you try next?"

Before there was time to answer, the secretary returned, handing Wainwright a paper sack and change. When the girl had gone, he took out the milk and sandwiches and set them down as Eastin watched, moistening his lips.

"You can eat those here if you like."

Miles moved quickly, removing the wrapping from the first sandwich with plucking fingers. Any doubts about the truth of his statement that he was hungry were banished as Wainwright observed the food devoured silently, with speed. And while the security chief watched, an idea began to form.

At the end, Miles emptied the last of the milk from a paper cup and wiped his lips. Of the sandwiches, not a crumb remained.

"You didn't answer my question," Wainwright said. "What will you try next?"

Perceptibly Eastin hesitated, then said flatly, "I don't know."

"I think you do know. And I think you're lying—for the first time since you came in."

Miles Eastin shrugged. "Does it matter any more?"

"My guess is this," Wainwright said; he ignored the question. "Until now you've stayed away from the people you knew in prison. But because you gained nothing here you've decided to go to them. You'll take a chance on being seen, and your parole."

"What the hell other kind of chance is there? And if you know so much, why ask?"

"So you *do* have those contacts."

"If I say yes," Eastin said contemptuously, "the first thing you'll do when I've gone is telephone the parole board."

"No." Wainwright shook his head. "Whatever we decide, I promise you I won't do that."

"What do you mean: 'Whatever we decide'?"

"There might just be something we could work out. If you were willing to run some risks. Big ones."

"What kind of risks?"

"Leave that for now. If we need to, we'll come back to it. Tell me first about the people you got to know inside and those you can make con-act with now." Sensing continued wariness, Wainwright added, "I give you my word I won't take advantage—without your agreement—of anything you tell me."

"How do I know this isn't a trick—the way you tricked me once before?"

"You don't. You'll take a chance on trusting me. Either that, or walk out of here and don't come back."

Miles sat silent, thinking, occasionally moistening his lips in the nervous gesture he had exhibited earlier. Then abruptly, without outward sign of a decision, he began to talk.

He revealed the approach first made to him in Drummonburg Penitentiary by the emissary from Mafia Row. The message relayed to Miles Eastin, he told Wainwright, had originated with the outside loan shark, Igor (the Russian) Ominsky and was to the effect that he, Eastin, was a "stand-up guy" because he had not disclosed the identity of the shark or the bookmaker at the time of his arrest or afterward. As a concession, interest on Eastin's loan would be waived during his time in prison. 'Mafia Row's messenger boy said that Ominsky stopped the clock while I was inside."

"But you're not inside now," Wainwright pointed out. "So the clock is running again."

Miles looked worried. "Yes, I know." He had realized that, and tried not to think about it while he searched for work. He had also stayed away from the location he had been told of where he could make contact with the loan shark Ominsky and others. It was the Double-Seven Health Club near the city's center, and the information had been passed to him a few days before leaving prison. He repeated it now under Wainwright's probing.

"Figures. I don't know the Double-Seven," the bank security chief mused, "but I've heard of it. It has the reputation of being a mob hangout."

The other thing Miles had been told at Drummonburg was that there would be ways for him, through contacts he would make, to earn money to live and begin paying off his debt. He had not needed a diagram to know that such "ways" would be outside the law. That knowledge, and his dread of a return to prison, had kept him resolutely removed from the Double-Seven. So far.

"My hunch was right then. You would have gone there from here."

"Oh, God, Mr. Wainwright, I didn't want to! I still don't."

"Maybe, between us, you can cut it both ways."

"How?"

"You've heard of an undercover agent?"

Miles Eastin looked surprised before admitting, "Yes."

"Then listen carefully."

Wainwright began talking.

Four months earlier, when the bank security chief viewed the drowned and mutilated body of his informer, Vic, he had doubted if he would send anyone undercover again. At that moment, shocked and with a sense of personal guilt, he had meant what he said and had done nothing since to recruit a replacement. But this opportunity—Eastin's desperation and ready-made connections—was too promising to be ignored.

Equally to the point: More and more counterfeit Keycharge credit cards were appearing, in what seemed a deluge, while their source remained unknown. Conventional methods of locating the producers and distributors had failed, as Wainwright knew; also hampering investigation was the fact that credit-card counterfeiting, under federal law, was not a criminal offense. Fraud had to be proven; intention to defraud was not enough. For all these reasons, law-enforcement agencies were more interested in other forms of counterfeiting, so their concern with credit cards was only incidental. Banks—to the chagrin of professionals like Nolan Wainwright—had made no serious effort to get this situation changed.

Most of this, the bank security chief explained at length to Miles Eastin. He also unfolded a basically simple plan. Miles would go to the Double-Seven Health Club, making such contacts as he could. He would try to ingratiate himself, and would also take whatever opportunities occurred to earn some money.

"Doing that will mean a risk two ways, and you'll have to realize it," Wainwright said. "If you do something criminal and get caught, you'll be arrested, tried, and no one else can help you. The other risk is, even if you don't get caught and the parole board hears rumors, that'll put you back in prison just as surely."

However, Wainwright continued, if neither mischance happened, Miles should try to widen his contacts, listening hard and accumulating information. At first, he should be wary of appearing curious. "You'd take it easy," Wainwright cautioned. "Don't hurry, be patient. Let word get around; let people come to you."

Only after Miles was accepted, would he work harder at learning more. At that time he could begin discreet inquiries about fake credit cards, exhibiting an interest for himself and seeking to move closer to wherever they were traded. "There's always somebody," Wainwright advised, "who knows somebody else, who knows some other guy who has a rumble of some action. That's the way you'd weasel in."

Periodically, Wainwright said, Eastin would report to him. Though never directly.

The mention of reporting was a reminder to Wainwright of his obligation to explain about Vic. He did so bluntly, omitting no details. As he spoke, he saw Miles Eastin go pale and remembered the night in Eastin's apartment, the time of the confrontation and exposure, when the younger man's instinctive fear of physical violence showed so clearly.

"Whatever happens," Wainwright said sternly, "I don't want you to say or think, later on, that I didn't warn you of the dangers." He paused, considering. "Now, about money."

If Miles agreed to go undercover on the bank's behalf, the security chief stated, he would guarantee a payment of five hundred dollars a month until—one way or another—the assignment ended. The money would be paid through an intermediary.

"Would I be employed by the bank?"

"Absolutely no."

The answer was unequivocal, emphatic, final. Wainwright elaborated: Involvement of the bank officially would be nil. If Miles Eastin agreed to assume the role suggested, he would be entirely on his own. If he ran into trouble and tried to implicate First Mercantile American, he would be disowned and disbelieved. "Since you were convicted and went to jail," Wainwright declared, "we never even heard of you."

Miles grimaced. "It's one-sided."

"Damn right! But remember this: You came here. I didn't come to you. So what's your answer—yes or no?"

"If you were me, which would it be?"

"I'm not you, nor likely to be. But I'll tell you how I see it. The way things are, you don't have many choices."

For a moment the old Miles Eastin humor and good nature flashed. "Heads I lose; tails I lose. I guess I hit the loser's jackpot. Let me ask one thing more."

"What?"

"If it all works out, if I get—if *you* get—the evidence you need, afterward will you help me find a job at FMA?"

"I can't promise that. I already said I didn't write the rules."

"But you've influence to bend them."

Wainwright considered before answering. He thought: If it came to it, he could go to Alex Vandervoort and present a case on behalf of

Eastin. Success would be worth it. He said aloud, "I'll try. But that'
all I promise."

"You're a hard man," Miles Eastin said. "All right, I'll do it."

They discussed an intermediary.

"After today," Wainwright warned, "you and I won't meet again di
rectly. It's too dangerous; either one of us may be watched. What w
need is someone who can be a conduit for messages—both ways—an
money; someone whom we both trust totally."

Miles said slowly, "There's Juanita Núñez. *If* she'd do it."

Wainwright looked incredulous. "The teller who you . . ."

"Yes. But she forgave me." There was a mixture of elation and ex
citement in his voice. "I went to see her and Heaven bless her, she for
gave me!"

"I'll be damned."

"*You* ask her," Miles Eastin said. "There's not a single reason why sh
should agree. But I think . . . just think, she might."

5

How sound was Lewis D'Orsey's instinct about Supranational Corporation? How sound was Supranational? That worry continued to vex Alex Vandervoort.

It was on Saturday night that Alex and Lewis had talked about SuNatCo. Over what remained of the weekend, Alex pondered *The D'Orsey Newsletter* recommendation to sell Supranational shares at whatever the market would pay and Lewis's doubts about the conglomerate's solidity.

The entire subject was exceedingly important, even vital, to the bank. Yet it could be a delicate situation in which, Alex realized, he would need to move cautiously.

For one thing, Supranational was now a major client and any client would be righteously indignant if its own bankers circulated adverse rumors about it, particularly if false. And Alex had no illusions: Once he began asking questions widely, word of them, and their source, would travel fast.

But were the rumors false? Certainly—as Lewis D'Orsey had admitted—they were insubstantial. But then so had the original rumors been about such spectacular business failures as Penn Central, Equity Funding, Franklin National Bank, American Bank & Trust, U. S. National Bank of San Diego, and others. There was also Lockheed, which hadn't failed, but came close to it, being bailed out by a U. S. Government welfare handout. Alex remembered with disquieting clarity Lewis D'Orsey's reference to SuNatCo's chairman, Quartermain, shopping in Washington for a Lockheed-type loan—except that Lewis used the word "subsidy," which wasn't far from truth.

It was possible, of course, that Supranational was merely suffering a temporary cash shortage, which sometimes happened to the soundest of companies. Alex hoped that that—or something less—was true. However, as an officer of FMA he could not afford to sit back and hope. Fifty million dollars of bank money had been funneled into SuNatCo; also using funds which it was the bank's job to safeguard, the trust department had invested heavily in Supranational shares, a fact which still made Alex shiver when he thought about it.

He decided the first thing he should do, in fairness, was inform Roscoe Heyward.

On Monday morning he walked from his office, down the carpeted 36th floor corridor, to Heyward's. Alex took with him the latest issue of *The D'Orsey Newsletter* which Lewis had given him on Saturday night.

Heyward was not there. With a friendly nod to the senior secretary Mrs. Callaghan, Alex strolled in and put the newsletter directly on Heyward's desk. He had already ringed the item about Supranational and clipped on a note which read:

> Roscoe—
> I thought you should see this.
> A.

Then Alex returned to his own office.

Half an hour later, Heyward stormed in, his face flushed. He tossed down the newsletter. "Did you put this disgusting insult-to-intelligence on my desk?"

Alex pointed to his own handwritten note. "It rather looks like it."

"Then do me the favor of not sending me any more drivel written by that conceited ignoramus."

"Oh, come on! Sure, Lewis D'Orsey is conceited, and I dislike part of what he writes, just as you obviously do. But he isn't an ignoramus, and some of his viewpoints are at least worth hearing."

"You may think so. Others don't. I suggest you read this." Heyward slapped an opened magazine on top of the newsletter.

Alex looked down, surprised at the other's vehemence. "I *have* read it."

The magazine was *Forbes*, the two-page article in question a slashing attack on Lewis D'Orsey. Alex had found the piece long on spite, short on fact. But it underscored what he already knew—that attacks on *The D'Orsey Newsletter* by the financial establishment press were frequent. Alex pointed out, "*The Wall Street Journal* had something similar a year ago."

"Then I'm amazed you don't accept the fact that D'Orsey has absolutely no training or qualifications as an investment adviser. In a way, I'm sorry his wife works for us."

Alex said sharply, "Edwina and Lewis D'Orsey make a point of keeping their occupations entirely separate, as I'm sure you know. As to qualifications, I'll remind you that plenty of degree-loaded experts haven't done well in financial forecasting. Quite frequently, Lewis D'Orsey has."

"Not where Supranational is concerned."

"Do you still think SuNatCo is sound?"

Alex asked the last question quietly, not from antagonism, but seeking information. But its effect on Roscoe Heyward seemed near-explosive. Heyward glared through his rimless glasses; his face suffused an even deeper red. "I'm sure that nothing would delight you more than to see a setback for SuNatCo, and thereby me."

"No, that isn't . . ."

"Let me finish!" Heyward's facial muscles twitched as anger poured out. "I've observed more than enough of your petty conniving and doubt-casting, like passing around this garbage"—he motioned to *The D'Orsey Newsletter*—"and now I'm telling you to cease and desist. Supranational was, and is, a sound, progressive company with high earnings and good management. Getting the SuNatCo account—much as you may be jealous about it personally—was my achievement; it's my business. Now I'm warning you: Stay out of it!"

Heyward wheeled and stalked out.

For several minutes Alex Vandervoort sat silently thoughtful, weighing what had just occurred. The outburst had amazed him. In the two and a half years that he had known and worked with Roscoe Heyward, the two of them had suffered disagreements and occasionally revealed their mutual dislike. But never before had Heyward lost control as he had this morning.

Alex thought he knew why. Underneath the bluster, Roscoe Heyward was worried. The more Alex thought about it, the more he was convinced.

Earlier, Alex had been worried himself—about Supranational. Now the question posed itself: Was Heyward worrying about SuNatCo, too? If so, what next?

As he pondered, memory stirred. A fragment from a recent conversation. Alex pressed an intercom button and told his secretary, "See if you can locate Miss Bracken."

It took fifteen minutes before Margot's voice said brightly, "This had better be good. You got me out of court."

"Trust me, Bracken." He wasted no time. "In your department store class action—the one you talked about on Saturday night—you told us you used a private investigator."

"Yes. Vernon Jax."

"I think Lewis knew him, or of him."

"That's right."

"And Lewis said he was a good man who'd done work for the SEC."

"I heard that, too. Probably it's because Vernon has a degree in economics."

Alex added the information to notes he had already made. "Is Jax discreet? Trustworthy?"

"Totally."

"Where do I find him?"

"I'll find him. Tell me where and when you want him."

"In my office, Bracken. Today—without fail."

Alex studied the untidy, balding, nondescript man seated opposite him in his office conference area. It was midafternoon.

Jax, Alex guessed, was in his early fifties. He looked like a small-town grocer, not too prosperous. His shoes were scuffed and there was a food stain on his jacket. Alex had already learned that Jax had been a staff investigator for the IRS before going into business for himself.

"I'm told you also have a degree in economics," Alex said.

The other shrugged deprecatingly. "Night school. You know how it is. Time on your hands." His voice tailed off, leaving the explanation incomplete.

"How about accounting? Do you have much knowledge there?"

"Some. Studying for CPA exams right now."

"Night school, I suppose." Alex was beginning to catch on.

"Yep." A pale ghost of a smile.

"Mr. Jax," Alex began.

"Most folks just call me Vernon."

"Vernon, I'm considering having you undertake an inquiry. It will require absolute discretion and speed is essential. You've heard of Supranational Corporation?"

"Sure."

"I want a financial investigation of that company. But it will have to be—I'm afraid there's no other word for it—an outside snooping job."

Jax smiled again. "Mr. Vandervoort"—this time his tone was crisper—"that's precisely the business I'm in."

It would require a month, they agreed, though an interim report would be made to Alex if it seemed warranted. Complete confidentiality concerning the bank's investigative role would be preserved. Nothing illegal would be done. The investigator's fee was to be fifteen thousand plus reasonable expenses, half the fee payable immediately, the balance after a final report. Alex would arrange payment from FMA operating funds. He realized he might have to justify the expense later, but would worry about it when the time came.

Late in the afternoon, when Jax had gone, Margot phoned.

"Did you hire him?"

"Yes."

"Were you impressed?"

Alex decided he would play the game. "Not really."

Margot laughed softly. "You will be. You'll see."

But Alex hoped he wouldn't. He hoped fervently that Lewis D'Orsey's instincts were wrong, that Vernon Jax would discover nothing, and that adverse rumors about Supranational would prove rumors—nothing more.

That night, Alex paid one of his periodic visits to Celia at the Remedial Center. He had come to dread the visits even more; he always came away deeply depressed, but continued them out of a sense of duty. Or was it guilt? He was never sure.

As usual, he was escorted by a nurse to Celia's private room in the institution. When the nurse had gone, Alex sat talking, chatting in an inane, one-sided conversation about whatever things occurred to him, though Celia gave no sign of hearing, or even an awareness of his presence. Once, on an earlier occasion, he spoke gibberish just to see if her blankness of expression changed. It hadn't. Afterward he felt ashamed and hadn't done it since.

Even so, he had formed the habit during these sessions with Celia, of prattling on, scarcely listening to himself, while half his mind was wandering elsewhere. Tonight, among other things, he said, "People have all kinds of problems nowadays, Celia; problems which no one ever thought of a few years ago. Along with every clever thing mankind discovers or invents, come dozens of questions and decisions we never had to face before. Take electric can openers. If you have one—and I do in my apartment—there's a problem of where to plug it, when to use it, how to clean it, what to do when it goes wrong; all problems nobody would have if there weren't electric can openers and, after all, who needs them? Speaking of problems, I have several at this moment—personal and at the bank. A big one came up today. In some ways you may be better off in here . . ."

Alex checked himself, realizing he was talking, if not gibberish, then rubbish. No one was better off here, in this tragic twilight quarter-life.

Yet nothing else was left for Celia; in the past few months that fact had become even clearer than before. As recently as a year ago there had been traces of her former girlish, fragile beauty. Now they were gone. Her once-glorious fair hair was dull and sparse. Her skin had a grayish texture; in places eruptions showed where she had scratched herself.

Where once her curled-up fetal position had been occasional, now she adopted it most of the time. And though Celia was ten years younger than Alex, she appeared hag-like and twenty years older.

It was nearly five years since Celia had entered the Remedial Center. In the meantime she had become totally institutionalized, and was likely to remain so.

Watching his wife, and continuing to talk, Alex felt compassion and sadness, but no sense of attachment or affection any more. Perhaps he ought to experience some of those emotions but, being honest with himself, he no longer found it possible. Yet he was tied to Celia, he recognized, by bonds he would never sever until one or the other of them died.

He remembered his conversation with Dr. McCartney, head of the Remedial Center, almost eleven months ago, the day after Ben Rosselli so dramatically announced his impending death. Answering Alex's question about the effect on Celia of a divorce and Alex's remarriage, the psychiatrist had said: *It might drive her over the brink into a totally demented state.*

And, later, Margot had declared: *What I won't have on my conscience, or yours, is shoving what's left of Celia's sanity into a bottomless pit.*

Tonight, Alex wondered if Celia's sanity was in some bottomless pit already. But even if true, it didn't change his reluctance to set in motion the final, ruthless machinery of divorce.

Nor had he gone to live permanently with Margot Bracken, or she with him. Margot remained agreeable to either arrangement, though Alex still wanted marriage—which obviously he couldn't have without divorcing Celia. Lately, though, he had sensed Margot's impatience at the lack of a decision.

How strange that he, accustomed at First Mercantile American to taking large decisions swiftly in stride, should wrestle with indecision in his private life!

The essence of the problem, Alex realized, was his old ambivalence about his personal guilt. Could he, years ago, by greater effort, love, and understanding, have saved his young, nervous, insecure bride from what she had become? If he had been more a devoted husband, less a devoted banker, he still suspected that he might.

It was why he came here, why he continued doing the little that he could.

When it was time to leave Celia, he rose and went toward her, intending to kiss her forehead as he did whenever she allowed him. But tonight she shrank away, curling her body even tighter, her eyes alert with sudden fear. He sighed and abandoned the attempt.

"Good night, Celia," Alex said.

There was no answer and he went out, leaving his wife to whatever lonely world she now inhabited.

Next morning Alex sent for Nolan Wainwright. He told the security chief that the investigator's fee to be paid Vernon Jax would be remitted through Wainwright's department. Alex would authorize the expense. Alex didn't state, and Wainwright didn't ask, the specific nature of Jax's investigation. For the moment, Alex decided, the fewer people who knew the target, the better.

Nolan Wainwright had a reciprocal report for Alex. It concerned his arrangement that Miles Eastin would be an undercover agent for the bank. Alex's reaction was immediate.

"No. I don't want that man ever again on our payroll."

"He won't be on the payroll," Wainwright argued. "I've explained to him that as far as the bank is concerned, he has no status. Any money he'll receive will be in cash, with nothing to show where it came from."

"That's hairsplitting, Nolan. One way or the other he'd be employed by us, and that I can't agree to."

"If you don't agree," Wainwright objected, "you'll be tying my hands, not letting me do my job."

"Doing your job doesn't require you to hire a convicted thief."

"Ever hear of using one to catch one?"

"Then use one who didn't personally defraud this bank."

They argued back and forth, at moments heatedly. In the end, Alex reluctantly conceded. Afterward he asked, "Does Eastin realize how much of a risk he's taking?"

"He knows."

."You told him about the dead man?" Alex had learned about Vic, from Wainwright, several months ago.

"Yes."

"I still don't like the idea—any of it."

"You'll like it even less if Keycharge fraud losses keep increasing, as they are."

Alex sighed. "All right. It's your department and you're entitled to run it your way, which is why I've given in. But I'll impress one thing on you: If you've reason to believe Eastin is in immediate danger, then pull him out at once."

"I intended that."

Wainwright was glad that he had won, though it had been a tougher argument than he expected. However, it seemed unwise right now to mention anything else—for example, his hope of enlisting Juanita Núñez as an intermediary. After all, he rationalized, the principle was established, so why bother Alex with details?

6

Juanita Núñez was torn between suspicion and curiosity. Suspicion because she disliked and distrusted the bank's vice-president of security, Nolan Wainwright. Curiosity because she wondered why he wanted to see her, apparently in secrecy.

There was nothing for her to be concerned about personally, Wainwright had assured Juanita on the telephone yesterday when he called her at the main downtown branch. He would merely like the two of them, he said, to have a confidential talk. "It's a question of whether you'd be willing to help someone else."

"Like you?"

"Not exactly."

"Then who?"

"I'd prefer to tell you privately."

From his voice, Juanita sensed that Wainwright was trying to be friendly. But she parried the friendliness, still remembering his unfeeling harshness when she had been under suspicion of theft. Not even his subsequent apology had wiped out that memory. She doubted if anything ever would.

Just the same, he was a senior officer of FMA and she a junior employee. "Well," Juanita said, "I'm here, and last time I looked the tunnel was open." She assumed that either Wainwright would walk over from the Headquarters Tower or she would be told to report there. However, he surprised her.

"It would be best if we didn't meet in the bank, Mrs. Núñez. When I've explained, you'll understand why. Suppose I pick you up in my car from your home this evening, and we talk while we drive."

"I can't do that." She was more wary than ever.

"You mean, not tonight?"

"Yes."

"How about tomorrow?"

Juanita was stalling, trying to decide. "I'll have to let you know."

"All right, call me tomorrow. As early as you can. And meanwhile, please don't tell anyone else we had this conversation." Wainwright hung up.

Now it *was* tomorrow—Tuesday in the third week of September. At midmorning, Juanita knew that if she failed to call Wainwright soon, he would call her.

She was still uneasy. Sometimes, she thought, she had a nose for trouble and scented it now. Earlier Juanita had considered asking the advice of Mrs. D'Orsey whom she could see, on the other side of the bank, at the manager's desk on the platform. But she hesitated, remembering Wainwright's cautionary words about not telling anyone else. That, as much as anything, had piqued her curiosity.

Today Juanita was working on new accounts. Beside her was a phone. She stared at it, picked it up, and dialed the internal number of Security. Moments later, Nolan Wainwright's deep voice asked, "Can you make it tonight?"

Curiosity won out. "Yes, but not for long." She explained that she would leave Estela alone for half an hour; no more.

"That will be long enough. What time and where?"

Dusk was settling in when Nolan Wainwright's Mustang II nosed to the curb outside the Forum East apartment building where Juanita Núñez lived. Moments later she emerged through the main floor entranceway, closing it carefully behind her. Wainwright reached over from behind the wheel to open the nearside door and she climbed in.

He helped fasten her seat harness, then said, "Thank you for coming."

"Half an hour," Juanita reminded him. "That's all." She made no attempt to be friendly and was already nervous about leaving Estela alone.

The bank security chief nodded as he eased the car away from the curb and into traffic. They drove two blocks in silence, then made a left turn onto a busier, divided road, lined with brightly lighted stores and eateries. Still driving, Wainwright said, "I hear young Eastin came to see you."

She responded sharply, "How did you know?"

"He told me. He also said that you've forgiven him."

"If he said it, then you know."

"Juanita—may I call you that?"

"It is my name. I suppose so."

Wainwright sighed. "Juanita, I already told you I'm sorry about the way things went between us once before. If you still hold that against me, I don't blame you."

She thawed slightly. "*Bueno*, you had better tell me what it is you want."

"I want to know if you'd be willing to help Eastin."

"So he is the one."

"Yes."

"Why should I? Isn't forgiving him enough?"

"If you ask my opinion—more than enough. But he was the one who said you might . . ."

She interrupted. "What kind of help?"

"Before I tell you, I'd like your promise that what we say tonight will go no further than the two of us."

She shrugged. "There is no one to tell. But you have the promise."

"Eastin is going to do some investigative work. It's for the bank, though unofficial. If he succeeds it may help him get rehabilitated, which is what he wants." Wainwright paused while he maneuvered the car around a slow-moving tractor-trailer. He continued, "The work is risky. It would be riskier still if Eastin reported directly to me. What the two of us need is someone to carry messages both ways—an intermediary."

"And you decided it should be me?"

"No one's decided. It's a question of whether you'd be willing. If you were, it would help Eastin help himself."

"And is Miles the only one this would help?"

"No," Wainwright admitted. "It would help me; also the bank."

"Somehow that is what I thought."

They had left the bright lights now and were crossing the river by a bridge; in the gathering darkness the water gleamed blackly far below. The road surface was metallic and the car wheels hummed. At the end of the bridge was the entrance to an interstate highway. Wainwright turned onto it.

"The investigation you speak of," Juanita prompted. "Tell me more about it." Her voice was low, expressionless.

"All right." He described how Miles Eastin would operate under cover, using his contacts made in prison, and the kind of evidence Miles would search for. There was no point, Wainwright decided, in holding anything back because what he didn't tell Juanita now she would find out later. So he added the information about the murder of Vic, though omitting the more unpleasant details. "I'm not saying the same will happen to Eastin," he concluded. "I'll do everything possible to make sure it won't. But I mention it so you know the risk he's running, and he understands it, too. If you were to help him, as I said, it would keep him safer."

"And who will keep *me* safe?"

"For you there'd be virtually no risk. The only contact you'd have would be with Eastin and with me. No one else would know, and you wouldn't be compromised. We'd make sure of that."

"If you are so sure, why are we meeting this way now?"

"Simply a precaution. To make certain we're not seen together and can't be overheard."

Juanita waited, then she asked, "And that is all? There is nothing more to tell me?"

Wainwright said, "I guess that's it."

They were on the interstate now and he held the car at a steady 45, staying in the right-hand lane while other vehicles speeded past. On the opposite side of the divided highway three lines of headlights streamed toward them, passing in a blur. Soon he would turn off at an exit ramp and return the way they had come. Meanwhile, Juanita sat silently beside him, her eyes directed straight ahead.

He wondered what she was thinking and what her answer would be. He hoped it would be yes. As on earlier occasions he found this petite, elfin girl-woman provocative and sexually attractive. Her perversity was part of it; so was the smell of her—a bodily feminine presence in the small closed car. There had been few women in Nolan Wainwright's life since his divorce, and at any other time he might have tried his luck. But what he wanted from Juanita now was too important to take a chance with self-indulgence.

He was about to break the silence when Juanita turned to face him. Even in the semidarkness he could see her eyes were blazing.

"You must be *mad, mad, mad!*" Her voice rose heatedly. "Do you think I am a little fool? *¡Una boba! ¡Una tonta!* No risk for me, you say! Of course there is a risk, and I take all of it. And for what? For the glory of Mr. Security Wainwright and his bank."

"Now wait . . ."

She brushed aside the interruption, storming on, her anger spilling out like lava. "Am I such an easy target? Does being alone or Puerto Rican qualify me for all the abuses of this world? Do you not care *who* you use, or how? *Take me home!* What kind of *pendejada* is this anyway?"

"Hold it!" Wainwright said; the reaction had astonished him. "What's *pendejada?*"

"Idiocy! *Pendejada* that you would throw a man's life away for your selfish credit cards. *Pendejada* that Miles would agree to do it."

"He came to me asking for help. I didn't go to him."

"You call *that* help?"

"He'll be paid for what he does. He wanted that, too. And it was he who suggested you."

"Then what is wrong with him that he cannot ask me himself? Has Miles lost his tongue? Or is he ashamed, and hiding behind your skirts?"

"Okay, okay," Wainwright protested. "I get the message. I'll take you home." An off ramp was close ahead; he turned onto it, crossed an overpass and headed back toward the city.

Juanita sat fuming.

At first, she had tried to consider calmly what Wainwright was suggesting. But while he had talked, and she had listened, doubts and questions besieged her, then afterward, as she considered each, her anger and emotion grew, and finally exploded. Coupled with her outburst was a fresh hate and disgust for the man beside her. All the old painful feelings of her earlier experience with him now returned and were augmented. And she was angry, not only for herself, but about the use which Wainwright and the bank proposed to make of Miles.

At the same time Juanita was incensed *at* Miles. Why had he not approached her himself, directly? Was he not man enough? She remembered that less than three weeks ago she had admired his courage in coming to her, facing her penitently, and asking forgiveness. But his actions now, the method of working on her through someone else, seemed more in keeping with his earlier deceit when he had blamed her for his own malfeasance. Suddenly her thinking veered. Was she being harsh, unjust? Looking inside herself, Juanita asked: Wasn't part of her frustration at this moment a disappointment that Miles had not returned after the encounter in her apartment? And wasn't there—exacerbating that disappointment here and now—a resentment that Miles, whom she liked despite everything, was being represented to her by Nolan Wainwright, whom she didn't?

Her anger, never long sustained, diminished. Uncertainty replaced it. She asked Wainwright, "So what will you do now?"

"Whatever I decide, I'm certainly not likely to confide in you." His tone was curt, the attempt at friendliness gone.

With sudden alarm, Juanita wondered if she had been needlessly belligerent. She *could* have turned down the request without the insults. Would Wainwright find some way to retaliate within the bank? Had she put her job in jeopardy?—the job she depended on to support Estela. Juanita's anxiety increased. She had a sense, after all, of being trapped.

And something else, she thought: If she were honest—which she tried to be—she regretted that because of her decision she would see no more of Miles.

The car had slowed. They were near the turnoff which would take them back across the river bridge.

Surprising herself, Juanita said in a flat, small voice, "Very well, I will do it."

"You'll what?"

"I will be—whatever it was—an . . ."

"Intermediary." Wainwright glanced sideways at her. "You're sure?"

"*Sí, estoy segura.* I am sure."

For the second time tonight he sighed. "You're a strange one."

"I am a woman."

"Yes," he said, and some of the friendliness was back. "I'd noticed."

A block and a half from Forum East, Wainwright stopped the car, leaving the motor running. He removed two envelopes from an inside jacket pocket—one fat, the other smaller—and handed the first to Juanita.

"That's money for Eastin. Keep it until he gets in touch with you." The envelope, Wainwright explained, contained four hundred and fifty dollars in cash—the agreed monthly payment, less a fifty-dollar advance which Wainwright had given Miles last week.

"Later this week," he added, "Eastin will phone me and I'll announce a code word we've already arranged. Your name will not be mentioned. But he'll know that he's to contact you, which he'll do soon after."

Juanita nodded, concentrating, storing the information away.

"After that phone call, Eastin and I won't contact each other directly again. Our messages, both ways, will go through you. It would be best if you didn't write them down, but carry them in your head. I happen to know your memory is good."

Wainwright smiled as he said it, and abruptly Juanita laughed. How ironic that her remarkable memory, which was once a cause of her troubles with the bank and Nolan Wainwright, should be relied on by him now!

"By the way," he said, "I'll need to know your home phone number. I couldn't find it listed."

"That is because I do not have a telephone. It costs too much."

"Just the same, you'll need one. Eastin may want to call you; so might I. If you'll have a phone installed immediately, I'll see that the bank reimburses you."

"I will try. But I have heard from others that phones are slow to be put in at Forum East."

"Then let me arrange it. I'll call the phone company tomorrow. I guarantee fast action."

"Very well."

Now Wainwright opened the second, smaller envelope. "When you give Eastin the money, also give him this."

"This" was a Keycharge bank credit card, made out in the name of H. E. LYNCOLP. On the rear of the card a space for signature was blank.

"Have Eastin sign the card, in that name, in his normal handwriting. Tell him the name is a fake, though if he looks at the initials and the last letter, he'll see they spell H-E-L-P. That's what the card is for."

The bank security chief said that the Keycharge computer had been programmed so that if this card was presented anywhere, a purchase of up to a hundred dollars would be approved, but simultaneously an automatic alert would be raised within the bank. This would notify Wainwright that Eastin needed help, and where he was.

"He can use the card if he's on to something hot and wants support, or if he knows he's in danger. Depending on what's happened up to then, I'll decide what to do. Tell him to buy something worth more than fifty dollars; that way the store will be certain to phone in for confirmation. After that phone call, he should dawdle as much as he can, to give me time to move."

Wainwright added, "He may never need the card. But if he does, it's a signal no one else will know about."

At Wainwright's request, Juanita repeated his instructions almost word for word. He looked at her admiringly. "You're pretty bright."

"¿De qué me vale, muerta?"

"What does that mean?"

She hesitated, then translated, "What good will it do me if I'm dead?"

"Stop worrying!" Reaching across the car he gently touched her folded hands. "I promise it'll all work out."

At that moment his confidence was infectious. But later, back in her apartment with Estela sleeping, Juanita's instinct about impending trouble persistently returned.

7

The Double-Seven Health Club smelled of boiler steam, stale urine, body odor, and booze. After a while, though, to anyone inside, the various effluvia merged into a single pungency, curiously acceptable, so that fresh air which occasionally blew in seemed alien.

The club was a boxlike, four-story brown brick building in a decaying, dead-end street on the fringes of downtown. Its façade was scarred by a half century of wear, neglect, and—more recently—graffiti. At the building's peak was an unadorned stub of flagpole which no one remembered seeing whole. The main entrance consisted of a single, solid, unmarked door abutting directly on a sidewalk notable for cracks, overturned garbage cans, and innumerable dog turds. A paint-flaking lobby just inside was supposed to be guarded by a punch-drunk bruiser who let members in and churlishly kept strangers out, but he was sometimes missing, which was why Miles Eastin wandered in unchallenged.

It was shortly before noon, midweek, and a dissonance of raised voices drifted back from somewhere in the rear. Miles walked toward the sound, down a main-floor corridor, none too clean and hung with yellowed prizefight pictures. At the end was an open door to a semi-darkened bar from where the voices came. Miles went in.

At first he could scarcely see in the dimness and moved uncertainly so that a hurrying waiter with a tray of drinks caromed into him. The waiter swore, somehow managed to keep the glasses upright, and moved on. Two men perched on barstools turned their heads. One said, "Thisa private club, buster. If you aina member—out!"

The other complained, "'S 'at lazy bum Pedro goofin' off. Some doorman! Hey, who are ya? Wadda ya want?"

Miles told him, "I was looking for Jules LaRocca."

"Look someplace else," the first man ordered. "No wunna that name here."

"Hey, Milesy baby!" A squat pot-bellied figure bustled forward through the gloom. The familiar weasel face came into focus. It was LaRocca who in Drummonburg Penitentiary had been an emissary from Mafia Row, and later attached himself to Miles and his protector Karl. Karl was still inside, and likely to remain there. Jules LaRocca had been released on parole shortly before Miles Eastin.

"Hi, Jules," Miles acknowledged.

"Come over. Meet some guys." LaRocca seized Miles's arm in pudgy fingers. "Frenna mine," he told the two men on barstools who turned their backs indifferently.

"Listen," Miles said, "I won't come over. I'm out of bread. I can't buy." He slipped easily into the argot he had learned in prison.

"Forget it. Hava coupla beers on me." As they passed between tables, LaRocca asked, "Whereya bin?"

"Looking for work. I'm all beat, Jules. I need some help. Before I got out you said you'd give it to me."

"Sure, sure." They stopped at a table where two other men were seated. One was skinny with a mournful, pockmarked face; the other had long blond hair, cowboy boots, and wore dark glasses. LaRocca pulled up an extra chair. "Thissa my buddy, Milesy."

The man with dark glasses grunted. The other said, "The guy knows about dough?"

"That's him." LaRocca shouted across the room for beer, then urged the man who had spoken first to, "Ask him sumpum."

"Like what?"

"Like about money, asshole," dark glasses said. He considered. "Where'da first dollar get started?"

"That's easy," Miles told him. "Lots of people think America invented the dollar. Well, we didn't. It came from Bohemia in Germany, only first it was called a *thaler*, which other Europeans couldn't pronounce, so they corrupted it to dollar and it stayed that way. One of the first references to it is in *Macbeth*—'ten thousand dollars to our general use.'"

"Mac who?"

"Macshit," LaRocca said. "You wanna printed program?" He told the other two proudly, "See what I mean? This kid knows it all."

"Not quite," Miles said, "or I'd know how to make some money at this moment."

Two beers were slapped in front of him. LaRocca fished out cash which he gave the waiter.

"Before ya make dough," LaRocca said to Miles, "ya gotta pay Ominsky." He leaned across confidingly, ignoring the other two. "The Russian knows ya outta the can. Bin askin' for ya."

The mention of the loan shark, to whom he still owed at least three thousand dollars, left Miles sweating. There was another debt, too—roughly the same amount—to the bookie he had dealt with, but the chance of paying either seemed remote at this moment. Yet he had known that coming here, making himself visible, would reopen the old accounts and that savage reprisals would follow if he failed to pay.

He asked LaRocca, "How can I pay any of what I owe if I can't get work?"

The pot-bellied man shook his head. "First off, ya gotta see the Russian."

"Where?" Miles knew that Ominsky had no office but operated wherever business took him.

LaRocca motioned to the beer. "Drink up, then you 'n me go look."

"Look at it from my point of view," the elegantly dressed man said, continuing his lunch. His diamond ringed hands moved deftly above his plate. "We had a business arrangement, you and me, which both of us agreed to. I kept my part. You've not kept yours. I ask you, where does that leave me?"

"Look," Miles pleaded, "you know what happened, and I appreciate your stopping the clock the way you did. But I can't pay now. I want to, but I can't. Please give me time."

Igor (the Russian) Ominsky shook his expensively barbered head; manicured fingers touched a pink clean-shaven cheek. He was vain about his appearance, and lived and dressed well, as he could afford to.

"Time," he said softly, "is money. You've had too much of both already."

On the opposite side of the booth, in the restaurant where LaRocca had brought him, Miles had the feeling of being a mouse before a cobra. There was no food on his side of the table, not even a glass of water, which he could have used because his lips were dry and fear gnawed at his stomach. If he could have gone to Nolan Wainwright now and canceled their arrangement, which had exposed him in this way, Miles would have done it instantly. As it was, he sat sweating, watching, while Ominsky continued his meal of Sole Bonne Femme. Jules LaRocca had strolled discreetly away to the restaurant's bar.

The reason for Miles's fear was simple. He could guess the size of Ominsky's business and knew the absoluteness of his power.

Once, Miles had watched a TV special on which an authority on American crime, Ralph Salerno, was asked the question: If you had to live illegally, what kind of criminal would you be? The expert's answer instantly: A loan shark. What Miles knew, from his contacts in prison and before, confirmed this view.

A loan shark like Russian Ominsky was a banker harvesting a staggering profit with minimal risk, dealing in loans large and small, unhampered by regulations. His customers came to him; he seldom sought them out, or needed to. He rented no expensive premises and did his business in a car, a bar—or at lunch, as now. His record keeping was the simplest, usually in code, and his transactions—largely in cash—were untraceable. His losses from bad debts were minor. He paid no federal, state, or city taxes. Yet interest rates—or "vig"—he charged were normally 100 percent p.a., and often higher.

At any given time, Miles guessed, Ominsky would have at least two million dollars "on the street." Some of it would be the loan shark's own money, the rest invested with him by bosses of organized crime for whom he made a handsome profit, taking a commission for himself. It was normal for an initial $100,000 invested in loan-sharking to be pyramided, within five years, to $1.5 million—a 1,400 percent capital gain. No other business in the world could equal it.

Nor were a loan shark's clients always small-time. With surprising frequency, big names and reputable businesses borrowed from loan sharks when other credit sources were exhausted. Sometimes, in lieu of repayment, a loan shark would become a partner—or owner—of another business. Like a sea shark, his bite was large.

The loan shark's main expenses were for enforcement, and he kept those minimal, knowing that broken limbs and hospitalized bodies produced little, if any, money; and knowing, too, his strongest collection aide was fear.

Yet the fear needed a basis in reality; therefore when a borrower defaulted, punishment by hired goons was swift and savage.

As to risks a loan shark ran, these were slight compared with other forms of crime. Few loan sharks were ever prosecuted, fewer still convicted. Lack of evidence was the reason. A loan shark's customers were closemouthed, partly from fear, some from shame that they needed his services at all. And those who were physically beaten never lodged complaints, knowing that if they did there would be more of the same to come.

Thus, Miles sat, apprehensive, while Ominsky finished his sole.

Unexpectedly, the loan shark said, "Can you keep a set of books?"

"Bookkeeping? Why, yes; when I worked for the bank . . ."

He was waved to silence; cold, hard eyes appraised him. "Maybe I can use you. I need a bookkeeper at the Double-Seven."

"The health club?" It was news to Miles that Ominsky owned or managed it. He added, "I was there today, before . . ."

The other cut him off. "When I'm talking, stay quiet and listen; just answer questions when you're asked. LaRocca says you want to work. If I give you work, everything you earn goes to me to pay your loan and vig. In other words, I *own* you. I want that understood."

"Yes, Mr. Ominsky." Relief flooded Miles. He was to be given time after all. The how and why were unimportant.

"You'll get your meals, a room," Russian Ominsky said, "and one thing I'll warn you—keep your fingers out of the till. If I ever find you didn't, you'll wish you'd stolen from the bank again, not me."

Miles shivered instinctively, less for concern about stealing—which he had no intention of doing—than his awareness of what Ominsky would do if he ever learned a Judas had come into his camp.

"Jules will take you and get you set up. You'll be told what else to do. That's all." Ominsky dismissed Miles with a gesture and nodded to LaRocca who had been watching from the bar. While Miles waited near the restaurant's outer door, the other two conferred, the loan shark issuing instructions and LaRocca nodding.

Jules LaRocca rejoined Miles. "You gotta swell break, kid. Let's move ass."

As they left, Ominsky began to eat dessert while another waiting figure slipped into the seat facing him.

The room at the Double-Seven was on the building's top floor and little more than a shabbily furnished cubicle. Miles didn't mind. It represented a frail beginning, a chance to reshape his life and regain something of what he had lost, though he knew it would take time, grave risk, and enterprise. For the moment, he tried not to think too much about his dual role, concentrating instead on making himself useful and becoming accepted, as Nolan Wainwright had cautioned him to do.

He learned the geography of the club first. Most of the main floor—apart from the bar he had been in originally—was taken up by a gymnasium and handball courts. On the second floor were steam rooms and massage parlors. The third comprised offices; also several other rooms which he learned the use of later. The fourth floor, smaller than the others, contained a few more cubicles like Miles's where club members occasionally slept overnight.

Miles slipped easily into the bookkeeper's work. He was good at the job, catching up on a backlog and improving postings which had been done sloppily before. He made suggestions to the club manager for making other record keeping more efficient, though was careful not to seek credit for the changes.

The manager, an ex-fight promoter named Nathanson, to whom office work did not come easily, was grateful. He was even more appreciative when Miles offered to do extra chores around the club, such as reorganizing stores and inventory procedures. Nathanson, in return, allowed Miles use of the handball courts during some of his free time, which provided an extra chance of meeting members.

The club's all-male membership, as far as Miles could see, was divided broadly into two groups. One comprised those who seriously used the club's athletic facilities, including the steam baths and massage parlors. These people came and went individually, few of them appearing to know each other, and Miles guessed they were salaried workers or minor business executives who belonged to the Double-Seven simply to keep fit. He suspected, too, that the first group provided a conveniently legitimate front for the second, which usually didn't use the athletic facilities, except the steam baths on occasion.

Those in this second group congregated mainly in the bar or the upstairs rooms on the third floor. They were present in greatest numbers late at night, when the exercise-seeking members seldom used the club. It became evident to Miles that this second element was what Nolan Wainwright had in mind when he described the Double-Seven as a "mob hangout."

Something else Miles Eastin learned quickly was that the upstairs rooms were used for illegal, high stakes card and dice games. By the time he had worked a week, some of the night regulars had come to know Miles, and were relaxed about him, being assured by Jules La-Rocca that he was "okay, a stand-up guy."

Shortly after, and pursuing his policy of being useful, Miles began helping out when drinks and sandwiches had to be carried to the third floor. The first time he did, one of a half-dozen burly men standing outside the gaming rooms, who were obviously guards, took the tray from him and carried it in. But next night, and on subsequent ones, he was allowed into the rooms where gambling was taking place. Miles also obliged by buying cigarettes downstairs and bringing them up for anyone who needed them, including the guards.

He knew he was becoming liked.

One reason was his general willingness. Another was that some of his old cheerfulness and good nature were returning, despite the problems and dangers of being where he was. And a third was that Jules LaRocca, who seemed to flit around the fringes of everything, had become Miles's sponsor, even though LaRocca made Miles feel, at times, like a vaudeville performer.

It was Miles Eastin's knowledge about money and its history which fascinated—it seemed endlessly—LaRocca and his cronies. A favorite item was the saga of counterfeit money printed by governments, which Miles had first described in prison. In his early weeks at the club he repeated it, under LaRocca's prodding, at least a dozen times. It always produced nods of belief, along with comments about "stinkin' hypocrites" and "goddam gumment crooks."

To supplement his fund of stories, Miles went one day to the apartment block where he had lived before imprisonment, and retrieved his reference books. Most of his other few possessions had long since been sold to pay arrears of rent, but the janitor had kept the books and let Miles have them. Once, Miles had owned a coin and banknote collection, then sold it when he was heavily in debt. Someday, he hoped, he might become a collector again, though the prospect seemed far away.

Able to dip into his books, which he kept in the fourth-floor cubicle, Miles talked to LaRocca and the others about some of the stranger forms of money. The heaviest currency ever, he told them, was the agronite stone discs used on the Pacific island of Yap up to the outbreak of World War II. Most of the discs, he explained, were one foot wide, but one denomination had a width of twelve feet and, when used for purchasing, was transported on a pole. "Waddabout change?" someone asked amid laughter, and Miles assured them it was given—in smaller stone discs.

In contrast, he reported, the lightest-weight money was scarce types of feathers, used in New Hebrides. Also, for centuries salt circulated as money, especially in Ethiopia, and the Romans used it to pay their workers, hence the word "salary" which evolved from "salt." And in Borneo, as recently as the nineteenth century, Miles told the others, human skulls were legal tender.

But invariably, before such sessions ended, the talk swung back to counterfeiting.

After one such occasion, a hulking driver-bodyguard who hung around the club while his boss played cards upstairs, took Miles aside.

"Hey, kid, you talk big about counterfeit. Take a looka this." He held out a clean, crisp twenty-dollar bill.

Miles accepted the banknote and studied it. The experience was not new to him. When he worked at First Mercantile American Bank, suspected bogus bills were usually brought to him because of his specialist knowledge.

The big man was grinning. "Pretty good, huh?"

"If this is a fake," Miles said, "it's the best I've ever seen."

"Wanna buy a few?" From an inner pocket the bodyguard produced nine more twenties. "Gimme forty bucks in real stuff, kid, that whole two hunnert's yours."

It was about the going rate, Miles knew, for high-grade queer. He observed, too, that the other bills were just as good as the first.

About to refuse the offer, he hesitated. He had no intention of passing any fake money, but realized it was something he could send to Wainwright.

"Hold it!" he told the burly man, and went upstairs to his room where he had squirreled away slightly more than forty dollars. Some of it had been left over from Wainwright's original fifty-dollar stake; the rest was from tips Miles had been given around the gaming rooms. He took the money, mostly in small bills, and exchanged it downstairs for the counterfeit two hundred. Later that night he hid the counterfeit money in his room.

The next day, Jules LaRocca, grinning, told him, "Hear ya didda stroka business." Miles was at his bookkeeper's desk in the third floor offices.

"A little," he admitted.

LaRocca moved his pot belly closer and lowered his voice. "Ya wanna piece more action?"

Miles said cautiously, "It depends what kind."

"Like makin' a trip to Louisville. Movin' summa the stuff you bought last night."

Miles felt his stomach tighten, knowing that if he agreed and were caught, it would not only put him back in prison, but for much longer than before. Yet if he didn't take risks, how could he continue learning, and gaining the confidence of others here?

"All it is, is drivin' a car from here to there. You get paid two C notes."

"What happens if I'm stopped? I'm on parole and not allowed a driver's license."

"A license ain't no problem if you gotta photo—front view, head 'n shoulders."

"I haven't, but I could get one."

"Do it fast."

During his lunch break, Miles walked to a downtown bus station and obtained a photograph from an automatic machine. He gave it to La-Rocca the same afternoon.

Two days later, again while Miles was working, a hand silently placed a small rectangle of paper on the ledger in front of him. With amazement he saw it was a state driver's license, embodying the photo he had supplied.

When he turned, LaRocca stood behind him, grinning. "Better service unna License Bureau, eh?"

Miles said incredulously, "You mean it's a forgery?"

"Can ya tella difference?"

"No, I can't." He peered at the license which appeared to be identical with an official one. "How did you get it?"

"Never mind."

"No," Miles said, "I'd really like to know. You know how interested I am in things like this."

LaRocca's face clouded; for the first time his eyes revealed suspicion. "Why ya wanna know?"

"Just interest. The way I told you." Miles hoped a sudden nervousness didn't show.

"Some questions ain't smart. A guy asks too many, people start wondering. He might get hurt. He might get hurt bad."

Miles stayed silent, LaRocca watching. Then, it seemed, the moment of suspicion passed.

"It'll be tomorrow night," Jules LaRocca informed him. "You'll be told wotta do, and when."

Next day, in the early evening, the instructions were delivered—again by the perennial messenger, LaRocca, who handed Miles a set of car keys, a parking receipt from a city lot, and a one-way airline ticket. Miles was to pick up the car—a maroon Chevrolet Impala—drive it off the lot, then continue through the night to Louisville. On arrival he would go to Louisville airport and park the car there, leaving the airport parking ticket and keys under the front seat. Before leaving the car he was to wipe it carefully to remove his own fingerprints. Then he would take an early-morning flight back.

The worst minutes for Miles were early on, when he had located the car and was driving it from the city parking lot. He wondered tensely: Had the Chevrolet been under surveillance by police? Perhaps whoever parked the car was suspect, and was followed here. If so, now was the moment the law was most likely to close in. Miles knew there had to be a high risk; otherwise someone like himself would not have been sought as courier. And although he had no actual knowledge, he presumed the counterfeit money—probably a lot of it—was in the trunk.

But nothing happened, though it was not until he had left the parking lot well behind and was near the city limits that he began to relax.

Once or twice on the highway, when he encountered state police patrol cars, his heart beat faster, but no one stopped him, and he reached Louisville shortly before dawn after an uneventful journey.

Only one thing happened which was not in the plan. Thirty miles or so from Louisville, Miles pulled off the highway and, in darkness, aided by a flashlight, opened the car's trunk. It contained two heavy suitcases, both securely locked. Briefly he considered forcing one of the locks, then commonsense told him he would jeopardize himself by doing so. After that he closed the trunk, copied down the Impala's license number, and continued on.

He found the Louisville airport without difficulty and after observing the rest of his instructions, boarded a flight back and was at the Double-Seven Health Club shortly before 10 A.M. No questions were asked about his absence.

Through the remainder of the day Miles was weary from the lack of sleep, though he managed to keep working. In the afternoon LaRocca arrived, beaming and smoking a fat cigar.

"Ya whacked off a clean job, Milesy. Nobody's pissed off. Everybody pleased."

"That's good," Miles said. "When do I get paid the two hundred dollars?"

"Y' awready did. Ominsky took it. Goes toward what ya owe him."

Miles sighed. He supposed he should have expected something of the kind, though it seemed ironic to have risked so much, solely for the loan shark's benefit. He asked LaRocca, "How did Ominsky know?"

"Ain't much he don't."

"A minute ago you said everybody was pleased. Who's 'everybody'? If I do a job like yesterday's, I like to know who I'm working for."

"Like I told ya, there's some things it ain't smart to know or ask."

"I suppose so." Obviously he would learn nothing more and he forced a smile for LaRocca's benefit, though today Miles's cheerfulness was gone and depression had replaced it. The overnight trip had been a strain and, despite the horrendous chances he had taken, he realized how little he had really learned.

Some forty-eight hours later, still weary and disheartened, he communicated his misgivings to Juanita.

8

Miles Eastin and Juanita had met on two earlier occasions during the month he had been working at the Double-Seven Health Club.

The first time—a few days after Juanita's evening ride with Nolan Wainwright and her agreement to act as intermediary—had been an awkward, uncertain encounter for them both. Although a telephone had been installed promptly in Juanita's apartment, as Wainwright promised, Miles had not known about it and came unannounced, at night, having traveled there by bus. After a cautious inspection through the partially opened apartment door, Juanita had taken off the safety chain and let him in.

"Hullo," Estela said. The small, dark child—a miniature Juanita—looked up from a coloring book, her large, liquid eyes regarding Miles. "You're the thin man who came before. You're fatter now."

"I know," Miles said. "I've been eating magic giant food."

Estela giggled, but Juanita was frowning. He told her apologetically, "There was no way to warn you I was coming. But Mr. Wainwright said you'd be expecting me."

"That hypocrite!"

"You don't like him?"

"I hate him."

"He isn't my idea of Santa Claus," Miles said. "But I don't hate him either. I guess he has a job to do."

"Then let *him* do it. Not make use of others."

"If you feel so strongly, why did you agree . . . ?"

Juanita snapped, "Do you think I have not asked myself? *Maldito sea el día que lo conocí.* Making the promise that I did was an instant's foolishness, to be regretted."

"There's no need to regret it. Nothing says you can't back down." Miles's voice was gentle. "I'll explain to Wainwright." He made a move toward the door.

Juanita flared at him, "And what of you? Where will you pass your messages?" She shook her head in exasperation. "Were you insane when you agreed to such stupidity?"

"No," Miles said. "I saw it as a chance; in a way the only chance, but there's no reason it should involve you. When I suggested that it might, I hadn't thought it through. I'm sorry."

"Mommy," Estela said, "why are you so angry?"

Juanita reached down and hugged her daughter. "*No te preocupes, mi cielo*. I am angry at life, little one. At what people do to each other." She told Miles abruptly, "Sit, sit!"

"You're sure?"

"Sure of what? That you should sit down? No, I am not even sure of that. *But do it!*"

He obeyed her.

"I like your temper, Juanita." Miles smiled, and for a moment, she thought, he looked the way he used to at the bank. He went on, "I like that and other things about you. If you want the truth, the reason I suggested this arrangement was that it would mean I'd have to see you."

"Well, now you have." Juanita shrugged. "And I suppose you will again. So make your secret agent's report and I will give it to Mr. Spider Wainwright, spinning webs."

"My report is that there isn't any report. At least, not yet." Miles told her about the Double-Seven Health Club, the way it looked and smelled, and saw her nose wrinkle in distaste. He described, too, his encounter with Jules LaRocca, then the meeting with the loan shark, Russian Ominsky, and Miles's employment as the health club book-keeper. At that point, when Miles had worked at the Double-Seven only a few days, that was all he knew. "But I'm in," he assured Juanita. "That was what Mr. Wainwright wanted."

"Sometimes it is easy to get in," she said. "As with a lobster trap, getting out is harder."

Estela had listened gravely. Now she asked Miles, "Will you come again?"

"I don't know." He glanced inquiringly at Juanita who surveyed them both, then sighed.

"Yes, *amorcito*," she told Estela. "Yes, he will come."

Juanita went into the bedroom and returned with the two envelopes

Nolan Wainwright had given her. She handed them to Miles. "These are for you."

The larger envelope contained money, the other the Keycharge credit card in the fictitious name of H. E. LYNCOLP. She explained the purpose of the card—a signal for help.

Miles pocketed the plastic credit card but replaced the money in the first envelope and gave it back to Juanita. "You take this. If I'm seen with it, someone might become suspicious. Use it for yourself and Estela. I owe it to you."

Juanita hesitated. Then, her voice softer than before, she said, "I will keep it for you."

Next day, at First Mercantile American Bank, Juanita had called Wainwright on an internal telephone and made her report. She was careful not to identify by name either herself, Miles, or the Double-Seven Health Club. Wainwright listened, thanked her, and that was all.

The second encounter between Juanita and Miles occurred a week and a half later, on Saturday afternoon. This time Miles had telephoned in advance and when he arrived both Juanita and Estela seemed pleased to see him. They were about to go shopping and he joined them, the three browsing through an open-air market where Juanita bought Polish sausage and cabbage. She told him, "It is for our dinner. Will you stay?"

He assured her he would, adding that he need not return to the health club until late that night, or even the following morning.

While they walked, Estela said suddenly to Miles, "I like you." She slipped her tiny hand into his and kept it there. Juanita, when she noticed, smiled.

Through dinner there was an easy camaraderie. Then Estela went to bed, kissing Miles good night, and when he and Juanita were alone he recited his report for Nolan Wainwright. They were seated, side by side, on the sofa bed. Turning to him when he had finished, she said, "If you wish, you may stay here tonight."

"Last time I did, you slept in there." He motioned to the bedroom.

"This time I will be here. Estela sleeps soundly. We shall not be disturbed."

He reached for Juanita and she came to him eagerly. Her lips, slightly parted, were warm, moist, and sensual, as if a foretaste of still sweeter things to come. Her tongue danced and delighted him. Holding her, he could hear her breathing quicken and felt the small, slim girl-woman body quiver with pent-up passion, responding fiercely to his own. As they drew closer and his hands began exploring, Juanita sighed deeply, savoring the waves of pleasure now, anticipating her ecstasy ahead. It had been a long time since any man had taken her. She made clear she was excited, urgent, waiting. Impatiently they opened the sofa bed.

What followed next was a disaster. Miles had wanted Juanita with his mind and—he believed—his body. But when the moment came in which a man must prove himself, his body failed to function as it should. Despairingly, he strained, concentrated, closed his eyes and wished, but nothing changed. What should have been a young man's ardent, rigid sword was flaccid, ineffectual. Juanita tried to soothe and aid him. "Stop worrying, Miles darling, and be patient. Let me help, and it will happen."

They tried, and tried again. In the end, it was no use. Miles lay back, ashamed and close to tears. He knew, unhappily, that behind his impotence was the awareness of his homosexuality in prison. He had believed, and hoped, it would not inhibit him with a woman, but it had. Miles concluded miserably: Now he knew for sure what he had feared. He was no longer a man.

At last, weary, unhappy, unfulfilled, they slept.

In the night Miles awoke, tossed restlessly for a while, and then got up. Juanita heard him and switched on a light beside the sofa bed. She asked, "What is it now?"

"I was thinking," he said. "And couldn't sleep."

"Thinking of what?"

It was then he told her—sitting upright, his head turned partially away so as not to meet Juanita's eyes; told her the totality of his experience in prison, beginning with the gang rape; then his "boy friend" relationship with Karl as a means of self-protection; the sharing of the big black man's cell; the homosexuality continuing, and Miles beginning to enjoy it. He spoke of his ambivalent feelings about Karl, whose kindness and gentleness Miles still remembered with . . . affection? . . . love? Even now he wasn't sure.

It was at that point Juanita stopped him. "No more! I have heard enough. It makes me sick."

He asked her, "How do you think I feel?"

"*No quiero saber.* I neither know nor care." All the horror and disgust she felt was in her voice.

As soon as it was light, he dressed and left.

Two weeks later. Again a Saturday afternoon—the best time, Miles had discovered, for him to slip away unnoticed from the health club.

He was still tired from his nerve-straining trip to Louisville the night before last, and dispirited at his lack of progress.

He had worried, too, about whether he should go to Juanita again; wondered if she would want to see him. But then he decided that at least one more visit was necessary, and when he came she was matter-of-fact and businesslike, as if what had happened on the last occasion had been put behind her.

She listened to his report, then he told her of his doubts. "I'm just not finding out anything important. Okay, so I deal with Jules La-Rocca and the guy who sold me those counterfeit twenties, but both are small fry. Also, when I ask LaRocca questions—such as where the fake driver's license came from—he clams up tight and gets suspicious. I've no more idea now than when I started of any bigger people in the rackets, or what goes on beyond the Double-Seven."

"You cannot find out everything in a month," Juanita said.

"Perhaps there isn't anything to be found—at least, not what Wainwright wants."

"Perhaps not. But if so, it is not your fault. Besides, it is possible you have discovered more than you know. There is the forged money you have given me, the license number of the car you drove . . ."

"Which was probably stolen."

"Let Mr. Sherlock Holmes Wainwright find that out." A thought struck Juanita. "What about your airline ticket? The one they gave you to come back?"

"I used it."

"There is always a copy that you keep."

"Maybe I . . ." Miles felt in his jacket pocket; he had worn the same suit when he went to Louisville. The airline envelope was there, the ticket counterfoil inside.

Juanita took both. "Perhaps it will tell somebody something. And I will get your forty dollars back that you paid for the bad money."

"You're taking good care of me."

"¿Por qué no? It appears someone must."

Estela, who had been visiting a friend in a nearby apartment, came in. "Hullo," she said, "are you going to stay again?"

"Not today," he told her. "I'll be leaving soon."

Juanita asked sharply, "Why do you need to?"

"No reason. I just thought . . ."

"Then you will have dinner here. Estela will like it."

"Oh, good," Estela said. She asked Miles, "Will you read me a story?"

When he said he would, she brought a book and perched herself happily on his knee.

After dinner, before Estela said good night and went to bed, he read to her again.

"You are a kind person, Miles," Juanita said as she emerged from the bedroom, closing the door behind her. While she had been helping Estela into bed, he had risen to go, but she motioned to him, "No, stay. There is something I wish to say."

As before, they sat beside each other on the living-room sofa. Juanita spoke slowly, choosing her words.

"Last time, after you had gone, I regretted the harsh things I thought and said while you were here. One should not judge too much, yet that is what I did. I know that in prison you suffered. I have not been there, but perhaps can guess how bad it was, and how can anyone know—unless they themselves were there—what they might do? As to the man you spoke of, Karl, if he was kind when so much else was cruel, that is what should matter most."

Juanita stopped, considered, then went on, "For a woman, it is hard to understand how men could love each other in the way you said, and do to each other what you did. Yet I know there are women who love each other in that way, as well as men, and perhaps when all is said, love like that is better than none, better than to hate. So wipe out, please, the hurtful words I spoke, and go on remembering your Karl, admitting to yourself you loved him." She raised her eyes and looked at Miles directly. "You did love him, didn't you?"

"Yes," he said; his voice was low. "I loved him."

Juanita nodded. "Then it is better said. Perhaps now you will love other men. I do not know. I do not understand these things—only that love is better, wherever it is found."

"Thank you, Juanita." Miles saw that she was crying and found his own face wet with tears.

They stayed silent a long time listening to the Saturday evening hum of traffic and voices from the street outside. Then both began to talk —as friends, closer than they had ever been before. They talked on, forgetting time, and where they were; talked far into the night, about themselves, their experiences, lessons learned, their once-held dreams, their present hopes, objectives they might yet attain. They talked until drowsiness eclipsed their voices. Then, still beside each other, holding hands, they drifted into sleep.

Miles awoke first. His body was uncomfortable and cramped . . . but there was something else which filled him with excitement.

Gently he awakened Juanita, guiding her from the sofa to the rug in front of it where he placed cushions for their pillows. Tenderly and lovingly he undressed her, then himself, and after that he kissed, embraced and confidently mounted her, thrusting himself strongly forward, gloriously inward, while Juanita seized and clasped him, and cried aloud with joy.

"I love you, Miles! *Cariño mío,* I love you!"

Then he knew that, through her, he had found his manhood once again.

9

"I'll ask you two questions," Alex Vandervoort said. He spoke less crisply than usual; his mind was preoccupied and somewhat dazed by what he had just read. "First, how in God's name did you get all this information? Second, how reliable is it?"

"If you don't mind," Vernon Jax acknowledged, "I'll answer those in reverse order."

They were in Alex's office suite in FMA Headquarters Tower, in the late afternoon. It was quiet outside. Most of the staff from the 36th floor had already gone home.

The private investigator whom, a month ago, Alex had retained to make an independent study of Supranational Corporation—an "outside snooping job," as they agreed—had stayed quietly seated, reading an afternoon newspaper, while Alex studied the seventy-page report, including an appendix of photocopied documents, which Jax had brought in personally.

Today, Vernon Jax was, if anything, more unimpressive in appearance than the last time. The shiny blue suit he was wearing might have been donated to the Salvation Army—and rejected. His socks drooped around his ankles, above shoes even less cared for than before. What hair remained on his balding head stuck out untidily like well-used Brillo pads. Just the same, it was equally clear that what Jax lacked in sartorial style he made up in espionage skill.

"About reliability," he said. "If you're asking me whether the facts I've listed could be used, in their present form, as evidence in court, the answer's no. But I'm satisfied the information's all authentic, and I haven't included anything which wasn't checked with at least two good sources, in some cases three. Another thing, my reputation for getting at the truth is my most important business asset. It's a good reputation. I intend to keep it that way.

"Now then, how do I do it? Well, people I work for usually ask me that, and I suppose you're entitled to an explanation, even though I'll be holding some things back which come under the heading of 'trade secrets' and 'protecting sources.'

"I worked for the U. S. Treasury Department for twenty years, most of it as an IRS investigator, and I've kept my contacts green, not only there but in a lot of other places. Not many know it, Mr. Vandervoort, but a way investigators work is by trading confidential information, and in my business you never know when you'll need someone else or they'll need you. You help another man this week, sooner or later he'll come through for you. That way, too, you build up debts and credits, and the payoffs—in tip-offs and intelligence—go both ways. So what I'm selling when you hire me is not just my financial savvy, which I like to think is pretty fair, but a web of contacts. Some of them might surprise you."

"I've had all the surprises I need today," Alex said. He touched the report in front of him.

"Anyway," Jax said, "that's how I got a lot of what's in there. The rest was drudgery, patience, and knowing which rocks to look under."

"I see."

"There's one other thing I'd like to clear up, Mr. Vandervoort, and I guess you'd call it personal pride. I've watched you look me over both times we've met, and you haven't much cared for what you've seen. Well, that's the way I prefer people to see me because a man who's nondescript and down-at-the-heel isn't as likely to be noticed or taken seriously by those he's trying to investigate. It works another way, too, because people I talk to don't think I'm important and they aren't on guard. If I looked anything like you, they would be. So that's the reason, but I'll also tell you this: The day you invite me to your daughter's wedding I'll be as well turned out as any other guest."

"If I should ever have a daughter," Alex said, "I'll bear that in mind."

When Jax had gone, he studied the shocking report again. It was, he thought, fraught with the gravest implications for First Mercantile American Bank. The mighty edifice of Supranational Corporation—SuNatCo—was crumbling and about to topple.

Lewis D'Orsey, Alex recalled, had spoken of rumors about "big losses which haven't been reported . . . sharp accounting practices among subsidiaries . . . Big George Quartermain shopping for a Lockheed-type subsidy." Vernon Jax had confirmed them all and discovered much, much more.

It was too late to do anything today, Alex decided. He had overnight to consider how the information should be used.

10

Jerome Patterton's normally ruddy face suffused an even deeper red. He protested, "Dammit!—what you're asking is ridiculous."

"I'm not asking." Alex Vandervoort's voice was tight with anger which had simmered since last night. "I'm telling you—do it!"

"Asking, telling—what's the difference? You want me to take an arbitrary action without substantial reason."

"I'll give you plenty of reasons later. Strong ones. Right now there isn't time."

They were in the FMA president's suite where Alex had been waiting when Patterton arrived this morning.

"The New York stock market has already been open fifty minutes," Alex warned. "We've lost that much time, we're losing more. Because you're the only one who can give an order to the trust department to sell every share of Supranational we're holding."

"I won't!" Patterton's voice rose. "Besides, what the devil is this? Who do you think you are, storming in here, giving orders . . ."

Alex glanced over his shoulder. The office door was open. He walked to close it, then returned.

"I'll tell you who I am, Jerome. I'm the guy who warned you, and warned the board, against in-depth involvement with SuNatCo. I fought against heavy trust department buying of the shares, but no one —including you—would listen. Now Supranational is caving in." Alex leaned across the desk and slammed a fist down hard. His face, eyes blazing, was close to Patterton's. "Don't you understand? Supranational can bring this bank down with it."

Patterton was shaken. He sat down heavily behind the desk. "But is SuNatCo in real trouble? Are you sure?"

"If I weren't, do you think I'd be here, behaving this way? Don't you understand I'm giving you a chance to salvage something out of what will be catastrophic anyway?" Alex pointed to his wrist watch. "It's now an *hour* since the market opening. Jerome, get on a phone and give that order!"

Muscles around the bank president's face twitched nervously. Never strong or decisive, he reacted to situations rather than created them. Strong influence often swayed him, as Alex's was doing now.

"For God's sake, Alex, for your sake, I hope you know what you're doing." Patterton reached for one of two telephones beside his desk, hesitated, then picked it up.

"Get me Mitchell in Trust . . . No, I'll wait . . . Mitch? This is Jerome. Listen carefully. I want you to give a sell order immediately on all the Supranational stock we hold . . . Yes, *sell*. Every share." Patterton listened, then said impatiently, "Yes, I know what it'll do to the market, and I know the price is down already. I saw yesterday's quote. We'll take a loss. But still sell . . . Yes, I do know it's irregular." His eyes sought Alex's as if for reassurance. The hand holding the telephone trembled as he said, "There's no time to hold meetings. So do it! Don't waste . . ." Patterton grimaced, listening. "Yes, I accept responsibility."

When he had hung up the telephone, Patterton poured and drank a glass of water. He told Alex, "You heard what I said. The stock is already down. Our selling will depress it more. We'll be taking a big beating."

"You're wrong," Alex corrected him. "Our trust clients—people who trusted *us*—will take the beating. And it would be bigger still if we'd waited. Even now we're not out of the woods. A week from now the SEC may disallow those sales."

"Disallow? Why?"

"They may rule we had insider knowledge which we should have reported, and which would have halted trading in the stock."

"What kind of knowledge?"

"That Supranational is about to be bankrupt."

"Jesus!" Patterton got up from his desk and took a turn away. He muttered to himself, "SuNatCo! Jesus Christ, SuNatCo!" Swinging back on Alex, he demanded, "What about our loan? *Fifty million.*"

"I checked. Almost the full extent of the credit has been drawn."

"The compensating balance?"

"Is down to less than a million."

There was a silence in which Patterton sighed deeply. He was suddenly calm. "You said you had strong reasons. You obviously know something. You'd better tell me what."

"It might be simpler if you read this." Alex laid the Jax report on the president's desk.

"I'll read it later," Patterton said. "Right now, *you* tell me what it is and what's in it."

Alex explained the rumors about Supranational which Lewis D'Orsey had passed on, and Alex's decision to employ an investigator—Vernon Jax.

"What Jax has reported, in total hangs together," Alex declared. "Last night and this morning I've been phoning around, confirming some of his separate statements. All of them check out. The fact is, a good deal of what's been learned could have been discovered by anyone through patient digging—except that no one did it or, until now, put the pieces together. On top of that, Jax has obtained confidential information, including documents, I presume by . . ."

Patterton interrupted peevishly, "Okay, okay. Never mind all that. Tell me what the meat is."

"I'll give you it in five words: Supranational is out of money. For the past three years the corporation has had enormous losses and survived on prestige and credit. There's been tremendous borrowing to pay off debts; borrowing again to repay *those* debts; then borrowing still more, and so on. What they've lacked is real cash money."

Patterton protested, "But SuNatCo has reported excellent earnings, year after year, and never missed a dividend."

"It now appears the past few dividends have been paid from borrowings. The rest is fancy accounting. We all know how it can be done. Plenty of the biggest, most reputable companies use the same methods."

The bank president weighed the statement, then said gloomily, "There used to be a time when an accountant's endorsement on a financial statement spelled integrity. Not any more."

"In here"—Alex touched the report on the desk between them—"are examples of what we're talking about. Among the worst is Horizon Land Development. That's a SuNatCo subsidiary."

"I know, I know."

"Then you may also know that Horizon has big land holdings in Texas, Arizona, Canada. Most of the land tracts are remote, maybe a generation from development. What Horizon's been doing is making sales to speculators, accepting small down payments with hedged agreements, and pushing payment of the full price away into the future. On two deals, final payments totaling eighty million dollars are due forty years from now—well into the twenty-first century. Those payments may never be made. Yet on Horizon and Supranational balance sheets, that eighty million is shown as current earnings. Those are just two deals. There are more, only smaller, utilizing the same kind of Chinese accounting. Also, what's happened in one SuNatCo subsidiary has been repeated in others."

Alex paused, then added, "What all of it has done, of course, is make everything look great on paper and push up—unrealistically—the market price of Supranational shares."

"Somebody's made a fortune," Patterton said sourly. "Unfortunately it wasn't us. Do we have any idea of the extent of SuNatCo borrowing?"

"Yes. It seems that Jax managed to get a look at some tax records which show interest deductions. His estimate of short-term indebtedness, including subsidiaries, is a billion dollars. Of that, five hundred million appears to be bank loans. The rest is mainly ninety-day commercial paper, which they've rolled over."

Commercial paper, as both men knew, were IOUs bearing interest but backed only by a borrower's reputation. "Rolling over" was issuing still more IOUs to repay the earlier ones, plus interest.

"But they're close to the limit of borrowing," Alex said. "Or so Jax believes. One of the things I confirmed myself is that buyers of commercial paper are beginning to be wary."

Patterton mused, "It's the way Penn Central fell apart. Everybody believed the railroad was blue chip—the safest stock to buy and hold, along with IBM and General Motors. Suddenly, one day, Penn Central was in receivership, wiped out, done."

"Add a few more big names since then," Alex reminded him.

The same thought was in both their minds: After Supranational, would First Mercantile American Bank be added to the list?

Patterton's ruddy face had gone pale. He appealed to Alex, "Where do we stand?" No pretense of leadership now. The bank president was leaning heavily on the younger man.

"A lot depends on how much longer Supranational stays afloat. If they can hang on for several months, our sales of their stock today might be ignored, and the breach of the Federal Reserve Act with the loan may not be investigated closely. If the breakup happens quickly, we're in serious trouble—with the SEC for not revealing what we know, with the Comptroller of Currency over abuse of trust, and, over the loan, with the Fed Reserve. Then, I need hardly remind you, we're facing an outright loss of fifty million dollars, and you know what that will do to this year's earnings statement, so there'll be angry shareholders howling for someone's head. On top of that there could be lawsuits against directors."

"*Jesus!*" Patterton repeated, "Jesus H. Christ!" He took out a handkerchief and mopped his face and egg-like dome.

Alex went on relentlessly, "There's something else we'll have to consider—publicity. If Supranational goes under there will be investigations. But even before that the press will be on to the story and do probing of their own. Some of the financial reporters are pretty good at it. When the questioning starts, it's unlikely our bank will escape attention, and the extent of our losses will become known and publicized. That kind of news can make depositors uneasy. It could cause heavy withdrawals."

"You mean a run on the bank! That's unthinkable."

"No, it isn't. It's happened elsewhere—remember Franklin in New York. If you're a depositor, the only thing you care about is whether your money's safe. If you think it might not be, you take it out—fast."

Patterton drank more water, then slumped into his chair. If possible, he looked even paler than before.

"What I suggest," Alex said, "is that you call the money policy committee together immediately and we concentrate, during the next few days, on attaining maximum liquidity. That way, we'll be prepared if there's a sudden drain on cash."

Patterton nodded. "All right."

"Apart from that there's not much else to do but pray." For the first time since coming in, Alex smiled. "Maybe we should get Roscoe working on that."

"*Roscoe!*" Patterton said, as if suddenly reminded. "*He* studied the Supranational figures, recommended the loan, assured us everything was great."

"Roscoe wasn't alone," Alex pointed out. "You and the board supported him. And plenty of others studied the figures and drew the same conclusion."

"You didn't."

"I was uneasy; suspicious, maybe. But I had no idea SuNatCo was in the mess it is."

Patterton picked up the telephone he had used earlier. "Ask Mr. Heyward to come in." A pause, then Patterton snapped, "I don't care if *God* is with him. I need him now." He slammed down the instrument and mopped his face again.

The office door opened softly and Heyward came in. He said, "Good morning, Jerome," and nodded to Alex coolly.

Patterton growled, "Close the door."

Looking surprised, Heyward did. "They said it was urgent. If it isn't, I'd like to . . ."

"Tell him about Supranational, Alex," Patterton said.

Heyward's face froze.

Quietly, matter-of-factly, Alex repeated the substance of the Jax report. His anger of last night and this morning—anger at shortsighted foolishness and greed which had brought the bank to the edge of disaster—had left him now. He felt only sorrow that so much was about to be lost, and so much effort wasted. He remembered with regret how other worthwhile projects had been cut back so that money could be channeled to the Supranational loan. At least, he thought, Ben Rosselli, by death, had been spared this moment.

Roscoe Heyward surprised him. Alex had expected antagonism, perhaps bluster. There was none. Instead, Heyward listened quietly, interjecting a question here and there, but made no other comments. Alex suspected that what he was saying amplified other information Heyward had received himself, or guessed at.

There was a silence when Alex was done.

Patterton, who had recovered some of his aplomb, said, "We'll have a meeting of the money policy committee this afternoon to discuss liquidity. Meanwhile, Roscoe, get in touch with Supranational to see what, if anything, we can salvage of our loan."

"It's a demand loan," Heyward said. "We can call it any time."

"Then do it now. Do it verbally today and follow up in writing. There isn't much hope SuNatCo will have fifty million dollars cash on hand; not even a sound company keeps that kind of money in the till. But they may have something, though I'm not hopeful. Either way, we'll go through the motions."

"I'll call Quartermain at once," Heyward said. "May I take that report?"

Patterton glanced at Alex.

"I've no objection," Alex said, "but I'd suggest we don't make copies. And the fewer people who know of this, the better."

Heyward nodded agreement. He seemed restless, anxious to get away.

11

Alex Vandervoort had been partly right in supposing Roscoe Heyward to have some information of his own. Rumors had reached Heyward that Supranational was having problems and he had learned, in the past few days, that some of SuNatCo's commercial paper was meeting resistance from investors. Heyward had also attended a Supranational board meeting—his first—and sensed that information supplied to directors was less than complete and frank. But, as a "new boy," he had withheld questions, intending to begin probing later. Subsequent to the meeting he had observed a decline in Supranational's share price and decided, only yesterday, to advise the bank's trust department to "lighten up" its holdings as a precaution. Unfortunately—when Patterton summoned him this morning—he had still not put the intention into effect. Yet nothing Heyward had heard or guessed suggested the situation was as urgent or as bad as the report, produced by Vandervoort, portrayed it.

Yet having heard the gist of the report, Heyward did not dispute it. Grim and jolting as it was, instinct told him that—as Vandervoort put it—everything hung together.

It was the reason Heyward had stayed mostly silent while with the other two, knowing—at this stage—there was little to be said. But his mind had been active, with alarm signals flashing while he weighed ideas, eventualities, and possible escape routes for himself. There were several actions which needed to be taken quickly, though first he would complete his personal knowledge by studying the Jax report. Back in his office, Heyward hurried through some remaining business with a visitor, then settled down to read.

He soon realized that Alex Vandervoort had been accurate in summarizing the report's highlights and the documentary evidence. What Vandervoort had not mentioned were some details of Big George Quartermain's lobbying in Washington for a government-guaranteed loan to keep Supranational solvent. Appeals for such a loan had been made to members of Congress, and at the Department of Commerce and the White House. At one point, it was stated, Quartermain took Vice-President Byron Stonebridge on a trip to the Bahamas with the objective of enlisting the Vice-President's support for the loan idea. Later, Stonebridge discussed the possibility at Cabinet level, but the consensus was against it.

Heyward thought bitterly: Now he knew what Big George and the Vice-President were discussing the night they had walked, deep in conversation, in the garden of the Bahamas house. And while, in the end, the Washington political machine made one of its wiser decisions in rejecting a loan to Supranational, First Mercantile American Bank—on Roscoe's urging—had bestowed one eagerly. Big George had proved himself the maestro of the soft sell. Heyward could hear him saying, even now: *If fifty million is bigger than you people can handle, let's forget the whole thing. I'll give it to Chase.* It was an ancient, con man's ploy and Heyward—the shrewd, experienced banker—had fallen for it.

One thing, at least, was to the good. In the reference to the Vice-President's journey to the Bahamas, details were sketchy and obviously little was known about the trip. Nor, to Heyward's great relief, did the report refer to Q-Investments.

Heyward wondered if Jerome Patterton had remembered the additional loan, totaling two million dollars, committed by FMA to Q-Investments, the private speculators' group headed by Big George. Probably not. Nor did Alex Vandervoort have any knowledge of it, though he was bound to find out soon. What was more important, though, was to ensure that Heyward's own acceptance of "bonus" Q-Investments shares should never be discovered. He wished fervently he had returned them to G. G. Quartermain, as he had at first intended. Well, it was too late for that now, but what he could do was remove the share certificates from his safe deposit box and shred them. That would be safest. Fortunately, they were nominee certificates, not registered in his name.

For the moment, Heyward realized, he was ignoring the competitiveness between himself and Alex Vandervoort, concentrating instead on survival. He had no illusions about what the collapse of Supranational would do to his own standing in the bank and with the board. He would be a pariah—the focus of everybody's blame. But perhaps, even now, with quick action and some luck, it was not too late for a recovery. If the loan money was regained, he might become a hero.

The first order of business was to get in touch with Supranational. He instructed his secretary, Mrs. Callaghan, to get G. G. Quartermain on the telephone.

Several minutes later she reported, "Mr. Quartermain is out of the country. His office is vague about where he is. They won't give any other information."

It was an inauspicious start and Heyward snapped, "Then get Inchbeck." He had had several conversations with Stanley Inchbeck, Supranational's comptroller, since they first met in the Bahamas.

Inchbeck's voice, with its nasal New York accent, came briskly on the line. "Roscoe, what can I do?"

"I've been trying to locate George. Your people don't seem to . . ."

"He's in Costa Rica."

"I'd like to speak to him. Is there a number I can call?"

"No. He left instructions he doesn't want calls."

"This is urgent."

"Then tell me."

"Very well. We're calling our loan. I'm advising you now, and formal written notice will follow in tonight's mail."

There was a silence. Inchbeck said, "You can't be serious."

"I'm entirely serious."

"But *why?*"

"I think you can guess. I also believe you wouldn't want me to go into reasons on the telephone."

Inchbeck was silent—in itself significant. Then he protested, "Your bank is being ridiculous and unreasonable. Only last week Big George told me he was willing to let you people increase the loan by fifty percent."

The audacity astounded Heyward, until he realized audacity had paid off—for Supranational—once before. It wouldn't now.

"If the loan were repaid promptly," Heyward said, "any information that we have here would remain confidential. I'd guarantee that."

What it came down to, he thought, was whether Big George, Inchbeck, and any others who knew the truth about SuNatCo, were willing to buy time. If so, FMA might steal an advantage over other creditors.

"Fifty million dollars!" Inchbeck said. "We don't keep that much cash on hand."

"Our bank would agree to a series of payments, providing they followed each other quickly." The real question was, of course: Where would SuNatCo find fifty million in its present cash-starved condition? Heyward found himself sweating—a combination of nervousness, suspense, and hope.

"I'll talk to Big George," Inchbeck said. "But he isn't going to like this."

"When you talk to him, tell him I'd like to discuss, also, our loan to Q-Investments."

Heyward wasn't sure but, as he hung up, he thought he heard Inchbeck groan.

In the silence of his office, Roscoe Heyward leaned backward in the upholstered swivel chair, letting the tenseness drain out of him. What had occurred in the past hour had come as a stunning shock. Now, as reaction set in, he felt dejected and alone. He wished he could get away from everything for a while. If he had the choice, he knew whose company he would welcome. Avril's. But he had not heard from her since their last meeting, which was over a month ago. In the past, she had always called him. He had never called her.

On impulse, he opened a pocket address book he always carried and looked for a telephone number he remembered penciling in. It was Avril's in New York. Using a direct outside line, he dialed it.

He heard ringing, then Avril's soft and pleasing voice. "Hello." His heart leaped at the sound of her.

"Hi, Rossie," she said when he identified himself.

"It's been a while since you and I met, my dear. I've been wondering when I'd hear from you."

He was aware of hesitation. "But Rossie, sweetie, you aren't on the list any more."

"What list?"

Once more, uncertainty. "Maybe I shouldn't have said that."

"No, please tell me. This is between the two of us."

"Well, it's a very confidential list which Supranational puts out, about who can be entertained at their expense."

He had the sudden sense of a cord around him being tightened. "Who gets the list?"

"I don't know. I know us girls do. I'm not sure who else."

He stopped, thinking nervously, and reasoned: What was done, was done. He supposed he should be glad he was not on any such list now, though found himself wondering—with a twinge of jealousy—who was. In any case, he hoped that back copies were carefully destroyed. Aloud he asked, "Does that mean you can't come here to meet me any more?"

"Not exactly. But if I did, you'd have to pay yourself, Rossie."

"How much would that be?" As he asked, he wondered if it were really himself speaking.

"There'd be my air fare from New York," Avril said matter-of-factly. "Then the cost at the hotel. And for me—two hundred dollars."

Heyward remembered wondering once before how much Supranational had paid out on his behalf. Now he knew. Holding the telephone away, he wrestled within his mind: Commonsense against desire; conscience against the knowledge of what it was like to be alone with Avril. The money was also more than he could afford. But he wanted her. Very much indeed.

He moved the telephone back. "How soon could you be here?"

"Tuesday of next week."

"Not before?"

"Afraid not, sweetie."

He knew he was being a fool; that between now and Tuesday he would be standing in line behind other men whose priorities, for whatever reason, were greater than his own. But he couldn't help himself, and told her, "Very well. Tuesday."

They arranged that she would go to the Columbia Hilton and phone him from there.

Heyward began savoring the sweetness to come.

He reminded himself of one other thing he had to do—destroy his Q-Investments share certificates.

From the 36th floor he used the express elevator to descend to the main foyer, then walked through the tunnel to the adjoining downtown branch. It took minutes only to gain access to his personal safe deposit box and remove the four certificates, each for five hundred shares. He carried them back upstairs, where he would feed them into a shredding machine personally.

But back in his office he had second thoughts. Last time he checked, the shares were worth twenty thousand dollars. Was he being hasty? After all, if necessary he could destroy the certificates at a moment's notice.

Changing his mind, he locked them in a desk drawer with other private papers.

12

The big break came when Miles Eastin was least expecting it.

Only two days earlier, frustrated and depressed, convinced that his servitude at the Double-Seven Health Club would produce no results other than enmeshing him deeper in criminality, the renewed shadow of prison loomed terrifyingly over him. Miles had communicated his depression to Juanita and, though tempered briefly by their lovemaking, the basic mood remained.

On Saturday he had met Juanita. Late Monday evening at the Double-Seven, Nate Nathanson, the club manager, sent for Miles who had been helping out as usual by carrying drinks and sandwiches to the card and dice players on the third floor.

When Miles entered the manager's office, two others were there with Nathanson. One was the loan shark, Russian Ominsky. The second was a husky, thick-featured man whom Miles had seen at the club several times before and had heard referred to as Tony Bear Marino. The "Bear" seemed appropriate. Marino had a heavy, powerful body, loose movements and a suggestion of underlying savagery. That Tony Bear carried authority was evident, and he was deferred to by others. Each time he arrived at the Double-Seven it was in a Cadillac limousine, accompanied by a driver and a companion, both clearly bodyguards.

Nathanson seemed nervous when he spoke. "Miles, I've been telling Mr. Marino and Mr. Ominsky how useful you've been here. They want you to do a service for . . ."

Ominsky said curtly to the manager, "Wait outside."

"Yes, sir." Nathanson left quickly.

"There's an old guy in a car outside," Ominsky said to Miles. "Get help from Mr. Marino's men. Carry him in, but keep him out of sight. Take him up to one of the rooms near yours and make sure he stays there. Don't leave him longer than you have to, and when you do go away, lock him in. I'm holding you responsible he doesn't leave here."

Miles asked uneasily, "Am I supposed to keep him here by force?"

"You won't need force."

"The old man knows the score. He won't make trouble," Tony Bear said. For someone of his bulk, his voice was surprisingly falsetto. "Just remember he's important to us, so treat him okay. But don't let him have booze. He'll ask for it. Don't give him *any*. Understand?"

"I think so," Miles said. "Do you mean he's unconscious now?"

"He's dead drunk," Ominsky answered. "He's been on a bender for a week. Your job is to take care of him and dry him out. While he's here—for three, four days—your other work can wait." He added, "Do it right, you get another credit."

"I'll do my best," Miles told him. "Does the old man have a name? I'll have to call him something."

The other two glanced at each other. Ominsky said, "Danny. That's all you need to know."

A few minutes later, outside the Double-Seven, Tony Bear Marino's driver-bodyguard spat in disgust on the sidewalk and complained, "For Chrissakes! The old fart stinks like a shithouse."

He, the second bodyguard, and Miles Eastin were looking at an inert figure on the rear seat of a Dodge sedan, parked at the curb. The car's nearside rear door was open.

"I'll try to clean him up," Miles said. His own face wrinkled at the overpowering stench of vomit. "But we'll need to get him inside first."

The second bodyguard urged, "Goddam! Let's get it over with."

Together they reached in and lifted. In the poorly lighted street, all that could be distinguished of their burden was a tangle of gray hair, pasty hollow cheeks stubbled with beard, closed eyes and an open, slack mouth revealing toothless gums. The clothes the unconscious man was wearing were stained and torn.

"You reckon he's dead?" the second bodyguard asked as they lifted the figure from the car.

Precisely at that moment, probably induced by movement, a stream of vomit emerged from the open mouth and cascaded over Miles.

The driver-bodyguard, who had been untouched, chuckled. "He ain't dead. Not yet." Then, as Miles retched, "Better you 'n me, kid."

They carried the recumbent figure into the club, then, using a rear stairway, up to the fourth floor. Miles had brought a room key and unlocked a door. It was to a cubicle like his own in which the sole furnishings were a single bed, a chest of drawers, two chairs, a washbasin and some shelving. Paneling around the cubicle stopped a foot short of the ceiling, leaving the top open. Miles glanced inside, then told the other two, "Hold it." While they waited he ran downstairs and got a rubber sheet from the gymnasium. Returning, he spread it on the bed. They dumped the old man on it.

"He's all yours, Milesy," the driver-bodyguard said. "Let's get outta here before I puke."

Stifling his distaste, Miles undressed the old man, then, while he was still on the rubber sheet, still comatose, washed and sponged him. When that was done, and with some lifting and shoving, Miles removed the rubber sheet and got the now cleaner, less evil-smelling figure into bed. During the process the old man moaned, and once his stomach heaved, though this time producing only a trickle of spittle which Miles wiped away. When Miles had covered him with a sheet and blanket the old man seemed to rest more easily.

Earlier, as he removed the clothing, Miles had allowed it to fall to the cubicle floor. Now he gathered it up and began putting it in two plastic bags for cleaning and laundering tomorrow. While doing so, he emptied all the pockets. One coat pocket yielded a set of false teeth. Others held miscellaneous items—a comb, a pair of thick-lensed glasses, a gold pen and pencil set, several keys on a ring and—in an inside pocket —three Keycharge credit cards and a billfold tightly packed with money.

Miles took the false teeth, rinsed them, and placed them beside the bed in a glass of water. The spectacles he also put close by. Then he examined the bank credit cards and billfold.

The credit cards were made out to Fred W. Riordan, R. K. Bennett, Alfred Shaw. Each card was signed on the back but, despite the name differences, the handwriting in each case was the same. Miles turned the cards over again, checking the commencement and expiration dates which showed that all three were current. As far as he could tell, they were genuine.

He turned his attention to the billfold. Under a plastic window was a state driver's license. The plastic was yellowed and hard to see through, so Miles took the license out, discovered that beneath it was a second license, beneath that a third. The names on the licenses corresponded to those on the credit cards, but the head and shoulders photographs on all three licenses were identical. He peered closer. Allowing for differences when the photograph was taken, it was undoubtedly of the old man on the bed.

Miles removed the money from the billfold to count it. He would ask Nate Nathanson to put the credit cards and billfold in the club safe, but should know how much he was handing over. The sum was unexpectedly large—five hundred and twelve dollars, about half in new twenty-dollar bills. The twenties stopped him. Miles looked at several of them carefully, feeling the texture of the paper with his fingertips. Then he glanced at the man on the bed who appeared to be sleeping deeply. Quietly, Miles left the room and crossed the fourth-floor corridor to his own. He returned moments later with a pocket magnifier through which he viewed the twenty-dollar bills again. His intuition was right. They *were* counterfeit, though of the same high quality as those he had bought, here in the Double-Seven, a week ago.

He reasoned: The money, or rather half of it, was counterfeit. So, obviously, were the three drivers' licenses and it seemed probable that they were from the same source as Miles's own fake license, given him last week by Jules LaRocca. Therefore, wasn't it likely that the credit cards were also counterfeit? Perhaps, after all, he was close to the source of the false Keycharge cards which Nolan Wainwright wanted to locate so badly. Miles's excitement rose, along with a nervousness which set his heart pounding.

He needed a record of the new information. On a paper towel he copied down details from the credit cards and drivers' licenses, occasionally checking to be sure the figure in the bed was not stirring.

Soon after, Miles turned out the light, locked the door from outside and took the billfold and credit cards downstairs.

He slept fitfully that night, with his door ajar, aware of his responsibility for the inmate of the cubicle across the hall. Miles spent time, too, speculating on the role and identity of the old man whom he began to think of as Danny. What was Danny's relationship to Ominsky and Tony Bear Marino? Why had they brought him here? Tony Bear had declared: *He's important to us.* Why?

Miles awoke with daylight and checked his watch: 6:45. He got up, washed quickly, shaved and dressed. There were no sounds from across the corridor. He walked over, inserted the key quietly, and looked in. Danny had changed position in the night but was still asleep, snoring gently. Miles gathered the plastic bags of clothing, relocked the door, and went downstairs.

He was back twenty minutes later with a breakfast tray of strong coffee, toast, and scrambled eggs.

"Danny!" Miles shook the old man's shoulder. "Danny, wake up!"

There was no response. Miles tried again. At length two eyes opened warily, inspected him, then hastily closed tight. "Go 'way," the old man mumbled. "Go 'way. I ain't ready for hell yet."

"I'm not the devil," Miles said. "I'm a friend. Tony Bear and Russian Ominsky told me to take care of you."

Rheumy eyes reopened. "Them sons-o'-Sodom found me, eh? Figures, I guess. They usually do." The old man's face creased in pain. "Oh, Jesus! My suffering head!"

"I brought some coffee. Let's see if it will help." Miles put an arm around Danny's shoulders, assisting him to sit upright, then carried the coffee over. The old man sipped and grimaced.

He seemed suddenly alert. "Listen, son. What'll set me straight is a hair of the dog. Now you take some money . . ." He looked around him.

"Your money's okay," Miles said. "It's in the club safe. I took it down last night."

"This the Double-Seven?"

"Yes."

"Brought me here once before. Well, now you know I can pay, son, just you nip down to the bar . . ."

Miles said firmly, "There won't be any nipping. For either of us."

"I'll make it worthwhile." The old eyes gleamed with cunning. "Say forty dollars for a fifth. Howzat?"

"Sorry, Danny. I had orders." Miles weighed what he would say next, then took the plunge. "Besides, if I used those twenties of yours, I could get arrested."

It was as if he had fired a gun. Danny shot upright, alarm and suspicion on his face. "Who said you could . . ." He stopped with a moan and grimace, putting a hand to his head in pain.

"Someone had to count the money. So I did it."

The old man said weakly, "Those are good twenties."

"Sure are," Miles agreed. "Some of the best I've seen. Almost as good as the U. S. Bureau of Engraving."

Danny raised his eyes. Interest competed with suspicion. "How come you know so much?"

"Before I went to prison I worked for a bank."

A silence. Then the old man asked, "What were you in the can for?"

"Embezzlement. I'm on parole now."

Danny visibly relaxed. "I guess you're okay. Or you wouldn't be working for Tony Bear and the Russian."

"That's right," Miles said. "I'm okay. The next thing is to get you the same way. Right now we're going to the steam room."

"It ain't steam I need. It's a short snort. Just one, son," Danny pleaded. "I swear that's all. You wouldn't deny an old man that small favor."

"We'll sweat some out you already drank. Then you can lick your fingers."

The old man groaned. "Heartless! Heartless!"

In a way it was like taking care of a child. Overcoming token protest, Miles wrapped Danny in a robe and shepherded him downstairs, then escorted him naked through successive steam rooms, toweled him, and finally eased him onto a masseur's table where Miles himself gave a creditable pummeling and rubdown. This early, the gym and steam rooms were deserted and few of the club staff had arrived. No one else was in sight when Miles escorted the old man back upstairs.

Miles remade the bed with clean sheets, and Danny, by now quietened and obedient, climbed in. Almost at once he was asleep, though unlike last night, he appeared tranquil, even angelic. Strangely, without really knowing him, Miles already liked the old man. Carefully, while he slept, Miles put a towel under his head and shaved him.

In late morning, while reading in his room across the hall, Miles drifted off to sleep.

"Hey, Milesy! Baby, stir ass!" The rasping voice was Jules LaRocca's. Startled, Miles jerked awake to see the familiar pot-bellied figure standing in the doorway. Miles's hand reached out, seeking the key of the cubicle across the hall. Reassuringly, it was where he had left it.

"Gotsum threads for the old lush," LaRocca said. He was carrying a fiberboard suitcase. "Ominsky said ta deliver 'em ta ya."

LaRocca, the ubiquitous messenger.

"Okay." Miles stretched, and went to a sink where he splashed cold water on his face. Then, followed by LaRocca, he opened the door across the hall. As the two came in, Danny eased up gingerly in bed. Though still drawn and pale, he appeared better than at any time since his arrival. He had put his teeth in and had his glasses on.

"Ya useless old bum!" LaRocca said. "Ya always givin' everybody a lotta trouble."

Danny sat up straighter, regarding his accuser with distaste. "I'm far from useless. As you and others know. As for the sauce, every man has his little weakness." He motioned to the suitcase. "If you brought my clothes, do what you were sent for and hang them up."

Unperturbed, LaRocca grinned. "Sounds like ya bouncin' back, ya old fart. Guess Milesy done a job."

"Jules," Miles said, "will you stay here while I go down and get a sunlamp? I think it'll do Danny good."

"Sure."

"I'd like to speak to you first." Miles motioned with his head and LaRocca followed him outside.

Keeping his voice low, Miles asked, "Jules, what's this all about? Who is he?"

"Just an old geezer. Once in a while he slips away, goes on a bender. Then somebody hasta find him, dry the old barfly out."

"Why? And where does he slip away from?"

LaRocca stopped, his eyes suspicious, as they had been a week ago. "Ya askin' questions again, kid. Whadid Tony Bear and Ominsky tell ya?"

"Nothing, except the old man's name is Danny."

"If 'n they wanna tell ya more, they'll tell ya. Not me."

When LaRocca had gone, Miles set up a sunlamp in the cubicle and sat Danny under it for half an hour. Through the remainder of the day, the old man lay quietly awake or dozed. In the early evening Miles brought dinner from downstairs, most of which Danny ate—his first full meal since arrival twenty-four hours ago.

Next morning—Wednesday—Miles repeated the steam room and sunlamp treatments and later the two of them played chess. The old man had a quick, astute mind and they were evenly matched. By now, Danny was friendly and relaxed, making clear that he liked Miles's company and attentions.

During the second afternoon the old man wanted to talk. "Yesterday," he said, "that creep LaRocca said you know a lot about money."

"He tells everybody that." Miles explained about his hobby and the interest it aroused in prison.

Danny asked more questions, then announced, "If you don't mind, I'd like my own money now."

"I'll get it for you. But I'll have to lock you in again."

"If you're worrying about the booze, forget it. I'm over it for this time. A break like this does the trick. Could be months before I'll take a drink again."

"Glad to hear that." Miles locked the door, just the same.

When he had his money, Danny spread it on the bed, then divided it into two piles. The new twenties were in one, the remaining, mostly soiled, assorted bills in another. From the second grouping, Danny selected three ten-dollar bills and handed them to Miles. "That's for thinking of some little things, son—like taking care of my teeth, the shave, the sunlamp. I appreciate what you did."

"Listen, you don't have to."

"Take it. And by the way, it's real stuff. Now tell me something."

"If I can, I will."

"How did you spot that those twenties were homegrown?"

"I didn't to begin with. But if you use a magnifier, some of the lines on Andrew Jackson's portrait show up blurred."

Danny nodded sagely. "That's the difference between a steel engraving, which the government uses, and a photo-offset plate. Though a top offset man can come awful close."

"In this case he did," Miles said. "Other parts of the bills are close to perfect."

There was a faint smile on the old man's face. "How about the paper?"

"It fooled me. Usually you can tell a bad bill with your fingers. But not these."

Danny said softly, "Twenty-four-pound coupon bond. Hundred percent cotton fiber. People think you can't get the right paper. Isn't true. Not if you shop around."

"If you're all that interested," Miles said, "I have some books about money across the hall. There's one I'm thinking of, published by the U. S. Secret Service."

"You mean *Know Your Money?*" As Miles looked surprised, the old man chuckled. "That's the forger's handbook. Says what to look for to detect a bad bill. Lists all the mistakes that counterfeiters make. Even shows pictures!"

"Yes," Miles said. "I know."

Danny continued chortling. "And the government gives it away! You can write to Washington—they'll mail it to you. There was a hot-shot counterfeiter named Mike Landress who wrote a book. In it he said *Know Your Money* is something no counterfeiter should be without."

"Landress got caught," Miles pointed out.

"That was because he worked with fools. They had no organization."

"You seem to know a lot about it."

"A little." Danny stopped, picked up one of the good bills, one of the counterfeits, and compared them. What he saw pleased him; he grinned. "Did you know, son, that U.S. money is the world's easiest to copy and to print? Fact is, it was designed so that engravers in the last century couldn't reproduce it with the tools they had. But since those days we've had multilith machines and high resolution photo-offset, so that nowadays, with good equipment, patience, and some wastage, a skilled man can do a job that only experts can detect."

"I'd heard some of that," Miles said. "But how much of it goes on?"

"Let me tell you." Danny seemed to be enjoying himself, obviously launched on a favorite theme. "No one really knows how much queer gets printed every year and goes undetected, but it's a *bundle*. The government says thirty million dollars, with a tenth of that getting into circulation. But those are government figures, and the only thing you can be sure of with *any* government figure is that it's set high or low, depending on what those in government want to prove. In this case they'd want it low. My guess is, every year, seventy million, maybe closer to a billion."

"I suppose it's possible," Miles said. He was remembering how much counterfeit money had been detected at the bank and how much more must have escaped attention altogether.

"Know the *hardest* kind of money to reproduce?"

"No, I don't."

"An American Express travelers check. Know why?"

Miles shook his head.

"It's printed in cyan-blue, which is next to impossible to photograph for an offset printing plate. Nobody with any knowledge would waste time trying, so an Amex check is safer than American money."

"There are rumors," Miles said, "that there's going to be new American money soon with colors for different denominations—the way Canada has."

"'Tain't just rumor," Danny said. "Fact. Lots of the colored money's already printed and it's stored by the Treasury. Be harder to copy than anything made yet." He smiled mischievously. "But the old stuff'll be around a bit. Maybe as long as I am."

Miles sat silent, digesting all that he had heard. At length he said, "You've asked me questions, Danny, and I answered them. Now I've one for you."

"Not saying I'll answer, son. But you can try."

"Who and what are you?"

The old man pondered, a thumb stroking his chin as he appraised Miles. Some of his thoughts were mirrored on his face: A compulsion to frankness struggled against caution; pride mingled with discretion. Abruptly Danny made up his mind. "I'm seventy-three years old," he said, "and I'm a master craftsman. Been a printer all my life. I'm still the best there is. Besides being a craft, printing's an art." He pointed to the twenty-dollar bills still spread out on the bed. "Those are my work. I made the photographic plate. I printed them."

Miles asked, "And the drivers' licenses and credit cards?"

"Compared with printing money," Danny said, "making those is as easy as pissing in a barrel. But, yep—I did 'em all."

13

In a fever of impatience now, Miles waited for a chance to communicate what he had learned to Nolan Wainwright, via Juanita. Frustratingly, though, it was proving impossible to leave the Double-Seven and the risk of conveying such vital intelligence over the health club's telephone seemed too great.

On Thursday morning—the day after Danny's frank revelations—the old man showed every sign of having made a full recovery from his alcoholic orgy. He was clearly enjoying Miles's company and their chess games continued. So did their conversations, though Danny was more on guard than he had been the day before.

Whether Danny could hasten his own departure, if he chose to, was unclear. Even if he could, he showed no inclination and seemed content—at least for the time being—with his confinement in the fourth-floor cubicle.

During their later talks, both on Wednesday and Thursday, Miles had tried to gain more knowledge of Danny's counterfeiting activities and even hinted at the crucial question of a headquarters location. But Danny adroitly avoided any more discussion on the subject and Miles's instinct told him that the old man regretted some of his earlier openness. Remembering Wainwright's advice—"don't hurry, be patient"—Miles decided not to push his luck.

Despite his elation, another thought depressed him. Everything he had discovered would ensure the arrest and imprisonment of Danny. Miles continued to like the old man and was sorry for what must surely follow. Yet, he reminded himself, it was also the route to his own sole chance of rehabilitation.

Ominsky, the loan shark, and Tony Bear Marino were both involved with Danny, though in precisely what way was still not clear. Miles had no concern for Russian Ominsky or Tony Bear, though fear touched him icily at the thought of their learning—as he supposed they must eventually—of his own traitorous role.

Late on Thursday afternoon Jules LaRocca appeared once more. "Gotta message from Tony. He's sending wheels for ya tomorra morning."

Danny nodded, but it was Miles who asked, "Wheels to take him where?"

Both Danny and LaRocca looked at him sharply without answering, and Miles wished he hadn't asked.

That night, deciding to take an acceptable risk, Miles telephoned Juanita. He waited until after locking Danny in his cubicle shortly before midnight, then walked downstairs to use a pay phone on the club's main floor. Miles put in a dime and dialed Juanita's number. On the first ring her voice answered softly, "Hello."

The pay phone was a wall type, in the open near the bar, and Miles whispered so he would not be overheard. "You know who this is. But don't use names."

"Yes," Juanita said.

"Tell our mutual friend I've discovered something important here. Really important. It's most of what he wanted to know. I can't say more, but I'll come to you tomorrow night."

"All right."

Miles hung up. Simultaneously, a hidden tape recorder in the club basement, which had switched on automatically when the pay phone receiver was lifted, just as automatically switched off.

14

Some verses from *Genesis*, like subliminal advertising, flashed at intervals through Roscoe Heyward's mind: *Of every tree of the garden thou mayest freely eat: But of the tree of the knowledge of good and evil, thou shalt not eat of it; for in the day that thou eatest thereof thou shalt surely die.*

In recent days, Heyward had worried at the question: Had his illicit sexual affair with Avril, which began that memorable moonlit night in the Bahamas, become his own tree of evil from which he would harvest the bitterest of fruit? And was all that was happening adversely now —the sudden, alarming weakness of Supranational, which could thwart his own ambition at the bank—intended as a personal punishment by God?

Conversely: If he severed all ties with Avril decisively and at once, and expunged her from his thoughts, would God forgive him? Would He, in acknowledgment, restore strength to Supranational and thereby revive the fortunes of His servant, Roscoe? Remembering *Nehemiah . . . Thou art a God ready to pardon, gracious and merciful, slow to anger, and of great kindness . . .* Heyward believed He might.

The trouble was, there was no way to be sure.

Also, weighing against severance from Avril was the fact that she was due in the city on Tuesday, as they had arranged last week. Amid his current mélange of problems, Heyward longed for her.

Through Monday and early Tuesday morning in his office, he vacillated, knowing he could telephone New York and stop her. But at midmorning Tuesday, aware of flight schedules from New York, he realized it was too late and he was relieved that no decision could be taken.

Avril phoned in late afternoon, using the unlisted line which rang directly on his desk. "Hi, Rossie! I'm at the hotel. Suite 432. The champagne's on ice—but I'm hot for you."

He wished he had suggested a room instead of a suite, since he would be paying. For the same reason, champagne seemed needlessly extravagant and he wondered if it would be ungracious to suggest sending it back. He supposed it would.

"I'll be with you shortly, my dear," he said.

He managed a small economy by having a bank car and chauffeur take him to the Columbia Hilton. Heyward told the man, "Don't wait."

As he entered Suite 432, her arms went around him immediately and those full lips hungrily ate at his own. He held her tightly, his body reacting at once with the excitement he had come to know and crave. Through the cloth of his trousers he could feel Avril's long slim thighs and legs, moving against him, teasing, shifting, promising, until all of him seemed concentrated in a few square inches of physique. Then, after several moments, Avril released herself, touched his cheek, and moved away.

"Rossie, why don't we get our business arrangements out of the way? Then we can relax, not worry any more."

Her sudden practicality jolted him. He wondered: Was this the way it always happened—the money first, before fulfillment? Yet he supposed it made sense. If left until afterward, a client—his urgency gone and appetite sated—might be disinclined to pay.

"All right," he said. He had put two hundred dollars in an envelope; he gave it to Avril. She took the money out and began counting it, and he asked her, "Don't you trust me?"

"Let me ask *you* something," Avril said. "Suppose I took money to your bank and paid it in, wouldn't someone count it?"

"They certainly would."

"Well, Rossie, people have as much right as banks to look out for themselves." She finished counting and said pointedly, "This is the two hundred for me. As well as that, there's my air fare plus taxis, which comes to a hundred and twenty; the rate on the suite is eighty-five; and the champagne and tip were twenty-five. Why don't we say another two hundred and fifty? That should cover everything."

Staggered by the total, he protested, "That's a lot of money."

"I'm a lot of woman. It's no more than Supranational spent when they were paying, and you didn't seem to mind then. Besides, if you want the best, the price comes high."

Her voice had a direct, no-nonsense quality and he knew he was meeting another Avril, shrewder and harder than the yielding, eager-to-please creature of a moment before. Reluctantly, Heyward took two hundred and fifty dollars from his wallet and handed it over.

Avril placed the full amount in an interior compartment of her purse. "There! That's business finished. Now we can attend to loving."

She turned to him and kissed him ardently, at the same time moving her long, deft fingers lightly through his hair. His hunger for her, which had briefly flagged, began to revive.

"Rossie, sweetie," Avril murmured, "when you came in, you looked tired and worried."

"I've had a few problems lately at the bank."

"Then we'll get you loosened. You'll have champagne first, then you can have me." Dexterously she opened the bottle, which was in an ice bucket, and filled two glasses. They sipped together, this time Heyward not bothering to mention his teetotalism. Soon, Avril began to undress him, and herself.

When they were in bed she whispered to him constantly, endearments, encouragement . . . "Oh, Rossie! You're so big and strong!" . . . "What a man you are!" . . . "Go slow, my dearest; slow" . . . "You've brought us to Paradise" . . . "If only this could last forever!"

Her ability was not only to arouse him physically, but to make him feel more a man than ever before. Never, in all his desultory couplings with Beatrice, had he dreamed of this all-encompassing sensation, a glorious progression toward fulfillment so complete in every way.

"Almost there, Rossie" . . . "Whenever you tell me" . . . "Yes, darling! *Oh, please, yes!*"

Perhaps some of Avril's response was acting. He suspected that it might be, but it no longer mattered. What did, was the deep, rich, joyous sensuality he had discovered, through her, in himself.

The crescendo passed. It would remain, Roscoe Heyward thought, as one more exquisite memory. Now they lay, sweetly languorous, while outside the hotel the dusk of early evening turned to darkness and the city's lights winked on. Avril stirred first. She padded from the bedroom to the suite living room, returning with filled glasses of champagne which they sipped while they sat in bed and talked.

After a while Avril said, "Rossie, I want to ask your advice."

"Concerning what?" What girlish confidence was he about to share?

"Should I sell my Supranational stock?"

Startled, he asked, "Do you have much?"

"Five hundred shares. I know that isn't a lot to you. But it is to me—about a third of my savings."

He swiftly calculated that Avril's "savings" were approximately seven times greater than his own.

"What have you heard about SuNatCo? What makes you ask?"

"For one thing, they've cut back a lot on entertaining, and I've been told they're short of money, and they aren't paying bills. Some of the other girls were advised to sell their shares, though I haven't sold mine because they're trading at a lot less than when I bought."

"Have you asked Quartermain?"

"None of us have seen him lately. Moonbeam . . . You remember Moonbeam?"

"Yes." Heyward was reminded that Big George offered to send the exquisite Japanese girl to his room. He wondered how it would have been.

"Moonbeam says Georgie has gone to Costa Rica and may stay there. And she says he sold a lot of his own SuNatCo shares before he went."

Why hadn't he sought out Avril as a source of information weeks ago?

"If I were you," he said, "I'd sell those shares of yours tomorrow. Even at a loss."

She sighed. "It's hard enough to earn money. It's harder still to keep it."

"My dear, you have just enunciated a fundamental financial truth."

There was a silence, then Avril said, "I'll remember you as a nice man, Rossie."

"Thank you. I shall think of you in a special way too."

She reached out to him. "Try again?"

He closed his eyes in pleasure while she caressed him. She was, as always, expert. He thought: Both of them accepted that this was the last time they would meet. One reason was practical: He couldn't afford Avril any more. Beyond that was a sense of events stirring, of changes imminent, of a crisis coming to a head. Who knew what would happen after?

Just before they made love, he remembered his earlier concern about the wrath of God. Well, perhaps God—the father of Christ who acknowledged human frailty, who walked and talked with sinners and died with thieves—would understand. Understand and forgive the truth —that in Roscoe Heyward's life a few sweet moments of his greatest happiness had been in the company of a whore.

* * *

On leaving the hotel, Heyward bought an evening paper. A two column heading, halfway down the front page, attracted his attention.

**Supranational Corp. Disquiet
How Solvent Is Global Giant?**

15

No one ever knew what specific event, if any, provoked the final collapse of Supranational. Perhaps it was one incident. Or it could have been the accumulated weight of many, causing gradual shifts in balance, like a growing strain on underpinning, until suddenly the roof falls in.

As with any financial debacle involving a big public company, isolated signs of weakness had been evident for weeks and months beforehand. But only the most prescient observers, such as Lewis D'Orsey, perceived them as a pattern and communicated warnings to a favored few.

Insiders, of course—including Big George Quartermain who, it was later learned, sold most of his shares through a nominee at SuNatCo's all-time high—had more warning than anyone and bailed out early. Others, tipped off by confidants, or friends returning favor for favor, had similar information and quietly did the same.

Next in line were those like Alex Vandervoort—acting for First Mercantile American Bank—who obtained exclusive information and swiftly unloaded all SuNatCo stock they had, hoping that in any later confusion their action would not be probed. Other institutions—banks, investment houses, mutual funds—seeing the stock price slide and knowing how the insider system worked, soon sized up the situation and followed suit.

There were federal laws against insider stock trading—on paper. In practice, such laws were broken daily and were largely unenforceable. Occasionally in a flagrant case, or as a whitewash job, an accusation might be leveled with a picayune penalty. But even that was rare.

Individual investors—the great, hoping, trusting, naive, beaten, suck-
ered public—were, as usual, the last to know that anything was wrong.

The first public intimation of SuNatCo's difficulties was in an AP
newswire story, printed in afternoon newspapers—the same news story
which Roscoe Heyward saw on leaving the Columbia Hilton. By the
following morning a few more details had been garnered by the press
and amplified reports appeared in morning papers, including *The Wall
Street Journal*. Even so, details were sketchy and many people had trouble believing that anything so reassuringly sizable as Supranational Corporation could be in serious trouble.

Their confidence was soon assailed.

At 10 A.M., at the New York Stock Exchange, Supranational shares
failed to open for trading with the rest of the market. The reason given
was "an order imbalance." What this meant was that the trading specialist for SuNatCo was so swamped with "sell" orders that an orderly
market in the shares could not be maintained.

Trading in SuNatCo did reopen at 11 A.M. when a big "buy" order
of 52,000 shares crossed the tape. But by then the stock, which had
traded at 48½ a month before, was down to 19. By the afternoon clo-
ing bell it was at 10.

The New York Stock Exchange would probably have halted trading
again the following day, except that overnight the decision was taken
from its hands. The Securities and Exchange Commission announced
that it was investigating the affairs of Supranational and, until its inquiry was completed, all trading in SuNatCo shares would be suspended.

There ensued an anxious fifteen days for the remaining SuNatCo
shareholders and creditors, whose combined investments and loans exceeded five billion dollars. Among those waiting—shaken, nervous, and
nail biting—were officers and directors of First Mercantile American
Bank.

Supranational did not, as Alex Vandervoort and Jerome Patterton
hoped it might, "hang on for several months." Therefore the possibility
existed that late transactions in SuNatCo shares—including the big
block sale by FMA's trust department—might be revoked. This could
come about in one of two ways—either by order of the SEC following
a complaint, or by purchasers of the shares bringing suit, claiming that
FMA knew the true condition of Supranational, but failed to disclose
it when the shares were sold. If that happened, it would represent an

even greater loss to trust clients than they already faced, with the bank almost certainly liable for breach of trust.

There was one other possibility which had to be faced—and it was even more likely. First Mercantile American's fifty-million-dollar loan to SuNatCo would become a "write-off," a total loss. If so, for the first time in FMA history the bank would suffer a substantial operating loss for the year. It raised the probability that FMA's own next dividend to shareholders would have to be omitted. That, too, would be a first.

Depression and uncertainty permeated the higher councils of the bank.

Vandervoort had predicted that when the Supranational story broke, the press would start investigative reporting and First Mercantile American would be involved. In this, too, he was right.

News reporters, who in recent years had been motivated by the example of the *Washington Post*'s Watergate heroes, Bernstein and Woodward, bored in hard. Their efforts were successful. Within several days, newspeople had developed sources inside and outside Supranational, and exposés of Quartermain's sleight-of-hand began emerging, as did the conglomerate's shady "Chinese accounting." So did the horrendously high figure of SuNatCo's indebtedness. So did other financial revelations, including FMA's fifty-million-dollar loan.

When the Dow Jones news service tapped out the first reference linking FMA with Supranational, the bank's public relations chief, Dick French, demanded and was granted a hastily summoned top-level conference. Present were Jerome Patterton, Roscoe Heyward, Alex Vandervoort, and the burly figure of French himself, the usual unlighted cigar in a corner of his mouth.

They were a serious group—Patterton glowering and gloomy, as he had been for days; Heyward seeming fatigued, distracted, and betraying nervous tension; Alex with a mounting inner anger at being involved in a disaster he had predicted, and which need never have happened.

"Within an hour, maybe less," the p.r. vice-president began, "I'm going to be hounded for details about our dealings with SuNatCo. I want to know our official attitude and what answers I'm to give."

Patterton asked, "Are we obliged to give any?"

"No," French said. "But then no one's obliged to commit hara-kiri either."

"Why not admit Supranational's indebtedness to us," Roscoe Heyward suggested, "and leave it at that?"

"Because we won't be dealing with simpletons, that's why. Some of the questioners will be experienced financial reporters who understand banking law. So their second query will be: How come your bank committed so much of its depositors' money to a single debtor?"

Heyward snapped, "It was not to a single debtor. The loan was spread between Supranational and five subsidiaries."

"When I say it," French said, "I'll try to make like I believe it." He removed the cigar from his mouth, laid it down, and drew a note pad toward him. "Okay, give me details. It'll all come out anyway, but we'll look a lot worse if we make this painful, like a tooth extraction."

"Before we go on," Heyward said, "I should remind you we're not the only bank to whom Supranational owes money. There's First National City, Bank of America, and Chase Manhattan."

"But they all headed consortiums," Alex pointed out. "That way, any loss is shared with other banks. So far as we know, our bank has the greatest individual exposure." There seemed no point in adding that he had warned all concerned, including the board of directors, that such a concentration of risk was dangerous to FMA and possibly illegal. But his thoughts continued to be bitter.

They hammered out a statement admitting First Mercantile American's deep financial involvement with Supranational and conceding some anxiety. The statement then expressed hope that the ailing conglomerate could be turned around, perhaps with new management which FMA would press for, and with losses minimized. It was a wan hope and everybody knew it.

Dick French was given some leeway to amplify the statement if he needed to, and it was agreed he would remain sole spokesman for the bank.

French warned, "The press will try to contact all of you individually. If you want our story to stay consistent, refer every caller to me, and caution your staffs to do the same."

That same day, Alex Vandervoort reviewed emergency plans he had set up within the bank, to be activated in certain circumstances.

"There's something positively ghoulish," Edwina D'Orsey declared, "about the attention that gets focused on a bank in difficulties."

She had been leafing through newspapers spread around the conference area of Alex Vandervoort's office in FMA Headquarters Tower. It was a Thursday, the day after the press statement by Dick French.

The local *Times-Register* bannered its page one story:

LOCAL BANK FACES HUGE LOSS
IN WAKE OF SUNATCO DEBACLE

With more restraint, *The New York Times* informed its readers:

FMA Bank Declared Sound
Despite Sour Loan Problems

The story had been carried, too, on last night's and this morning's TV network news shows.

Included in all reports was a hasty assurance by the Federal Reserve that First Mercantile American Bank was solvent and depositors need have no cause for alarm. Just the same, FMA was now on the Fed's "problem list" and this morning a team of Federal Reserve examiners had quietly moved in—clearly the first of several such incursions from regulatory agencies.

Tom Straughan, the bank's economist, answered Edwina's observation. "It isn't ghoulishness, really, that excites attention when a bank's in trouble. Mostly, I think, it's fear. Fear among those with accounts that the bank might be forced out of business and they'd lose their money. Also a wider fear that if one bank fails, others could catch the same disease and the entire system fall apart."

"What *I* fear," Edwina said, "is the effect of this publicity."

"I'm equally uneasy," Alex Vandervoort agreed. "It's why we'll continue to watch closely to see what effect it has."

Alex had called a midday strategy meeting. Among those summoned were heads of departments responsible for branch bank administration, since everyone was aware that any lack of public confidence in FMA would be felt in branches first. Earlier, Tom Straughan had reported that branch withdrawals late yesterday and this morning were higher than usual, and deposits lower, though it was too early yet to be sure of a definable trend. Reassuringly, there had been no sign of panic among the bank's customers, though managers of all eighty-four FMA branches had instructions to report promptly if any were observed. A bank survives on its reputation and the trust of others—fragile plants which adversity and bad publicity can wither.

One purpose of today's meeting had been to ensure that actions to be taken in event of a sudden crisis were understood, and communications functioning. Apparently they were.

"That's all for now," Alex told the group. "We'll meet tomorrow at the same time."

They never did.

At 10:15 next morning, Friday, the manager of the First Mercantile American branch at Tylersville, twenty miles upstate, telephoned Headquarters and his call was put through immediately to Alex Vandervoort.

When the manager—Fergus W. Gatwick—identified himself, Alex asked crisply, "What's the problem?"

"A run, sir. This place is jammed with people—more than a hundred of our regular customers, lined up with passbooks and checkbooks, and more are coming in. They're withdrawing everything, cleaning out their accounts, demanding every last dollar." The manager's voice was that of an alarmed man trying to stay calm.

Alex went cold. A run on a bank was a nightmare any banker dreaded; it was also—in the last few days—what Alex and others in top management had feared most. Such a run implied public panic, crowd psychology, a total loss of faith. Even worse, once news of a run on a single branch got out, it could sweep through others in the FMA system like a flash fire, impossible to put out, becoming a catastrophe. No banking institution—not even the biggest and most sound—ever had enough liquidity to repay the majority of its depositors at once, if all demanded cash. Therefore, if the run persisted, cash reserves would be exhausted and FMA obliged to close its doors, perhaps permanently.

It had happened before to other banks. Given a combination of mismanagement, bad timing, and bad luck, it could happen anywhere.

The first essential, Alex knew, was to assure those who wanted their money out that they would receive it. The second was to localize the outbreak.

His instructions to the Tylersville manager were terse. "Fergus, you and all your staff are to act as if there is nothing out of the ordinary. Pay out *without question* whatever people ask for and have in their accounts. And don't walk around looking worried. Be cheerful."

"It won't be easy, sir. I'll try."

"Do *better* than try. At this moment our entire bank is on your shoulders."

"Yes, sir."

"We'll get help out to you as quickly as we can. What's your cash position?"

"We've about a hundred and fifty thousand dollars in the vault," the manager said. "I figure, at the rate we're going, we can last an hour, not much more."

"There'll be cash coming," Alex assured him. "Meanwhile get the money you have out of the vault and stack it up on desks and tables where everyone can see it. Then walk among your customers. Talk to them. Assure them our bank is in excellent shape, despite what they've been reading, and tell them everyone will get their money."

Alex hung up. On another phone he immediately called Straughan. "Tom," Alex said, "the balloon's gone up at Tylersville. The branch there needs help and cash—fast. Put Emergency Plan One in motion."

16

The municipality of Tylersville, like many a human being, was engaged in "finding itself." It was a neo-suburb—a mixture of bustling market town and farmland now partially engulfed by the encroaching city, but with enough of its origins remaining to resist, for a while, ex-urban conformity.

Its populace was a hybrid assortment of the old and new—conservative, deep-rooted farming and local business families, and freshly resident commuters, many of the latter disgusted with decaying moral values of the city they had left, and seeking to absorb—for themselves and growing families—something of peaceful, rustic mores before these disappeared. The result was an unlikely alliance of real and would-be ruralists, mistrusting big business and city-style maneuverings, including those of banks.

Unique, too, in the case of the Tylersville bank run, was one gossipy mail carrier. All day Thursday, while delivering letters and packages, he had also handed out the rumor, "Did you hear about First Mercantile American Bank going bust? They say anyone who has money in there and doesn't get it out by tomorrow is going to lose everything."

Only a few who heard the mailman believed him implicitly. But the story spread, then was fueled by news reports, including those of evening television. Overnight, among farm folk, trades people and the new migrants, anxiety grew so that by Friday morning the consensus was: Why take a chance? Let's get our money now.

A small town has its own jungle telegraph. Word of people's decisions circulated rapidly and, by midmorning, more and more of the populace was heading for the FMA branch bank.

So, out of small threads, are large tapestries woven.

* * *

At FMA Headquarters Tower, some who had scarcely heard of Tylersville were hearing of it now. They would hear more as the chain of events in Vandervoort's Emergency Plan One went forward quickly.

On instructions from Tom Straughan, the bank's computer was consulted first. A programmer tapped the question on a keyboard: What are the totals of savings and demand deposits at Tylersville Branch? The answer was instantaneous—and up to the minute since the branch was on-line to the computer.

SAVINGS ACCOUNTS $26,170,627.54
DEMAND DEPOSITS $15,042,767.18
TOTAL $41,213,394.72

The computer was then instructed: Deduct from this total an allowance for dormant accounts and municipal deposits. (It was a safe assumption that neither of these would be disturbed, even in a run.) The computer responded:

DORMANT & MUNICIPAL .. $21,430,964.61
BALANCE $19,782,430.11

Twenty million dollars more or less which depositors in the Tylersville area could, and might, demand.

A subordinate of Straughan's had already alerted Central Cash Vault, a subterranean fortress below the FMA Tower. Now the vault supervisor was informed, "Twenty million dollars to Tylersville Branch—rush!"

The amount was still more than might be needed, but an objective—decided on during advance planning by Alex Vandervoort's group—was to make a show of strength like running up a flag. Or, as Alex expressed it, "When you fight a fire, make sure you have more water than you need."

Within the past forty-eight hours—anticipating exactly what was happening now—the normal money supply in Central Cash Vault had been augmented by special drawings from the Federal Reserve. The Fed had been informed of, and had approved, the FMA emergency plans.

A Midas fortune in currency and coin, already counted and in labeled sacks, was loaded onto armored trucks while an array of armed guards patrolled the loading ramp. There would be six armored trucks in all, several recalled by radio from other duties, and each would travel sepa-

rately with police escort—a precaution because of the unusual amount
of cash involved. However, only three trucks would have money in them.
The others would be empty—dummies—an extra safeguard against
holdup.

Within twenty minutes of the branch manager's call, the first armored
truck was ready to leave Headquarters and, soon after, was threading
downtown traffic on its way to Tylersville.

Even before that, other bank personnel were en route by private car
and limousine.

Edwina D'Orsey was in the lead. She would be in charge of the support operation now under way.

Edwina left her desk at the main downtown branch at once, pausing
only to inform her senior assistant manager and to collect three staff
members who would accompany her—a loan officer, Cliff Castleman,
and two tellers. One of the tellers was Juanita Núñez.

At the same time, small contingents of staff from two other city
branches were being instructed to go directly to Tylersville where they
would report to Edwina. Part of over-all strategy was not to deplete any
branch seriously of staff in case another run should begin elsewhere. In
that event, other emergency plans were ready, though there was a limit
to how many could be managed at once. Not more than two or three.

The quartet headed by Edwina moved at a brisk pace through the
tunnel connecting the downtown branch with FMA Headquarters.
From the lobby of the parent building they took an elevator down to the
bank's garage where a pool car had been assigned and was waiting. Cliff
Castleman drove.

As they were getting in, Nolan Wainwright sprinted past, heading for
his own parked Mustang. The security chief had been informed of the
Tylersville operation and, with twenty million dollars cash involved,
intended to oversee its protection personally. Not far behind him would
be a station wagon with a half-dozen armed security guards. Local and
state police at Tylersville had been alerted.

Both Alex Vandervoort and Tom Straughan remained where they
were, in FMA Headquarters Tower. Straughan's office near the Money
Trading Center had become a command post. On the 36th floor, Alex's
concern was to keep close tab on the remainder of the branch system,
and to know instantly if fresh trouble erupted.

Alex had kept Patterton informed and now the bank president waited
tensely with Alex, each mulling the unspoken questions: Could they
contain the run in Tylersville? Would First Mercantile American make
it through the business day without a rash of runs elsewhere?

* * *

Fergus W. Gatwick, the Tylersville branch manager, had expected that his few remaining years until retirement would pass unhurriedly and uneventfully. He was sixtyish, a chubby apple of a man, pink-cheeked, blue-eyed, gray-haired, an affable Rotarian. In his youth he had known ambition but shed it long ago, deciding wisely that his role in life was supportive; he was a follower who would never blaze a trail. Managing a small branch bank ideally suited his ability and limitations.

He had been happy at Tylersville, where only one crisis had marred his tenure until now. A few years ago a woman with an imagined grudge against the bank rented a safe deposit box. She placed in the box an object wrapped in newspaper, then departed for Europe leaving no address. Within days, a putrid odor filtered through the bank. At first, drains were suspect and examined, to no effect, while all the time the stench grew greater. Customers complained, staff were nauseated. Eventually suspicion centered on the safe deposit boxes where the awful smell seemed strongest. Then the crucial question arose—which box?

It was Fergus W. Gatwick who, at duty's call, sniffed his way around them all, at length settling on one where the malodor was overpowering. After that, it took four days of legal proceedings before a court order was obtained permitting the bank to drill the box open. Inside were the remains of a large, once-fresh sea bass. Sometimes, even now in memory, Gatwick still sniffed traces of that ghastly time.

But today's exigency, he knew, was far more serious than a fish in a box. He checked his watch. An hour and ten minutes since he had telephoned Headquarters. Though four tellers had been paying out money steadily, the number of people crowding the bank was even greater, with newcomers pouring in, and still no help had come.

"Mr. Gatwick!" A woman teller beckoned him.

"Yes?" He left the railed management area where he normally worked and walked over to her. Across a counter from them both, at the head of a waiting line, was a poultry farmer, a regular bank customer whom Gatwick knew well. The manager said cheerfully, "Good morning, Steve."

He received a cool nod in return while silently the teller showed him checks drawn on two accounts. The poultryman had presented them. They totaled $23,000.

"Those are good," Gatwick said. Taking the checks, he initialed both.

In a low voice, though audible across the counter, the teller said, "We haven't enough money left to pay that much."

He should have known, of course. The drain on cash since opening had been continuous with many large withdrawals. But the remark was unfortunate. Now there were angry rumblings among those in line, the teller's statement being repeated and passed back. "You hear that! They say they don't have any money."

"By Christ!" The poultry farmer leaned wrathfully forward, a clenched fist pounding. "You just better pay those checks, Gatwick, or I'll be over there and tear this goddam bank apart."

"There's no need for any of that, Steve. Not threats or shouting either." Fergus W. Gatwick raised his own voice, striving to be heard above the suddenly ugly scene. "Ladies and gentlemen, we are experiencing a temporary cash shortage because of exceptional demands, but I assure you a great deal more money is on the way and will be here soon."

The last words were drowned by wrathful shouts of protest. "How come a bank runs out of money?" . . . "Get it now!" . . . "Forget the bullshit! Where's the cash?" . . . "We'll camp here till this bank pays what it owes."

Gatwick held up his arms. "Once again I assure you . . ."

"I'm not interested in your sleazy assurances." The speaker was a smartly dressed woman whom Gatwick recognized as a newish resident. She insisted, "I want my money out now."

"Damn right!" a man behind her echoed. "That goes for all of us."

Still others surged forward, voices raised, their faces revealing anger and alarm. Someone threw a cigarette package which hit Gatwick in the face. Suddenly, he realized, an ordinary group of citizens, many of whom he knew well, had become a hostile mob. It was the money, of course; money which did strange things to human beings, making them greedy, panicked, at times sub-human. There was genuine dread, too—the possibility, as some saw it, of losing everything they had, along with their security. Violence, which moments ago appeared unthinkable, now loomed close. For the first time in many years, Gatwick felt physical fear.

"Please!" he pleaded. "Please listen!" His voice disappeared under growing tumult.

Abruptly, unexpectedly, the clamor lessened. There seemed to be some activity in the street outside which those at the rear were craning to see. Then, with a bravura flourish, the bank's outer doors flung open and a procession marched in.

Edwina D'Orsey headed it. Following her were Cliff Castleman and the two young women tellers, one of them the petite figure of Juanita Núñez. Behind was a phalanx of security guards shouldering heavy canvas sacks, escorted by other protective guards with drawn revolvers. A half dozen more staff who had arrived from other branches filed in behind the guards. In the wake of them all—a vigilant, wary Lord Protector —was Nolan Wainwright.

Edwina spoke clearly across the crowded, now near-silent bank. "Good morning, Mr. Gatwick. I'm sorry we all took so long, but traffic was heavy. I understand you may require twenty million dollars. About a third of it just arrived. The rest is on the way."

While Edwina was speaking, Cliff Castleman, Juanita, the guards and others continued through the railed management area to the rear of the counters. One of the newly arrived relief staff was an operations man who promptly took charge of incoming cash. Soon, plentiful supplies of crisp new bills were being recorded, then distributed to tellers.

The crowd in the bank pressed around Edwina. Someone asked, "Is that true? Do you people have enough money to pay us all?"

"Of course it's true." Edwina looked over heads around her and spoke to everyone. "I'm Mrs. D'Orsey, and I'm a vice-president of First Mercantile American Bank. Despite any rumors you may have heard, our bank is sound, solvent, and has no problems which we cannot handle. We have ample cash reserves to repay any depositor—in Tylersville or anywhere else."

The smartly dressed woman who had spoken earlier said, "Maybe that's true. Or maybe you're just saying so, hoping we'll believe it. Either way, I'm taking my money out today."

"That's your privilege," Edwina said.

Fergus W. Gatwick, watching, was relieved at no longer being the focus of attention. He also sensed that the ugly mood of moments earlier had eased; there were even a few smiles among those waiting as increasing amounts of money continued to appear. But less obdurate mood or not, a purposefulness remained. As the process of paying out continued briskly, it was clear that the run on the bank had not been halted.

While it continued, once more like Caesar's legionaries, the bank guards and escort who had returned to their armored trucks outside, marched in again with still more loaded canvas sacks.

No one who shared that day at Tylersville would ever forget the immense amount of money eventually displayed on public view. Even those who worked at FMA had never seen so much assembled at a single time before. On Edwina's instructions and under Alex Vandervoort's plan, most of the twenty million dollars brought to fight the bank run was out in the open where everyone could see it. In the area behind the tellers' counter, every desk was cleared; from elsewhere in the bank more desks and tables were moved in. Onto them all, great stacks of currency and coin were heaped while the extra staff who had been brought in somehow kept track of running totals.

As Nolan Wainwright expressed it later, the entire operation was "a bank robber's dream, a security man's nightmare." Fortunately, if robbers learned of what was happening, they learned too late.

Edwina, quietly competent and with courtesy to Fergus W. Gatwick, supervised everything.

It was she who instructed Cliff Castleman to begin seeking loan business.

Shortly before noon, with the bank remaining crowded and a lengthening line outside, Castleman carried a chair forward and stood up on it.

"Ladies and gentlemen," he announced, "I'd like to introduce myself. I'm a loan officer from the city, which doesn't mean a lot except that I have authority to approve loans for larger amounts than are normally dealt with at this branch. So if any of you have been thinking of applying for a loan and would like a fast answer, now's the time. I'm a sympathetic listener and I try to help people who have problems. Mr. Gatwick, who is busy doing other things right now, has kindly said I can use his desk, so that's where I'll be. I hope you'll come and talk to me."

A man with a cast on his leg called out, "I'll be right over, soon's I get my other money. Guess if this bank's going bust I should grab a loan. I'd never have to pay it back."

"Nothing's going bust here," Cliff Castleman said. He inquired, "What did you do to the leg?"

"Fell over in the dark."

"From the sound of you, you're still in the dark. This bank is in better shape than either of us. What's more, if you borrow money you'll pay it back or we'll break the other leg."

There was some laughter as Castleman climbed down from his chair, and later a few people drifted over to the manager's desk to discuss loans. But withdrawals continued. The panic eased, but nothing, it seemed—neither a show of strength, assurances or applied psychology —would stop the bank run at Tylersville.

By early afternoon it appeared, to despondent FMA officials, that only one question still remained: How long would it take for the virus to spread?

Alex Vandervoort, who had talked several times by telephone with Edwina, left for Tylersville himself in midafternoon. He was now even more alarmed than this morning when he had hoped the run could be terminated quickly. Its continuance meant that, over the weekend, panic among depositors would spread, with other FMA branches certain to be inundated Monday.

So far today, while withdrawals at some other branches had been heavy, nothing comparable to the Tylersville situation had occurred elsewhere. But clearly that same luck could not hold for long.

Alex went by chauffeured limousine to Tylersville and Margot Bracken rode with him. Margot had concluded a court case earlier than she expected that morning and joined Alex at the bank for lunch. Afterward at his suggestion she stayed on, sharing some of the tensions by then pervading the tower's 36th floor.

In the car Alex leaned back, savoring the relaxed interval which he knew would be brief.

"This year has been hard for you," Margot said.

"Am I showing the strain?"

She reached over, running a forefinger across his forehead gently. "You've more lines there. You're grayer at the temples."

He grimaced. "I'm also older."

"Not that much."

"Then it's a price we pay for living with pressures. You pay it too, Bracken."

"Yes, I do," Margot agreed. "What matters, of course, is which pressures are important and if they're worth the part of ourselves we give to them."

"Saving a bank is worth some personal strain," Alex said sharply. "Right now if we don't save ours, a lot of people will be hurt who shouldn't be."

"And some who should?"

"In a rescue operation you try to save everybody. Any retribution can come later."

They had covered ten of the twenty miles to Tylersville.

"Alex, are things really that bad?"

"If we have an unstoppable run on Monday," he said, "we'll have to close. A consortium of other banks may then get together to bail us out —at a price—after which they'll pick over what's left, and in time, I think, all depositors would get their money. But FMA as an entity would be finished."

"The most incredible part is how it can happen so suddenly."

"It points up," Alex said, "what a lot of people, who ought to, don't fully understand. Banks and the money system, which includes big debts and big loans, are like delicate machinery. Monkey with them clumsily, let one component get seriously out of balance because of greed or politics or plain stupidity, and you imperil all the others. And once you've endangered the system—or a single bank—and if word leaks out as usually happens, diminished public confidence does the rest. That's what we're seeing now."

"From what you've told me," Margot said, "and from other things I've heard, greed is the reason for what's happening to your bank."

Alex said bitterly, "That and a high percentage of idiots on our board." He was being franker than usual but found it a relief.

There was a silence between them until Alex exclaimed, "God! How I miss him."

"Who?"

"Ben Rosselli."

Margot reached out for his hand. "Isn't this rescue operation of yours exactly what Ben would have done himself?"

"Maybe." He sighed. "Except it isn't working. That's why I wish Ben were here."

The chauffeur let down the dividing window between the front seat and his passengers. He spoke over his shoulder. "We're coming into Tylersville, sir."

"Good luck, Alex," Margot said.

From several blocks away, they could see a lineup of people outside the branch. New arrivals were joining it. As their limousine pulled up outside the bank, a panel truck screeched to a halt across the street and several men and a girl jumped out. On the side of the truck in large letters was WTLC-TV. "Christ!" Alex said. "That's all we need."

Inside the bank, while Margot looked around her curiously, Alex talked briefly with Edwina and Fergus W. Gatwick, learning from both that there was little if anything more that anyone could do. Alex supposed it had been a wasted journey but had felt the need to come. He decided it would do no harm, and might even help, if he chatted with some of those waiting. He began to walk down the several lines of people, quietly introducing himself.

There were at least two hundred, a sizable cross-section of Tylersville —old, young, middle-aged, some well-to-do, others obviously poorer, women with babies, men in work clothes, some carefully dressed as if for an occasion. The majority were friendly, a few not, one or two antagonistic. Almost everyone showed some degree of nervousness. There was relief on the faces of those who received their money and left. An elderly woman spoke to Alex on the way out. She had no idea he was a bank official. "Thank heaven that's over! It's been the most anxious day I ever spent. This is my savings—all I have." She held up a dozen or so fifty-dollar bills. Others left with much larger or smaller sums.

The impression Alex got from everyone he talked to was the same: Maybe First Mercantile American Bank was sound; maybe it wasn't. But no one wanted to take a chance and leave their money in an institution which might collapse. The publicity linking FMA with Supranational had done its work. Everyone knew that First Mercantile American was likely to lose a huge amount of money, because the bank admitted it. Details didn't matter. Nor did the few people to whom Alex mentioned Federal Deposit Insurance trust that system either. The amount of federal insurance was limited, a few pointed out, and FDIC funds were believed to be inadequate in any major crunch.

And there was something else, Alex realized, perhaps even more profound: People didn't believe any more what they were told; they had become too accustomed to being deceived and lied to. In the recent past they had been lied to by their President, other government officials, politicians, business, industry. Lied to by employers, by unions. Lied to in advertising. Lied to in financial transactions, including the status of stocks and bonds, stockholder reports and "audited" corporate statements. Lied to at times—through bias or omission—by communications media. The list was endless. Deception had been piled on deception until lying—or, at best, distortion and failure to make full disclosure— had become a way of life.

So why should anyone believe Alex when he assured them that FMA was not a sinking ship and their money—if they left it there—was safe? As the hours slipped by and afternoon waned, it was clear that no one did.

By late afternoon Alex had become resigned. What would happen would happen; for individuals and institutions, he supposed, there came a point where the inevitable must be accepted. It was about that time— near 5:30, with dusk of the October evening closing in—that Nolan Wainwright came to him reporting a new anxiety in the waiting crowd.

"They're worried," Wainwright said, "because our closing time is six o'clock. They figure in the half hour that's left we can't deal with everybody."

Alex wavered. It would be simple to close the Tylersville branch bank on schedule; it would also be legal, and no one could seriously object. He savored an impulse born of anger and frustration; a spiteful urge to say, in effect, to those still waiting: *You've refused to trust me, so sweat till Monday, and the hell with you!* But he hesitated, swayed by his own nature and a remark of Margot's about Ben Rosselli. What Alex was doing now, she had said, was "exactly what Ben would have done himself." What would Ben's decision have been about closing? Alex knew.

"I'll make an announcement," he told Wainwright. First he sought out Edwina and gave her some instructions.

Moving to the doorway of the bank, Alex spoke from where he could be heard by those inside and others still waiting on the street. He was conscious of TV cameras directed at him. The first TV crew had been joined by a second from another station, and an hour ago Alex made a statement for them both. The TV crews stayed on, one of their people confiding they were getting extra material for a weekend news feature since "a bank run doesn't happen every day."

"Ladies and gentlemen"—Alex's voice was strong and clear; it carried easily. "I am informed that some of you are concerned about the time of our closing tonight. You need not be. On behalf of the management of this bank I give you my word that we will remain open here in Tylersville until we have attended to you all." There was a murmur of satisfaction and some spontaneous handclapping.

"However, there is one thing I urge on all of you." Once more, voices quietened as attention returned to Alex. He went on, "I strongly advise that over the weekend you do not keep large sums of money on your person or in your homes. It would be unsafe in many ways. Therefore I urge you to select another bank and deposit there whatever you withdraw from this one. To help you in this, my colleague Mrs. D'Orsey is at present telephoning other banks in this area, asking them to remain open later than usual in order to accommodate you."

Again there was an appreciative hum.

Nolan Wainwright came to Alex, whispered briefly and Alex announced, "I am informed that two banks have already agreed to our request. Others are still being contacted."

From among those waiting in the street a male voice called, "Can you recommend a good bank?"

"Yes," Alex said. "My own choice would be First Mercantile American. It's the one I know best, the one I'm surest of, and its record has been long and honorable. I only wish that all of you felt that way too." For the first time there was a hint of emotion in his voice. A few people smiled or laughed half-heartedly, but most faces watching him were serious.

"Used to feel that way myself," a voice behind Alex volunteered. He turned. The speaker was an elderly man, probably nearer eighty than seventy, wizened, white-haired, stooped, and leaning on a cane. But the old man's eyes were clear and sharp, his voice firm. Beside him was a woman of about the same age. Both were tidily dressed, though their clothing was old-fashioned and well worn. The woman held a shopping bag which, it could be seen, contained packages of currency. They had just come from the bank counter.

"The wife and me, we've had an account at FMA for more'n thirty years," the old man said. "Feel kinda bad taking it away now."

"Then why do it?"

"Can't ignore all them rumors. Too much smoke for there not to be some truth somewhere."

"There is some truth and we've admitted it," Alex said. "Because of a loan to Supranational Corporation, our bank is likely to suffer a loss. But the bank can withstand it, and it will."

The old man shook his head. "If I was younger and working, maybe I'd take a chance on what you say. But I ain't. What's in there"—he pointed to the shopping bag—"is pretty well all we got left until we die. Even that ain't much. Them dollars don't go half as far as when we worked and earned 'em."

"That's for sure," Alex said. "Inflation hits good people like you hardest. But, unfortunately, changing banks won't help you there."

"Let me ask you a question, young fellow. If you was me and this here was your money, wouldn't you be doing the same as I am now?"

Alex was aware of others closing in and listening. He saw Margot a head or two away. Just behind her, TV camera lights were on. Someone was leaning forward with a microphone.

"Yes," he admitted. "I suppose I would."

The old man seemed surprised. "You're honest, anyways. Just now I heard that advice you gave about getting to another bank and I appreciate it. I guess we'll go to one and put our money in."

"Wait," Alex said. "Do you have a car?"

"Nope. Live just a piece from here. We'll walk."

"Not with that money. You might be robbed. I'll have someone drive you to another bank." Alex beckoned Nolan Wainwright and explained the problem. "This is our chief of security," he told the elderly couple.

"No sweat," Wainwright said. "Be glad to drive you myself."

The old man didn't move. He stood looking from one face to the other. "You'd do that for us? When we've just moved our money out of your bank? When we've good as told you we don't trust you any more?"

"Let's say it's all in our service. Besides," Alex said, "if you've been with us thirty years, we ought to part as friends."

Still the old man paused uncertainly. "Maybe we don't have to. Let me ask you one more question, man to man." The clear, sharp, honest eyes regarded Alex steadily.

"Go ahead."

"You told me the truth once already, young fellow. Now tell me it again, remembering what I said about being old and knowing what them savings mean. Is our money safe in your bank? *Absolutely safe?*"

For measurable seconds Alex weighed the question and all its implications. He knew that not only the old couple was watching him intently, but many others, too. The omnipresent TV cameras were still turning. He caught a glimpse of Margot; she was equally intent, a quizzical expression on her face. He thought of the people here, and of others elsewhere affected by this moment; of those relying on him—Jerome Patterton, Tom Straughan, the board, Edwina, more; of what might happen if FMA failed, of the wide and damaging effect, not just at Tylersville but far beyond. Despite all this, doubt rose. He thrust it down, then answered crisply and confidently, "I give you my word. This bank is absolutely safe."

"Aw shucks, Freda!" the old man told his wife. "Looks like we been barkin' up a tree about nothing. Let's go put the damn money back."

In all the post-mortem studies and discussions over the following weeks, one fact stayed undisputed: The bank run at Tylersville effectively ended when the old man and his wife turned back into the FMA branch and redeposited the money from their shopping bag. People who had been waiting to withdraw their own money, and who witnessed the exchange between the old man and the bank executive either avoided each other's eyes or, if they didn't, grinned sheepishly and turned away. Word passed speedily among the remainder of those outside and inside; almost at once the waiting lines began dispersing, as quickly and mysteriously as they had formed. As someone said later: It was the herd instinct in reverse. When the few remaining people in the bank were dealt with, the branch closed only ten minutes later than was normal on a Friday night. A few FMA people, at Tylersville and in Headquarters Tower, had worried about Monday. Would the crowd return, the run begin again? In the event, it never did.

Nor, on Monday, did a run develop anywhere else. The reason—most analysts agreed—was an explicit, honest, moving scene involving an old couple and a good-looking, open, bank vice-president as it appeared on weekend television news. The film, when cut and edited, was so successful that stations used the item several times. It came through as an example of the intimate, effective *cinema verité* technique which

TV can do so well, but seldom does. Many viewers were moved to tears.

During the weekend, Alex Vandervoort saw the TV film but reserved his comments. A reason was that he alone knew what his thoughts had been at the vital, decisive moment when he was asked the question: *Is our money . . . absolutely safe?* Another was that Alex knew the pitfalls and problems which still lay ahead for FMA.

Margot also said little about the incident on Friday night; nor did she mention it Sunday when she stayed at Alex's apartment. She had an important question she wanted to ask but wisely decided that now was not the time.

Among First Mercantile American executives who watched the telecast was Roscoe Heyward, though he didn't see it all. Heyward turned on the TV after arriving home on Sunday night from a church vestry meeting but snapped it off in jealous anger part way through. Heyward had serious enough problems of his own without wishing to be reminded of a Vandervoort success. And quite apart from the bank run, several matters were likely to surface during the coming week which made Heyward highly nervous.

One other postscript developed from that Friday evening in Tylersville. It concerned Juanita Núñez.

Juanita had seen Margot Bracken arrive during the afternoon. She had recently debated whether or not to seek out Margot and ask advice. Now she decided to. But for reasons of her own, Juanita preferred not to be observed by Nolan Wainwright.

The opportunity Juanita had been waiting for occurred shortly after the bank run ended, while Wainwright was busy checking branch security arrangements for the weekend, and the day-long pressure on the staff had eased. Juanita left the counter where she had been assisting a regular branch teller and crossed to the railed management area. Margot was seated there alone, waiting until Mr. Vandervoort could leave.

"Miss Bracken," Juanita said, speaking softly, "you once told me that if I had a problem I could come and talk to you."

"Of course, Juanita. Do you have one now?"

Her small face creased in worry. "Yes, I think so."

"What kind of problem?"

"If you don't mind, could we talk somewhere else?" Juanita was watching Wainwright, near the vault on the opposite side of the bank. He seemed about to end a conversation.

"Then come to my office," Margot said. "When would you like to make it?"

They agreed on Monday evening.

17

The reel of tape, retrieved from the Double-Seven Health Club, had been lying there on the shelf above the test bench for six days.

Wizard Wong had glanced at the tape several times, reluctant to wipe out what was on it, yet uneasy about passing on the information. Nowadays, recording *any* telephone conversation was risky. Even riskier was to play the recording back for someone else.

Yet Marino, Wizard was certain, would very much like to hear a portion of that tape, and would pay well for the privilege. Whatever else Tony Bear Marino might be, he was generous about payment for good service, which was the one reason Wizard did work for him periodically.

Marino was a professional crook, he was aware. Wong himself was not.

Wizard (his real first name was Wayne, though no one who knew him ever used it) was a young, clever, second-generation Chinese-American. He was also an electronics-audio expert, specializing in the detection of electronic surveillance. His genius in the subject had earned him his name.

For a long list of clients, Wong provided guarantees that their business premises and homes were not bugged, their phones untapped, their privacy—from surreptitious electronics—inviolate. With surprising frequency he did discover planted listening devices and when it happened his clients were impressed and grateful. Despite official assurances to the contrary—including some recent presidential ones—bugging and wiretapping in the U.S. continued to be widespread and flourishing.

Heads of industrial companies retained Wong's services. So did bankers, newspaper publishers, presidential candidates, some big-name lawyers, a foreign embassy or two, a handful of U.S. senators, three state governors, and a Supreme Court justice. Then there were the other executives—the Don of a Mafia family, his consigliori, and various wheels at slightly lower level, of whom Tony Marino was one.

To his criminal clients Wizard Wong made one thing plain: He wanted no part of their illicit activities; he was making an excellent living within the law. However, he saw no reason for them to be denied his services, since bugging was almost always illegal, and even criminals were entitled to protect themselves by lawful means. This ground rule was accepted and worked well.

Just the same, his organized crime clients intimated to Wizard from time to time that any usable information he acquired as a result of his work would be appreciated and rewarded. And occasionally he *had* passed on tidbits of knowledge in return for money, yielding to that oldest and simplest of all temptations—greed.

He was being tempted by it now.

A week and a half ago, Wizard Wong had made a routine anti-bug survey of Marino's haunts and telephones. These included the Double-Seven Health Club where Marino had a financial interest. In course of the survey—which showed everything to be clean—Wizard amused himself by briefly bugging one of the club lines, a practice which he sometimes followed, rationalizing that he owed it to himself and his clients to maintain his own technical expertise. For the purpose he chose a pay phone on the health club's main floor. Through forty-eight hours Wizard left a tape recorder spliced across the pay-phone circuit, the recorder hidden in the basement of the Double-Seven. It was a type which switched itself on and off each time the phone was used.

Though the action was illegal, Wizard reasoned that it didn't matter since no one but himself would hear the tape played back. However, when he did play it, one conversation, especially, intrigued him.

Now, on Saturday afternoon, and alone in his sound lab, he took the tape from the shelf above the test bench, put it on a machine and listened to that portion once again.

A coin was inserted, a number dialed. The sound of dialing was on the tape. A ringing tone. One ring only.

A woman's voice (soft, with slight accent): Hello.

A male voice (whispering): You know who this is. But don't use names.

The woman's voice: Yes.

The first voice (still whispering): Tell our mutual friend I've discov-

ered something important here. Really important. It's most of what he wanted to know. I can't say more, but I'll come to you tomorrow night. .

A woman's voice: All right.

A *click*. The caller, in the Double-Seven Health Club, had hung up.

Wizard Wong wasn't sure why he thought Tony Bear Marino would be interested. He simply had a hunch, and his hunches had paid off before. Making up his mind, he consulted a private notebook, went to a telephone and called a number.

Tony Bear, it transpired, could not see him until late Monday afternoon. Wizard made an arrangement for then and—having committed himself—set out to extract more information from the tape.

He rewound it, then carefully played it several times again.

"Judas Priest!" Tony Bear Marino's husky, thick features contorted in a savage scowl. His incongruous falsetto voice rose even higher than usual. "You had that goddam tape, and you sat on your goddam ass a week before you came here!"

Wizard Wong said defensively, "I'm a technician, Mr. Marino. Mostly, the things I hear are none of my business. But after a while I got to thinking this one was different." He was relieved in one sense. At least there had been no angry reaction because he had bugged a Double-Seven line.

"Next time," Marino snarled, "think faster!"

Today was Monday. They were at the trucking terminal where Marino maintained an office and, on the desk between them, was a portable tape player which Wong had just switched off. Before coming here he had re-recorded the significant part of the original tape, transferring it to a cassette, then erased the rest.

Tony Bear Marino, in shirtsleeves in the stuffy, heated office, appeared physically formidable as usual. His shoulders were a prizefighter's; his wrists and biceps thick. He overflowed the chair he sat in, though not with fat; most of him was solid muscle. Wizard Wong tried not to be intimidated, either by Marino's bulk or his reputation for ruthlessness. But, whether from the hot room or other reasons, Wong began to sweat.

He protested, "I didn't waste all that time, Mr. Marino. I found out some other things I thought you'd want to know."

"Such as?"

"I can tell you the number that was called. You see, by using a stop watch to time the length of each dial turn as recorded on the tape, then comparing it . . ."

"Cut the crap. Just give me the number."

"There it is." A slip of paper passed across the desk.

"You've traced it? Whose number is it?"

"I have to tell you, tracing a number like that isn't easy. Especially since this particular one is unlisted. Fortunately, I have some contacts in the phone company . . ."

Tony Bear exploded. He slammed a palm on the desktop, the impact like a gunshot. "Don't play games with me, you little bastard! If you got information, give!"

"The point I'm making," Wizard persisted, sweating even more, "is that it costs. I had to pay off my phone company contact."

"You paid a goddam lot less than you'll squeeze out of me. Get on with it!"

Wizard relaxed a little, aware that he had made his point and Tony Bear would meet the price to be asked, each of them knowing there might be another time.

"The phone belongs to a Mrs. J. Núñez. She lives at Forum East. Here's the building and apartment number." Wong passed over another slip. Marino took it, glanced at the address, and put it down.

"There's something else might be of interest to you. The records show the phone was installed a month ago as a hurry-up job. Now normally, there's a long waiting list for phones at Forum East, but this one wasn't on the list at all, then all of a sudden it was put on at the top."

Marino's growing scowl was part impatience, part anger at what he heard. Wizard Wong went on hastily, "What happened was, some pressure was applied. My contact told me there's a memo in the phone company files showing it came from a guy named Nolan Wainwright who's head of security for a bank—First Mercantile American. He said the phone was needed urgently for bank business. Billing for it is going to the bank, too."

For the first time since the audio technician's arrival, Tony Bear was startled. Momentarily the surprise revealed itself on his face, then vanished, to be replaced by a blank expression. Under it, his mind was working, relating what he had just learned to certain facts he already knew. The name Wainwright was the connection. Marino was aware of the attempt six months ago to plant a stoolie, a creep named Vic who, after they busted his balls, said "Wainwright." Marino knew of the bank dick by reputation. In that earlier series of events Tony Bear had been very much involved.

Was there another one now? If so, Tony Bear had a strong idea what action he was after, though there was a lot of other business through the Double-Seven he had no wish to see disclosed. Tony Bear did not waste time in speculation. The caller's voice, a whisper only, you couldn't tell. But the other voice—the woman's—had been traced, so whatever else was needed they could get from her. It did not enter his mind that the woman might not co-operate; if she was foolish, there were plenty of ways.

Marino paid Wong off quickly and sat thinking. For a while, he followed his usual cautious pattern, not rushing a decision and leaving his thoughts to simmer for several hours. But he had lost time, a week.

Later that night he summoned two musclemen. Tony Bear gave them a Forum East address and an order. "Pick up the Núñez broad."

18

"If everything you just told me turns out to be true," Alex assured Margot, "I'll personally administer the biggest kick in the ass that Nolan Wainwright ever had."

Margot snapped back, "Of course it's all true. Why would Mrs. Núñez invent it? In any case, how could she?"

"No," he admitted, "I don't suppose she could."

"I'll tell you something else, Alex. I want more than your man Wainwright's head on a platter—or his ass. A whole lot more."

They were in Alex's apartment where Margot had come a half hour ago, following her Monday-night talk with Juanita Núñez. What Juanita had revealed amazed and enraged her. Juanita had nervously described the month-old agreement in which she had become the link between Wainwright and Miles Eastin. But recently, Juanita confided, she had begun to realize the risk she was running and her fears had grown, not just for herself but for Estela. Margot had gone over Juanita's report several times, questioning her on details, and at the end Margot went directly to Alex.

"I knew about Eastin going under cover." Alex's face was troubled, as it had been so often recently; he paced the living room holding an untasted scotch. "Nolan told me what he planned. At first I opposed it and said no, then I gave in because the arguments seemed convincing. But I swear to you that no arrangement with the Núñez girl was ever mentioned."

"I believe you," Margot said. "He probably didn't tell you because he knew you'd veto it."

"Did Edwina know?"

"Apparently not."

Alex thought peevishly: Then Nolan was out of line there, too. How *could* he have been so shortsighted, even stupid? Part of the trouble, Alex knew, was that department heads like Wainwright got carried away by their own limited objectives, forgetting the larger view.

He stopped pacing. "A minute ago you said something about wanting 'a whole lot more.' What does that mean?"

"The first thing I want is immediate safety for my client and her child, and by safety I mean placing her somewhere where she's out of jeopardy. After that, we can discuss compensation."

"Your *client?*"

"I advised Juanita tonight that she needs legal help. She asked me to represent her."

Alex grinned and sipped his scotch. "So you and I are now adversaries, Bracken."

"In that sense, I suppose so." Margot's voice softened. "Except you know I won't take advantage of our private conversations."

"Yes, I do. That's why I'll tell you privately we *will* do something—immediately, tomorrow—for Mrs. Núñez. If it means sending her out of town for a while, to be certain she's safe, then I'll approve it. As to compensation, I won't commit us on that, but after I hear the whole story, and if it agrees with yours and hers, we'll consider it."

What Alex left unsaid was his intention to send for Nolan Wainwright in the morning and order the entire undercover operation terminated. That would include safeguarding the girl, as he had promised Margot; also, Eastin must be paid off. Alex wished fervently he had stayed firm by his original judgment and forbidden the entire plan; all his instincts had been against it and he had been wrong in backing down under Wainwright's persuasion. The risks, in every way, were far too great. Fortunately it was not too late to remedy the error, since nothing harmful had occurred, either to Eastin or Núñez.

Margot regarded him. "One of the things I like about you is that you're a fair man. So you do concede the bank has a liability to Juanita Núñez?"

"Oh, Christ!" Alex said, and drained his scotch. "Right now we're liable for so much, what the hell is one thing more?"

19

Only one more piece. Just one more needed to complete the tantalizing jigsaw. A single lucky break could yield it, and answer the question: Where was the counterfeiter's base?

When Nolan Wainwright conceived the second undercover mission, he did not anticipate spectacular results. He considered Miles Eastin a long shot from whom some minor information might accrue, and even that could take months. But instead, Eastin had moved quickly from one revelation to another. Wainwright wondered if Eastin himself realized how outstandingly successful he had been.

On Tuesday at midmorning, alone in his plainly furnished office at FMA Headquarters Tower, Wainwright once more reviewed the progress made:

—*The first report from Eastin had been to say "I'm in" at the Double-Seven Health Club. In light of later developments that, in itself, had been important. Confirmation followed that the Double-Seven was a hangout for criminals, including the loan shark, Ominsky, and Tony Bear Marino.*

—*By gaining access to the illegal gambling rooms, Eastin had improved his infiltration.*

—*Soon after, Eastin had made a "buy" of ten counterfeit $20 bills. These, when examined by Wainwright and others, proved to be of the same high quality as those circulating in the area over the past several months and were undoubtedly from the same source. Eastin had reported his supplier's name and the man was being watched.*

—*Next, a three-pronged report: the forged driver's license; the license number of the Chevrolet Impala which Eastin had driven to*

*Louisville, apparently with a consignment of counterfeit money in the
trunk; and the counterfoil of the airline ticket given Eastin for his return journey. Of the three items, the airline ticket had proven the most
useful. It had been purchased, along with others, with a Keycharge bank
credit card, counterfeit. At last the bank security chief had a sense of
closing in on his main objective—the conspiracy which had, and still
was, defrauding the Keycharge system of huge amounts. The fake
driver's license confirmed the existence of a versatile, efficient organization to which there was now an additional lead—the ex-con, Jules
LaRocca. The Impala, inquiry showed, had been stolen. A few days
after Eastin's journey it was found abandoned in Louisville.*

*—Finally, and most important, had been identifying the counter-
feiter, Danny, along with a cornucopia of information including the
fact that the source of the counterfeit Keycharge credit cards was now
known with certainty.*

As Wainwright's knowledge had accumulated because of his pipe-
line from Miles Eastin, so had an obligation grown—to share what he
knew. Therefore a week ago he had invited agents of the FBI and U. S.
Secret Service to a conference at the bank. The Secret Service had to
be included because money counterfeiting was involved, and theirs was
the constitutional responsibility for protecting the U.S. money system.
The FBI special agents who came were the same team—Innes and
Dalrymple—who investigated the FMA cash loss and arrested Miles
Eastin almost a year ago. The Secret Service men—Jordan and Quimby
—Wainwright had not met before.

Innes and Dalrymple were complimentary and appreciative about
the information Wainwright gave them, the Secret Service men less so.
Their beef was that Wainwright should have notified them sooner—as
soon as he received the first counterfeit bills from Eastin—and that
Eastin, through Wainwright, ought to have advised them in advance
about the Louisville journey.

The Secret Service agent Jordan, a dour, hard-eyed, runtish man
whose stomach rumbled constantly, complained, "If we'd been warned,
we could have made an intercept. As it is, your man Eastin may be
guilty of a felony, with you as an accessory."

Wainwright pointed out patiently, "I already explained there was no
chance for Eastin to notify anybody, including me. He took a risk and
knew it; I happen to think he did the right thing. As to a felony, we
don't even know for sure there was counterfeit money in that car."

"It was there all right," Jordan grumbled. "It's been surfacing in
Louisville ever since. What we didn't know was how it came in."

"Well, you do now," the FBI agent Innes injected. "And thanks to Nolan, we're all that much further ahead."

Wainwright added, "If you'd made an intercept, sure you might have got a batch of counterfeit. But not much else, and Eastin's usefulness would have been ended."

In a way, Wainwright sympathized with the Secret Service point of view. The agents were overworked, harassed, their service understaffed, yet the quantity of counterfeit money in circulation had increased by staggering amounts in recent years. They were fighting a hydra-headed monster. No sooner did they locate one source of supply than another sprang up; others remained permanently elusive. For public purposes the fiction was maintained that counterfeiters were always caught, that their kind of crime didn't pay. In reality, Wainwright knew, it paid plenty.

Despite the initial friction, a big plus from involving law enforcement agencies was recourse to their records. Individuals whom Eastin had named were identified and dossiers assembled against the time when a series of arrests could be made. The counterfeiter, Danny, was identified as Daniel Kerrigan, age seventy-three. "Long ago," Innes reported, "Kerrigan had three arrests and two convictions for forgery, but we haven't heard of him in fifteen years. He's either been legit, lucky, or clever."

Wainwright recalled and repeated a remark of Danny's—relayed by Eastin—to the effect that he had been working with an efficient organization.

"Could be," Innes said.

After their first conference Wainwright and the four agents maintained frequent contact and he promised to inform them immediately of any new report from Eastin. All were agreed that the remaining key piece of information was the location of the counterfeiters' headquarters. So far, no one had any idea where that might be. Yet hopes of obtaining a further lead were high, and if and when it happened the FBI and Secret Service were ready to close in.

Abruptly, as Nolan Wainwright meditated, his telephone jangled. A secretary said that Mr. Vandervoort would like to see him as soon as possible.

Wainwright was incredulous. Facing Alex Vandervoort, across the latter's desk, he protested, "You can't be serious!"

"I'm serious," Alex said. "Though I have trouble believing you were, making use of the Núñez girl the way you have. Of all the insane notions . . ."

"Insane or not, it worked."

Alex ignored the comment. "You put the girl in jeopardy, consulting no one. As a result we're obligated to take care of her, and may even have a lawsuit on our hands."

"I worked on the assumption," Wainwright argued, "that the fewer people who knew what she was doing, the safer she would be."

"No! That's your rationalization now, Nolan. What you really thought was that if I had known, or Edwina D'Orsey, we'd have stopped you. *I* knew about Eastin. Was I likely to be less discreet about the girl?"

Wainwright rubbed a knuckle along the surface of his chin. "Well, I guess you have a point."

"Damn right I do!"

"But that's still no reason, Alex, for abandoning the entire operation. For the first time in investigating Keycharge frauds we're close to a big breakthrough. Okay, my judgment was wrong in using Núñez. I admit it. But it wasn't wrong about Eastin, and we've got results to prove it."

Alex shook his head decisively. "Nolan, I let you change my mind once before. This time I won't. Our business here is banking, not crime busting. We'll seek help from law enforcement agencies and co-operate with them all we can. But we will *not* sustain aggressive crime-fighting programs of our own. So I tell you—end the arrangement with Eastin, today if possible."

"Look, Alex . . ."

"I already have looked, and don't like what I see. I will not have FMA responsible for risking human lives—even Eastin's. That's definite, so let's not waste time in further argument."

As Wainwright looked sourly despondent, Alex went on, "The other thing I want done is a conference set up this afternoon between you, Edwina D'Orsey, me, to discuss what to do about Mrs. Núñez. You can start considering ideas. What may be necessary . . ."

A secretary appeared in the office doorway. Alex said irritably, "Whatever it is—later!"

The girl shook her head. "Mr. Vandervoort, Miss Bracken's on the line. She said it's extremely urgent and you'd want to be interrupted, whatever you were doing."

Alex sighed. He picked up a phone. "Yes, Bracken?"

"Alex," Margot's voice said, "it's about Juanita Núñez."

"What about her?"

"She's disappeared."

"Wait." Alex moved a switch, transferring the call to a speaker phone so that Wainwright could hear. "Go ahead."

"I'm terribly worried. When I left Juanita last night, and knowing I was going to see you later, I arranged to telephone her at work today. She was deeply concerned. I hoped to be able to give some reassurance."

"Yes?"

"Alex, she didn't get to work." Margot's voice sounded strained.

"Well, maybe . . ."

"Please listen. I'm at Forum East now. I went there when I learned she wasn't at the bank and I couldn't get an answer on Juanita's home phone either. Since then I've talked to some other people in the building where she lives. Two of them say Juanita left her apartment this morning, at her usual time, with her little girl Estela. Juanita always takes Estela to nursery school on her way to the bank. I found out the name of the school and phoned. Estela isn't there. Neither she nor her mother arrived this morning."

There was a silence. Margot's voice asked, "Alex, are you still listening?"

"Yes, I'm here."

"After that, I phoned the bank again and this time talked to Edwina. She's checked personally. Not only has Juanita not appeared, she hasn't phoned in, which isn't like her. That's why I'm worried. I'm convinced something's gone terribly, terribly wrong."

"Do you have any ideas?"

"Yes," Margot said. "The same one you have."

"Wait," he told her. "Nolan's here."

Wainwright had hunched forward, listening. Now he straightened and said quietly, "Núñez has been picked up. There isn't any doubt of it."

"By?"

"By someone from that Double-Seven crowd. They're probably on to Eastin, too."

"You think they've taken her to that club?"

"No. That's the last thing they'll do. She's somewhere else."

"Do you have any idea where?"

"No."

"And whoever it is has the child, too?"

"I'm afraid so." There was anguish in Wainwright's eyes. "I'm sorry, Alex."

"You got us into this," Alex said fiercely. "Now, for God's sake, you've got to get Juanita and the kid out of it!"

Wainwright was concentrating, thinking as he spoke. "The first thing is to see if there's a chance of warning Eastin. If we can get to him, and get him out, he might know something which could lead us to the girl." He had a small black notebook open and was already reaching for another phone.

20

It happened so swiftly and was so totally unexpected that car doors had slammed, the big black limousine was moving, before she had a chance to cry out. By then Juanita knew instinctively it was too late, but screamed just the same—"Help! Help!"—until a fist slammed savagely into her face, followed by a gloved hand clamped across her mouth. Even then, hearing Estela's shriek of terror alongside her, Juanita went on struggling until the fist hit hard a second time and vision blurred while sounds receded far away.

The day—a clear, fresh, early-November morning—had begun normally. Juanita and Estela were up in time to have breakfast, then watch the NBC *Today* news on their small black and white portable. After that, they hurried to leave as usual at 7:30, which allowed Juanita just enough time to accompany Estela to nursery school before catching a bus to downtown and the bank. Juanita always liked mornings, and being with Estela was a joyous way to start any day.

Coming out of the building, Estela had skipped ahead, calling back, "Mommy, I'm missing all the lines," and Juanita smiled because evading lines and cracks in the sidewalk was a game they often played. It was about then that Juanita took vague notice of the dark-windowed limousine parked just ahead, with its rear curbside door open. She had taken more notice, though, as Estela neared the car and someone inside it spoke to her. Estela moved closer. As she did, a hand reached out and yanked the little girl inside. Instantly, Juanita had run to the car door. Then, from behind, a figure whom she hadn't seen closed in and shoved Juanita hard, making her trip and fall forward into the car, scraping her legs painfully. Before she could recover, Juanita was dragged inside and pushed to the floor with Estela. The door behind her slammed, also a door in front, and the car was moving.

Now, as her head cleared and full consciousness returned, she heard a voice say, "For chrissakes, why ya bring the goddammed kid?"

"Hadda do it. If we don't, the kid's gonna make a big fat fuss, then some jerk hollers cops. This way we got away clear, fast, no sweat."

Juanita stirred. Hot knives of pain, originating where she had been hit, surged through her head. She moaned.

"Listen, bitch!" a third voice said. "Ya make trouble, y'll get hurt plenty more. And don't get ideas about anyone outside seein' in. This car's got one-way glass."

Juanita lay still, fighting off panic, forcing herself to think. There were three men in the car, two on the back seat above her, one in front. The remark about one-way glass explained her earlier impression of a big car with dark windows. So what had been said was right: It was no good trying to attract attention. Where were she and Estela being taken? And why? Juanita had not the least doubt that the answer to the second question had something to do with her arrangement with Miles. What she had dreaded had come true. She was, she realized, in gravest peril. But, *Mother of God!—why Estela?* The two of them were sandwiched together on the car floor, Estela's body heaving in desperate sobs. Juanita moved, trying to hold and comfort her.

"There, *amorcito!* Be brave, little one."

"Shaddup!" one of the men commanded.

Another voice—she believed the driver's—said, "Better gag and blindfold 'em."

Juanita felt movements, heard a cloth-like substance tear. She pleaded frantically, "Please, no! I'll . . ." The remaining words were lost as a wide adhesive tape was slapped over her mouth and pressed down. Moments later a dark cloth covered her eyes; she felt it being fastened tightly. Next her hands were seized and tied behind her. Cords cut her wrists. There had been dust on the car floor which filled Juanita's nostrils; unable to see or move, choking under the gag, she blew frantically to clear her nose and breathe. From other movements beside her she sensed the same treatment was being meted out to Estela. Despair enveloped her. Tears of rage, frustration filled her eyes. *Damn you, Wainwright! Damn you, Miles! Where are you now?* . . . Why had she ever agreed . . . made it possible . . . *Oh, why? Why? . . . Mother of God, please help me! And if not me, save Estela!*

As time passed, with pain and helplessness increasing, Juanita's thoughts drifted. She was aware vaguely of the car moving slowly, stopping and starting as if in traffic, then of a long burst of speed followed by more slowness, twists, and turns. The journey, wherever it was to, seemed endless. After perhaps an hour—or was it much more or even much less?—Juanita felt the force of brakes applied fully. Momentarily the car's motor was louder, as if in a confined space. Then the motor stopped. She heard an electric hum, a rumble as if a heavy door was closing mechanically, a "thunk" as the rumble stopped. Simultaneously the limousine's doors clicked open, hinges creaked and she was pulled roughly to her feet and impelled forward. Juanita stumbled, striking her legs painfully again, and would have fallen, but hands seized her. One of the voices she had already heard ordered, "Goddamit—walk!"

With the blindfold still in place, moving clumsily, her fears remained centered on Estela. She was conscious of footsteps—her own, others—resounding on concrete. Suddenly the floor fell away and she stumbled, partly held, partly shoved down stairs. At the bottom, more walking. Abruptly she was pushed backward off balance, her legs shooting out until the fall was stopped by a hard wooden chair. The same voice as before told someone, "Take off the shade and tape."

She felt the movement of hands, and fresh pain as the tape was pulled carelessly away from her mouth. The blindfold loosened, then Juanita blinked as darkness gave way to a bright light directed into her eyes.

She gasped only, "*¡Por Dios!* where is my . . ." when a fist struck her.

"Save the singing," one of the car voices said. "When we tell ya, y'll spill plenty."

There were certain things which Tony Bear Marino liked. One was erotic sex—by his standards, erotic meant things women did to him which made him feel superior and themselves degraded. Another was cockfighting—the bloodier the better. He enjoyed detailed, graphic reports of gangland beatings and executions which he ordered, though he was careful to stay away from evidential involvement. Another, though milder, taste was for one-way glass.

Tony Bear Marino so liked one-way (or mirror pane) glass, which permitted him to observe without being seen, that he had it installed in multiple places—his cars, business premises, hangouts including the Double-Seven Health Club, and his secluded, guarded home. In the house, a bathroom and toilet which women visitors used had an entire wall of one-way glass. From the bathroom side it was a handsome mirror, but on the other was a small closed room in which Tony Bear would sit, enjoying a cigar and the personal privacies unknowingly revealed to him.

Because of his obsession, some one-way glass had been installed at the counterfeiting center and though, out of normal caution, he seldom went there, it had proved useful occasionally, as was the case now.

The glass was built into a half-wall—in effect a screen. Through it he could see the Núñez woman, facing him and tied to a chair. Her face was bruised and bleeding, and she was disheveled. Beside her was her child, secured to another chair, the little girl's face chalk white. A few minutes ago, when Marino learned the child had been brought in, he exploded angrily, not because he cared about children—he didn't —but because he smelled trouble. An adult could be eliminated, if necessary, with virtually no risk, but killing a child was something else. It would cause squeamishness among his own people, and emotion and danger afterward if rumors leaked. Tony Bear had already made a decision on the subject; it related to the blindfold precautions taken while coming here. He was also satisfied to be out of sight himself.

Now he lit a cigar and watched.

Angelo, one of Tony Bear's bodyguards who had been in charge of the pick-up operation, leaned over the woman. Angelo was an ex-prize fighter who had never made the big time but was built like a rhino. He had thick, protruding lips, was a bully and enjoyed what he was doing. "Okay, you two-bit hooker, start talkin'."

Juanita, who had been straining to see Estela, turned her head toward him. "¿De qué? Talk, what about?"

"Whassa name o' da guy who phoned ya from the Double-Seven?"

A flicker of understanding crossed Juanita's face. Tony Bear saw it and knew it would be only a matter of time, not long at that, before they had the information.

"You bastard! . . . Animal!" Juanita spat at Angelo. "¡Canalla! I know of no Double-Seven."

Angelo hit her hard, so that blood ran from her nose and the corner of her mouth. Juanita's head drooped. He seized her hair, holding her face up while he repeated, "Who's the guy who phoned you from the Double-Seven?"

She answered thickly through swollen lips. "Maricón, I will tell you nothing until you let my little girl go."

The broad had spirit, Tony Bear conceded. If she had been built differently he might have amused himself breaking her in other ways. But she was too scrawny for his taste—no hips worth a damn, half a handful of ass, and little peanut tits.

Angelo drew back his arm and punched her in the stomach. Juanita gasped and doubled forward as far as her bonds allowed. Beside her, Estela, who could see and hear, was sobbing hysterically. The sound annoyed Tony Bear. This was taking too long. There was a quicker way. He beckoned a second bodyguard, Lou, and whispered. Lou looked as if he didn't like what he was being told, but nodded. Tony Bear handed over the cigar he was smoking.

While Lou stepped out past the partition and spoke in an undertone to Angelo, Tony Bear Marino glanced around him. They were in a basement with all doors closed, eliminating the chance of sounds escaping, though even if they did it wouldn't matter. The fifty-year-old house, of which this was part, stood in its own grounds in a high-class residential district and was protected like a fortress. A syndicate which Tony Bear Marino headed had bought the house eight months ago and moved the counterfeiting operation in. Soon, as a precaution, they would sell the house and move on elsewhere; in fact, a new location was already chosen. It would have the same kind of innocuous, innocent-appearing background as this one. That, Tony Bear sometimes thought with satisfaction, had been the secret of the long, successful run: frequent moves to quiet, respectable neighborhoods, with traffic to and from the center kept to a minimum. The ultra-caution had two advantages—only a handful of people knew exactly where the center was; also, with everything buttoned down, neighbors weren't suspicious. They had even worked out elaborate precautions for moving from one place to the next. One of them: wooden covers, designed to look like household furniture, which fitted over every piece of machinery, so to a casual watcher all that was happening was a domestic move. And a regular house moving van, from one of the organization's outwardly legit trucking companies, was brought in for the job. There were even standby arrangements for an emergency, extra-fast trucking move if ever needed.

The fake furniture gimmick had been one of Danny Kerrigan's notions. The old man had had some other good ones, as well as proving a champion counterfeiter since Tony Bear Marino brought him into the organization a dozen years ago. Shortly before that time, Tony Bear heard about Kerrigan's reputation as a craftsman, and that he had become an alcoholic, skid row bum. On Tony Bear's orders the old man had been rescued, dried out, and later put to work—with spectacular results.

There seemed to be nothing, Tony Bear had come to believe, that Danny couldn't print successfully—money, postage stamps, share certificates, checks, drivers' licenses, Social Security cards, you name it. It had been Danny's idea to manufacture thousands of fake bank credit cards. Through bribery and a carefully planned raid, they had been able to obtain blank plastic sheets from which Keycharge cards were made, and the quantity was enough to last for years. Profit so far had been immense.

The only beef about the old man was that once in a while he went back to hitting the sauce and could be out of business for a week or more. When it happened there was danger of him talking, so he was kept confined. But he could be crafty and sometimes managed to slip away, as happened last time. Lately, though, the lapses had been fewer, mostly because Danny was happily stashing away his share of the dough in a Swiss bank account and dreamed of going there in a year or two to pick up his loot, then retire. Except that Tony Bear knew that was one move of the old drunk's which wouldn't happen. He intended to use the old man as long as he could function. Also Danny knew too much ever to be let go.

But while Danny Kerrigan was important, it had been the organization which protected him and made the most of what he produced. Without an efficient distribution system the old man would have been like most others of his breed—small time or a nothing. Therefore it was the threat to the organization which concerned Tony Bear most. Had it been infiltrated by a spy, a stool pigeon? If "yes," from where? And how much had he—or she—learned?

His attention swung back to what was happening on the other side of the one-way glass. Angelo had the lighted cigar. His thick lips were twisted in a grin. With the side of his foot he shoved the two chairs so the Núñez woman and her brat now faced each other. Angelo puffed on the cigar until its tip was glowing. Casually he moved to the chair where the child was seated and bound.

Estela looked up, visibly trembling, eyes wild with fright. Without hurrying, Angelo took her small right hand, lifted it, inspected the palm, then turned it over. Still slowly he removed the glowing cigar from his mouth and ground it, as if into an ashtray, on the back of her hand. Estela cried out—a piercing shriek of agony. Opposite her, Juanita, frantic, weeping, shouting incoherently, struggled desperately against her bonds.

The cigar was not out. Angelo puffed it into fresh redness then, with the same leisureliness as before, lifted Estela's other hand.

Juanita screamed, "No, no, *déjela quieta*. I will tell you."

Angelo waited, the cigar poised as Juanita gasped, "The man you want . . . is Miles Eastin."

"Who's he work for?"

Her voice a despairing whisper, she answered, "First Mercantile American Bank."

Angelo dropped the cigar and ground it out with his heel. He looked interrogatively at where he knew Tony Bear Marino to be, then came around the screen.

Tony Bear's face was tight. He said softly, "Get him. Go get that fink. Bring him here."

21

"Milesy," Nate Nathanson said with unusual grouchiness, "whoever your friend is keeps phoning, tell him this place ain't run for the staff, it's run for members."

"What friend?" Miles Eastin, who had been away from the Double-Seven for part of the morning taking care of club errands, looked uncertainly at the manager.

"How in hell would I know? Same guy's phoned four times, asking for you. Wouldn't leave a name; no message." Nathanson said impatiently, "Where's the deposit book?"

Miles handed it over. Among his calls had been one to a bank to deposit checks.

"Shipment of canned goods came in just now," Nathanson said. "Cases in the storeroom. Check 'em against the invoices." He handed Miles some papers and a key.

"Sure, Nate. And I'm sorry about the calls."

But the manager had already turned away, heading for his office on the third floor. Miles felt some sympathy for him. He knew that Tony Bear Marino and Russian Ominsky, who owned the Double-Seven jointly, had been leaning hard on Nathanson lately with complaints about running of the club.

On his way to the storeroom, which was on the main floor at the rear of the building, Miles wondered about those phone calls. Who would be calling him? And insistently. As far as he knew, only three people connected with his former life were aware that he was here—his probation officer; Juanita; Nolan Wainwright. The probation officer? Highly unlikely. Last time Miles made his required monthly visit and report, the p.o. had been rushed and indifferent; all he seemed to care about was that he wouldn't be caused trouble. The probation man had made a note of where Miles was working and that was that. Juanita then? No. She knew better; besides, Nathanson had said a man. That left Wainwright.

But Wainwright wouldn't call either . . . *Or would he?* Might he not take the risk if it were something truly urgent . . . *like a warning?*

A warning of what? *That Miles was in danger? That he had been exposed as a spy, or might be?* Abruptly, icy fear seized him. His heart hammered faster. Miles realized: Lately he had assumed an invulnerability, had taken his safety for granted. But in reality there was no safety here, never had been; only danger—even greater now than in the beginning, for now he knew too much.

Approaching the storeroom, as the thought persisted, his hands were trembling. He had to steady himself to put the key in the lock. He wondered: Was he becoming frightened about nothing, reacting cravenly to shadows? Perhaps. But a sense of foreboding warned him—no. *So what should he do?* Whoever had telephoned would probably try again. But was it wise to wait? Miles decided: Risk or not, he would call Wainwright directly.

He had pushed the storeroom door open. Now he began to close it, to go to a pay phone nearby—the one from which he had called Juanita a week and a half ago. At that moment he heard activity in the club's front lobby at the other end of the main floor corridor which ran from front to rear. Several men were entering from the street. They seemed in a hurry. Without knowing why, Miles reversed direction and slipped into the storeroom, out of sight. He heard a mix of voices, then one ask loudly, "Where's that punk, Eastin?"

He recognized the voice. Angelo, one of Marino's bodyguards.

"Up in the office, I guess." That was Jules LaRocca. Miles heard him say, "What's with . . ."

"Tony Bear wants . . ."

The voices faded as the men hurried upstairs. But Miles had heard enough, knowing that what he feared had come true. In a minute, maybe less, Nate Nathanson would tell Angelo and the others where he was. Then they would be down here.

He felt his entire body quaking, yet forced himself to think. To leave by the front lobby was impossible. Even if he didn't encounter the men returning from upstairs, they had probably left someone on guard outside. The rear exit, then? It was seldom used and opened near an abandoned building. Beyond that was a vacant lot, then an elevated railway arch. On the far side of the rail line was a maze of small, mean streets. He could try dodging through those streets, though the chance of eluding a pursuit was slim. There could be several pursuers; some would have a car or cars; Miles had none. His mind flashed the message: *Your only chance! Don't lose more time! Go now!* He slammed the storeroom door closed and took the key; perhaps the others would waste precious minutes battering the door down, believing him to be inside.

Then he ran.

Through the small rear door, fumbling first with a bolt . . . Outside, stopping to close the door; no sense in advertising the way he had gone . . . Then down a lane beside the disused building . . . The building had been a factory once; the lane was littered with debris, old packing cases, cans, the rusty skeleton of a truck beside a caved-in loading dock. It was like running an obstacle course. Rats scampered away . . . Across the vacant lot, stumbling over bricks, garbage, a dead dog . . . Once Miles tripped and felt an ankle twist; it pained him sharply, but he kept on . . . So far he had heard no one following . . . Then as he reached the railway arch, with comparative safety of the streets ahead, there were running feet behind, a shout, "There's the son of a bitch!"

Miles increased his speed. He was now on the firmer ground of streets and sidewalks. He took the first turning he came to—sharply left; then right; almost at once, left again. Behind him he could still hear the pounding feet . . . These streets were new to him but his sense of direction told him he was headed for the city center. If he could only make it there he would disappear in midday crowds, giving him time to think, to telephone Wainwright, perhaps, and ask for help. Meanwhile he was running hard and well, his wind good. His ankle hurt a little; not too much. Miles's fitness, the hours spent on the Double-Seven handball court, were paying off . . . The sounds of running behind him receded, but their absence didn't fool him. While a car could not travel the route he had come—down the blocked lane and over the vacant lot—there were ways around. A detour of several blocks to cross the railway line would create delay. Not much, though. Probably, even now, someone in a car was trying to outguess him, head him off. He doubled left and right again, hoping, as he had from the beginning, for any kind of transportation. A bus. A taxi better still. But neither came . . . *When you needed a taxi badly, why was there never one around?* . . . *Or a cop.* He wished the streets he was passing through were busier. Running made him conspicuous, but he could not afford to slow down yet. A few people whom Miles passed looked at him curiously, but citizens here were used to minding their own business.

The nature of the area, though, was changing as he ran. Now it was less ghetto-like, showing signs of more prosperity. He passed several sizable stores. Ahead were larger buildings still, the city skyline coming into view. But before getting there, two major intersecting streets would have to be crossed. He could see the first one now—wide, busy with traffic, divided by a center boulevard. Then he saw something else—on the far side of the boulevard a long black Cadillac with dark windows, cruising slowly. *Marino's.* As the car crossed the street which Miles was on, it seemed to hesitate, then speeded up, passing quickly out of sight. There had been no time to try to hide. Had he been seen? Had the car gone on to switch lanes and come back, or had he stayed lucky and been unobserved? Again fear struck him. Though he was sweating, Miles shivered but kept on. There was nothing else to do. He moved close to buildings, slowing his pace as much as he dared. A minute and a half later, with the intersection only fifty yards away, a Cadillac—the same car—nosed around the corner.

He knew that luck had run out. Whoever was in the car—most likely Angelo, for one—could not fail to see him, probably had already. So was anything to be gained by more resistance? Wouldn't it be simpler to give up, to allow himself to be taken, to let what was going to happen, happen? *No!* Because he had seen enough of Tony Bear Marino and his kind, in prison and since, to know what happened to people who incurred their vengeance. The black car was slowing. They *had* seen him. *Desperation.*

One of the stores Miles had noticed moments earlier was immediately alongside. Breaking his stride, he turned left, pushed open a glass door and went in. Inside, he saw it was a sporting goods store. A pale, spindly clerk, about Miles's own age, stepped forward. "Good day, sir. Is there something I can show you?"

"Er . . . yes." He said the first thing that came into his head. "I'd like to see bowling balls."

"Certainly. What kind of price and weight?"

"The best. About sixteen pounds."

"Color?"

"Doesn't matter."

Miles was watching the few yards of sidewalk outside the street door. Several pedestrians had gone by. None had paused or looked in.

"If you come this way, I'll show you what we have."

He followed the clerk past racks of skis, glass cases, a display of handguns. Then, glancing back, Miles saw the silhouette of a single figure, stopped outside and peering in the window. Now a second figure joined the first. They stood together, not moving from the storefront. Miles wondered: Could he get out through the back? Even as the thought occurred to him, he discarded it. The men who were after him would not make the same error twice. Any rear exit would already have been located and guarded.

"This is an excellent ball. It sells for forty-two dollars."

"I'll take it."

"We'll need your hand measurement for the . . ."

"Never mind."

Should he try to phone Wainwright from here? But Miles was sure if he went near a phone the men outside would come in instantly.

The clerk looked puzzled. "You don't want us to drill . . ."

"I said never mind."

"As you wish, sir. How about a bag for the ball? Perhaps some bowling shoes?"

"Yes," Miles said. "Yes, okay." It would help postpone the moment of returning to the street. Scarcely aware of what he was doing, he inspected bags put in front of him, chose one at random, then sat down to try on shoes. It was while slipping on a pair that the idea occurred to him. *The Keycharge card which Wainwright had sent through Juanita . . . the card in the name of H. E. Lyncolp . . . H-E-L-P.*

He motioned to the bowling ball, bag, and the shoes he had chosen. "How much?"

The clerk looked up from an invoice. "Eighty-six dollars and ninety-five cents, plus tax."

"Listen," Miles said, "I want to put it on my Keycharge." He took out his wallet and offered the LYNCOLP card, trying to stop his hands from trembling.

"That's okay, but . . ."

"I know, you need authorization. Go ahead. Phone for it."

The clerk took the card and invoice to a glassed-in office area. He was gone several minutes, then returned.

Miles asked anxiously, "Get through?"

"Sure. Everything's okay, Mr. Lyncolp."

Miles wondered what was happening now at the Keycharge Center in FMA Headquarters Tower. Would it help him? Could *anything* help? . . . Then he remembered the second instruction relayed by Juanita: After using the card, dawdle as much as possible. Give Wainwright time to move.

"Sign here, please, Mr. Lyncolp." A Keycharge account slip was filled in for the amount he had spent. Miles leaned over the counter to add a signature.

Straightening up, he felt a hand touch his shoulder lightly. A voice said quietly, "Milesy."

As he turned, Jules LaRocca said, "Don't make no fuss. It won't do no good and you'll get hurt the worse."

Behind LaRocca, their faces impassive, were Angelo and Lou, and a fourth man—another bruiser type—whom Miles hadn't seen before. The four moved around him, seizing him, pinioning his arms.

"Move, shitass." The order was from Angelo, low-voiced.

Miles considered crying out, but who was there to help him? The milquetoast clerk, watching open-mouthed, could not. The hunt was ended. The pressure on his arms tightened. He felt himself propelled helplessly toward the outer door.

The bewildered salesclerk ran after them. "Mr. Lyncolp! You've forgotten your bowling ball."

It was LaRocca who told him, "You keep it, buster. This guy don't even need the balls he's got."

The black Cadillac was parked a few yards down the street. They pushed Miles roughly into it and drove off.

Business in the Keycharge authorization center was near its daily peak. A normal shift of fifty operators was on duty in the semidarkened auditorium-style center, each seated at a keyboard with a TV-like cathode ray tube above it.

To the young operator who received the call, the H. E. LYNCOLP credit query was simply one of thousands dealt with routinely during a working day. All were totally impersonal. Neither she nor others like her ever knew where the calls they handled came from—not even which city or state. The credit sought might be to pay a New York housewife's grocery bill, provide clothing for a Kansas farmer, allow a rich Chicago dowager to load herself with unneeded jewelry, advance a Princeton undergrad's tuition fees, or help a Cleveland alcoholic buy the case of liquor which finally would kill him. But the operator was never told details. If really needed later, the specifics of a purchase could be traced back, though it seldom happened. The reason: No one cared. The money mattered, the money changing hands, the ability to repay the credit granted; that was all.

The call began with a flashing light on the operator's console. She touched a switch and spoke into her headset mike. "What is your merchant number, please?"

The caller—a sporting goods clerk attending to Miles Eastin—gave it. As he did, the operator typed the number. Simultaneously it appeared on her cathode ray screen.

She asked, "Card number and date of expiry?"

Another answer. Again, details on the screen.

"Amount of purchase?"

"Ninety dollars, forty-three."

Typed. On screen. The operator pressed a key, alerting a computer several floors below.

Within a millisecond the computer digested the information, searched its records and flashed an answer.

> APPROVED.
> AUTH. NO. 7416984
> URGENT . . . EMERGENCY . . . DO NOT, REPEAT DO NOT,
> ALERT MERCHANT . . . ADVISE YOUR SUPERVISOR . . .
> EXECUTE IMMEDIATELY EMERGENCY INSTRUCTION 17 . . .

"The purchase is approved," the operator told the caller. "Authorization number . . ."

She was speaking more slowly than usual. Even before she began, she had flashed a signal to an elevated supervisors' booth. Now in the booth another young woman, one of six supervisors on duty, was already reading her own duplication of the cathode ray tube display. She reached for a card index, seeking emergency instruction 17.

The original operator deliberately stumbled over the authorization number and began again. Emergency signals were not flashed often, but when it happened there were standard procedures which operators knew. Slowing down was one. In the past, murderers had been caught, a kidnap victim saved, disappearances solved, stolen art treasures recovered, a son brought to his dying mother's bedside—all because a computer had been alerted to the possibility that a particular credit card might be used, and if and when it was, prompt action was essential. At such moments, while others took the needed action, a few seconds' foot-dragging by an operator could help significantly.

The supervisor was already implementing instruction 17 which informed her that N. Wainwright, v/p Security, was to be advised immediately by telephone that the special Keycharge card issued in the name H. E. LYNCOLP had been presented, and where. By depressing keys on her own keyboard, the supervisor summoned from the computer the additional information:

PETE'S SPORTING GOODS

and a street address. Meanwhile she had dialed the office number of Mr. Wainwright who answered personally. His interest was instant. He responded crisply to the supervisor's information and she sensed his tension while he copied details down.

Seconds later, for the Keycharge supervisor, operator, and computer, the brief emergency was over.

Not so for Nolan Wainwright.

Since the explosive session an hour and a half ago with Alex Vandervoort, when he learned of the disappearance of Juanita Núñez and her child, Wainwright had been tensely and continuously on telephones, sometimes two at once. He had tried four times to reach Miles Eastin at the Double-Seven Health Club to warn him of his danger. He had had consultations with the FBI and U. S. Secret Service. As a result the FBI was now actively investigating the apparent Núñez kidnapping, and had alerted city and state police with descriptions of the missing pair. It had been arranged that an FBI surveillance team would watch comings and goings at the Double-Seven as soon as the manpower could be spared, probably by this afternoon.

That was all that would be done concerning the Double-Seven for the time being. As FBI Special Agent Innes expressed it, "If we go in there with questions, we tip our hand about knowing the connection, and as for a search, we've no grounds to seek a warrant. Besides, according to your man Eastin, it's mostly a meeting place with nothing illegal—except some gambling—going on."

Innes agreed with Wainwright's conclusion that Juanita Núñez and her daughter would not have been taken to the Double-Seven.

The Secret Service, with fewer facilities than the FBI, was working the hideout angle, contacting informers, probing for any scintilla of fact or rumor which might prove to be a lead the combined law enforcement agencies could use. For the moment, unusually, inter-force rivalry and jealousies were put aside.

When Wainwright received the Keycharge H. E. LYNCOLP alert, he promptly dialed the FBI. Special Agents Innes and Dalrymple were out, he was informed, but could be contacted by radio. He dictated an urgent message and waited. The reply came back: The agents were downtown, not far from the address given, and were on their way there. Would Wainwright meet them?

Action was a relief. He hurried through the building to his car.

Outside Pete's Sporting Goods, Innes was questioning bystanders when Wainwright arrived. Dalrymple was still inside, completing a statement by the clerk. Innes broke off and joined the bank security chief. "A dry hole," he reported glumly. "It was all over when we got here." He related the little they had learned.

Wainwright asked, "Descriptions?"

The FBI man shook his head. "The store guy who served Eastin was so shit scared, he's not sure if there were four men came in or three. Says it all happened so fast, he can't describe or identify anyone. And no one, inside the store or out, remembers seeing a car."

Wainwright's face was drawn, the strain of anxiety and conscience showing. "So what comes next?"

"You were a cop," Innes said. "You know how it is in real life. We wait, hoping something else will turn up."

22

She heard scuffling and voices. Now she knew they had Miles and were bringing him in.

For Juanita, time had drifted. She had no idea how long it was since she had gasped out Miles Eastin's name, betraying him, to end the horror of Estela's torture. Soon after that she had been gagged again and the bonds holding her to the chair were checked and tightened. Then the men left.

For a while, she knew, she had dozed—or, more accurately, her body had released her from awareness since any real rest was impossible, bound as she was. Alerted by the new noise, her constricted limbs protested agonizingly, so that she wanted to cry out, though the gag prevented it. Juanita willed herself not to panic, not to struggle against her bonds, knowing both would be futile and make her situation worse.

She could still see Estela. The chairs they were bound to had been left facing each other. The little girl's eyes were closed in sleep, her small head drooping; the noises which awakened Juanita had not disturbed her. Estela, too, was gagged. Juanita hoped that sheer exhaustion would spare her from reality for as long as possible.

Estela's right hand showed the ugly red burn from the cigar. Shortly after the men had left, one of them—Juanita had heard him addressed as Lou—came back briefly. He had a tube of ointment of some kind. Squeezing the tube, he covered Estela's burn, glancing quickly at Juanita as if to tell her it was the best he could do. Then he, too, had gone.

Estela had jumped while the ointment was being applied, then whimpered for a while behind her gag, but soon after sleep had mercifully come.

The sounds Juanita had been hearing were behind her. Probably in an adjoining room, and she guessed a connecting door was open. Briefly she heard Miles's voice protesting, then a thud, a grunt, and silence.

Perhaps a minute passed. Miles's voice again, this time more distinct. "No! Oh, God, no! Please! I'll . . ." She heard a sound like hammer blows, metal on metal. Miles's words stopped, changing to a high-pitched, piercing, frenzied scream. The screaming, worse than anything she had ever heard, went on and on.

If Miles could have killed himself in the car, he would have done so willingly. He had known from the beginning of his deal with Wain-wright—it had been the root of his fears ever since—that straightforward dying would be easy compared with what awaited an exposed informer. Even so, what he had feared was nothing beside the unbelievably awful, excoriating punishment being meted to him now.

His legs and thighs were strapped tightly, cruelly together. His arms had been forced down onto a rough wooden table. *His hands and wrists were being nailed to the table . . . nailed with carpenter's nails . . . hammered hard . . . A nail was already in the left wrist, two more in the wide part of the hand between the wrist and fingers, fastening it tightly down . . . The last few strokes of the hammer had smashed bone . . . One nail was in the right hand, another poised to tear, to hack through flesh and muscle . . . No pain was ever, could be ever . . . Oh, God, help me! . . . would be ever greater.* Miles writhed, screamed, pleaded, screamed again. But the hands holding his body tightened. The hammer blows, which had briefly paused, resumed.

"He ain't yelping loud enough," Marino told Angelo, who was wielding the hammer. "When you get through with that, try nailing down a couple of the bastard's fingers."

Tony Bear, who was puffing on a cigar while he watched and listened, had not bothered concealing himself this time. There would be no possibility of Eastin identifying him because Eastin would soon be dead. First, though, it was necessary to remind him—and others to whom the news of what had happened here would filter out—that for a stool pigeon there was never any easy death.

"That's more like it," Tony Bear conceded. Miles's agonized shrieks rose in volume while a fresh nail penetrated the center finger of his left hand, midway between the two knuckles, and was hammered home. Audibly, the bone in the finger split apart. As Angelo was about to repeat the process with the middle finger of the right hand, Tony Bear ordered, "Hold it!"

He told Eastin, "Stop the goddam noise! Start singing."

Miles's screaming turned to racking sobs, his body heaving. The hands holding him had been removed. They were no longer needed.

"Okay," Tony Bear told Angelo, "he ain't stopped, so go right ahead."

"No! No! I'll talk! I will! I will!" Somehow Miles choked back his sobs. The loudest sound was now his heavy, rasping breathing.

Tony Bear waved Angelo back. The others in the room remained grouped around the table. They were Lou; Punch Clancy, the extra bodyguard who had been one of the four in the sporting goods store an hour earlier; LaRocca, scowling, worried about how much he would be blamed for sponsoring Miles; and the old printer, Danny Kerrigan, ill at ease and nervous. Although this was normally Danny's domain— they were in the main printing and engraving shop—he preferred to keep out of the way at moments such as this, but Tony Bear had sent for him.

Tony Bear snarled at Eastin, "So all the time you were a stoolie for a stinking bank?"

Miles gasped out, "Yes."

"First Mercantile?"

"Yes."

"Who'd you report to?"

"Wainwright."

"How much you found out? What'd you tell him?"

"About . . . the club . . . the games . . . who went there."

"Including me?"

"Yes."

"You son of a bitch!" Tony Bear reached over and slammed his clenched fist in Miles's face.

Miles's body sagged away with the force of the blow, but the strain tore at his hands and he pulled back desperately to the painful, bent-over position he was in before. A silence followed, broken only by his labored sobs and groans. Tony Bear puffed his cigar several times, then resumed the questioning.

"What else you find out, you stinking turd?"

"Nothing . . . nothing!" Every part of Miles was shaking uncontrollably.

"You're lying." Tony Bear turned to Danny Kerrigan. "Get me that juice you use for the engravings."

During the questioning until now, the old printer had been eying Miles with hatred. Now he nodded. "Sure thing, Mr. Marino."

Danny crossed to a shelf and hefted down a gallon jug with a plastic cap. The jar was labeled *NITRIC ACID: Use for Etching Only.* Removing the cap, Danny poured carefully from the jar into a half-pint glass beaker. Being careful not to spill the beaker's contents, he carried it to the table where Tony Bear faced Miles. He put it down, then laid a small engraver's brush beside it.

Tony Bear picked up the brush and dipped it in the nitric acid. Casually he reached over and dabbed the brush down one side of Eastin's face. For a second or two, while the acid penetrated surface skin, there was no reaction. Then Miles cried out with a new and different agony as the burning spread and deepened. While the others watched in fascination, the flesh under the acid smoldered, turning from pink to brownish black.

Tony Bear dipped the brush in the beaker again. "I'll ask you one more time, asshole. If I don't get answers, this goes on the other side. What else did you find out and tell?"

Miles's eyes were wild, like a cornered animal's. He spluttered, "The counterfeit . . . money."

"What about it?"

"I bought some . . . sent it to the bank . . . then drove the car . . . took more to Louisville."

"And?"

"Credit cards . . . drivers' licenses."

"You know who made them? Printed the phony money?"

Miles motioned his head as best he could. "Danny."

"Who told you?"

"He . . . told me."

"And afterwards you spilled your guts to that cop at the bank? He knows all that?"

"Yes."

Tony Bear swung savagely to Kerrigan. "You drunken stupid fart! You're no better than him."

The old man stood quaking. "Mr. Marino, I wasn't drunk. I just thought he . . ."

"Shaddup!" Tony Bear seemed about to hit the old man, then changed his mind. He returned to Miles. "What else do they know?"

"Nothing else!"

"Do they know where the printing's done? Where this place is?"

"No."

Tony Bear returned the brush to the acid and withdrew it. Miles followed every movement. Experience told him the expected answer. He shouted, "Yes! Yes, they know!"

"You told that bank security bum?"

Despairingly, Miles lied. "Yes, yes!"

"How'd you find out?" The brush stayed poised above the acid.

Miles knew he had to find an answer. *Any* answer which would satisfy. He turned his head to Danny. "*He* told me."

"You're a liar! You lousy, stinking goddammed liar!" The old man's face was working, his mouth opening and closing and jaw quivering as emotion gripped him. He appealed to Tony Bear. "Mr. Marino, he's lying! I swear he's lying! It isn't true." But what he saw in Marino's eyes increased his desperation. Now Danny rushed at Miles. "Tell him the truth, you bastard! Tell him!" Demented, knowing the potential penalty for himself, the old man looked around him for a weapon. He saw the acid beaker. Seizing it, he tossed the contents in Miles's face.

A fresh scream started, then abruptly stilled. As the odor of acid and the sickly smell of burning flesh mingled, Miles fell forward, unconscious, across the table where his mangled, bleeding hands were nailed.

Though not wholly understanding what was happening to Miles, Juanita suffered through his cries and pleadings and finally the extinction of his voice. She wondered—dispassionately, because her feelings were now dulled beyond the point where more emotion could affect her—if he were dead. She speculated on how long it would be before she and Estela shared Miles's fate. That they would both die now seemed inevitable.

Juanita was grateful for one thing: Estela had not stirred, despite the uproar. If sleep would only stay with her, perhaps she would be spared whatever awfulness remained before the end. As she had not done in many years, Juanita prayed to the Virgin Mary to make death easy for Estela.

Juanita was aware of new activity in the adjoining room. It sounded as if furniture was being moved, drawers opened and slammed, containers set down heavily. Once there was the jangle of metal cascading on cement and curses afterward.

Then, to her surprise, the man she had come to recognize as Lou appeared beside her and began unfastening her bonds. She supposed she was being taken somewhere, exchanging one perdition for another. When he had finished, he left her where she was and started to untie Estela.

"Stand up!" he ordered both of them. Estela, coming awake, complied, though sleepily. She began crying softly, the sound muffled by her gag. Juanita wanted to go to her but could not yet move forward;

she supported her weight against the chair, suffering as blood flowed through her cramped limbs.

"Listen to me," Lou told Juanita. "You got lucky because of your kid. The boss is gonna let you go. You'll be blindfolded, taken in a car a long ways from here, and then let out. You don't know where you've bin, so you can't bring nobody back. But *if* you blab, tell *anybody*, we'll find you wherever you are and kill your kid. Understand?"

Hardly able to believe what she was being told, Juanita nodded.

"Then get goin'." Lou pointed to a door. Evidently it was not his intention to blindfold her yet. Despite her inertia of moments earlier, she found her normal mental sharpness coming back.

Partway up a flight of concrete stairs, she leaned against the wall and wanted to be sick. In the outer room they had just passed through, she had seen Miles—or what was left of him—his body slumped across a table, his hands a bloody pulp, his face, hair, and scalp burned beyond recognition. Lou had pushed Juanita and Estela quickly past, but not fast enough to prevent Juanita taking in the grim reality. She had also learned that Miles was not dead, though he was surely dying. He had stirred slightly and moaned.

"Move it!" Lou urged. They continued up the stairs.

The horror of Miles as she had seen him filled Juanita's mind. *What could she do to help him?* Clearly, nothing here. But if she and Estela were to be released, was there some way she could bring aid back? She doubted it. She had no idea where they were; there seemed no chance of finding out. Yet she must do *something*. Something to expiate—at least a little—her terrible sense of guilt. She had betrayed Miles. Whatever the motivation, she had spoken his name, and he was caught and brought here with the consequence she had seen.

The seed of an idea, not wholly thought out, came to her. She concentrated, developing the notion, blotting other things from her mind, even Estela for the moment. Juanita reasoned: it might not work, yet there was a slim chance. Success depended on the acuity of her senses and her memory. It was also important that she not be blindfolded until *after* getting in the car.

At the head of the stairway they turned right and entered a garage. With cement block walls, it looked like an ordinary two-car garage belonging to a house or business and, remembering the sounds she had heard on arrival, Juanita guessed they had come in this same way. There was one car inside—not the big car in which they had arrived this morning, but a dark green Ford. She wanted to see the license number but it was beyond her view.

In a quick glance around, something puzzled Juanita. Against a wall of the garage was a chest of drawers of dark polished wood, but like no other chest that she had seen before. It appeared to have been sawn vertically in half, with the two halves standing separated and she could see the inside was hollow. Beside the chest was what looked like a dining-room sideboard cut in the same peculiar way, except that half the sideboard was being carried out of another doorway by two men, one shielded by the door, the other with his back to her.

Lou opened a rear door of the Ford. "Get in," he ordered. In his hands were two thick dark cloths—the blindfolds.

Juanita entered first. Doing so, she tripped intentionally and fell forward, supporting herself by grabbing the back of the car's front seat. It gave her the opportunity she wanted—to look toward the front on the driver's side and read the odometer mileage. She had a second only to take in the figures: 25714.8. She closed her eyes, committing them —she hoped—to memory.

Estela followed Juanita. Lou came in after them, fastened the blindfolds and sat on the rear seat. He pushed Juanita's shoulder. "Down on the floor, botha ya. Make no trouble, ya won't get hurt." Squatting on the floor with Estela close beside her, Juanita curled her legs and managed to keep facing forward. She heard someone else get in the car, the motor start, the garage doors rumble open. Then they were moving.

From the instant the car moved, Juanita concentrated as she had never done before. Her intention was to memorize time and direction —if she could. She began to count seconds as a photographer friend had once taught her. *A thousand and ONE; a thousand and TWO; a thousand and THREE; a thousand and FOUR* . . . She felt the car reverse and turn, then counted eight seconds while it moved in a straight line forward. Then it slowed almost to a stop. Had it been a driveway? Probably. A longish one? The car was again moving slowly, most likely easing out into a street . . . *Turning left. Now faster forward.* She recommenced counting. *Ten seconds. Slowing. Turning right . . . A thousand and ONE; a thousand and TWO; a thousand and THREE . . . Turning left . . . Speed faster . . . A longer stretch . . . A thousand FORTY-NINE; a thousand FIFTY* . . . No sign of slowing . . . *Yes, slowing now. A four-second wait, then straight on.* It could have been a traffic light . . . *A thousand and EIGHT* . . .

Dear God! For Miles's sake help me to remember!

. . . *A thousand and NINE; a thousand and TEN. Turning right . . .*

Banish other thoughts. React to every movement of the car. Count the time—hoping, praying that the same strong memory which helped her keep track of money at the bank . . . which once saved her from Miles's duplicity . . . would now save *him*.

. . . *A thousand TWENTY; One thousand and twenty dollars. No!* . . . *Mother of God! Keep my thoughts from wandering* . . .

A long straight stretch, smooth road, high speed . . . She felt her body sway . . . *The road was curving to the left; a long curve, gentle* . . . *Stopping, stopping*. It had been sixty-eight seconds . . . *Turning right*. Begin again. *A thousand and ONE; a thousand and TWO* . . .

On and on.

As time went by, the likelihood of remembering, of reconstructing, seemed increasingly less likely.

23

"This's Sergeant Gladstone, Central Communications Bureau, City Police," the flat, nasal voice on the phone announced. "Says here to immediately notify you people if Juanita Núñez or child Estela Núñez located."

Special Agent Innes sat up taut and straight. Instinctively he moved the phone closer. "What do you have, Sergeant?"

"Car radio report just in. Woman and child answering description and names found wandering near junction of Cheviot Township and Shawnee Lake Road. Taken into protective custody. Officers bringing 'em to 12th Precinct now."

Innes covered the mouthpiece with his hand. To Nolan Wainwright, seated across the desk at FBI Headquarters, he said softly, "City Police. They've got Núñez and the kid."

Wainwright gripped the desk edge tightly. "Ask what condition they're in."

"Sergeant," Innes said, "are they okay?"

"Told you all we know, chief. Want more dope, you better call the 12th."

Innes took down the 12th Precinct number and dialed it. He was connected with a Lieutenant Fazackerly.

"Sure, we got the word," Fazackerly acknowledged crisply. "Hold it. Follow-up phone report just coming in."

The FBI man waited.

"According to our guys, the woman's been beaten up some," Fazackerly said. "Face bruised and cut. Child has a bad burn on one hand. Officers have given first aid. No other injuries reported."

Innes relayed the news to Wainwright who covered his face with a hand as if in prayer.

The lieutenant was speaking again. "Something kind of queer here."

"What is it?"

"Officers in the car say the Núñez woman won't talk. All she wants is pencil and paper. They've given it to her. She's scribbling like mad. Said something about things being in her memory she has to get out."

Special Agent Innes breathed, "*Jesus Christ!*" He remembered the bank cash loss, the story behind it, the incredible accuracy of Juanita Núñez's circus freak memory.

"Listen," he said. "Please take this from me, I'll explain it later, and we're coming out to you. But radio your car right now. Tell your officers not to talk to Núñez, not to disturb her, help her in any way she wants. And when she gets to the precinct house, the same thing goes. Humor her. Let her go on writing if she wants. Handle her like she was something special."

He stopped, then added, "Which she is."

> Short reverse. From garage.
> Forward. 8 secs. Almost stop. (Driveway?)
> Turn left. 10 secs. Med. speed.
> Turn right. 3 secs.
> Turn left. 55 secs. Smooth, fast.
> Stop. 4 secs. (Traffic light?)
> Straight on. 10 secs. Med. speed.
> Turn right. Rough road (short dist.) then smooth. 18 secs.
> Slowing. Stop. Start immed. Curve to right. Stop-start. 25 secs.
> Turn left. Straight, smooth. 47 secs.
> Slow. Turn right . . .

Juanita's finished summation ran to seven handwritten pages.

They worked intensively for an hour in a rear room at the precinct house, using large-scale maps, but the result was inconclusive.

Juanita's scribbled notes had amazed them all—Innes and Dalrymple, Jordan and Quimby of the U. S. Secret Service who had joined the others after a hurry-up call, and Nolan Wainwright. The notes were incredibly complete and, Juanita maintained, entirely accurate. She explained she was never confident that whatever her mind stored away could be recalled—until the moment came to do so. But once the effort had been made, she knew with certainty if her recollections had been correct. She was convinced they were now.

Besides the notes, they had something else to go on. Mileage.

The gags and blindfolds had been removed from Juanita and Estela moments before they were pushed from the car on a lonely suburban road. By contrived clumsiness and luck, Juanita had managed to catch a second glimpse of the odometer. 25738.5. They had traveled 23.7 miles.

But was it a consistent direction, or had the car doubled back, making the journey seem longer than it was, merely to confuse? Even with Juanita's summary, it was impossible to be certain. They did the best they could, working painstakingly backwards, estimating that the car might have come this way or that, turned here or there, traveled thus far on this road. Everyone, though, knew how inexact it was since speeds could only be guessed at and Juanita's senses while she was blindfolded might have deceived her so that error could be piled on error, making their present exercise futile, a waste of time. But there *was* a chance they could trace the route back to where she had been captive, or come close. And, significantly, a general consistency existed between the various possibilities worked out so far.

It was Secret Service Agent Jordan who made an assessment for them all. On an area map he drew a series of lines representing the most likely directions in which the car carrying Juanita and Estela would have traveled. Then, around the origins of the lines, he drew a circle. "In there." He prodded with a finger. "Somewhere in there."

In the ensuing silence, Wainwright heard Jordan's stomach rumble, as on all the occasions they had met before. Wainwright wondered how Jordan made out on assignments where he had to stay concealed and silent. Or did his noisy stomach preclude him from that kind of work?

"That area," Dalrymple pointed out, "is at least five square miles."

"Then let's comb it," Jordan answered. "In teams, in cars. Our shop and yours, and we'll ask help from the city police."

Lieutenant Fazackerly, who had joined them asked, "And what will we all be looking for, gentlemen?"

"If you want the truth," Jordan said, "damned if I know."

Juanita rode in an FBI car with Innes and Wainwright. Wainwright drove, leaving Innes free to work two radios—a portable unit, one of five supplied by the FBI, which could communicate directly with the other cars, and a regular transmitter-receiver linked directly to FBI Headquarters.

Beforehand, under the city police lieutenant's direction, they had sectored the area and five cars were now crisscrossing it. Two were FBI, one Secret Service, and two from the city. The personnel had split up. Jordan and Dalrymple were each riding with a city detective, filling in details for the newcomers as they drove. If necessary, other patrols of the city force would be called for backup.

One thing they were all sure of: Where Juanita had been held was the counterfeit center. Her general description and some details she had noticed made it close to a certainty. Therefore, instructions to all special units were the same: Look for, and report, any unusual activity which might relate to an organized crime center specializing in counterfeiting. All concerned conceded the instructions were vague, but no one had been able to come up with anything more specific. As Innes put it: "What else have we got?"

Juanita sat in the rear seat of the FBI car.

It was almost two hours since she and Estela had been set down abruptly, ordered to face away, and the dark green Ford had sped off with a screech of burned rubber. Since then Juanita had refused treatment—other than immediate first aid—for her badly bruised and cut face, and the cuts and lacerations on her legs. She was aware that she looked a mess, her clothing stained and torn, but knew too that if Miles was to be reached in time to save him, everything else must wait, even her own attention to Estela, who had been taken to a hospital for treatment of her burn and for observation. While Juanita did what she had to, Margot Bracken—who arrived at the precinct house shortly after Wainwright and the FBI—was comforting Estela.

It was now midafternoon.

Earlier, getting the sequence of her journey down on paper, clearing her mind as if purging an overburdened message center, had exhausted Juanita. Yet, afterward, she had responded to what seemed endless questioning by the FBI and Secret Service men who kept on probing for the smallest details of her experience in the hope that some unconsidered fragment might bring them closer to what they wanted most —a specific locale. So far nothing had.

But it was not details Juanita thought about now, seated behind Wainwright and Innes, but Miles as she had last seen him. The picture remained etched—with guilt and anguish—sharply on her mind. She doubted it would ever wholly disappear. The question haunted her: If the counterfeit center were discovered, would it be too late to save Miles? Was it already too late?

* * *

The area within the circle Agent Jordan had drawn—located near the city's eastern edge—was mixed in character. In part, it was commercial, with some factories, warehouses, and a large industrial tract devoted to light industry. This last, the most likely area, was the segment to which the patrolling forces were paying most attention. There were several shopping areas. The rest was residential, running the gamut from regiments of box bungalows to a clutch of sizable mansion-type dwellings.

To the eyes of the dozen roving searchers, who communicated frequently through the portable radios, activity everywhere was average and routine. Even a few out-of-the-ordinary happenings had commonplace overtones. In one of the shopping districts a man buying a painter's safety harness had tripped over it and broken a leg. Not far away a car with a stuck accelerator had crashed into an empty theater lobby. "Maybe someone thought it was a drive-in movie," Innes said, but no one laughed. In the industrial tract the fire department responded to a small plant blaze and quickly put it out. The plant was making waterbeds; one of the city detectives inspected it to be sure. At a residential mansion a charity tea was beginning. At another, an Alliance Van Lines tractor-trailer was loading household furniture. Over amid the bungalows a repair crew was coping with a leaky water main. Two neighbors had quarreled and were fistfighting on the sidewalk. Secret Service Agent Jordan got out and separated them.

And so on.

For an hour. At the end of it, they were no further ahead than when they started.

"I've a funny feeling," Wainwright said. "A feeling I used to get in police work sometimes when I'd missed something."

Innes glanced sideways. "I know what you mean. You get to believe there's something right under your nose if you could only see it."

"Juanita," Wainwright said over his shoulder, "is there *anything*, any little thing you haven't told us?"

She said firmly, "I told you everything."

"Then let's go over it again."

After a while Wainwright said, "Around the time Eastin stopped crying out, and while you were still bound, you told us something about there being a lot of noise."

She corrected him, "No, *una conmoción*. Noise and activity. I could hear people moving, things being shifted, drawers opening and closing, that sort of thing."

"Maybe they were searching for something," Innes suggested. "But what?"

"When you were on the way out," Wainwright asked, "did you get any idea what the activity was about?"

"*Por última vez, yo no sé*." Juanita shook her head. "I told you I was too shocked at seeing Miles to see anything else." She hesitated. "Well, there *were* those men in the garage moving that funny furniture."

"Yes," Innes said. "You told us about that. It's odd, all right, but we haven't thought of an explanation for it."

"Wait a minute! Maybe there is one."

Innes and Juanita looked at Wainwright. He was frowning. He appeared to be concentrating, working something out. "That activity Juanita heard . . . Supposing they weren't searching for something but were packing up, preparing to move?"

"Could be," Innes acknowledged. "But what they'd be moving would be machinery. Printing machines, supplies. Not furniture."

"Unless," Wainwright said, "the furniture was a cover. *Hollow* furniture."

They stared at each other. The answer hit them both at the same time. "For God's sake," Innes shouted. "That moving van!"

Wainwright was already reversing the car, spinning the wheel hard in a tight, fast turn.

Innes seized the portable radio. He transmitted tensely, "Strongthrust group leader to all special units. Converge on large gray house, stands back near east end Earlham Avenue. Look for Alliance Van Lines moving van. Halt and detain occupants. City units call in all cars in vicinity. Code 10-13."

Code 10-13 meant: Maximum speed, wide open, lights and siren. Innes switched on their own siren. Wainwright put his foot down hard.

"Christ!" Innes said; he sounded close to tears. "We went by it twice. And last time they were almost loaded."

"When you leave here," Marino instructed the driver of the tractor-semi, "head for the West Coast. Take it easy, do everything the way you would with a regular load, and rest up every night. But keep in touch, you know where to call. And if you don't get fresh orders on the way, you'll get them in L.A."

"Okay, Mr. Marino," the driver said. He was a reliable joe who knew the score, also that he would get a king-sized bonus for the personal risk he was running. But he had done the same thing other times before, when Tony Bear had kept the counterfeit center equipment on the road and out of harm's way, moving it around the country like a floating crap game until any heat was off.

"Well then," the driver said, "everything's loaded. I guess I'll roll. So long, Mr. Marino."

Tony Bear nodded, feeling relief. He had been unusually antsy during the packing and loading operation, a feeling which had kept him here, overseeing and keeping the pressure on, though he knew he was being un-smart to stay. Normally he kept safely distant from the working front line of any of his operations, making sure there was no evidence to connect him in the event that something fouled up. Others were paid to take those kinds of risks—and raps if necessary. The thing was, though, the counterfeit caper, starting as chickenshit, had become such a big-time moneymaker—in the real sense—that from once having been the least of his interests, it was now near the top of the list. Good organization had made it that way; that and taking *ultra*-precautions—a description Tony Bear liked—such as moving out now.

Strictly speaking, he didn't believe this present move was necessary —at least not yet—because he was sure Eastin had been lying when he said he had found out this location from Danny Kerrigan and had passed the information on. Tony Bear believed Kerrigan on that one, though the old fart *had* talked too much, and was going to have some unpleasant surprises soon which would cure him of a loose tongue. If Eastin *had* known what he said he did, and passed it on, the cops and bank dicks would have swarmed here long ago. Tony Bear wasn't surprised at the lie. He knew how people under torture passed through successive mental doors of desperation, switching from lies to truth, then back to lies again if they thought it was something their torturers wanted to hear. It was always an interesting game outguessing them. Tony Bear enjoyed those kinds of games.

Despite all that, moving out, using the emergency rush arrangements set up with the mob-owned trucking company, was the smart thing to do. As usual—ultra-smart. If in doubt, *move*. And now the loading was done, it was time to get rid of what was left of the stoolie Eastin. Garbage. A detail Angelo would attend to. Meanwhile, Tony Bear decided, it was high time he got the hell away from here himself. In exceptional good humor, he chuckled. *Ultra*-smart.

It was then he heard the faint but growing sound of converging sirens and, minutes later, knew he had not been smart at all.

"Better move it, Harry!" the young ambulance steward called forward to the driver. "This one doesn't have time to spare."

"From the look of the guy," the driver said—he kept his eyes directed ahead, using flashers and warbling siren to weave daringly through early rush hour traffic—"from the look of him, we'd both be doing the poor bastard a favor if we pulled over for a beer."

"Knock it off, Harry." The steward, whose qualifications were somewhat less than those of a male nurse, glanced toward Juanita. She was perched on a jump seat, straining around him to see Miles, her face intent, lips moving. "Sorry, miss. Guess we forgot you were there. On this job we get a bit case-hardened."

It took her a moment to absorb what was said. She asked, "How is he?"

"In bad shape. No sense fooling you." The young paramedic had injected a quarter grain of morphine subcutaneously. He had a blood-pressure cuff in place and now was sloshing water on Miles's face. Miles was semiconscious and, despite the morphine, moaning in pain. All the time the steward went on talking. "He's in shock. That can kill him, if the burns don't. This water's to wash the acid away, though it's late. As to his eyes, I wouldn't want . . . Say, what the hell happened in there?"

Juanita shook her head, not wanting to waste time and effort in talk. She reached out, seeking to touch Miles, even through the blanket covering him. Tears filled her eyes. She pleaded, uncertain she was being heard, "Forgive me! Oh, forgive me!"

"He your husband?" the steward asked. He began putting splints, secured by cotton bandages, around Miles's hands.

"No."

"Boyfriend?"

"Yes." The tears were flowing faster. Was she still *his* friend? *Need* she have betrayed him? Here and now she wanted forgiveness, just as he had once asked forgiveness of her—it seemed long ago, though it was not. She knew it was no use.

"Hold this," the steward said. He placed a mask over Miles's face and handed her a portable oxygen bottle. She heard a hiss as the oxygen went on and grasped the bottle as if, through her touch, she could communicate, as she had wanted to communicate ever since they had found Miles, unconscious, bleeding, burned, still nailed to the table in the house.

Juanita and Nolan Wainwright had followed the federal agents and local police into the big gray mansion, Wainwright having held her back until he made sure there was not going to be any shooting. There had been none; not even any resistance apparently, the people inside having decided they were outflanked and outnumbered.

It was Wainwright, his face more strained than she had ever seen it, who carefully, as gently as he could, pried loose the nails and released Miles's mangled hands. Dalrymple, ashen, cursing softly, held Eastin while, one by one, the nails came out. Juanita had been vaguely aware of other men, who had been in the house, lined up and handcuffed, but she hadn't cared. When the ambulance came she stayed close to the stretcher brought for Miles. She followed it out and into the ambulance. No one tried to stop her.

Now she began praying. The words came readily; words from long ago . . . *Acordaos, oh piadosísima Virgen María . . . that never was it known that anyone who fled to thy protection, implored thy help or sought thy intercession was left unaided. Inspired by that confidence I fly unto you . . .*

Something the ambulance steward had said, but she hadn't taken in, played back in her subconscious. *Miles's eyes.* They were burned with the remainder of his face. Her voice trembled. "Will he be blind?"

"The specialists will have to answer that. Soon's we get to Emergency he'll get the best treatment. There isn't a lot more I can do right here."

Juanita thought: there wasn't anything she could do either. Except to stay with Miles, as she would, with love and devotion for as long as he wanted and needed her. That, and pray . . . *¡Oh Virgen Madre de las vírgenes! . . . To thee I come, before thee I stand, sinful and sorrowful. O Mother of the Word Incarnate, despise not my petitions but hear and answer me. Amen.*

Some colonnaded buildings flashed by. "We're almost there," the steward said. He had his fingers on Miles's pulse. "He's still alive—"

24

In the fifteen days since official investigation was begun by the SEC into the labyrinthine finances of Supranational, Roscoe Heyward had prayed for a miracle to avert total catastrophe. Heyward himself attended meetings with other SuNatCo creditors, their objective to keep the multinational giant operating and viable if they could. It had proven impossible. The more deeply investigators probed, the worse the financial debacle appeared. It seemed probable, too, that criminal charges of fraud would eventually be laid against some of Supranational's officers, including G. G. Quartermain, assuming Big George could ever be enticed back from his Costa Rica hideaway—at the moment an unlikely prospect.

Therefore, in early November, a petition of bankruptcy under Section 77 of the Bankruptcy Act was filed on behalf of Supranational Corporation. Though it had been expected and feared, the immediate repercussions were worldwide. Several large creditors, as well as associated companies and many individuals, were considered likely to go down the drain along with SuNatCo. Whether First Mercantile American Bank would be one of them, or if the bank could survive its enormous loss, was still an open question.

No longer an open question—as Heyward fully realized—was the subject of his own career. At FMA, as the author of the greatest calamity in the bank's one-hundred-year history, he was virtually finished. What remained at issue was whether he, personally, would be legally liable under regulations of the Federal Reserve, the Comptroller of the Currency, and the SEC. Obviously, there were those who thought so. Yesterday, an SEC official, whom Heyward knew well, advised him, "Roscoe, as a friend, I suggest you get yourself a lawyer."

In his office, soon after the opening of the business day, Heyward's hands trembled as he read *The Wall Street Journal*'s page one story on the Supranational bankruptcy petition. He was interrupted by his senior secretary, Mrs. Callaghan. "Mr. Heyward—Mr. Austin is here."

Without waiting to be told, Harold Austin hurried in. In contrast to his normal role, the aging playboy today merely looked an overdressed old man. His face was drawn, serious, and pale; pouches beneath his eyes were rings of age and lack of sleep.

He wasted no time in preliminaries. "Have you heard *anything* from Quartermain?"

Heyward motioned to the *Journal*. "Only what I read." In the past two weeks he had tried several times to telephone Big George in Costa Rica, without success. The SuNatCo chairman was staying incommunicado. Reports filtering out described him as living in feudal splendor, with a small army of thugs to guard him, and said he had no intention, ever, of returning to the United States. It was accepted that Costa Rica would not respond to U.S. extradition proceedings, as other swindlers and fugitives had already proved.

"I'm going down the tube," the Honorable Harold said. His voice was close to breaking. "I put the family trust heavily into SuNatCo and I'm in hock myself for money I raised to buy Q-Investments."

"What *about* Q-Investments?"

Heyward had tried to find out earlier the status of Quartermain's private group which owed two million dollars to FMA in addition to the fifty million owing by Supranational.

"You mean you didn't hear?"

Heyward flared, "If I did, would I be asking?"

"I found out last night from Inchbeck. That son of a bitch Quartermain sold out all Q-Investments holdings—mostly stock in SuNatCo subsidiaries—when the group share prices were at their peak. There must have been a swimming pool full of cash."

Including FMA's two million, Heyward thought. He asked, "What happened to it?"

"The bastard transferred everything into offshore shell companies of his own, then moved the money out of them, so all Q-Investments is left with is shares in the shells—just worthless paper." To Heyward's disgust, Austin began to blubber. "The real money . . . my money . . . could be in Costa Rica, the Bahamas, Switzerland . . . Roscoe, you've got to help me get it back . . . Otherwise I'm finished . . . broke."

Heyward said tersely, "There's no way I can help you, Harold." He was worried enough about his own part in Q-Investments without concerning himself with Austin's.

"But if you hear anything new . . . if there's any hope . . ."

"If there is, I'll let you know."

As quickly as he could, Heyward eased Austin out of the office. He had no sooner gone than Mrs. Callaghan said on the intercom, "There's a reporter calling from *Newsday*. His name is Endicott. It's about Supranational and he says it's important that he speak to you personally."

"Tell him I have nothing to say, and to call the p.r. department." Heyward remembered Dick French's admonition to the senior officers: *The press will try to contact you individually . . . refer every caller to me.* At least that was one burden he need not bear.

Moments later he heard Dora Callaghan's voice again. "I'm sorry, Mr. Heyward."

"What *is* it?"

"Mr. Endicott is still on the line. He asked me to say to you: Do you wish him to discuss Miss Avril Deveraux with the p.r. department, or would you prefer to talk about her yourself?"

Heyward snatched up a phone. "What is all this?"

"Good morning, sir," a quiet voice said. "I apologize for disturbing you. This is Bruce Endicott of *Newsday*."

"You told my secretary . . ."

"I told her, sir, that I thought there were some things you'd prefer me to check with you personally, rather than lay them out for Dick French."

Was there a subtle emphasis on the word "lay"? Heyward wasn't sure. He said, "I'm extremely busy. I can spare a few minutes, that's all."

"Thank you, Mr. Heyward. I'll be as brief as I can. Our paper has been doing some investigating of Supranational Corporation. As you know, there's a good deal of public interest and we're running a major story on the subject tomorrow. Among other things, we're aware of the big loan to SuNatCo by your bank. I've talked to Dick French about that."

"Then you have all the information you need."

"Not quite, sir. We understand from other sources that you personally negotiated the Supranational loan, and there's a question of when the subject first came up. By that I mean when did SuNatCo first ask for the money? Do you happen to remember?"

"I'm afraid I don't. I deal with many large loans."

"Surely not too many for fifty million dollars."

"I think I already answered your question."

"I wonder if I could help, sir. Could it have been on a trip to the Bahamas in March? A trip you were on with Mr. Quartermain, Vice-President Stonebridge, and some others?"

Heyward hesitated. "Yes, it might have been."

"Could you say definitely that it was?" The reporter's tone was deferential, but it was clear he would not be put off with evasive answers.

"Yes, I remember now. It was."

"Thank you, sir. On that particular trip, I believe, you traveled in Mr. Quartermain's private jet—a 707?"

"Yes."

"With a number of young lady escorts."

"I'd hardly say they were escorts. I vaguely recall several stewardesses being aboard."

"Was one of them Miss Avril Deveraux? Did you meet her then, and also in the several days which followed in the Bahamas?"

"I may have done. The name you mentioned seems familiar."

"Mr. Heyward, forgive me for putting it this way, but was Miss Deveraux offered to you—sexually—in return for your sponsorship of the Supranational loan?"

"Certainly not!" Heyward was sweating now, the hand holding the telephone shaking. He wondered how much this smooth-voiced inquisitor really knew. Of course, he could end the conversation here and now; perhaps he should, though if he did he would go on wondering, not knowing.

"But did you, sir, as a result of that trip to the Bahamas, form a friendship with Miss Deveraux?"

"I suppose you could call it that. She is a pleasant, charming person."

"Then you *do* remember her?"

He had walked into a trap. He conceded, "Yes."

"Thank you, sir. By the way, have you met Miss Deveraux subsequently?"

The question was asked casually. But *this man Endicott knew*. Trying to keep a tremor out of his voice, Heyward insisted, "I've answered all the questions I intend to. As I told you, I'm extremely busy."

"As you wish, sir. But I think I should tell you that we've talked with Miss Deveraux and she's been extremely co-operative."

Extremely co-operative? Avril would be, Heyward thought. Especially if the newspaper paid her, and he supposed they had. But he felt no bitterness toward her; Avril was what she was, and nothing could ever change the sweetness she had given him.

The reporter was continuing. "She's supplied details of her meetings with you and we have some of the Columbia Hilton hotel bills—your bills, which Supranational paid. Do you wish to reconsider your statement, sir, that none of that had anything to do with the loan from First Mercantile American Bank to Supranational?"

Heyward was silent. What could he say? *Confound* all newspapers and writers, their obsession with invading privacy, their eternal digging, digging! Obviously someone inside SuNatCo had been induced to talk, had filched or copied papers. He remembered something Avril had said about "the list"—a confidential roster of those who could be entertained at Supranational's expense. For a while, his own name had been on it. Probably they had that information, too. The irony, of course, was that Avril had not in any way influenced his decision about the SuNatCo loan. He had made up his mind to recommend it long before involvement with her. But who would believe him?

"There's just one other thing, sir." Endicott obviously assumed there would be no answer to the last question. "May I ask about a private investment company called Q-Investments? To save time, I'll tell you we've managed to get copies of some of the records and you are shown as holding two thousand shares. Is that correct?"

"I have no comment to make."

"Mr. Heyward, were those shares given to you as a payoff for arranging the Supranational loan, and further loans totaling two million dollars to Q-Investments?"

Without speaking, Roscoe Heyward slowly hung up the phone.

Tomorrow's newspaper. That was what the caller had said. They would print it all, since obviously they had the evidence, and what one newspaper initiated, the rest of the media would repeat. He had no illusions, no doubts about what would follow. One newspaper story, one reporter, meant disgrace—total, absolute. Not only at the bank, but among friends, family. At his church, elsewhere. His prestige, influence, pride would be dissolved; for the first time he realized what a fragile mask they were. Even worse was the certainty of criminal prosecution for accepting bribes, the likelihood of other charges, the probability of prison.

He had sometimes wondered how the once-proud Nixon henchmen felt, brought low from their high places to be criminally charged, fingerprinted, stripped of dignity, judged by jurors whom not long before they would have treated with contempt. Now he knew. Or shortly would.

A quotation from *Genesis* came to him: *My punishment is greater than I can bear.*

A telephone rang on his desk. He ignored it. There was nothing more to be done here. Ever.

Almost without knowing it, he rose and walked out of the office, past Mrs. Callaghan who regarded him strangely and asked a question which he neither absorbed nor would have answered if he had. He walked down the 36th floor corridor, past the boardroom, so short a time ago an arena for his own ambitions. Several people spoke to him. He took no notice of them. Not far beyond the boardroom was a small door, seldom used. He opened it. There were stairs going upward and he ascended them, through several flights and turns, climbing steadily, neither hurrying nor pausing on the way.

Once, when FMA Headquarters Tower was new, Ben Rosselli had brought his executives this way. Heyward was one of them, and they had exited by another small door, which he could see ahead. Heyward opened it and went out, onto a narrow balcony almost at the building's peak, high above the city.

A raw November wind struck him with blustering force. He leaned against it and found it somehow reassuring, as if enfolding him. It was on that other occasion, he remembered, that Ben Rosselli had held out his arms toward the city and said: "Gentlemen, what was once here was my grandfather's promised land. What you see today is ours. Remember—as he did—that to profit in the truest sense, we must give to it, as well as take." It seemed long ago, in precept as well as time. Now Heyward looked downward. He could see smaller buildings, the winding, omnipresent river, traffic, people moving like ants on Rosselli Plaza far below. The sounds of them all came to him, muted and blended, on the wind.

He put a leg over the waist-high railing, separating the balcony from a narrow, unprotected ledge. His second leg followed. Until this moment he had felt no fear, but now all of his body trembled with it, and his hands grasped the railing at his back tightly.

Somewhere behind him he heard agitated voices, feet racing on the stairs. Someone shouted, "Roscoe!"

His last thought but one was a line from *I Samuel: Go, and the Lord be with thee.* The very last was of Avril. *O thou fairest among women . . . Rise up, my love, my fair one and come away . . .*

Then, as figures burst through the door behind him, he closed his eyes and stepped forward into the void.

25

There were a handful of days in your life, Alex Vandervoort thought, which, as long as you breathed and remembered anything, would stay sharply and painfully engraved in memory. The day—little more than a year ago—on which Ben Rosselli announced his impending death was one. Today would be another.

It was evening. At home in his apartment, Alex—still shocked from what had happened earlier, uncertain and dispirited—was waiting for Margot. She would be here soon. He mixed himself a second scotch and soda and tossed a log on the fire, which had burned low.

This morning he had been first through the door to the high tower balcony, having raced up the stairs after hearing worry expressed about Heyward's state of mind and deducing—from swift questioning of others—where Roscoe might have gone. Alex had cried out as he hurled himself through the doorway into the open, but was too late.

The sight of Roscoe, seeming to hang for an instant in air, then disappear from view with a terrible scream which faded quickly, left Alex horrified, shaking, and for moments unable to speak. It was Tom Straughan, who was right behind him on the stairway, who had taken charge, ordering the balcony cleared, an order with which Alex had complied.

Later, in an act of futility, the door to the balcony had been locked.

Below, returning to the 36th floor, Alex had pulled himself together and gone to report to Jerome Patterton. After that, the rest of the day was a mélange of events, decisions, details, succeeding and merging with each other until the whole became a Heyward epitaph, which even now was not concluded, and there would be more of the same tomorrow.

But, for today, Roscoe's wife and son had been contacted and consoled; police inquiries answered—at least, in part; funeral arrangements overseen—since the body was unrecognizable, the coffin would be sealed as soon as the coroner agreed; a press statement drafted by Dick French and approved by Alex; and still more questions dealt with or postponed.

Answers to other questions became clearer to Alex in the late afternoon, shortly after Dick French advised him that he should accept a telephone call from a *Newsday* reporter named Endicott. When Alex talked to him, the reporter seemed upset. He explained that just a few minutes earlier he had read on the AP wire of Roscoe Heyward's apparent suicide. Endicott went on to describe his call to Heyward this morning and what transpired. "If I'd had any idea . . ." he ended lamely.

Alex made no attempt to help the reporter feel better. The moralities of his profession were something he would have to work out for himself. But Alex did ask, "Is your paper still going to run the story?"

"Yes, sir. The desk is writing a new lead. Apart from that, it will run tomorrow as intended."

"Then why did you call?"

"I guess I just wanted to say—to somebody—I'm sorry."

"Yes," Alex said. "So am I."

This evening Alex reflected again on the conversation, pitying Roscoe for the agony of mind he must have suffered in those final minutes.

On another level there was no doubt that the *Newsday* story, when it appeared tomorrow, would do the bank great harm. It would be harm piled on harm. Despite Alex's success in halting the run at Tylersville, and the absence of other visible runs elsewhere, there had been a public lessening of confidence in First Mercantile American and an erosion of deposits. Nearly forty million dollars in withdrawals had flowed out in the past ten days and incoming funds were far below their usual level. At the same time, FMA's share price had sagged badly on the New York Stock Exchange.

FMA, of course, was not alone in that. Since the original news of Supranational's insolvency, a miasma of depression had gripped investors and the business community, including bankers; had sent stock prices generally on a downhill slide; had created fresh doubts internationally about the value of the dollar; and now appeared to some as the last clear warning before the major storm of world recession.

It was, Alex thought, as if the toppling of a giant had brought home the realization that other giants, once thought invulnerable, could topple, too; that neither individuals, nor corporations, nor governments, could escape forever the simplest accounting law of all—that what you owed you must one day pay.

Lewis D'Orsey, who had preached that doctrine for two decades, had written much the same thing in his latest *Newsletter*. Alex had received a new issue in the mail this morning, had glanced at it, then put it in his pocket to read more carefully tonight. Now, he took it out.

> Do not believe the glibly touted myth [Lewis wrote] that there is something complex and elusive, defying easy analysis, about corporate, national or international finance.
>
> All are simply housekeeping—ordinary housekeeping, on a larger scale.
>
> The alleged intricacies, the obfuscations and sinuosities are an imaginary thicket. They do not, in reality, exist, but have been created by vote-buying politicians (which means *all* politicians), manipulators, and Keynesian-diseased "economists." Together they use their witch doctor mumbo-jumbo to conceal what they are doing, and have done.
>
> What these bumblers fear most is our simple scrutiny of their activities in the clear and honest light of commonsense.
>
> For what they—the politicians, mostly—on one hand have created is Himalayas of debt which neither they, we, nor our great-great-great-grandchildren can ever pay. And, on the other hand, they have printed, as if producing toilet tissue, a cascade of currency, debasing our good money—especially the honest, gold-backed dollars which Americans once owned.
>
> We repeat: It is all simply housekeeping—the most flagrantly incompetent, dishonest housekeeping in human history.
>
> This, and this alone, is the basic reason for inflation.

There was more. Lewis preferred too many words, rather than too few.

Also, as usual, Lewis offered a solution to financial ills.

> Like a beaker of water for a parched and dying wayfarer, a solution is ready and available, as it has always been, and as it always will be.
>
> Gold.
>
> Gold as a base, once more, for the world's money systems.
>
> Gold, the oldest, the *only* bastion of monetary integrity. Gold, the *one* source, *incorruptible*, of fiscal discipline.

Gold, which politicians cannot print, or make, or fake, or otherwise debase.

Gold which, because of its severely limited supply, establishes its own *real*, lasting value.

Gold which, because of this consistent value and when a base for money, protects the honest savings of all people from pillaging by knaves, charlatans, incompetents and dreamers in public office.

Gold which, over centuries, has demonstrated:

—without it as a monetary base, there is inevitable inflation, followed by anarchy;

—with it, inflation can be curbed and cured, stability retained.

Gold which God, in His wisdom, may have created for the purpose of curtailing man's excess.

Gold of which Americans once stated proudly their dollar was "as good as."

Gold to which, someday soon, America must honorably return as its standard of exchange. The alternative—becoming clearer daily —is fiscal and national disintegration. Fortunately, even now, despite skepticism and anti-gold fanatics, there are signs of maturing views in government, of sanity returning . . .

Alex put *The D'Orsey Newsletter* down. Like many in banking and elsewhere he had sometimes scoffed at the vociferous gold bugs—Lewis D'Orsey, Harry Schultz, James Dines, Congressmen Crane, Exter, Browne, Pick, Richard Russell, a handful more. Recently, though, he had begun wondering if their simplistic views might not after all be right. As well as gold, they believed in laissez-faire, the free, unhampered function of the marketplace where inefficient companies were allowed to fail and efficient ones succeed. The obverse of the coin were the Keynesian theorists, who hated gold and believed in tinkering with the economy, including subsidies and controls, calling it all "fine tuning." Could the Keynesians be the heretics, Alex wondered, and D'Orsey, Schultz, et al., true prophets? Perhaps. Prophets in other eras had been lonely and derided, yet some lived to see their prophecies fulfilled. One view Alex shared in totality with Lewis and the others was that grimmer times were close ahead. Indeed, for FMA they were already here.

He heard the sound of a key turning. The outer door of the apartment opened and Margot came in. She removed a belted camel's-hair coat and tossed it on a chair.

"Oh God, Alex. I can't get Roscoe out of my mind. How could he do it? *Why?*"

She went directly to the bar and mixed a drink.

"It seems there were some reasons," he said slowly. "They're beginning to come out. If you don't mind, Bracken, I don't feel like talking about it yet."

"I understand." She came to him. He held her tightly as they kissed.

After a while he said, "Tell me about Eastin, Juanita, the little girl."

Since yesterday Margot had masterminded arrangements concerning all three.

She sat facing him, sipping her drink. "It's all so much; coming together . . ."

"Often things seem to happen that way." He wondered what else, if anything, there would be before this day was done.

"Miles first," Margot began. "He's out of danger and the best news is that by a miracle he won't be blind. What the doctors believe is that he must have closed his eyes an instant before the acid hit, so the eyelids saved him. They're terribly burned, of course, like the rest of his face, and he'll be having plastic surgery for a long time."

"What about his hands?"

Margot took a notebook from her purse and opened it. "The hospital has been in touch with a surgeon on the West Coast—a Dr. Jack Tupper in Oakland. He has the reputation of being one of the best men in the country for surgical repair of hands. He's been consulted by phone. He's agreed to fly here and operate the middle of next week. I assume the bank will pay."

"Yes," Alex said. "It will."

"I've had a talk," Margot continued, "with Agent Innes of the FBI. He says that in return for Miles Eastin's testifying in court, they'll offer him protection and a new identity somewhere else in the country." She put down her notebook. "Has Nolan talked to you today?"

Alex shook his head. "There hasn't been much chance."

"He's going to. He wants you to use your influence in helping Miles get a job. Nolan says if necessary he'll pound on your desk to make you do it."

"He won't need to," Alex said. "Our holding company owns consumer finance shops in Texas and in California. We'll find something for Eastin in one or the other."

"Maybe they'll hire Juanita as well. She says wherever he goes, she's going with him. Estela, too."

Alex sighed. He was glad there would be at least one happy ending. He asked, "What did Tim McCartney say about the child?"

It had been Alex's idea to send Estela Núñez to Dr. McCartney, the

Remedial Center psychiatrist. What mental harm, if any, Alex wondered, had befallen the little girl as a result of her kidnapping and torture?

But the thought of the Remedial Center now was a dismal reminder to him of Celia.

"I'll tell you one thing," Margot said. "If you and I were as sane and balanced as little Estela, we'd both be better people. Dr. McCartney says the two of them talked the whole thing out. As a result, Estela won't bury the experience in her subconscious; she'll remember it clearly —as a bad nightmare, nothing more."

Alex felt tears spring to his eyes. "I'm glad of that," he said softly. "Really glad."

"It's been a busy day." Margot stretched, kicking off her shoes. "One of the other things I did was talk with your legal department about compensation for Juanita. I think we can work something out without taking you to court."

"Thanks, Bracken." He took her drink, and his own, to refill them. While he did, the telephone rang. Margot got up and answered it.

"It's Leonard Kingswood. For you."

Alex crossed the living room and took the phone. "Yes, Len?"

"I know you're relaxing after a rough day," the Northam Steel chairman said, "and I'm shook up about Roscoe, too. But what I have to say can't wait."

Alex grimaced. "Go ahead."

"There's been a caucus of directors. Since this afternoon we've had two conference calls, with other calls between. A full meeting of the FMA board is being summoned for noon tomorrow."

"And?"

"The first order of business will be to accept the resignation of Jerome as president. Some of us demanded it. Jerome agreed. In fact, I think he was relieved."

Yes, Alex thought, Patterton would be. He clearly had no stomach for the sudden avalanche of problems, along with the critical decisions needed now.

"After that," Kingswood said with his usual blunt directness, "you will be elected president, Alex. The appointment to take effect immediately."

While talking, Alex had cradled the telephone against his shoulder and lit his pipe. Now he puffed it while he considered. "At this point, Len, I'm not sure I want the job."

"There was a feeling you might say that, which is why I was elected as the one to call you. You could say I'm pleading, Alex; for myself and the rest of the board." Kingswood paused, and Alex sensed he was having a hard time. Beseeching did not come easily to a man of Leonard L. Kingswood's stature, but he plowed on just the same.

"We all know you warned us about Supranational, but we thought we were wiser. Well, we weren't. We ignored your advice and now what you predicted has come true. So we're asking you, Alex—belatedly, I admit—to help us out of this mess we're in. I might say that some of the directors are worried about their personal liability. All of us remember your cautioning about that, too."

"Let me think a minute, Len."

"Take your time."

Alex supposed he should feel some personal satisfaction, a sense of superiority, perhaps, at being vindicated, able to say, *I told you so*; a conviction of power at holding—as he knew he did—trump cards.

He felt none of those things. Only a great sadness at the futility and waste, when the best that could happen for a long time to come, assuming he succeeded, was for the bank to regain the state in which Ben Rosselli left it.

Was it worth it? What was it all about? Could the extraordinary effort, deep personal involvement and sacrifice, the stress and strain, be justified? And for what? To save a bank, a money store, a money machine, from failure. Wasn't Margot's work among the poor and disadvantaged far more important than his own, a greater contribution to their times? Yet it wasn't all that simple because banks were necessary, in their way as essential and immediate as food. Civilization would break down without a money system. Banks, though imperfect, made the money system work.

Those were abstract considerations; there was a practical one. Even if Alex accepted the leadership of First Mercantile American at this late stage, there was no assurance of success. He might merely preside, ignominiously, over FMA's demise or take-over by another bank. If so, he would be remembered for it, his reputation as a banker liquidated, too. On the other hand, if anyone could save FMA, Alex knew he was the one. As well as ability, he possessed the inside knowledge which an outsider would not have time to learn. Even more important: Despite all the problems, even now, he believed that he could do it.

"If I accepted, Len," he said, "I'd insist on a free hand to make changes, including changes on the board."

"You'd get your free hand," Kingswood answered. "I personally guarantee it."

Alex drew on his pipe, then put it down. "Let me sleep on it. I'll give you my decision in the morning."

He hung up the phone and retrieved his drink from the bar. Margot had already taken hers.

She regarded him quizzically. "Why didn't you accept? When both of us know you're going to."

"You guessed what that was all about?"

"Of course."

"Why are you so certain I'll accept?"

"Because you can't resist the challenge. Because your whole life is banking. Everything else takes second place."

"I'm not sure," he said slowly, "that I want that to be true." Yet it *had* been true, he thought, when he and Celia were together. Was it still? Possibly the answer was yes, as Margot said. Probably, too, no one ever changed his basic nature.

"There's something I've been wanting to ask you," Margot said. "This seems as good a time as any."

He nodded. "Go ahead."

"That night in Tylersville, the day of the bank run, when the old couple with their life savings in that shopping bag asked you the question: *Is our money absolutely safe in your bank?* you answered yes. Were you really sure?"

"I've asked myself that," Alex said. "Right afterwards, and since. If I own up, I suppose I wasn't."

"But you were saving the bank. Right? And that came first. Ahead of those old people, and all the others; ahead of honesty even, because 'business as usual' was more important." Suddenly there was emotion in Margot's voice. "It's why you'll go on trying to save the bank, Alex— ahead of everything else. It's the way it was with you and Celia. And," she said slowly, "as it would be—if you had to make the choice—with you and me."

Alex was silent. What could you say, what could anyone say, confronted with the naked truth?

"So in the end," Margot said, "you aren't all that different from Roscoe. Or Lewis either." She picked up *The D'Orsey Newsletter* with distaste. "Business stability, sound money, gold, high share prices. All those things first. People—especially little, unimportant people—a long way after. It's the big gulf between us, Alex. It will always be there." He saw that she was crying.

A buzzer sounded in the hallway beyond the living room.

Alex swore. "Goddam the interruptions!"

He strode toward an intercom unit connecting with a doorman on the street floor. "Yes, what is it?"

"Mr. Vandervoort, there's a lady here asking for you. Mrs. Callaghan."

"I don't know any . . ." He stopped. Heyward's secretary? "Ask if she's from the bank."

A pause.

"Yes, sir. She is."

"All right. Send her up."

Alex told Margot. They waited curiously. When he heard the elevator on the landing outside, he went to the apartment door and opened it.

"Please come in, Mrs. Callaghan."

Dora Callaghan was an attractive, well-groomed woman, nearing sixty. She had, Alex knew, worked at FMA for many years, at least ten of them for Roscoe Heyward. Normally she was poised and confident, but tonight she looked tired and nervous.

She wore a fur-trimmed suede coat and carried a leather briefcase. Alex recognized it as belonging to the bank.

"Mr. Vandervoort, I'm sorry to intrude . . ."

"I'm sure you have a good reason for coming." He introduced Margot, then asked, "Could you use a drink?"

"I really could."

A martini. Margot mixed it. Alex took the suede coat. They all sat by the fire.

"You can speak freely in front of Miss Bracken," Alex said.

"Thank you." Dora Callaghan took a gulp of the martini, then put it down. "Mr. Vandervoort, this afternoon I went through Mr. Heyward's desk. I thought there would be some things to clear, papers perhaps that should be sent to someone else." Her voice thickened and stopped. She whispered, "I'm sorry."

Alex told her gently, "Please don't be. There's no hurry."

As her composure returned, she continued, "There were some locked drawers. Mr. Heyward and I both had keys, though I didn't use mine often. Today I did."

Again a silence while they waited.

"In one of the drawers . . . Mr. Vandervoort, I heard there would be investigators coming tomorrow morning. I thought . . . that you'd better see what was in there, that you'd know, better than I, what to do."

Mrs. Callaghan opened the leather briefcase and took out two large envelopes. As she handed them to Alex, he observed that both had been slit open previously. Curiously, he removed the contents.

The first envelope contained four share certificates, each for five hundred shares of Q-Investments common stock and signed by G. G. Quartermain. Though they were nominee certificates, there could be no doubt they had belonged to Heyward, Alex thought. He remembered the *Newsday* reporter's allegations of this afternoon. This was confirmation. Further proof would be needed, of course, if the matter were pursued, but it seemed certain that Heyward, a trusted, high-ranking officer of the bank, had accepted a sordid bribe. Had he lived, exposure would have meant criminal prosecution.

Alex's earlier depression deepened. He had never liked Heyward. They were antagonists, almost from the time that Alex was recruited into FMA. Yet never for an instant, until today, had he doubted Roscoe's personal integrity. It demonstrated, he supposed, that however well you thought you knew another human being, you never really did.

Wishing none of this was happening, Alex removed the contents from the second envelope. They proved to be enlarged photographs of a group of people beside a swimming pool—four women and two men in the nude, and Roscoe Heyward dressed. As an instant guess, Alex suspected the photos were a souvenir from Heyward's much-vaunted trip to the Bahamas with Big George Quartermain. Alex counted twelve prints as he spread them out on a coffee table while Margot and Mrs. Callaghan watched. He caught a glimpse of Dora Callaghan's face. Her cheeks were red; she was blushing. *Blushing?* He'd thought no one did that any more.

His inclination, as he studied the photos, was to laugh. Everyone in them looked—there was no other word for it—ridiculous. Roscoe, in one shot, was staring fascinated at the naked women; in another he was being kissed by one of them while his fingers touched her breasts. Harold Austin exhibited a flabby body, drooping penis, and foolish smile. Another man, with his behind to the camera, faced the women. As to the women—well, Alex thought, some people might consider them attractive. For himself, he would take Margot, with her clothes on, any day.

He didn't laugh, though—out of deference to Dora Callaghan who had drained her martini and was standing up. "Mr. Vandervoort, I'd better go."

"You were right to bring these things to me," he told her. "I appreciate it, and I'll take care of them personally."

"I'll see you out," Margot said. She retrieved Mrs. Callaghan's coat and went with her to the elevator.

Alex was by a window, looking out at the city's lights, when Margot returned.

"A nice woman," she pronounced. "And loyal."

"Yes," he said, and thought: Whatever changes were made tomorrow and in ensuing days, he would see that Mrs. Callaghan was treated considerately. There would be other people to think of, too. Alex would immediately promote Tom Straughan to Alex's own previous post as an executive vice-president. Orville Young could fill Heyward's shoes well. Edwina D'Orsey must move up to senior vice-president in charge of the trust department; it was a post Alex had had in mind for Edwina for some time, and soon he expected her to move higher still. Meanwhile she must be named, at once, a member of the board.

He realized suddenly: he was taking for granted that he himself would accept the bank presidency. Well, Margot had just told him that. Obviously she was right.

He turned away from the window and the outside darkness. Margot was standing at the coffee table, looking down at the photographs. Suddenly she giggled, and then he did what he had wanted to, and laughed with her.

"Oh, God!" Margot said. "Funny-sad!"

When their laughter ended he bent down, collected the prints and returned them to their envelope. He was tempted to throw the package on the fire, but knew he mustn't. It would be destruction of evidence which might be needed. But he would do his best, he decided, to keep the photos from other eyes—for Roscoe's sake.

"Funny-sad," Margot repeated. "Isn't it all?"

"Yes," he agreed, and in that moment knew he needed her, and always would.

He took her hands, remembering what they had been speaking of before Mrs. Callaghan came. "Never mind any gulfs between us," Alex urged. "We have a lot of bridges, too. You and I are good for each other. Let's live together permanently, Bracken, starting now."

She objected, "It probably won't work, or last. The odds are against us."

"Then we'll try to prove them wrong."

"Of course, there *is* one thing in our favor." Margot's eyes sparkled mischievously. "Most couples who pledge 'to love and to cherish, till death us do part,' wind up in divorce courts within a year. Maybe if we start out not believing or expecting much, we'll do better than the rest."

As he took her in his arms, he told her, "Sometimes bankers and lawyers talk too much."

Hailey, Arthur   FICTION
  The moneychangers.

IDEAS & MEN · *The Story of*

WESTERN THOUGHT

Crane Brinton

MCLEAN PROFESSOR OF ANCIENT & MODERN HISTORY
HARVARD UNIVERSITY

Prentice-Hall, Inc.   ENGLEWOOD CLIFFS, N. J.

Copyright, 1950, by

PRENTICE-HALL, INC.

Englewood Cliffs, N. J.

First printing............June, 1950
Second printing......September, 1950
Third printing.........February, 1951
Fourth printing...........July, 1951
Fifth printing.........October, 1952
Sixth printing......September, 1953
Seventh printing........ May, 1954
Eighth printing......November, 1955
Ninth printing...........June, 1957
Tenth printing.......November, 1958

PRINTED IN THE UNITED STATES OF AMERICA
44923

To My Wife

ACKNOWLEDGMENTS

I wish to thank the following publishers for permission to quote from copyright works:

APPLETON-CENTURY-CROFTS, INC., for permission to quote from Machiavelli, *The Prince*, translated and edited by Thomas G. Bergin, copyright 1947.

BENZIGER BROTHERS, INC., New York, N. Y., for permission to quote from the Complete American Edition of the *Summa Theologica*.

GEORGE ROUTLEDGE & SONS, London, for permission to quote from F. A. Wright, *A History of Later Greek Literature*, page 169.

HARVARD UNIVERSITY PRESS, Cambridge, Mass., for permission to quote from the Loeb Classical Library edition of *Diogenes Laertius*, translated by R. D. Hicks.

LONGMANS, GREEN & COMPANY, New York, for permission to quote from *The Bacchae* of Euripides translated by Gilbert Murray.

THE MACMILLAN COMPANY, for permission to quote from Oscar Levy, *Complete Works of Frederic Nietzsche*.

OXFORD UNIVERSITY PRESS, for permission to quote from the *Social Contract* (Galaxy Edition of the World's Classics), and from Thucydides, *Peloponnesian War*, edited by Sir R. W. Livingston (World's Classics).

CRANE BRINTON

Contents

CONTENTS

Ideas and Men

I

Introduction

*T*HIS IS A BOOK about the ideas men in our Western tradition have held and still hold on the Big Questions—cosmological questions, which ask whether the universe makes sense in terms of human capacity to comprehend, and if so, what kind of sense; and ethical questions, which ask whether what we do and what we want to do make sense, ask what we *really* mean by good and bad, by beautiful and ugly. The total of recorded answers to these and similar questions —that is, most of our Western philosophy, art, literature, and in some senses, natural science—fills millions of volumes. Any account of them, therefore, must omit vastly more than it can possibly include.

There are many possible schemes for guiding the historian of these ideas and attitudes, for what we may call figuratively the cartography of ideas. The figure is more apt than such analogies often are, for neither the historian nor the cartographer can ever reproduce the reality they are trying to communicate to the reader of books or of maps; they can but give a plan, a series of indications, of this reality. There are contrasting schemes for choosing from enormous numbers of details. You may have a map in which every feature that can be named, every hill, brook, crossroads, is crowded in; or you may have a map in which many details are omitted in the effort to show the reader the lay of the land, the shape of the mountain systems, the relations of drainage, relief, communications, and so on. Both kinds are useful, depending on the needs of the user. In mapping the history of ideas, this book will definitely attempt to follow the second scheme. It will try to show the lay of the cultural and intellectual land; it will omit many famous names, and perhaps even a few landmarks, in an effort to make clear what large groups of men and women in the West have felt about the answers to the great questions of human destiny.

There is, however, another important, contrasting set of schemes for guiding the intellectual historian. This may be put as the contrast between picking out the ideas and attitudes the historian thinks are right, or true, and setting forth a fair selection of ideas and attitudes for the reader to exercise his own judgment upon. The first, translated into educational terms, is based on the principle "To teach is to affirm"; the second is based on the principle "To teach is to put problems." In the real world, these two are by no means mutually exclusive. The most dogmatic approach—at least in the West—hardly means that the learner repeats by rote exactly what he hears or reads; and the most tentative and open-minded approach hardly means that no one takes anything on authority, that everybody works out his own ideas in his own private world. Both poles are as bleak and as uninhabited as the poles of this earth. Nevertheless, this book will try to keep to the hemisphere of the second pole, to the principle that the individual should do a great deal of his own thinking and choosing— that, to use Alfred North Whitehead's expressive phrase, intellectual history is an "adventure of ideas" for anyone who will embark on it. But all adventure implies uncertainty.

These two choices—for the broad lines instead of the details, and for independent thinking instead of absorbing "correct" information and interpretation—are in accord with a growing feeling in the United States that we have in the past absorbed too many facts and thought about them too little.

This feeling is clear in the movement for general education, by whatever name it may be called. Like most such movements, that for general education may well go too far. Folk wisdom recognizes the danger of throwing the baby out with the bath. The "baby" of good sound command of the necessary facts is one that no sensible person wants to throw out. On the whole, however, our culture is admirably organized to permit the rapid and accurate accumulation of and ready access to the facts necessary to useful thinking about a given problem. Libraries, encyclopedias, textbooks that are really reference books, all abound.

The "baby" of sound generalizations, or theories, is also one that no sensible person wants to throw out. But there is a difficulty here, that of determining which generalizations are sound and which are not. In fields such as natural science, there exists a core of theories that are known by all competent persons and must be accepted by all who work in the field. This, as we shall shortly see, is simply not so in the fields of theology, philosophy, literature, and art, where it is plain that men of education and taste do differ widely. For in these fields we are not just asking ourselves *what is,* but rather we all feel, more or less strongly, that *something else ought to be.*

Now in a democratic society it is believed that each member of the society has a part to play in the complex process by which *ought* —that is, men's wants and the communicable forms they give those wants—slowly, imperfectly, unpredictably perhaps, alters *is.* (The problems encountered in this process, indeed, the problem of whether or not the process is an illusion—that is, the old question of determinism or freedom of the will—are good examples of the insoluble but persistent and by no means unimportant problems that have vexed the Western mind for millennia.) In a democratic society, the individual must exercise his judgment on questions like this, for if he does not, they may be answered by authoritarian enemies of democracy in a way he will not like. The word "exercise" was chosen deliberately; it means mental as well as physical effort. But mental effort means making decisions, trying to solve problems not decided in advance, trying to balance and choose among conflicting generalizations. This book should give the serious reader ample opportunity for such exercise.

It is not a book designed primarily to impart information, not a book that will help the reader to shine in quiz programs. It is not a history of any one of the great disciplines, theology, philosophy, scholarship, science, literature, art. A brief book that covered all these fields would be no more than a list of names and a few more or less appropriate labels, like the "ethereal Shelley" and the "sweet-voiced Keats." More especially, this book is not a history of philosophy; it is not written by a professional philosopher and it treats no philosopher fully and in the round. It makes an effort to deal with that part of a philosopher's work that went into the climate of opinion of the intellectual classes. It is, to use Mr. D. C. Somervell's distinction, rather a history of opinion than a history of thought. It is no substitute, for those who wish to undergo such discipline, for a thorough study of the history of formal philosophy.

One final word of explanation. The serious reader may find our approach to many of these problems the reverse of serious, may find it light, undignified. This is a genuine difficulty. It seems to the writer that many of the grand questions about the beautiful and the good have commonly been approached, especially among English-speaking peoples, with so much reverence that *ought* has been disastrously confused with *is*. Americans like to think they are idealists, and many of them are. But foreigners often accuse us of keeping our ideals and our actions in separate compartments. They are unfair, but their position has a base in fact. We tend as a people to revere certain abstract ideas so much that we are likely to fall into the error of thinking that once we have got the ideas on paper, once we have verbal acceptance of a goal as virtuous, then we have attained the goal. Witness Woodrow Wilson's career from the announcement of the Fourteen Points to the completion of the Treaty of Versailles. Witness the Eighteenth Amendment. In this book an attempt is made at a clinician's attitude toward these matters, an attitude that demands working over a good deal of the petty and the undignified in order to understand what we are really dealing with when we study ideas at work among real living human beings. It is an attitude not of *irreverence,* but of *nonreverence* while the clinical work is being done. In no sense does it involve a denial of the existence—and desirability—

of the beautiful and the good, any more than the attitude of the medical clinician involves a denial of the existence and the desirability of the healthy and the sane.

The Limits of Intellectual History

The field of study known as intellectual history or history of ideas is not a clear-cut and simple one. Under some such labels there can be found a wide range of actual subject matter, from the writings of very abstract philosophers to expressions of popular superstition like triskaidekaphobia, which in simpler language is excessive fear of the number thirteen. Intellectual historians have dealt with the ideas of the philosopher and with those of the man in the street. Their main job, however, is to try to find *the relations between the ideas of the philosophers, the intellectuals, the thinkers, and the actual way of living of the millions who carry the tasks of civilization.*

It is a job that should chiefly differentiate intellectual history from such old, established disciplines as the history of philosophy, the history of science, and the history of literature. The intellectual historian is interested in ideas wherever he finds them, in wild ideas as well as in sensible ideas, in refined speculation and in common prejudices; but he is interested in these products of men's mental activity as they influence, and are influenced by, men's whole existence. He will not, then, deal solely with abstract ideas that breed more abstract ideas; he will not deal, for instance, with that very abstract political theory known as the social contract as though it were just a bit of legal reasoning. But he will treat even the most abstract ideas as these ideas filter into the heads and hearts of ordinary men and women; he will explain what the social contract meant to those eighteenth-century rebels who held that their rulers had violated it.

This is a difficult task. The intellectual historian is trying to work out a very complex set of relations between what a few men write or say and what many men actually do. He finds it very easy, at least for the last twenty-five hundred years of our Western society, to discover and analyze what the few have written and said. That record is not perfect, but it is extraordinarily good, even for ancient Greece and Rome, thanks to the labors of generations of scholars. But, until the printing press and popular education gave the historian in newspapers, periodicals, pamphlets, and the like a record of what ordinary men thought and felt, the rest of the intellectual historian's task was very difficult. The historian can describe pretty clearly how all sorts of people in Germany and outside Germany regarded Adolf Hitler; he can never know just how the common, unheard millions of people in the Graeco-Roman world regarded Julius Caesar. There were no Gallup polls in those days, no letters to the editor, no popular magazines. Nevertheless, if he is not to limit himself to analyzing ideas in terms of still more ideas, the intellectual historian must make an effort to piece together from scattered sources some notion of how ideas got to work among the crowd.

There is, indeed, some justification for limiting intellectual history to what the late J. H. Robinson called the "intellectual classes." Professor Baumer of Yale has defined the intellectual class as "not only the comparatively small group of really profound and original thinkers, not only the professional philosophers, scientists, theologians and scholars in general, but also creative literary men and artists, the popularizers, and the intelligent reading public." In a way, it would seem sensible that intellectual history should be confined to the doings, sayings, and writings of intellectuals; and yet Professor Baumer's definition seems a bit too narrow. Not until the eighteenth century was there anything like a reading public. Moreover, quite unintellectual, even, in a scholarly, bookish, verbal sense, quite unintelligent, human beings do entertain ideas about right and wrong, have purposes that can be, and are, stated in words, and are moved by all sorts of beliefs, creeds, superstitions, traditions, and sentiments. The history of the intellectual classes is worth writing, but it is not the whole of intellectual history; or if it is, some other name must be found for what this book is concerned with.

Sources for the study of the ideas (in the broadest sense) of ordinary men and women are, in fact, many. Literature is obviously less purely intellectual, less highbrow, than formal philosophy or science. What has survived from the days before printing is, of course, relatively highbrow. From Greek, Roman, medieval, and even Renaissance times we have more of the equivalent of *The New York Times* and less of the equivalent of the tabloids, more of the equivalent of Bernard Shaw and less of the equivalent of *Little Orphan Annie*. Still, we have a great deal that is obviously nearer to earth than philosophy. We can check on the philosopher Socrates as he appeared to his disciple Plato by reading Aristophanes' *Clouds,* in which a popular and successful playwright makes fun of Socrates. We can see medieval men and women, not only as the theologians and philosophers described them, but as men of the world like Chaucer described them in his *Canterbury Tales.*

The ordinary man has, indeed, left many traces other than those left in what we call literature. Of religions we have not only the theologies—that is, the more obviously intellectual elements corresponding to what in secular matters is called philosophy—but also the rituals, the daily practices, and even what, if we feel patronizing, we call the superstitions of ancient and medieval men. A great deal of what the intellectual historian must draw on has been amassed by specialists called social historians, who have set themselves the task of finding how men and women of all classes actually lived. These social historians have often been interested, not only in what men and women ate, and wore, and did to earn a living, but also in what they believed to be right and wrong, in what they hoped for in this world and the next. Many social historians became, in a sense, intellectual historians, focusing on what went on in the heart and head of the man in the street.

The full task of the intellectual historian, then, is to gather into an intelligible whole materials ranging from abstract philosophic concepts to concrete acts of men. At one end of his spectrum, he comes close to being a philosopher, or at least a historian of philosophy, and at the other end he comes close to being a social historian, or just a plain historian, concerned with the daily lives of human beings. But his special task is to bring the two ends together, to follow ideas in their often tortuous path from study or laboratory to the market, the club, the home, the legislative chamber, the law court, the conference table, and the battlefield.

In carrying out this ambitious task, the intellectual historian may find himself invading still another field of study long cultivated by scholars. This is the vague, all-embracing field traditionally known as the philosophy of history. The philosopher of history tries to use his knowledge of what has happened in the past to unlock all the mysteries of man's fate. A complete philosophy of history (like any and all philosophies) seeks to give final answers to all the Big Questions: What is the good life? How can human beings lead the good life? What are the prospects that human beings will be able to lead the good life? In short, where are we, and where are we going?

In a later chapter, we shall try to see how it comes about that in this mid-twentieth century some of the most popular philosophical systems are in fact philosophies of history, and that names like Spengler, Sorokin, and Toynbee are known wherever high intellectual matters are discussed. For the present we need only note that the intellectual historian, though he may well be tempted to put on the mantle of the prophet and philosopher of history, ought to resist the temptation to do so. He will work more profitably if he confines himself to the more modest but still arduous task of tracing the ways in which the answers men have given to the Big Questions—Life, Destiny, Right, Truth, God—have apparently affected their conduct. He may—and indeed if he is a normal human being he will—have his own answers to some, at least, of the Big Questions. But if he is true to the traditions of science and scholarship as they have matured for the historian of today, he will do his best to keep his own answers from affecting his report of other men's answers. Again, we shall in later chapters have more to say about this whole matter of scientific method and objectivity and their relation to the study of human behavior. Here it should be sufficient to note that intellectual history as interpreted in this book is not offered as an answer to all the problems that beset modern men, but rather as a help toward putting some of those problems more clearly, and, perhaps, toward indicating what consequences are likely to follow upon various attempts to solve them.

Indeed, the reader should be warned that the task of tracing the work ideas have done and still do among the great masses of human beings in Western society can be but imperfectly done. It is not merely that the historical sources before modern times are lacking or difficult to assemble; competent specialists, once their attention is turned to this problem, can over the next few generations do something to supplement our lack of materials. There is a graver difficulty. We do not yet understand sufficiently well, despite the work of psychologists, sociologists, and philosophers, just what goes on in men's minds and hearts, just how they are moved to action—or to inaction. Above all, men who have long studied these problems are by no means agreed concerning the part played in human behavior by reason, logic, ideas, knowledge, in contrast with emotion, sentiment, drives, urges. There is among such men a by no means complete agreement that there is to be found in concrete human behavior some such components as the rational and the nonrational, but there is no universally accepted set of effective working definitions of these terms.

The Role of Ideas

There remain, therefore, a few bothersome questions of methods, perhaps even of philosophy, before we can begin the study of our Western intellectual heritage at its major Greek and Hebraic sources. The intellectual historian will try to see how ideas work in this world, will study the relation between what men say and what men actually do: What does he mean by ideas and what does he mean by saying that ideas do work in this world? Now these are themselves philosophical questions, about which men debate without agreeing. This fact alone should make it clear that these are not questions that can be answered as any American boy could answer such questions as: What does the automotive engineer mean by carburetor? and what does he mean when he says a carburetor does work?

Ideas are clearly different from carburetors, but do not make the mistake of thinking they are less real than carburetors, less important in our lives, or that they are mere words and not important at all. We

11

shall here take "ideas" in a very broad sense indeed as almost any coherent example of the workings of the human mind expressed in words. Thus, the word "ouch" uttered by a man who hits his finger with a hammer is probably not an idea at all. His statement "I hit my finger with a hammer" is a very simple proposition, and therefore an idea. A further statement, "My finger hurts because I hit it with a hammer," begins to involve more complicated ideas. Statements such as "My finger hurts because the hammer blow affected certain nerves which carried to my central nervous system a kind of stimulus associated with what we call pain" and "My finger hurts because God is punishing me for my sins" are both very complex propositions, taking us into two important realms of human thought, the scientific and the theological.

Now the classification of all the kinds of ideas that go to make up what we commonly call knowledge is in itself the major task of several disciplines, among them logic, epistemology, and semantics. And then there follows the task of deciding what knowledge is true, or how far given knowledge is true, and many other tasks that we cannot here undertake. In our own day, the study of semantics, the analysis of the complicated ways in which words get interpreted as they are used in communication among human beings, has aroused widespread interest. For our present purposes, it will be sufficient to make a basic distinction between two kinds of knowledge, cumulative and noncumulative.

Cumulative knowledge is best exemplified by the knowledge we call commonly natural science, or just science. From the beginnings of the study of astronomy and physics several thousand years ago in the eastern Mediterranean, our astronomical and physical ideas have *accumulated,* have gradually built up into the astronomy and physics we study in school and college. The process of building up has not been regular, but on the whole it has been steady. Some of the ideas or theories of the very beginning are still held true, such as the ideas of the ancient Greek Archimedes on specific gravity, but many, many others have been added to the original stock. Many have been discarded as false. The result is a discipline, a science, with a solid and universally accepted core of accumulated knowledge and a growing outer edge of new knowledge. Dispute—and scientists dispute quite as much as do philosophers and private persons—centers on this growing outer edge, not in the core. This core all scientists accept as true.

New knowledge can, of course, be reflected back through the whole core, and cause what may not unfairly be called a "revolution" in the science. Thus quantum mechanics and relativity theories have been reflected back into the core of Newtonian physics.

Noncumulative knowledge can here be illustrated best from the field of literature. Men of letters make certain propositions, entertain certain ideas, about men, about right and wrong action, about beautiful and ugly things. Over two thousand years ago, men of letters were writing in Greek on these matters; at the same time others were writing in Greek about the movements of the stars or about the displacement of solids in water. But our contemporary men of letters are today writing about the very same things the Greek men of letters wrote about, in much the same way and with no clear and certain increase in knowledge. Our men of science, on the other hand, have about astronomy and physics far more knowledge, far more ideas and propositions, than the Greeks had.

To put the matter most simply: A Greek man of letters like Aristophanes, a Greek philosopher like Plato, if miraculously brought to earth in the mid-twentieth century and given speech with us (but no knowledge since his death) could quite soon talk about literature or philosophy with a G. B. Shaw or a John Dewey, and feel quite at home; a Greek scientist like Archimedes in the same position would, even though he were a genius, need to spend a good many days grinding over elementary and advanced textbooks of physics and acquiring enough mathematics before he could begin to talk shop with a modern physicist like Bohr or Einstein. To put it another way: A modern American college student is not wiser than one of the sages of antiquity, has no better taste than an artist of antiquity, but he knows a lot more physics than the greatest Greek scientist ever knew. He knows more *facts* about literature and philosophy than the wisest Greek of 400 B.C. could know; but in physics he not only knows more facts—he understands the relations between facts, that is, the theories and the laws.

This distinction between cumulative and noncumulative knowledge is useful and obvious, which is about all one need expect from a distinction. *Such a distinction does not mean that science is good and useful, and that art, literature, and philosophy are bad and useless, but merely that in respect to the attribute of cumulativeness they are different.* Many people do take this distinction as a statement that art is somehow inferior to science, and are offended by it to the point of rejecting any truth or usefulness the distinction may have. This is a common habit of men, and one the intellectual historian must reckon with.

Perhaps it is merely that in the last three hundred years science has accumulated very *rapidly,* while art, literature, and philosophy have accumulated *slowly* for several thousand years. Our great men may in some senses be wiser than the great men of old; and the average wisdom, or good sense, of American citizens may be greater than that of Athenian citizens. But these matters are very hard to measure, very hard to get agreement on; and the cumulative character of scientific knowledge is well-nigh indisputable. The most hopeful defender of progress in art and philosophy would hardly maintain as a formula: Shakespeare is to Sophocles as Newton is to Archimedes.

The foregoing necessarily oversimplifies the distinction between cumulative and noncumulative knowledge. Notably, for generations of Western thinkers, as for many thinkers today, that part of human knowledge not subsumed under "science" is given less than justice by the tag "noncumulative." It can be argued that what are commonly called the social sciences have in their own right, not just as rather feeble imitations of the natural sciences, an accumulated body of knowledge about the interrelations of human beings. This knowledge is an accumulation not merely of facts, but also of valid interpretations of the facts. Thus economists, in the century and a half from Adam Smith to Lord Keynes, have come to *understand* more about economic activity. It can be argued that philosophers, though they still face some of the questions that faced Plato and Aristotle, have over the centuries improved their methods of analysis, and have refined into greater precision the questions they ask themselves. Finally, though the cynic may say that all we learn from history is that we never learn from history, most of us would hold that over the centuries Western men have built up a body of wisdom and good taste that was not available to the Greeks. How widely such wisdom and taste are spread in our society is another question.

Indeed, for both cumulative and noncumulative knowledge the problem of *dissemination,* the problem of correcting common errors in public thinking, is at least as important as, and in a democratic society perhaps more important than, the problem of getting the experts to agree. This should be evident, save to the most determined scorners of economic thought, in a field like economics. Of course the economists disagree. So do the doctors. Even in modern America, where medicine has a very high prestige among all classes, it is by no means easy to educate the public to the point where it will act intelligently in medical matters. In economic matters, the public remains even in mid-twentieth century largely unable to make use of the amount of accumulated knowledge the experts possess, or we should not be attempting to restore something like a balanced international world trade while retaining a high general level, and often very high particular levels, of protective tariffs.

The intellectual historian clearly must concern himself with *both* cumulative and noncumulative knowledge, and must do his best to distinguish one kind of knowledge from another, to trace their mutual relations, and to study their effect on human behavior. Both kinds of knowledge are important, and each does its own work on this earth.

We thus come to the second of our questions: How do ideas work in this world? Any answer must take into account the fact that often *ideas* are really *ideals*—expressions of hopes and aspirations, goals of human desire and effort. We say, for instance, that "all men are created equal," or, with the poet Keats,

> "Beauty is truth, truth beauty,"—that is all
> Ye know on earth, and all ye need to know.

What can statements like these mean? If you assert that a heavy weight and a lighter weight will drop through the air at different rates, you can drop them from a height and see. Galileo did this, though not, we now know, from the Leaning Tower of Pisa. Witnesses can also see, and should agree after they have checked what they saw. But you cannot possibly test the assertion of human equality or the identity of truth and beauty in any such fashion, and you can be very sure that after argument on such propositions, a random sample of human beings will not in fact agree about them.

In a general way, the kind of knowledge we have called cumulative, that is, scientific knowledge, is subject to the kind of test that makes it possible for all sane, properly trained men to agree upon its truth or falsehood; and the kind of knowledge we have called noncumulative is not subject to such a test, nor capable of producing such an agreement. Hence, as stated earlier, some have concluded that noncumulative knowledge is of no use, is not really knowledge, has no meaning, and, above all, has no real effect on human behavior. These people often fancy themselves as hard-boiled realists, as sensible people who know what the world really is like. They are actually very mistaken people, as narrow-minded as the most innocent of the idealists they condemn.

For, at the very least, a proposition like "all men are created equal" means that somebody *wants* all men to be equal in some respects. In the form "all men ought to be equal" the proposition would be frankly what we call an ideal. This confusion of "ought" and "is" turns out for the intellectual historian to be another of the abiding habits of men thinking. Moreover, he will realize that "ought" and "is" influence one another mutually, are parts of a whole process, not independent, and not—at least not often—mutually contradictory. Indeed, he will know that the effort to close the gap between ideal and real, between "ought" and "is," supplies one of the main interests of intellectual history. The gap has never been closed, certainly not by idealists who deny the "is," nor by realists who deny the "ought." Men do not consistently act in logical (rational) accordance with their professed ideals; here the realist scores. But their professed ideals are not meaningless, and thinking about ideals is not a silly and ineffective activity that has no effect on their lives. Ideals, as well as appetites, push men into action; here the idealist scores.

Today in the United States we are perhaps more liable to be led astray by the realist's than by the idealist's error, though throughout our history we have been lured by many ideals. Again, the study of intellectual history ought to help us understand why. But for the moment we can content ourselves with the observation that in human history there are no important facts unrelated to ideas, no important ideas unrelated to facts. The debate, a favorite one between Marxists and their opponents, whether economic changes are more basic than other changes, is logically pointless. No automotive engineer would dream of debating whether the gasoline or the spark makes an internal-combustion engine run, let alone which came first, the gasoline or the spark. No intellectual historian need debate whether ideas OR interests move men in their relations in society, nor which comes first. Without BOTH gasoline and spark, no working motor; without BOTH ideas and interests (or appetites, or drives, or material factors) no live, working human society, and no human history.

Contemporary Importance of Intellectual History

The study of intellectual history is especially important in our time, for such study should contribute to clearer thinking on one of the main issues of our day. This issue has been put before us all by many forms of education and propaganda. It is sometimes put temperately, sometimes quite hysterically. The columnists like to put it something like this: Science and technology have made possible weapons that can destroy the human race in the next war. Political and moral wisdom, on the other hand, seem not to have devised any way of preventing the next war. We must, they say, find a way to bring our political and moral wisdom (hitherto noncumulative, or at best very slowly cumulative) and its application up to a level with our scientific knowledge (rapidly cumulative) and its application in technology, and we must find it quickly, so that there will be no next war.

17

The matter can be put in the less excited terms we have already used. What we have called cumulative knowledge has, especially within the last three centuries, enabled human beings to attain an extraordinary mastery over their nonhuman environment. Not only do men manipulate inorganic matter, but they can do a great deal to shape living organisms. They can breed animals for maximum use of mankind. They can control many microorganisms, and have prolonged human life in advanced countries far beyond what seemed possible only a few generations ago.

But men have not yet won comparable triumphs in the control of the human environment at the highest levels of conscious human behavior. Knowledge of why men want certain things, of why they will kill other men to get those things, of how their desires can be changed or satisfied, of much of the whole range of human behavior, seems to belong rather to noncumulative than to cumulative knowledge. Now this noncumulative knowledge, whether philosophy, theology, practical wisdom, or plain horse sense, has never yet been sufficient to preserve peace on earth, let alone to banish all kinds of evil in human relations. Unless we get another kind of knowledge of human behavior, say the alarmists, cumulative knowledge of the sort the physicist or biologist has, we shall get affairs in such a mess that our civilization, and possibly even the human race, will be destroyed.

In short, one of the great problems of our day is this: Can the so-called *social sciences* enable man to control his human environment to anything like the extent the natural sciences have enabled him to control his nonhuman environment? An intellectual historian today is almost bound to focus his work on this problem, and to concentrate primarily on the way men in the past have dealt with the basic problems of human relations. He will write, in a sense, a history of the social sciences.

Intellectual history will not, it should be noted very clearly, in itself give the answers to the problems that are worrying us all today. Those problems will be answered only by the collective effort of us all, and in ways that the wisest philosopher or scientist—even the wisest columnist—cannot predict. If the social sciences follow the course the natural sciences have taken, the answers to the great problems will be given by the kind of people we call geniuses; but the geniuses will be able to get their answers only because of the full, patient work of thousands of workers in research and in practical life. Still more important, the answers can be translated into effective social action in a democratic society only if the citizens of that society have some basic understanding of what is going on. Both for those engaged in active work on problems of human relations and for those whose main work lies in other fields, the study of intellectual history can be useful.

For those engaged directly in the field of human relations, either as social scientists or as practical workers, a knowledge of how men have behaved in the past is of major importance. We shall see in a later chapter that the problem of the uses and limitations of historical study has been a much-debated topic at certain stages of our Western civilization. There have always been individuals to whom the study of history seems unprofitable, even vicious, a limitation on the possibilities of soaring that the human spirit not dragged down by history might have. But the general verdict of our Western civilization has been that a knowledge of history is at the very least a kind of extension of individual experience, and therefore of value to the human intelligence that makes use of experience. And certainly the kind of knowledge we have called cumulative—natural science—is committed to the view that valid generalizations must depend on wide experience, including what is commonly called history. Thus, the historical or genetic sciences, such as historical geology or paleontology, are as essential as analytical sciences like chemistry in the achievement of the natural sciences. History is quite as essential in the social sciences.

History should, in fact, supplement field work and experimentation if the social sciences are to advance. The record of what men have done in the past is essential to save us today from wasting our time in blind alleys. UNESCO, the United Nations Educational, Scientific, and Cultural Organization, is engaged on a vast co-operative study of the tensions that threaten to break out into violent conflict. None of these tensions can be understood without some attention to their histories—their *case histories*. History thus provides some of the essential data, the raw material of facts, the record of trial and error, necessary to an understanding of human behavior today.

But more important is the use a knowledge of history, and especially of intellectual history, can have for those of us who do the many important tasks of our civilization that do not call for specialized knowledge of the social sciences, or for creative work in them. One can imagine a society in which a few experts manage the masses of men skillfully and efficiently; indeed, Mr. Aldous Huxley in his *Brave New World* has imagined just such a society, and Mr. B. F. Skinner has devised a most ingenious one in his *Walden Two*. It is an ideal that often tempts the engineering temperament. But this product of "cultural engineering" would not be a *democratic* society, and, even were it attainable, which is most doubtful, Americans brought up in our national traditions could not possibly bring themselves to work for it. We are committed to the democratic, widespread, voluntary solutions of our problems, to solutions arrived at by free and extensive discussion and decisions made by some form of counting individual decisions. The scientists, the creative minority, will of course initiate solutions; but solutions will not be attained until we all understand them and put them into practice because we understand, approve, and want them ourselves.

Here again we can get light from what has happened in the natural sciences. Pathologists, immunologists, practicing physicians have done the creative work that has all but stamped out certain diseases, typhoid and diphtheria for instance. But in our society this great progress in public health has been possible only because the great majority of the people have in the last few decades had some understanding, however imperfect, of the germ theory of disease, have wished to eradicate disease, and have collaborated freely and intelligently, for the most part, in the work of the experts.

Some progress in the eradication of such diseases as typhoid and diphtheria has indeed been made by experts working with an ignorant population, a population holding ideas about disease quite different from those we hold. Even in India and Africa public health has been improved. But this improvement has been slower than with us, and less secure, just because the experts could not really share their knowledge with the rest of the populations, but had to use authority, prestige, persuasion, and tricks to put their prescriptions across.

The process of successful innovation, from the idea in the mind of the genius to its widespread working out among human beings—the subject of the last few paragraphs—is one of the many important problems we still know relatively little about. We can be sure there is a problem, and that the catchy phrase attributed to Emerson, "if a man make a better mouse-trap, the world will beat a path to his door," is at the very least misleading. There will be a confusing criss-cross of paths, or perhaps no path. Vaccination had first to win the medical profession, and then the public, though on the whole its course was relatively simple. But how about the ideas Marx had? What is the tortuous set of paths that led from the British Museum to the Kremlin? Note that here, even among the experts, there is nowhere near the general agreement on the truth and value of Marx's ideas that holds for vaccination.

If our experts do find ways of curing, or at least palliating, such social ills as war, depressions, unemployment, inflation, delinquency, crime, and all the long tale of evil, they will not succeed in making those ways effective unless the rest of us have some knowledge of what they are about. And if in our own time the progress of the social sciences is not very great, if we have to rely on the kind of leaders and the kind of ideas about human beings that our predecessors had to rely on—why then, it is still more important that all citizens of a democratic society should have some knowledge of intellectual history. If the experts fail us in our time and we have to fall back on common sense, it is important that that common sense be really common. History, like all forms of experience, is a most useful guide in the formation of common sense. It is a guide, not an infallible Leader, not a worker of miracles. If you want miracles—certainly a very human want—you must look elsewhere than to history. Clio is a very limited goddess.

Some Patterns of Intellectual History

In this mid-twentieth century we possess in printed form so complete a record of what human beings have said and done in the past, both original records and the comments of successive generations of historians and critics, that no one person could ever read everything pertaining to any considerable part of the record. One life would not be sufficient to read every word we possess written by the ancient Greeks and every word written about them. Writers and readers of history alike must pick and choose from this immense body of writings. This is commonplace, but none the less important.

The critical problem we must all face is how we choose, how we sort out the important from the unimportant, how we know the important when we run up against it. A full answer to such questions would demand a whole book on the methodology of the historian; here we can only attempt to justify in broad lines the choices exercised in this book. But first we may examine some other possible choices that have been rejected.

A plausible principle of choice, and one very popular in America nowadays, is to choose what is said to be "living" for us today and reject what is said to be "dead." The former is held to be important, the latter of no interest save to the pedant and the specialist. Hence, we are told, let us by all odds have the "living thought" of Plato, but not the part of his thought that was applicable only to the Greeks of his own day.

The difficulty lies in knowing what you mean by *living* in such a context. You may mean "accepted as true by the great majority of men." Now in this sense it may be argued that all the physicist needs to know about Greek physics is the part that is still accepted as true. Yet even the scientist can learn much from the history of science; he can learn how easily mistakes can be made, how difficult, even in a field like his, sound innovation is. And he can learn that science is no ivory tower, but a part of full human life.

Physics, however, is clearly an example of cumulative knowledge.

Plato was not a physicist, but a philosopher, whose main concern was problems of right living and wrong living, the existence of God, the immortality of the soul, the relations between permanence and change, and many more of the sort. These are matters of noncumulative knowledge, about which it is by no means easy to decide what is true and alive today, and what is false and dead. It is a fact of experience that twentieth-century readers of what Plato himself wrote range from those who think it all sublime wisdom to those who think it all nonsense, with many variants between these extremes.

Sometimes those who talk about choosing only what of the past is alive today seem to mean by alive what is familiar, and by dead what is strange. Take, for instance, a classic Greek tragedy, the *Antigone* of Sophocles. The play deals with the efforts of Antigone to secure the proper funeral rites for the corpse of her brother Polyneices, who has been slain in rebellion against Creon, lawful ruler of Thebes. Creon, holding that the fate of Polyneices must be held up as an example of what happens to rebels and lawbreakers, refuses proper burial, and when Antigone makes a pathetic attempt to perform ritual burial for her brother, condemns her to death.

Now the universality, the applicability to human beings like ourselves, of the struggle between Antigone and Creon is clear enough. Antigone sets her own sense of right and wrong against the commands of the legal system she lives under. There are those who maintain, however, that what stirs her sense of right and wrong—the treatment of her brother's corpse—is so strange, almost so trivial, to modern Americans that they miss the whole point of the drama unless they are carefully told what it is. According to these critics and teachers, the masterpiece of Sophocles can only be made alive for us if it is made clear that Antigone was really a kind of Thoreau or Gandhi, indulging in "civil disobedience."

Of course she was not these, but a Greek maiden of the great age of Greece, moved profoundly by notions of human dignity in part alien to us. Now what is alien in Antigone is most important to us. History—even intellectual history—is above all useful because it takes us out of the narrow and limited range of our own lives, and makes

23

us aware of how wide human experience has been, how complicated what we carelessly label "human nature" is, how much men are alike and predictable, how much unlike and unpredictable.

If we take the familiar, the things we find least difficult to accept as human, as our principle of choice in the welter of historical facts, we shall vastly lessen the value of any study of the past. Were our knowledge of men and women truly and simply cumulative, like our knowledge of physics, we could keep the living parts and reject the dead parts of the record of the past. But our knowledge of men and women is not cumulative, and we cannot exercise sensibly any *simple* principle of choice between alive and dead, valid and invalid, important and unimportant. Some choice there must be, and everyone who writes or reads history makes a choice. But it should be a wide choice, as good a sampling as possible, and not a choice determined by any closed system of ideas. A history of democratic thought should not pass over antidemocratic thought.

Still another principle of choice, in intellectual history at least, might be to take the figures the general opinion of cultivated people today has marked out as classics, as the great thinkers and writers, and outline as clearly and as succinctly as possible what they wrote. Now this is worth doing, and has been well done. It is not, however, what we mean in this book by intellectual history. It is rather the history of philosophy, or the history of literature, or the history of political theory. What we mean by intellectual history is something more and less than a record of the achievements of the great minds in the fields of noncumulative knowledge. It is more in that it seeks to find how quite ordinary men and women, not the geniuses, not the great, felt and thought and acted; it is less in that it cannot, without reaching interminable lengths, analyze thoroughly the formal thought of the great and near-great thinkers as this thought is analyzed professionally, technically, in the standard manuals of philosophy, art, and literature. We are not here interested so much in Plato's thought in and of itself as in how far that thought is part of the Greek way of life, how far it rejects that way of life, how far it was accepted by ordinary educated men in later societies; in short, we are

24

interested less in Plato-in-himself than in what men have made of Plato, or Kant, or Nietzsche.

Finally—and this is the thorniest problem of all—there is the kind of choosing among the almost infinite details of the past which arranges them with a view to proving something. All historians do, in fact, arrange their materials in such a way as to lead the reader to believe that some propositions—often very big and very philosophical propositions—about men and their destiny are true. St. Augustine in his *City of God* used the facts of history as he collected them to prove that Christianity had not weakened the Roman Empire, that the Empire fell because God punishes the wicked. George Bancroft in his history of the United States used his selected facts to show that we Americans are the real chosen people of a truly democratic God, that our Manifest Destiny is to lead the world to better living. The nineteenth-century English philosopher Herbert Spencer found that history clearly showed men progressing from warlike competitive societies to peaceful, collaborating, industrial societies.

History is still, and may always remain, a part of noncumulative rather than of cumulative knowledge. Some of its research methods, its ways of deciding reliability of evidence, are indeed scientific or cumulative. But sooner or later the historian comes up against the problem of what his evidence means in terms of human loves and hates, hopes and fears; sooner or later he makes judgments of value, decides about good and bad, brings in purpose. Science *as science* itself does none of these things, but confines itself to establishing uniformities or laws at bottom descriptive, not normative.

This book has a pattern of values, a thesis, an explanation of the course of human events, which should come out definitely enough for those who pursue it to the end. Here, briefly, too briefly for clarity, we may anticipate and say that this book will try to show that in the course of the last two thousand years Western intellectuals have helped build up very high standards of the good life and rational conduct; that in the last three hundred years, especially through the doctrines of progress and democracy, the notion has been widespread that everybody here and now on this earth can, or ought to, live up to these standards and be "happy"; that the two world wars of our day and their attendant evils, the Great Depression, and much else have made the postponement of this good democratic life, if not its abandonment, seem likely to many thoughtful people; that the most plausible explanation of the comparative failure of the ideals of democracy and progress lies in the overestimation their holders made of the reasonableness, the powers of analytical thought, of the average man today; that therefore all interested in man's fate should study with great care the way men actually behave, the relation between their ideals and their acts, their words and their deeds; finally, that this relation is not the simple, direct, causal relation most of us were brought up to believe it is.

Throughout this book, there runs a very great problem indeed, one that is today much in the minds of all concerned with human relations. It is a problem that you will find very early in Western intellectual history, among the Greeks of the fifth century B.C. It is a problem implicit in our distinction between cumulative and non-cumulative knowledge. Let it be granted that science, cumulative knowledge, can tell us in many concrete cases what is true and what false, even what will "work" and what will not. Is there any reliable knowledge that will tell us what is good and what is bad? Is there a science, a knowledge, of *norms?* Or are what are usually called value-judgments (we cannot here go into all the depths a rigorous treatment of these terms would demand) incapable, at bottom, of being rated by the instrument of thought?

Now clearly in matters of right and wrong, beautiful and ugly, Western men have not in fact attained the kind of agreement they have attained in matters of natural science. But there is a very strong current indeed in the Western tradition that refuses to accept the thesis, which has cropped up every now and then in Western history from the sophists to the logical positivists, that there is no use reasoning about men's morals and tastes, about their *wants.* In spite of popular sayings like "there's no use disputing about tastes" and assertions like "might makes right," Western men reject the belief that values are the mere random outcome of conflicting human desires. This rejection is in itself a major fact.

In this book we shall attempt, not to dodge this great question of the existence of a normative knowledge of values, but to stimulate the reader to do his own thinking on this question. The writer must confess that in his own thinking he has gone rather far toward the position that value-judgments cannot for Western men be given a solid ranking order save by the intervention of a human activity commonly called *faith*. Men can and do believe that Bach is a better composer than Offenbach as firmly as they believe that Mt. Everest is higher than Mt. Washington. They can think about the Bach-Offenbach relationship and their judgment on that relationship; they can communicate much of what they think (*and feel*) about that relationship to their fellows; they can even persuade their fellows to accept their own views of that relationship.

We cannot here do more than touch the surface of the question of normative judgments. Clearly one does not use the same criteria in judging the relation between the music of Bach and the music of Offenbach that one uses in judging the relation between the height of Mt. Everest and the height of Mt. Washington. To decide the latter problem, most of us would go to a good reference book and accept its authority, rather than try to measure the mountains ourselves. Such use of an appeal to authority in a question of fact (in a sense, of "science") is often pounced upon by defenders of the validity of normative judgments in ethics, aesthetics, and other fields, who then urge we accept the authority of, say, the Church concerning the existence of God. There really is, however, a difference between the use of authority in the two instances. Any properly trained person can go through the steps, accepted as valid by all geographers, that ended in the measurement of the two mountains. Such an operation is impossible for the existence of God. Properly trained persons can indeed follow the reasoning by which theologians prove the existence of God; but they will find many conflicting reasonings, including some that end up by proving that God does *not* exist.

Properly trained persons can also follow the reasoning by which a musical critic shows that the music of Bach is better than that of Offenbach. Here he will find differences enough, but much more agreement than on the existence of God. He will find the argument from authority—that the most competent judges agree that Bach's music is better than Offenbach's. He will find complex arguments, edging into the field of ethics, to show that Bach was a more elevated musician than Offenbach, that he wrote music more exacting and more satisfying by aesthetic standards. He will find very technical explanations based on the mathematics and physics of music. Finally, and happily, he will find the explanation that Bach writes serious music very well, and that Offenbach writes light music very well, and that a man may well enjoy both in their proper places.

Reason is thus by no means helpless in problems of value. It can do much; above all it can persuade men and teach men. But it cannot achieve the impossible task of eliminating what to the pure rationalist is the perverseness of men—each man's conviction that beyond some irreducible point he is not like other men, that he has a will, a personality of his own. That will, at some point, must bolster itself with faith, "the evidence of things not seen."

The Hellenic Fountainhead

THERE HAVE SURVIVED writings in classic, or ancient, Greek, dating very roughly from 750 B.C. to 1000 A.D., which cover almost the whole range of thinking men have done in the fields of noncumulative knowledge. Greek philosophers, Greek observers of human nature, Greek historians, Greek men of letters have expressed in some form or other almost all the kinds of intellectual and emotional experience Western men have recognized and named. This may seem an extreme statement, and is not of course a denial of the force, weight, beauty, wisdom, and in many senses, originality of medieval or modern achievement in these fields.

You can test this assertion in almost any field. In literature, the Greeks tried all of what we call the genres, including, toward the end, something very close to the novel. Especially in epic, lyric, and dramatic poetry and in history they set standards never yet surpassed—some would say, never yet equaled. In philosophy, their schools put all the Big Questions—being and becoming, the one and the many, mind and body, spirit and matter—and gave all the big answers. Among the Greek philosophers were idealists, materialists, rationalists, monists, pluralists, skeptics, cynics, relativists, absolutists. Their painting has not survived physically; the decline in most phases of civilization that followed the breakup of the Graeco-Roman world was so great that men could not, at any rate did not, take care of these paintings. There is some doubt whether Greek painting was as great an art as Greek sculpture and Greek architecture; there is no doubt of the greatness of these latter, which have managed to survive, though often in imperfect condition, from the very solidity of their materials. Finally, in science or cumulative knowledge the Greeks, building in part on earlier achievements in Egypt and Mesopotamia, carried to high development the theoretical side of mathematics and astronomy and did creditably in physics and in medicine; the Romans, building in part on Greek achievements, attained high standards in engineering. In political and economic life, this culture attained great complexity. These people, in short, were fully "civilized."

Indeed, so great was the prestige acquired by this classical civilization that it was not until nearly 1700 A.D., in France and in England, that writers and thinkers came to wonder whether they, the moderns, couldn't come somewhere near the old Greeks and Romans as writers, artists, scientists—in short, as civilized human beings. The prestige of the "classical" in this sense has now, however, almost disappeared in mid-twentieth-century America. In formal education, the classicists have lost even the rear-guard actions. Greek is no longer taught in secondary schools, and Latin survives as hardly more than a genteel formality.

Although many educated Americans are wholly ignorant of an achievement that once meant so much to all educated men, the Greek achievement remains an essential part of the capital stock of our culture. It is by no means mere pedantry, nor even mere scientific custom, that has sent our psychologists, after so many humanists and men of letters, back to Greece. If from Greek sources the psychologists have named their Oedipus complex, their narcissism, their phobias and their manias, it is because the so-called mythology of the Greeks is in fact an amazingly rich treasury of realistic, and in the unromantic sense of the word, imaginative, observations on human behavior, on human aspirations, on that never-to-be-exhausted commonplace, human nature. Compared with Greek mythology, Norse or Celtic mythology is simply thin, poverty-stricken, naive about human nature. We cannot know ourselves well if we know the Greeks not at all.

30

Moreover, the Graeco-Roman experiment in civilization was in some senses completed; it exhibits, as philosophers of history all remind us, something like a full cycle, from youth to age and death, from spring to winter; it has a beginning and an ending.

Finally, in this civilization was matured the Christian religion. Christianity clearly has Jewish origins largely outside Greek influences. But in its growth and organization it was an integral part of the Graeco-Roman world in the last few centuries of that civilization's active life. We cannot understand Christianity today unless we understand Christianity then.

The origins of the Greeks are unrecorded in history, but are clearly reflected in Greek legend and mythology and in archaeological remains. It is clear that the Greek-speaking peoples were outsiders, Northerners from the Danube basin or even further north, and related by language at least to the Germans, the Celts, and the Slavs. In various waves, of which the latest, the Doric, finished its wanderings almost in historic time, at the beginning of the first millennium before Christ, these Greeks—or Hellenes, as they called themselves— came down on an earlier native culture we now call Minoan. Almost certainly Hellenes and Minoans mixed their genes and their cultures, with the Hellenes the dominant group, and with the usual falling off of cultural standards that accompanies the conquest of more civilized by less civilized peoples. For the Minoans had a high civilization, as we can tell from their architectural and sculptural remains. From this dark age the Greeks emerged clearly by the eighth century B.C., already traders as well as fighters, already artists, perhaps even thinkers, and already organized in the most famous of Greek institutions, the *polis,* or self-governing, sovereign city-state. In the *polis* was bred the classical culture of Greece. Athens and its surrounding territory, Attica, had in the fifth century B.C., the century of its greatness, a population of at most 200,000—the size of a modest American city today.

The thousand years of the classical civilization of the Mediterranean offer something we cannot afford to turn down—a chance to see a kind of trial run of ideas that are still part of our daily living.

31

Perhaps we behave as we do more because of what a great many generations of our ancestors did as prehistoric men than because of what the relatively few generations of our ancestors did as members of this classical Mediterranean culture; human bodies, from liver to brain, were twenty-five hundred years ago substantially what they are today. Many of our habits of mind, our sentiments, our psychological needs, were no doubt formed long before the Greeks were ever heard of, but history can tell us little of these, intellectual history least of all. Indeed, Western intellectual history in a great measure begins with the Greeks, for they were the first to use the mind in a striking and novel way. The Greeks have left the first permanent and extensive record in our Western society of the kind of thinking we all do a great deal of (sometimes rather against the grain) in our lives. There is no good, unambiguous word for this kind of thinking; let us simply call it *objective reasoning*.

Now the Greeks were by no means the first people to think, nor even the first to think scientifically: Egyptian surveyors and Chaldean stargazers used mathematics, and therefore thought scientifically. But the Greeks first reasoned about the whole range of human experience. The Greeks even reasoned about how they should behave. Perhaps every human being tries to do what the Greeks did by reasoning—that is, adjust himself to the strange, bewildering, sometimes hostile universe that is clearly not himself, that seems to run on most of the time with no regard for him, that seems to have will, strength, purpose often at odds with his. Probably Australian Bushmen, Iroquois, Kalmucks, and all other peoples reason about these matters, and if we really knew how their minds worked we could understand them. But the point is, some of the Greeks, as early as the great age, did it *our way*. Their minds worked the way ours work.

Their own primitive ancestors had not done it quite our way. They had heard thunder, and seen lightning, and been frightened. The thunder and lightning were clearly not human, they realized, but they must be alive—everything, for some primitive men, is alive. So they ultimately came to believe that a very powerful being, whom they called the god Zeus, was hurling his monster bolts through the sky and causing all the row. Sometimes, they thought, he was hurling them at other gods, sometimes just displaying his anger, sometimes, of course, hurling them at mortal men, whom he thus struck dead. A good Greek believed, or hoped, that if he showed proper respect for Zeus, the god would not throw thunderbolts at him. For right into the great days of Athenian culture, the man in the street believed in Zeus and his thunderbolts.

Note that the early Greek "explained" the thunderstorm. He explained almost everything by the actions of gods, or spirits, or nymphs, or giants, or the kind of supermen he called heroes. But some Greeks—we do not know just where and when—came to the conclusion that a good deal went on in the universe without any god's doing anything about it. They became convinced, for instance, that the weather made itself. They did not know much about electricity, certainly not enough to connect the simple instances of magnetism they had observed with anything as potent as thunder and lightning. But they did believe, as we might put it, that a thunderstorm was a natural phenomenon, subject to a reasonable and scientific explanation.

The conflict between the older, supernatural explanation and the newer, natural explanation is recorded in a play of Aristophanes, *The Clouds*, first performed in 423 B.C. In spite of the burlesque and deliberate nonsense in which the playwright puts the scientific case, you can gather that some Athenians held the respectable meteorological theory that winds go from high-pressure areas to low-pressure areas. Aristophanes was—or to cater to the popular audience perhaps pretended to be—shocked at these newfangled ideas, and leaves the impression that the old Zeus theory was sounder. But in spite of the absurdities he puts in the mouth of the philosopher Socrates, for him the type of the new thinker, you can see the Greek mind at work, trying to understand the weather.

This does not mean that the new thinkers were antireligious, that they were materialists. Some of them were, and later many Greek and Roman thinkers were to be what we now call complete rationalists. But for the Greeks of the great era reasoning was a tool, an exciting new one, to be used on all human experience, including human experience of the divine. At most, one can say that the early Greeks used reason rather confidently and broadly, that they liked to spin out theories, that they were not very good at the kind of slow amassing, observing, and testing of facts that modern science employs. Later Greeks amassed many facts in scholarship and science; few men since have amassed more facts than Aristotle.

It is worth our while to go a bit further into this problem of the way the Greek mind worked. At least two very old philosophical problems confront us at this stage—the problem of universals and the related problem of like and unlike.

First, we have just written "the way the Greek mind worked." But was there ever a Greek mind? Weren't there just the millions and millions of individual Greeks, each with a mind of his own? In what actual brain-case was this mysterious "Greek mind" ever lodged? We shall have to turn seriously to this problem of universals when we come to medieval Europe, where it held the center of the stage for a while among intellectuals. Here we may note that there are at least ways around the problem, ways of avoiding the conclusion that there were as many Greek minds as there were Greeks, and ways of avoiding the conclusion (even more absurd to ordinary Americans) that there was only one Greek mind, the essence, the pattern, of all Greek thinking.

A clue lies in that worn phrase "with a mind of his own." Each of *us,* of course, likes to think he has a mind of his own. But do we really think there are 100,000,000 adult Americans with minds of their own? Aren't many millions of these minds filled most of the time with pretty much the same thoughts, thoughts made uniform by radio, press, Hollywood, school, church, all the agencies that work on our minds? There are of course the rebels, the unorthodox, the deliberately "different"—though even these come together in little groups which share many ideas. The fact is that phrases like the "Greek mind" or the "American mind" are useful because they correspond to facts of ordinary experience. They can be abused by being made too

34

simple, too unchanging, too little related to facts, but they are indispensable at the stage of mental growth we moderns have attained.

Let us then grant that there is a Greek mind, and that it works often very much the way the American mind works. But are not all minds—the Egyptian mind, the Chinese mind, the Bushman mind—more alike than unlike? We have here a special phase of the basic logical problem we have just hastily considered. Again, as a working solution we may suggest that among *homo sapiens,* and groups of *homo sapiens,* there are both identities and differences, and that our task is to try to describe both. For instance, it is probably safe to say that the digestive system in human beings is pretty much the same, that variations in its functioning, though great and due to complex causes, are rather individual than group differences. Or, to put it another way, though you might sort humanity into two groups, those with good digestions and those with bad digestions, individuals in each of the two groups would hardly have anything else in common. These would therefore hardly be real groups, groups of the kind historians and sociologists study.

On the other hand, human beings vary greatly in skin pigmentation. All human beings might, though the experimental data would be hard to obtain, be arranged in a kind of spectrum of color, each shading into the other, from very black to albino. Individual variation is of great importance. And yet the groups—the white men, the yellow men, the black men—are of even greater importance. These groups, or races, are not what the ignorant or prejudiced think they are, *but they are undeniably facts of life.* Perhaps an average Chinese, an average American, and an average African Negro are, if you add up all possible attributes and activities of *homo sapiens,* more like than unlike. But in color of skin they are clearly unlike, and on that unlikeness a good deal of great importance in human relations has been based.

When we come to differences and likenesses in men's minds, there is certainly at least as complex a set of problems as for differences of color. Individual differences here are very great, and clearly cut across group lines of nationality, class, color, and the like. If by "mind" we mean what the physiologist means by "brain," individual variation is obvious. If we mean the "group mind," there are real groups that share ideas, sentiments, and mental habits different from the ideas, sentiments, and mental habits of other groups. Certainly this is true if one judges the *products* of mental activity. Even in translation into English, a passage from Homer sounds different from a passage from the Hebrew Old Testament or the Egyptian *Book of the Dead*. A Greek statue does not look like an ancient Hindu statue. A Greek temple does not look like an American skyscraper.

Now when we say that the Greeks first used objective reason in a certain way, that the Greeks lived in an intellectual climate in many ways like ours and quite different from that of their neighbors in Egypt, in Palestine, and in Mesopotamia, we are making a rough generalization of the kind that must be made in such matters. A chemist possesses analytical methods that enable him to define, weigh, and measure with great exactness; he can tell you in what respects a given compound is like another, in what respects the two are unlike. No student of men can tell you whether men in general are more unlike than alike. Men are just too complicated compounds.

Of course, there were ancient Greeks who did not reason—we shall meet some of them. There were ancient Greeks who by temperament at least might have been at home in Palestine or India, or in the present USA. All we can safely assert is that the range of Greek mental activity was very great; and that within that range there seems to be a norm, a pattern, a most characteristic way of thinking, which we have called objective reasoning, and which marks both Greek formal thought (philosophy) and the wider general culture we think of as peculiarly Greek.

Greek Formal Thought

The Greeks were too impatient, too ambitious, perhaps merely too early in the history of Western thought, to content themselves with the slow, limited, and always tentative use of reason we call natural science. They wanted answers to the Big Questions that the scientist has not yet answered, and probably never will answer: How did the universe begin? What is human destiny on this earth? Is there an afterlife? Is sense evidence an illusion? Is change or permanence the more real? Yet even in science, there are Greeks who reasoned as rigorously and observed as carefully as the best modern scientists. We may well begin a brief survey of the range of Greek reasoning in the great age with two examples of this sort of scientific thinking.

First, there are writings attributed to Hippocrates, a fifth-century physician. Hippocrates or his pupils have left clinical descriptions of concrete individual illnesses which could stand today. Not only has he gone beyond the devil or medicine-man stage of thinking about disease, but he has also gone beyond the next stage, that of crude and ambitious general theories about disease—for example, always bleed a patient to relieve a fever, always give a physic. He simply gets his facts straight, so that he can identify the disease next time and not confuse it with diseases that show similar but not identical symptoms.

This is no simple task. Hippocrates knew he knew very little about disease, but that little he wished to know carefully and systematically. He held that nature tends to re-establish in the patient the equilibrium we call health. He was skeptical about medicines, especially medicines tied up with big theories about health and disease. Therefore, as a physician, his great axiom was "do no harm"; make the patient comfortable, and let nature get in its healing work. Some of his contemporaries thought he was rather heartless, more concerned with the study of disease than with its cure, but Hippocrates has come to be admired as the real founder of medical science. Even today, our physicians repeat the celebrated summary of the ethics of the profession, the "Hippocratic oath," though that oath is almost certainly from a later period.

Second, there is the historian Thucydides, who came as near writing history scientifically as anyone has ever done. Thucydides, like Hippocrates, from whom he may have learned, writes a kind of clinical report. He tries to show what actually went on during the great

Peloponnesian War between Athens and Sparta, when men's passions were roused to an almost pathological fury. He has no great theories of human history, and he does not hope to cure the evil of war. He is neither pro-Athenian nor pro-Spartan, though he had earlier held command in the Athenian army. He is not interested in anecdotes, scandal, or the romantic events of history. He does have notions of right and wrong—prejudices, if you like. He pretty clearly prefers order, quiet, and the decencies of social life to rebellion, intense competition, uncertainties, cruelties, and violence. But he is no preacher. He is observing and checking the records of a dramatic struggle among certain human beings, and preserving it so that those who follow him may be wiser in human ways.

The great field of learning the Greeks cleared for themselves in these early centuries was not, however, science, but philosophy. The word itself is Greek and means, literally, love of wisdom or love of knowledge. But even for later Greeks, it came to have a technical meaning close to the one it has for us: the attempt to answer the Big Questions we have just noted. The Greeks asked all the Big Questions, and answered them all. Men have made subtle variants on both questions and answers since the Greeks, but our contemporary philosophers are still going over the ground the Greeks disputed. Philosophy, if it is at all a cumulative knowledge, is not cumulative in the way physics is; philosophers are still disputing over everything save some of their methods of thinking, whereas physicists are agreed on the core of their discipline. Philosophers—save perhaps for the logical positivists of our own day—do not, of course, admit that their discipline lacks ways of testing the validity of its conclusions. Their criteria of determining truth, they maintain, are simply *different* from those of the scientist. Their discipline has improved, they maintain, just as logic and mathematics have improved.

Though the writings of most Greek philosophers up to about 400 B.C. exist only in fragments, odds and ends of quotations, and accounts in surviving textbooks, we know that the Greeks had ranged widely by the time of Aristotle and Plato. Here we need only sample from the range.

An early school, the Ionians, thought everything had developed from some simpler matter, the original stuff of the world, such as water or air. One of them, Anaximander, seems to have held that human beings evolved from fishes. This, of course, was a mere guess; the Ionian philosopher had not anticipated Darwin by long and careful biological studies. Indeed, those hostile to the Greek philosophic temperament would say he was a typical philosopher—a man with ideas but with no way of testing their validity.

Another Greek, Heraclitus, held that all things flow, that becoming is the only reality. This river you look at, he said, and give a single name to, is never for an instant the same river. Parmenides held almost the polar opposite of this Heraclitan doctrine of flux; for Parmenides, change is an illusion, reality one great whole, perfect and indivisible.

Democritus, a pretty extreme materialist, believed that everything, including man and man's mind or soul, is made up of tiny, invisible, and indivisible particles he called atoms. Again, note that this is a philosophical theory, not an anticipation of modern physics. Pythagoras, who was also a mathematician, his name forever attached to the theorem that the square on the hypotenuse of a right-angled triangle is equal to the sum of the squares on the other two sides, as a philosopher was definitely on the nonmaterialist, or spiritual, side. He believed in immaterial souls and in some form of metempsychosis, the transmigration of souls.

So fascinated were the Greeks with this newly exercised faculty of reason that they pursued it into the nooks and crannies of the purely logical puzzle. Most famous—and of course readily shown up as the mere brain teaser it is—was the problem of the tortoise and the hare, originally stated by Zeno of the Eleatic school. Agreed that Achilles, swiftest of men, runs ten times as fast as the tortoise. But give the tortoise a ten-foot start, and Achilles will never catch up with it. Why? Because while Achilles is going ten feet, the tortoise will have gone one foot; while Achilles goes the next foot, it will have gone a tenth of a foot—and so on forever. They will always be separated by a fraction of an inch.

Or there is the puzzle of the Liar, attributed to a certain Eubulides of Megara. Epimenides of Crete says "All Cretans are liars"; but Epimenides himself who says so is a Cretan, therefore he is a liar; therefore what he says is not so; therefore Cretans are not liars; therefore . . . and so on.

Even the puzzle makers, however, were doing something more than playing with a new tool. They had discovered that custom and common sense are sometimes misleading, that things are not always what they seem, that a reasonable or scientific explanation of phenomena sometimes contradicts sense impressions. Zeno (one hopes) knew that in this real world Achilles would be past the tortoise in a flash. But he also knew that common-sense notions of space, time, and motion were clearly not the last word in these matters. A modern physicist would say that Zeno's researches into the relations of time and space led up a blind alley. Nevertheless, they were explorations into unknown country, evidence of the restless, inquiring Greek mind.

Nor was this intellectual activity pursued in cloistered detachment. The Greek philosophers of these early centuries were certainly what we now call intellectuals, but they appear to have mixed more readily with their fellow citizens in the market place than have the intellectuals of the modern world. They by no means converted all their fellow citizens into philosophers. We shall see in the next chapter that many of their religious and ethical ideas left the man in the street far behind. The conflict between new ideas and old ways comes out clearly in the first of the philosophers we know much about, Socrates, a man whose name has stood for over two thousand years as a symbol of philosophic inquiry.

Socrates was an Athenian citizen, a stonecutter by trade, an incurable teacher and preacher by calling. We know him not by his own writings—he was a talker, not a writer—but chiefly by the writings of two of his pupils, the philosopher Plato and the historian Xenophon. His pupils loved him. The rest of Athens seems to have had mixed feelings toward him. He used to buttonhole his fellow citizens and draw them into philosophical discussion. He compared himself to a gadfly, whose purpose was to sting his fellows out of their self-satisfied acceptance of conventional ways, their lazy indifference to the evil in this world. For Socrates was a child of the new intellectual movement that questioned convention, appearance, the accepted things, and sought for something better. He was rather a moralist than a metaphysician, however, and he put his main challenge to the Babbitts of Athens on a moral basis.

The basic notions Socrates had of right and wrong were at bottom those of most of the great moral codes, among them the Golden Rule and the Beatitudes. He did not like lying, cheating, thieving, cruelty. The gods he and his countrymen had been brought up to believe in (the gods of what we today call "Greek mythology") lied, cheated, stole, and did worse. These actions were bad in a man. How could they be good in a god? Socrates thought there were better things inside himself, things told him by his conscience, than these stories he had learned in his youth. He would follow his conscience, not convention. He maintained that "knowledge is virtue," that if you *really* know the good, you cannot do evil. The old traditions, the old lazy ways, he maintained, were not knowledge but ignorance.

Socrates might buttonhole an Athenian citizen in the market place in Athens, and fall into conversation, asking innocently, "Do you not believe that Zeus leads the good life?" "Certainly," he replies. "Do you believe that Zeus has had children by mortal women?" He does indeed—he was brought up on tales of Zeus's love for Leda, Danaë, Europa and many, many others, and he knows all about their heroic progeny. "Do you believe then that Zeus committed adultery?" The harassed citizen does not quite like to put it this way, but Socrates can readily badger him into a "yes," for after all Zeus is duly married to the goddess Hera. "Do you believe that adultery is good?" He has the poor man. There is no way out of the Socratic conclusion: If Zeus commits adultery he is not good, and therefore not a god; or if Zeus is a god, he is good, and therefore does not commit adultery.

The foregoing account is, no doubt, a simplification of the famous Socratic method, but it does show what the Athenians were up against in Socrates. He disturbed them. He doubted the old gods, and seemed to conventional Athenians to have invented new ones of his

41

own. But they put up with him for a long time. When he was an old man, Athens was in the midst of the letdown that followed her defeat by Sparta. Through some political intrigues that we do not know in detail, Socrates was made a scapegoat and tried for what really seemed to his opponents atheism, treasonous freedom of speech, corrupting the youth. He was convicted, though by a close vote of the jury, and, refusing to compromise by accepting exile, chose to die. He was, of course, a martyr to the cause of freedom of speech, and therefore of democracy and progress. But before you condemn too wholeheartedly those who condemned him, ask yourself whether you like gadflies.

Later Greek philosophers developed all the implications of the first ones, refined them, formed "schools" that pretty well cover in detail the philosophical spectrum. But the broad lines are clear even in these early days of the fifth and fourth centuries B.C.

The American philosopher William James once made a famous rough-and-ready separation of philosophers into the "tender-minded" and the "tough-minded." Or, if you find the distinction clearer, you may divide them into other-worldly and this-worldly philosophers, understanding by "this world" the world of the senses and common sense (perhaps also science), and by "other world" everything *not* evident to the unaided senses and common sense.

Like most such simple, two-parted divisions, these divisions of the sheep and the goats are not really satisfactory for close work. But they provide a handy first approximation. The early Greeks produced in Plato as good a specimen of the tender-minded philosopher as you will find. They produced a number of less distinguished but quite adequate specimens of the tough-minded philosopher. And in perhaps their most famous philosopher, Aristotle, they produced a man who tried very hard to straddle, to be both tough- and tender-minded. We shall have to analyze briefly and untechnically the central position of all three of these philosophic types.

Once more the reader should be warned that many, perhaps most, professional philosophers question the validity of James's distinction between the tough- and the tender-minded. And indeed the changing terms in which some such polarity has been put—nominalist *vs.* realist, realist *vs.* idealist (the term "realist" changed sides between the thirteenth and the nineteenth centuries), empiricist *vs.* rationalist—have by their very alterations in time shown how philosophers have sought to transcend or get around the difficulty. But to the outsider the difficulty of making a distinction remained. Many of the judgments on professional philosophers made in this book are from the point of view of the professional philosopher hopelessly wrong-headed, as, for example, the judgments we are about to make on Plato and Aristotle. The reader who wishes to be fair should sample the philosophers himself. Plato's *Republic* and Aristotle's *Nicomachean Ethics* and *Politics* should give him a good start.

Plato's importance in philosophy can be judged by the late Alfred North Whitehead's remark that all Western philosophy since Plato is a series of footnotes to Plato's writings. The footnotes are by no means in agreement, even on what Plato meant. The problem is further confused by the fact that Plato wrote dialogues in which various speakers present their points of view, agree, disagree, and pursue the search for truth according to the method known since then as *dialectical*. Plato himself does not appear as a speaker, although it is usual to assume that, notably in the *Republic* and other dialogues of Plato's maturity, he talks through the mouth of Socrates. Even those who admit that Plato is no mere reporter, but an original thinker, vary greatly in their interpretations; some make him almost tough-minded; others make him wholly tender-minded.

For our purposes as intellectual historians, it will be sufficient to note that Plato's works are a rich mine in which men still quarry, and that over the ages his influence has been on the whole to push Western thought toward the other-worldly pole. We cannot attempt a detailed outline of Plato's metaphysics—that is, of his most abstract and general thought. But he is identified in metaphysics with a most important doctrine, one that will serve as an admirable sample of his thought—the doctrine of Ideas. The doctrine is perhaps Plato's attempt to get beyond the stark contrast between Heraclitus's doctrine of Change and Parmenides's doctrine of Permanence, an attempt by

Plato to *reconcile* the One and the Many, Being and Becoming. It is a difficult doctrine to summarize in untechnical language; but if you find the following exposition *wholly* incomprehensible, you have learned something of value—that you are not meant to study philosophy (a good many intelligent men and women are not so meant); and if you find it *wholly* repugnant, you have also learned something of value—that you are not tender-minded, not other-worldly.

Plato maintained that all objects we learn through sense experience to recognize and name are merely imperfect, this-worldly approximations of ideal, other-worldly objects ("ideas," "forms"). That is, all the particular horses we see are faulty copies of the ideal, heavenly horse. There can, of course, be but one perfect horse, timeless, changeless, and not to be seen or otherwise experienced, as are the imperfect horses on earth. *But there is a relation between the imperfect, or actual, horses and the perfect, or ideal, horse.* It is only because the actual dimly reflects, in its effort to resemble, the ideal that we can have anything like knowledge at all. Note we say "actual," not "real"; for to the idealist, *the ideal is the real*.

To some minds, this idealism is a profound insight into something more real than the easy reality of touching, seeing, and feeling, than even the somewhat more difficult reality of organized scientific thought. To other minds, it is nonsense—puzzling nonsense. Plato made a valiant effort to make his doctrine of ideas clear to ordinary intellectuals in one of the most famous passages in human writings, his metaphor of the prisoners in the cave in the *Republic*.

Imagine, says Plato, a group of prisoners chained immovably in a cave in such a position that their backs are toward the light that pours in through the mouth of the cave. They cannot see the source of light, nor the goings on in the outside world. All they see are the reflections on the wall in front of them. What do they really know about the sunlight and the world outside? Only its dim, imperfect reflections. What the prisoners, ordinary people like you and me, fondly think is the real world, the world we eat, drink, sleep, strive, love, and live in, is actually only a shadow world. Now if one of the prisoners should by chance be able to escape and see the true world of God's sunshine, and then come back and try to tell his fellow prisoners about it, he would have a very hard time making his fellow prisoners (whom he can't unchain) understand what he was talking about. He would, in fact, be like Plato trying to explain his doctrine of ideas to his fellow countrymen.

Now Plato himself was fully aware of a difficulty other-worldly philosophers have always had trouble with. He had to use *words,* put together in grammatical form as language, in order to try to communicate to his fellows this knowledge, this description, of true reality—for to him this other world was the only real world. But words are noises made in human throats, grammar an arrangement made in human central nervous systems. Both words and grammar are thoroughly stained with the sounds, sights, and smells of this world. It is impossible to use the word "horse" without such a stain. Even the inventor's "idea" of his contraption is to the tough-minded a *combination* of this-worldly, already concrete, bits of experience of given data.

Now "God" is the word that for most ordinary human beings can come nearest to escaping these stains of the senses; and yet the great modern monotheistic religions—Judaism, Christianity, Mohammedanism—have always had to struggle against the tendency of the faithful to imagine God as a bearded, benign, yet awful person. (The learned word for this tendency is *anthropomorphism.*) Moreover, though it seems pretty clear that Plato, at least at moments, went very far indeed toward complete denial of the reality of the sense world—or, in positive language, toward a complete, mystic, self-annihilation in the contemplation of the One, the Perfect, the Good—another whole side of his activity, and of his writings, is wholly immersed in the problems of this world of the senses. As a matter of fact, even in his metaphysics, Plato does not take consistently the position one might think from his famous allegory of the cave he should take— that is, the position that this imperfect world of the senses is simply an illusion, that it just doesn't exist.

We have, in fact, arrived at one of the Big Questions that has tortured—really tortured, in the case of sensitive men—the human mind. It may be put summarily in this way: We feel—some of us,

45

at any rate, *know*—that there is *one* immutable perfect being, a perfect God, wholly beyond the petty and imperfect beings who live and die. But how and why did that perfect God permit, or even create, imperfection? How make the leap from the One to the Many, from the Unchanging to the Changing, from Good to Evil? Or, why did God chain up those prisoners in the cave in the first place? One logical answer we have noted above: This imperfect world is unreal, does not exist. This is an answer rarely given in Western intellectual history. Generally the answer in the West has been a variant of a fundamental theme that may be stated as follows: The Perfect One could not attain the fullness, the plenitude, of perfection unless, paradoxically, this perfection could also cope with imperfection; or, this Perfect One could not really be perfect in a universe wholly static; hence out of perfection came imperfection, which must ever strive for perfection. There are grounds for holding that Plato justified himself metaphysically in some such way—certainly Platonists have so justified themselves.

But at this point we can turn from Plato the metaphysician to Plato the moralist and political thinker. However far toward complete denial of the reality of this world the interpretation of Plato's metaphysics can be pursued, he was certainly the kind of man who wants to have human beings in this world behave in certain ways. He was an idealist, not only in pure metaphysics, but in a sense more obvious to Americans, in the reforming, practical, worldly sense. Here too we shall have to treat summarily ideas of great complexity that have continued to occupy the minds of thinking men for twenty-five hundred years.

Just as interpreters vary in the degree of metaphysical otherworldliness they assign to Plato, so they vary in the degree to which they make him a moral and political authoritarian—or, to use a not too misleading contemporary word, a totalitarian. If you set up a spectrum from defense of maximum liberty of individuals to defense of maximum authority over individuals, you would have to put Plato on the side away from liberty. It is significant that libertarians like Thomas Jefferson and H. G. Wells disliked Plato's political writings extremely. It is hard to read his best-known and generally considered most characteristic work, the *Republic,* and not place him very far along the spectrum toward absolute authority.

Plato grew up a sensitive, intelligent young man of good family in an Athens that had just been badly beaten in a war against Sparta and her allies. It was the fashion among Athenian intellectuals to blame this defeat on the defects of Athenian democratic government and society. Moreover, Athens was in the midst of a series of crises, spiritual as well as material, as we shall see in the next chapter. Plato clearly revolted against his environment, which he found vulgar, harsh, insufferable. In contrast with the imperfect Athens he knew he describes in the *Republic* a perfect state, the best worldly embodiment of the idea of justice.

It is *not* a democratic state. Of its three classes, the great working masses have no voice in its running. They produce; they are the belly. A smaller group, that of warriors, is trained to the soldier's life, for Plato's Utopian world was not to be one of international peace. These warriors have courage; they are the heart. Finally a very small group of guardians, brought up from infancy for the task, guides the destiny of the state. They have virtue and intelligence; they are the head. They rule because they really are fit to rule, not just because they have persuaded the ignorant common people that they are fit to rule. They culminate in a philosopher-king, the fittest of all.

Plato's guardian class will be no conventional hereditary aristocracy. He is fully aware that such aristocracies have in the past tended to degenerate in many ways, and he makes in his Utopia various provisions for eugenic improvement of the stock of his guardians, as well as careful provisions for their training in all the virtues he thinks a ruling class needs. Plato was perhaps a democrat in the sense that Napoleon was a democrat, for he believed in the career open to talents —but always the kind of talents he approved.

For his guardians he proposes a kind of austerely aristocratic Communism, modeled in part on what some Athenian intellectuals held to be the life of the Spartan ruling classes in their best days.

47

For the guardians he would abolish the family, since the family was to him a nest of selfishness, a focus of loyalties that took a man away from the state, away from virtue. Women in the Republic are rather surprisingly, and in contrast with common Athenian notions, given a large degree of freedom, and in many ways are to be regarded as the equals of men. Plato is, in a sense, a feminist.

Children would be the children of the community, brought up by the community and trained to regard all the elders as their parents. They would be brought up with the Spartan physical discipline and the intellectual discipline of Plato's own definitely puritanical other-worldliness. They would, for instance, not be allowed to read Homer and the lyric poets, for such reading would soften them, give them misleading notions about the gods, generally corrupt them. Plato is a bit apologetic, almost wistful, about poetry. Poetry and art were to him at least a kind of effort to transcend the vulgar world of common sense he hated so; poets were on the road toward the ideal. But they had taken somewhere a wrong turning, and he had to part company with them. Certain kinds of music too.were forbidden the young guardians—soft, languorous music. Austere and martial music they might have.

The warriors too were a chosen group. They were taught many of the virtues of the guardians, with the important exception of the philosophic ones. As for the producers, the great majority, the belly-men, Plato is not really interested in them. They may marry and have conventional family lives; they may eat and drink, work and play, pretty much as they like, as long as they keep the state going and make no attempt to influence politics. They should in general behave themselves and know their place, but they cannot really lead the good life.

Plato, then, is no democrat. He trusts neither the intelligence nor the good will of the average man. He leaves him rather disdainfully a certain kind of animal freedom—the freedom of a well-domesticated animal. But note that even for his superior people Plato has no belief in freedom in the common-sense meaning of the word; in fact, the guardians are most rigorously disciplined. His warriors and guardians do not gain the virtues necessary to their responsibilities by experiment, by trial and error, or by full exposure to the amazing variety of this world. They are carefully kept by authority of their elders—and the philosopher-king Plato—from any exposure to alternative paths. They are strictly indoctrinated; they think only very high thoughts—which to the tough-minded is hardly to think at all.

It is not hard to account for the spell Plato's Utopia has always worked on men's minds. In the first place, he was a stylist, a poet; even in translation his writings have a charm rarely attained by philosophical works. His other-worldliness—his mysticism, if you prefer—has always made an appeal to sensitive natures. We shall see how readily much of Plato was built into the intellectual scaffolding of later Christianity. But Plato was no simple refugee from the world of the senses. As a moralist, a reformer, he wanted to push this poor world a lot further along the path of the ideal. Very much in our Western tradition, this seeker after perfection felt driven to lead an imperfect life teaching, urging, bullying his imperfect fellow men toward the perfection they could not reach. Plato had to return to the cave and enlighten the chained prisoners.

Perhaps, too, the cave was not without its attractions for him. Plato, like many a Christian after him, felt the fascinations of this world—not so much the crude satisfactions of food and drink and sex the vulgar think are the temptations of this world, but rather the subtle satisfactions of mind and body that make the world of the artist. Plato was too good a poet to leave this world entirely. Yet surely for the One, the Good, the Perfect, even poetry can hardly be more than another disturbance.

Plato is the earliest Greek philosopher of whom we possess entire works. Of the earlier ones, known usually as the pre-Socratic philosophers, we have only fragments, mostly citations by later scholars. These fragmentary materials have been lovingly worked over by generations of scholars, and we know at least that most varieties of philosophic thought are represented. But we have nothing complete on any early hard-boiled, this-worldly, tough-minded philosopher. Democritus, whom we have noted already as the "inventor" of the atom, was probably a thoroughgoing materialist and, like most materialists, a denier of human free will. But we really lack a consistent body of Democritus's doctrine.

Perhaps our best choice of early this-worldly philosophers would be the Sophists, who flourished in the fifth century B.C., at the climax of Greek (or rather, Athenian) culture. The Sophists were perhaps not true philosophers but free-lance teachers and lecturers who taught learners—for a price—how to use the new tool we have called "reasoning." They took up a position not unknown today, claiming that ultimate metaphysical problems, the kind Plato wrestled with, are incapable of solution and better left alone. Human intelligence, the Sophists maintained, should concentrate on problems of human nature and human relations; "man is the measure of all things." The world of the senses they accepted as perfectly real, and in this world they thought men's desires could be made an adequate guide.

Some of them came, at least according to their enemies, to the doctrine that the measure of an individual man is what he can get away with; in other words, that might makes right, that justice is the decision of the stronger. The new tool of critical, logical thought they considered an admirable instrument in the hands of intelligent and ambitious persons, and they set themselves up in the business of guiding such persons. Their pupils could argue their way to success over the conventionally moral and therefore limited common people. Aristophanes, who disliked the Sophists, shows them in the *Clouds* teaching a young man how to avoid paying his debts. The Sophists have probably had a bad press. They were worldly fellows for philosophers and, like most such, a bit naive in their worldliness. They were professors, trying hard not to be professorial, but not altogether succeeding.

Aristotle has survived in many volumes. He is not a polished writer; indeed many scholars have maintained that we do not have what he wrote, but only students' notes on his lectures. He is sometimes considered a polar opposite of Plato, under whom he studied as a young man. But though Aristotle noted and analyzed his differences from his master—notably in the matter of the aristocratic Communism of the *Republic,* and in the matter of women—Aristotle is not really the tough-minded philosopher as opposed to the tender-minded philosopher Plato. Indeed, Aristotle is perhaps better classed as an eclectic, a compromiser, a mediator between the extremists of this world and the other world. He was interested in everything, had, indeed, the kind of collector's instinct which, when it is applied to matters of the intellect, we call scholarship. His works cover encyclopedically all the field of knowledge of his day, from metaphysics through comparative political institutions to biology. Yet he was also the philosopher, the man who tries to bring everything into a system, to find in the universe moral purposes that can be ranked in objective value.

The central point of his doctrine is really an amended, rather more worldly, version of Plato's doctrine of Ideas. Aristotle puts this central metaphysical problem as that of form and matter. Matter is by nature not indeed lifeless, but purposeless, save for a kind of dumb persistence and striving. Form, which is really mind or spirit at work in this world, transforms matter into something that has life and purpose, that human beings can understand, that can strive after what Plato called the idea. Form is creative, active, purposive; matter just drifts, or just accumulates. One almost feels that Aristotle would like to say that form is a Good Thing, matter a Bad Thing. He does indeed say that the male is form, the female matter.

Clearly his "form" is close to Plato's "ideas," his "matter" to that world of sense impressions Plato so often seems to regard as almost unreal. Yet Aristotle never quite crusades against matter. He accepts it, is indeed as a scientist with a fondness for classifying, quite fascinated by its variety. It is true that as he goes to work on the clearer definition of the good life he gradually comes to a position not so far from Plato's—or Buddha's, or any good mystic's. This is the famous doctrine of *theoria,* the undisturbed meditation on God, who is the Unmoved Mover, the Final Cause. *Theoria* is undoubtedly a most other-worldly state of mind—and of body, for the sage still has a body even in this mystic ecstasy; the textbooks commonly compare it with the Buddhist *nirvana.* But Aristotle clearly thinks that only a very few wise men can approximate the stage of *theoria,* and the great bulk

51

of his writings on human relations urges a very Greek middle way in all things, including choice between demands of the flesh and demands of the spirit. As we shall shortly see, Aristotle's ethical recommendations for the average upper-class Greek are best summed up in the folk wisdom of "nothing in excess" and come to be pretty characteristic of the generally accepted ideas and perhaps even the practices of the time. They are Greek in much the same way that Benjamin Franklin's moral aphorisms are American.

Aristotle's notions of causation, fitting in neatly as they did with his notions about form and matter, have had a long philosophic life, for they are still alive in Catholic neo-Thomism. Aristotle finds in every effect four causes: material, efficient, formal, and final. The *material* cause is the stuff, the ingredients—let us say, the beef, vegetables, water, and seasoning for a stew. The *efficient* cause is the cook, the "agent." The *formal* cause is the *nature,* the *character,* the "form" in that typical Aristotelian-Platonic sense in which there may be said to be a type, an ideal of a stew. The *final* cause is the purpose of the stew—nutritive, aesthetically satisfying, stimulating to the appetite. These are undignified concrete illustrations, of which Aristotle might not have approved. And they suggest many difficulties: After all, is the cook the only "efficient" cause? How about the gardener who raised the vegetables? How can you ever stop a chain of cause and effect? And so on.

To these four ordinary causes, Aristotle adds what is in a sense a fifth—God, the First Cause, himself uncaused, who started the universe off on its puzzling career. This is the God we have already met as the object contemplated in *theoria.* As the necessary beginning of a chain of cause and effect for which otherwise no beginning can be found, this kind of God has had a long life. But he has never been a very warmly worshiped God.

In political thinking as in so much else, Aristotle is the compromiser, the man who tries to reconcile the extremes. Very characteristically, he wrote no *Republic* about an ideal state. He made very careful comparative studies of the actual working of governmental institutions in various Greek city-states, studies of the kind familiar to American students of political science and government. These, save for the "Constitution of Athens," have not survived, but generalizations based on them survive in Aristotle's *Politics,* still a carefully studied book.

Aristotle has contributed one of the most celebrated of phrases to political literature, the statement that "man is a political (or social) animal." Much of the *Politics* is an expansion of that statement, an effort at a sociology of politics that will also be an ethics. For Aristotle, as, one suspects again, for the conventional educated Athenian of the great tradition, such a phrase as Herbert Spencer's "the man vs. the state" would have been nonsense. Man, for Aristotle, is inseparably part of the group we call the state, and can lead the good life only within the state. But Aristotle is no totalitarian. Man is not for him a mere subject of an all-powerful state. In a healthy state, the citizen has what political theory traditionally calls rights. The state is not a unity, but a plurality, within which the moral struggle—which implies individual rights—goes on.

Aristotle is no egalitarian; he believes that slavery is natural, that some men are born to be slaves. He anticipates, in a sense, what later became the organic theory of the state—the notion that men are born to a place, to a status, and that the good state is one in which each man has the place for which he was designed by nature.

A good deal of the book is taken up with the classification and criticism of existing forms of government. Plato's *Republic* contains a classification of governments which Aristotle takes as a base for his own. For us the important fact is that from these classifications came much of the vocabulary of political theory, and indeed of just plain political discussion, still in use today. Aristotle distinguishes six types of government—three desirable types and a perversion of each. Each of the three good types has its own virtues; each can, under conditions suited to it, be a good government. Each can degenerate into a very bad kind of government.

The six types are: *monarchy,* the rule of one superior man, and its perversion *tyranny,* in which the one ruler, though not in fact superior in virtue, rules by reason of possessing force; *aristocracy,* the rule of the few, but the wiser, better few, and its perversion, *oligarchy,* again the rule of the few, but not the wise few, merely the powerful few, whose power may depend on wealth, on arms, or on ability to manipulate others; *polity* (or constitutional republic—there is no good translation), a state based on popular government and rough equality, but one in which the citizens are all pretty virtuous, and *democracy,* a perversion of polity, in which the many rule, the ordinary, undisciplined, unvirtuous many.

Aristotle studies the way in which one of these forms passes over into another. In other words, he does not content himself with static descriptions of given forms of government, but attempts a dynamics of government. Moreover, as we noted in pointing out how he admits the possibility of different forms of good government, Aristotle is interested in bringing out the relations between ideals and actual conditions. There is not one perfect form, but only forms better or worse adapted to the limitations set by conditions. Aristotle is thus in some degree what later came to be called a relativist. Much of this side of his thinking suits the tough-minded, the scientist, the man interested in knowing the earthly limits of human effort in politics.

Yet Aristotle is by no means hard-boiled in the modern manner; he is far from Machiavelli, for example. What he calls democracy he lists as a perversion of the quiet, law-abiding polity, in which men are apparently equal, but not too equal. And note that his distinctions between the good and the bad forms of government are that the former have "virtue," "goodness," the latter only "force," "riches," "numbers" and the like. Aristotle is surely no realist in the conventional modern sense of the word. Almost as strongly as Plato he feels that merely succeeding on this earth is not enough, not even in politics. Worldly success, unless it is moral success, success in accordance with the plan, or purpose, of the universe, is but the beginning of failure.

Like Plato, Aristotle has turned away from the harsh world of conflicting city-states, of class struggle, of chaotic ups and downs, to a better, neater, more stable world. It is not quite as rigorously unworldly a world as that of Plato's philosopher-king. Indeed, Aritotle was properly shocked at Plato's proposal to do away with the family and give women equal place with men. His ideal world is only a little removed from our—and his—real one. But that little interval between us and a better world seems to many a long way, and Aristotle never succeeds in telling us how to cross it.

Aristotle is obviously no materialist. His concept of purposiveness (*teleology*), of life here on earth as a striving after something better, as form striving to dominate matter, has been attractive to generations of thinkers and was readily adapted to Christian use. His vocabulary has never wholly fallen out of philosophy. To the founders of modern science in the sixteenth and seventeenth centuries, who led a revolt against his influence, he seemed to use a barren, deductive logic that left no place for fruitful experiment and induction. But he has never lacked disciples, and may long live on as the great mediator among the impatient seekers after the ideal—or the real.

The Classical Culture

One of the most difficult tasks of intellectual history is that of describing clearly the complex thing we call variously the culture of a given place and time, or the spirit of an age, or, to use a fashionable German term, a *Zeitgeist*. There *is* such a thing, a total impression made by a huge number of details that somehow fit together. In terms of simple recognition, one may illustrate this by, for instance, late eighteenth-century culture in the Western world, what most Americans mean when they speak of "colonial" styles. The costumes of both ladies and gentlemen, the architecture, as in restored Williamsburg, the furniture, the music of Mozart and Haydn, the paintings of Gainsborough and Copley, all this and a lot more could be nothing else in space-time but eighteenth-century Western culture.

Now the Greeks, and especially the Athenian Greeks of the fifth and fourth centuries before Christ, produced one of these cultures, one of these wholes of many parts, which has never ceased to fascinate educated men and women. We have already seen that in formal philosophic thought the Greeks laid foundations Western philosophers have built upon, but never gone beyond. But the great culture of the Greeks was much more than formal philosophy; it was, at least for a cultured minority, a way of life.

We judge this great culture by those of its monuments—architecture, sculpture, minor arts, and literature—that have survived over two thousand years of attrition by neglect, wars, decay, and disorder of all sorts. It is possible that this attrition has worked to preserve the best rather than the average, and that therefore what we have of the great culture of Greece is better than a true sample would be. It may be we have the best of Greek art, and not its worst or its average. Perhaps it is as if in 4000 A.D. archaeologists were to have recordings of some work of Bach, Mozart, and Brahms, but no trace of lighter music, no trace of jazz, no trace of a single crooner; they could hardly judge our modern Western music. At any rate, the question inevitably arises whether or not we can judge Athenian standards of life by the standards of what we have of Athenian art.

We shall attempt some answer to this question in the next chapter. Here it must be noted that in our Western society one perfectly clear strain of cultural history is the creation of great works of art, philosophy, and science by a very few men and women of genius who usually work and live in the midst of a relatively small cultured group. There is, in spite of partial interruption during the Dark Ages, a continuous chain of this kind of culture from the Greeks to ourselves. This we may frankly call the highbrow chain. It is not the sole chain linking us to the past, nor is it the only stuff of intellectual history. But it remains the central core of our subject.

But doubts concerning the representative character of what we know of the great Greek culture can be better focused than in the question of the relation between highbrow and lowbrow culture. The question can be put sharply: Haven't the humanists, the educators, the classicists of Europe and America since the Renaissance actually *idealized* the Athens of Pericles? Haven't they taken a few buildings, a few statues, a few poems, a few heroes, and put together a very genteel Shangri-la of the past? Perhaps our modern lovers of ancient Greece have exaggerated the virtues of their loved one, as lovers so often do. But you need not take their word for it. Photography and the printing press have made it possible for everyone to know something at almost firsthand of this Greece that has so long fascinated Western men. The following generalizations are no more than a few guideposts on your road to understanding the Greeks.

The first thing to note is that the great Greek culture of our classical tradition is very much of this earth. For these artists, dramatists, craftsmen, athletes, there seems at first sight no afterlife worth worrying about or hoping for. There is no heaven and no hell, probably nothing at all after death, at most a monotonous kind of purgatory, or limbo, not nearly as good or as bad, not nearly as enjoyable and exciting, as this earth. We shall see that for many, many Greeks, even at the time of Pericles, the problems of the life to come were very real indeed. But little of these feelings of ordinary men comes into the great culture. Antigone had, indeed, to see that the proper funeral rites were performed over the corpse of her brother. And she does say "I owe a longer allegiance to the dead than to the living: in that world I shall abide forever." Yet the whole emphasis of the play is on Antigone's plight in this world, *not on the plight of her brother's soul.*

In the great culture, then, this life is the thing. And in this life the satisfaction of natural human needs—which are, of course, natural human desires—is what we should all look forward to. From the Greek word for nature, *physis,* we get our word "physical," which is appropriate enough. Physical pleasures, physical appetites, were for the Greeks of the great culture perfectly natural, and naturally respectable. Eating, drinking, making love, sleeping, playing games, dancing, listening to music, making music, writing poetry, gossiping, philosophizing, all seemed worth doing to these Greeks, and worth doing well.

Worth doing well—a very important qualification. The Greeks recognized in all their activities the differences between good and bad, better and worse. They did not assume that these natural human needs could be satisfied easily, automatically, by letting each individual do always what came easiest to him. They did not believe in turning on the tap and letting their desires run on in a stream. On the contrary, they believed in disciplining, in training, in limiting their desires. Their folk wisdom (always a useful source for the intellectual historian) has the phrase "nothing in excess," which is a good start at understanding the major Greek principle of restraint. But the classic statement is in Aristotle's writings, and especially in his *Nicomachean Ethics.*

The right way to live, says Aristotle, is to attain the Golden Mean between too much and too little. You like your food—fine, nature meant you to like it. But if you eat too much you get fat, you look ridiculous, you are not virtuous. Suppose, however, you worry so much over the danger of gaining weight that you don't enjoy your food, or you get concerned about vitamins and iron and such dietary notions (of course, the Greeks knew nothing about vitamins), or you turn vegetarian on principle. In all these cases, the classic Greeks would say you were starving yourself, foolishly denying yourself a good thing, getting to look indecently thin, were guilty, in fact, of the evil of abstemiousness. (Note carefully that abstemiousness became, in some formal Christian ethics, not an evil but a virtue, and that gluttony became one of the more simple Christian sins.) In between gluttony and abstemiousness for the Greeks lay the virtue of good eating.

You can easily work out concrete examples of this Greek ethics for yourself. Thus abstention from sexual intercourse, celibacy, would be to the Greeks unnatural, excessive, and therefore not virtuous; promiscuity in sex life, obsessive indulgence in or preoccupation with sexual intercourse, would also be a bad thing, and therefore also not virtuous. The Golden Mean here, as with the other appetites, involves self-control, balance, decency. Or, as a final illustration, courage is clearly a virture, and a fine manly one. Cowardice—insufficiency of courage—is most obviously a vice. But so too is excess of courage, which we commonly call foolhardiness or rashness, and which is the attribute, not of the brave man, but of the show-off.

This last example can give us a clue to the way the classic Greeks felt about an eternal human problem—that of the relation of the individual to the society of which he is a part. The show-off is thinking always about himself and how he can hold the limelight. This excessive preoccupation with one's self the classic Greeks disapproved of. Indeed, they cast such discredit on the individual who tried to go his own way regardless of his fellow members of the citystate that their root word for *private* has come to be our word *idiot*.

The Athenian of the great age would hardly have understood and certainly would not have approved of what many Americans mean by the phrase "rugged individualism." On the other hand, the great Greek culture was almost literally based on competition among individuals. Their athletes competed in the Olympic games, and in many others; even their poets competed for the honor of having their tragedies officially performed, and were awarded specific prizes—first, second, third. The individual who did something worth doing in Greek eyes, and did it supremely well, was singled out and honored as an individual. And it is clear from what we know of Athenian life in the great age that personality, character, even perhaps a mild degree of eccentricity, were appreciated and encouraged.

So again we find the characteristic Greek attempt to attain a middle way between too little and too much. They wanted neither a society of conformists nor a society of nonconformists. They did not want men in society to behave like ants or bees, regularly, unthinkingly, like so many automata—though enemies of Sparta thought the Spartans came near so behaving. Nor did they want men in society to behave like cats, each for himself, each proudly out to have his own way, each ready always to pounce on his prey—though enemies of Athens thought the Athenians came near so behaving. They wanted men to be at once citizens and individuals, to conform to common laws and common customs, yet not to live by rote and habit, to be good team players and yet to stand out as stars. It goes without saying that they did not consistently attain in performance the ideal they set themselves.

They best attained it—or did so most obviously to us two thousand years after them—in what has survived of their art. Critics have for centuries tried to describe in words what the Greeks achieved as artists. They talk of measure, balance, restraint, harmony, repose, dignity. They use adjectives like calm, self-contained, orderly, disciplined. Yet most of them insist also that this is not a formal, lifeless, unemotional art, but a profound, moving, energetic art. In short, the critics hold that at least some few Greek geniuses achieved something like perfection in art—the true Golden Mean, not a mere average, not a mere compromise, but something that, like life itself, transcends "too little" and "too much."

You will have to judge for yourself by looking at concrete examples of this art, preferably in contrast with other, non-Greek, forms of art. The Greek has, of course, persisted ever since, and in our society has come to be known as classical. The critics have commonly contrasted with this Greek art the art of later, more northern peoples, which they call romantic. We shall have to come back to this dualism of classical-romantic when we reach modern times. Here it will be sufficient to note that, however abstract and unreal the schoolbooks make the contrast, the concrete works of art are very different indeed.

First, look at a Greek temple, perhaps at the Parthenon at Athens, both as it now stands ruined, and as it has been restored (in models) by archaeologists. Then look at a Gothic cathedral, best at a French one such as that of Chartres or that of Amiens. Then look at Rockefeller Center or the Empire State Building in New York, or at almost any very tall American building. Then think of the critics' phrases we have just listed. There is something in them. The Greek temple stops; the Gothic cathedral and the American skyscraper look as if they really ought to keep on going up. The Greek temple, in spite of its vertical pillars, seems to emphasize the horizontal; the Gothic and the American buildings certainly emphasize the vertical. One seems contented and earth-bound, the others aspiring and heaven-bound. One looks like a box, the others like a tree—or a forest.

There is, of course, no lack of rationalistic or naturalistic explanations of this difference—that is, explanations that try to find the cause of the difference ultimately in something outside the will (or ideals, ideas, plans, hopes) of human beings. Some maintain that the lines of the Greek temple were determined by the clear Mediterranean climate, those of the Gothic temple by the misty northern climate. There is the theory that Greek masons merely translated the lines of the simpler wooden buildings of the early Greeks into stone. There is the theory that the Gothic cathedral took to the air because in the closely confined walled medieval city there wasn't horizontal space for it. A variant theory explains the American skyscraper by the restricted space of Manhattan Island. There is the theory that the respective forms of worship (ritual, liturgy) of Olympian Greek religion and Western Christianity determined the shapes of the buildings that housed them. And there are many more theories.

Most of them make some sense, contribute something to our final understanding. But none of them explains everything, and some of them if taken as sole explanations are inconsistent with all the facts we know. Thus the area within a walled Greek city (the acropolis) was at least as restricted as that within a medieval city, yet the Greek temple did not soar. Granted that the Greek masons and architects were conventional and rather poor engineers, it still remains true that had they wanted the colossal or the aspiring, they had adequate *technical skills,* though perhaps not economic resources, to secure it in a simple form. The Egyptians before them had achieved the colossal, as in the pyramids, by the simple expedient of piling stone on stone.

We are, indeed, forced to the conclusion that the Greeks *wanted* what they built just as clearly as Americans *want* skycrapers, for we have built them on the limitless prairies as well as on tight Manhattan Island. The Greeks of the great culture did not want the colossal or the heaven-storming. However useful naturalistic and rationalistic theories are in explaining the beginnings of an art, we must remember, if we are to understand the whole development of the art, that the ideas human beings come to hold about what is beautiful, useful, and desirable help keep the art alive and growing. At a certain stage these ideas perpetuate, and even slightly modify, themselves. The Greeks of the age of Pericles built as they did in part because they thought and felt in certain ways, desired certain things.

Much the same experience can be felt with Greek sculpture. Look at the gods and goddesses on the pediment of the Parthenon,

61

and at the saints on the west front of Chartres Cathedral. Again the Athenians seem contented, well fed, well built, unworried; the medieval Christians seem a trifle gaunt, aspiring, overflowing with unearthly gentleness, or austerity, or saintliness. Here a later Greek work, beyond the great culture we are now trying to understand, can give us even more perspective. Look at the often reproduced statue of Laocoön and his sons overwhelmed by the snakes, a technically admirable work of the century after the great culture. There is nothing serene about this work, no Golden Mean. Laocoön and his sons suffer visibly, and perhaps in Aristotle's terms, indecently. This is an extreme—perhaps true to life, but not true to the ideals of the great culture.

Or take examples from literature, always remembering that the Greek inevitably loses something in translation. Here are two lines by Simonides written as an inscription for the funeral monument of the three hundred Spartan (Lacedemonian) soldiers who died at Thermopylae rather than surrender to the Persians (ever afterward, Thermopylae had for all Greeks—not just Spartans—the kind of meaning the Alamo has for Texans):

> Go, passer-by, and tell the Lacedemonians that we lie here, having obeyed their commands.

H. L. Seaver has put this into English verse:

> Stranger, report in Sparta, where they gave
> Command, that we obey, here in the grave.

And now turn your mind to another battle, and another commemorative poem:

> By the rude bridge that arched the flood,
> Their flag to April's breeze unfurled,
> Here once the embattled farmers stood
> And fired the shot heard round the world.

The first is as classical in its restraint, its spare understatement, as the second is romantic in the arresting overstatement of the final phrase. Make no mistake. The Greeks were as proud of Thermopylae as any

Yankee was of Concord Fight. The special quality of Simonides's verse is not humility; in its way, it boasts as much as does Emerson's. Nor should we say that Simonides is a good poet and Emerson a bad one, or the reverse, but merely that they are different poets in different cultures.

One final illustration, through the refraction of a critic in another tongue. The nineteenth-century English writer Matthew Arnold discerned a Greek or classical strain and a Celtic or romantic strain in English literary tradition, even in a single poet, and used an illustration from the work of Keats. When Keats writes

> What little town, by river or seashore
>   Or mountain-built with peaceful citadel,
> Is emptied of this folk, this pious morn?

he is, says Arnold, writing in the authentic Greek tradition. When, however, he writes of

> . . . magic casements, opening on the foam
>   Of perilous seas, in fairy lands forlorn

he is writing with the magic of Celtic romanticism.

You may, of course, like or dislike the qualities of classic Greek culture as they appear in its art. Iconoclastic critics have found derogatory terms to replace those we have so far, following tradition, used in this book. They have found Greek art and literature of the great culture overformal, shallow, limited, overintellectual, static, lifeless, lacking feeling for mystery and the many-sidedness of human existence—aristocratic in the bad, snobbish sense. Indeed, so great a lover of old Greece as Gilbert Murray has suggested that the fact that what has survived of Greek culture has survived only through transmission by the later Byzantines, Christians, Renaissance humanists, educators—in short, the overrespectable—may well mean that in fact we have an unrepresentative selection of Greek achievements. Perhaps there were in fifth-century Athens more extremists, more heaven-stormers, more hell-benders, more disheveled romantic figures than our canon has preserved. Yet the concrete reality is there still, in temples and statues as well as in poetry and prose. No one has yet been quite iconoclastic enough to suggest that the Parthenon and its sculptures were regarded by fifth-century Athenians as the work of an alien aristocracy. It is still fair to say that the tastes of these men who set the standards of the great culture were classical, not romantic.

You can see what the hostile romantic critics are getting at if you will recollect that statue of Aphrodite, goddess of love, found in the Aegean island of Melos and known to everybody by its Latin-Italian name as the Venus de Milo. This is probably the most familiar statue in the world. Its proportions, we are told, still are standard in Hollywood and Atlantic City, at least as ideals. Yet this Aphrodite could hardly move anyone to more than admiration. It is hard to think of her in relation to love. She seems pretty frigid, even for a goddess.

The figure of the Venus de Milo may in a sense be a kind of Aristotelian mean between extremes of too tall and too short, too fat and too thin; her classic measurements may even be a kind of arithmetical average of the measurements of all her millions of European sisters. But in the living flesh such figures are rare. The Venus de Milo is one of the things that even the most democratic of us have to call aristocratic. And the whole culture we have been discussing is clearly aristocratic.

It is aristocratic in an obvious, and to most modern Americans somewhat unpleasant sense, because its major apologists insist that only those who do not have to work for a living can really pursue its ideals, can really lead a good life. Here again Aristotle, who, though he came late in the great age of Greek culture, was in some senses most representative of his society, is the best witness. Aristotle thinks that not only sweaty manual labor, but also the vulgar calculations of business, prevent those who must work from living the good life. Such people cannot spare the time to acquire the intellectual and moral discipline necessary to the well-rounded man. They have to exaggerate something, do something in excess, and so their bodies are not harmoniously developed. Think of the bulging muscles of the blacksmith, the undeveloped muscles of the clerk or bookkeeper. Aristotle seems not to have been at all shocked by this state of affairs. On the contrary, he defends slavery as natural and therefore good. Some men are born to do the kind of work slaves have to do, and it is fitting that they should do it. Plato, with whom Aristotle is by no means always in agreement, felt quite as strongly that the good life—the best life— is open only to the few. In one of the famous parables of the *Republic,* he talks of three kinds of men, the golden men (guardians, the head), the silver men (warriors, the heart), and bronze or iron men (workers, the belly). Naturally the golden men are few and valuable, and deserve to be on top.

The culture of the great days of Greece was aristocratic because its standards are observably the kind many men find it impossible to live up to. To attain the Golden Mean in all things, to cultivate good taste in many fields, to lead a well-rounded, diversified life is not easy even for those who need not work for a living. But this culture was aristocratic for still another, and perhaps deeper, reason. The Greek of the great culture was prepared to accept the world in something like the way the scientist accepts it. He worked with the stuff his sense experience gave him, tried to organize it so that he would be sensuously satisfied, but made no attempt to transcend it, save in the sense that the Venus de Milo transcends this world of sense experience. He had no hope of personal immortality, no belief in a God morally interested in his fate, and, though he had clear notions of right and wrong, had no feelings quite equivalent to what we mean by a sense of sin. To put the thing very simply: He had to be happy over what he had in this world of sense experience; he could not compensate, sublimate his feelings, secure self-esteem vicariously; he could not gain strength and consolation by most of the means we associate with religion. The patriotism of the city-state he did indeed have, in the great age, to uplift himself; but, as we shall see, this resource was soon to fail him. Few men can make the spiritual effort (which may, of course, be a mistaken one) needed to accept this harsh world simply, as the Greek of the great age accepted it.

The Crisis of Greek Culture

I N THE FIRST YEAR of the great war between Athens and Sparta (431 B.C.) Pericles, the democratically chosen leader of Athens, delivered a speech at the memorial service for the Athenians who had died in the first year of the fighting. This funeral speech, as reported by the historian Thucydides, is an eloquent and confident appraisal of the greatness of Athens.

Our constitution is named a democracy, because it is in the hands not of the few but of the many. But our laws secure equal justice for all in their private disputes, and our public opinion welcomes and honours talent in every branch of achievement, not for any sectional reason but on grounds of excellence alone. . . . Yet ours is no work-a-day city only. No other provides so many recreations for the spirit—contests and sacrifices all the year round, and beauty in our public buildings to cheer the heart and delight the eye day by day. . . . We are lovers of beauty without extravagance, and lovers of wisdom without unmanliness. Wealth to us is not mere material for vainglory but an opportunity for achievement; and poverty we think it no disgrace to acknowledge but a real degradation to make no effort to overcome. . . . We secure our friends not by accepting favours but by doing them. And so we are naturally more firm in our attachments: for we are anxious, as creditors, to cement by kind offices our relation towards our friends. If they do not respond with the same warmness it is because they feel that their services will not be given spontaneously but only as the repayment of a debt. We are alone among mankind in doing men benefits, not on calculations of self-interest, but in the fearless confidence of freedom. In a word I claim that our city as a whole is an education to Greece, and that her members yield to none, man by man, for independence of spirit, many-sidedness of attainment, and complete self-reliance in limbs and brain.

Americans will detect familiar notes in this speech. It is a speech full of confidence and hope, sure that Athens has a mission to make the rest of the world as great a success as she has been, a speech delighting in the here and now, in the activities, the struggles, of a busy life, a good life. Yet an infant born when Pericles made this speech, had he lived to a very old but not impossible age, would have seen an Athens beaten in war, deprived of her independence, an Athens still physically prosperous enough, but the prey of constant class and factional struggles, an Athens no longer capable of producing great culture in any field, and hardly capable of sustaining it.

The problems focused around what may be called in no misleading metaphor the birth, life, and death of a culture are central to any study of intellectual history. Why did Athens cease to be the Athens of Pericles? The Athenians did not die out, nor did grass grow in the streets of Athens—not, at least, until a good many centuries later. A group, a society, as long as it holds together at all, is in a sense immortal. Biological decline, sheer physical decadence of a given stock, takes a relatively long time. Yet nothing is more certain than that over the five thousand years of recorded history of the Western world, all sorts of groups, all sorts of societies, have risen, flourished, and died. Only the most matter-of-fact historian can write straight narration, can wholly avoid conceiving the history of the groups he studies in terms of rise and fall, of the cycle of spring, summer, autumn, and winter, or the cycle of birth, youth, maturity, old age, and death.

Our grandfathers were reasonably sure that they had achieved a culture that would change only in the direction of improvement, that would never decline. To this familiar doctrine of progress we shall return in a later chapter. But two world wars have made many men, especially in countries like France and Germany, realize that in their own lifetimes their countries have in fact regressed, at least in certain respects measurable in statistics such as population and real wealth. The problem, then, of the decline of once-established, successful, prosperous groups of human beings—groups once in the mood of Pericles's famous speech—is a problem that should nowadays seem real, even to us Americans, in a way it could not to our grandparents.

The problem of the rise and fall of human societies has not been solved. It may well be too big a problem ever to be solved—solved in the sense of permitting human beings to take action to prevent the decline of their societies, solved in the sense that solving the problem of the causes of tuberculosis has enabled us to come within striking distance of stamping tuberculosis out. Yet the long tradition of our Western society, a tradition stemming in part from these very Athenians, a tradition the very existence of which shows that in one sense groups like the Athens of Pericles, cultures like the classical culture of Greece, never wholly die—this tradition would have us make the attempt to understand social processes in order to guide or control them.

We may at least hope, if the social sciences prove genuinely cumulative, to get partial answers to problems of the decline of specific societies, and these partial answers may in the long run add up to most useful knowledge. In the case of fifth- and fourth-century Greece, there are many elements, many variables in the complex equation (far beyond mathematics) of decline. Many of these elements are rather the concern of economic and political history than of intellectual history; but, since one of the tasks of intellectual history is to set and attempt to answer major problems of the course of human life on this earth, we shall attempt at the end of this chapter a brief summary of this crisis of the great Greek culture. For the present, we shall be concerned with the elements more narrowly intellectual. We shall attempt to see what went wrong with the way of life—surely an attractive way of life to many human beings—we have sketched in the last chapter. Perhaps, indeed, nothing went wrong. Greek culture may simply have developed into an old age we subjectively find less attractive than its youth. Such organic determinism, however, still goes against the grain of modern Western thought.

How Deep Did the Classical Culture Go?

It is possible that the great culture we associate with ancient Athens was no more than the culture of a privileged minority, and that the masses, even in Athens, were in fact excluded from the enjoyment of this culture. The question is worth investigating, though the answer to it will not necessarily in itself help to show why this culture declined. For there have been many human societies, and relatively long-lived ones, in which privileged upper classes held ideas of virtue and beauty shared hardly at all by the masses. Yet *some* such sharing would seem to be a condition of a really healthy society, certainly of a society that considers itself, in our sense of the word, a democracy. In the ante-bellum American South the split between the small group of the plantation aristocracy and the great masses of poor whites and slaves is a clear example of the kind of social separation inconsistent with our notions of democracy, and probably inconsistent with the way of life reflected in Pericles's funeral speech. Probably for Western man *a really great gap* between the culture of a ruling class and that of the ruled is already a sign of crisis, of threatening decline.

Yet it is very difficult to answer the question, How deep did the great culture go in fifth-century Athens? We can only assemble bits of evidence and attempt to weigh them.

The literary evidence is ambiguous. Plato with his metaphor of golden, silver, and iron and bronze men, Aristotle with his assertion that some men are born slaves, and many other writers give evidence that the intellectuals, at least, regarded as desirable a sharp separation between a privileged class capable of living up to the great culture and an inferior class of workers not capable of sharing in such a culture. On the other hand, there are no signs, save our independent knowledge that slavery did exist, that Pericles in his funeral speech was addressing himself to anything less than the whole population of Athens, no signs that he thought in terms of grade A citizens and grade B citizens. It is probable that writers like Plato and Aristotle were actually disappointed intellectuals, witnesses to the beginnings of the breakdown of the great culture, and that they both, in a sense, wrote as political escapists.

In fact, there is a sense in which the attacks on democracy made by these writers, and in a different way by men like the historian Xenophon, the comic dramatist Aristophanes, the admirable anonymous pamphleteer scholars call the "Old Oligarch," and others, are an indication that the culture of late fifth-century Athens had seeped pretty well down into the lives of ordinary men and women, that Athens was in some senses a practicing democracy. These writers could hardly have worked themselves up so warmly against a mere abstraction.

Unfortunately, we have for Athens nothing like the kind of information that enables us to measure in some fashion the depth of contemporary culture. We have no statistics on Athenian literacy, for instance, and indeed very little on formal education in Athens. There was no state-directed school system. There was, of course, no printing and nothing like our periodical and newspaper press. Books were hand-copied rolls of expensive materials, and there was no such thing as a public library. When later on in the third century B.C. large public libraries were founded, they were scholars' libraries, not mass-circulation libraries. Only the well-to-do could actually own books.

Yet even at the level of general education and literacy, there is good evidence that in Athens, at least, the kind of culture we have been studying was really widespread. We are today so completely under the domination of the written word that we find it hard to understand how a community can be intellectually cultured without extensive recourse to the written word. Our descendants, of course, may be equally dominated by television, or something of the sort, and wonder how book-ridden creatures like ourselves could have thought ourselves educated. At any rate, the literary culture of Athens was based on the spoken word, rather than the written; its market places, theaters, temples, and other public centers were in their best days filled with all sorts of men gossiping, trading, talking politics, weather, philosophy. Moreover, the arts of sculpture, painting, and architecture visible to all in public buildings, in religious rites, and in dramatic performances were a constant public education in the appreciation of beauty.

Again, we know that in Athens and in many other city-states with something like democratic forms of government, public affairs were the direct concern of all male citizens. Even the more oligarchic governments like Sparta were not absolutisms; their citizens were aware of sharing in something, had at least the right to approve or disapprove in assemblies of the decisions of their rulers. These little city-states—and even Athens was small by our standards—were perhaps more like the older New England towns than like anything else in our experience. Matters of common concern were always talked out in public. In the formal democracies, like Athens, ultimate decisions were made by vote of thousands of citizens assembled for public debate. In short, the Greeks had government by discussion; they had politics, of the sort we recognize as politics—indeed, the word *politics* is Greek in origin.

Now politics of this sort is a kind of education, a kind of culture, for those who take part in it. Tender-minded critics insisted then as they do today that the average man was swayed by oratory, moved by narrow selfish emotions, prone to undiscerning mob action, intolerant of real excellence and distinction—was, in short, the belly of Plato's *Republic,* unfortunately put where head and heart should be. No more vigorous attack on democracy in action has ever been made than in Aristophanes's *Knights,* where Demos (i.e. the people) is a comic figure, half villain, half fool. Yet Demos in his thousands apparently sat in the theater and laughed at this lampoon of himself, much as American businessmen bought, and read, Sinclair Lewis's *Babbitt.* At the very least, then, in Athens and many other Greek city-states in the fifth century, men of all sorts were aware of possible choices in politics, had to make up their minds, even though this process was not the rarified intellectual one the philosophers wanted. Perhaps really these Greeks had only that metropolitan smartness and alertness, that superficial up-to-the-minute concern with what is going on, that common sophistication we know in the London cockney, the Parisian *midinette,* the New Yorker. But we may grant the lover of Greece a small concession: It is possible, even probable, that the general level of thought and taste was higher in Periclean Athens than it has ever been in any comparable group in Western civilization.

Some scraps of evidence bear out those who hold a very high opinion of the average level of culture among the Athenians of the great age. The funeral speech of Pericles is the most famous indication from Athenian literature that its level was indeed high. Pericles was, however, a politician, and he may have been flattering his audience. We know that thousands of Athenians sat hour after hour in the theater listening to the plays of the great Greek dramatists. These plays, especially the tragedies, are at a very high intellectual level throughout. There are no letdowns, no concessions to the lowbrows or to the demands of "realism," such as the scene of the gravediggers in *Hamlet.* The music and dancing woven into these plays were almost certainly at an equally high level. Our opera—not Italian opera, not even Wagner, but the restrained, difficult opera of the eighteenth century—is probably the best modern parallel. The comparison is no doubt dangerous, but can you imagine almost the entire population of an American city (in suitable installments, of course) sitting through performances of Mozart's *Don Giovanni* or Gluck's *Orpheus?* Perhaps the Athenian masses went to these plays because of a lack of other amusements. They could at least understand something of what went on, since the subjects were part of their folklore. For the American people, the subjects of grand opera are not part of their folklore. The real parallel may be *Oklahoma!*

It can plausibly be maintained, of course, that these Athenian dramas were actually religious performances, part of the cult of the god Dionysus, and that the audience behaved well simply because, so to speak, they felt they were in church, indeed, that the masses went to the tragedies *because* it was the decent religious thing to do. They may not have understood the lofty words; they may even have been bored. Moreover, in comedy, where the conventions were different, there is much coarseness and obscenity. Aristophanes at times was certainly trying to catch the attention of human beings not precisely wrapped in high thought. But nothing in Aristophanes is inane, nothing is as bad as a Hollywood "B" picture, nothing as silly as the soap operas of our radio. And much of his work is quite as subtle and witty, much of it demands as much alertness of mind in his hearers, as do the plays of a modern dramatist like G. B. Shaw.

The reputation of the Greeks has no doubt suffered from the nineteenth-century reaction against the worship of things Greek, initiated in the West at the time of the Renaissance. Even today there are admirers of ancient Greece—and especially of fifth-century Athens —for whom all Athenians were capable of appreciating the best in human thought and aspiration. These are the classicists who insist that even slavery at Athens wasn't really slavery, and that the Greek word for slave, *doulos,* is best translated "fellow worker." It is natural for our realistic generation to wonder whether, even in the field of art and literature, there wasn't some Athenian equivalent of our sentimental music, our comic strips, our pulp magazines, our chromos, our gimcrack souvenirs, our main motor highways lined with ugly buildings. These equivalents have not survived, but time may well have been selective.

Between Plato's judgment of his fellow citizens and that of Pericles no final objective decision is possible today. Perhaps we can apply here too the Greek principle of the Golden Mean. Athenian culture at its best was in some senses the property of all Athenians; but not all Athenians lived up to its standards at all moments. Its widest spread was probably in aesthetic fields rather than in more purely intellectual ones; in political and moral life, the Athenian-in-the-street was far from the Golden Mean, far from the "civic virtues" of the New England town meeting. At bottom, romantics like Gilbert Murray are not wholly wrong; there is a zest, an indecent energy, an adventurousness in the real Athens not reflected in the textbook notions of the great culture. Or one may go on to actual debunking. Perhaps the Greeks of the classical culture set up the ideals of moderation, self-restraint, harmony *just because they were actually addicted to excesses of all kinds.* Perhaps the classical Greeks were quarrelsome extremists, fickle, unstable, untamed. Their cultural ideals may have been a kind of compensation for what they lacked.

There is no better summing up of the flavor of Athenian life than that of Thucydides, himself a moderate conservative, who has the Corinthians make a vivid contrast between the liveliness of Athenians and the sluggishness of Spartans:

> The Athenians are revolutionary, and their designs are character-ized by swiftness alike in conception and execution; you [Spartans] have a genius for keeping what you have got, accompanied by a total want of invention, and when forced to act you never go far enough. They are adventurous beyond their power, and daring beyond their judgement, and in danger they are sanguine; your way is to attempt less than your power justifies, to mistrust even what your judgement sanctions, and to think that there will be no end to your dangers. They are prompt, you procrastinate; they are never at home, you are never from it: they hope by leaving it to extend their acquisitions, you fear that any new enterprize will endanger what you possess. They are swift to follow up a success, and slow to recoil from a reverse. Their bodies they spend ungrudgingly in their country's cause; their intellect they jealously husband to be employed in her service. A scheme unexecuted is with them a positive loss, a successful enterprize a comparative failure. If they fail in some attempt, they compensate for the miscarriage by con-ceiving new hopes: unlike any other people, with them to hope is to have, so quick are they to put an idea into practice. So they toil on in trouble and danger all the days of their life, with little opportunity for enjoying, ever engaged in getting: their only idea of a holiday is to do what the occasion demands, and to them laborious occupation is less of a misfortune than inaction and rest. In a word, one might truly say that they were born into the world to take no rest themselves and to give none to others.

Greek Religion as a Measure of Culture

We have found no ready answer for the question, How far did the great culture penetrate Greek society? The modern American intellectual can hardly help projecting his feelings, assumptions, ques-tionings about American culture back into Greek culture. He believes firmly that Emerson and Whitman are really, in spite of the school marms, hardly more than names to most Americans, and he suspects that in ancient Athens, where there weren't even any schoolmarms, Socrates and Aeschylus were hardly more than names to most Athenians. Finally, we have found it very likely that such a view is a distortion, that in the relatively small Athens of the fifth century no such sharp distinction between highbrow and lowbrow actually existed.

Fortunately, intellectual history finds sources other than art and philosophy. One of the best of these is the history of religion. Even in this field it is not easy to find what the common man believed and how he behaved, but that he has held religious beliefs, that these beliefs have had some relation to his practices, is clear enough. There are no doubt extreme intellectuals who really hold that the French moralist La Bruyère's description of the French peasantry before the great Revolution, "animals which look like human beings," is an objective description of ordinary men and women, that such men and women are incapable of intellectual life. But such an extreme position, if it makes its occupier feel comfortably superior, does not conform to the facts of human behavior. The idea of God, one may hold, means much to a trained theologian that it cannot mean to the run of the inarticulate faithful. But to assert that the idea of God means *nothing* to the inarticulate faithful is nonsense.

There was in the great period of Greek culture an official, even in some senses an established, Greek religion. What makes it hard for us to describe, let alone understand, this official religion is that it had no theological dogmas, no real Bible, no professional priesthood, and no churches—at least, none of these elements in forms that our own Christian training makes familiar to us. This belief in the gods of Olympus meant no more in terms of dogma than belief that the gods, each with certain powers and attributes, existed, and that what these gods did could affect your life. There was no creed, no catechism, above all, no belief that these were the *only* gods in existence. Priests and priestesses did indeed carry out numerous rites in temples, but they were not, like the Jewish Levites or the Catholic clergy, a group wholly set apart from the rest of the people. They were in a sense part-time priests. There were temple buildings, of course, but in the sense that the word *church* has come to mean for us a body of the faithful existing within the wider society of the state, the Greek religion of the Olympian gods had no churches. The American notion of freedom of religion, of separation of church and state, would have been meaningless to a Greek. When he took part in the festival of the goddess Athena in Athens, for instance, and entered Athena's temple of the Parthenon, he was partly in the mood we call patriotic, partly in the mood we call religious. His *whole* state of mind we should find it very hard to enter into.

All this is not to say that the average Greek did not believe in his gods. Even by 400 B.C. a minority of intellectuals had come to disbelieve in these gods, and were seeking for a simpler, ethically higher belief in one god; another minority had become skeptics, agnostics, rationalists, had cast aside the old gods without feeling the need for new ones; and some Greeks had, either in addition to or in place of the official religion, come to practice more mystical faiths. But the great majority of Greeks of the great culture appear to have practiced the official religion. How warmly and how deeply they believed we cannot ever know; perhaps they did no more than go through the motions. But going through the motions means taking part in a formal religious ritual, and such taking part is a socially important act. In the next six or seven centuries to come, the official Greek religion was to die out as completely as a religion can. But we have no reason to believe that it was not an important part of Greek life at this period.

Even in a modern America that has broken more completely than any other great country the spell the great culture of Greece laid on our Renaissance forefathers, there remains something of classical mythology. We know that Zeus (in Latin, Jupiter) was father or chief of the gods, threw thunderbolts, and had love affairs with both goddesses and mortal women. Pandora's box, the Gorgon's head, the labors of Heracles (in Latin, Hercules) and other tales are vaguely in our minds. The sum total of these tales of gods and heroes, which makes up the substance of the Greek Olympian religion, is very great indeed and was never fixed and codified in any Bible.

Most educated Greeks may have learned about the gods chiefly from the poems of Homer, which many learned by heart in their youth. But there were many other sources, some of them deep in the past of the primitive Greeks, some perhaps carried over from those who inhabited Greece before the Greeks came down from the north or central Europe into the Mediterranean basin to conquer them. The developed polytheism of fifth- and fourth-century Greece represents a long history, one that anthropologists, sociologists, and historians of religion have long worked over. It is not for us here, however, to attempt to answer questions about the origin of religions, about belief in ghosts or in the existence of life (spirit) in winds, trees, waterfalls, in all of what modern men call nature. The Greeks by 400 B.C. had been through centuries of questioning, thinking, and believing, and had achieved a set of beliefs and practices, not neatly systematized, not universal even among Greeks, but still a definite attitude toward the Big Questions of human existence.

One final simple descriptive generalization: There were many local divinities, nymphs, heroes, even local gods or goddesses, or local quirks in the worship of more universal gods and goddesses. Athena was in a sense the peculiar local divinity of Athens, but as goddess of wisdom she had a wide acceptance through the Greek-speaking world. And in spite of this intense localism, in spite of the fact that new gods might spring up almost anywhere, there was something more like a federal Greek organization in religion than in any other human activity. Shrines to Zeus at Olympia, where the Olympian games were celebrated, and to Apollo at Delphi, were regarded as the spiritual property of all Greece.

Most commentators on things Greek are agreed on a few more definitely evaluative generalizations about the Olympian religion. First, the gods and goddesses are *human beings,* deathless, and in the good meaning of that abused word, glorified; they are incredibly more powerful than mortals; they are to the believer really transcendent, ineffable, creatures. They are, perhaps, what such characters of our comic strips as Superman are to a child—and not only to a child! But, otherwise, they are like human beings. The family of gods and goddesses eat, drink, quarrel, and make love, indulge in every pos-

77

sible desire, as humans would like to, forever. They cannot always have what they want, because the wishes of other gods and goddesses may go contrary to theirs. Not even Zeus is omnipotent; indeed, as one reads of Zeus's attempts to control his unruly family, one feels that Zeus is the most frustrated of gods. But he can always take it out on humans, for in relation to mere men and women he is omnipotent.

It follows, then, that human beings must do their best to win the approval, and avoid the dislike, of the gods. This was often a difficult task, if one accepted what Homer himself said. For his hero Odysseus pleased Athena very much but mortally offended her rival and uncle Poseidon, god of the sea. In the long run, Odysseus came through very well, for on the whole—and certainly in this instance—Athena rates higher than Poseidon. But you, a mere mortal, can never be any surer about which god will win than about which horse will win at the race track.

This uncertainty will, of course, not discourage most people from betting. And, in a sense, the Greeks did bet on their gods. The mortals put in ritual acts—sacrifices of animals, erection of votive tablets, and the like—and expected, or hoped, to get favors from the god in return. The usual descriptive phrase is that this aspect of Greek religion was determined by the Latin formula *do ut des, I give in order that you may give.* And the modern writer usually points out, and quite rightly, that the Greek worshiper in sacrificing a lamb to Poseidon that he might have a safe overseas voyage was not praying to a personal god, was not trying to atone for any sin he had committed or might commit, was not communing with a god of righteousness concerned with the inner as well as the outer life of his worshipers on earth. In short, the religion of the Olympian gods was not the religion of Christ, nor of Mohammed, nor of Buddha.

One of the great Greek religious institutions was the oracle. The greatest of the oracles was that of Apollo at Delphi. Almost every one at some time or other consulted an oracle, about a pressing family problem, a financial crisis, a dangerous journey about to be undertaken, or something of the sort. The reply of the god, speaking through the temple priests, was often pretty ambiguous, or "oracular," but it was also usually consoling, and it never urged unconventional or romantic action. No doubt these priests helped greatly to preserve the steady ways of Greek life. The range of attitude toward oracles was probably, at least by the time of Pericles, something like the range of attitudes toward miracles among modern Christians. There is ample evidence that many educated Greeks did not believe in them. Yet they were clearly a part of the official religion.

The oracles were, however, inconsistent with the new tool of the human mind we have called objective reasoning. The priests too often hedged; moreover, it seemed unreasonable for a busy god to concern himself with quite so many intimate, private affairs. The tender-minded modern admirer of the old Greeks is apt to be troubled by the appeal to oracles, as by the many other examples of crass superstition among these children of the light. In part, he consoles himself by noting the many advertisements of astrologers and fortune tellers in the quite respectable American press. He also notes, quite rightly, that the Greeks were far nearer than we to the primitive society from which they sprang, that inevitably there were even in their great culture survivals of the kind of practices our modern anthropologists associate with "primitive" people. And finally, he reflects that the Greeks were no narrow-minded rationalists, but a people fully aware of the depth and mystery of life, of all that part of human experience that does not yield neatly to the calculating mind. Oracles, vows, sacrifices, intimate dealings with not-so-noble gods and goddesses—all this is not too distantly related to the more spiritual struggles of the dramatists and philosophers in a universe that seemed hauntingly, perversely, not really made for men to be happy in.

The trouble is that the net impression of all this on the average American reader is likely to be that the Greeks really had no religion at all, or at least that they didn't have the kind of feelings we associate with religion. That impression is almost certainly wrong. The Greek did not feel about his gods as we feel, or think we ought to feel, about our God; but he clearly felt that they were real, that they had power over him and over the rest of the universe, and that he could by behaving in certain ways (*i.e.* by ritual acts) get that power used in ways beneficial to himself—and, of course, that by neglecting so to behave he ran the risk of that power being used in ways harmful to himself. This is by no means the highest flight man's religious imagination has taken. But it is a genuine religion, and while it was believed in it had its part in maintaining the social discipline, the sense of sharing something common, needed to keep any human society going. Its ritual prescriptions were numerous, complicated, and covered pretty well the whole range of human interests, at least at the conventional level of daily life. Just as the good Jew observed the Mosaic Law, the good Greek observed these rites.

Its inadequacies seem clear to us now, with centuries of experience behind us. It was not a very consoling religion. It was, perhaps, enough for the satisfied. It was enough for the successful. But for the losers, for the perpetual failures, it offered almost nothing—not even a very satisfactory explanation for their failure. It held out no hope of rewards in another life to make up for sufferings undergone in this one. If political and economic failure came upon the city-states, if more and more people found that on the whole the gods didn't give them the good things in life, the things the great culture valued so highly, then the ordinary mortal was bound to try to find elsewhere the satisfaction he had not found in the Olympians.

Not only was this official Olympian religion without a firm Heaven and a firm Hell; it did not in the present provide a kind of satisfaction hard to describe, but perhaps best put as shared religious ecstasy. One form of this ecstasy, sufficient to define it roughly for Americans, is the kind of behavior we associate with evangelical revivalism, with camp meetings, with the Holy Rollers. We need not here debate the question how far this ecstasy is refined, ennobled, in certain religions. The point is that, as far as we can judge, no such ecstasy emerged from the dignified civic services in honor of Athena or from the games in honor of Zeus. Excitement, yes, and a feeling not wholly unlike the feelings we should have on the Fourth of July; but no specific religious ecstasy, no frenzy.

Finally, this collection of tales about the gods began to many to seem scientifically absurd and morally shocking. Zeus, for instance, was supposed to have assumed the shape of a swan in order to make love to Leda, a mortal woman. From this union came the heroic warrior twins, Castor and Pollux. Now, as we should put it today, the biological processes involved in this story began to seem to some a bit unusual. But even if you could bring yourself to accept the story of Leda and the swan as a miracle, an event outside natural history, you might still feel, as Socrates and Plato felt, that seduction and adultery were not godlike actions. It is not possible to weigh at this date the relative influence of these two approaches, the scientific and the moral, in undermining the old Olympian religion. The average educated man was probably affected by both approaches. Yet in general this intellectual criticism had probably not seeped down very far into the population, even in Athens, by 400 B.C. Blasphemy—freely expressed doubts about the established religion—was one of the counts on which Socrates was condemned to die.

What one finds, then, at the end of the great age of Greece, is the conventional religion we have described, with much local variation, established as the belief of the mass of Greeks. One also finds, broadly speaking, two kinds of deviation from, or development of, this conventional religion: one, the philosophical, about which we know a great deal, and another, the emotional or mystical, about which we know much less, but which may well have been more important.

From very early times we find scattered references in Greek writings to group practices, or cults, within the very wide range of conventional religion, which seem to have certain emotional elements the conventional religion has not, or has to only a very slight degree. The subject is very complicated and has a large literature of research. Here we can only note that these "mysteries" are associated with Demeter, a goddess of growth, of life forces, or with Dionysus or Bacchus, god of intoxication, or with Orpheus, the supreme musician who charmed even the god of the underworld. How far these cults are based on foreign gods, on cultural importations from the Orient, how far they may be survivals of very primitive worship of earth forces, how far they are independent growths in a civilized Greece, are questions for scholarly debate. All seem to have elements absent from, or already refined out of, the Olympian religion.

Notably they promised a very real personal immortality to the initiate. Orphism, indeed, preached the doctrine of metempsychosis, or transmigration of souls. With this doctrine went something very close to the notion of original sin, the identification with sin of matter, the life of the senses, the life of this world. If the soul cannot get free from the body, according to Orphism, it is condemned to an eternal cycle of reincarnation, and therefore of suffering. But by initiation into the Orphic mysteries, the converted could escape this cycle, could free his soul for eternal life in bliss. Just what rites and practices were necessary for this achievement, and above all, what kind of continued discipline here on earth was necessary to make this salvation sure, we do not know. Hostile critics have said that Orphism was merely a kind of magic, without high moral notions, that the initiate secured salvation by repeating certain formulae, by purifying himself ritually, and by paying the priests. But this sort of anticlerical argument continually crops up in the history of religions.

Again in these cults there is the idea of a god who dies and is resurrected, thus proving to the faithful that death deceives, that personal immortality exists despite the appearance of death. The body dies, but the soul lives—if the soul has been properly made part of the god's soul. This identification of the soul of man with the immortal god is effected by initiation and maintained by ritual. Again, we do not know accurately the details of these ceremonies. At the height of religious ecstasy, some Bacchic worshipers may well have felt that they themselves were now Bacchus. The faithful ate ceremonial meals, and at these meals some of them may have felt that they were eating the flesh of their god, and thus quite simply and directly acquiring his immortal strength.

We said that the Olympian religion did not encourage, indeed did not permit, holy rolling. The mystery cults clearly did. Again, details are confused and contradictory, but it is certain that the initiates of these cults were able to work off a good deal of excitement and nervous tension by participating in their rites. The devotees of Bacchus danced their way to frenzy. Yet even the worship of Bacchus was no mere whipping-up of the lower depths of human nature. To take the word of the dramatist Euripides, who was almost certainly no initiate, and who may have had a rationalist's distrust of religious ecstasy, those who sought Bacchus were seeking the peace that all the higher religions seek. In a famous chorus of his play, *The Bacchae,* some maidens sing

> Will they ever come to me, ever again,
>   The long long dances,
> On through the dark till the dim stars wane?
> Shall I feel the dew on my throat, and the stream
> Of wind in my hair? Shall our white feet gleam
>   In the dim expanses?
> Oh, feet of a fawn to the greenwood fled,
>   Alone in the grass and the loveliness;
> Leap of the hunted, no more in dread,
>   Beyond the snares and the deadly press:
> Yet a voice still in the distance sounds,
> A voice and a fear and a haste of hounds;
> O wildly labouring, fiercely fleet,
>   Onward yet by river and glen . . .
> Is it joy or terror, ye storm-swift feet? . . .
>   To the dear lone lands untroubled of men,
> Where no voice sounds, and amid the shadowy green
> The little things of the woodland live unseen.
>
> What else is Wisdom? What of man's endeavour
>   Or God's high grace, so lovely and so great?
>   To stand from fear set free, to breathe and wait;
>   To hold a hand uplifted over Hate;
> And shall not Loveliness be loved for ever?

How common were these ecstatic religions? Did they perhaps really provide the religion of the man in the street? Was the Olympian religion, perhaps, like what we have called the great culture, really only part of the lives of a minority, an aristocracy, even at Athens? The answers to these questions are by no means certain. But it seems unlikely that at any time in the great age of Greece these mystery cults were in fact the religion of the majority of Greeks. We learn about Orphism, the cult of Dionysus, even the more conventional mysteries of Demeter at Eleusis near Athens, only by piecing together fragments, stray references, scraps of information here and there. True, these cults were secret cults, and the facts about their practices were not published at the time. True, these cults were outside the dignified traditions of the great culture, and the writers of that culture were usually hostile or indifferent to them. True, we have at best but scrappy records of Greek culture, and nothing remotely like a census of religious sects. Nevertheless, it looks as though the mystery cults were peripheral to the core of Greek life in the great age, that they were *not* the faith of the man in the street. They seem to have been, quantitatively and measured against the main stream of Greek culture, not the Baptists or the Methodists, let alone the Catholics, but rather the Holy Rollers, the Jehovah's Witnesses.

About the reaction of the philosophers and men of letters against the Olympian religion we are well-informed, for we have here whole treatises, not just scraps of information. In this book, we have already seen in the work of Socrates an example of how the philosophers sought to explain the universe more reasonably than the old tales did, and how they sought for better standards of conduct than the old tales afforded. Some of them stayed content with the reasonableness, the acceptance of this world, characterized by the ethical and aesthetic standards of the Golden Mean. Others, and notably Plato, were not so content; they wanted a much better world—or another world. Gradually the philosophers came to influence the mysteries, to equip them with a sophisticated theology—a theology destined to have a great influence on Christian theology, as for instance in the concept, already noted, of a God that dies and is reborn.

Most cultivated Athenians of the late fifth century had probably gone well beyond the conventional beliefs and practices of the Olympian faith, but not so far as Socrates or Plato. After all, the worship of Athena was a sharing in the hopeful, active Athens of its great days. These cultivated Athenians had been brought up on the tales of Homer. As they saw these and other tales translated into the

84

works of their dramatists, they must at least have been moved as the Elizabethans were moved by Shakespeare's historical plays. Moreover, as the dramatists treated them, even the most primitively ferocious of these tales, full of murder and atrocious revenge, became elevated discussions of man's fate. The tragedies of Aeschylus, Sophocles, and Euripides are lofty, poetic, and concrete discussions of the kind of questions that were agitating the philosophers: What is justice? What is virtue? Is the world we live in a just place? Is man free to choose between right and wrong? How can man tell right from wrong? The dramatists did not all give the same answers; even the three whose works we possess were of quite different temperaments.

Nevertheless, it is not unfair to say that these tragedies have in common an ethics far above the level reflected in the actual inheritance of Greek mythology, that they have an attitude of dignified and courageous acceptance of this harsh world which is not far from the more optimistic worldliness we have previously outlined in our study of the great culture. Attic tragedy is not rationalistic, not indifferent to the depths of human feelings, not unaware of many mysteries. But it certainly does not make the sharp distinction between this world of the senses and another world of divine reality such as Plato and the Christians made. This universe is to these cultivated Athenians by no means made for man's easy happiness. Men suffer often for their good deeds, not only for their sins. The gods, if there are gods, are not the innocent magnifications of men they seem in the old tales to be. The gods too are subject to fate, to necessity, to the mysterious and inevitable linkings that bind all men. Men carry their fate in their character, which they have not wholly made for themselves, for they bear the heavy weight of inheritance, a social as well as a physical inheritance. Yet men can face this fate, this necessity, with courage and dignity, and win from the struggle honor and even a kind of peace. The good life is not an easy life, not a cheap life, not always a successful life in the common meaning of success, and it must be led here on earth if it is to be led at all. But it is a possible life.

This austere acceptance of the world was not enough for Plato, nor for many other educated Greeks. Indeed, Plato drew in part from an organized group called the Pythagoreans, a body that forms a link between the more popular mystery cults and the work of the philosophers. The Pythagoreans were a kind of highbrow cultists. They were named from their leader and founder, the philosopher and mathematician Pythagoras, whose notions about right-angled triangles we have already encountered. They believed in transmigration of souls, and in a lot else of Orphic or Oriental origin, and they mixed their mathematics (which was good, advanced mathematics for the time) and their mystic faith and practice in a way perhaps analogous to the way certain modern astronomers mix their science with their mystical search for the Infinite God. Their basic feeling that science does not reveal a world mechanical, finished, automatic (that is, a world like that of the average nineteenth-century physicist), that it does reveal a mysterious world inviting to the adventure of thought, is quite consonant with the attitude of many of our contemporary scientists. They were clearly intellectually respectable, and Plato probably learned a lot from them.

Plato comes out in the end with moral standards which, if they do not wholly deny, repudiate, and attempt to lacerate the flesh, are at least extremely other-worldly. Appetite, even temperate appetite, is not for Plato a good thing. The many are hopelessly enmired in the mud of their senses, but the redeemed few may see the light, and live purely, live the life of the idea and the ideal. The flesh will perish, but the idea—the soul—is immortal. Plato may well have held at one time some form of the Pythagorean doctrine of transmigration of souls. But in the end he comes out as a singularly pure idealist, almost, indeed, a Christian and a puritan. His god is one, eternal, perfect, infinite, and real. The human soul can—nay, must—aspire to union with this godhead, but not by ritual, not by magic, not by any earthly transaction. The soul must purge itself of the material body by scorning the things the body wants. We do not know whether Plato himself was personally an ascetic; and in many of his dialogues—for instance, the *Philebus*—he comes near the conventional Greek notion of bodily pleasure. Nor, though in his more radical moments he equates body, matter, and evil, does he ever suggest liberating the soul by suicide. Salvation rests on a life as little physical, as much spiritual, as possible. This is a pedestrian, and to the follower of Plato misleading, formula for what Plato puts into very beautiful words; but it brings out how far Plato had gone, not merely from the man in the street, but from the conventions and ideals of the great culture. At the very least such ideas are a sign that many men no longer found this world the fresh, exciting, inviting place it must have been to Pericles, and to the artists and men of letters of the great age.

The Crisis of the Fourth Century

In the century from the beginning of the Peloponnesian War in 431 B.C. to the victory of the Macedonian King Philip over the Greek city-states in 338 B.C. the culture we have been studying was greatly altered. The city-state or *polis*, in which it had grown up much as our culture has grown up in the nation-state, ceased to be genuinely independent. Though all the Greek city-states preserved much local autonomy and many of the old forms, they fell under the ultimate control first of the Macedonians and then of the Romans, and were incorporated into a new kind of state we shall study in the next chapter. With the end of their independence something vanished from their culture; the Greeks after the fourth century never regained the freshness, the originality, the union of strength and grace, the range and variety, of what we have called the great culture. Indeed, historians have devised as a label for the culture of the last three centuries before the birth of Christ the term "Hellenistic," as distinguished from "Hellenic" or "Greek"; and this term has always had unfavorable connotations of pedantry, academicism, imitativeness, of technical skills without depth or inspiration.

We must here pause a moment again over one of the difficulties of intellectual history, a difficulty we have already encountered, that of the life and death, the flourishing and the weakening, of a culture. There is a sense in which our Western society has preserved a continuous existence. Occasionally a city, like the desert city of Palmyra, becomes a total ruin, without a single inhabitant. Athens itself sank by 1600 to a few scattered huts among the ruins on the Acropolis—though at present, in spite of war and civil disturbance, it contains more inhabitants than at the time of Pericles. Rome never sank nearly so low as Athens. And the living continuity of generations has obviously never been wholly interrupted. Moreover, no generation has ever lived without some civil disturbances, some quarreling, some economic uncertainty, some intellectual complaints.

Nevertheless, to be concrete, one may say that the early and middle fifth century B.C. in Greece was a high point—a time of great cultural achievements, a time of comparative stability and security, a happy time; and that the century after the outbreak of the Peloponnesian War was a decline, a time of troubles, a time of insecurity, a time when even the great cultural achievements bear the stamp of struggle, an unhappy time. Though such comparisons are never accurate, never more than suggestive, it may be that in the perspective of history the nineteenth century will seem a high point of security and culture, the twentieth century a time of troubles.

The Peloponnesian War, then, was a turning point. There were happy Greeks after that war, and unhappy ones before it; there were great writers and artists after that war. But something, the thing still best made real by the funeral speech of Pericles, had gone out of Greek life. The Greeks failed to meet successfully the crisis that confronted them in 431 B.C.

That crisis was a most complex one, by no means solely a spiritual or an intellectual crisis. It was, of course, felt by men as a living whole within their experience of life. When for purposes of analysis we break it up into political, economic, social, and intellectual elements, we are breaking up a whole in some senses as the chemist breaks water down into hydrogen and oxygen. Neither alone is water. Neither the Peloponnesian War, nor the grievous class struggles of the time, nor the breakdown of the *polis,* nor the decay of the old moral restraints, was alone the crisis of Greek culture.

The *political* crisis took most conspicuously a form startlingly similar to that of our day. The sovereign Greek city-states could not live in fact independent of one another like so many tiles in a mosaic or colored blobs on a map. Yet their constant interrelations always culminated in wars. These wars were getting more and more serious, more and more long-drawn-out, and were reaching a point where the victorious coalition was as badly exhausted as the losing one. Once, in the 490's and 480's, these Greek city-states had combined, with only a little backsliding and no more than normal bickering among allies, to beat the alien, Asiatic, great power of Persia. From the lift of this victory over Persia dates the culminating upswing of the culture we have studied. Athens, especially, grew in wealth and strength, and began building up the city-states of the Aegean area into a kind of Athenian system, at first a defensive league against the ever present danger of a Persian comeback, then something close to what we call a sphere of influence, and finally into an Athenian Empire. It was this threat to the old system of quite independent city-states, joined only into shifting alliances, that brought Sparta into war to preserve the independence of Greece.

The Greek city-states could not stop fighting one another, and yet this fighting was getting so serious that sooner or later an outside power, non-Greek, was bound to be tempted to come in and conquer the Greeks—all of them. The Athenian Empire was never a conscious effort to transcend the city-state system. It was absorption by conquest, which made little attempt to gain the active loyalty of the absorbed. In the Peloponnesian War, these city-states absorbed by Athens almost all took the opportunity of Spartan victories to desert Athens and reassert their "independence." Nor, after the defeat of Athens, were Sparta and Thebes any more successful in making the Greek world a united one.

Read "twentieth-century nation-state" for "fifth-century city-state" and you have a situation clearly in some respect like ours. It hardly seems likely that our sovereign nation-states can bear the physical and spiritual cost of fighting wars like the last two; and it hardly seems likely that, as long as they continue to be sovereign, they can avoid fighting such wars. The dilemma seems clear today to many of us.

It was perhaps not quite so clear to the old Greeks, but you have only to read the pacifist plays of Aristophanes (the amusing *Lysistrata* for instance) at the beginning of the troubles—or, at the end, the great debate between Demosthenes and his opponents over the intervention of Macedonia in Greek politics—to realize that the Greeks felt the nature of the crisis.

Much too late, in the third century, they did attempt to bring the city-states voluntarily into a real federal unit, as the thirteen American colonies were brought together in 1787-1789. But though the Achaean League and the Aetolian League were both interesting experiments in transcending the sovereign city-state, they were only partly successful, and they came much too late. By this time, the greatest of imperial states in our Western tradition, Rome, was ready to take the place of weakened Macedonia.

There was, then, not as much explicit planning for a supergovernment, not as much agitation and conscious attempt to transcend the political form that gave trouble, as there is today. The two great political theorists of this time of troubles, Plato and Aristotle, seem both rather blind to the inadequacies of the city-state. Both seem to assume that Greeks can go on indefinitely living in the city-state of the great culture or in an improved version of this city-state. In a sense, the Greeks entered the One World that was being prepared for them without much awareness of what they were doing. Meanwhile, in the hundred years of the troubles we are concerned with, one can safely say that the evil of continuous wars was one of the main factors in unsettling the minds of men.

The wars were in part wars for wealth as well as for power and prestige, wars to gain tribute from the beaten, to assure trade monopolies, perhaps—though in the absence of statistics one cannot be sure of this—to assure livelihood and living space to increasing populations pressing on living standards. Certainly fifth-century Athens, with its dependence on overseas trade to feed its crowded population, looks to be very much in a position where economic motives count heavily in war-making. We know that on the whole the Greek city-states had been growing richer and more populous for several centuries. This growth had led, especially in great trading cities like Athens and Corinth, to the growth of a monied trading class. It had uprooted peasants from the soil, thrown them into the uncertainties and excitements of urban life. It had culminated, notably in Athens, in a most varied society where rich, middle-class, and poor rubbed elbows, where even an enterprising slave might make money, a society built on class lines, but not rigidly so—a society in many ways like our own. In prosperous times, there was enough to go around, there was hope of something better, and this mixed society was not subject to too great strain. But as war piled on war, deficit on deficit, tension on tension, the class struggle was added to the war among the city-states. Rich against poor, aristocracy against democracy, Right against Left, became ultimately Athens against Sparta. For at the great crisis of the war the democratic or popular party in every town lined up with Athens, the oligarchic or aristocratic party with Sparta.

The result has been simply put by Thucydides, writing about the first great outbreak of class warfare within the frame of the Peloponnesian War, which took place at Corcyra on the west coast of Greece:

> So civil war broke out in the cities, and the later revolutionaries, with previous examples before their eyes, devised new ideas which went far beyond earlier ones, so elaborate were their enterprises, so novel their revenges. Words changed their ordinary meanings and were construed in new senses. Reckless daring passed for the courage of a loyal partisan, far-sighted hesitation was the excuse of a coward, moderation was the pretext of the unmanly, the power to see all sides of a question was complete inability to act. Impulsive rashness was held the mark of a man, caution in conspiracy was a specious excuse for avoiding action. A violent attitude was always to be trusted, its opponents were suspect. To succeed in a plot was shrewd, it was still more clever to divine one: but if you devised a policy that made such success or suspicion needless, you were breaking up your party and showing fear of your opponents.

To some minds, this generalized description may seem abstract and unreal. Then let Thucydides continue in a concrete narrative form more common among historians. Some Corcyraeans of the aristocratic party had fled to a mountain stronghold, and had come down under Athenian safe conduct. By a dishonorable trick to which their Athenian allies gave at least passive consent, the Corcyraean democrats got individuals out of custody, and massacred them. Thucydides goes on:

> As many as sixty men were taken out and killed in this way without the knowledge of their friends in the building, who fancied they were merely being moved from one prison to another. At last, however, someone opened their eyes to the truth, upon which they called upon the Athenians to kill them themselves, if they wished, and refused to leave the building, and said they would do all they could to prevent anyone coming in. The Corcyraeans, not liking to force a passage by the doors, got up on the top of the building, and breaking through the roof threw down the tiles and shot arrows at them, from which the prisoners sheltered themselves as well as they could. Most of them, meanwhile, killed themselves, cutting their own throats with the arrows shot by the enemy, or hanging themselves with the cords taken from some beds, that happened to be there, and with strips made from their clothing; adopting, in short, every possible means of self-destruction, and also falling victims to the missiles of their enemies on the roof. Night came on while these horrors were in progress, and most of it had passed before they ended. When it was day the Corcyraeans threw the dead in heaps upon wagons and carried them out of the city. All the women taken in the stronghold were sold as slaves. In this way the Corcyraeans of the mountain were destroyed by the commons; and so after terrible excesses the class war came to an end, at least as far as the period of this war is concerned, for of one party there was practically nothing left.

These political, economic, and social difficulties fused in the Greek mind to produce the crisis of the fourth century. Intellectually, that crisis appears as a revolt against the old beliefs, the old morality of the city-state, the ways of "the men who fought at Marathon." It appears in the work of men as different as Aristophanes, who would escape by going back to the good old days, and Plato, who would escape by going forward into Utopia. It appears in the soul searchings of Socrates and in the confident cynicism of the Sophists. Again, it has a very modern flavor. One can imagine that psychoanalysis would have been most popular during this Greek time of troubles.

The Corcyraean aristocrat who by a miracle escaped the annihilation Thucydides describes can hardly have found consolation for the loss of everything and everybody dear to him by reflecting on the good life according to the Golden Mean and "nothing in excess." He had just been through something very much in excess. And what happened at Corcyra was happening all over the Greek world. A determined few of the cultivated classes might still preserve the ethical and aesthetic standards of the great culture; but even these had to harden and codify their way of life into the self-conscious and pessimistic discipline of Stoicism.

Or take an ordinary middle-class Athenian lad, not too bright in verbal matters. Expose him to the subtleties of Socrates, to the lively exchange of ideas we know went on in the Athens of the time. He is almost certain to come to the conclusion that the old tales of the gods he learned in childhood are not true, but he is unlikely to have followed Socrates or Plato on through to a high ethical monotheism. He is much more likely to end in confusion and doubt, or in the sort of cheap cynicism not unknown to our own generation. In any case, he is no fit man to carry on the tasks of Athenian government and culture.

Multiply these cases, and add many more, refugees, disabled veterans, those who have lost property and business, the defeated and the victors alike, and you have the human material in which the intellectual discontents of the time did their work. Here again, we must avoid exaggeration. Many a Greek of the time of troubles kept his faith in the gods, in the *polis,* in the way of life he had learned from Homer, from his parents, from the men he mixed with in market place and council hall and army. Ways of life, beliefs, habits, die hard on this earth. But the new troubles had upset the balance between old and new; the disasters had taken the heart out of the old ways. The more enterprising and intelligent, especially, felt driven to repudiate the old, as so many Frenchmen after the debacle of 1940 felt driven to repudiate the Third Republic.

For the more educated, the trouble may be put a bit abstractly as the relative dissolution of the ties that bound them together in the *polis,* the relative widening of the areas in which they had to act on their own. This is the commonplace that the regularities of Greek life broke down under increasing individualism. Left to themselves, the individuals pursued varied but mostly worldly goals—wealth, pleasure, power, all in the tense competitive spirit always characteristic of the Greeks. For the successful few, this harrowing competition might be tolerable, even welcome; to the unsuccessful, it left life an almost intolerable thing to bear.

Nor were the masses exempt from this crisis. They bore the brunt of the disasters of the time of troubles. And yet, as we have seen, the conventional religion of the city-state gave them little consolation for the evils of this life, gave them very little hope of another life. It seems unlikely that they were faced with the complexities of the intellectual problems that faced the upper classes, but the very prevalence of class warfare shows clearly that they had lost confidence in the ruling classes.

Let us sum the matter up briefly, and in concrete terms for a single city. Athena, the goddess of Athens, was for the Athenians what church *and* state are for us. Athena was Washington, Lincoln, and the divine power that controls our lives, all bound together. Yet by 400 B.C. Athena had failed in both roles. She had not preserved her city from defeat, not kept Athens the serene city of light. Surely now in her defeat the words of Pericles must have been almost unbearable:

> No other city of the present day goes out to her ordeal greater than ever men dreamed; no other is so powerful that the invader feels no bitterness when he suffers at her hands, and her subjects no shame at the indignity of their dependence.

No, Athena had not been enough. Temperance, moderation, serenity, the discerning cultivation and satisfaction of the natural appetites, "nothing in excess," all the catalogue of Apollonian virtues had not been enough, had not even been possible these last few years. Men must look elsewhere for guidance—ultimately, very far afield, to a little-known part of what was always to the Greek the barbaric orient—to the land we now again call Israel.

4

One World

THE LATER CLASSICAL CULTURE

*T*HE FOURTH CENTURY B.C., the century of Plato and Aristotle, was the last century of the truly independent Greek city-state, on which was built the culture we have just studied. In the next three centuries roughly, there grew up in the Mediterranean world much bigger political units. These units were the "successor states" to the ephemeral empire of Alexander the Great, namely, Macedon, Egypt, Syria, and lesser states in Asia Minor; and in the West, Rome and Carthage. These "superpowers" fought among themselves until, by 100 B.C., Rome had beaten and absorbed all the others. Then, for some three centuries, Greek culture worked itself out in a society politically under Roman control. The warring world of tribes and city-states had become the One World of later Graeco-Roman culture. And it was, to an extraordinary degree, one world, a world in which good roads and organized seaways permitted men—and ideas—to circulate freely, a world in which the educated classes, at least, whatever their local origins, British, Gallic, Spanish, Italian, African, Greek, Egyptian, shared a genuinely cosmopolitan culture, a world freed for a while from wars among its constituent units, and, on the whole, peacefully administered by administrators trained in Roman Law.

In these centuries there grew up great urban centers, Rome itself, Antioch, Alexandria, and in these centers were libraries and universities that brought scholarship, and even some of the sciences, to a very high point. The scholarship, save as, by multiplying texts, it made the survival of the great work of the great culture more likely, is of little meaning to most of us now. The science, and especially the mathematics, the astronomy, and the physics, formed the basis of what we know today, and was transmitted in large part to us through the medieval schoolmen and the Arabs.

Still more important, these half-dozen centuries saw the working out, in the wider frame of the new world of Macedon and Rome, of many of the ideas, many of the attitudes toward life, that had grown up in the *polis* of the great age. Ideas consciously developed from the ethics and metaphysics of the original thinkers of Greece were spread abroad, perhaps not among the masses of the people, but at least among educated minorities of half-a-hundred tribes and races. Greek ideas lost their sharpness, their original flavor, and were softened and blended, made suitable to the use of a cosmopolitan elite. This process still seems to the pure lover of the great culture of Greece a cheapening, a vulgarizing, of the original. But it is an important process for us, since by it Greek ideas came to exercise whatever influence they did exercise—and the degree of that influence is still debatable and debated—on Christianity.

Most important of all, then, in these centuries was the growth of Christianity which, together with Roman Law, *as a living institution* alone survives of this One World of Graeco-Roman culture. Philosophers of history may seek in the thousand years of the life of Graeco-Roman culture some clues to the life span of all cultures, or may try to find out by analogy with that culture whether we ourselves are now in the twilight or in the noon of our day. Historians of law and institutions, of language and literature, may seek a thousand direct links between us and our Graeco-Roman predecessors. Or those who revel in the richness of detail with which we can reconstruct this age of urbanity and complexity may rejoice in the Graeco-Roman world for its own sake. But for those who must have a clear and certain link with the past, the overwhelmingly central fact of these centuries is that they were the seedbed of Christianity.

In this chapter we shall examine successively the Jewish, the later

Greek (or Hellenistic), and the Roman contributions to our intellectual heritage.

The Jewish Element

The seed itself of Christianity came from without the Graeco-Roman world. Jesus Christ was a Jew. He himself was, indeed, born at a time when the Jewish homeland, ruled by the Hellenized Herod, was articulated as a semi-independent unit in the vast complex of nations called the Roman Empire. And it is true that by the time of Jesus's birth there were many Jews who spoke Greek, and even Latin, who were fully citizens of that cosmopolitan world of conflicting ideas, religious cults, and emotions. Nevertheless, the background of early Christianity is overwhelmingly Jewish, stamped with the unique experience of the Jews, an experience (the paradox is unavoidable) at once more parochial and more universal than that of any great Greek city-state.

Right here we encounter a difficulty we shall encounter in an even more acute form in the study of Christianity itself. The historian must ask himself why the Jews, alone among all the tribes and peoples of the eastern Mediterranean who shared similar geographical and other material environments, and not greatly dissimilar early histories, should have produced the religion that is still, two thousand years later, the formal religion of our Western world. Perhaps he should answer, as the fundamentalist Christian must tell him to answer, that God chose the Jews, that all went according to divine plan. This answer is a clear and irrefutable answer, and one that greatly simplifies the task of the historian. It is not one that will be given here.

Now short of acceptance of the full divine inspiration of the Bible, both Old Testament and New, there are many, many possible positions, indeed a whole spectrum from complete acceptance to dogmatic denial that the Bible is anything more than a set of historical documents to be treated like any other similar documents, say Homer's *Iliad* and *Odyssey,* the *Nibelungenlied,* the *Koran.* Anti-Christians like Nietzsche, whom we shall meet toward the end of this book, sometimes lean over very far backward, and announce that what is written in the Bible is especially likely to be false.

We shall attempt in this book to take no dogmatic position, certainly not a dogmatically anti-Christian position. We shall, however, assume here that the ideas and practices of Judaism and of Christianity are, for purposes of historical analysis, products of human culture in historic time. It is, however, perfectly possible to regard the truths of Christianity, like the truths of Platonism, as transcending history, as not, and certainly not finally, explicable in terms of historical process. Perhaps no one can be a skeptic in time and a believer in eternity. At any rate, we shall attempt in this book to maintain an inoffensive skepticism, and even a certain amount of humility.

Now the Jews, seen in this light, were a small desert tribe closely related to the peoples later known as Arabs or Bedouins and originating probably in Arabia. After various wanderings they settled down, probably sometime between 1700 and 1500 B.C., in the hilly area just west of the Jordan valley. The whole area between the Nile valley and the Tigris-Euphrates valley, between the great powers—Egypt in one valley and Babylonia, or Assyria, or Persia in the other—was in ancient times a zone of fragmentation, inhabited by various tribes at war among themselves, and periodically subject to invasion and "pacification" by one or another of their powerful neighbors to the east or west. On the surface of politics, at least, the Jews seem to have had a history much like that of their smaller neighbors. After a brief period as a united people, when under David and Solomon the Jews were the dominant people of the region, Israel split into two kingdoms, Israel in the north and Judah in the south. There were rivalries between the kingdoms and among the Jews and their neighbors. There were alliances, intrigues, expeditions, battles, all the complexities of history as they are related in the Books of Kings and Chronicles. Meanwhile, there was growing up in the east a great and ambitious power, Assyria, which made an end to Israel in the eighth century B.C. Judah, with its sacred capital at Jerusalem, struggled on until 586 B.C., when it was captured by another great eastern power, Babylonia. Some ten thousand Jews, including most of the educated elite, were taken as captives to Babylon, probably as part of a definite Babylonian policy of dispersing recalcitrant nationalist groups. Though these displaced Jews came finally back to Jerusalem, though the Jews again enjoyed some kind of political status (they were never really independent), their great scattering had in fact begun. The Jewish homeland was part of the great Achaemenid Persian Empire in the sixth and fifth centuries B.C., and after the conquests of Alexander the Great came under the influence of Greek culture. At the time of Christ, there was a Jewish state under the Hellenized King Herod, a sort of native kingdom under the complex Roman Empire; but there were also thousands of Jews scattered about, usually in specifically Jewish quarters, in Antioch, in Alexandria, in Corinth, indeed all over the eastern part of the Empire. Already, save in Palestine itself, the Jews were predominantly urban merchants, traders, moneylenders, intellectuals, cut off from the land.

It is clear, even from this bare sketch, that something differentiates the Jews from the Philistines, the Amalekites, the Moabites, the Amorites, and all the other neighboring peoples whose names are scattered through the Old Testament. At its simplest, this something is the will to persist, to be themselves, to be a people. Now, once more, two thousand years after the Romans destroyed the Jewish client-state, the land of Israel has appeared on the political map of the world.

There is no consensus of agreement on why the Jews have had this unique history. The religious Jew can, of course, assert simply that God created and preserved the Jews and will yet carry out his promise of the Messiah. But the outsider attempting a naturalistic or positivistic explanation has no such easy solution at hand. It has been held that the Jews really are a race, really have certain inherited bodily and mental traits that have determined their history. Such naive beliefs in race and racial inheritance are not, however, today accepted by any serious students of human relations. Yet the currently fashionable explanation of human relations in terms of economic and geographic environment, the materialist interpretation of history, is here quite obviously inadequate. For the material conditions under which

Amalekites, Moabites, Amorites, and the forgotten rest grew up were probably identical with those that helped mold the Jews.

Part of the explanation of Jewish uniqueness must be sought in intellectual history. The Jews, first among the peoples of our Western world, came to believe ardently, fanatically, in a single God, all-powerful, jealous, and fiercely determined to protect his people, *as long as they proved by their acts that they were his people.* As we shall see, the greater Jewish writers of antiquity put a lot more, and a lot nobler, ideas than this into their god, but there was always at least this much: Jehovah, god of battles, a jealous god, a god that would have no truck with Zeus, or Dionysus, or Baal, or, worse yet, *female* deities like Aphrodite or Astarte. The Jews held together, through all their tribulations, because they had Jehovah.

You may, of course, fairly ask how the Jews came to hold these views of their god. Granted that what differentiates them from their neighbors is, to use a familiar abstract term, their ultimate achievement of a lofty ethical monotheism, why did they alone among their neighbors achieve this belief? As is so often the case, the historian cannot answer, not at least in any simple, quantitative terms. These beliefs were hammered out of Jewish history, notably in the years between 1500 B.C. and 600 B.C. They may depend in part on the existence of certain great men, such as Moses, shadowy and legendary to the mere historian. They may depend on some genes, some inherited toughness, among the sons of Abraham. They depend, in part certainly, on the earlier priestly caste that preserved the early records of Jewish nationalism, since their highest ethical form depends on those later priestly characters known as prophets. They depend in part on the pressures exerted on the gifted minority that was exiled to Babylon in 586 B.C., pressures that made this minority conscious of their mission to restore their "in-group" to what they felt was its rightful place, pressures that drove them to idealizing that place by making their Jehovah a better God, a more moral God. Like the political achievements of the Romans and the artistic achievements of the Athenians, the religious achievements of the Jews were the product of a long history that we cannot wholly understand or wholly restore.

We have for the Jews a remarkable record, known to us as the Old Testament. These writings, from the point of view of a modern lay historian, were put together at various times and by various people. Some are epic writings, the Jewish equivalents of Homer; some are priestly rules, meant for direct use in the Temple; others are poems, aphorisms, patriotic ethical studies. By the time of Christ, most of this material had been put together, more or less as officially approved, and had come to serve the Jews as a sacred collection, as what we all know as a *Bible*. For the faithful, the Bible became the word of God, dictated by God to his scribes, and not by any means a mere book.

Incorporated with the New Testament into the Christian Bible, this collection of Jewish national literature remained for centuries the word of God, and hence not subject to any critical study, subject only to interpretation, or exegesis. Then slowly after the Renaissance and Reformation, and rapidly during the eighteenth century, men began to study these texts critically, as they had studied the texts of Homer and Vergil, Thucydides and Herodotus. They produced by the nineteenth century that triumph of scholarship, the so-called "higher criticism," which so troubled the conscience of our great-grandparents. The higher criticism has not produced complete agreement. At the highest level, the Old Testament deals with those most important problems of human destiny we simply do not have agreement on.

Moreover, modern criticism, based on archaeological work, has come to question some of the factual material of the higher criticism of the last century. Yet as an illustration of the concrete achievements of a method, the labors of several generations of scholars in this field are a remarkable monument to the possibilities of achieving some kind of cumulative knowledge in a most difficult field. Only the fundamentalist now refuses to accept *in its broad lines* the result of this scholarship.

Thus it is clear to the historian that the Old Testament was put together from varied sources at various periods. Scholars are by no means in agreement over details; they still dispute over just what person or group wrote specific passages. For a concrete example of what the higher criticism has done, we may take the Pentateuch, the first five books of the Old Testament, traditionally attributed to Moses. Here the scholars discern at least three sources. One, called J, from the fact that God is referred to as Yahweh, or in our English spelling Jehovah, is probably the oldest and most primitive. This Jehovah is the Jewish tribal God, and still a pretty familiar, manlike (anthropomorphic) god, a god Homer himself could have understood. The second source, called E, from the fact that God is called Elohim, is probably later, and certainly has already a more ethical, more abstract, more universal notion of God. A third source, called P, is much later, and was written almost certainly by priests concerned with the laws, ritual, and outward performances that tied the Jews together in a social and religious body—in what we should call a church. These three sources were combined much later, perhaps as late as the fifth century B.C., into the biblical account of Jewish origins we are familiar with. The combination was not made hypocritically to delude anybody; it represents the ideas that earnest Jewish intellectuals of the years after the exile had of the Jewish national mission and national history.

Much of the rest of the Old Testament is in fact essentially this same kind of history, history written from earlier sources, and with some contemporaneous documents, but written to make Jews better Jews, written always with the horrors of the exile in mind, written ultimately as poetry, philosophy, and theology, not just history. And so the traditional epic history of the Jews becomes the works of the prophets, or the "writings," books like those of Job, Proverbs, Ecclesiastes.

To make a digest of this great mass of writings is even less profitable than usual. The Old Testament is not a book, but the record, fragmentary yet not misleading, of the experience of a gifted people. There is little resembling what we call science in it, indeed little of that attitude toward the relation of man to the universe sometimes called objective reasoning. Nothing in the Old Testament sounds like Thucydides, or Hippocrates, or even Aristotle; you cannot think of the Old Testament in terms of a phrase like "clinical report." Even that set of aphorisms called the Book of Ecclesiastes, which begins with the famous phrase "vanity of vanities, all is vanity," is no attempt to analyze human behavior realistically, but the despairing complaint of a man who somehow finds profundity is not enough. This great body of literature is then, overwhelmingly, a literature of feeling, of grasping for the ultimate, for the poetic, for something transcendental. This is a literature that simply will not accept this world of senses, tools, and instruments—not even long enough to study it.

What the Old Testament does do superbly is to trace the development of the Jewish conscience, of the Jewish view of the relation of mere men to their divine master. Such a relation is the main part of Jewish experience that passed over into Christian experience. As we have noted, Jehovah at first looks like the kind of god common enough in ancient days. He is never a very kindly God. When we first meet him he is already, as the Jewish tribal God, supreme, single, no mere member of a wrangling pantheon of gods. But he is God of the Jews alone.

Other tribes were supposed to have other gods. Jehovah was a jealous God, and he did not want his own people to adopt any of these other tribal gods. In fact, from the point of view of a modern humanitarian or rationalist, some of the most unpleasant passages in the Bible recount Jehovah's long and successful struggle to defend himself and his people from the allurements of competing gods and goddesses. This Jehovah was no Sunday-school character. Moreover, he had other traits of a god of primitive people: he walked on earth, talked with Abraham, wrestled with God's messenger, appeared fleetingly but quite corporeally in his majesty before Moses on Sinai.

Anticlericals, positivists, modern religious rationalists of all sorts may tend to exaggerate the primitive, anthropomorphic, tribal character of this Jehovah of the Pentateuch. Perhaps, without intending it, we have exaggerated in the preceding paragraph. And yet it is very hard to read with any care a book like Genesis and not feel that the god there pictured is very far indeed from the god of any modern higher religion we may be familiar with—Jewish, Christian, Mohammedan, Buddhist.

In the later books of the Old Testament, in the so-called Deutero-Isaiah (the last twenty-six chapters of the Book of Isaiah), in Jeremiah, in Job, there can be no doubt: The Jews have worked their way through to the concept of a single universal religion, a high ethical monotheism, held by its prophets to be true for all mankind. The second Isaiah says specifically, "I the Lord . . . give thee for a covenant of the people, for a light of the Gentiles." The Jews are indeed, perhaps more than ever, a Chosen People. But they are not chosen by a thunderous old shepherd-god to enjoy green pastures after breaking a suitable number of Philistine heads; they are chosen to show all men by their example that God wants men to live in peace and justice. "Ye are my witnesses . . . and my servant whom I have chosen; that ye may know and believe me, and understand that I am he; before me there was no God formed, neither shall there be after me. I even I am the Lord: and beside me there is no savior."

The Book of Job is the work of a late Jewish poet and philosopher (or of several, for most scholars hold that there is at least one major interpolation in the book) wrestling with a problem that confronts all the higher religions. This is the problem of theodicy, the problem of justifying God's ways to man. God is all-powerful, all-knowing, all-good. How then can we explain the existence of evil? We cannot say that God would destroy evil, but is powerless to do so; even less can we say that he, by permitting evil, does evil himself. Still, as we noted in Plato, the determined other-worldly mind can see in the need for each individual's overcoming evil, or incompleteness, the final and necessary step to good, or completeness.

Job's trouble, however, is in a sense more concrete: It is a form of the problem of theodicy that has always troubled Christians. Let it be granted that God permits evil that we may have a chance to overcome it, that we may lead a good life in spite of temptations to lead a bad one. Surely it follows that goodness leads to success and happiness, badness to failure and unhappiness? And yet all about us we see the wicked prosper and the good suffer. Job was a righteous man, wealthy and happy. God permitted Satan to test Job's faith by inflicting upon him a series of misfortunes. Job responded to loss of wealth with the famous words: "The Lord gave, and the Lord hath taken away: blessed be the name of the Lord." Job stood physical afflictions. But as suffering piled on suffering, as his friends showed their belief that behind such spectacular sufferings must be some great wickedness, Job began, not to doubt God, but to be most self-righteous about his own sufferings. God himself finally appeared and reminded Job that man is so infinitely petty, God's wisdom so infinitely great, that self-pity in man is really a presumption, and wickedness. Job then repents: "I know that thou canst do everything . . . therefore have I uttered that I understood not; things too wonderful for me, which I knew not. . . . Wherefore I abhor myself, and repent in dust and ashes." Job's health and prosperity then returned and he lived happily ever afterward.

This is a bare, perhaps in the bad sense a rationalistic, summary of something that cannot be readily summarized. The meaning of the Book of Job is an emotional meaning, something aroused by the poet himself, even though most of us can know him only in translation. Yet if something earthly must be made of the Book of Job, it is that our little calculating human minds cannot measure God in any way, cannot approach him. There is no problem of theodicy, for the very assumption that there is one is the height of wicked human self-assertion. Our relation to God is not in any sense a measuring, a questioning, a problematical relation, about which we should think, as the lawyer, the scientist, or the merchant thinks about his problems. "Behold, God is great, and we know him not." We do not and cannot know him, for could we, we should not be men; but just because we cannot know him, we believe in him.

Not all Jews reached the levels of thought and feeling we have attempted to note, any more than all Athenians attained the levels of Plato and Aristotle. But out of their long experience the Jewish people did make an organized religion, a set of institutions, a way of life, and it was in this way of life that Christianity had its beginnings. We must once more note that intellectual history is concerned, not only with the great achievements of the human mind, like the work of the

Jewish prophets, but with the way these ideas are reduced to the daily round of conventional life.

The Jewish people did not all see their God as Isaiah saw him. As a people, they could never quite lose their tribal Jehovah in the universal Jehovah. Religion meant to many of them, certainly, the observation of the Law, that is, the preservation of ritual purity by carrying out in perfect detail an immensely complicated set of rules and regulations. Many of the rules were prohibitions, of the kind most of us are nowadays familiar with under the names of taboos, such, for instance, as the law forbidding the Jew to eat pork; others, like the law of circumcision, enjoin positive acts. The prophets were rebels against the strict letter of the Law; they were at the very least religious idealists who sought to go beyond the Law, and did in fact widen and deepen the religious life of their people.

By the time of Christ, there was then a Jewish way of life, not identical with the highest ideals of the prophets, any more than our American way of life is identical with the highest ideals of an Emerson or a Whitman, but still a way very different from the Greek way, or the Roman way. The Jew believed in one omnipotent God who, for reasons the wisest man cannot quite penetrate, permits, indeed wills, on earth the kind of struggle we mortals feel as the struggle between good and evil. He believed that God had chosen the Jewish people as the spearhead of good in this struggle, that, indeed, God had destined the Jews to lead mankind to its final victory over evil. For that purpose, he would send to guide them a very great man indeed, a new Moses, the Messiah who should build the New Jerusalem.

Certainly many, perhaps most, ordinary Jews felt in all this rather a promise of worldly glory for the Jews, a righting of all the wrongs they had suffered at the hands of Babylonians, Egyptians, Persians, Greeks, Romans—in short, what we can easily recognize and label satisfaction of nationalist aspirations. Some Jews must have thought of this final triumph, not as an other-worldly, mystical triumph of good over evil, but as the very this-worldly setting up of Israel, the scorned, the broken, the "small nation," in the place of Rome.

Yet even this form of the dream could scarcely have been purely materialistic. You can hardly read anywhere in the prophets without finding evidence that they felt this coming Jewish greatness was to be God's greatness first of all. For instance, in Zechariah: "In those days it shall come to pass, that ten men shall take hold out of all languages of the nations, even shall take hold of the skirt of him that is a Jew, saying, We will go with you; for we have heard that God is with you." The Jews could no more hope to be Rome or Persia— granting the differences between the modern and the ancient worlds— than the Irish can hope to be the United States or the USSR. For some, the Messiah no doubt would merely restore the greatness of Solomon in a limited area of this earth, in Palestine. For those who went beyond such an ideal, the Messiah had to be the herald rather of spiritual than of material triumph.

One more generalization: The Jew, even the unimaginative, conforming Jew for whom the Law was enough, had what few Greeks had, a sense of sin. The Greek—the Greek in the street—had a sense of right and wrong, but of right and wrong as, in effect, a kind of trial and error. Wrongdoing was a mistake, which if you were sensible you could correct next time. Of course, some men weren't sensible, and the consequences of a lack of sense could indeed be serious, even tragic. The gods themselves were not quite clear on the distinction between right and wrong, and they too were subject to the inscrutable decrees of fate. But at the very worst, if this world was not designed for man's convenience, the ordinary Greek felt it was not designed to torture him into a marked preference for another world.

The Jew, however, felt wrongdoing to be a sin, a sign that the wrongdoer was foul, corrupt, deep inside him. Wrongdoing was not a mistake, it was a disease. You could try medicines; perhaps your correct ritual behavior would be medicine. But only God could cure you, and God could always go behind your behavior into your inmost thoughts and feelings. These had to be clean, had to be righteous, for God cannot be fooled. If you can really be righteous, righteous all through, you are saved. The Jews, indeed, made much less of the doctrine of immediate, personal immortality than did the Christians later, but it is likely that by the time of Christ the notion of personal salvation through righteousness was common among them. But righteousness for the Jew is hard to attain. God tests the soul fearfully. This world is not really a pleasant place, not even a sensible place. It is not, in fact, meant for men to live in as men—common, sensible, selfish, unheroic, rational men—think of living. Such men are living the life that Satan, the tempter, wants them to live, the obvious sort of life, the life of sin. Sin is all about us, and we can never be sure we are not sinning.

Do not misunderstand. The ordinary Jew can hardly have spent his life amid obsessive fear of sinning. Above all, the specific conduct that seemed to him sinful was not identical with the conduct we Americans, if we remember the doctrine at all, think of as sin. The Jew was not quite a puritan, and certainly not what our stereotyped thinking calls a puritan. He was not ascetic, and he was permitted the temperate enjoyment of much of what we call sense pleasures. Nevertheless, he was nearer even to our stereotyped notion of a puritan than he was to the Greek way of life. He did not condemn the flesh, but he distrusted it. And above all, he did not have the reasoning mind, the mind of the geometer, the mind that seeks to understand the universe in terms of measurable things. The world was to him an immeasurable and really rather hostile place in which a man had to feel his way in blindness, unless the Lord lighted it up for him with a very special light not of this world at all, a light that sinful man could easily miss.

The Hellenistic Element

In between the great days of the *polis* in the sixth to the fourth centuries and the political unification of the Mediterranean world under Rome in the first century B.C. lies a period of confused struggle among great powers—Egypt, Syria, Macedonia, Rome, Carthage. Under Alexander, the Greeks had overflowed the whole eastern part of the Mediterranean and had made their culture in some senses the culture of all educated persons in what we now call the Levant, or Near East. The culture thus spread was not identical with that of the *polis;* just by its spread it was bound to alter. Historians as we earlier noted have fastened on this period the epithet "Hellenistic," usually with the connotation of an unfavorable alteration, a cheapening.

For the intellectual historian, the Hellenistic period has two main points of interest. First, as an important stage in the development of Graeco-Roman civilization—indeed, as the dramatic stage of over-ripeness, the beginning of decline—it has always fascinated those philosophers of history who see in the history of the ancient world a kind of pattern, even an inevitable foreshadowing, of what will happen to us moderns. As such a pattern, however, the Hellenistic centuries fit in so closely with the Roman centuries that we shall do better to postpone to a later chapter consideration of the problem: Is Western society today following a course closely resembling that of Graeco-Roman society?

Second, Hellenistic culture is part of our whole inheritance. Its science, art, literature, and philosophy helped make up, perhaps quite as much as the work of earlier Greek ages, that formal education we still call "liberal" or "classical." Its scholars, librarians, and copyists were an essential link in passing on to us the work of earlier generations. And most important of all for us, these Hellenistic Greeks, ordinary folk as well as intellectuals, were the people in whose heads and hearts was chiefly worked the transformation of Christianity from a Jewish sect or heresy to the universal faith that survived the universal empire of Rome.

These first three centuries before Christ are the great centuries of Greek science. The Hellenistic Greeks did best in mathematics (especially geometry), astronomy, and physics. In medicine and in biology the promise of Hippocrates and Aristotle was not fully realized, and chemistry was hardly a recognized field of study. The sum total of scientific advance was, however, very considerable. Science today for us means trained research personnel, endowed institutions for their support, communication of results to fellow workers, and a tireless search for theories to explain facts, and for facts to test theories. It is probable that science in this modern sense was, until the late seventeenth century, most nearly attained at the Museum in Alexandria under the earlier Ptolemies.

We do not know accurately the organization of the Museum at Alexandria. The nine muses of the Greeks from whom it was named were, as a matter of fact, rather literary than scientific ladies. But literature under the Alexandrian system for endowing the pursuit of knowledge was cared for by the great Library, the staff of which took care of what in a modern university we call the humanities. The Museum seems in part to have been what museums of natural history now are, a place where specimens of interest were exhibited; but it was also in part an institute for scientific research, and, at least in the direct master-apprentice relation, for teaching.

One of the main conditions for the flourishing of science, an adequate center for teaching and research, clearly existed in Hellenistic times. There is not much use in running through the catalogue of names. Archimedes of Syracuse was a physicist of Newtonian range. Euclid wrote a textbook that was used to teach geometry for over two thousand years. Aristarchus of Samos, though since his key writings did not survive we must take chiefly the word of Archimedes for this, worked out a system of celestial mechanics that put the sun at the center of our planetary system, with the earth and other planets revolving about it. Erastosthenes, accepting an earlier scientific theory that the earth is a sphere, worked out its circumference at a figure surprisingly close to its true one. Just how close he came depends on the exact modern equivalent of his unit of measurement, the stadium, of which we cannot be sure; but he probably arrived at a figure of about 28,000 miles instead of the approximate 25,000 miles of modern geographers.

Though much of this scientific work is pure theory, done in the study much as philosophy is done, the Alexandrians by no means shrank from the hard, undignified work of observation and experiment. Erastosthenes, for instance, arrived at his figure for the circumference of the earth by careful measurement of the shadow cast by perpendicular pole at Alexandria at exact noon on the day of the summer solstice. He knew that at Syene, due south of Alexandria the sun at that moment on that day cast no shadow whatever—or, in modern terms, that Syene was on the Tropic of Cancer. The distance from Alexandria to Syene he knew. By some very simple geometry he was able to measure the arc of the earth's surface represented by the distance between Alexandria and Syene, which he found to be 7° 12′, or 1/50 of the circle. His total error came chiefly from a series of minor ones; Syene is not *quite* due south of Alexandria; it is not *quite* on the Tropic of Cancer; he may not have allowed for the half-diameter of the sun itself in measuring his original angle. But still, his was a remarkable job, a scientific doctrine made up of theory and facts.

Some of the later Alexandrians, though by no means technicians or inventors in the modern sense, did a great deal of actual experimentation in mechanics. Inheriting from their predecessors—science was already clearly cumulative—a good deal of basic knowledge about the behavior of fluids and gases, about levers, siphons, pumps, and the like, they achieved toy steam engines, penny-in-the-slot machines, birds that whistled and stopped whistling automatically, temple doors that opened automatically when a fire was lighted. It seems likely that some of these inventions were deliberately used by the priests to heighten the effect of their ceremonies. But we have no record of any Alexandrian businessman making use of the slot machines to sell his goods, nor of any Alexandrian engineer using the steam engine to move anything.

The record of science in the later Graeco-Roman world is, then, potty. There were great minds devoted to its pursuit, and there were at least the beginnings of an educational system and a social organization capable of carrying on the cumulative study of science. Yet no fruitful relation among science, technology, and economic production ever arose; and in the early centuries of Roman world rule science ceased to grow, ceased to push forward its frontiers. The problem of why the growth of science was thus arrested is one of the most interesting in intellectual history. No simple answer is possible. Here, as almost always in human history, we are confronted with many factors, many variables, all of which had some part in the process.

We cannot arrange them in an equation; we can but weigh them roughly.

One factor is often exaggerated, though it was undoubtedly there. This is what one might call the "genteel" element in the great Greek tradition, the notion that gentlemen of culture pursue graceful subjects like music and philosophy, but not the precise, difficult, undignified work of the laboratory or of field research; or, put more intellectually, the notion that the truth is arrived at by introspection, inspiration, the reading of the great works of the masters, and not by the ferreting out and manipulating of facts of sense experience. In other words, the Greek and Roman intellectuals chose to follow Plato rather than Hippocrates.

Now this is in part true, but it is unlikely that the genteel tradition in itself blocked ancient science. There were plenty of individual scientists, from Hippocrates to Archimedes and Erastosthenes, who did submit themselves to the undignified task of digging out the facts. Perhaps the best minds were not attracted to science, but we have no conclusive evidence for such an explanation.

Still another factor should be given short shrift. We shall encounter again the notion that the triumph of Christianity, with its emphasis on the next world, was responsible for the failure of the Greeks and Romans to cope with the manifold problems of this world including, naturally, those of science. But in this specific case, at least, the timing is such as to exonerate Christianity. The Christians did not attain real influence in the Roman Empire until the close of the second century A.D. Hellenistic science had reached its peak and begun to decline, or mark time, several centuries earlier.

The really important factor here must be sought in the failure of pure science to influence, and be influenced by, engineering and other economic activities. We can be pretty sure that modern science has taken the shape it has, and that it has developed and survived, largely because of the commercial and industrial revolutions of modern times. Science, to be vulgar, has paid. In the ancient world, it did not pay. Actually, we are here driven back to a further question: Why was there no industrial revolution in ancient times? The beginnings of industrial know-how were there, both in banking and in technology. But there was no labor shortage; indeed, with slavery, there can hardly be said to have been a labor problem. And there was thus no incentive to produce labor-saving machinery.

In short, of the whole complex matrix out of which came the modern scientific world—intellectual, economic, social, spiritual—only the intellectual was fully developed in the Graeco-Roman world. Whether a fuller development of science and attendant industry would have made the ancient world proof against the decline that finally overcame it is a question impossible to answer. Nineteenth-century Western optimists inclined to believe that an industrial and scientific revolution would have saved the ancient world. Many intellectuals today are not quite so sure that such a revolution has in fact saved our own world.

Hellenistic and indeed all later Greek artistic and literary achievement has seemed to most modern critics inferior to that of the great age just preceding it. Yet some of those who played the greatest part in the classical education of generations of later Europeans and Americans belong to these later years—the moralist and biographer Plutarch, the historian Polybius, the poet Theocritus, the meditative emperor Marcus Aurelius. Moreover, it was in these years that, for better or for worse, the cultural phenomenon we call scholarship first clearly appeared in the Western world.

The literary counterpart of the scientific Museum at Alexandria was the Library. At its height, this library probably had some 500,000 separate rolls, or as we should say, volumes. These books were hand-written on long strips of papyrus, a paper made from a common reed, and rolled up into something not unlike old-fashioned player-piano rolls. They had, of course, to be unrolled as they were read. They were "published" by the laborious process of copying by hand, work usually done by superior slaves.

In spite of the lack of our modern mechanical apparatus of scholarship, the Alexandrian scholars, like their contemporary scientists, developed what is recognizably the modern pursuit of their guild. They were the ancient equivalent of our Ph.D.'s. They edited,

catalogued, footnoted, analyzed, and abstracted the work of their predecessors, the giants from Homer to Aristotle. Their marginal or
interlinear comments, written on actual manuscripts and called glosses,
have survived to make possible much modern classical scholarship.
The Alexandrians are thus an essential link in the chain that binds
us to the great culture of Greece. As is true of scholars ever since,
their work has been scorned by the imaginative souls, by the creative
writers, held in low esteem by the utilitarians, and generally regarded
with mild puzzlement by the masses. Yet anything that has survived
as successfully as scholarship has survived would seem, if only on
Darwinian grounds, to have value for society. At any rate, it is risky
to maintain that the rise of scholarship is in itself a sign of cultural
decay.

The libraries in which these scholars worked were not much like
our American circulating libraries. They were not accessible to the
public. They were places where books were preserved, to be used
only by scholars. Yet one must not exaggerate the degree to which
literacy—still confined to a small portion of the population—is a test
of accessibility to ideas. We have noted that the Athenians talked
about ideas rather than reading about them. As the Greek way of
life spread through the East, the Greeks carried their habits of lively
public discussion with them. They carried their language, which,
losing some of its Attic elegance but by no means degenerating into
the equivalent of pidgin English, became the *koiné,* the common
tongue, the language of St. Paul. Moreover, the old Greek institution
of the lecturer was developed still further, so that it was possible for
intellectuals to make a living—in later times, for exceptionally gifted
or lucky ones, a very good living—on something like the early American Chautauqua or lyceum circuit. Most of us know that successful
gladiators, like good baseball players today, were well rewarded in
the Graeco-Roman world. But so too were successful rhetoricians, or
public lecturers. The literary and philosophic culture of the Graeco-
Roman world was clearly in some senses a widespread one, certainly
not confined to a very small upper class. Christianity spread among
people used to the exchange of ideas in public.

For the rest, Hellenistic culture is clearly different from the culture of the great age, though as a style the classical is to be recognized even in decay and perversion. Here we can but indicate certain notes, or characteristics, of Hellenistic culture.

In the first place, the range and variety of the great culture is even further extended. In later Greek and Roman art and writing you will find recorded almost every variety of human experience. To take an undignified but not unimportant example: Modern Western man has probably added very little new to the stock of Graeco-Roman pornography. This variety is probably in large part a reflection of the individualism that replaced the common discipline and common standards of the *polis*. In the Hellenistic world there was a scramble for place, power, riches—and (a human goal sociologists and political scientists often underestimate) public attention. To do the unusual, to go to the extreme, to be original, was one way of making your mark. There is, for instance, the young man who set fire to the temple of Diana in Ephesus in order that his name might go down in history—as indeed it has. There are psychologists who call an inordinate desire for fame a "Herostratean complex."

The patterns of the great culture were, then, extended, altered, caricatured in various ways. One direction, especially clear in sculpture, was to seek the expressive, the moving, the pathetic, the exciting. In place of the calm of the statues of the Parthenon we get Laocoön and his sons writhing in the coils of the serpents, we get the dying Gaul, we get pathetically sightless Homers. True, the older ways also persist: The Venus de Milo and the Winged Victory of Samothrace are works of the Hellenistic time.

Another direction is toward greater adornment, greater luxury, especially in private dwellings. Even in temple building, however, the simpler Doric order gave place to the acanthus-leaved Corinthian order, which was a favorite with the Romans. People began to boast of bigness in buildings, though in general the architects of the ancient Graeco-Roman world did not attempt to achieve great vertical height, as did the medieval builders of cathedrals and modern builders of skyscrapers.

Still another direction is toward what we moderns are familiar with as escapism. Perhaps scholarship and science were escapes for the Hellenistic Greek, but the most obvious example is the vogue of pastoral poetry in an urban society. Men and women of the upper class, surrounded by the comforts and conveniences of a very advanced civilization, liked to read about shepherds and shepherdesses, about sylvan dells and meals of bread and watercress, about true love. Most of them no doubt turned from the reading to their warm baths, cosmetics, slaves, banquets, and untrue loves. A few could no longer stomach these things. They were, however, hardly escapists in any simple sense; they were rebels, and ready for something more serious than Theocritan idylls. They were, in fact, ready for Christianity, and we shall return to them.

Wit, too, is a characteristic Hellenistic device, and one that seems always to crop up in a mature culture. Wit indeed is present in Aristophanes, along with much gusto and frankness. Hellenistic wit, however, is more malicious, more refined, and runs easily into irony, a device by which the author says one thing on the surface, to the vulgar, and another by implication, to the clever and initiate. Sometimes the wit is expended on the foibles and weaknesses of our common human nature. The later Greeks, and their Latin followers, were fond of the subtle character sketch, the satire, which might be very bitter or very gay. These satirists were often also realists. Here, for instance, is a poem by a later writer, preserved in a remarkable collection of Greek poetry known as the Palatine Anthology. Incidentally, it shows us that there were vegetarians even in the pagan world.

> He went among his garden roots
> And took a knife and cut their throats,
> Then served us green stuff heap on heap
> As though his guests were bleating sheep.
> Rue, lettuce, onion, basil, leek,
> Radishes, chicory, fenugreek,
> Asparagus and peppermint
> And lupines boiled—he made no stint.
> As last in fear I came away:
> I thought the next course would be hay.

To us, however, the most familiar direction taken by Hellenistic culture is toward realism, toward the faithful reproduction by human effort of some bit of the external world, or nature. Realism, in this sense, runs right through Hellenistic culture, even to its extremes. For in this world truth really can keep up with fiction. There is a spectrum, or range, of concrete instances in the external world quite as great as human imagination can compass. The extreme is rare, sometimes very rare, and its deliberate use in a work of art, especially in the plastic arts, would have disturbed the Greek of the great age; such use did not disturb, indeed it seemed to satisfy, the Greek of Hellenistic times. At any rate, the Hellenistic Greek went in for reproducing every last wrinkle, every wart and every bulge.

It is in this period that we get, for example, the admiring anecdotes of the realism achieved by great painters, stories of observers attempting to pluck fruit from paintings or to draw curtains painted on the wall. The Old Comedy of Aristophanes, still tied to ritualistic conventions of the Dionysian festival, gave place to the realistic New Comedy of Menander, who put ordinary men and women on the stage and had them behave as such. Of Menander an admiring later critic wrote the epigram: "Menander! Life! I wonder which of you copied which?" We have Menander's works only in fragments, and it must be said that by our standards the epigram is somewhat exaggerated, for Menander's obsession with foundlings, seductions, sudden changes of fortune, and recognition scenes seems to us rather forced and artificial.

Yet on the whole we can recognize this artistic and literary realism as something familiar to us. If these realists find reality quite often ugly or trivial, or both, so too did the realists of the nineteenth century. If sometimes the realists leap from the ordinary, the commonplace, to the marvelous, the stupendous, we too know that leap. And we can see ourselves in the men and women of Hellenistic art, much more easily than in the men and women of the art of the great culture, somehow removed from us by their perfection—and by their imperfections. Here is a bit from a mime of Theocritus that has been cited for generations with the remark that this could have been written yesterday. Gorgo, an Alexandrian lady, is calling on her friend Praxinoe, who is at home with her infant and her maid.

GORGO.

PRAXINOE in?

PRAXINOE.

My dear! at last! I am here, quite ready.

GORGO.

It's a marvel I ever got here!

PRAXINOE.

(*To the maid*)—Eunoe, a chair for the lady. Fetch a cushion.

GORGO.

It does very well as it is.

PRAXINOE.

Sit down for a spell.

GORGO.

O why can't folks stop at home?   I scarce got hither alive!
Crowds everywhere aimlessly roam, and hundreds and hundreds that
   drive!
High boots here, and there regimentals—and oh, the road
Is endless!   'Tis too far, where you have taken up your abode.

PRAXINOE.

That madman it was!—took flight to the world's end: hither he
   came,
Took a hole, not a house, that we might not be neighbours: his only
   aim,—
The jealous brute—is to spite us: it's like him, always the same.

GORGO.

Mind how you talk, my dear, of your husband—be careful, do,
When the little fellow is near!   How hard he is looking at you!
(*To the child*)—All right, Zopyrion, my pet!   She doesn't mean Pa,
   doesn't Ma!
He takes notice—it *is* early yet, by our Lady!   Pretty Papa!

PRAXINOE.

That "pretty papa" t'other day—though I *told* him to take special
   care,
Soap and rouge being wanted—away he goes to the shop, and there
He buys me—the booby, the great long looby brings salt, I declare!

118

Hellenistic formal thought rounds out Greek philosophy. In the biggest of problems, those of metaphysics and cosmology, little is added to the work of the philosophers of the great culture. But in problems of daily living, in ethics, the Hellenistic thinkers work out in some detail and in great variety leads given them by earlier philosophers. Scholarship was expended lovingly on philosophers as on men of letters. And the range of philosophy was widened, or at least made more explicit, so that again we can say that the modern West has hardly added anything new to its classical philosophical heritage.

First, then, the varieties and subvarieties of philosophical experience are all there. As in the anecdotes about painting, this variety is reflected in popular versions of what the philosophers thought. There are the skeptics, who doubted that they doubted that they doubted. There is Diogenes the Cynic, or Dog-Philosopher, who lived in a tub, and who has come down to us less as the ascetic, other-worldly person he may have been than as the bitter-tongued, witty rebel against convention. There are the confident, innocent rationalists or positivists, who could explain (rationalize) everything, especially the religious beliefs they had cast aside. They went relentlessly through what we call Greek mythology, explaining it all neatly. Thus the tale of Actaeon, hunter devoured by his hounds because he had offended the goddess Artemis, was explained by the rationalists as the story of a wild, spendthrift young man who used up all his money building up a hunting pack, and was hounded by his creditors.

The irrationalists—if one may use neutrally an abusive name— were also present. It is in Roman, not strictly speaking in Hellenistic, times that the other-worldly philosophy of Plato was pushed to the extremes our textbooks label "Neoplatonism." But Plotinus, born in 204 A.D., the greatest of the Neoplatonists, is part of a long line of mystics, some Christian, some pagan. Plotinus held that common belief of mystics, that the properly trained person can attain a state of ecstasy in which he is *unaware* of himself as animal, sense-experiencing, conscious man. For Plotinus, the choice soul could literally make the physical world disappear into the nonexistence that is its reality, and be at one with God-Light.

In this period, too, philosophers and their pupils came to form more definite groupings, known as schools, which preserved the attitude of a master and passed it on to posterity—with inevitable alterations. The followers of Plato took their name from the Academy, the Athenian grove in which he taught. Those of Aristotle were called Peripatetics, "movers about," presumably because they walked around as they lectured and philosophized. But the characteristic schools of Hellenistic philosophy, both clearly derived from earlier ones, were those known as Stoics and Epicureans. Both are concerned less with the great questions of metaphysics than with those of man's adjustment to his natural and human environment. Both are consoling philosophies, ways of fortifying the individual in a harsh world.

Epicureanism, named from Epicurus, master of the school, has been ever since the days of the master himself one of the most abused of philosophies. The Epicurean believes in a remote but kindly God, in a quiet life on earth, in an avoidance of struggle and pain. Epicurus held the aim of the good life to be pleasure (in Greek, hēdonē, hence the term "hedonism" by which Epicurean and similar philosophies are known). The word "pleasure" was enough for his opponents, and for the general public. They at once assumed that Epicurus meant sensual indulgence and all kinds of improper things. That is exactly what he did not mean. As he himself put it:

> When we say that pleasure is the aim and end, we do not mean the pleasures of the prodigal or the pleasures of sensuality, as we are understood by some to do through ignorance, prejudice, or wilful misrepresentation. By pleasure we mean the absence of pain in the body and of trouble in the soul. It is not an unbroken succession of drinking-bouts and of revelry, not sexual love, not the enjoyment of the fish and other delicacies of a luxurious table which produce a pleasant life; it is sober reasoning, searching out the grounds of every choice and avoidance, and banishing those beliefs through which the greatest tumults take possession of the soul.

Naturally a philosophy setting up pleasure as the good could be adapted to most varied temperaments. There have no doubt been wicked Epicureans, but there have been wicked men of all philosophic beliefs. Epicureanism as a philosophy tended to be welcomed chiefly by those of the privileged classes whose tastes ran toward art, poetry, and the quieter pursuits. Occasionally an Epicurean was of very stern stuff indeed, such as the Latin poet Lucretius, whose *De Rerum Natura* is a moving defense of atheism. Generally, however, the upper classes, above all the people who gradually came to rule the One World of the Roman Empire, were Stoics.

Stoicism is, then, the most important set of beliefs of the later Greek and Roman world, save, of course, for emerging Christianity. Its founder, Zeno, of whose work we have but the merest of fragments, taught in the Stoa Poikile in Athens, whence the name "Stoics," those of the porch or *stoa*. Stoicism as it grew into a way of life became for the elite of the Roman Empire as much a religion as a philosophy. It pretty clearly never had much of a hold on the common people anywhere. It was an austere but not ascetic faith, basically rationalistic, charged with an awareness of moral obligation, not too hopeful of this world or the next. We shall not meet a belief much like this one, nor held so widely among educated men, until we reach the deism of the eighteenth century.

The Stoic believed in one god, worshiped though he be under many names. He was a kindly and omnipotent god, who cared for his children and meant them to live virtuously. Why they did not all live virtuously—that is, the problem of evil—was as much a stumbling block to the Stoics as to other theists. But the average Stoic accepted sin as something to be fought, and duty as the call to fight it. The good life in practice for the Stoic was not so very far from the good life for the Epicurean—simplicity, decency, quiet accomplishment of the tasks to which one is called. Nor, as an ethics, is practical Stoicism very far from practical Christianity. Its best-known work, the *Meditations* of the emperor Marcus Aurelius, has long been admired by Christian writers. Stoicism, however, never became a church, an ecclesiastical organization, and it never had a formal set of dogmas. But its contribution to the Roman Empire was immense. Most of the men who held that empire together were Stoics—not sectarian ·believers, not rigorous thinkers, not the men who write books—but men to whom Stoicism was a way of life. Moreover, as we shall see in the next section, the Stoic rationalist view of human equality was an essential part of the cosmopolitan citizenship of the Roman Empire.

In all these ethical systems, as indeed in much of the artistic and literary culture of the period, you can discern an element of escapism. The good life for both Epicurean and Stoic *can* mean, and in the late Empire clearly did mean to many gentlemen, an avoidance of vulgar things, an avoidance of the sweat and dirt of conflict, a retreat into something like the mystic other world we have seen in Plato and Plotinus. Slogans of other schools suggest escape even more clearly— the skeptic's *ataraxia,* restfulness, the cynic's *autarkeia,* self-sufficiency. But, especially for Stoicism, this element of escapism must not be exaggerated. At least as they penetrated into the minds of ordinary educated men, these suggested ways of life are not as extreme, not as paradoxical, as their literary expression. They have this in common: They tend to accept the world, not quite as it is, but as something that, by and large, cannot be greatly changed; and they try to reconcile the individual to a modest, dignified acceptance of what God or the gods or Fate or Providence has brought him. This is not quite passive acceptance. The individual, especially the Stoic individual, does his duty here and now and helps actively to keep this world going. Indeed, no one summed up this point of view better than a Frenchman nearly two thousand years later. Voltaire, who could well have been a later Greek like Lucian, ended his *Candide* with: "We must cultivate our garden."

The Roman Element

By the end of the second century B.C. the series of great international wars that began with Alexander the Great had been ended by the victory of one of the contending superpowers, the Roman Republic. There was another century of disturbance as the leaders of the republic, Julius Caesar, Pompey, Mark Anthony, Augustus, and the rest, struggled among themselves in what was, from the historian's point of view, really an attempt to adapt the machinery of a single state to world rule. That adaptation was achieved under Augustus, and roughly at the beginning of the Christian era what we call the Roman Empire came into being. For some four centuries afterward, our Western society, from Britain and western Germany to Egypt and Mesopotamia, was a single political entity, the One World of the Romans. It was by no means wholly a peaceful world. Civil wars among contestants for the imperial throne were at times almost endemic. There was constant pressure in the later centuries from migrant Germanic barbarians. In the East the Persians and the Parthians, never quite great powers, were none the less independent, and a frequent threat. Even so, especially in the Age of the Antonines, 96 A.D. to 180 A.D., peace was general over a wider territory than has since enjoyed such peace in our Western society.

Rome itself began as simply another city-state built up by a people speaking Latin, an Indo-European tongue, and perhaps, like the Ionians of Attica, of fairly mixed stock. Situated on hills in a strong position some miles up from the mouth of the Tiber, the chief river of the western side of Italy, Rome no doubt owes some of its greatness to its geographical position. It owes something, perhaps, to the fact that it came late on the scene of international politics and fought the final struggle in comparative freshness. But the fact remains that Rome carried a united Italy with it into that struggle. In a sense, Rome solved the problem neither Athens nor Sparta nor any Greek unit ever solved, the problem of transcending the *polis*, or city-state. Roman Italy by the first century B.C. was, if not quite a modern nation-state, at least a great territorial unit with common citizenship and common laws, a commonwealth and not a mere oriental despotism. The political and legal achievements of the Romans remain the most striking thing about them, even for the intellectual historian.

It is a commonplace that the philosophical, literary, and artistic culture of the Romans is derived from that of the Greeks. Some put the matter more strongly: *imitated* from that of the Greeks. Yet the sum total of pagan Latin writings, and of surviving examples of Roman art, deserves a less scornful summing up. After all, until roughly

1450, the direct Greek inheritance was unknown to us in the West. Rome was to all western Europe the great transmitter of Greek culture, and from this point of view alone is of great importance in the history of our civilization. Moreover, if in formal philosophy there is scarcely any distinguished Latin writing (the emperor Marcus Aurelius wrote in Greek), Latin literature, the Latin of Vergil, Cicero, Tacitus, Catullus, and their peers is, precisely because of its debt to Greek, one of the world's great literatures. It has its own flavor, and its individual writers have their own personalities.

Generalization about such matters is not, as we have already noted, capable of scientific formulation. Those who try to describe the Roman spirit, the Roman way, the Roman *Weltanschauung,* disagree, as do those who try to describe what is American, or French, or Russian. It is easy to say that Roman culture is more practical, more matter-of-fact than the Greek, less eager to push through to the ultimate knowable—or imaginable—about the universe, that the Roman is the fit culture of a people who could rise from compromise through compromise to world rule. And all this would be true. Latin is, all told, even as a language, *tamer* than Greek.

Yet Latin writers by no means always stand on their dignity. And, if they cannot scale the heights, they can sound the depths. Catullus, one of the earliest Latin poets, bares his soul with as much abandon as any nineteenth-century romantic. Satire, the reflection of a kind of moral nausea, is in Latin hands even more skillfully developed than in Greek. The Roman, like many other hard-headed practical men, could sometimes break loose into coarseness, excess, debauchery. This indecency of the barracks-room is reflected directly in much Latin writing, indirectly by the moralist's reaction against it.

But at its best, the Roman spirit as expressed in letters attains great dignity, as in Vergil—though, as always in these matters, there is at least a minority that finds this Roman dignity heavy, stiff, dull. Not only schoolboys have found Cicero something of a stuffed shirt. At any rate, since so much of Roman attention was focused on human behavior rather than on metaphysics or theology or natural science, you can cull from the whole mass of Roman literature a great deal of wisdom about human beings. Some of it is astonishingly modern, as when Catullus writes of his Lesbia "odi et amo"—"I hate and I love"—thus anticipating a great deal of modern writing on psychological ambivalence. Again, the Roman as moralist seems to some critics commonplace and preachy—Seneca, for instance—or a little too ripely aristocratic—for example, Horace.

In the arts that deal with things rather than words, the Romans are seen at their best in public buildings designed for worldly use. Their temples, like the admirably preserved Maison Carrée at Nîmes in southern France, were closely modeled on the Greek. But Roman engineers developed the arch, as the Greek never did, and were able to build great aqueducts, circuses, stadia, and huge public halls called basilicas. The remains of their aqueducts—again there is an admirable one near Nîmes, the Pont du Gard—are today perhaps the most effective visible monuments of their greatness, admirable examples of functional architecture. The Romans built these great arched canals across valleys, not because they were ignorant of the principles of the siphon or of water pressure, but because they could not make cheaply enough the necessary pipes to carry a great deal of water under pressure.

In sculpture, and presumably in painting, the Romans were outright imitators of the Greeks. One exception to this rule—though the Hellenistic Greeks were fond of sculptural realism also—is the series of surviving portrait busts of late Roman times. The men depicted were, of course, of the top rank, emperors, senators, rich landowners; ordinary men do not get themselves portrayed in stone. These rulers of the Roman world were striking men, often heavy-set and heavy-jowled, quite often bald, not very like the sculptured Greek males of the Age of Pericles, but pretty obviously men who knew how to get on in this world. In fact, as a group, they look extraordinarily like portraits of successful American businessmen and politicians.

Any such American group would contain some lawyers. So too did the Roman; most Roman men of affairs had some knowledge of the law. And indeed what we associate first of all with pagan Rome is not its literature, not even its engineering, but the achievement of Roman Law. Nor is this law by any means dead. In one form or another it survives in the living legal systems of Western society outside the English-speaking countries. And even in English-speaking countries Roman jurisprudence has had a great influence in molding the modern legal system. If you are practically rather than aesthetically or philosophically inclined, you may well feel that Rome with her law and her engineering did far more for our civilization than did the brilliant Greeks.

Now *law* is, especially in the English language, a word of many meanings, the kind of word that worries the semanticist. Not only is it used of uniformities in the fields of science—for example, the law of gravity—but it is also in common language our sole word for what in most other Western tongues is distinguished by two: the *loi* and the *droit* of the French, the *Gesetz* and the *Recht* of the German, the *lex* and the *jus* of Latin. English does indeed have the professional lawyer's term *equity,* which arose in England out of a conscious attempt to remedy the injustices a rigid adherence to the letter of the law might bring. Roughly, the first of these pairs is law in the sense of any actual rule the legal authorities apply, and the second is law in the sense of an ethically sound rule; equity is the attempt to modify the first by an appeal to the second. By and large, for satisfied members of a society, the two kinds (or conceptions) of law tend to coincide; for dissatisfied members, they tend to be readily distinguishable. Incidentally, the fact that the word *law* in English and American covers *both* senses, though it may be a sign of our toughmindedness, is probably a mere accident; in practice, we are fully aware of the distinction involved between a law that just *is,* and a law that *ought to be.*

So, obviously, were all the ancient peoples with whom we have been concerned in this book. Indeed, it seems likely that the most primitive of men make a distinction between existing conditions and more desirable conditions, which is psychologically the basic simple distinction we have been discussing. But, not to go too far into the complex problems of the philosophy of law, there is another, related distinction that will bring out more fully the originality and importance of Roman Law in its mature form. The Law may be regarded as so holy that in fact all its practical prescriptions belong in the class of law as "ought to be." Such law can be broken in this world of "is," but—and here a modern American must use his imagination to understand primitive peoples—under such conditions it is for the primitive broken almost in the sense that we think of breaking the law of gravity. One could jump off a roof in an attempt to break the law of gravity, but the attempt could not of course succeed. A primitive Jew could touch the ark of the covenant even though Jehovah's law forbade it, but of course he perished on the spot if he tried it. The Law is thus from this point of view something above human contrivance, something revealed or found, not made by human beings, but perfect, unchanging, an absolute.

The analogy we have made above between revealed law, of which the Mosaic Law is a familiar example, and the law of gravity as most of us understand it has, like most analogies, logical imperfections, but it is psychologically useful, and it can profitably be pursued a bit further. You may have thought of the would-be defier of gravity, "Ah, but perhaps he has a parachute" (or a balloon, or a helicopter). He would then not precisely *break* or *defy* the law of gravity, but at least he would in some sense *get around it,* or better, adapt it to his purpose. Now, at least from our own modern point of view, the men who managed these early societies under Revealed Law did something of the sort with this majestic, absolute set of rules. They got around them. They invented what *we* (not they) call legal fictions. They did in fact do something new, something different, made an adjustment; but they used the old forms, the old words, the old "right" ways. The Law says only a son can do certain things. Sempronius has no son. But he can adopt a son, pretend that someone else's son is in fact his son. He will go through certain ritual forms, and will then have a son to do the things only a son can do. He will not have defied the Law, but he will certainly have got around it. This sort of behavior is by no means as extinct even in modern societies as some of our rationalists think it is.

Nevertheless, we moderns are well used to the notion that laws are arrangements for getting things done in human relations, and if we want to do something new, we are quite used to repealing an old law and making a new one. The eighteenth and twenty-first amendments to the American Constitution afford a neat example. The Jews, the Greeks, the Romans, all seem to have started with the notion of a revealed and unchanging Law, and they all did in practice change this Law. How far their leaders, especially in early times, were aware of what they were doing, how far they were actually pretending to conform when they weren't doing so, is an interesting but pretty involved question. We may here pass it by.

The Romans more definitely than any other ancient people got beyond the stage of changing their laws while pretending they were not changing them. By imperial times, indeed, the Roman Law was a complex body of doctrine that the jurists themselves acknowledged to have many sources, basically the laws of the Republic modified by statutes, by decisions of judges, by interpretations of scholarly experts, and, since Augustus, by decrees of the emperor, the *princeps*. It had obviously changed, and was changing. Full awareness of what we today might call the sociology of the law was attained, however, just about the time when Roman Law had, in its original form and scope, ceased to grow. The greatest of codifications, that under the emperor Justinian in the sixth century A.D., was made in the East just before the Dark Ages closed in on the Empire in the West. The later development of Roman Law, its adaptation to the Christian Church (canon law), to medieval and modern European societies, is a different story.

The Romans first clearly made law a living, growing thing consciously adapted by lawmakers to changing human demands. They have another related achievement to their credit. Law to earlier peoples, to the Jews for example, was not merely a set of divine rules, perfect and unchanging; it was a set of such rules designed *exclusively for them*. Only a Jew could obey the Mosaic Law. Only an Athenian could be tried under the Law of Athens. We have seen that the Jewish prophets rose to the conception of a Jehovah, and a divine law, shared by all mankind; and philosophically the Greeks even at the height of the independent *polis* could conceive a humanity transcending the distinction between Greeks and barbarians. The Romans, characteristically, did something of the sort not in a philosophical or theological, but in a practical way. *They extended their laws to other peoples.*

As the little *polis* on the seven hills by the Tiber, Rome seems to have had originally divine and exclusive laws, the privilege and the possession of born Roman citizens. Only gradually did the Romans come to extend the basis of Roman citizenship. Their rulers, working cautiously through the Senate, would confer Roman citizenship on individual foreigners they wished to win over, on communities, later on bigger areas. In an earlier period, they invented a sort of halfway citizenship, the Latin, in which the useful commercial and suchlike privileges were shared, but the personal, political, quasi-religious privileges of full Roman citizenship were not. And, certainly in these formative days of 500 B.C. to 100 B.C., all this was done neither in accordance with a conscious theory of widening political sovereignty nor, like the American process of citizenship by naturalization, as a kind of deliberate Romanization.

Roman citizenship, and Roman political rule generally, were widened by men of affairs trying to get things done, to lessen the tensions, the pulling and hauling, among many peoples. By the time Rome faced the international struggles of the last few centuries B.C., she had what no Greek *polis* could count on, an extended territorial area in which her rule was accepted—and in which her laws prevailed. Yet it is characteristic of the slowness of this process of political unification that as late as 90 B.C. Rome's Italian allies revolted against her, and for motives not worlds apart from those that made the allies of Athens revolt in the fifth century. Rome beat the rebels in the field— and then gave them what they wanted, full Roman citizenship. Ultimately, under the emperor Caracalla, all freeborn persons, all the mixed peoples from Britain to Syria, were made Roman citizens. The Romans, though they had a fully developed law of agency, never hit upon agency as a political device, and did not have representative assemblies. A Roman citizen had to be in Rome itself to vote. Naturally, the Roman universal state had to be ruled by an emperor, a bureaucracy, and an army. Actually, citizenship by Caracalla's time meant little politically.

One further generalization about Roman Law needs to be made. We have described it as a growing thing, the product not of abstract thinking but of the practical needs of a people not much given to abstract thinking. But it must not be thought that the Roman Law is the product of unthinking men, opportunists operating on hunches, men hostile to logic and proud of muddling through. On the contrary, Roman Law is obviously the product of generations of hard, logical thinking; and what is more, the lawyers never wholly kept from their sight the notion of an ideal, of something the law *ought to be*—of justice, in short, which is a Latin word. But they could not in the sophisticated world of later Rome retain the old simple belief that the gods had directly revealed a code of justice. Being practical and sensible men, used to responsibility, they had to believe in justice. They could not take the position that justice is a noble but unreal abstraction, or that justice is what you can get away with, or that might makes right. What they did was to put nature in place of the gods. They produced the concept of *natural law* that was to play so important a part in all subsequent political thinking.

Natural law in this sense is not a generalized description of what actually goes on in this natural world of our sense experience. It is not a law of nature in the sense that the law of gravity is a law of nature. It is, in fact, a prescription for, and a description of, a world that *ought to be*. Yet the Latin *natura,* and its Greek equivalent *physis,* certainly carry connotations of the existing, of the here-and-now, of *this* world. Perhaps one of the great reasons for the success of the concept of natural law is that though in fact it is an otherworldly concept, an ideal, it manages to suggest this world so firmly that it seems practical, not at all visionary. The natural is not only good; it seems quite possible.

Into the specific content of natural law as it was developed in the Graeco-Roman world there went several different trains of thought and experience. In a way, the ripened classical concept of natural law is one of the most successful fusions of Greek and Roman thought.

The simplest of these trains of thought is that of the practicing lawyers in Rome. We have seen that the Roman state early extended its citizenship, or part citizenship, to various individuals and groups. Some remained, however, though allies, actually foreigners. Business dealings among these individuals of varying status soon produced problems that came up for judgment in the Roman courts. The lawyers could not apply full Roman Law, which was still the property, the quasi-religious monopoly, of true Roman citizens. Yet the two litigants—a Neapolitan and a Latin, for example—themselves had grown up under different laws. What the Roman *praetor peregrinus,* or judge handling such cases, did was to try to find a common rule, a sort of least common denominator in all these varying local laws, customs, usages. A business contract in one place meant one set of forms to be complied with; a business contract in another place meant quite a different set of forms. But what was common to both, what underlay both, what was a valid contract for both places? These were the questions the Roman lawyers asked themselves, and in answering them they worked out what they called the *jus gentium,* or law of peoples, as distinguished from the *jus civile,* the Roman Law proper.

They arrived at this working international law, these rules for adjudicating cases among men of different citizenship, or among different political units, by comparing existing national, city, or tribal laws, and trying to find what was common to them. They did this by a kind of thinking that involves classification according to characteristics *abstracted* from the living, perceptible wholes they started with. As wholes experienced, the laws they compared did not seem much alike. If you have a smattering of botany, you can see that what they did is much like what the taxonomist does when he finds that plants apparently as little alike as the strawberry, the rose, the apple, and the steeplebush (hardhack) are actually members of the same family. This kind of thinking about classification, pigeonholing, is a very common kind of thinking, and one that is used at various levels from common sense to science.

So far, the Roman lawyers had done no more than produce a working instrument for adjusting law cases involving different legal systems. They had done no more, really, than extend to differing systems what they had done with conflicting separate rules of law within their own system. But they could hardly help feeling that their new *jus gentium* was somehow more "universal," somehow more perfect, more valid for all men, than the separate local systems they started with. And here the Greek philosophers, and especially the Stoics, came in to help them, and transform *jus gentium* into *jus naturale*.

For the Stoics had arrived at a kind of aristocratic cosmopolitanism that emphasized what men have in common as opposed to their apparent differences. What the unwise, ordinary man notices, so the Stoics reasoned, is the variegated appearance of this world and its human inhabitants. What the wise Stoic notices is the underlying unity of all God's work. He sees the permanent, not the temporary, the accidental. Nature fools the unwise into thinking she is fickle, many-sided, changing. Actually nature is, to him who can penetrate her secrets, regular, orderly, consistent, uniform. For the Stoic philosopher, the *jus gentium,* this international law common to many peoples, seemed more natural than did the various separate codes and systems of the cities, tribes, and nations. To the ruling classes of the Roman world, trained both in law and in Stoic ideas, the *jus gentium* became a kind of pattern, never wholly realized, for the *jus naturale.*

It is important to note that neither for the lawyer nor for the philosopher did the general, the universal, the "natural" they were seeking mean quite what most of us mean by "average," or "most common." Many of their hostile critics have maintained that their ideal of natural was a deadening mediocrity, the unexciting middle of a regular frequency curve. They themselves certainly did not equate *universal* with *average*. The lawyer's universals were not the commonest legal practices, but what his mind could distinguish as the underlying unifying principles of all legal systems. The Stoic's ideal was not the behavior of the average man, the man-in-the-street (far from it!), but rules of behavior worked out from long communion with the wisdom of the ages. The "natural" of natural law is *not what is, but what ought to be;* yet it rests on one kind of "is"—the "is" of faith.

The natural is an "ought to be" which, we know from history, appealed at least to educated citizens of the most various racial origins —Britons, Gauls, Spaniards, Greeks, Romans, Egyptians, Syrians. Natural law, or what seemed its nearest earthly embodiment, the great system of developed Roman Law, unlike the Jewish or Athenian law, was designed for all men; it was not an exclusive tribal possession. On the other hand, this natural law was not a mere collection of practical rules for keeping things as they are. It too was a set of ideals, a higher law, an attempt to bring justice down to earth. Natural law, the offspring of Roman Law and Greek philosophy, has been one of the most important abstract ideas in Western society. We shall encounter it again, especially in the Middle Ages and in the eighteenth century. We shall also, toward the end of this book, encounter modern anti-intellectual thinkers who maintain that a concept like that of natural law is meaningless nonsense, or at most an attempt to disguise the fact that human societies are always ruled by small privileged groups. For the moment, we may waive the problem of the importance of abstract ideas like natural law in human relations, and content ourselves with noting that the Graeco-Roman concept of natural law was *as an ideal* a concept of the unity of all mankind, a basically democratic concept.

5

The Doctrine of Christianity

No ONE in the Western world can wholly escape the influence of Christianity. Even those who set themselves against what they consider the Christian religion are unavoidably affected by what they oppose. For Christianity has colored the thinking and feeling of nearly seventy generations of Western men and women. Through the work of missionaries it has in the last few centuries followed expanding Western society throughout the world. As a way of life, Christianity has in the two thousand years of its existence seemed capable of extraordinary range and variety. In one form or another it has manifested itself throughout the activity of Western man.

"Range and variety," "in one form or another"—these simple, obvious phrases bring us squarely up against a difficulty we have already encountered in discussing the religious beliefs of the Jews. Christianity is a *revealed* religion. Its God is perfect, above such human categories as time and space, above the historical process itself. But Christianity is also a religion much concerned with human conduct on this earth, with its mission in historical time. It is, though its theologians have struggled very hard indeed to make it satisfyingly monistic, in some senses a dualistic belief; it recognizes the existence ("reality") of the supernatural and the natural, the soul and the body, the spiritual and the material. To an observer from outside, Christianity has displayed great ingenuity and adaptability in adjusting itself

134

to the natural world without losing grip on the concept of the supernatural world.

In this book, an attempt will be made to study Christianity from the outside, from a position that denies the *existence* of the supernatural, though not, of course, the reality of human aspirations toward the supernatural. Especially since the Enlightenment of the eighteenth century Christianity has often been expounded from a wholly naturalistic point of view, sometimes by men calling themselves Christians. More often those writers on Christianity who have denied the real existence of the supernatural have been hostile to Christianity as an organized religion, have been in fact anti-Christians, often dogmatic materialists or positivists. Still others, though clearly unable to accept the supernatural aspect of Christian belief, have written wistfully, romantically of its beauties, or have admired its ethics while regretting its theology. In fact, the behavior of writers who reject Christianity is clear evidence of the fact that no Westerner can quite escape the influence of Christianity.

We shall in this book attempt to avoid the errors of non-Christian writers on Christianity. But no Christian reader should have a moment's doubt: The core of Christian faith, the belief in the existence of the supernatural, the divine, is forever proof not merely against naturalistic and historical attacks, *but involves rejection of naturalistic and historical explanation.* When an English rationalistic clergyman obtained from a High Church altar consecrated bread and wine, which by consecration had become the flesh and blood of God, turned them over to a chemist, and published the chemist's report that they were nothing more than bread and wine, he did nothing at all to confute the High Church position. Chemistry, which is wholly concerned with facts and theories in nature, with natural processes, has nothing to say about anything outside such natural processes.

The Growth of Early Christianity

The New Testament is an account of the life, death, and resurrection of Jesus Christ and of the labors and difficulties of the first generations of missionaries of the new faith called Christian. To a Christian, this account is divinely inspired, its final truth not subject to historical interpretation. None the less, just as with the Old Testament, scholars for the last few centuries have in fact submitted the texts of the New Testament to the same kind of rigorous philological and historical study they have used on texts no longer considered in any sense inspired or holy. What Albert Schweitzer calls the "quest of the historical Jesus" has gone on for several generations, and has produced some strange results. Perhaps the strangest is the conclusion of one school that there was no historical Jesus, that the Christian figure of Jesus is legendary, or rather, a sort of synthesis of various legends. It is fair to note that even in the learned world such skepticism is regarded as rather extreme.

No more than on the exact roles of "J," "E," and "P" in the Pentateuch are scholars in absolute agreement on the sources and accuracy of the New Testament accounts of the life and teaching of Jesus and the early Christian mission of St. Paul and his co-workers. But there is among these scholars a general agreement that we have *no direct contemporaneous account of anything Jesus said or did.* The following analogy will offend precise scholars, but it should be clear and real to ordinary Americans, and not in essentials misleading: Suppose no copies, no contemporaneous written records of Lincoln's speeches and letters existed, no newspapers, no histories, nothing printed or written between his birth in 1809 and his death in 1865 that referred to him at all, except a possible ambiguous reference or two in the private memoirs of a British statesman; suppose, however, that there had been a few brief accounts of his life written in their old age by men who had known him mostly in Washington, perhaps a bit in Illinois, and who had been a little too young to know him really well; they had, however, seen manuscript collections of Lincoln tales, and amateur stenographic reports of some of Lincoln's speeches, and a manuscript copy of a brief life of Lincoln by his secretary Hay, written in the 1870's; from such sources in our own time three good Republican party writers had drawn up brief popular accounts, and one rather excited Professor of Political Science, also Republican, had done the same; in all this there had survived many phrases "with malice towards none," "government of the people, by the people, for the people," but no whole speech, except perhaps the Gettysburg Address; there had survived accounts of how he pardoned the sleeping sentry from Vermont, how he issued the Emancipation Proclamation, how he stood by Grant, but no complete, consecutive account of his life and times.

Obviously under such conditions we should not know about Lincoln anything like as much as we know today. On the other hand, we should know most of what is essential about him; we should by no means have a misleading conception of the real Lincoln. So from the often complementary accounts of Matthew, Mark, and Luke, from the parables he is reported to have told, from the Sermon on the Mount (which may well be almost as much the words of the historical Jesus as the Gettysburg Address is the words of the historical Lincoln), even from the confused and contradictory accounts the Gospels give us of the final mission in Jerusalem, we almost certainly get no really misleading sense of what Jesus was like.

But the analogy with Lincoln is at best suggestive. Though Lincoln is part of a national American cult, though many Americans have in a sense worshiped him, no great theological and philosophical system has grown up around him. He has been variously interpreted, but not on the full band or spectrum of theology, which is a very wide one indeed. Here we can but state certain major problems about Jesus and his mission.

First, did the historical Jesus claim to be the son of God, a God himself? Christian theologians, as we shall soon see, had grave difficulties in the formative years of the Church in solving satisfactorily what came to be known as problems of Christology. In the three Synoptic Gospels, as they are called, the narrative accounts of Matthew, Mark, and Luke, and of course in the much more metaphysical account of the Fourth Gospel, that of John, Jesus is reported as using many phrases that cry out for theological explanation—"kingdom of God," "Son of man," "my Father," "Son of God." The Gospel of John is most explicit: It is written, the author tells us, "that ye might believe that Jesus is the Christ, the Son of God; and that believing ye might have life through his name." And indeed the weight of Christian thought has through the centuries been on the side of the divinity of Christ; Unitarian ideas, under whatever name they have taken, have been unorthodox, heretical.

Yet it is quite possible to argue, accepting the naturalistic historical interpretation of the origins of the New Testament, that Jesus never claimed divinity for himself, that phrases like those we cite above were badly reported or meant metaphorically, or both, that Jesus in fact had no interest in theology or indeed in organized religion, but was very much interested in persuading his fellow men to lead what we may colorlessly call the simple life on earth. Men have even gone further and maintained that the historical Jesus was a crank, a back-to-nature faddist, even—if they were themselves shallow and cock-sure enough—that Jesus was a deliberate faker, charlatan, nature-healer. The point is that, once you admit the fragmentary and inexact nature of our historical sources, you cannot wholly rule out any interpretation of the personality of Jesus that seems humanly possible and plausible.

Thus, if we treat the New Testament as a mere historical source like any other, we cannot *finally* decide by naturalistic-historical methods problems such as the problem of whether Christ claimed to be divine, or whether he claimed to be the Jewish Messiah, or even such important and untheological questions as whether or not Christ believed in and preached passive resistance, or nonresistance. The texts are there, clashing neatly for the rationalist.

On this problem of nonresistance, we may pick two very familiar extremes: "Ye have heard that it hath been said, An eye for an eye, and a tooth for a tooth: But I say unto you, that ye resist not evil: but whosoever shall smite thee on thy right cheek, turn to him the other also," and the apparent contradiction, "Think not that I am come to send peace on earth: I came not to send peace, but a sword." These two quotations from Jesus are given on almost the same page in Matthew. They can be reconciled—indeed they have been reconciled in millions of words, printed and preached. You may say that in the first passage Jesus warned against vulgar contentiousness, truculence, fighting of the cheap Hollywood or comic-strip sort; and that in the second passage he was urging on his disciples and followers spiritual warfare of the noblest sort. The fact remains that there is something to explain. The Bible, including both the Old and the New Testaments, has been—again from an outsider's point of view—for Western man until very recent times indeed the major source of what we have in the introduction to this book called noncumulative knowledge. This statement does not mean that the study of the Bible is unimportant; on the contrary, its study is of very great importance.

After such an introduction, there is some temerity in attempting any positive account of the historical Jesus. The reader, especially if he suffers from modern ignorance of the Bible, will do well to read, in a modernized version if he likes, at least the two Gospels of St. Luke and St. John, and form some opinion of his own. This writer inclines, by weight of many influences subconscious and unconscious as well as conscious, to the view that the historical Jesus was what the Germans call a *Schwärmer,* a religious enthusiast, a gentle but determined soul, a paradoxically this-worldly mystic not at all contemptuous of sensuous delights, but anxious that their enjoyment be free of jealousies, indeed free of competition, a man of great attraction for bewildered and unhappy people, and with a great gift (which makes our earlier Lincoln instance seem not unnatural) for making himself understood by ordinary people. Jesus was probably a much more masculine figure than later religious art made him out to be. And he seems clearly to have been able to attain the bitter exaltation of the prophets.

Again, the tradition of naturalistic-historical study of Christianity insists that there is a great deal in developed Christianity that is in no sense the work of Jesus. Here too the hostile critics go very far, some maintaining that in most important respects organized Christianity is the *opposite* of what Jesus stood for—ascetic instead of joyous, persecuting instead of tolerant, militant instead of pacific. Even allowing that these are overstatements, there is clearly in organized Christianity much that is not explicit in our fragmentary historical knowledge of Jesus. There is, at least by the second century, a complete and very subtle theology, a code of ethics, a disciplined mass of believers, a consecrated group of leaders, in short, a major religion. Christianity had gone beyond Christ—at least beyond the Christ who gathered together the fishermen of Galilee:

> At the same time came the disciples unto Jesus, saying, Who is the greatest in the kingdom of heaven? And Jesus called a little child unto him and set him in the midst of them, and said, Verily I say unto you, except ye be converted, and become as little children, ye shall not enter into the kingdom of heaven. Whosoever therefore shall humble himself as this little child, the same is greatest in the kingdom of heaven.

The man who seems to have done most to change Christianity from an obscure Jewish sect to a universal religion was Saul of Tarsus, in Christianity St. Paul, a Hellenized Jew and a Roman citizen. We have, by the usual standards of historical source material, more accurate direct knowledge of Paul than of Jesus. Scholars are generally agreed that the most famous of the Epistles of the New Testament that bear his name are in fact his work, and that the account of the labors of Paul and his co-workers in the Book of Acts is in its main outline accurate. Of course, we do not have for Paul the many intimate biographical details we have for many moderns of less importance than he—Napoleon, for instance. But we have at least enough so that no one has yet doubted his historical existence.

About Paul, his work and his ideas, the spectrum of modern opinion is quite as wide as for Jesus. There is a certain polarity discernible, well brought out in the title of a work by the English nineteenth-century radical Bentham: *Not Paul But Jesus*. Broadly speaking, one extreme of interpretation holds that the humanitarian aims of the kindly Jesus were perverted by the power-seeking, harshly puritanical Paul into just another organized tyranny. This is a frequent position among sentimental radicals outside the Christian Church, like Bentham himself. The polar opposite view is that Jesus was an ineffective but somehow dangerous Communist agitator, and Paul the wise administrator and realistic disciplinarian who curbed the excesses of Jesus' disciples and made the Christian Church a sound, sensible means of keeping the masses in their place. This view also can hardly be held by good Christians, though it approximates that of such would-be Machiavellians as the *Action française* group in the Third French Republic.

Christians have usually held, as Paul himself did, that the work of the apostle was a fulfillment of that of the Master, a widening but by no means a corruption of his mission. Paul himself never knew Jesus. Indeed, as an orthodox Jew Saul of Tarsus had at one time helped in the persecution of the little group of Jewish Christians after the crucifixion. The biblical account of his conversion to Christ while he was on the road to Damascus has become the classic instance of the sudden, apparently miraculous change of heart. From the fact that from this account Paul seems to have been in some sort of trance, and from odds and ends of information scattered through our sources, some have concluded that Paul was an epileptic. Of course, this kind of distant medical diagnosis is quite impossible scientifically. Paul was clearly no dull, conventional, unimaginative person, but a genius. One of the characteristics of our modern age is the recurrent cropping up of the notion that great men are pathological specimens. That view can teach us more about certain implications of modern democratic notions—especially the belief that the average is an ethical and aesthetic norm—than it can about great men.

Paul's major contribution to the spread of Christianity was to smooth the way from Jewish sectarianism to universalism; and the first stage to universalism at that time and place was, of course, through the Greek. Paul wrote and spoke the Greek of Hellenistic universalism, and he was familiar with Greek religious and philosophical ideas. He seems early in his life as a Christian to have taken a stand against the Judaizing wing of the new religion, and his work as an organizer has given him the title of "Apostle to the Gentiles." The great stumbling block for Gentiles who found the Christian way of life attractive was the Law of the Jews, the complex set of ritual ways that a born Jew learned as part of growing up. Somewhat oversimply the problem could be put: Can an uncircumcised man be a Christian? It was asking a lot of poor human nature to expect an adult Gentile to go through with what must then have been a dreaded operation. Paul answered clearly: The Greek, Egyptian, or Roman who accepted Christ need not be circumcised, need not abstain from pork, need not worry about the letter of the law. "For the letter killeth, but the spirit giveth life."

Do not let this famous text mislead you. Paul was no anarchist, and this was not an invitation to newly converted Christians to do what they liked. The spirit, according to Paul's life and works, was indeed an exacting, if comforting, spirit, and the life of the spirit a definite, prescribed way of life. *To an outsider,* Paul seems in fact to have substituted a Christian Law for a Jewish Law. Indeed, to the rationalist he seems to have been willing to play a bit on words: "All things are lawful for me, but all things are not expedient: all things are lawful for me, but all things edify not."

For we meet here one of the great, recurring human intellectual and emotional difficulties. The man who wants men to follow new ways must turn them from old ways. He must tell them they are, and ought to be, *free* to go new ways, that the Law, the prescriptions, the habits they were brought up to follow do not *really* bind them. The reformer is inevitably a rebel in the name of freedom. But he does not really want men to do the astonishing variety of things they would do were they free to follow their natural impulses and desires, free from conscience, laws, priests. He wants them to do the *right* things. It is true—and he really believes it—that "the spirit giveth life." But, as one of Paul's co-workers said, "believe not every spirit, but try the spirits whether they are of God; because many false prophets are gone out into the world." The reformer, too, finds he must appeal to law. Men are free, but free only to do right. The result can only be put in a paradox, like Rousseau's famous "forcing a man to be free." Jesus himself put it better: "For whosoever will save his life shall lose it: and whosoever will lose his life for my sake shall find it."

Paul as an administrator, as one of the great figures in a long line of leaders who helped make the Christian Church the extraordinarily effective organization it became, clearly belongs on the authoritarian side. His letters show him skillfully keeping a tight rein on the struggling little groups scattered throughout the Greek world and already established in Italy. Not that Paul was a harsh, tyrannical, or —worse—systematic authoritarian. He relied on his very great eloquence, on what must have been a very great personal appeal, on the human knowledge of one born to the cure of souls. But as a practical man Paul was in no sense soft, in no sense what we modern Americans think of as liberal or humanitarian.

Yet Paul was more than an administrator. He was also a theologian who, as we have seen, lent his full strength to the process of universalizing the new Church, of making its message attractive to the Gentiles. He has remained among the Fathers of the Church the great authority for the doctrine known as "justification by faith," to which we shall recur. At this point, we may focus rather on the practical Christianity of Paul, the kind of life he wanted Christians to lead.

But first it must be noted that almost certainly Paul, like most of his generation, did not believe Christians would live very long anyway on this earth. Christ himself had said, according to the First Gospel, "There be some standing here, which shall not taste of death, till they see the Son of man coming in his kingdom." The first Christians believed that Christ would return any day and bring an end to this world of sense experience. There would be a final judgment, and then bliss or damnation forever in another world. Naturally men who believed this were not concerned with long plans, with measurement of trends and tendencies, with the slow work of common sense. Paul might conceivably have compromised more with human nature had he believed human beings were to exist for at least the next two thousand years.

For much of Paul's teaching is puritanical in the generally current modern American sense of that word. Paul's views on sex relations, for instance, have shocked many even before our Freudian generation. The famous seventh chapter of I Corinthians, with its flat statement "it is better to marry than to burn," is actually rather ambiguous. Paul would apparently like to have the whole human race abstain from sexual intercourse. But the practical and experienced man of action in him knew this to be impossible, even with the end of the world at hand. So he counseled Christian marriage, and has some interesting and by no means intolerant advice on mixed marriages between Christians and pagans.

The good life according to Paul is, then, ascetic as to sense pleasures, whether those of the bed or those of the table. ("But meat commendeth us not to God: for neither, if we eat, are we the better; neither, if we eat not, are we the worse.") It is a simple life, free from the intellectual vanities the Greeks, especially, call wisdom ("Hath not God made foolish the wisdom of this world?") It is a life free from the backbiting, pettiness, quarrels, jealousies of daily life in this vulgar world, as well as—even more than—a life free from the more heroic sins. For again, Paul was used to working with ordinary men and women, and it is to them that he constantly addresses himself. He wants them to pull themselves out of their selfish little individual courses, into the great eddyless stream that is the life of the spirit.

For Paul, like so many other striking figures in the history of Christianity, combined the practical man with the mystic. He wants men free from entanglements with this dirty world of the senses so that they may live in the clean world of the spirit. But Paul's other world of the spirit is *not* the world of the lone individual who has attained *nirvana* for himself, or who has followed Plotinus into solitary philosophic ecstasy. Paul's other world remains a human world, a world of common effort, of sharing, of faith, hope, and charity. And Paul's best-known words are those of the thirteenth chapter of Corinthians:

Charity suffereth long, and is kind; charity envieth not; charity vaunteth not itself, is not puffed up, doth not behave itself unseemly, seeketh not her own, is not easily provoked, thinketh no evil; rejoiceth not in iniquity, but rejoiceth in the truth; beareth all things, believeth all things, hopeth all things, endureth all things. Charity never faileth: but whether there be prophecies, they shall fail; whether there be tongues, they shall cease; whether there be knowledge, it shall vanish away. For we know in part, and we prophesy in part. But when that which is perfect is come, then that which is in part shall be done away. When I was a child, I spake as a child, I understood as a child, I thought as child: but when I became a man, I put away childish things. For now we see through a glass, darkly; but then face to face: now I know in part; but then shall I know even as also I am known. And now abideth faith, hope, charity, these three; but the greatest of these is charity.

And, finally, salvation. Even in this passage with its emphasis on love (which some think a better translation of the Greek than "charity") Paul brings in the great promise of Christianity: "now I know in part; but then shall I know even as also I am known." This world ("now"), even this world as Christians try to make it, is but a testing ground for life in the next world ("then"). Those who are saved will enjoy in that world eternal bliss; those who are not saved will suffer there eternal torture. All true Christians will be saved.

What is the test of a true Christian? Paul, to an outsider, seems to impose a dual test, which, however, he clearly regards not as twofold but as one. First, the true Christian must belong to an organized Christian group (Church) and have carried out, and continue carrying out, certain ritual acts, such as baptism and communion; second, he must be Christian inside, in his soul, must have attained that state the mystic never quite succeeds in putting in words, though he call it "grace" or "faith" or something else.

The contrast between works and faith, ritual performance and inner light, runs all through the history of Christianity. *To the orthodox, one is impossible without the other.* A Christian not right inside himself can obviously not behave right outside. *But,* we can all see his outside, and only God can see inside him. That is why, though religious innovators almost always start by an appeal to the doctrine of justification by faith ("the spirit"), they end, if they succeed in gathering a flock of their own, by returning to some external test, some justification by works ("the letter"). We shall come back to this problem again with Luther.

The other great name in the earliest Christian thought is John, to whom are attributed the Fourth Gospel, three brief pastoral letters, and that extraordinary final book of our New Testament, Revelation. Now this John, the youthful beardless apostle of Christian painting and sculpture, who stands out among the bearded rest, must have been prodigiously old when he wrote the Fourth Gospel, if the scholars are right about the date of its composition. In fact, so much scholarly doubt exists about the historical reality of John that even very orthodox and very sincere Christian learned men write habitually of "the author or authors of the Fourth Gospel," and "the author of Revelation."

Revelation is an apocalyptic book full of the most cryptic prophecies. It has served for two thousand years as an arsenal for the kind of person the rationalist, and even the sober, conventional Christian, has to consider a crank. Revelation is a book before which the non-believer, and even the ordinary pedestrian believer, is simply helpless. The searcher for hidden things can find almost anything in it. Almost everything that has happened in the last millennia has been found in Revelation.

The Fourth Gospel is, however, one of the most important Christian writings. Its author is a shadowy person compared to Paul. Just because we know so little about him, we are tempted to see him in his work. The author of the Fourth Gospel does not seem to have been an administrator, a practical man charged with cure of souls. On the other hand, it is probably erroneous to see in him the meta-physician, the theologian, the man withdrawn from the world. The author of the Fourth Gospel obviously wrote under an acute moral tension: In his opinion so-called Christians, men who had never known Christ, were missing the great point of Christianity, that Christ *is* the impossible union of God and man, the other world and this world, the infinite and the finite. What earlier mystics had striven in vain to achieve Christ achieved by the mere fact of his being Christ. But this union of God and man was in constant danger of being misinterpreted by ordinary human beings, constantly tempted to make understanding easier for themselves by thinking of Christ either as all-man or as all-god.

The term the author of the Fourth Gospel uses to express this miraculous union of God and man is *Logos,* "the Word":

In the beginning was the Word, and the Word was with God, and the Word was God. . . . And the Word was made flesh, and dwelt among us, (and we beheld his glory, the glory as of the only begotten of the Father,) full of grace and truth.

Thousands of pages have been written about this Word, and the related theological concept of the Holy Ghost, by which orthodox Christianity has ever since sought to provide for the faithful an intelligible link between the divided worlds of God and man. The whole Fourth Gospel focuses around this miracle of the man-god; but it is not, save for the famous introductory sentences, an abstract theological treatise. It is a life of Christ, but a life always centered on Christ as the Word made flesh:

> If I do not the works of my Father, believe me not. But if I do, though ye believe not me, believe the works: that ye may know, and believe, that the Father is in me, and I in him.

The ideas and ideals of early Christianity are only part of its story, even for the intellectual historian. The ideas of Paul, John, and hundreds of less well-known laborers in the vineyard were made real to the faithful in a ritual, in a series of communal ceremonies; and the faithful were disciplined, held together, strengthened by what, in a lay society, we frankly call government. Both of these subjects—ritual or liturgy, and church organization—are of enormous importance. We can here but indicate their importance for the Christian way of life.

The central ritual act of Christianity is the Eucharist. The central source for the Eucharist is the account, roughly the same in Matthew, Mark, and Luke, of Christ's last supper with his disciples. Matthew tells it as follows:

> And as they were eating, Jesus took bread, and blessed it, and brake it, and gave it to the disciples, and said, Take, eat; this is my body. And he took the cup, and gave thanks, and gave it to them, saying, Drink ye all of it; for this is my blood of the new testament, which is shed for many for the remission of sins.

Now this is an excellent example of what seems to some naturalistic historians a tampering with the facts, or at least a later addition. There is too much theology here, especially in the words "remission of sins." Such historians suppose that Christ himself may well have had a last sorrowful meal with his disciples and may even have asked them to remember him. They suppose that the very first Christians, practicing the communism of goods as we know they did, marked out certain of their common meals, their *agapes* or love feasts, in memory of Christ. Finally, they suppose that fairly soon this ceremony came to be in fact a sacrament, a constantly renewed miraculous sharing of the life of Christ the God, a sharing, even a theophagy such as we have noted already in the Greek mystery religions. Then, and only then, were the Gospels as we know drawn up, and Christ made to say: *this is my body.*

Whatever the historical process involved, the Church clearly did very early develop the sacrament. The Eucharist, or Holy Communion, involved first definite acts (ritual) and second a goal achieved —a spiritual goal, of course—by such acts. At the central point of the Eucharist, the believer ate a small piece of bread and sipped a bit of wine from a stock that the miraculous power of God, transmitted in an unbroken line through Christ to his disciples and thence to all priests, had altered to a divine substance, respectively the body and blood of Christ. By this act, if his whole behavior and state of mind at the time was truly Christian—that is, if he was in a state of grace —his earlier sins were forgiven, canceled out, and his membership in the band of the elect, those who would be saved and granted eternal life in blessedness, was ratified before man and God. An ever recurring miracle once more challenged this daily and evil life.

Now it ought to be evident even from this brief paragraph that the doctrine of the Eucharist, if seen as a free intellectual problem invites many interpretations. The simple word *altered* as used above would offend many theologians. They would insist that the bread and wine are not "altered" in the vulgar sense of the word, not "altered" chemically. Then there are problems about the role of the priest. Suppose he is an unworthy priest, himself a sinner? Is the sacrament he gives valid? The Catholic Church later answered yes to this question, when challenged by an active heresy, the Donatist which answered no. There are problems about the communicant, the one who takes the sacrament. Just what is a state of grace? How can the believer be sure he is in a state of grace? Ought he to be sure? There are problems about the very form of the sacrament, such as the one that later divided Catholics and Protestants: Shall the communicant take communion in both kinds (both bread and wine) or in one kind only?

Important though these intellectual problems are in the early history of Christianity, they must not be taken as all-important. Christianity owes much to its organization as well as to its theology. Now the central fact about the organization of early Christianity is the growth of a differentiation between laymen and clergy. Christianity, in contrast to Greek and Roman paganism, came to have a priestly caste very markedly set apart from the lay believers. Again, many critics believe that Jesus planned no such church, but again no proof is possible. Certainly the beginnings of the differentiation between lay and clerical come almost as early as organized Christianity, certainly by the beginning of the second century.

Here once more we may pause to emphasize the *interrelation* of ideas and the rest of human life. A pure intellectualist might say that because Christianity made so sharp, indeed so absolute a distinction between God and man, this world and the other world, it had to work out a sharply defined clergy to mediate between God and man, just as the author of the Fourth Gospel had to have his *Logos*. A pure anti-intellectualist might say that because Christianity got started among a power-hungry group of "natural" priests, a theology justifying the priests, together with a set of sacraments calling for priests with a monopoly on the necessary miraculous powers, had to be devised. Both intellectualist and anti-intellectualist would be quite wrong. Christianity starts in a cosmopolitan world of wars, slavery, all sorts of widespread human misery, and its basic appeal is the appeal of salvation, of mental, spiritual wholeness in a divided world. Its theology, its ethics, its government are all *mutually determining factors in its growth*. Each influences the others, and is influenced by them.

The remarkable thing about early Christian organization is the

effectiveness of the network of individual cells, or churches. The
Christians held together—held together in the earliest years against
the excessive enthusiasms, the holy rolling, of some of the brothers and
sisters, held together in later years against severe if sporadic persecutions by Roman officials who regarded Christian refusal to sacrifice
to the God-Emperor as evidence of treason to the state, held together
even against the internal theological bickerings, the wave of heresies
that accompanied the great successes of the new religion.

The form of organization taken on by the Church is closely
parallel to the civil organization of the Roman Empire. Indeed, one
of the key units of Christian organization, the diocese, was under the
same name an administrative area of the Empire. The clergy, early
differentiated from the laymen, were organized in a chain of authority
much as in an army; they formed a *hierarchy* from altar boys and
other lesser ministrants through priest to bishop to archbishop to pope.
In these first Christian centuries the critical office is that of the bishop,
a name deriving from the Greek word *episcopos*, "overseer." The
bishop, like a good regimental officer, worked directly with the priests
and important laymen in his jurisdiction. Above the bishops, the
metropolitans (archbishops), patriarchs, and the pope himself tended,
like staff officers, to be concerned with the higher strategy and tactics
of the movement, and to lose touch with rank and file.

In the very earliest Christian communities there was probably no
distinction between laymen and clergy. And the first clergy were
probably self-elected, but confirmed in their functions by the good will
of their brethren among the faithful. Ordination, the formal sacrament that qualified a man for the miraculous office of priest, grew up
not only because of doctrines like the Eucharist, which required it,
but also because the wild enthusiasms of the brothers and sisters so
readily went to excesses. Indeed, you can find the problems and the
answers of the organizers clear enough even in the writings of Paul.
Yet from these democratic origins there remained, especially for the
office of bishop, some sense that these chosen officials were chosen by
the voice of the community, by what we call "election." Early bishops
were chosen by vote of clergy and certain active laymen, and even

the Middle Ages the bishops of the Catholic Church were canonically (legally) elected by the clergy organized in the chapter of the cathedral. Actually, however, the hierarchy of the organized church was fairly early established as an appointive one. The bishop was certainly, if not king, at least colonel in his diocese. Bishops assembled in councils were the active, organized, and organizing groups that gave final direction to growing Christianity.

For during the first three or four centuries with which we are here concerned, the Church had no single head on earth. The final establishment of the complete hierarchy, with the pope at the apex, had to await the separation between the East and the West of the Empire, between what became the Greek Orthodox Church and what became the Roman Catholic Church. It is true that very early the Bishop of Rome set up special claims to predominance among bishops. The skeptically inclined outside the Church believe that as early as the third or fourth generation after Christ interested Romanists inserted in the New Testament the passages that gave scriptural basis for the Petrine tradition, according to which Jesus himself planned the Roman papacy. Matthew has Jesus say to his disciple: "And I say also unto thee, that thou art Peter; and upon this rock I will build my church; and the gates of hell shall not prevail against it." There is here what in undignified matters is called a pun, since the Greek words for Peter and for stone are the same—*petros.* Very early tradition had Peter go to Rome itself, found the Church there, and die a martyr.

What was planned and what accidental in this chain no man can now tell. At any rate, by the Petrine tradition the Bishop of Rome is marked as head of the Church. The prestige of Rome, the place of Rome in the by then age-old scheme of things, the later abandonment of Rome by the emperors in favor of Constantinople—all this made the headship of the Bishop of Rome what we like to call inevitable. In these first centuries, however, each of the Patriarchs—an Eastern title—of Constantinople, Antioch, and Alexandria had firm notions of his own importance, if not supremacy, and in the great debates over the heresies the Roman see was by no means always in a dominating position. Indeed, as we have noted, the Eastern and

Western churches finally separated. Some efforts were made to bring them together, for it seemed scandalous that there should be two competing ways to heaven, but by the eleventh century the separation was final.

The great wave of heresies, at its height in the third century, marks the coming of the age of Christianity. Men and women of the now powerful faith debated about almost everything debatable. We cannot in a book of this sort attempt an account even of the major heresies. They range through a wide spectrum of what we have called noncumulative knowledge. They represent what to an outsider seems the normal reaction of a large number of educated and partly educated persons confronted with an opportunity to discuss quite freely these great questions of right and wrong, of salvation and damnation, of the ways of God to man. What makes them heresies instead of mere differences of opinion (as in a debating club) is that such differences of opinion in troubled times get translated into action, social and common action. But continued subdivision into competing groups ruins the unity of action with which the movement sets out, and to which it tries hard to adhere.

The main group of Christians, the group that won its way through persecutions and heresies as the Roman Catholic Church, preserved and strengthened its unity, as it seems to an outsider, precisely because it had to struggle against, and make compromises with, the heretics. For the prevalence of heresies—that is, of disagreements over value-judgments—is in the youth of a movement probably a sign of strength rather than of weakness. Too much division over ideas can probably kill a movement; but a certain amount strengthens it. Apparently the Catholic Church was strengthened by the heresies it overcame.

These heresies ranged over most of human conduct and belief. Some were centered on the sacraments, such as that over the validity of a sacrament administered by a sinful priest; others on actual liturgy, such for instance as the quarrel over the way to determine the date for Easter; others on matters of conduct, such as priestly abstention from sexual intercourse; others on very high matters of theology (philosophy) indeed. One whole group of heresies, labeled Gnostic from the

Greek word for knowledge, forms a fascinating study in the chesslike complexities the human mind can build in words and emotions. The Gnostics were mostly intellectuals of the Graeco-Roman world in search of magic—sophisticated magic. They knew about most of the other competing cults of the Graeco-Roman world, and about its philosophies, especially Neoplatonic philosophy. They tended, in spite of their bewildering variety, to have one thing in common, a belief that this sense world is evil, or nonexistent, or more simply, that the everyday world is an evil illusion. The figure of Jesus they found appealing, but it was Jesus the miracle-worker, Jesus the God. His human nature, his sharing in this world, they could not for a moment admit.

We may, however, take the final controversy over the relation between Jesus and the One God—God the Father—as typical of the whole period of the heresies. Here much more than Gnosticism was involved. Official Christianity finally accepted in 325 at the Council of Nicaea, near Constantinople, the trinitarian, or Athanasian, position. According to this the persons of the Trinity, God the Father, Jesus Christ the Son, and the Holy Ghost, are real persons, three in number, and yet they are also one. Christianity remained a monotheism, its Trinity well above mathematics. The opposing doctrine of Arius, if not exactly Unitarianism as we know it in twentieth-century America, was at least on the Unitarian side in many ways, tending to subordinate Jesus to God, to make him later in time, an emanation of God, or—theology is a subtle thing—in some other way less than God the Father. The critical phrases of the struggle were the Athanasian *homoousion* (of one [same] essence with the Father) and the Arian *homoiousion* (of like [similar] essence to the Father). Popular wit, always alert for this sort of thing, lighted on the letter *i* (the Greek *iota,* by later Latin transliteration made *jota*) as the whole difference between these parties of dignified churchmen. Hence, by fairly direct inheritance, our still-used expression "not a jot"—not a tiny bit.

This early example of semantic skepticism need not persuade us that there was no real difference between Athanasians and Arians, and hence that the Council of Nicaea might just as well have chosen for

Arius as for Athanasius. We have already noted in connection with the Fourth Gospel how real, how crucial for Christianity is its fruitful tension between this world and the other world. Christianity cannot afford the logic required to make a choice between these two logically incompatible beliefs. Gnosticism accepted would have led it into a jungle of magic, swooning, and denial of this world. Arianism accepted might have led it into a mere scientific or common-sense acceptance of this world. Catholicism—traditional Christianity—has kept a foot, a solidly planted foot, in each world.

The Council of Nicaea was called by an emperor, Constantine, himself politically at least a Christian. By 325 the once obscure Jewish heresy had come to dominate the Graeco-Roman world. Remnants of pagan groups were to exist for several more centuries, and the triumphant Church was to adopt as local saints, as local uses and superstitions, many pagan beliefs and habits. Still, the victory was amazingly complete. Christianity by the fourth century had become the religion of the Western world.

Christian Belief

At this point, with the Church triumphant, we must attempt a schematic view of Christian belief among common men and women. This we shall have to do without the subtleties of theology, concentrating on that mythical figure, the average man. But the reader will understand that on nearly every point recorded in the next few pages differences of opinion, some of them on very subtle points indeed, have existed somewhere, sometime, and often most of the time, among men calling themselves Christian.

By the fourth century, belief in the immediate second coming of Christ and the consequent end of the world had naturally enough died down. From time to time Christian prophets arise to predict the immediate second coming, and to gather little bands of believers. So in central New York state, in the enlightened nineteenth century, the Millerites gathered in confidence and white robes to await the end of the world. But these chiliastic beliefs, as they are technically called, are crank beliefs, outside formal, accepted Christian belief. Besides, it must be noted that from the point of view of the fate of the individual, Christianity has by no means lost a sense of the immediacy and finality of divine judgment on human beings: At death every Christian expects to face such final judgment.

The Christian believes in a single God, embodied in the Trinity, a perfect being who created this world and man, intending man to live the happy life recorded in the Garden of Eden. But Adam, the first man, whom God made a free agent, chose to disobey God by sinning. As a result of Adam's sin, mankind was driven from Eden by a just God and condemned to an imperfect life on earth. God, however, did not desert his own. As it is recorded in the Old Testament, his chosen people kept alive in this harsh world his worship, and after two thousand years of darkness, God sent his only-begotten son, Jesus Christ, to bring to mankind the possibility of redemption from sin, of a return, not precisely to Eden, but to an Eden-like state not on this earth but in heaven. Christ, God become man, died on the cross that all men might have the chance to avoid death.

The possibility of redemption, a chance to avoid death through Christ's resurrection—this was the gift. To achieve redemption, a man had to be a true Christian. He had to have had the emotional experience of *conversion,* of spiritual awareness of the gift of grace Christ had brought. He had to be a church member in good standing, conforming to certain prescribed ritual practices: When he was received into the Church he underwent the sacrament of baptism, by which he was ritually cleansed of his sins; he shared by the sacrament of the Eucharist in the periodic renewal of the miracle by which Christ brought redemption to mankind; should he lapse into sinning, he was restored to spiritual wholeness again by confession to a priest, and by the sacrament of penance; his marriage, too, was a sacrament. Finally, as death approached, he would receive from a priest, if it were at all possible, the sacrament of extreme unction, which prepared him decently to meet his final judgment.

The Christian, then, had his own law, which he had to observe. He had also somewhat less precise ethical prescriptions to follow. No longer was Christianity in the fourth century a sect of humble or re-bellious folk, practicing communism of consumer's goods, disdainful of rank and wealth. The Christian could be rich, and he could be what this world calls powerful. Indeed, already there were Christian moralists who complained that rich Christians were trying to buy themselves salvation, though they failed to live up to Christian ideals in practice. These ideals are in part the ideals of most of the higher religions—honesty, kindness, modesty, sobriety, a life on the ascetic side, but not, for the ordinary Christian, a life in sackcloth and ashes. For the ordinary Christian, we must insist, the life of the senses was not, as it was in many oriental faiths, an illusion; it was not wholly evil; it was not even in any clear sense a mere stage in the soul's progress, certainly not such a stage in any elaborate oriental cult of metempsychosis. For the Christian, this world could not be wholly bad, since God had made it. For the Christian, this world presented an opportunity to lead a good life preparatory to the perfect life of salvation.

Moreover, though Christianity as a great Church accepted social and economic inequalities on this earth, Christian doctrine never ceased to affirm the equality of all human beings before God. Human souls cannot be given an order of rank. In the final event, they will be numbered among the saved or among the damned, but neither rank nor wealth nor power will influence that dread decision. Indeed, to be realistic, one must admit that Christian teaching has tended to tell the ordinary man that rank, wealth, or power, if not barriers to salvation, are at any rate handicaps. Now to certain temperaments, this steadily affirmed Christian doctrine of the equality of souls before God is either meaningless or a kind of opiate to keep the poor poor. We may more modestly conclude that this doctrine has provided for Western culture a kind of minimal estimate of the dignity of man, a sharp separation of human beings from other animate beings.

Finally, the Christian, and especially the early and the medieval Christian, before the great growth of modern science, thought of God and his ministers (angels, saints) as constantly taking part in what went on in this world. The Christian did indeed distinguish between the natural occurrence, which was usual, and the supernatural occurrence, which was unusual. But he clearly did not have scientific or rationalist notions about the usual events in this world, did not even think of the average as normal. God could and did do things that men, animals, and the elements couldn't do of themselves. If you wish, you may say that the Christian was superstitious, that he lived in a world of unreasonable fears and hopes. To him, Judas Iscariot had been the thirteenth in a supremely tragic context, and he did not wish to get involved in anything that might repeat in any form that badness of thirteen. The supernatural, therefore, if not indeed as common as the natural, was in his mind not only quite as real, but often *quite as predictable.* It was something you could cope with, by the old, tried religious ways. The devil was likely to turn up, of course; but the Christian knew a way—indeed by medieval times many ways—of exorcising him. Neither the natural nor the supernatural aspects of the universe were to the true Christian basically hostile. Both were part of God's plan, and the true Christian, though he ought never to be wholly, indecently, priggishly sure of his own salvation, at least *knew* enough to adjust his conduct in this world to both natural and supernatural occurrences, and *believed* enough to feel that he had a good chance of salvation.

The Reasons for the Triumph of Christianity

There is a simple answer to the question of why Christianity won its way among the many competing cults of the Graeco-Roman world: It is true, and truth prevails by God's will. But even quite good Christians, at least since the beginnings of modern critical historical and sociological writing, have been unable to resist the temptation to give more concrete naturalistic-historical reasons for that triumph. Answers have been many and varied, often motivated by hatred of Christianity. Thus some anti-Christian rationalists have maintained that Christianity won out because it appealed to the ignorance, superstition, and weakness of the enslaved proletariat of the Graeco-Roman world. Others have insisted that Christianity offered something to everybody, that it borrowed without compunction from all its competitors. Others have emphasized what we should now call the escapist side of Christianity, its appeal to the tired and disappointed men and women of a sick society.

We must insist here, as throughout this book, that if the triumph of Christianity be regarded as a natural event in history, then many, many factors went into that triumph. These factors we cannot in our present state of knowledge weigh and measure and turn into a formula. We can but insist that there has been no explanation of the rise of Christianity without *some* element of truth. Here we can but go over old ground and familiar elements, and attempt a rough adjustment among them.

First, there is a whole series of factors centering around the syncretic element in Christianity. This syncretic factor (syncretism is the combining of elements drawn from various religions) is taken by the simplifiers as being the whole explanation, whereas it is only a part. You can find in the Greek mystery cults, in the cult of Isis, in the cult of Mithra, in Judaism, and in other cults of the Hellenistic world *samples* of almost everything the Christian believed—ritual cleansing, a god that dies and is resurrected, a virgin that bears a child, a day of judgment, spring festivals, winter-solstice festivals, devils, saints, and angels. What you do not find outside Christianity is the *whole* that is Christian belief and practice. To say that Christianity borrowed from other cults is, from the naturalistic-historical point of view, no more and no less a complete explanation of Christianity than a source study of Shakespeare's works is an explanation of their greatness. Of course it is important to note that Christianity has in it elements of belief and practice derived from various sources. It may even be true that the known few and the nameless many who formed Christian beliefs in the early centuries were particularly skillful in choosing here an Orphic, there a Mithraic bit for the new faith. But this picture of the early Fathers deliberately planning a cult, like the directors of an American firm planning to market a new product, besides being vulgar and offensive, is historically and psychologically unsound. The Founding Fathers of Christianity were not such deliberate planners, above all not such intellectuals. Their syncretic work was in large part an unconscious work. Christianity has something in common with the cult of Isis, for instance, not so much because Christians deliberately thought the Virgin Mary out in Isiac terms, but rather because both Isis and Mary helped fulfill the need for a consoling mother-figure.

Second, there is also some truth in the assertion that Christianity, with its promise of salvation in another world to compensate for poverty, suffering, oppression in this world, proved a most attractive faith to the proletariat of the declining Roman Empire; there is truth in the closely related assertion that to the tired, bored, blasé, as well as to the naturally idealistic of the privileged classes, Christianity was either a most attractive way of escape from a world they did not like or a stimulating challenge to make that world better. Christianity, not so much because of its syncretic origins as because of its firm refusal to opt exclusively either for this world or the next, offered a wide range of satisfactions to human beings. Many of those satisfactions, it is true, were of the kind the modern psychologist suggests by words like compensation and escapism, and for which we have always had a good common word: consolation. There is, then, truth in the statement that Christianity is a religion for the weak, for the simple, for the oppressed. The Gospels are explicit on this point.

Third, Christianity also made striking progress among the upper classes and the intellectuals, both Greek and Roman. Very early indeed we find scattered instances of conversion of men and women of good family to the despised sect. No doubt, from the point of view of the sociologist, such conversions are much like a present-day conversion of a banker's son to Communism. Obviously, Christianity in its first few centuries did not appeal to the satisfied. Those who turned to Christianity had already turned away from the ways in which they had been brought up. But it is a mistake to think of the appeal of Christianity as wholly an emotional one. The growing theology of the new sect was complex enough, indeed intellectually respectable enough, to attract men of philosophic bent. One of the factors in the ultimate triumph of Christianity. then, was its theology, which by the end of the second century had been well integrated with the Greek intellectual tradition. Indeed, for the later Greeks theological debates in a sense took the place of the old political debates of the *polis,* and like them, went far down into classes of the population not ordinarily given to abstract discussion. At the height of the Arian controversy, your barber in Constantinople or Alexandria might well have asked you whether you thought the Son was, in fact, coeval with the Father.

Fourth, Christianity made an appeal to still another, and very important, kind of person, the active, organizing, "practical" person. One of the illusions satisfied, conservative people sometimes have about revolutionaries—*and the early Christians were revolutionaries*—is that revolutionary movements are wholly staffed by impractical people. This, of course, is true only of small, marginal, crank movements—and even in such movements there are likely to be a few hardheaded men. Great revolutionary movements early attract men who see in them no doubt a chance to satisfy ambition, drive for power, even desire for wealth, but also a chance to get things done, to clean up this messy world and make it a better place. The men who staffed the early Christian Church, the deacons, priests, and bishops, the men responsible for the admirable Christian organization, for those qualities of internal *political* strength in which Christianity so markedly excelled its competitors among the oriental cults—these men, whatever else they were, deserve those blessed modern American words of praise, "efficient" and "practical."

Fifth, Christianity inherited from its Jewish origins, and managed during the crucial years of its growth to hold on to, an exclusiveness that stood it in good stead. Christianity always refused to make alliances with any other cult. Even Christian syncretism—and we have seen that from our point of view Christianity has a syncretic element—deserves a stronger term than "borrowing"; the Christians annexed, appropriated a belief or a ritual for themselves, jealously insisting it was a Christian monopoly. Notably, the other cults all compromised with emperor worship. The Christian could not put a pinch of incense on the altar of divine Caesar and remain a good Christian. Now

Christian tradition has no doubt exaggerated the horrors of the persecutions, official and unofficial, that the faithful were subjected to, and it has exaggerated the extent to which persecuted Christians preferred the lions to apostasy. Still, the Christians were persecuted when the believers in Mithra, for instance, were the favorites of the powerful Roman army. And up to a point, persecution strengthens in a purely worldly way the group persecuted. At the very least, persecution drives the persecuted into a more efficient, disciplined unity. And unity, in spite of the outbreak of heresies as pressure lessened, the early Christians clearly had.

To sum up: From a naturalistic and historical point of view Christianity overcame its competitors for no single reason, but rather through a concurrence of favorable factors, *mutually interacting*. Its promise of salvation was as concrete and attractive a promise as any of its competitors made. The fact that salvation came only after death, and could in a sense be made more certain if the individual were poor, humble, underprivileged, gave Christianity great attractiveness for the proletarian masses of the Roman Empire. Yet the theological subtleties of the new faith gave room for the intellectuals, its mystical ranges made escape from this world possible for many emotional and imaginative souls, and the practical problems of organizing what was clearly a great power on this earth had a great appeal for the practical man of reforming energy. A sense of mission, a sense of separateness from and superiority to their pagan fellows, the persecutions undertaken by a government to which the behavior of the new sect was puzzling and probably treasonous, combined to make the early Christians a working team. Christians stuck together, Christians helped one another throughout the Empire. At the same distance of time from Christ that we are from the first settlers of Virginia and New England, the Christians were running the Empire.

They were not much like the fisher folk of Galilee who listened to the words of Jesus. Yet the words were there, as they are today: "It is easier for a camel to go through the eye of a needle, than for a rich man to enter into the kingdom of God." "Blessed are the meek: for they shall inherit the earth." "Therefore I say unto you, Take no thought for your life, what ye shall eat, or what ye shall drink; nor yet for your body, what ye shall put on." The confrontation we are now making is unfair, as we hope to make clear, but it is not unreal. For some seventy generations now rich men, proud men, and men very much concerned with what they eat, drink, and wear have sat calmly in church, listened to the above texts, and continued to be rich, proud, and much concerned with what they ate, drank, and wore.

There is, then, a problem here. Was the triumph of Christianity at the same time the failure of *true* Christianity, of primitive Christianity, of the Christianity of Jesus? For something like these seventy generations rebels within and without the Christian Church have accused it of forsaking the Christian way for the way of the world. They have flung back at these successful Christians the words of Christ himself: "For what shall it profit a man, if he shall gain the whole world, and lose his own soul?" It is time we attempted the difficult task of appraising the place of organized Christianity in the tradition of Western society.

The Christian Way of Life

The reader is perhaps wearied with our frequent insistence that we are writing of Christianity from the outside, as a series of relations among human beings. But the point must be made again firmly, for if Christianity is so regarded, one would expect the triumphant Christianity of the Council of Nicaea, the official faith of the world's greatest empire, to be quite different from the Christianity of the fishermen of Galilee. On the other hand, if one takes the New Testament as the final assertion of Christian truth, one is bound to conclude, not just that the Christianity of the fourth century was different from that of the first, but that the Christianity of the fourth century was not Christian.

We may take a lay analogy. The United States of 1950 is not much like early New England. Stand for a while in Plymouth by the elegantly housed and protected boulder known as Plymouth Rock;

watch the crowds of tourists drive up in their cars, get out and inspect the rock (with a variety of comments, many of them wisecracks), buy souvenirs, salt-water taffy, soda pop from the hawkers, and then drive off. You are inevitably tempted to wonder what the Pilgrim Fathers would think of it all. Would they recognize their descendants, their successors? Or would they feel that this enormously successful America had gained a world but lost its own soul?

Ever since the fourth century, we Westerners have been Christians of one sort or another, at the very least *professed* Christians. Only within the last few centuries has it been possible for many members of Western society openly and collectively to profess atheism, or agnosticism, or theosophy, or any faith other than Christianity. Avowed unbelievers were rare in the thousand years of the Middle Ages. Since all men have been Christians, it was inevitable that Christianity be all things to all men. St. Francis, Erasmus, Loyola, Machiavelli, Pascal, Wesley, Napoleon, Gladstone, and John D. Rockefeller were all Christians. You can, of course, say that only certain of these were *real* Christians. But you cannot classify Christians as the taxonomist classifies plants; at any rate, you will not in your classification get the kind of agreement the taxonomist gets.

Indeed, to avoid the abstractions and unrealities that must inevitably accompany any attempt to generalize at a high level, one must go to the Fathers themselves, to those citizens of the universal Roman state who sought in Christianity a way out of the difficulties they confronted in pagan society. They are in many ways the elite of their society, men determined to go to the roots of the troubles they feel. They are not, in modern jargon, mere escapists. Some of them are scholars, men who in another society and another culture might have been no more than scholars—Jerome, for instance. Some of them are born administrators, turned to intellectual and emotional questioning by the crises they faced, like Ambrose, or even Augustine. Some of them are seekers, reformers, idealists, perfectionists not content even with the other world, like Tertullian. But they have in common a sense of mission, a sense of belonging to something that is going to go beyond anything men have known or felt before. They have, though some are pedants and some are men of action, a focus in a new, adventurous, conquering, fresh emotional faith.

Historically, the Christian Church has actually allowed a variety of ways of life, even a considerable variety of intellectual explanations of life, to go on under the common label of Christianity. We are all familiar with the proliferation of sects that has gone on since the Protestant Reformation of the sixteenth century. From Unitarian through Holy Roller to High-Church Episcopalian there is surely a great emotional and intellectual range. But even before Luther, in the days when the Catholic Church gave religious unity to the West, that unity was no doctrinaire, no totalitarian unity; it did not mean uniformity.

The Mass, the creeds, the catechisms, and much else were of course uniform. The language of the priest in the services was Latin. There was a hierarchically organized church government that could settle disputes, if necessary by the harsh means of excluding one party from the Christian community. All this, so characteristic of medieval Christianity, is pretty well established by the fourth century. But consider a perfectly possible cross-section of actual services of the Mass in the West during the first centuries of established Christianity. Here in a monastery the monks pause from their silent labors in garden or library. Here at the court of a Germanic chieftain who has carved himself out a rich principality in the decay of Roman rule the prince's chaplain gives the Eucharist to the prince's court, including his numerous concubines. In Rome, the pope himself officiates at a great Mass at the Church of the Lateran, attended by beggars, merchants, soldiers, officials, all that is left of a decaying city. In a small French village a priest stumbles through a ritual he hardly understands before a congregation of illiterate field workers. Nearby, in a villa just fortified against increasingly numerous marauding bands, the master, a Gallo-Roman proud of his culture, at heart and in private a pagan, yawns through a Mass his wife has made him attend. On the Rhine, a little band of soldiers hear Mass from a military chaplain just before they set out on patrol. The point should be clear: The way of life, the *practice,* of monk, chieftain, concubine, merchant, beggar, peasant, gentleman, and soldier were very different indeed, very differently related to what Christian theology means by "this world."

Yet Christianity has always driven strongly toward what the philosophers call monism. At the very bottom, what usually makes a man a monist is the belief that the universe is somehow designed around *homo sapiens,* or at least around some part, some faculty, of man. The Christian cannot accept the pluralist view that man is one organism among many, in a universe not designed for man or any other organism—a universe not, in fact, designed in advance. The Christian wants to understand, for Christianity is a highly intellectual religion. But he wants to understand wholly, completely, not partially, as the scientist understands. Some Christians, indeed, can content themselves with complete submission to a God who understands all, but who cannot be understood by his creatures. But, like the analogous position of the mystic, that is, that this sense world is an illusion, this belief in the final impotence of man's understanding has been in the history of established Christianity heretical, or dangerously on the edge of heresy.

This drive toward monism (not merely monotheism) has, then, been one great intellectual trait of Christianity. And in spite of the very important distinctions orthodox Christian thought has always made between this world and the other world, body and soul, natural and supernatural, Christianity has resisted firmly the temptation to accept a *formal* dualism. Indeed, of all the heresies of the first few centuries, the orthodox probably feared and hated most a frank dualism, hardly Christian at all, but Persian in origin, known as Manichaeanism. The Manichaeans solved the problem of theodicy by allowing God (light) and his satanic opponent (darkness) to fight it out on something like even grounds. Their God was good, but not omnipotent. The virtuous on this earth should fight on God's side, but they could not count on victory. This position, which historically has proved attractive to a good many people, was firmly rejected by orthodox Christianity, and by none more firmly than the greatest of the Latin fathers, St. Augustine, who had been a Manichaean before his conversion.

Now this drive toward monism meant in practice that orthodox Christianity as a corporate body pursued none of its characteristic doctrines, judgments, and ways of life to an extreme. Had it done so, it would have had to give up its great claim to catholicity, to universality. Monistic doctrines by no means lead to compromise and breadth by any logical sequence—indeed, quite the contrary. Monistic idealism or monistic materialism can be narrow, intolerant, exclusive beliefs. It was the practical needs of a great Catholic Church in a universal Empire—a Catholic Church succeeding, in a sense, to the role of such an Empire—that made Christian monism so illogically, even so unexpectedly, broad and all-inclusive. At bottom, certainly, Christianity is an idealistic, other-worldly monism; but something has always kept it right in the heat and dust of this world. In the West, even the monks who fled this material world took to cleaning up its material swamps and waste places, improving its crops, copying and cataloguing its books. They did indeed mortify the flesh, at least as long as the spiritual drive of their particular order was strong. After this drive weakened, even the monks took a good deal of this world as it came, with the result that new, reforming orders were organized.

All this is not to say that Christianity is organized hypocrisy, as so many generations of rationalistic critics have repeatedly accused it of being. It is rather that at least many of the men who guided organized Christianity acquired very early a kind of wise patience with human beings, something of the patience of the good physician. They still believed in the Kingdom of God, but not on earth, and certainly not in their time. Meantime, on this earth, was it not wiser to take God's creatures somewhat as they came and not attempt to change them too violently? After all, even Paul had admitted that, if virginity were best, it was apparently not quite universally possible, even with the second coming at hand. Even Paul would rather have his flock marry than burn.

The other-worldly, idealistic elements in Christianity were, then, never permitted to turn the Church into a small exclusive sect determined to live up to the very highest ideals or—still more difficult—so to control the masses that these masses lived up to the very highest ideals. In part, through monasticism and through its insistence on special qualifications for secular priesthood, the Church did allow a role for the idealistic minority, and as we shall see in the next chapter, succeeded until the time of Luther in controlling, sometimes by absorption, sometimes by rejection, those who really wished to bring heaven—their own God's heaven—to earth. But these other-worldly phases of Christian belief are none the less of extreme importance. They are the true notes of Christianity, which together make it something more than an empirical, opportunistic adjustment to a complicated world. Millions of words have been written about this subject. We can here but pick out certain of the clearest notes.

One of the clearest, indeed a sort of ground-tone in all forms of Christianity, can be most simply put as a distrust of the flesh, a rejection of the adequacy of natural human appetites, human instincts, as a guide to human conduct. This distrust is stated intellectually—though it is obviously a very profound sentiment rather than a theory—in one of the major doctrines of Christianity, that of original sin, of the *natural wickedness* of man. (We shall see in a later chapter that the most formidable modern heresy Christianity confronts is the doctrine, first popularized by the Enlightenment of the eighteenth century, of the *natural goodness* of man.) Now this sentiment of distrust of the natural man of flesh and blood runs all through Christianity and takes many forms. Our Freudian time is tempted to believe that the early Christians were obsessed with sex, that the original sin of Adam and Eve was sexual intercourse, that the appetite in natural man most distrusted by Christianity is sexual appetite. And certainly there is a great deal in Christian literature to confirm this impression. From the whole corpus of Christian writings you could extract a set of case histories that would keep a psychoanalyst busy all his life.

Yet it is fairer to say that most Christian thought distrusts the whole natural man—his appetites for food, drink, gaming, fighting, vainglory, as well as for sexual indulgence. Catholic Christianity has always provided a place for the rare individual who wished to subdue the flesh—though it has not, of course, been willing to allow the individual to subdue his flesh to the point of suicide. Protestant Christianity has been less successful with such people, who under Protestantism have generally had to turn their ascetic drive toward reforming the conduct of others on earth. For the ordinary person, Catholic Christianity has taken no heroic measures. Indeed, in practice the traditional Catholic way of life has not been as different from that of the Greeks of the great culture as a pure intellectual, starting with the doctrine of original sin and with early Christian writings, might conclude. We noted that for the Greek of the great age overeating and undereating, gluttony and abstinence, were *both* evils, and that the sensible man ate moderately but well. So too, in fact, with the good Catholic. Gluttony was no doubt for the Christian much worse than abstemiousness—or at any rate, more likely, and therefore more dangerous. There remains in the background of Christian (perhaps only Protestant) feeling on this subject something well reflected in the popular saying "it is better to eat to live than to live to eat." But the view that Christianity is a gloomy faith, that the Christian may not enjoy food, drink, and love-making on this earth is false. The note of asceticism is in Christianity, and if you listen for it with either a friendly or a hostile ear, you can always hear it. But there are many other notes, sounding simultaneously in chords of unbelievable complexity.

Another note is that of unselfishness, unselfconsciousness. Here again we find one of the great abstract problems of philosophy, that of individualism and collectivism. And here again we find in the huge literature of Christianity almost a full range from pole to pole. From one point of view Christianity is a very individualistic faith, concerned with the salvation of the soul of each individual. The Christian at his highest moments is alone with God, responsible to God alone. State, vocation, family are all distractions of this world. Jesus himself could be quoted against family ties:

> While he yet talked to the people, behold, his mother and his brethren stood without, desiring to speak with him. Then one said unto him, Behold, thy mother and thy brethren stand without, desiring to speak with thee. But he answered and said unto him that told him, Who is my mother? and who are my brethren? And he stretched forth his hand

toward his disciples, and said, Behold, my mother and my brethren! For whosoever shall do the will of my Father which is in heaven, the same is my brother, and sister, and mother.

Yet precisely this passage shows the way to one phase of Christian collectivism. In the true Christian life all men are one, and subsidiary groups a distraction, or worse, a padding for the selfish ego. The important thing is for the individual to avoid all kinds of personal triumphs over others, all competitive successes, all the things that set off, sharpen his ego. Now just as Christianity as a great world religion, especially in its Catholic form, has never carried asceticism to extreme, so it has not carried this annihilation of the individual ego to an extreme. Very successfully competitive individuals have in this world been professing Christians; even Napoleon was a professed Christian. Nevertheless, the ideal of unselfishness is there. Christianity tries to tame the more extravagant flights of the competitive human spirit, tries to subdue self-assertiveness, truculence, boasting, pride, and other such manifestations of the "natural man," manifestations it distrusts quite as much as it distrusts his simpler appetites for food, drink, and sex.

A third note of Christianity is but the other side of unselfconsciousness. The Christian should not only subdue his own ego; he should open his heart in loving-kindness to all his fellow men. Modern rationalists have often been so shocked by the fact that some Christians burned, imprisoned, or otherwise silenced fellow men who disagreed with them on matters theological that they have refused to hear this note of love (charity) in Christianity. But it is there, and without it Christianity is incomplete. The note is not quite the one we today recognize as sentimental humanitarianism, not quite the note of miscellaneous pity for criminals, defectives, failures, and all other underdogs we know so well among crusading reformers of a certain kind. For one thing, an important thing, the Christian should love the upperdog as well as the underdog, a duty most secular humanitarian reformers seem not to acknowledge. Christian loving-kindness, for all its affinities with softer emotions, has a touch of iron, of resignation and humility in face of a universe not to be shaped wholly by

169

man's will. For the Christian regards sin as a fact. He must forgive the sinner, he must pity the sinner, he must indeed in a sense love the sinner. But he may not love the sinner for his sin, and in hating the sin he must also in a sense hate the sinner. Above all, he may not regard sin as an illusion, or as the result of bad physical and social environment alone, or as the result of purely human influences. Christian loving-kindness can therefore never be universalist optimism as to the perfectibility of man, nor can it ever be pure humanitarianism.

A fourth note of Christianity is its distrust of certain kinds of thinking. There are semantic difficulties here, as well as the usual difficulties with the range and universality of Christian thought. Christianity is in no simple sense anti-intellectual. We have already seen that its theology is an intellectual structure of great subtlety and complexity; we shall see that at its medieval climax organized Christianity held reason in highest esteem. But Christianity has always distrusted the kind of thinking we nowadays call "rationalism"; it has always been afraid that the human mind will reason away the supernatural. Thus, though it is rankly unfair to Christianity to say that it has always opposed full intellectual freedom, rankly unfair to say that modern science has developed *in spite of* Christian obscurantism, there remains a grain of truth in these extreme statements. At the very least, the Christian must at some point begin to believe what his sense experience, his instruments, and his science give him no direct evidence for. Indeed, pure rationalism must remain for the Christian the indecent self-assertion of the rationalist, a sin perhaps worse than the self-assertion displayed by the sensualist or the show-off. The natural man can think as well as lust. Only the spiritual man can have faith, "the substance of things hoped for, the evidence of things not seen."

For throughout the ages Christianity has firmly maintained its theism. This universe is for the Christian ultimately a problem—an intellectual as well as a moral and emotional problem. There is a God for whom nothing is a problem, a God who—if one may use so human a term of him—understands the universe. Men cannot possibly put themselves in God's place, certainly not by the kind of activity they are used to in daily relations one with another on earth.

Through God's free and miraculous intercession they can by a quite different kind of activity acquire a kind of certainty well beyond what we call knowledge.

They can be certain, though they cannot know as they know, for instance, that oaks grow from acorns, that God does exist, that the universe is not the puzzling, even hostile place it seems to man thinking, man planning, man worrying, that indeed the universe is made for man and the drama of his salvation. The kind of activity—and here even the word "activity" is theologically suspect—by which men arrive at this certainty must, since we humans are hopelessly word-bound, be given a name, even as other human activities. This activity we call *faith*. It is not thinking, not feeling, not anything the psychologist or physiologist in the laboratory can ever get at, any more than the chemist in his laboratory can get at the miracle of the Eucharist.

Christianity, then, is resolutely theistic, firm in the belief that this world of the senses is not the whole universe. But—and this is the last note we shall dwell on—it attaches a very great importance, a very great degree of reality, to this world of the senses. This world is the testing ground for entrance to the next world. The faith of the Christian, which we have above sought to separate sharply from other human activities, does teach him that these other activities are indispensable to his salvation, that they must be well conducted here on earth. The good Christian is a good man, good in a sense that the ancient Greek and Hebrew moralists made quite explicit. But more than this—the good Christian wants other men to be good; he wants to make this imperfect world as nearly as possible like that perfect world his faith tells him about.

Christianity is ethically an intensely melioristic faith. It is, as we shall see in contrast when we come to the optimistic belief in human perfectibility of our own eighteenth-century forefathers of the Enlightenment, in many ways a pessimistic faith, with no concrete notions of its own about progress on this earth, indeed with quite definite notions about this earth as almost necessarily a vale of tears. And yet, long before the eighteenth century, long before accepted theories of progress or evolution, Christianity was in practice a reforming religion, anxious to make this world a better place for human beings, more peaceful, more prosperous, more friendly, more decent. It believed in improvement, if not in formal progress.

Although humility is one of the greatest of Christian virtues, to an outsider the ideals of the Christian way of life seem *aristocratic,* at least as aristocratic as the ideal of the Greek way of life. To tame one's grosser appetites, to extinguish entirely less obviously sensual appetites like those for fame, wealth, and power, to hold reason and faith in due balance, to labor steadfastly but always with imaginative sympathy for one's fellows in order to make this world a better place— to live like this has never been possible for the great majority of men. Yet the Christian must always hope that all men can so live. Here is the true difference between the high and difficult ideals of the great age in Greece and those of Christianity. The Greek gentleman, as we see him reflected in Aristotle, does not hope to raise the masses to his standards; he is quite content to let them provide the material basis on which he can live the life of the beautiful and the good. The Christian gentleman can never be a gentleman in the exclusive, snobbish sense that word has gained in our own time. He must want the whole world to be truly Christian. He must extend aristocratic standards to a democracy.

Roughly, very roughly, we may say that over the centuries *organized Christianity,* Protestant as well as Catholic, has made what its leaders thought were necessary compromises with this world of the flesh, that it has not attempted to force the notes of asceticism, complete annihilation of the ego, love of one's fellows, lofty, mystic transcending of prudential reason, ardent missionary desire to clean up this dirty world. It has tempered the wind to the shorn lamb—and most decidedly, its opponents would say, to the lamb's shearer also. That is, the Church has taken the world of rich and poor, saint and sinner, pretty much as it came, and sought no more than to keep things on a not too uneven keel. This unheroic, everyday Christianity has over the centuries been subject to two kinds of attack, the attack from the inside and the attack from the outside.

The attack from the inside comes from men and women who wish to push Christianity beyond these compromises with the flesh. The attempt to understand the Christian experience from the outside, by naturalistic-historical methods, inevitably deforms that experience. But we must stick to our last. In one sense, which we have here deliberately chosen to follow, St. Francis of Assisi, Calvin, Wesley, and Mrs. Mary Baker Eddy, however different their inward Christian experiences, were all Christians who attacked formal and established Christianity in the name of a purer, a more ideal Christianity. They were otherwise, of course, very different persons, and their work on earth was very different. But the pattern should be clear. The Church at a given moment in space and time begins to seem to one of its members to be false to Christian ideals. It seems to let Christians grow rich and powerful, to let them commit adultery, to let them be stuffy and proud and ordinary, as long as they go to church. This the rebellious one cannot stand. He will go back to Christ, will purge the Church of its laxity, will prod or inspire ordinary men and women into taking their religion seriously.

This idealistic rebel is a constant problem to the conservatives who run Christian churches, Catholic and Protestant, as indeed they run most human institutions. No doubt many of these conservatives would also say, in public at least, that this rebel is on the whole a stimulant and an inspiration. At any rate, the conservative has to cope with him. Up to Luther, the Roman Catholic Church was generally—not always—successful in taming these rebels, in absorbing them into the body of Christian tradition, within which they undoubtedly served as a valuable leaven. Such, for instance, seems to the outsider the fate of St. Francis of Assisi, who under harsher treatment from the authorities of his Church might have been driven to heresy. Since Luther, the more extreme Christian idealists and innovators have in fact been heretics—have indeed revolted even from churches that seemed to have no fixed beliefs to revolt from. Short of these extreme rebels, who were also extreme idealists, there are always practicing Christians well beyond the unheroic center of ordinary Christianity—men and women who are constantly spurring their fellows to a life at least somewhat closer to Christian ideals than that of the majority.

The attack from the outside rejects Christian ideals, or many of them. Organized Christianity has had to face the difficulty of reconciling its aristocratic ideals with the necessity for reaching the vulgar and accepting in some part this imperfect world. It has also had to face men who did not like its ideals, not even the diluted ideals that Christianity at most times accepted in practice. These opponents have been many and varied, especially since in the last four hundred years or so they have enjoyed something like freedom of speech. They have included hedonists, naturalists, men who believe that human beings should as far as possible do what they want to do, that human wants are essentially good, that the human body is a fine thing, that bodily pleasures are a fine thing. These are the men who find Christianity, even in its ordinary practice, gloomy, ascetic, distrustful of the body and its pleasures. The opponents of Christianity have included the philosophical materialists, the tough-minded who dislike Plato and the author or authors of the Fourth Gospel, the positivists who recoil from words like *spirit, faith,* and *soul.* They have included true skeptics, men as uncertain about heaven as about this world. They have included all who, whatever their positive views of the universe, deny the possibility of the supernatural, the miraculous, the divine. They have included the humanitarian sentimentalists who, rejecting the doctrine of original sin, hold that men are naturally good, and that some are bad only because society makes them bad..

The attack from the outside has in the last few centuries attained an importance it has not had since the last days of Graeco-Roman paganism. Christianity has in modern times had to confront not merely those, like St. Francis, for whom Christians were not enough like Christ; it has had to confront those for whom Christ himself was a myth, or a crank, or a primitive, or even a psychopath. It has had, in short, to meet many challenges on many fronts. The story of the origins of these challenges, of their rise, and of their conflict with the established values of Christianity occupies a central position in the intellectual history of the West.

6

The Middle Ages~I

THE VERY TERM "Middle Ages" is a judgment of value, originally a derogatory one. It stood for what its coiners considered the thousand-year valley or depression between the great peaks of Ancient and Modern. The term, and its Latin derivative "medieval," was firmly established in popular usage by the eighteenth-century Enlightenment. By the nineteenth century the tripartite division of Ancient, Medieval, and Modern had become fixed, to the extent that it has even been used by Westerners for such histories as that of China, where it has no meaning at all.

A fixed, conventional nomenclature, however, has one distinct advantage: It loses most of its original flavor of praise or blame. We think now of "medieval" as denoting in European history roughly the thousand years from 500 to 1500. Its earliest centuries, from 500 to 900 or 1000, are still sometimes known as the Dark Ages, a term from which even constant use can hardly wash the element of dispraise. The Middle Ages proper are considered as lasting, with some overlapping and much imprecision, from Charlemagne in the ninth century to Columbus in the fifteenth. Just as the fifth century B.C. is commonly regarded as the flowering of the culture of the *polis,* so the thirteenth century is commonly regarded as the flowering of medieval culture. Finally, this culture was that of the western part of the old

Roman Empire, with the addition of the newer extensions into central Europe, Ireland, Scotland, and Scandinavia. The eastern part of the Empire, constantly encroached upon by the Slavs, Arabs, and Turks, lasted in Constantinople until 1453. But its history is really the history of a separate society, and even its direct cultural influences on the West were probably less than those made by Islam.

The reputation of the Middle Ages has varied greatly in the few centuries since their end. Only quite recently, and among men scornful of classical education, has Graeco-Roman culture been attacked. But the writers and artists of the late fifteenth and the sixteenth centuries were already most contemptuous of their medieval predecessors. Many of the famous slanders on medieval culture, such as the statement that medieval philosophers spent their time debating how many angels could stand on the point of a pin, have their origin in these early years of modern times. Our own contemporary slander on the Middle Ages characteristically takes such forms as "a thousand years without a bath." Even the adjective "Gothic," which we now apply with overtones of praise to the architecture of medieval times, was originally a term of scorn, equivalent to "barbarous."

The reputation of the Middle Ages was at its low point in the mid-eighteenth century, the "age of prose and reason." The romantic movement of the next generation, headed by Sir Walter Scott, fell in love with the poetry and unreasonableness of what they thought of as the Middle Ages. People actually began building again in the medieval style; at one noted American university, it is said, the new Gothic stone steps were deliberately hollowed out to look worn by generations of use, as Gothic steps should. Boys during the romantic revival of medievalism played at Robin Hood, and their elders illuminated manuscripts and wrote ballads.

There was in the later nineteenth century a reaction that quelled though it did not extinguish, this enthusiasm for the Middle Ages. Today the average American student is indifferent enough about the Middle Ages; on the whole, he tends to a vague condemnation of them as unprogressive and superstitious. But the minority of lovers and haters are both very vocal, and furnish us with our major problem in this chapter. For some, many but by no means all of them Roman Catholics, the Middle Ages, and especially the thirteenth century, represent the peak of human achievement, a society without modern wealth and scientific technology, but with a basic social and moral equilibrium, a practical social justice, and a Christian way of life that more than make up for the absence of material abundance. For others, many but not all of them positivists, radicals, anti-Christians, firm believers in progress, the Middle Ages remain a barbarous, superstitious, caste-ridden, unprogressive time of suffering for the many, of violence and empty show for the few. Each of these views contributes important elements to an understanding of the Middle Ages; each, taken as an unmodified whole, is false.

The Institutions of Medieval Culture

The first thing to get clear about medieval culture is that it had to be built slowly on what it is no mere metaphor to call ruins. The Dark Ages, though not a complete break in the complicated set of threads that tie us to the past, did see the breaking of many and the fraying of almost all these threads. We cannot here attempt to measure all these breaks. They were most probably complete at the higher levels of politics and administration and in economic life. No one could run anything extensive—business, state, association of any sort—save, of course, the Catholic Church. The Church remained for these centuries the one *European* institution that really worked, that really held together, for one can hardly count the tradition of the Roman Empire, nor even its Law, as persisting, effective institutions in these centuries. At most, some Roman municipalities seem to have carried on. Even the Church had by the tenth century accumulated a number of abuses, marriage or concubinage of priests, sale of clerical offices, worldliness of all sorts, that cried out for reform.

From this Europe urban civilization almost vanished. Towns in western Europe were but local market centers, and those towns which came nearest our notions of urban life were commonly centers of church administration, seats of bishops or archbishops, or were growing up around the great monastic centers. Men lived for the most part in small, economically autarkic (self-sufficient) farming villages. Trade was rare, and mostly limited to articles of luxury, or to the minerals necessary to the feudal lords' armor and swords. Even the Roman roads were abandoned, and travel confined to foot or horseback. Society was sharply divided into the feudal warrior-chieftains and the peasants and craftsmen. There was hardly any middle class. The warrior-chieftains fought among themselves, usually to the detriment of the commoners' crops and other property. But the peasants at least did not have to fight.

At the low points of the seventh or the tenth century, many other threads of culture were nearly severed. Formal thought was preserved by the Church, and Latin was never wholly lost. The Latin of the Dark Ages was, however, a simplified and sometimes a most ungrammatical Latin. What new writing there was concerned itself almost wholly with religion, and was mostly mere compilation from and comment on earlier work. What is sometimes called the Carolingian Renaissance of the eighth and ninth centuries, associated with the emperor Charlemagne, is hardly more than an elementary revival of rather more grammatical Latin, and a beginning of the characteristically medieval formal education to which we shall come in a moment.

Yet we must not exaggerate. At the top the Catholic Church held together, and at the bottom, in local life, in the things that touch the individual, many threads held. On the whole, techniques of getting a living probably suffered less than nineteenth-century historians thought. Agricultural skills fell off from the highest Roman standards, but those standards had been far from universal in the Empire. Artistic skills in a technical sense probably suffered; the lines from master to apprentice were broken. Still, there was some excellent stone carving in almost every century, and it may be that the desire rather than the ability to be photographically faithful to nature in art was lost. The typical craftsman's skills in textiles, weapons, furniture, and the like were roughened, but again by no means lost. The monks who cleared the forests and drained the swamps introduced new methods; they improved, invented.

Gradually the full fabric of civilization was restored, so that in the high Middle Ages, the twelfth, thirteenth, and fourteenth centuries, only a blind hater of things medieval would deny the existence of a fully developed culture. Even materially, the culture of the centers of this new world, France, England, the Low Countries, northern Italy, the Rhineland, had reached as high a level as that attained by the Greeks and the Romans. Intellectually and emotionally this new culture represents a way of life which, as we have noted, still fascinates many of us today.

The Church remained in the high Middle Ages the great center of intellectual life. For the first time in Western society, there came to be a systematic, graded education under common control. It was not universal education, but it was an education open to really bright, bookish boys (not, of course, girls) even from the lowest classes. The common control was not a single bureaucratic one, like a state superintendent of education; it was that of the Catholic Church, with its numerous organs of education and administration, with its admirably organized clergy, and with its supreme head in the pope.

The elementary schools had grown up around monastic centers, or as adjuncts of cathedrals, occasionally as town schools. They taught the very elementary things, and especially Latin, which was no longer spoken as a common tongue except among the learned. Note, however, that for the learned it was a spoken as well as a written tongue, and the bright little boys began it very young. Education of the upper classes, neglected in the Dark Ages, gradually resulted in the literacy or semiliteracy of a large number of noblemen; but even so, most upper-class education was in the arts of war and the chase and in the practice of running estates.

The characteristic educational institution of the Middle Ages, and one of its major legacies to us, is the university. Next to the Roman Catholic Church itself, certain universities, Paris, Oxford, and Bologna for instance, are the oldest unbroken human institutions in the Western world today. (France and England, it may be argued, are older as nations, but they are certainly not politically unbroken institutions.) Most of these universities had their start very early in the Middle Ages, as church schools or the like. By the twelfth and thirteenth centuries they had attained their characteristic form, a formal association of teachers and scholars into a corporate whole with very great freedom from political authorities, and with at least freedom of status within the ecclesiastical organization. These universities, after proper examination, conferred degrees, that of Master of Arts qualifying the recipient for most intellectual occupations, though the doctorate was very soon established as a qualification for the highest posts.

These universities taught the higher reaches of the subjects that formed the established basis of medieval formal education—the famous *quadrivium* (geometry, astronomy, music, and arithmetic) and the *trivium* (grammar, logic, and rhetoric). Do not let these formal names mislead you. Actually under these strange names there lies concealed most of what still forms the basis of liberal education. The experimental sciences are not there, and neither, of course, are the amazing variety of practical subjects, from the internal combustion engine to success in marriage, that have somehow got into modern American educational curricula. The medieval student, after grounding in Latin as a living scholarly tongue and literature and in the mathematical sciences (*quadrivium*), could go on to study one of the two genuinely learned professions, law or medicine, or he could go on to what is basically the equivalent of our graduate work in philosophy and literature. Both the philosophy and the literature (Latin) would seem restricted to a modern scholar used to the great *à la carte* list of courses in a modern graduate school. But, as we shall see, the formal thought of the Middle Ages grappled with all the major problems of learning.

By the thirteenth century the learned career had come to be a fully recognized part of medieval social organization at the intellectual level. There was *imperium,* the function of political administration, *sacerdotium,* the priestly function, and *studium,* the scholarly function. There was even, among the university students themselves, something we should recognize as college life. The contrast of "town and gown" dates from medieval times. The students played, drank, sang and organized hoaxes and practical jokes; there were student riots, not infrequently accompanied by bloodshed. The whole thing was infinitely less organized, less a mirror of the adult world, than our own American "youth culture." Still, as compared with the life of the young in Greece or Rome, this medieval student life has a very modern flavor.

Admirers of the Middle Ages—indeed, some very distinguished and scholarly students of the Middle Ages—have insisted that the basic underlying spirit of the medieval *studium* was very different indeed from that of modern higher education. The absence of experimental science from formal medieval education and the presence of a single, universally acknowledged religious faith, are obvious differences; they characterize, however, the whole of medieval intellectual life, and to them we shall return. The difference more usually noted for student life in itself is the absence, in medieval times, of our acute modern spirit of competition, an acceptance of one's position in life. And indeed, although in purely intellectual matters medieval Schoolmen were extremely competitive and seem to have had the scholar's full complement of vanity, quarrelsomeness, and desire to out-argue an opponent, poor students clearly did not usually expect to use the medieval university as a steppingstone to a bank presidency or a board chairmanship. There may have been in the medieval student more self-consecration to learning for learning's sake than there is in the modern. Even so, the *studium* was in many senses a career open to talents, and here as elsewhere in the Middle Ages one is struck with the fact that there is, for a society in which everyone is supposed to know his place, a great deal of pushing and shoving.

Most of the members of the *studium,* even in the high Middle Ages, had taken some kind of ecclesiastical orders, were in some sense a part of the Church. Most of them, it is true, did not have cure of souls, that is, the charge of a parish with the priestly duties of shepherd of the flock, and the Church understandably was less strict in supervising their private lives than it was with parish priests. But to an extent we can hardly understand today, the Church penetrated and controlled all human activity, especially intellectual activity. In the earlier Middle Ages, the ability to read was in itself taken as a sign that a man was a priest. Hence the term not yet quite dead, "benefit of clergy," which meant that a man who could prove he could read could thereby count, if he got in difficulty with the authorities, on being tried in an ecclesiastical, not in an ordinary lay court. In the Dark Ages all work requiring literacy—keeping of accounts and registers, letter writing, drafting documents—was done by priests, for only priests had the necessary education. Though this monopoly no longer existed in the high Middle Ages, the clergy even then bore a much larger part of the administrative work of the world than they do now.

Again, in thousands of rural parishes, even in town parishes, the priest was the effective link with the outside world, the world of ideas as well as of wars, taxes, intrigues. The sermon, though never in Catholic practice the overwhelming thing it came to be in some Protestant sects, was nevertheless a way of spreading ideas. Indeed, the pulpit gave to the medieval Church the very great advantage of a near-monopoly of the ways of influencing public opinion. In the absence of newspapers, radio, or anything like the classical traveling lecturer (rhetorician), the Church alone could make effective propaganda. Ideas otherwise could spread among the masses only by informal word of mouth. The fact that the papacy possessed this medieval equivalent of the power of the press and radio is surely one of the reasons why the medieval popes so long held their own against the growing power of lay rulers.

Finally, it is to the Church that we owe the preservation of Greek and Latin literature. Of course, extremists among the Christians thought of pagan literature as the devil's work and would have had it destroyed; even for the ordinary pious cleric, there remained something of the attraction of forbidden fruit in pagan imaginative literature. Still, the monks collected and the monks copied, both in the East and in the West. Losses were great, especially during the long years of the breakup of the Roman Empire. But enough survived so that we know well the culture of the Greeks and Romans. Nor was the work of the monastic copiers limited to the transmission of the classics. They also copied—in modern terms, published—the

Latin writings of contemporary medieval theologians and philosophers, and the vernacular writings of medieval poets and storytellers. We owe to them not only Cicero, but also Aquinas and the *Chanson de Roland*.

Men trained in the Church had, then, almost a monopoly of the intellectual life. The Church was lecture platform, press, publisher, library, school, and college. Yet it is not accurate to think of the Middle Ages as priest-ridden, and certainly not as dominated by a fundamentalist, puritanical, censorious Church. Moreover, there are important phases of medieval intellectual life by no means monopolized by clerics. If the upper classes of the Dark Ages were hardly more than professional fighters, by the high Middle Ages they had acquired much broader interests—in law and administration, in poetry and romance, in the extraordinary way of life known as chivalry, even occasionally in scholarship. The greatest of medieval philosophers, St. Thomas Aquinas, was by birth an Italian nobleman. In the vernacular literatures, Italian, French, English, and others well launched by the high Middle Ages, we get all sorts of elements from popular life, including a good deal of ribaldry and coarseness to prove that the old Adam had not been spirited away. It is not, perhaps, as easy to show for the Middle Ages a relation between the more formal level of thought and the life of the ordinary man as it is, say, for the century of Voltaire, Rousseau, Jefferson, and their fellows of the Enlightenment. Still, the formal scholastic philosophy of the Middle Ages was by no means a system in a vacuum. Precisely because of the structure of medieval society, because of the prestige of clerics, formal philosophy is a safer guide to ordinary human aspirations than it is in a period like the present, where philosophy is actually a very isolated academic pursuit.

Medieval Theology and Philosophy

In medieval thought, theology was indeed the "Queen of the Sciences." The medieval thinker did use the separate words "theology" and "philosophy," but in fact they are inseparably mixed.

There remained always a part for mystery, for faith; but the theologian, like the philosopher, was a thinker, a man who reasoned about
what went on in the universe. He believed that, if no man could
wholly penetrate God's place, still there was such a place, and by
reasoning the human thinker could get an imperfect, but useful
indeed essential, series of notions about God's place.

The medieval thinkers built, of course, on the basis of the work
of the early Christian Fathers, and on the Church practices and attitudes we have described in the previous chapter. Of all the writing
of the Fathers the most important for the Middle Ages, and indeed for
all subsequent Christianity, are those of St. Augustine, Bishop of
Hippo, who lived in the late fourth and early fifth centuries. Augustine was of Roman-African noble stock, with a pagan father and a
Christian mother (canonized as St. Monica). He died in 430, during
the siege of his episcopal seat by the Vandals, a Germanic tribe. He
is thus a child of the ancient world, yet also in a sense a man of the
medieval world. Certainly that world later was to adopt him as the
greatest of the Latin.fathers.

Augustine is one of the major figures in Western thought, on a
par with Plato and Aristotle. We cannot in a book of this sort do
him justice. He should be read directly, if only in his *Confessions*
one of the few autobiographies that have survived from the classical
world. Thanks to this book, and to the very full survival of his many
incidental polemical writings, as well as the great, systematic *City of
God,* we can know Augustine as a person much better than almost any
other figure in the classical world. He is full of contradictions, of the
twistings and turnings of a richly endowed personality cast into the
strange, disintegrating world of Roman culture. One is tempted to
think that he embraced Christianity as the one sound integrating
principle in a world of confusion—in other words, that this descendent
of practical Romanized gentlemen was true to the balanced, worldly
common-sense Roman tradition. Yet Augustine, if a Roman, was of
African blood. One can equally well discern a deep emotional drive,
a sounding of the depths from which somehow came to Augustine
the miraculous quiet of God. At any rate, before his conversion to

184

Christianity he had sampled most of the carnal delights, and many of the spiritual consolations of his world, including Manichaeanism and Neoplatonism.

In Augustine the Christian bishop there is still this extraordinary activity, and this tension—so very Christian—between the flesh and the spirit. The flesh no longer draws Augustine to self-indulgence; the world is now a world a bishop can and must deal with, help put in order, help rescue from the evils of disorder. Augustine, like Paul, had a tireless cure of souls, a practical man's absorption in the countless details of running things. Note that, in the pure mystical tradition, the world as a place to clean up is more subtly and more dangerously the devil's lure than is the world as a place to wallow in. Yet seen from outside that tradition, Augustine seems one kind, and a perfectly genuine kind, of mystic. His was no practical cleaner's chore, which could seem to make progress, but rather the eternal and impossible task of perfect spiritual cleansing. Augustine was in the City of Earth only that he might make it the City of God. Clearly, as he went about his daily tasks this other-worldliness could not have been obsessive or he would not have remained Bishop of Hippo. But it remains at the basis of his doctrine, and gives him his characteristic place in Christian thought.

Of this vast work we can here note but three things. First, Augustine's whole work is a synthesizing and encyclopedic one. He touched upon almost every matter of doctrine and in important matters went into great detail. His point of view is in most respects central enough to Latin Christian experience to serve as a basis for medieval orthodoxy. On the Trinity, on the sacraments, above all on the manifold reaches of the Christian drama of sin and salvation, Augustine was an admirable source and foundation.

Second, Augustine's great work, the *City of God,* put the Christian point of view, the Christian cosmology, in a form that has always had a pronounced attraction for Western men, that of a philosophy of history. Augustine made Christianity not merely a drama, but a process in time. The *City of God* was written partly because Augustine wished to refute the common pagan accusation that the increasingly evident weakness of the Roman Empire was due to Christian other-worldliness, if not to plain Christian wickedness. Augustine has no trouble in showing that many cities and empires had already decayed and fallen long before the revelation of Christianity had been made. It is the nature of the cities of this world to decay. Only the City of God is eternal. That city is not yet on earth, though it is promised us even here; meanwhile, God has revealed its existence to us, and through his son Jesus has given us all a chance to become citizens of it. But that other City of Earth lives on, and the two cities are in eternal civil war until at the day of judgment they are finally to be separated forever, their citizens no longer torn by the possibility of changing citizenship, the saved forever blessed, the damned forever tortured.

Third, as it seems to an outsider at least, there remains a part of Augustine that is a constant invitation to heresy, the heresy of the perfectionist. This side of Augustine's work comes out clearly in what was perhaps the most influential of his theological doctrines, that of determinism, or predestination. It was sharpened in conflict with Pelagius, a British monk who defended a heretical degree of freedom of the will. The basic issue is one of the oldest that confronts man thinking, that of individual freedom of choice against some form of determinism. Now Christianity has always had difficulty admitting that human beings can make free choices (possess freedom of the will) if only because such freedom would seem a derogation from the overwhelming power Christianity attributes to its God. How can a mere worm like man will something that God has not willed? God is literally everything, including my thoughts and yours, my desires and yours. He has made, he rules, both the City of God and the City of Earth. If indeed some of us become citizens of the City of God, it is not because we had the power, so to speak, to naturalize ourselves but because God from the beginning had chosen us as citizens, because he bestowed upon us the gift of irresistible grace. This gift of grace—a gift no man can win, or even, in one sense, deserve—is the free gift of God to his chosen ones, and for them makes salvation, the escape from the consequences of original sin, possible. Mere men can hirst after grace, can ask God for this gift. The decision is God's, n his infinite wisdom that has already made all decisions for all time.

Now all this is good logic (once you postulate an omnipotent God) and it is good logic of the sentiments, also. For the emotionally stirred, complete submission to such a God is the wiping out of the self, is peace. Men have exhausted themselves in metaphors to express this feeling; we have used a very common one, that of the worm. There are, however, especially from the point of view of those trying hard to keep things going in this world, some difficulties with these deterministic doctrines. The most obvious of these difficulties is by no means the most common, though it has always worried the sensibly orthodox: If God has determined everything in advance, why hasn't he determined a man's desire to get drunk, or steal, or fornicate? If man has no free will, how can he have any moral responsibility? God is responsible for all man's desires. How can he resist them, since in resisting them he resists God?

Actually this position is very rarely taken. It simply is a fact that those who believe most rigorously in determinism act as if their every moment were a portentous decision for the right and against the wrong. Nevertheless, the logical threat of moral irresponsibility hovers over all doctrines of determinism, and there is something in ordinary human nature that clings to some common-sense belief in the reality of individual choices, in free will. The Catholic Church itself is in practice semi-Augustinian on this point. It accepts the awful necessity of determinism by reason of God's ineffable majesty; obviously man cannot really resist God. But for the sake of the drama God wills to take place on this earth, in order that the fight may be real, we must accept for man a sort of delegated moral responsibility.

There is, however, another and more common danger to orthodoxy in extreme determinism. It would seem that the notion of a great irresistible force *sweeping things away from the vulgar, ordinary, obvious state of things* is of great attraction to men of strong temperament in rebellion against their surroundings. Now the Bishop of Hippo was by no means always in such a state of rebellion; he believed man's free will was reconcilable with God's foreknowledge absolute—but Augustine the mystic, Augustine the ardent lover of God, *was* such a rebel. The man who wants this world to be very much what it is not seems peculiarly likely to hold that he knows just how and why it must change into something else. The reformer —not always, but often—wants to know that his plans are God's plans, or the plans of Dialectical Materialism. It is surely significant that, after Augustine, two of the greatest supporters of rigid determinism, Calvin and Karl Marx, have also been leaders of great reforming movements, movements inspired above all by contempt for the commonplace, the comfortable, the daily routine of living. There is a tendency within Catholicism for reformist groups to appeal to Augustine, as conformist groups appeal to St. Thomas Aquinas.

From Augustine a line, dim and uncertain at first, leads on to the culmination of medieval formal thought in Scholasticism. Now Scholasticism is a mature system of thought, ripened in one of the great ages of Western culture. Its original works are numerous and have been well preserved; modern comment on it is copious. Again, in accordance with the scale of this book, we can but suggest certain major points of interest in Scholasticism, with the hope that the reader will go directly to some of the writings of the Scholastics.

First, however, it should be noted that for that special kind of intellectual history concerned with the transmission of learning, with the complex study of manuscripts, translations, and cultural cross-fertilization, the background of medieval thought presents a fascinating story. To the small ·but solid stock of materials preserved in the West throughout the Dark Ages there was added, notably in the eleventh century, a mass of materials translated from the Arabic. The Arabs under Mohammed and his successors had conquered widely in the eastern part of the old Roman Empire, and by the mid-eighth century had swept over Spain, Sicily, and southern Italy. In this general region they held on through the next few centuries; indeed they were not wholly driven out of Spain until the end of the Middle Ages. Anti-clerical historians have long delighted to contrast the intellectual freedom and prowess of the Arabs in these centuries with the torpor and obscurantism they find among Western Christians. It is a fact that from 700 to about 1100 the Arabs had an active intellectual class, interested above all in science and philosophy. We shall return shortly to their scientific work. Philosophically, they were not in fact strikingly original, but they did have access to Greek originals, especially to much better and more complete versions of Aristotle than those available in the West. These were translated into Arabic, and as the West grew well out of the Dark Ages and the Crusades increased Christian-Moslem contacts, above all as the learned communities we have described above grew and thirsted for more books, translators rendered this Greek work from Arabic into Latin. The most famous of these translators, Gerard of Cremona, who worked at Toledo in Spain, is said to have translated some ninety separate works from the Arabic.

There were, then, the original materials of the *trivium* and the *quadrivium* and the fast-growing libraries of new works, Greek, Arabic, and in the case of some mathematical work, ultimately Hindu, all now available in Latin. There was, if still no printing press, a large class of devoted monkish copyists, good libraries, and scholarly communities. Indeed, from the eleventh century on active thinkers in these communities were adding to the stock, were working out the foundations of medieval philosophy. To get the general spirit of this philosophy, let us look at the problem that was perhaps the central one of the time, the very old problem of universals.

The problem, which we have seen in a somewhat different form in Plato, centers for the medieval thinkers in the reality of class-concepts. The horse is a favorite example. One polar position, that of the *nominalist,* asserts that though there are a great many separate, individual horses, each of which is real, the class-concept "horse" corresponds to nothing real, and is merely a convenience for human thinking, merely a word, a kind of intellectual shorthand. For though actually Dobbin, and Ranger, and Silver, and Bucephalus are separate and individual horses—a fact we recognize by giving each a proper name—there is no such thing as a horse-in-general. Actually not even one oak tree is *exactly* like another; but it would be inconvenient to recognize this fact by giving each oak tree a proper name. The generic name, then, is a convenience, not a reality.

The polar opposite of this view is that of the *realist*. The medieval realist held that individual horses are but imperfect approximations to the perfect horse, the ideal horse which alone is real. It is true, the realist admits, that in this sense world we encounter through our receptor experiences (sensations) only separate individual horses; nevertheless, the fact that we can rise to the concept of horse-in-general should persuade us that what we find out through this high faculty of reason is truer than what we learn from sense experience alone. The supremely real is not the individual but the class.

Now nominalism, if carried at all toward its extreme, is a doctrine very hard to reconcile with Christianity. It tends to the position that that alone exists which I can apprehend as an individual, a specimen linked to my knowing through my senses or their refinement in instruments. A horse, a blade of grass, even, when a few centuries later the microscope is invented, a microbe—these are real to the nominalist. But God? Or even the Church, as apart from the individuals that make it up? It is difficult for the extreme nominalist to make these very real. And in fact the logical implications of medieval nominalism put it in a class with what later came to be called materialism, positivism, rationalism, or empiricism.

Realism, also, had its dangers from the point of view of Christian orthodoxy, though less pressing and less obvious dangers. Realism took care of God and the Church, of justice and all the other moral ideas. But like any other other-worldly doctrine, it ran the risk of being pushed in the hands of a very logical—or a very mystical— thinker into a denial of what ordinary men find it rather hard to get away from, this vulgar world of eating, drinking, working, calculating, and other un-Platonic activity. And the Catholic Church for two thousand years has been very concerned with ordinary men and women, anxious not to get too far away from their minds and hearts.

Scholasticism, then, is in a sense a doctrine of compromise, and the greatest of the Scholastics, Aquinas, has been called "the first Whig," after the moderate, compromise-loving British statesmen of the eighteenth century. Yet it must be emphasized that in medieval formal thought there was room for the full philosophic spectrum, except perhaps for skepticism, which, although occurring occasionally in such a man as the emperor Frederick II, was condemned almost unanimously by the literate. One must not be misled by terms like "medieval unity," nor by the notion that since the Church in the West was established supreme there was no opportunity for debate over basic philosophical issues. On the contrary, the Schoolmen belabored one another on the lecture platform and in writing quite as heartily as in any other great period of Western philosophy. One of them, Abelard, for instance, is a fairly hard-boiled nominalist much liked by modern positivists who generally loathe the Middle Ages; conversely, those moderns who love the Middle Ages for their supposed serenity and other-worldliness generally loathe Abelard. Indeed, by a man's reaction to Abelard you can often predict his reaction to all medieval culture. But Abelard as a person was in many ways the eternal protesting philosopher—vain, quarrelsome, marvelously gifted in debate, a teacher who made ardent followers, quite lacking in Christian humility, and by temperament always against the established, the conventional, the moderate, the dull, and the successful of this world. Now you expect to find this temperament in free societies, a Socrates, a Tom Paine, a Bertrand Russell; but unless you have been spared the common American notions on the subject, you are surprised to find it so conspicuous in the Middle Ages. The answer is that in the West the Middle Ages were at their height one of the free societies. Abelard was in that society honored by a conspicuous position, and naturally felt the opposition of the people he so bitterly attacked. He was treated very badly indeed by his enemies, but he was not silenced.

At the very beginning of systematic medieval thinking we find in the ninth-century Scotus Erigena a kind of pre-realist, a thinker who comes so close to Neoplatonism that later ages found him rather dangerous. Toward the end of the thirteenth century we find in Duns Scotus another example of the dangers of scholastic realism, for this philosopher could never rest content with the imperfect arguments by which men prove that perfection exists, and wrote devastating criticisms of his predecessors, realists as well as nominalists. Duns Scotus spun out his own arguments for the realist position so that his works became a byword for oversubtlety, and helped add to the general discredit that came over Scholasticism at the end of the Middle Ages. William of Ockham, on the other hand, is the most famous of extreme nominalists. His philosophical position, he came to see, made it impossible for him to accept as reasonable many of the essential doctrines of the Church. Accordingly—and, one is tempted to say, like the good Englishman he was—Ockham chose to believe these doctrines anyway. In more formal language, he abandoned the characteristic medieval attempt to show that the truths of Christianity can be proved by human reason, and returned to something very near the position of one of the early Fathers, Tertullian, *credo quia impossibile*—I believe *because* it's impossible.

To such a position, of course, many ardent mystics had come in the beginning. In the range of medieval thought there is plenty of that anti-intellectualism of the anchorite, the flagellant, the romantic wild man. Yet medieval mysticism is by no means all of one piece. Most of the great mystics were not in fact anti-intellectuals in the sense of opposing as wicked or ineffective the ordinary uses of the mind. They simply lived above calculation, spiritually at a level that has made many of them saints. The best-known medieval work of piety, the *Imitation of Christ* attributed to Thomas à Kempis, is an admirable example of contained mysticism, which reconciles and consoles instead of prodding. We saw in the last chapter that one of the abiding notes of Christianity is a distrust of the intellect. Certainly this distrust appears in so Christian an age as the medieval. Adam of St. Victor, St. Bernard, St. Francis of Assisi—the role of those who opposed the scholastic appeal to reason is long and varied.

At the thirteenth-century climax of medieval culture, then, there is the variety and spontaneity of philosophical reflection that we found in the great age of Greece. But there is also, again as in Greece, a balance, a middle point, a golden mean. In the Middle Ages, that balance is mature Scholasticism, one of the most successful efforts to resolve the tension between this world and the other, between the real and the ideal. The mature Scholastics appealed to reason, but to reason working from bases set up by authority, the authority of the Church seconded by that of Aristotle. Their reason was not the restless, probing, basically discontented and nonconforming force it has been at many times in human history—including, probably, our own. We have cited Abelard indeed as an example of just this sort of revolutionary reason, but Abelard is far from being a good Scholastic. The good Scholastic has the intellectual humility that seems to the nonconformist intellectual cowardice.

An excellent example of this moderating but basically intellectual force of medieval formal thought can be found in some of the theological doctrines to which final form was given in these years. The Eucharist, for instance, put rather starkly in the form of appearance and reality the never-ending Christian problem of this world and the other. The elements could not be bread and wine, but they could not help looking and tasting like bread and wine. The other-worldly way out was simply to deny that the elements, once consecrated, were in any way anything except the body and blood of Christ; the this-worldly way out was to accept the elements as bread and wine, and say that they merely symbolized Christ, refreshed the communicant's memory of Christ. The latter way seemed always to orthodox Catholics a dangerous way out, for it eliminated the miracle and opened up other ways to the inroads of reason or common sense. And although the Catholic Church has always found a place for both reason and common sense, it has sought to keep them both in the place it thought fitting.

The characteristic medieval doctrine of transubstantiation, formally accepted by the fourth Lateran Council in 1215 after several centuries of debates among theologians, takes a sound other-worldly view, but preserves the common-sense decencies. The bread and wine have *substance* (Latin, *substantia*), a basic being or character, and *accidents* (Latin, *accidentia*), the qualities we feel and see and taste, and which in normal conditions help us build up approximate knowledge of their substance. By the miracle of the Mass the priest changes the substance of the bread and wine into the substance of the body

and blood of Christ, but he effects no change whatever in the acci
dents, which remain those of bread and wine. We taste only accidents
never substance, so that in taking communion we naturally taste wha
we always taste at the home table. The chemist analyzes only acci
dents, never substance, so that the chemist who impiously analyze
consecrated bread and wine also reports no change. But change ther
is, the miraculous change of transubstantiation which transcends, bu
never crushes, our senses.

Earlier doctrines of redemption, though they did not present a
grave dangers of heresy as did that of the Eucharist, were lacking i
logical and emotional depth. The Fathers of the early Church ha
come to rest with the doctrine of ransom, according to which Chris
had come to buy back man from Satan's clutches by his suffering o
the cross. This was a belief quite acceptable to ordinary men and fo
centuries held great popularity. But to subtler minds such ransom
seemed almost a commercial transaction; moreover, it put God in
position unworthy of his omnipotence and dignity. The first of th
great medieval realists, and perhaps the most creative of medieva
thinkers in the field of theology, St. Anselm, brought forward in th
doctrine of the atonement a much more satisfactory logical explana
tion of how Jesus brought redemption. Adam's sin against God coul
not be canceled out by any sort of bookkeeping, and certainly not b
any transaction with the devil. Man owed God reparation, but in hi
fallen state he could not possibly make such reparation. Jesus as Go
could take the necessary initiative to pay the debt he actually paid a
a suffering man. Jesus was sinless, both as God and man, and coul
therefore freely atone for the sin of Adam, could, so to speak, satisf
by his intercession God's justified anger with his children. Jesus th
perfect voluntarily took on imperfection—and the suffering that goe
with imperfection, for as man he suffered pain—that men might mak
the great and otherwise impossible first step toward human perfec
tion. This is a subtle doctrine, and nonsense to many modern mind
But it is an attempt—and to the ardent other-worldly temper a dange
ous attempt—to satisfy the intellectual element in man. Once mor
it would be much simpler to echo Tertullian and say that Jesus save

in a way that must always be unfathomable to the man who strings words together in thought.

But this was not the scholastic way, and certainly not the way of the greatest of the Scholastics, St. Thomas Aquinas, who, though he died at the age of forty-nine, has left a voluminous body of writings. Two of his books, the *Summa contra gentiles* and the *Summa theologica,* are encyclopedias of medieval learning and philosophy, but systematic encyclopedias in which everything is co-ordinated from a central point of view, not mere miscellaneous information put together, like a modern encyclopedia, in alphabetical order. The central point of view is orthodox Catholic Christianity interpreted by a moderate realist (in the medieval sense of the word we have been using in this chapter), an orderly logician never tempted to excess even in logic, a prodigious scholar who somehow kept his links with the world of common sense.

For Aquinas, this is a sensible world, though by no means a serene, happy, easygoing one. In the main, God has designed this earth as a fit place for man, whom he created in his own image. Clearly, therefore, no such important human activity as thinking can be contrary to his design; nor indeed are any of the activities clearly natural to man to be considered in themselves wrong. There are indeed many possibilities for men to do wrong, and life on this earth is a constant struggle against the very real powers of evil. But here again God has given us his only Son, and in the Church founded on earth by that Son he has given us an unmistakable guide in the task of fulfilling his will.

Aquinas, then, started with the authority of revealed faith, with those truths we possess direct from God; according to Aquinas, all our thinking, *if rightly done,* merely confirms these truths, and helps us in this daily life to apply them. In that eternal Christian problem of faith against reason (remember the *credo quia impossibile!*) Scholasticism took a firm stand; there is no problem, because there is no opposition between faith and reason rightly understood. If a man put a series of arguments together and came out with a conclusion contrary to what orthodox Catholics believed, he was simply guilty of faulty logic, and the use of correct logic could readily show where he erred. Indeed Thomas Aquinas, like most of the later Scholastics, delighted in the game of inventing arguments against accepted beliefs, matching them with a set of even more ingenious arguments that usually went a little bit beyond the simpler require-ments of the faith, and then reconciling them with an intellectual skill reminiscent of the trained athlete's ability to master timing and co-ordination. Nor is the figure of speech misleading. The athlete like the scholastic thinker must avoid too much and too little, too early and too late, must focus the right amount of energy at the right place.

The right logic for Aquinas was the revived and once more fully understood method of Aristotle. We have noted that Aristotle him-self was by temperament a middle-of-the-roader, that he could not accept Plato's ideal other world, and that he could not by any means take this world as it came. Aristotle's feeling for purposiveness in human life fitted admirably with the melioristic tendencies of Chris-tianity. Aristotle's method of thinking, which was to start with evident truths and by a process apparently natural to the human, or at least to the Western, mind, keep on spinning out a neat and con-sistent pattern of propositions, fitted well with the scholastic acceptance of revealed truths and with scholastic habits of reflection. You have heard this process of thinking referred to as deduction, and almost certainly you have been led to contrast it unfavorably with another process of thinking, rendered respectable by the triumphs of modern science, and known as induction. Actually this is an oversimple, if not a false contrast, to which we shall return when we come to the great figure of Francis Bacon.

For the moment, it may be noted that if you work by this method of deduction from a starting point for half-a-dozen steps in a row without checking up on your facts (sense experience) you will prob-ably arrive at a conclusion not in accordance with the facts. But this is not necessarily disastrous unless you are the kind of person known to us as an experimental scientist, or unless, like a physician or a garage mechanic, you are trying to work on a common-sense level much as the scientist works. You may wish, for instance, as the

Scholastics wished, to find patterns of conduct that satisfy your desire to lead a good life. You may wish to find something better than the facts. You may wish to see where your mind leads you, as the mathematician does. For all these and many other purposes deduction will serve you well, especially if, like the Scholastics, you do return from your thinking from time to time at least to the facts of human behavior.

Aquinas certainly does have a base from which he never gets very far, even in his subtlest and most "scholastic" arguments. That base is the body of revealed truths of the Christian faith, supplemented by common sense and experience in many phases of human relations, and interpreted by an essentially moderating, reconciling mind with full access to the works of the Fathers, the earlier Schoolmen, and in particular Aristotle, who is often quoted in the *Summa* as simply "the Philosopher."

Here, for instance, is an example of the mind and method of Aquinas. It is a relatively unimportant part of the *Summa theologica,* but it is fairly easy to follow and brings out more clearly than some of the grander parts, such as that on the freedom of the will, how close to common sense Aquinas can be. He is discussing the specific conditions of "man's first state," the state of innocence before the Fall. He comes to the question—a traditional one, odd as it may seem to moderns, in the literature—of what children were like in a state of innocence? Even more specifically, were they born with such perfect strength of body that they had full use of their limbs at birth, or were they like human children nowadays, helpless little wrigglers at birth? In the Garden of Eden, one might think that any form of helplessness would derogate from perfection, and that since God was making human life so different from what it later became he might well have made the human infant strong and perfect from the.start, or even had the men and women born adult. And indeed the all-out perfectionist, other-worldly tradition tended to make Eden as unearthly as possible. Not so Aquinas; even his Eden was as "natural" a one as he could make it.

By faith alone do we hold truths which are above nature, and what we believe rests on authority. Wherefore, in making any assertion, we must be guided by the nature of things, except in those things which are above nature, and are made known to us by Divine authority. Now it i clear that it is as natural as it is befitting to the principles of human na ture that children should not have sufficient strength for the use of their limbs immediately after birth. Because in proportion to other animals man has naturally a larger brain. Wherefore it is natural, on account of the considerable humidity of the brain in children, that the sinews which are instruments of movement, should not be apt for moving the limbs. On the other hand, no Catholic doubts it possible for a child to have, by Divine power, the use of its limbs immediately after birth.

Now we have it on the authority of Scripture that *God made man right* (Eccles. vii. 30), which rightness, as Augustine says, consists in the perfect subjection of the body to the soul. As, therefore, in the primi-tive state it was impossible to find in the human limbs anything repug-nant to man's well-ordered will, so was it impossible for those limbs to fail in executing the will's commands. Now the human will is well ordered when it tends to acts which are befitting to man. But the same acts are not befitting to man at every season of life. We must, there-fore, conclude that children would not have had sufficient strength for the use of their limbs for the purpose of performing every kind of act; but only for the acts befitting the state of infancy, such as suckling, and the like.

There is much typical of Thomism in this apparently trivial pas-sage—the clear supremacy granted to "truths which are above nature," which we hold by faith and receive through divine authority; the ready acceptance of divine omnipotence; the belief that generally God pre-fers to let nature run its course; that there is a "fitness" in human action conforming to observable laws of nature; that these laws of nature are basically purposeful in terms of human life; and finally, the appeal to authority, in this case the Old Testament and Augustine.

Certainly Aquinas is difficult for a twentieth-century American layman to read, though not more so than Kant, or than Aristotle him-self. Part of the difficulty, then, lies in the fact that Aquinas is a professional philosopher of great technical ability and with the tech-nician's interest in refinements and precision that escape the amateur. Especially in the *Summa theologica* he did indeed write as simply as he could, for he meant the work for serious students and not just for his fellow professors. No doubt, however, that part of the difficulty an unprepared modern has in reading Aquinas lies in the very different assumptions a medieval philosopher made, lies in the strangeness (to us) of the intellectual climate of the Middle Ages. To this strangeness we shall return later in an effort to put into words the *Zeitgeist* of the Middle Ages.

In spite of these difficulties, it should be clear that Aquinas belongs among the great philosophical systematizers of Western thought. His is a beautifully constructed system, which has been praised for this excellence, perhaps somewhat grudgingly, even by modern positivists and materialists who disagree with almost all that Scholasticism holds true. It is a system which, in its general bearing, sets man comfortably but not too comfortably in a world understandable to the human mind, in a world the human will cannot indeed wholly transform, but to which it can adjust. The world of Aquinas is a Christian world where man belongs, where he is at home. Finally, the system of Aquinas is a marvelously balanced system, holding the middle way in all the great problems of philosophy, and holding it with the ease of supreme skill. Again the image of the athlete occurs, and one thinks of the tightrope walker. But Aquinas is never showy, and never seems to strive after this middle way. It is, to use a favorite word of his, which troubled him much less than it troubles our semantically worried age, part of his *nature*.

Like most such balanced achievements, that of Aquinas is bound to seem dull to many ardent, curious, or otherwise discontented spirits. Aquinas is no crusader. Like Burke, he would reform in order to conserve. He never laughs, never lets himself risk the light touch. Of course, theology and philosophy were in his day subjects of supreme seriousness. But Aquinas has not even a touch of the ironist. We have just remarked that the Eden of Aquinas was as natural as he could make it. He probably had no emotional conception of Eden, and he had a good deal of common sense. But you must not think that he ever brings in common sense to chasten, correct, or lighten the very great load of not-common sense that Christianity—and the whole human race—carries. Aquinas, who seems to this writer very little indeed of a mystic, none the less takes the concrete heritage of Christian mysticism, of Christian other-worldliness, with admirable ease, without struggling, as part of what was given him. He makes his peace with it, in a sense tames it. Aquinas is not the philosopher for the Christian anxious to storm heaven; he is an admirable philosopher for the Christian seeking peace of mind, and a disturbing one for the peace of mind of the non-Christian.

Medieval Theories of Human Relations

We have attempted to show how medieval philosophers and men of learning, working on the materials left them by the Fathers of the Church, and on a good deal of the classical tradition, arrived at the formal philosophy we call Scholasticism. We have seen that within medieval formal thought is to be found almost as great a range as within classical thought; and we have found that the culminating system of Scholasticism is the all-embracing, almost eclectic, almost common-sense moderation of Aquinas. The medieval answers to the Big Questions were very different from the Greek answers; the medieval methods of thought were not so different. That is one reason why Aristotle could be so readily used by the Schoolmen. In the somewhat lesser but still big questions of human conduct and political organization the medieval answers are also new. Inevitably in morals and politics Christian notions of good and evil, and the concrete circumstances of medieval life, show up more clearly than in the more abstract fields of theology and philosophy. And, above all, the insistent problem of the relation between theory and practice, which can always be dismissed as irrelevant or undignified by the sufficiently determined metaphysician, can hardly be suppressed in problems of human relations.

It is sometimes maintained that the gap between ideal and practice in human relations is, for Western man, at its widest in the Middle Ages. Now the problem of the relation between ideal type and actuality in society is a continuing one in our tradition. Certainly

Plato was well aware of it. The gap is hardly one that can be measured on a graph, like the difference between the goal for a charity drive and the actual contributions made. Just conceivably, if we could measure for various Western societies the gap between ideals and actuality, we might find it a constant. Those who hold that the gap was wider in the Middle Ages argue as follows. In ideal, the Middle Ages provided for men on earth a well-organized and orderly life: The Church took care of men's souls, the feudal nobility preserved civil order, the peasants and craftsmen worked unenviously and steadily at useful tasks; a beautifully ordered nexus of rights and duties bound each man to each, from swineherd to emperor and pope; each man knew his place, was secure in his place, happy in it; this was a society of *status* instead of the mad competitions and uncertainties of modern society, but a society in which the Christian concept of the equality of all men before God had, so to speak, put a firm floor under the humblest and poorest of men; in short, an orderly, stratified society of morally free men.

In practice—and those hostile to the Middle Ages can cite horrendous details—even in the thirteenth, "greatest of centuries," and even in that center of medieval achievement northwestern Europe (modern France, England, the Low Countries, and the Rhineland), there were constant gangster wars among the feudal barons, corruption, laziness, worldliness, and worse among the clergy, poverty among the great masses, endemic disease, frequent famine, outbursts of class warfare—in short, and at the best, the customary misbehavior and unhappiness one finds in the human race, perhaps in some ways rather worse than usual.

The gap between the ideal and the real exists in all societies. We hardly need to be reminded of the gap between American democratic theory and practice. The above statements exaggerate the innocent perfectionism of the "ought to be" of the Middle Ages, and they exaggerate (perhaps even more) the miseries of the Middle Ages "is." Yet again we must insist that there remains a grain of truth in the commonly held notion that there is a striking gap between medieval theory and medieval fact, between the excellent intentions of medieval moralists, and what even so great an admirer of the Middle Ages as Henry Osborn Taylor calls the "spotted actuality."

The width of the gap may be due in part to the fact that during the Dark Ages and the early Middle Ages the intellectual class was even more removed than in other Western societies from the daily give and take of life. It may be that, faced with the disorders, the breakdown of central authority, the partial relapse into barbarism of the Dark Ages, the intellectual leaders of the growing new society tended to emphasize the importance of order, of fixed arrangements binding each man to a set role in society. At any rate, one is struck by the fact that the moral and political ideals of most medieval thinkers are geared to a stable society. But from the eleventh century on medieval society was in fact a dynamic society, growing in population, wealth, technical command over resources, and therefore subject to stresses and strains its social theory tended to assume were nonexistent. Let us, without attempting to cover the field by individual writers, take a characteristic concrete phase of the field, and try to make the problem real.

One of the commoner polarities of social theory and practice is that between a caste society and a society of complete individual social mobility. At one pole each individual is born to a place in society—a job, an income, a social role, a set of opinions—which he retains all his life. Plato's ideal society seems to some interpreters pretty close to this extreme, and of course the bees and the ants actually live in this sort of society. At the other pole is a society in which all members are as free of all the others as possible, each individual doing what seems desirable to him at any time, with no one tied to job, family, or social position—to a status, in short. Naturally there has never been such a society as this last, but we can say that many Americans think of our society as composed of free, mobile, and equal individuals; and we can further say that in fact our society is, as human societies have gone in the past, closer than most to the pole of individual social mobility. The popular saying "three generations from shirt sleeves to shirt sleeves" is a good concrete example of this attitude.

Now no such saying would have made sense to men of the Middle Ages. But in the later Middle Ages, such a saying was by no means wholly wide of the facts. The fifteenth century especially saw many impoverished feudal noblemen, many newly rich merchants and court favorites. In theory among the Scholastics, and even among thinkers whose training was legal rather than theological, society was a well-arranged whole, or organism, of which the individuals were parts or members. We have in the twelfth-century *Policraticus* of the English monk, John of Salisbury, a very complete statement of what came to be called the "organic theory" of society. According to John of Salisbury, the prince is the head of the body of the commonwealth, the senate (legislative body) the heart, judges and governors of provinces the eyes, ears, and tongue, officials and soldiers the hands, financial officers the stomach and intestines, and the husbandmen "correspond to the feet, which always cleave to the soil." This figure of speech, or if you think it deserves a more ambitious name, this organic theory of state or society, is a great favorite with those who wish to oppose change. For obviously the foot does not try to become the brain, nor is the hand jealous of the eye; the whole body is at its best—its very parts are at their best—when each part does what nature meant it to do.

The field worker, the blacksmith, the merchant, the lawyer, the priest, and the king himself all have assigned to them a part of God's work on earth. Medieval thought is insistent on the dignity and worth of all vocations, even the humblest; and of course even the humblest person on this earth could in the next world hope to enjoy a bliss as full and eternal as any king's. You do not find the contempt for, or at least indifference toward, a class of belly-men you find in Plato. Moreover, medieval political theory is by no means absolutist. One might assume that in an organized society as it appears in this body of thought there would be no means of resisting the acts of a superior. And certainly medieval thinkers were not democratic in the sense of believing that the people have a right to cashier their rulers. Jefferson's famous statement that there ought to be a revolution every nineteen years or so would have shocked most of these thinkers—would indeed have been unintelligible to them. But they did not hold, as they might perhaps logically have held, that since God has arranged authority and dignity as it now is in this world, we should preserve the *status quo*.

Their way out of this dilemma was readily found. God has ordained an order of rank in this world, and has made the relation of superior-inferior one of the keystones of his work on earth. For this relation one of the characteristic medieval terms was *dominium*, first clearly used in this sense early in the fourteenth century by Egidius Romanus, an apologist for the papal power. If I am placed above you you owe me service, and I have *dominium* over you. But I may abuse my *dominium*, may treat you as if you were a mere animal and not an immortal soul. In that case I do not exercise *dominium* (authority), but mere *proprietas* (possession, ownership). *Dominium* is the right, the decent human relation, *proprietas* the wrong, the unbearable human relation. One may own a thing, but not a person. You must accept my *dominium*, but you must reject my *proprietas*, if its exercise outrages your moral sense. No man ought to be treated as a thing, an instrument, by another. Should the prince himself abuse the power he has from God, says John of Salisbury, he may justly be killed as a tyrant. His killer will simply be the agent of God, not really a responsible human being committing murder. John's doctrine is a good concrete illustration of the fact that medieval thinkers did differ, did not in fact display that "unity" sometimes made a catchword for the Middle Ages. His doctrine of tyrannicide was *not* orthodox.

In this stratified society where every man has his rightful place, every man received, at least in theory, his just economic due. Medieval economic notions have been greatly admired by modern intellectuals in revolt against what they regard as our crassly competitive business life. Work was to the medieval theorist wholly honorable, a part of God's design for man. Work was not a way of advancing the worker in the social scale; above all, one did not work to "make money" in the modern sense. For making money in this sense could only come by cheating someone else, by taking more than one's rightful share. A piece of work, say a pair of shoes made by a skilled craftsman, is not to be considered as a commodity on the open market, fetching what the buyer will pay for it, sold at a high price if there is a scarcity of shoes at the moment, at a low price—even at a loss—if there is a glut of shoes. The shoes are worth a fixed price, their "just price." This just price includes the cost of the raw materials, the amount needed to sustain the worker at his usual standards of life while making the shoes (i.e., cost of labor), and a small item not so much of profit as of wages of management for the seller.

To ensure this economic justice, medieval society, especially in the later centuries, worked out an elaborate system of what we should now call controls. Merchants and artisans were both organized in trade associations called guilds. These guilds set prices and standards and controlled admission of new workers and masters into the trade. They did not exactly set a quota for each firm in the trade, nor did they "plan" production in the modern sense of the word. Obviously in a static society a given firm (master and workmen) did the amount of business it had been doing from time immemorial; custom set its quota. As for planning, that had been done a long time ago by God himself. Custom took the place of planning too in medieval society. These controls were reinforced by the regulations of local governments.

Finally, medieval society had in theory no place for finance capitalism, had no fluid supply of money or credit from which the man who wished to expand his business could draw. Medieval theory— and here Aquinas is an especially clear and good source—regarded the taking of interest for money lent as getting something for nothing, as the exploiting by the lender of the temporary needs of the borrower. If I lend a sum for twelve months and get it back intact, I have neither gained nor lost. If I get back more than I lent, I am getting unearned income. True, if the borrower does not pay within the time agreed, I may claim a kind of indemnity, since my plans are disturbed. But this and a few similar adjustments do not amount to a recognition of the legitimacy of interest; and indeed in the Middle Ages what we call interest was regarded as mere usury. What the men of the

Middle Ages refused to admit—and in a static and autarkic society this refusal is wholly natural—is that money lent to an enterpriser can be productively invested so that *more economic goods* exist at the end of the loan period than at the beginning. Even when such increased economic goods began to come in, even when the economy of the later Middle Ages became in fact dynamic, the medieval thinkers could not—certainly did not—see the change. We shall return to this distinction between dynamic and static, which is of major importance in understanding the medieval outlook in contrast with the modern.

Let us take one final illustration. We have already noted that in most early and simple societies the modern notion of making law, of passing statutes changing existing legal arrangements, does not exist. Indeed in such societies the term "arrangements" that we have just now used almost instinctively would seem highly inappropriate if applied to something so dignified and sanctified as the law. To the medieval mind, even to that of the lawyer, the law was not made but found. Law for common, everyday purposes indeed was what we should call custom. The way to find that was to inquire among the experienced and established men of a given locality, find out what had been done in a given respect from time immemorial. Customs might conflict in a given case, but due inquiry among the people most concerned would establish a weight of evidence for one solution or another of the case.

There was indeed something beyond custom, something beyond law in the sense of what people were used to doing. Medieval thought at its height provided a heavy reinforcement for that notion of a "law of nature" that we have seen emerging from the Graeco-Roman world, a notion never wholly lost even in the Dark Ages. The law of nature was to the medieval thinker something like God's word translated into terms usable by ordinary men on earth. It was the norm, the ethical ideal, the "ought to be" discernible by men of good will thinking rightly. When men like Egidius Romanus and later the famous English radical Wycliffe made the distinction we have noted above between *dominium* and *proprietas,* they would put behind

universe is at bottom dynamic. The one assumes that laws for right human action have been, so to speak, designed for all time by God in heaven, and that those laws are clear to the good Christian; the other assumes that laws for right human action are in fact worked out in the very process of living, fighting, loving, planning, earning money, that no one can be sure of them in advance, that new ones are constantly being created in the course of human life. Since human beings do not live in neatly polar climates of opinion, the medieval man mixed with his static view much practical adaptability to change; and the modern man, however inconsistently, does for the most part believe in some absolutes above the process of evolutionary change—or at the very least, that evolutionary change is somehow purposeful. But in many fields of human activity the mental attitudes of medieval and modern men work out clearly in different behavior.

The medieval man, puzzled, tends to resolve this problem by an appeal to authority, the best or the natural authority in which he has been trained to place faith—Aristotle if he is a Schoolman, the customary law of the land if he is a lawyer, his father's farming practices if he is a farmer; and—this is very important—he tends to believe that no perfectly satisfactory solution of his problem is actually available, tends to feel that he cannot be much better off until he goes to heaven. The modern man, puzzled, tends at least to consult several different authorities and compare them before making up his own mind, and if he is well trained in some disciplines of scientific or practical character, he may try to experiment, to make tentative essays in new directions suggested by his appeal to different authorities and to his own particular experiences; and he tends to feel that if he goes about it the right way, he can in fact solve his difficulty. The right way for the medieval man already exists, and has at most to be *found;* the right way for the modern man may have to be *made, created.*

In spite of these contrasting attitudes, there is much in medieval social and political thought that has proved basic to our own. True, you will not find the idea of systematic material progress or evolution in medieval thought, and you will not find much emphasis on competition, individualism, or, indeed, on organized planning. You will

not find an atmosphere of "bigger and better," nor will you find discussion of the "democratic way of life." Medieval theory, as we have
noted, emphasizes obedience, status, custom, fixed class structure,
authority. But medieval social relations were not as stable and fixed
in fact as in theory. From some of the actual conflicts of medieval life
came the material changes, the progress, that helped break down
medieval attitudes; and there also came, even at the height of the
Middle Ages, ideas (or sentiments) that are with difficulty reconcilable
with the principles of authority, obedience, an unchanging order of
rank. To the first sort of change we shall come in the next chapter.
The second sort of change is by no means independent of the first,
but it depends also on conflicts long antedating the kind of economic
conflict that ushered in modern times.

Briefly and oversimply, the point can be made as follows: A
relatively rigid, authoritarian, unchanging society among human
beings needs a final sovereign authority whose decisions really are
final. As long as Sparta was such a society, for instance, the decisions
of the elders were unanimous and accepted. In the eastern part of the
old Roman Empire the emperor, and his Russian successor the tsar,
were such final authorities, able to dictate their will even to the
Church. Hence the somewhat heavy term "caesaropapism" for the
absolutism of the Eastern heirs of Caesar. But the slightest acquaintance with the political history of the West during the medieval period
makes it clear that in the West there was never that unquestioning
acceptance of a single and final authority which is essential for the
kind of society many Western thinkers thought they had—or better,
were about to have. At the very highest level, the popes and the
emperors each claimed supreme authority in the West. Able and
lucky emperors had tastes of such authority, which was perhaps most
nearly attained in fact by Pope Innocent III in the early thirteenth
century. Each side had its triumphs in the long struggle. Both sides
had very able theorists, and indeed almost all medieval thinkers
sooner or later took sides in the dispute. Dante, for instance, spent a
great deal of energy on a long political pamphlet, *De Monarchia,* in
which he urges the world rule of the emperor as a solution for the

evils brought on by the wars of his time. Papal supremacy had its defenders, among them Egidius Romanus. Thomas Aquinas concluded that the pope had "an indirect rather than a direct authority in temporal matters," another example of his bent toward moderation.

A great deal of what the specialist finds fascinating speculation went into this struggle of pope and emperor. But one obvious upshot was that by the later Middle Ages the extreme claims of each were discredited. It is not merely that in the strife of propaganda—for such it was—the imperialists insulted the papalists and the papalists the imperialists, and that, again as is usual with propaganda, the insults stuck more firmly than the praise of their own side. It is also that each side had to find a backing for its claim to authority, and that some of the backing came to be quite modern. Marsiglio of Padua, the fourteenth-century author of *Defensor Pacis,* an imperialist tractate, found the only true source of authority in a commonwealth to be the *universitas civium,* the whole body of the citizens. Marsiglio was no doubt carried away by his enthusiasm, and probably did not mean to be as modern as some of his commentators have made him out to be. He still uses medieval terms, and the constitutionalism, the notions of popular sovereignty, attributed to him are a long way from our notion of counting heads to determine political decisions. But Marsiglio did in all earnestness mean what a great many other medieval thinkers, even those on the papal side, meant: No man's place in the order of rank, even if he is at the top of it, is such that what he commands must always and unquestioningly be accepted and acted on by those of lower rank.

The feudal relation itself, by which throughout the nobility men were bound together as lord and vassal, is an admirable example of medieval insistence that its order of rank is not one of mere might. The term "vassal" has cheapened with time, and insofar as it survives at all today it comes near suggesting involuntary servitude. Moreover, there is still common today a mistaken view of the Middle Ages as a period of chaos and personal tyranny. Actually only gentlemen could be vassals to a lord. The relation was marked by elaborate ceremonies at its beginning (*homage*) and was always regarded as a mutual relation of give and take, indeed, as a contractual relation. The vassal owed the lord certain services; the lord owed the vassal the great service of protection. The elaborate way of life known as chivalry, which gradually developed in this feudal class, is one of the most insistent of all human codes on the personal dignity and standing of each of its initiates.

Not even here was the theory identical with the practice; and the practice had much to do with the emergence of modern from medieval society. In theory the feudal relation was a fixed order of rank, as in an army, from the lowest knight to the emperor (or was it the pope?). If the count was vassal to the duke, and the duke to the king, then each owed services and was owed them in a neat, prearranged way. The trouble was that the count might acquire lands bearing feudal obligations to another duke, or directly to the king, or even to someone below himself in rank. There might be disputes, and in the confusion of feudal ties a vassal might find himself—in spite of theory—fighting *against* his lord. In short, though feudalism might have hardened into a fixed caste society, it did not do so because its members were rarely contented with, and sometimes not at all sure of, their place in the order of rank. That place, ultimately, in the medieval mind, depended on right, not might. And though *right* here as elsewhere in the Middle Ages was most easily and frequently interpreted as *custom,* "the way things have always been," there remained always the final bottoming of right on God's will expressed in the law of nature.

We come again to the great medieval generalization of the natural order, the law of nature, which is on earth the nearest we can come to God's law. This characteristic Western doctrine is an always available argument in favor of change, if necessary of revolutionary change. For it sets up clearly, as we have already noted, the notion of a better order, yet an order which, since it is "natural," is obviously attainable, not an other-worldly ideal. When, as in the eighteenth century, many men's notions of what is natural are quite radically different from those of their social and political superiors, you have a revolutionary situation. When, as briefly in the thirteenth century, there is at least general agreement among educated men on what is natural, you have a relatively stable society. But in the later Middle Ages, as growing class antagonisms were accentuated by wars, plagues, and other disorders of a time of troubles, the concept of natural law came to be an inspiration to rebellion against authorities who were not achieving the order—the justice—for which natural law strives. The fifteenth century has, in spite of the obvious differences of vocabulary and, to some extent, habits of mind, much in common with the eighteenth.

Yet even in its earlier years, even at its height, the Middle Ages was not the impossible combination of chaos and disorder in fact [practice] and of unity in ideals it sometimes appears to be in American textbooks. And very definitely, the Middle Ages in the West was no time for absolutism. In medieval theory, only God was absolute; the men through whom he worked on earth were no more than his agents, and as men could be judged by other men if they went against God's law—and nature's. In medieval Western practice, division of authority between lay and spiritual powers, the conflicting claims of thousands of feudal lords, and the universal appeal to custom as authority made established absolute rule quite impossible. The roots of modern Western democracy lie in the Middle Ages, whereas it was not until the first few centuries of the modern period that the doctrine of absolutism gained prominence.

7

The Middle Ages ~ II

THERE IS a not uncommon notion that the Middle Ages—the whole thousand years between the end of Graeco-Roman culture and the Renaissance—added nothing to the body of cumulative knowledge we call science. That notion is incorrect. We now know that the social, economic, and even the intellectual foundations for modern science in the West were laid down in the high Middle Ages. From the twelfth century on the rise of towns and commerce, the growth of an adventurous class of merchant enterprisers eager for technical improvements, the amassing of capital to permit investment in improvements, made for social conditions in which science could prosper. Intellectually, the study of logic, mathematics, and the liberal arts underlay the habits of mind which, once turned toward the familiar world of objects of sense perception, slowly grew into modern science.

Of course, the notion that the Middle Ages were unscientific, indeed antiscientific, has some basis in fact. Few such widespread notions, or stereotypes, are *wholly* false. Many of the great thinkers of the Middle Ages wrote much in a vein wholly contrary to what we consider that of science; and in a sense the spirit of the age was not conducive to formal scientific thought. But here, as so often in complex problems of this sort, two precautions need to be taken. On any given point, the full range, the full spectrum, of actual opinion should be ascertained as far as possible; and an attempt should be made to find out what is being done as well as what is being said or written. Such a study will show that at the speculative or philosophical level much useful work was done in science in the later Middle Ages, and that even more was achieved at the practical level of technology and invention.

Extreme other-worldliness is quite irreconcilable with science, and even with learning. In support of the thesis that science was utterly dead in the Middle Ages you can find many quotations, such as the common one from St. Ambrose: "To discuss the nature and position of the earth does not help us in our hope of the life to come." And you can call up anti-intellectuals, mystics, fundamentalists of all sorts in these years. But so you can at any period in Western history, including our own. Indeed it is only within the last few generations that the natural sciences have risen to the topmost rank in intellectual prestige. The question is always one of balance among many conflicting attitudes. In the later Middle Ages, the highest prestige went to the kind of learning we call Scholasticism: and Scholasticism is by no means anti-intellectual. It is indeed one of the sources of modern science.

It is certainly true that medieval Scholasticsm as a whole is very different from modern science. Scholasticism puts its emphasis on deduction from principles it takes on authority; science puts its emphasis on experimentation to test its own kind of authority (that is, previous theories on a given subject). But do not fall into the prejudices of the Baconians who damned the Scholastics. Science is not all *induction,* is by no means the piling up of fact on fact until by miracle facts breed their own explanation. Science is in part *deduction,* and as such owes a great deal to the spadework of the Scholastics. Indeed, there are those to whom medieval Scholasticism seems the beginning of the end of true mystic belief, the beginning of that—to them—fatal modern effort to *understand* the universe which has gone so far that man can *now* perhaps destroy at least his own universe.

The medieval intellectual's reverence for authority was a much greater obstacle to the growth of science than were his deductive ways of thinking. It may be that the *habit* of taking the established written word as authority even against common sense had its origins in Christian acceptance of the Bible as the word of God. But Biblical fundamentalism was in the Middle Ages less a stumbling block in the way of scientific experimentation than the works of Aristotle and the surviving classical literature of antiquity. Notably in the whole range of what we now call biology the Middle Ages tended to take the word of Aristotle, Pliny, a most credulous Roman natural historian, and Galen, a good but perhaps too theoretical physician.

Moreover, the Middle Ages was a time of great human credulity and what seems to us superstition. After all, the thirteenth century was very close indeed to the Dark Ages; medieval thinkers had to struggle out of depths of ignorance. Yet credulity and superstition—indeed, unquestioning acceptance of a given authority in matters where this authority is wrong or irrelevant—have by no means been banished from modern Western society. You will find books on astrology in almost any American drugstore; and why should a movie actress be an authority on the effect of cigarette smoking on the throat? Sea serpents crop up in the newspapers with great regularity.

It is true that our professional biologists think it extremely unlikely that sea serpents or unicorns exist; and it is true that in the Middle Ages many educated men apparently believed that such creatures, and even stranger ones, existed. That is, certain kinds of belief that we today find contrary to our experience were in the Middle Ages held to be true by individuals of a very high social and intellectual rank. These medieval intellectuals were brought up in a living tradition of Christian theism that set the boundary between the natural and the supernatural much lower in the scale of ordinary experience than we can possibly do, unless we have had a very exceptional upbringing indeed. For them, the appearance of the *stigmata* (marks on hands and ankles where Christ was nailed to the cross) on a saint like Francis of Assisi required neither proof to establish it as a fact nor a theory to establish it as plausible. Even quite good Catholics today would be very happy with a medical explanation of such a phenomenon, and, indeed, such explanations have been attempted.

This ready acceptance of the miraculous was not conducive to the slow, patient study of natural events in which no miraculous breaks occur. But a still greater obstacle to medieval experimental science was the set of taboos that prevented—though in the later Middle Ages these taboos merely hindered—the study of human anatomy. Such taboos, as much social as religious, prevented the dissection of the human body. Christian belief, holding firmly to the doctrine of the resurrection in the flesh, could not permit mutilation of the body that must someday appear before its maker. Even so, in the famous medical schools of the Middle Ages, such as those of Salerno in Italy and Montpellier in France, there was a good deal of what we might somewhat grimly call bootlegging of cadavers, and with the addition of classical and Arab work in the field a broad foundation was laid on which later experimental science could build.

We must, then, grant that in the Middle Ages experimental science in all its fields, and particularly the sciences of life, faced many hindrances: comparatively wide prevalence of an other-worldliness scornful of a scientific concern with things of this world; a deductive habit of thought unwilling to admit the necessity of testing from time to time a chain of thinking by appeal to what the scientist calls "facts"; an uncritical reverence for classical authority; a very great credulousness, or, negatively, an absence of the kind of skepticism the scientist believes necessary; so wide an acceptance of the miraculous as to undermine the study of the commonplace, which study is one of the essentials of science; and finally, an acceptance of the commonplace as the miraculous work of God, and therefore as not really understandable in scientific terms. Yet in spite of these obstacles the scientific achievement of the thousand years of the Middle Ages is very great.

In the first place, the Middle Ages greatly improved the mathematical tools without which there would be no modern science. With the help of borrowings from the Arabs and the Hindus they retained what the Greeks had done in geometry and created the new science of algebra. Here again they made a broad foundation from which Newton and others could go on to the calculus and the rest of modern mathematics. But perhaps these achievements are less important than a not very lofty technical device, almost a gadget, which has been indispensable to us all. Ultimately from the Hindus and through Arabic intermediaries medieval arithmeticians took the simple device we call "zero," and the rest of our common numeration. If you think this an unimportant thing, try such a simple problem as dividing MDCCIV by LXVI—sticking throughout, of course, to Roman numerals.

The most striking of medieval achievements in formal science was in this very deductive field of mathematics, in which some of the obstacles we have just noted were of much less importance than in the experimental fields. Nevertheless, well before the end of the fifteenth century, which usually serves to mark the beginning of modern times, definite progress had been made in many other formal sciences. Almost everyone is familiar with the name of Roger Bacon, a thirteenth-century English monk whose work anticipates in its praise of induction and experiment that of his famous namesake Francis Bacon over three centuries later. Roger Bacon was not the lone scientist of the Middle Ages, nor did he suffer persecution because of his opinions. In his long life—he lived to be eighty—he took part in the intellectual life of his age, which then as now meant taking sides in the Big Questions. Bacon seems clearly to have been some kind of nominalist or empiricist, and to have been opposed to the realists or idealists. But he was no heretic, no secret materialist, and much of his hopes for the method of experience were directed toward making more clear the truths of the Christian faith. Still, he can sound unquestionably modern, or perhaps merely British: "Of the three ways in which men think that they acquire a knowledge of things, authority, reasoning, and experience, only the last is effective and able to bring peace to the intellect."

Roger Bacon was once thought to have been an altogether exceptional figure in medieval thought. But the researches of men like C. H. Haskins, Lynn Thorndike, and George Sarton have in our day brought to light again the work of generations of patient medieval scientists, from scholars devotedly translating Arabic treatises on mathematics or astronomy to alchemists seeking, it is true, a goal not quite in accord with the ethics of modern science, but none the less building up within their eccentric guild the real beginnings of a knowledge of chemistry. Alchemy was a somewhat irregular, if not shady, pursuit that became a science. Another sort of marginal science in the Middle Ages was falconry, established to improve the methods of this aristocratic sort of hunting, but which led to a great deal of accurate and methodical investigation in one of the fields of the later ornithologist.

Falconry brings us squarely to one of the great facts about the growth of modern science, a fact we often lose sight of today. We are used, especially since the last war, to the idea of pure science as the fountainhead, the origin, of actual technological change. We agree that American industrial know-how was essential to the production of the atomic bomb, but we give chief credit for the bomb to the theoretical physicists. Now historically, in the medieval and early modern periods, the situation is reversed: It is the pure scientists who follow after, who take leads from, the practical workers, craftsmen, artisans, budding industrialists, estate owners working to improve their livestock. Of course, the relation between pure science and practical needs must not be seen in the terms of the old chicken-egg dilemma. At all times, one stimulates the other. The point is that in earlier times technology (the practical) at almost every step stimulated pure science; nowadays pure science can be self-nourishing and self-developing without being noncumulative, and yet without constant return to the technologists.

The list of medieval improvements and inventions would be a very long one. Very typical was one of the earliest, a product of the Dark Ages. This was the horse collar, a simple device, but one unknown to the Greeks and Romans. By means of this padded collar that slipped on over the head, it was possible to use the full tractive power of the horse without cutting off his windpipe. The Anglo-Saxons in Britain used a better plow than their Romano-British predecessors, and were thus able for the first time to plow up the rich, heavy lands of the valleys. The monks who cleared the forests and drained the swamps were responsible for many technical advances.

Metal workers paved the way for the formal study of mineralogy and metallurgy. Papermaking, another European borrowing from the Orient through the Arabs, was improved in European hands, and by the fifteenth century true paper was being made from rags and flax cheaply enough so that when in that last of the medieval centuries printing was invented (or borrowed from the Chinese) printed books quickly became, if not cheap, at least cheaper and more numerous than written manuscripts had ever been.

The printed work is certainly indispensable to modern science. But the connection between these medieval workmen and modern science is perhaps even clearer in clockmaking. Exact measurement of time is essential to any physical science. The Alexandrians unquestionably had for their purposes adequate clockwork. The Dark Ages brought a complete relapse to sundials and water clocks. By the thirteenth century clockworking had become a recognized craft, which gradually improved its product until by the fourteenth century hours, minutes, and seconds could be measured. Elaborate clocks adorned some of the later churches and city halls, clocks where little figures swung into view and hammered out the hour, clocks that showed the time of year, and so on. The workers who built these intricate machines were the true predecessors of modern precision workers.

The compass is perhaps the most familiar of the critical inventions made at this time. It was in use certainly a century or so before Columbus undertook his voyage, one that he could not possibly have made without this tiny instrument. But there is no use piling instance on instance. The important point for the intellectual historian is that from the thirteenth century on—that is, from the full blossoming of that Scholasticism we are sometimes told is the polar opposite of modernity—we find in the medieval West a spirit of material enterprise, a willingness to try new ways, a desire to master nature. We find, in short, the soil from which modern science grew.

Medieval Culture

We have already stressed, perhaps unduly, the fact that the Middle Ages are not a mere depression between the two peaks of

Graeco-Roman culture and our own. They are one of the flowering periods of Western culture in their own right, related to what came before and after, but still a whole that the historian of culture can attempt to understand and describe. No more than other periods are they static, nor are they at all simple. Unfortunately, one must make about them the almost impressionistic generalizations that are all the human mind can yet encompass in these matters.

The word one always comes to sooner or later in discussing the Middle Ages is "unity." These were the years when our Western culture really was one, when there existed a single Christian community, spiritual and temporal inextricably bound together, with no rival religious sects, no rival nationalities. Now it should be clear from the preceding chapter that on the whole this description of medieval culture applies rather to the theory than to the practice of that varied civilization. That this theoretical unity of Christianity should be proclaimed is in itself an important fact for us in our attempt to understand the Middle Ages. We know at least what the intellectuals wanted. And it is likely that to some extent this professed unity of Western Christendom set limits on the divisions and struggles that filled medieval life even at its high point in the thirteenth century.

Certainly within these limits there was a rich variety. The true lover of the Middle Ages likes to maintain that just *because* men were agreed on fundamentals—on the essentials of the Christian view of the universe—they could afford those picturesque local differences which make the Middle Ages so fascinating to moderns weary of the regimented regularities of a large-scale machine civilization. On this one can only comment that we do not know enough about sociology to know whether the basic principle invoked in such a statement—that is, that professed agreement on religious principles permits individuals to enjoy greater latitude of individual variation—is true. We cannot, indeed, even be sure that comparisons between modern uniformity and medieval variation are quite accurate as statements of fact.

It is true enough that in medieval France, for instance, people in adjoining valleys might speak dialects so different as to be mutually incomprehensible and that in those same valleys in modern France the people all speak standard French, with at most slight differences in accent. In medieval France each valley might have its own system of weights and measures; today both use that neat example of modern standardization, the metric system. And yet variety surely persists today, in spite of the alarms of intellectuals who hold that we are all going to be stamped out by modern totalitarian methods into identical patterns, that we are already robots or Babbitts. It may well be that in fact the range and variety of personality and temperament are greater in modern society than in medieval. Human beings obstinately vary as long as there is any choice before them; and actually modern culture, if it has diminished our choices in dialects, measures, and many other material things, has multiplied our choices among the extraordinary variety of things and services available to us—and (though not all our philosophers will agree to this) among *ends*, among good lives.

At any rate, we may content ourselves with the obvious assertion that one of the striking characteristics of medieval culture in the West is its diversity. If Latin remained the language of learning, there grew up from the twelfth century onward literatures in a dozen of the popular tongues, or vernaculars, which were to become the languages of modern Europe. If the great churches were built in a style we have since called "Gothic," this style varies so greatly from region to region that no one would mistake the Gothic of the Ile de France for the Gothic of the Low Countries or of England. Even chivalry, the ideal of the way of life of the medieval upper classes in the West, though it aspires to unity and certainly rises above parochialism, still is by no means the same thing all over Europe. Indeed, it may be questioned whether feudalism and chivalry were any more universal and uniform in the upper classes of the West than were the ideals and the way of life of the *noblesse* of the early modern period, which, like chivalry, were basically French in inspiration.

The geographical variants in medieval culture are not yet quite the modern nation. These nations, especially France, England, Spain, and (culturally, at least, if not politically) Germany and Italy, do however emerge clearly out of the Middle Ages. There is even a kind of "nationalism"—enough to be worth studying—in many phases of medieval life, such as that of the university world, the *studium* that on the surface looks to be wholly cosmopolitan. Some universities, notably the famous one at Paris, were organized into groups according to the nationality of the students. By 1300 most of the great modern tongues had at least the beginnings of a literature well beyond the purely popular level. Most serious writing—philosophy (including "natural philosophy," by which name science was understood), theology, political theory, learned work generally—was done in Latin until the late seventeenth century. Even in such fields the need to appeal to the people, as in the reform movements of the fourteenth and fifteenth centuries, brought much serious writing in the vernaculars.

Printing, in fact, came some two or three centuries after the clerical monopoly on the written word, on the making of manuscripts that was the equivalent of what we call publication, had ceased. Two of the greatest figures of our Western literature, Dante and Chaucer, wrote in Italian and English long before the printed book; their work was "published" in much the same way the work of Vergil or Horace had been published. The copyists did not disdain making collections of *fabliaux,* French popular verses that quite deserve to be called lowbrow. Of course, the traditional heroic poetry of the upper classes—the French *Chanson de Roland* is the most famous—were put down in manuscript form, as were the later lyrical works of the traveling singers. The encyclopedic works of learned monks, the chronicles or histories they laboriously compiled, often contain concrete details of popular beliefs and customs.

All told, then, we know a great deal about the ideas and sentiments of all sorts of medieval men and women, especially in the last few centuries of the period. We have a more rounded set of sources than we do for the Greeks and Romans. Inevitably we still know more about the learned and the upper classes. We have not yet printing, let alone newspapers, periodicals, and Gallup polls. But for generations antiquarians have been rummaging in muniment rooms and libraries, collecting and publishing every scrap of record of thing medieval they could lay their hands on.

We shall have to take the Middle Ages at their own estimate and accept the fact that theirs was a stratified society. The learned world still in the later Middle Ages mostly a clerical world, we have studied in the last chapter. Through Christian beliefs and practices, there i some influence of this learned world on that of the nobility, but the upper classes in the West have a culture of their own, that of chivalry Chivalry is not a way of abstract thinking, not a philosophy in the usual sense; but it involves all sorts of ideas and ideals, and just because of its association with a privileged class it has left an ample record. Finally, chivalry grows, changes, has a history. Indeed, the history of the word itself is fascinating. Its earliest meaning is apparently no more than "cavalry"; its latest, in America, apparently no more than somewhat quaint politeness to ladies. In the high Middle Ages, however, chivalry was a way of life.

The origins of chivalry lie in the formation of the feudal ruling class during the Dark Ages. This was a class of landed proprietors fighting men by profession, for centuries the sole police and military power of society. By the feudal and manorial system of landholding these lords were after a fashion integrated in a system of authority culminating in king or emperor. But the chain of command was often an obscure one, and a great deal of initiative, a good deal of independence in action, was left to the individual member of this upper class. Indeed, within the class, there was always, in spite of great differences of wealth and power, a certain basic equality. A knight was a knight, as later a gentleman was a gentleman.

In its earliest centuries, and to a certain extent well into the high Middle Ages, membership in the class was open to talent—talent closer to that which gets the ambitious American lad his varsity letter rather than the kind that gets him scholarship honors, but definitely talent The outward sign of membership in the group was knighthood (the English knight is the French *chevalier*). Knighthood was conferred by a feudal superior upon a young man when he came of age, or upon deserving followers in their later years. It was almost never withheld

224

from those of noble birth; but in addition it could be conferred for good reason, such as bravery in battle, on commoners. There was always in feudal society a group of non-noble fighting men, or helpers to fighting men. In earlier years, these not infrequently rose by being knighted into the privileged class. Later, as so often in the history of such groups, access from below became difficult, if not impossible.

Now this feudal class lived by fighting, usually among themselves. There were, of course, crusades against the Mohammedans, against heretics like the Albigenses, and against the heathen Slavs. There came to be, especially with the Hundred Years' War between France and England, something like our standard national wars. And there were truly punitive expeditions against barons who had really gone beyond the bounds and become frank robbers. Yet it is still true that much feudal warfare was private warfare among men who could do little except fight, and who enjoyed unusual opportunities for fighting. Under these conditions, the anarchical tendencies were gradually balanced, and then overbalanced, by a set of voluntarily imposed rules, restrictions, decencies. By the fifteenth century, knightly fighting was hardly more dangerous than any very rough sport. Indeed, what happened in chivalry was roughly like what happened in American football from its brawling early days to the restrained game of today.

Even in its very early days, this fighting class was—so its members would earnestly have insisted—Christian. In the hard violence of its life one is tempted to see something of what we call gangsterism; and certainly a French count of the tenth century was nearer to being a gangster than to being the perfect gentle knight modern lovers of the Middle Ages have made him out to be. He could not read or write. He mastered as a youth the necessary skills in horsemanship, swordsmanship, and the like. He could, and often did, leave to stewards and clerks the administration, the governing, the dealing with human beings a ruling class usually has to take on to hold its power. He had, in short, much time on his hands, much chance to brood over insults, take revenge, maintain his reputation, which he called his honor. He could have fits of ungovernable rage—one guesses that he sometimes cultivated them—and could in passion kill, maim, seduce, violate most of the precepts Christianity never quite ceased to put before him.

But he believed in Christianity. He believed very much in heaven and especially in hell. He had a conscience, not infrequently a bad conscience. Nowhere can the sort of slick cynicism one often finds in modern America err more seriously than in assuming a similar cynicism in a ruling class like that of the Middle Ages. The knight who had given way to his passions knew quite well that he had sinned. He might make an extravagant gesture of repentance. He might take the cross, mortgage all his possessions to join a crusade to the Holy Land; he might give or will substantial property to the Church. Indeed, in the course of these thousand years the Church accumulated, from men of bad conscience as well as of good, such immense endowments of worldly goods that it became a major economic power. There are still those who believe that the Protestant Reformation was essentially an economic movement, the spoliation of the Church by a new set of robber barons without any conscience at all.

But it would be a mistake to think even of the earlier knighthood as merely an unruly group of athletes somehow come into positions of economic and political power, and held to some minimum standard of conduct only by the fear of hell-fire. Readers of this book should be amply warned of the dangers of taking any piece of literature as an accurate account of how men actually behave. Nevertheless, it would be absurd to hold that literature has no relation, or a purely negative relation, to real life. The ideal side of early European chivalry has been embodied in a series of epics, of which the best known and most representative is the *Chanson de Roland*. This poem, which deals with the historical ninth-century figure of Charlemagne, was recited for generations by poets who went from castle to castle offering entertainment. It was reduced to written form comparatively late in the Middle Ages. It is, then, the folk poetry of an upper class; it shows almost certainly how the earlier Western nobility liked to think of itself.

Charlemagne and his paladins as they are seen in this poem (and King Arthur and his knights as they are seen in others of roughly the same origin) are still athletes, but nice, simple, unsubsidized athletes who play the game fairly, even against the heathen, and who love God and the emperor in the old school spirit. If you consider this comparison unduly flippant and prefer to see the *Chanson de Roland* treated with loving care, read the first few pages of Henry Adams's *Mont St. Michel and Chartres*. Here the tired, soured New England intellectual turns with relief from his crazy, perverse modern world (as he felt it) to this fresh, simple, strong world of manly dignity, manly action, and manly certainties. But do not be too persuaded. Turn also to a few pages—any pages—of a monkish chronicler of Frankish times, Gregory of Tours. Frankish life as reflected in Gregory is rather more like life reflected in an American tabloid, at least as violent, and hardly more dignified. Once more, we meet the eternal medieval—and human—contrast between the real and the ideal.

There can be no doubt, however, that as a way of life European chivalry began as the simple creed of fighting men, and that like most things medieval it ripened to its best about the thirteenth century. It came to have a rather more complex code of action, one better integrated into the elaborate series of personal relations that made up medieval society at its height. It came, in short, nearer to being a tried and balanced system of human relations, a way of getting things done on this earth. As such, it is seen in its best in the memoirs of the Sieur de Joinville, crusading companion of the saintly King Louis IX of France. Joinville clearly has the traditional feudal virtues, loyalty to his king, unquestioning faith in Catholic Christianity, above all that quality of athletic innocence we have tried above to convey. Joinville is not only no intellectual, he is not even much of a thinker. He and his comrades fight as they have been trained to fight. He clearly is not in the least inventive, not in the least used to thinking of the world as changing, certainly not as developing. On the other hand, Joinville is quite as clearly a sensible and practical man, a good handler of his fellows, quite without any of the picturesqueness our nineteenth-century romantics insisted on finding in the Middle Ages. In him, as in a very different field in Aquinas, you get a sense of balance quite contrary to what we have so often been taught about the Middle Ages.

Joinville served in a crusade with Louis IX, later canonized as St. Louis. He revered the memory of the king, who, he noted "so loved the truth that even when he dealt with the Saracens, he was not willing to go back on his word." But the saintly Louis could not quite take the younger man with him into absolute, other-worldly virtue. Joinville in a famous passage tells how the king, calling in two monks, began to talk to him about religion:

> "Now I ask you," said the king, "which would you prefer, to be a leper, or to have committed a mortal sin." And I who had never lied to him, I replied that I had rather commit thirty mortal sins than be a leper. When the monks had left he called me to him quite alone, had me sit down at his feet and said, "What did you tell me just now?" And I told him that I would still say the same thing. And he said to me, "You spoke like a madman; for you should know that there is no leper as ugly as one who is in a state of mortal sin, because the soul which is in a state of mortal sin is like the devil; that is why there cannot be a leper so ugly. And it is indeed true that when a man dies his body is cured of leprosy but when a man who has committed mortal sin dies he does not know whether he has in his life so far repented that God has pardoned him. That is why he ought really to fear that this kind of leprosy will last him as long as God shall be in paradise. So I beg you as strongly as I can to accustom your heart for the love of God and of me to prefer that any evil come to your body through leprosy or some other ill rather than that mortal sin seize hold of your soul."

The balance was, as it usually is in Western history, a brief, precarious one. Chivalry was a way of life which lent itself readily to exaggeration; it did not have an altogether graceful old age. The formalism, the following-in-the-rut, the hardening of the arteries of fashion that seems to come upon all cultures and subcultures in the West came rather quickly on this culture of chivalry, which had not the virtues of old age. Most strikingly and most obviously, the fighting that had perhaps once been a justification and an explanation of the existence of a feudal privileged class began with the rise of modern hired professional armies in the fourteenth century to be quite frankly a game. As such, it grew to be a very complicated and rather dull game, the knightly tourney or jousting. The rules grew very elaborate, the protective armor very strong, and in the end no one suffered very much physical damage, although accidents did occur.

Even at its most balanced period, the attitude of chivalry toward love and women was hardly an enshrinement of common sense—if indeed there is a common sense of such matters. As we in the twentieth century learn more of non-Western peoples, we become aware of the fact that what can perhaps best be called the tradition of romantic love is in many ways unique to our society, that Chinese, Hindus, and many other peoples do not share it. Even in the West, that tradition is far from unchanging—is probably nowadays changing rather fast. But it is an elaborate and deep-set tradition, with all sorts of local variants and with many complex roots. One of these roots is certainly Christianity.

But another and very important one represents the variants introduced by medieval chivalry. We cannot today read even so moderate a statement of the ideals and ways of courtly love as Chaucer's "Knight's Tale" without a sense of strangeness. In this poem two cousins, Palamon and Arcite, two Theban knights taken prisoner in war by the Duke of Athens (the Middle Ages did not bother much with historical accuracy) both fall in love with the lovely Emelie, whom they barely glimpse from their prison. In the course of several years in prison and out the two cousins, bound together though they are by blood and knightly honor, conduct a mortal feud over Emelie— and all this without knowing her at all, without any response from her. She does indeed learn finally of this strife for her love; but on the eve of the great jousting between Palamon and Arcite that the poet finally arranges, he has her pray to Diana

> Chaste goddesse, wel wostow that I
> Desire to ben a mayden al my lyf,
> Ne never wol I be no love, ne wyf.
> I am, thow woost, yet of thy compaignye,
> A mayde, and love huntynge and venerye,
> And for to walken in the wodes wilde,

And noght to ben a wyf and be with childe;
Noght wol I knowe the compaignye of man.
Now helpe me, lady, sith ye may and kan,
For tho thre formes that thou hast in thee.
And Palamon, that hath swich love to me,
And eek Arcite, that loveth me so soore,
This grace I preye thee withoute moore;
As sende love and pees bitwixe hem two,
And fro me turne awey hir hertes so
That al hire hoote love and hir desir,
And al hir bisy torment and hir fir,
Be queynt, or turned in another place.
And if so be thou wolt do me no grace,
Or if my destynee be shapen so
That I shal nedes have oon of hem two,
As sende me hym that moost desireth me.
Bihoold, goddesse of clene chastitee,
The bittre teeres that on my chekes falle.
Syn thou art mayde, and kepere of us alle,
My maydenhede thou kepe and wel conserve
And whil I lyve a mayde I wol thee serve.

Arcite's horse makes a false step, and he is wounded to death. Palamon wins the maiden.

This is a moderate romance. Chaucer in another of the *Canterbury Tales,* the "Rime of Sir Thopas," gives a ridiculous parody of the literary romance; and even in the "Knight's Tale" he is no more than poetically persuaded of the reality of courtly love. Others were less bound to this earth, so that lovers in medieval romance went through all the horrors and trials imaginable, indulged in abstract, indeed metaphysical variations on the possible conflicts among Duty, Honor, and Love, and kept to their virtue as a Christian martyr kept to his faith. Vaguely, faintly, behind all this one guesses there exists some notion of the fact of sexual intercourse; but perhaps not—perhaps only our Freudian age puts it there. Yet in fairness one must note that chivalry made a serious and often successful effort to control a phase of human activity that in a privileged class especially tends to get out of control, and to end in a promiscuity disastrous to the discipline such a class needs. Chivalry involved a real institutional sublimation of very powerful drives—a sublimation many who are not mere alarmists feel is lacking in the modern West.

The convention of courtly love has, however, left its mark on Western culture. It has put woman on an ideal pedestal she nowadays finds it rather inconvenient even to pretend to fit. In that eternal struggle between this world and the ideal other world that is certainly in intensity one of the unique marks of Western culture, even sexual love has, thanks to Christianity and the Middle Ages, taken on an otherworldly side. Do not mistake. Even ancient Greeks knew love between man and woman, and so clearly do many modern peoples not yet fully in the Western tradition; but they do not know *romantic love,* the impossible, unearthly, unbedded love of the ideal, love beyond loving. We no longer know this romantic love as did our nineteenth-century ancestors, but it has left its mark of unrealism upon us—and especially upon Hollywood.

There is much else in the decline or overripeness of chivalry worth attention—the way in which the chivalric virtue of consideration for inferiors, for the weak and unfortunate, becomes a maudlin pose, the way the appetite for the marvelous grows until monsters begin to seem quite normal, the way chivalry comes to be a kind of protection for the nobleman's ego against the rising power of the men of money, the merchants and bankers. But here we can only dwell on one more point, perhaps even more central to the whole notion of chivalry than religion or love, certainly more central in the decline of chivalry, the point of honor. If early chivalry seems at bottom a code that tries to subdue the individual to the group, if it seems in many ways to make the fighting man into a member of a team, it nevertheless puts, in contrast with the discipline of a Sparta, much emphasis on the individual. The knight was always acutely conscious of his honor, of himself as an individual and a final arbiter of what suited and what did not suit his dignity. In the later years of chivalry everything was focused on the point of honor, and the knight became a nysterically sensitive person quite cut off from the world of prosaic values, ready, in fact, for the pen of Cervantes. And it is probably more than a coincidence that it was the nation whose aristocracy carried the point of honor farthest, the Spanish, who also produced in *Don Quixote* a book that most of the world has taken to be a devastating attack on the ideals of chivalry.

Chivalry is one of those great compounds or clusters of ideas, sentiments, and habits—like romanticism, or democracy, or collectivism—that challenge our understanding. A useful way to tackle such a challenge is to compare one such compound with another with which it has something in common. Now chivalry clearly has something in common with Christianity. The earliest chivalry is in part an attempt to Christianize a body of primitive, pagan fighting men. The rituals of knighthood form a part of Christian rituals; the knight as crusader is often the knight seen in his best light. The crusaders were indeed rarely saints—the crusading Joinville we have just met may seem to the idealist far more a pagan than a Christian. Yet Joinville's sense of honor and duty, his conscience, his very awareness that there can be saints, are marks of Christianity—everyday, practicing, unheroic Christianity.

Even in the extremes of the chivalric ideal, in courtly love and in knightly honor, we may see something of the prick of the ideal, the transcendental, that never quite deserts the Christian. But in the balance chivalry looks to be one of the social forces that have tended to disrupt Christianity. If one of the abiding notes of Christianity is the attempt to subdue the self, if humility is really one of the great goals of the Christian life, then chivalry is not very Christian. At its most altruistic, chivalry still points up the knightly ego, still makes ornamental and honorific competition an act of social virtue; at its ordinary level it sharpens the ego in its struggle with the world; and in its decline it glorifies in the individual's honor a frequently hysterical self-centeredness, a worried vanity, which in the West has been mostly limited to intellectuals. But the knight of later chivalry was after all an intellectual. What else was Don Quixote?

Chivalry, to sum up, was a way of life among the upper classes of the medieval West, in some ways much as Stoicism was a way of life among the upper classes of the Graeco-Roman imperial world.

The ordinary count or baron was of course no more like Don Quixote, or even Palamon and Arcite, than was the ordinary Roman official like Zeno, the Stoic philosopher. That is why we have used the phrase "way of life" in both cases. But the extreme—the ideal if you prefer—does in human mass conduct in some way influence the mean. The count or baron, the count's steward, the hard-working abbots and bishops who ran so much of the medieval world, reflect even in their practical bent some of the goals set by chivalry, as chivalry itself reflects some of their customary activities. Through all medieval life there runs the contrast between theory and practice, between the knight's devotion to God, his lady, and his duty and the knight's addiction to fighting, gambling, hunting, love-making, to what are, in fact, still the great manly addictions. There run the knight's frequent bouts with his conscience as awareness of this contrast becomes unavoidable. There runs the knight's restless energy, his proud individualism, that striving quality that almost all moderns feel in the Middle Ages, even when they insist that it was an age of quiet stability and balance.

One must jump directly from the culture of the medieval ruling classes to that of the people. It is not quite true that there is no middle class in the medieval period. Especially in the fourteenth and fifteenth centuries the merchants, enterprisers, bankers are of growing numbers and importance. But their way of life, their ideas, are only slowly formed into something apart from the common ways of non-nobles, and we may postpone to a later chapter an analysis of what the rise of a ruling middle class means to our intellectual history.

The great mass of population in the West in the Middle Ages was rural. The small market towns and even the few larger cities—Paris, London, and Florence among them—were walled urban areas with farmlands at their gates, and were in constant relations with the nearby peasants from whom they got most of their foodstuffs. The craftsmen might live either in villages or towns, and might well be part-time farmers. This popular culture is, then, a simple, relatively unchanging, clear-cut one, lacking that curiously ambiguous surface sophistication we have come to know among the naive masses of our great modern cities. But it is not exactly an innocent one. Indeed, in the French *fabliaux* and in other odds and ends of evidence of how the medieval masses felt, one is struck by a hard, earthy realism, an admiration for the cunning fellow, the successful hoodwinker of the gullible, a skepticism of fine words and fine professions. This rural medieval constant must be noted; it suggests again the limitations of the view that the Middle Ages represent a serene, stable, Christian way of life.

We should expect to find much coarseness in this culture, and indeed we do. The monosyllables everyone knows and only the very highbrow print nowadays appear even in Chaucer, at least when he has the commoner speak. Just as his "Knight's Tale" is a very good mirror for chivalry in some of its phases, so is nis "Miller's Tale" an admirable literary reflection of some phases of popular taste. It is a broad, farcical, bawdy tale, in which the jealous, stupid husband is properly cuckolded in the best traditions of folklore. It is so un-Christian that one never even thinks of it in relation to Christian ideals. And yet there it is; and the miller, who tells it, is on his way to the shrine of Canterbury, there to worship as will his companions, the gentle knight, the kindly clerk of Oxenford, the hearty wife of Bath, the much more subtly un-Christian Prioress, and all the rest of those Canterbury pilgrims whose present-day antitypes might be assembling at this moment for a tour of the Yellowstone.

Coarseness and obscenity would seem to be roughly constants in our Western culture. There are all sorts of interesting problems of taste in connection with such matters. Perhaps in certain periods, such as the Middle Ages, there is an unaffected simplicity one no longer finds when conventions of decency have sunk down from more refined classes. What is merely coarseness in the Middle Ages may become pornography in modern times. But these are very difficult problems, for the solution of which we certainly have no cumulative means. At any rate, it would seem that the streak of obscenity in human nature is well established, not to be eliminated, or even successfully suppressed, by the most high-minded of cultures.

Some of this bawdy humor is directed against priests and clerks.

Again, if we are to have a balanced picture we must take account of what has to be called the popular anticlericalism of the Middle Ages. For the most part, this fairly widespread sentiment was not in the Middle Ages the bitter hatred it became in the eighteenth century. It is, indeed, often humorous and even good-natured, and some of it seems to have amused the clergy themselves. Visitors to medieval French churches are still shown carvings on the underside of choir stalls, in which apparently the wood carver was given free rein, for many of them show intimate and amusing details of daily life that seem to us somewhat out-of place in a church. The greedy priest, the lecherous priest, the vain and worldly priest occur often enough in medieval popular literature. And again in Chaucer, who certainly knew what was going on in the popular mind, the men of God, with the exception of the clerk of Oxford, come off none too well. They have their full burden of human weaknesses.

Yet there is little bitterness in all this, but rather a bringing down of the priest to the common human level. The philosophical and theological structure of Christianity—its whole world-view—are not challenged as they were to be challenged in the days of Voltaire and Tom Paine. The *fabliaux,* and we may be pretty sure, the peasants and the craftsmen, did not doubt the existence of God, nor the need to go to Mass, nor indeed the whole complex mass of superstitions that grew up in medieval popular Christianity. Sometimes there is in this medieval anticlericalism a strain of dislike for the Church as a wealthy corporation exploiting the poor, to which we shall return in a moment. But for the most part, one feels that the medieval man-in-the-field distrusted the priest just because the priest, with his celibacy, his poverty, his humility, the whole burden of his Christian ideals, seemed a denial of common humanity. That the medieval man himself had absorbed from Christian teaching some distrust of his own common humanity only sharpened the joke when he heard about the girl smuggled into a monastery in a laundry basket. For the medieval man, though with part of his mind he thought of the priest as no better than he should be, or as just a bit lacking in manliness, with another part of his mind he thought of the priest as the agent of God on earth, as standing for something respectable, powerful, admirable, and generally elevated. In short, the medieval man felt toward the priest and the Church in something like the same ambiguous fashion the average American feels toward professors and education.

Nothing could be more misleading than to think of the medieval masses as mere brutes, without ideas at all. We have already made clear that in the West medieval men and women of the masses, in spite of the lack of literacy, printing, and the rest of the modern apparatus of mass culture, shared the common inheritance of Christianity. That inheritance was in part one of rebellion, an ever-renewed effort to realize a larger part, at least, of Christian ideals here and now. These ideals, we have already noted, were—and are—as complex and many-sided as Western culture. There was in many medieval popular uprisings, and even in specifically religious movements like the Franciscan, an element of what we today call socialism or social democracy. Of course, medieval popular revolts were not inspired by Marxist ideals; the rebels simply wanted a return to early Christian virtue and simplicity. But it is no anachronism to say that for well over a thousand years men in the West working for greater economic and social equality, men trying to break down a society with clear-cut stratification—social revolutionaries, in short—have appealed to what they regard as the true Christian tradition. There is clearly an egalitarian element in historical Christianity.

Naturally enough, men of the Middle Ages used the language of religion to justify their revolt. The best-known of medieval revolts in the English-speaking world is the late fourteenth-century movement associated with Wat Tyler. One of its leaders was John Ball, a priest; and its slogan still survives in the history books:

> When Adam delved and Eve span
> Who then was the gentleman?

We need not here concern ourselves with the narrative history of this or other late medieval social movements, such as the Jacquerie in France or the Peasants' War in Luther's sixteenth-century Germany, which might as well be considered the last of these medieval movements as the first of modern ones. Indeed, the Peasants' War is in many ways *more* medieval than modern. None of them was outwardly successful for long. All of them would be to the sociologist of revolution "abortive" revolutions. Yet they are interesting for the light they throw on the failure of the medieval, at least the late medieval, stratified society to satisfy the lower strata; they emphasize once more the potentially revolutionary elements in Christian belief; and they are interesting examples of the spread of ideas in a relatively illiterate society. They are also full of violence and cruelty, on the part both of the rebels and of the ultimately successful defenders of the established order. It would be very hard to prove that man's inhumanity to man was greater in the Terror of 1794 than in the fourteenth-century Jacquerie in France, greater in the genocide of the 1940's than in the Peasants' War of the 1520's in Germany.

They have no single great theoretician or ideologist, no Rousseau, no Marx. They get many of their ideas from intellectuals—priests or monks—who are themselves to a certain extent leaders of the movement. This is notably true of a man like Wycliffe in England, a trained scholar, one of the numerous ones known as the "last of the Schoolmen," who in later life wrote pamphlets in English instead of in academic Latin, and translated the Bible into English. But even their less intellectual leaders were familiar with a great deal of the medieval intellectual heritage. In fact, these later movements, like the earlier monastic reforms, and the earlier popular heresies, Albigensian, Waldensian, and the like, are all still centered about the great Christian drama, are all, in a sense, Christian heresies. It would be an oversimplification to say that the first great wave of heresies, that of the Gnostics, Arians, and the rest, in the second and third centuries was basically theological and philosophical, and that the second, from the Albigensians to the finally successful revolt of Luther, was basically social and economic. You cannot thus neatly divide movements that draw on all human wants and capacities. Nevertheless, these medieval revolts are clearly focused on this world. They use the vocabulary of Christian theology, and are in some of their forms quite wildly chiliastic, but they do not for the most part anticipate the actual second coming of Christ. They do set out to redistribute the wealth of this world, to humble the rich and the proud, to change radically the carefully ordered world of medieval social stratification. They fail in their central purpose, which is to solve the problem of poverty. But cumulatively, and aided, as we shall see in the next chapter, by the rise of a money economy and a middle class, they do break down feudal society, at any rate in the west of Europe.

Wycliffe and his followers, the poor priests or "Lollards" (babblers), went direct to the people, and whether or not they intended it, stirred them up to the Peasants' Revolt. They were suppressed by a coalition of the old privileged classes and the new men of wealth. This is not, however, the sole pattern of such medieval attempts to go to the people. One of the most remarkable of medieval popular movements is that of the mendicant friars of the thirteenth century. Seen, we must again insist, from the outside, from the point of view of historical naturalism, the great orders of St. Francis and St. Dominic illustrate another pattern of action by the Church in the face of grave unrest among the masses.

Briefly and oversimply, the pattern is this. Changing social conditions, any breaking down of order and regularities, such as undue incidence of wars, famines, disease, unsettling movements of large numbers of people (as in the Crusades), technological changes that make old ways of living impossible (as in a shift from grain raising to pasturing, or the rise of big towns specializing in textiles)—any combination of changes of this sort drives home to the displaced, the unsettled, sometimes even the starving, the gap between Christian ideals and actual practice. A gifted person, almost always by birth a member of the privileged classes, takes this gap to heart, and takes on once more the role of prophet and leader.

In the Middle Ages, the inspiration of such a person, his way of thinking, was inevitably set in Christian terms. He preached a revival of the old Christian spirit that would not let the world rest in sloth and evil. He would have Christ brought to earth again, not in the simple literal sense of the first few Christian generations who expected to see Christ in the flesh, but in the sense that men should try to live as Christ wanted them to live. He himself—if he is a Francis of Assisi—would give up his worldly position and imitate Christ in his poverty and contempt for this world of the flesh. He would himself live with the poor and gather disciples about him who would further carry the word of God to the poor and the unhappy, not to stir them up to hatred of the rich, not to produce a social revolution of the sort we moderns associate with Marxism or Communism, but to produce a spiritual revolution in them and in all men that would bring them peace through union with God. His disciples and his followers would many of them take him as an example, and the Order he founded would for a time live up fairly well to his standards.

The line between the spirit and the flesh, however, is hard to draw. The masses tended to gravitate toward the more material ends of social revolution, or to relapse into acceptance of their lot. The leaders found subtler and more varied ways of compromise with the world. St. Francis himself had the mystic's distrust of the rationalizing intellect, the nonconformist's dislike for the organized and pretentious world of book learning. He wanted his Order to go to the people unencumbered with corporate property and unspoiled by books. Yet within a generation of his death the Franciscan Order had already amassed great wealth, and Franciscans were taking full part in the medieval scholarly world. Roger Bacon, whom we have already met as a major figure in the history of science, was an Oxford Franciscan.

The other great mendicant Order, the Dominican, had origins less close to that spirit of integral revolt against the established order of society than that of St. Francis. St. Dominic too felt deeply the plight of the masses, revolted against the failure of the ordained pastors to take care of their sheep. But he and his friars were from the first less extreme evangelists. They brought the gospel to the people by skillful and ardent preaching, and they took in earnest their cure of souls. Like the Franciscans, they too made their compromise with the world, and came in later years to be distinguished for their scholarly devotion to the history of their Church.

There existed, then, among the medieval population in the West, especially toward the end of the period, two attitudes that were difficult to reconcile with the notion that these masses were contented sheep in the care of their priest and warrior shepherds: first, a rather coarse streak of humor, even irreverence, which delights in pointing the contrast between idyllic theory and mundane performance; and second, a series of popular revolts, Christian in inspiration and often led by priests or monks, which aim toward the realization here on earth of something like a Christian communism. Despite these disruptive forces, however, the Middle Ages brought to Western man a degree of social equilibrium, a kind of security, that is rare in the West today.

The medieval village or town community of the best days of the Middle Ages was indeed a community in which custom, backed by the authority of religion, had established a network of reciprocal rights and obligations within which each man, from serf to feudal lord, could have the kind of security that comes with the knowledge that one has a place, a *status,* in a set of orderly rules of behavior resting on a well-worked-out conception of the universe and of man's place in it. Of course the peasant didn't read Aquinas; but something of Aquinas and of the whole medieval cosmology seeped down to the peasant. You can see how this social equilibrium worked out in detail, from the planting of the crops to their distribution, from the rules of inheritance of land to the rules for daily living, in books like Mr George Homans's *English Villagers of the Twelfth Century* and the late Marc Bloch's *Les caractères originaux de l'histoire rurale française.* It was not, as we know already, a perfect equilibrium, and it was soon broken by the rise of what we now call a capitalist economy—and by much else we think of as modern. Perhaps the simplest and most temperate way of putting it is this: In the high Middle Ages life for the ordinary person in the West, though subject to much that we should find hardship or discomfort, was psychologically more secure, *less competitive,* than life today; and it was a life almost wholly free from fundamental religious and ethical doubt and uncertainty.

An Evaluation of Medieval Culture

The historian who attempts to make generalizations about the rise, maturing, and fall of cultures (or societies, or civilizations) confronts in the Middle Ages a serious problem. The more common classification adopted by such historians—or philosophers of history—in recent times is to set up a Graeco-Latin culture lasting roughly from the Greeks of Homer to the Romans of the fifth century A.D. and a modern Western culture beginning in the Dark Ages and going on to the present (which present many of them regard as the decadent last days of our culture). A good example is the twentieth-century German Oswald Spengler, who thinks of these cultures as a kind of organism with a life span of roughly a thousand years and possessing a youth, maturity, and old age, or a spring, summer, fall, and winter. For Spengler, the Graeco-Roman was the "Apollonian," our own the "Faustian" culture. But many others, including Mr. Arnold Toynbee, though they do not accept all of Spengler's notions about life spans of cultures and much else, do see the ancient, or classical, as one culture, our own modern Western as another, related to the first, perhaps, but for their purposes a separate culture. Now in such a view, the Dark Ages appears as the infancy, the Middle Ages as the youth, of our modern culture. The Middle Ages, in other words, is not in itself a culture. On the other hand, many of those who have most deeply studied the Middle Ages, including most of the modern lovers of the period, regard it as, so to speak, a culture-in-itself, not merely a prelude to our own. They think of the Middle Ages as rising to a peak in the thirteenth century and then falling off in the next two centuries. Those of them who most dislike the modern world think of the decline as continuous to the present. Mr. Pitirim Sorokin, for instance, finds but two cultural high points in the history of the West—fifth-century Athens and thirteenth-century Western Europe. Others will grant the moderns a peak, which nowadays they incline to find in the nineteenth century.

Now the variables involved in any attempt to measure ups and downs in the life of human groups are so complex that nothing like accuracy or indeed agreement can be achieved in their study. We are obviously here dealing with noncumulative knowledge. On the other hand, groups do have their ups and downs. To deny this fact is to strip all meaning from history.

A grave initial difficulty in the study of Western society is that this society has never, except perhaps briefly at the time of the Roman Empire, been a *political* unity. It has been divided politically into independent groups—city-states, feudal states, nation-states—and these units have themselves had periods of flourishing and decline. When Rome was at its height, Athens was a mere university town. Spain, after attaining a peak in the sixteenth century, sank into insignificance. Any journalist now feels free to label France, once *la grande nation*, a second-rate power. Again, the very diversity of human activity sets a problem here. The "flowering" of a culture is not the production of a single flower, but of a most complex organism. Some kinds of human activities may flourish with a given society when others languish. One kind of activity may seem more significant a part of culture than another. One may argue that the cultural peak attained by tiny Elizabethan England was a higher one than that attained by the rich and powerful Britain of Victorian days. So widespread have been the economic and technological advances common to Western society in the last two centuries that the actual standard of living in twentieth-century decadent Spain is almost certainly higher than in the Spain of Cervantes, Lope de Vega, and the *conquistadores*. Almost all would agree that the cultural peak of Germany, from Bach, Kant, and Goethe to the great scientific and scholarly achievements of the nineteenth-century German university, antedates the political, military, and economic peak of the Germany of William II and Hitler.

With these warnings, we may return to the problem with which we set out. It is possible, though the formula is oversimple, to reconcile the view of the Middle Ages as a beginning, a youth, of modern Western society with the view of the Middle Ages as in itself a peak, a flourishing, a kind of maturity. If you focus on the political and economic integration of the territorial subgroups in Western society (nations), then there are two clear sequences in our history—one from the diversity of independent, economically primitive city-states, tribes, and nations of roughly 1000 B.C. to the unified, wealthy, complex One World of the Roman Empire, and another from the extreme feudal disintegration and economic primitiveness of the Dark Ages to the present, when there are but seventy-odd independent political units in the whole world, when economic development has reached heights unknown before, and when this process of integration seems to many well on its way toward a universal state. If you focus on smaller and more detailed problems, such as that of the development of representative parliamentary institutions, or that of the growth of banking, or of scientific thought, you find a low point which is almost a break (not quite) in the Dark Ages, and you find unmistakable beginnings in the Middle Ages, from which development has been in some sense continuous to the present. In such lights, the Middle Ages appear clearly as a beginning of things modern.

If, however, you focus as well as you can on medieval culture *as a whole,* on what we have somewhat weakly called a "way of life," on medieval notions of right and beauty and man's place in the scheme of things, you can hardly help accepting something of the thesis that the Middle Ages deserves to be ranked as an achievement in living different from, though clearly related to, our own. You cannot read Dante, or Aquinas, or Chaucer, or look at the cathedral of Chartres, or even study a detailed map of a medieval self-sustaining manor, without feeling that you are in another world. Indeed that world will probably seem to a twentieth-century American who will take the trouble to live himself into both, a world more different from his own than that of fifth-century Athens.

We can here do no more than indicate certain broad generalizations about this medieval world, certain notes of medieval culture, certain signs of its taste or flavor.

First of all, there is the immediacy, the common-sense acceptance, of the supernatural, which we have of course already encountered. There are millions of men and women in the twentieth century who as good Christians believe in Christianity. Many of them would be gravely offended were we to suggest that their belief is one whit less strong than that of their medieval ancestors. But even for believers today the boundaries of the supernatural have been pushed back, and whole regions of their conscious life made subject to the regularities we think of as natural. They may pray for rain; but they also read the weather reports drawn up by meteorologists who, whatever their religion, do not believe that God interferes directly with cold fronts. Moreover, there are today millions of men and women—no one knows quite how many—who do not believe in the immortality of the human soul, and for whom, therefore, the notion of heaven and hell is meaningless, or actually offensive. There are a great many more for whom heaven and hell have become very vague concepts indeed; they believe in immortality, heaven, and hell, but as rather remote things, closer acquaintance with which can be indefinitely postponed. Hell, particularly, has for many moderns lost its bite; it has become for them a place for distinguished sinners only, much like the Greek hell.

Not so for the men of the Middle Ages. God, as we have pointed out, was as real, as present for them, as the weather is for us, heaven or hell for each man as certain as sunshine or rain. Medieval intellectuals for the most part held that God made things happen on this earth in accordance with certain regularities basically directed for man's good—that is, that the universe was basically moral and therefore that much was known and predictable. Their God was a reliable God, in something of the same sense that modern scientists think nature reliable. Some of this sense of regularity, if only in the form of what we like to call common sense, undoubtedly was shared by the masses, or they could hardly have gone about their daily living. None the less, there is widespread among the medieval masses, and even among the intellectuals, a feeling of the irrationality, the uncertainty, the *unexpectedness* of life on this earth. At one most obvious level, this comes out in the prevalence of what we now call superstition in the Middle Ages. The slightest dip into medieval writing brings up an example—that eggs laid on Good Friday are good to put out fires, that elves sour milk, that the king's touch can cure scrofula, and many, many more. True, many of these same superstitions are still alive, and we have added some of our own. But the ange and depth of medieval superstition puts ours in the shade. At the very least, the spread of popular science has relegated most of our superstitions to the purely emotional side—"touch wood," for instance; they are not, as they were in the Middle Ages, considered basically as explanations, as theories.

The immediacy of the supernatural (of which superstition is merely the trivial and undignified part) is clear in a work that must at least be sampled by anyone attempting to understand the Middle Ages. The hell, purgatory, and heaven of Dante's *Divine Comedy* were as real to him as London was to Dickens. His hell, as has often been remarked, is the most concrete of the three. Dante was a very great poet, but he was also an embittered and exiled politician who saw his Florence and his Italy take a course that outraged his moral sense. He put his enemies in hell—in his book—as part of a polemic process as natural to him as the much more abstract fulminations that have to satisfy a modern Trotskyite. The quality of fantasy, which a modern attempting to deal with the supernatural can hardly avoid, is simply not in Dante's *Inferno*. He takes his reader to a hell so convincing that any attempt of an illustrator to paint it takes the edge off, makes it less true. This applies notably to the work of the best-known of Dante's illustrators, the French nineteenth-century artist Gustave Doré, who only succeeds in making Dante's hell what we call "romantic"—which it is not.

Nevertheless, the romantic writers of the nineteenth century— Walter Scott will come to mind at once—found something they were looking for in the Middle Ages, which they brought back into good cultural repute. That something they distorted by overemphasis, but it is there, and is the second note of medieval culture we must try to bring out. It is another phase of the medieval acceptance of the supernatural as natural. Truth, we like to say, is stranger than fiction. But we moderns do not really mean by that saying that we believe our daily life is filled with wonders. We mean, for example, that out of hundreds of real murder cases that come up in our courts *one* shows a degree of human depravity and ingenuity that goes beyond the imaginings of the wildest of detective fiction. The overwhelming

majority of actual murders we know to be by no means up to fiction:
standards in interest. They are, in fact, routine affairs, as crime goe
Put in more general terms, we accept a sort of common-sense statist
cal view, in which instances are strung along a classical distributio
curve; 100 per cent is as rare as 0 per cent, and there is a great bulg
around 50 per cent.

The men of the Middle Ages were not statistically minded. W
should overdo paradox if we asserted that for the medieval mind th
rare instance was as common as the usual instance; but we should no
greatly overdo paradox if we asserted that for the medieval min
the rare instance is, humanly speaking, quite as *typical,* quite as goo
as, or even better than, the usual instance as a sign to man of wha
the universe is like. The medieval man was not put off by the e:
treme; he expected it, looked for it, put it concretely into his ar
The world of his imagination (he would not have admitted it *was*
world of mere imagination) was filled with horrors and marvel
perfect heroes and perfect villains, monsters and saints. And som
how, for most of us today, the monsters stay in the mind better tha
the saints. We find Dante's Inferno more convincing than his Par
dise. Were those of us who have been exposed at all to medieval cu
tural history to call up at random some sort of concrete image of th
Middle Ages, the most frequent would probably be that broodin
gargoyle of Notre Dame in Paris which has been reproduced o
thousands of post cards.

This medieval push toward the extreme, toward the grotesque o
toward the sublime, is often described as a striving toward the infinit
the endless, a refusal to accept the apparent limits of the materi
world of sense experience. A favorite practice among philosophic
historians of culture—Spengler again will do as a concrete instance-
is to contrast the Greek temple and the Gothic cathedral. The Gree
temple stands foursquare on solid ground, accepting man's own con
monplace dimensions, its basic shape no more heroic and heave:
storming than a box; the Gothic cathedral soars, transcends by darin
inventions like the pointed arch and the flying buttress the vertic
limitations of earlier building, seeks to translate into stone the longin

of the medieval soul for the infinite. The Greek temple is geometry; the Gothic cathedral, algebra. The Greek temple accepts; the Gothic cathedral aspires. The Greek temple looks as if man made it; the Gothic cathedral looks as if the forest grew it.

Now these contrasts are fundamentally sound. A Greek temple and a Gothic cathedral are very different things, and the differences are in part expressions of different human attitudes toward the beautiful and the good. You can argue that there are material or technical reasons why the medieval architects built one way, the Greeks another—differing religious ceremonies needing to be housed, differing engineering techniques that set differing problems. But the fact remains that the men of the Middle Ages wanted something the Greeks had not wanted. They wanted height; the architects of the cathedral at Beauvais in France wanted it so much that they built the seemingly impossible apse that exists today and tried to construct an even more impossible tower, which unfortunately but quite naturally fell.

Nor is the famous simile of the Gothic forest without suggestiveness. We go from suggestiveness to the fanciful if we say that because their Germanic and Celtic ancestors had grown up in the primeval forest of a northern climate they built their church aisles to look like forest aisles, while the Greeks had no such pattern in their Mediterranean environment. But certainly the finished Gothic church, not only in its structural lines but in its ornamental details—the leafy foliage of its capitals, the tracery of its vaults, its statues, which seem to grow out of the whole building, the thousand details of ornamentation flowering from it—looks less planned, more spontaneous, than a Greek building, or one of our own.

The impression is helped by the fact that very few Gothic cathedrals were built all of a piece. They were strung out over several generations, as the money came in, and the builders of each part built in the variant of the Gothic style fashionable in their day. (Remember that the practice of picking from the grab bag of history a particular style, Doric, Gothic, Colonial, Mission, and the like is strictly limited to modern times; until these times men have always built in their own contemporary style, just as, for example, they always dressed their actors in the style of their own day.) So the favorite Gothic church of the connoisseur, the cathedral of Chartres in France, still has in its crypt the round arches of the pre-Gothic romanesque style; it has on its west front a south tower in the simple, relatively un-ornamented style of early Gothic, a north tower richly ornamented in a later style, and elsewhere statues, porches, rose windows made by many different hands over several centuries. Yet the building is a magnificent whole, and no hodgepodge; neither, of course, is a forest

This second note of medieval culture—call it spontaneity, imagina-tive exuberance, the search for the extraordinary, the striking, the ro-mantic, the striving for the infinite, no phrase quite spans the reality —this note can be heard in everything medieval. We have chosen to find it in architecture, but it could be found equally well in the rich tangle of medieval literature. Dante's was—for a man of the Middle Ages—a disciplined mind, and his style has none of the looseness, quaintness, exuberance of the knightly romances; but the effect of his epic as a whole, when contrasted with that of his master Vergil, is quite like that of a Gothic cathedral contrasted with a Greek temple. Even his great political work, the Latin *De Monarchia,* is a welter of argument and fancy compared with the logical neatness of Aristotle's political writing.

A third note of medieval culture, less pleasing to its modern ad-mirers, is the frequence of violence. Murder and sudden death were not as unusual to medieval man as to modern man. We must be careful here, as always with big generalizations. The lover of the Middle Ages may well reply that modern warfare kills far more ef-fectively than did the medieval, that nothing in medieval annals is any worse than what went on in the concentration camps of the last war. He is right, of course, but he must be reminded of our modern suc-cesses in medicine and in provisioning large populations. For all our terrible wars, we have up to the moment maintained a larger popula-tion in the West than ever before. But the real point is the absence in the Middle Ages, in spite of the Christian tradition, of a feeling for the relative permanence of human life. Men simply did not expect life to be without hazard. Indeed, they saw the hand of God in the decision of violence. One of the best known of medieval institutions is that of trial by combat, a procedure limited to conflicts among the knightly class. As a last resort, a dispute could be settled by combat between the disputants or between their champions, and the decision was seen as the direct intervention of God who gave victory to the right. Gradually through the Middle Ages this procedure was supplanted by legal processes that became the foundation of our own.

We need not labor the point. The upper classes, heirs of the rough fighter of the Dark Ages, carried on well into the more advanced culture of the Middle Ages the tradition of violence in which their fathers had been bred. We have seen how this tradition was gradually formalized into the mock violence of late chivalry. The Church and the growing territorial states both had a part in the gradual substitution of orderly processes of law for this appeal to force. Growing trade brought with it growing protection of industry and commerce, until the robber baron was tamed. Even so, the grave social conflicts of the later Middle Ages brought renewed violence of another kind, and terrible plagues, like the Black Death of the fourteenth century, added their toll. Later medieval literature and art, as admirably described in Huizinga's *Waning of the Middle Ages,* came to be obsessed with death.

If we put all this together, we have a whole that does not altogether fit with some of the things we have said earlier about the Middle Ages. Our notes sum up as a pervading sense of the uncertainties and irregularities of life, indeed as the *cultivation* of these qualities. We have a culture that hardly distinguishes between the supernatural and the natural, a culture of credulity and superstition, a culture of unearthly mysticism and of very earthly crudity and violence, a culture of extremes and contradictions, a culture forever oscillating between a search for the Holy Grail and a search for the next meal. What has become of the moderation, the "whiggishness" of Aquinas? Where is that quality of maturity that made us rank the thirteenth century in some respects with the fifth century B.C.? It looks as if this medieval culture really were a sort of childhood or at best obstreperous youth, for which the gargoyle is a fitting symbol.

We shall have to let many of our contradictions about the Middle Ages stand. Indeed, they can stand the more serenely because, though all human cultures contain contradictory, logically mutually inconsistent elements, the Middle Ages is conspicuous in Western history as an age of strongly marked contrasts. One of the firmest notes of medieval culture is that of contrast and contradiction, at its clearest perhaps in the contradiction between the high Christian ideals of its formal culture, of Scholasticism and chivalry, and the "spotted actuality." Just because the Middle Ages at their best took the Christian way of life so seriously, indeed so literally, does the coarseness, the violence the eccentricity, and also the *routine* and dullness, of much of their daily life force itself on our attention.

But if our notes of other-worldliness, belief in the supernatural striving after the infinite, violence, and contrast between Christian ideals and a not very Christian performance must stand, we must none the less make several qualifications in them. First, though much of medieval culture seems like the culture of an age of immaturity— credulity, love of extremes, more pleasing traits like the freshness of imagination, the unbuttoned joy, the simplicity that so captivated the later romantics—the notion that medieval culture did attain a real maturity is by no means false. This maturity comes out clearly in almost any form of medieval art. We have in our account perhaps focused overmuch on an analytical approach that has neglected the chronological development of medieval culture. The Middle Ages are by no means all of one piece. They have their own youth, their own primitive stage, which we call the Dark Ages. They flower in the thirteenth, to modern Neo-Scholastics the "greatest of centuries." They have their own falling off in the fourteenth and fifteenth centuries.

Let us take a few examples. The world of the *Chanson d' Roland,* the ninth-century world as it was preserved in epic tradition has the qualities of the youthful, the primitive. It is a simple, dignified world of strong men with clear-cut loyalties. It is a simple world economically and socially, as far as we can discern these matters. But no sensible man would call the world reflected in Dante's *Divin*

Comedy a simple, youthful world. Dante, like Aquinas, is a mature man living in a most complex civilization. And if we go on to the fifteenth century we come to a poet like François Villon, in whose work we find an awareness of a world already grown old. Villon lived in the underworld of an already urban Paris, and he wrote of beggars, thieves, and prostitutes with nothing of innocence. He was an intellectual in a society where being an intellectual no longer meant inevitably being a priest and therefore having an assured status. He was an intellectual who had slipped down the ladder. The French have a better word for it than we—*déclassé*. Only in an already old society is a career like Villon's possible.

This cycle from youth to age appears perhaps at its clearest in medieval church architecture. Here the beginnings lie in the rather heavy, round-arched romanesque of the early Middle Ages. With the invention of the pointed arch true Gothic begins. In its early period —which some today think its best—Gothic architecture is relatively simple. It is content with vaulting lighter and higher than romanesque, a vaulting that does not, however, seem to strain for height. Its carving is natural, graceful, and subordinated to the lines of the building. Its statues are also skillfully adapted to the architect's purpose. The best of them—for example, those of the west front at Chartres—have the quality historians of art have labeled "primitive," a quality also found in Athenian sculpture just before the great age of Phidias. The window tracery—perhaps the easiest sign of a particular Gothic period for the layman—is still simple. Gradually the style gets more complicated, more ornamented. There is a mature middle period in which daring use of the flying buttress and other devices enables the architects to give an impression of great height, and to flood their churches with light from many windows. Sculpture attains a perfection that is not the realism of the Greeks, but another high realism with no trace of the primitive distortion of anatomy. Such, for instance, are the statues of the cathedrals at Amiens and Rheims. Window tracery is freer, more flowing, more decorated.

Then in the later medieval centuries comes the overripeness which is a sign that the style is growing old. Notably in France there is a striving for impossible height which brings on disaster like the fall of the central tower at Beauvais. Ornamentation, both inside and outside the building, gets out of hand, so that one finds western fronts like that at Rouen which are adorned like a wedding cake. The Virgin no longer smiles naturally—she smiles ineffably. The natural is again distorted, but melodramatically, not simply as with the primitives; or the distortion is "realistic," and the Virgin looks like an attractive peasant girl. The window tracery, carrying out in great complexity the suggestion of the flame, sets the tone for what in France especially is called the *flamboyant* (flaming) period of late Gothic. The word "flamboyant" itself has come in this way to suggest overelaboration and ostentation. In England, later Gothic did not follow French models into striving for great height. Characteristically, those who believe the English are congenitally moderate like to say, English architects never did attempt the soaring naves and towers of the French. Yet English Gothic, too, shows the excesses of an exhausted style. The tracery of its later period, instead of following the theme of a flame, adopts that of vertical lines, and is called the "perpendicular." English perpendicular is thus in its ornamentation almost obsessed with the theme of height, and carries this out in tracery and vaulting.

So too in many other phases of cultural life one can trace in the later Middle Ages a falling off from an earlier balance and maturity. Even in formal philosophical thought, Scholasticism, after the great peak of the thirteenth century, begins to abandon the moderation of Aquinas and to spin out its arguments into the hair-splitting logic that gave its humanist opponents of the Renaissance good grounds for attack. We have already noted how in its decay chivalry became a series of formal acts divorced from the new life around it.

Our remaining difficulty is less serious than it may appear at first sight to be. We have maintained that especially in its great period the Middle Ages was a society of status in which the individual had a relatively secure place, a society in which the individual had known duties and rights, had *roots*. In contrast to our still very competitive modern society, we have argued that the medieval man had a peace of mind most of us moderns do not have. And yet the notes of medieval culture as we have tried to sum them up suggest anything but balance, moderation, security. Striving for the infinite, the ineffable, expecting the miraculous as we expect the statistically established, living in an age of violence and sudden death, never free from the menace of famine and disease, imperfectly protected by little more than custom and religious feeling from abuse of power by feudal authorities, the medieval man seems on the surface to have been intolerably insecure.

Three considerations should soften this contradiction. First, the balance we have found in medieval life is at its best only briefly, at the height of medieval culture in the twelfth, thirteenth, and early fourteenth centuries. Even then there was violence and uncertainty enough, but not the widespread violence and change we find in the fifteenth century, which was unmistakably a time of troubles for Western man.

Second, the phrase we have used above, "little more than custom and religious feeling," gives things a misleading modern twist. Again, in the high Middle Ages, custom and religious feeling were of incalculably more strength than we moderns can easily realize. Consider the relation of feudal lord and serf. If the lord were to beat the serf, seduce his daughter, take away his holding of land, there was in most of the medieval West no court, no police power, no civil organization to which the serf could apply for redress. There was no "constitution," no "bill of rights" in our modern sense. Even the English Magna Charta of 1215 was not, in fact, a legal document for the protection of the common man. But most lords did not commonly beat serfs, seduce their daughters, take away their livelihood. One simple set of facts shows this, and is a refutation of the widespread view that the Middle Ages was a chaos of poverty and oppression from which the West was somewhat inexplicably freed by the Renaissance and Reformation. From the eleventh century on, in spite of private wars, pestilence, famine, imperfect protection of commerce, the lot of the western European peasant steadily improved, at least until the breakup of the relatively self-sufficient manorial economy began to produce the modern uncertainty associated with production for sale in money. Serfs in France as well as in England gradually attained the status of freemen, not by any statute of wholesale emancipation as in nineteenth-century Russia, but by the slow working of economic and legal processes which, basically, enabled western European serfs to *earn* their freedom. They could not have done this in a chaotic society without the steadying force of law and custom, nor, of course, in an absolutely fixed society of caste.

Finally, and most important, if hardest for us to understand, the security of medieval life was a very different thing from what we in the mid-twentieth century understand by security. The medieval man did not count on the kind of life on earth we accept as something given. He did not expect our physical comforts and luxuries, did not expect to avoid smallpox by vaccination, did not expect good roads, did not, in short, expect a thousand things we take for granted. He was used to a hard life (in our terms), used to violence and uncertainty. Nothing in his philosophy—and we use the word philosophy advisedly, even of the common man—led him to expect that his life on earth could actually be very different from what it had always been. Such beliefs do not mean that the medieval man expected nothing, that he was never discontented. A shrewish wife, for instance, was as unpleasant to live with in the thirteenth as in the twentieth century.

But—and we are getting toward the heart of the matter—in no class of society would the thirteenth-century husband dream of trying to divorce his wife for "mental cruelty," or indeed for any other reason. Marriage was for him made in heaven, even if it were not well made. God had made marriage indissoluble. So too with many other aspects of human life, which we tend to regard as arrangements a man can make or unmake on his own initiative, and on his own responsibility. For the medieval man, much of his life was out of his own hands, in the hands of God working through society. We come back to the inescapable fact of the penetration of medieval life by the Christian attitude—not the Christian attitude at its perfection of spiritual striving, though the Middle Ages made a more natural place for this than our own—but the Christian attitude in its acceptance of the world as a place of probation, of toil and sorrow for the human soul. It is no accident that one of the best-known passages of Dante is

> E'en la sua volontate è nostra pace;
> Ella è quel mare al qual tutto si move
> Ciò ch' ella crea, e che natura face.

"And in his will is our peace: that will is the ocean to which moves everything that it creates or that nature makes."

The Christian promise of salvation in an afterlife for the man or woman who lives on earth according to the precepts of the Church no doubt helps explain the Christian hold over the medieval mind. But the notion of religion as an opiate is a product of the modern mind, which thinks—or hopes—that suffering is not in the order of things. Christianity for the medieval man not merely gave promise of a better life in the next world; it gave to this uncertain life of violence, striving, imperfection, and want on earth meaning, limits, and purpose that came near to closing, for most men, the gap between what they had and what they wanted. Medieval man was more nearly than we *resigned* to a world he could not greatly change. He felt secure in the midst of what we should regard as insecurity—violence, physical want, hardship, even fears bred of ignorance of what we regard as natural phenomena. He felt this security precisely because he was keenly aware of his own weakness. He was neither ashamed of nor disturbed by this weakness; it was not his fault, nor was it, humanly speaking, anyone's fault—certainly one could not be impious enough to attribute the fault to God. The medieval man *felt* as truth what in a later philosopher, Leibnitz, was no more than a rather insincere intellectual formula—that this is the best of all possible worlds. Not a happy, not a contented world, for in such a world men would usurp the place of God. It was, quite simply, God's world.

255

8

Making the Modern World ~ I

MEN HAVE ALWAYS lived in "modern" times but they have not always been as much impressed with the fact. Our own time, conventionally considered as beginning about 1500 A.D., is the first to coin so neat a term and apply it so consistently. *Modern* derives from a late Latin adverb meaning *just now,* and in English is found in its current sense, contrasted with *ancient,* as early as Elizabethan days. This awareness of a shared newness, of a way of life different from that of one's forebears—and by 1700 awareness of a way of life felt by many to be much *better* than that of their forebears—this is in itself one of the clearest marks of our modern culture.

This culture is a most complex one. We cannot define *modern* neatly here, but must hope to build up a definition slowly in the following chapters. At this point we face the problem of disentangling *modern* from *medieval.* It is a very difficult problem, for the millions of concrete situations we try to sum up in these general terms are not related in the simple way our rhetorical habit of thinking conveys. Medieval does not stop, and modern begin, at any one point in space-time. The modern is not a sunrise ending the medieval night. The modern is not the child of the medieval, nor even the medieval grown to manhood.

Indeed, the distinction between medieval and modern has bothered professional historians greatly in the last fifty years or so, as research has dimmed the clearer distinctions our grandfathers drew. In late nineteenth-century times the periodization of medieval and modern was clear in all the textbooks: Renaissance and Reformation, humanism, the geographical discoveries, the invention of printing, and the breaking down of medieval religious unity all come neatly between 1453 and 1517. Americans, particularly, found for modern history a very convenient starting point: 1492. Nowadays all this has been changed. The Renaissance, in particular, has been pushed back so far into what was once considered the unadulterated Middle Ages that the distinction between medieval and modern seems to vanish; the two are telescoped, like a train wreck in time.

Is your criterion the "revival of learning," a truer appreciation of pagan Latin culture? The late Charles H. Haskins has in his *Renaissance of the Twelfth Century* pushed this back well into medieval times. Is your criterion achievement in science and technology? We have already seen that the last few centuries of the Middle Ages are centuries of marked scientific advancement. Indeed, as Professor George Sarton likes to point out, the humanists proper of the Renaissance, the men of letters, theologians, moralists, were at least as contemptuous of grubbing natural science, at least as "deductive" and as respectful of written authority, as were the Schoolmen. It is even possible to defend the thesis that the Renaissance proper means a *regression* in the growth of modern science. Is your criterion economic, the growth of a money economy, banking, extensive trade? Modern research pushes most of these back to the Crusades, to the high Middle Ages. Is your criterion the establishment of the territorial state in the place of the feudal congeries of holdings? Surely France and England are both territorial states by the time they begin their Hundred Years' War in the fourteenth century.

But the reverse approach is possible. When did the Middle Ages end? Apparently, for purposes of controversy, never. Any editorial can use pejoratively today "medieval" or "feudal"—"Boston's medieval streets," "our feudal officeholders in Washington." More seriously, if you take concrete examples in various fields of human culture, you will find medieval ways persisting quite clearly in western Europe as late as the seventeenth century—the legal system in England, the land-holding system in France, medieval weights and measures everywhere, and everywhere much, in Protestant as well as in Catholic Europe, of what in preceding chapters we have tried to bring out as the Christian way of life. The seventeenth-century British colonists who came to Virginia and New England brought with them a surprising amount of the Middle Ages—commons, stocks and pillories, belief in witches, traces of medieval domestic architecture. The colonists of New France even brought with them *seigneurs* and the manorial system, the impress of which still remains in the province of Quebec.

The Middle Ages, then, *grows into* the Modern Age in a way that the life of no single organism really illustrates. Nor can conventional narrative history really embrace the complexities of cultural change. We shall here not by any means abandon the historical approach, but attempt to combine it with an analytical approach. In the next three chapters we shall deal with the building up of the modern way of life in the late fifteenth, the sixteenth, and the seventeenth centuries; and for purposes of analysis we shall consider separately art and letters, religion, and science and technology, trying not to forget that in the real life of our society they were inseparably combined.

By so doing, we shall abandon the roughly chronological approach we have hitherto employed, and shall go contrary to the established canon of historical writing, which accepts a periodization roughly by centuries—though the Renaissance has to be pushed back into the fifteenth and even the fourteenth century. We shall treat humanism, Protestantism, and rationalism as constituent parts of Western intellectual life that can for purposes of analysis be separated out from the whole and treated as a unit over the centuries, roughly from 1450 to 1700, which separate the Middle Ages from the Age of Enlightenment. Our central theme is how the medieval view of life was altered into the eighteenth-century view of life. This eighteenth-century view of life, though modified in the last two centuries, is still at bottom *our* view of life, especially in the United States. The late fifteenth, the sixteenth, and the seventeenth centuries are from this point of view essentially *transitional,* essentially the years of preparation for the

Enlightenment. In this transition, humanism, Protestantism, and rationalism (and natural science) do their work of undermining the medieval, and preparing the modern, cosmology.

They work, as ideas always do, through the hearts and heads of men and women who are by no means pure intellectuals. They do not explain all modern history. They are even, in a sense, abstractions that we build up in our own minds in our effort to make sense of the past. But they do make sense. We believe what we believe today, behave as we do, in part because of what the men we label humanists, Protestants, or rationalists said and did several centuries ago.

The Terms "Renaissance" and "Reformation"

Once upon a time a pair of fair-haired twins named Renaissance and Reformation, persecuted and abused, turned against their wicked but doddering stepmother, the Catholic Church of the Middle Ages. . . . Of course, our history books never came to such a simple and undignified way of putting the matter; they couldn't quite begin like a fairy tale. But, except for Roman Catholics, most Americans who have had to learn some European history have come out with the notion that the movements we call the Protestant Reformation and the Renaissance were somehow the same in inspiration and purpose. One was directed toward religious freedom, the other toward artistic freedom, and both together worked for moral freedom, and, of course, for what became in the nineteenth century democracy. Both worked to *emancipate* ordinary men and women from restraints that custom and superstition had combined to lay upon them in the Middle Ages.

Now even this very misleading view is not *wholly* mistaken. Many a follower of Luther must have felt a kind of exaltation, a sense of being freed from routine obligations that confined him, a new confidence in his own powers. We know well that artists and men of letters, scientists and explorers, all felt the lift of new worlds to conquer, new opportunities to do things—all sorts of things—in ways no one had ever yet made use of, ways therefore of *being themselves,* of being striking personalities. Vague, loose, though the terms are, there is some sense in equating the Middle Ages with *authority,* and both Renaissance and Reformation with *liberty.* But not much sense, if you stop there.

For the facts are too complex for the formula that seeks to explain them. Luther used his authority to help suppress the Peasants' Revolt. Many of the emancipated humanists of the Renaissance set up the masters of Greek literature as authorities beyond their questioning, as models for everything they wrote. Cicero and Plato were worshiped as blindly as any literary masters have ever been worshiped. In politics the Renaissance tyrant, the Renaissance despot are common figures. Neither Renaissance nor Reformation worked consciously toward individual freedom of a democratic sort.

Even less true is it that Renaissance and Reformation always worked harmoniously together for the same ends. A good Calvinist had to hold in horror the Renaissance artist who sculptured nude models, lived recklessly and prodigally, took no thought of the morrow. Luther came to hate the humanist Erasmus, and the feeling was reciprocated. Here we have no simple antithesis between the religious ascetic and the frankly sensuous artist. Erasmus loved Christianity, he loved flawless Greek and the after-dinner conversation of scholars, and in a rather academic way he loved common sense; he made a very poor rebel. The career and personality of Erasmus, indeed, fit in poorly with a cut-and-dried formula for either Renaissance or Reformation.

Humanism, indeed, is an attitude toward life that is fundamentally out of harmony with that side of democracy that is concerned with the common man, with the welfare of the masses. The artist, the man of letters of the Renaissance, believed in a privileged class—not the old feudal nobility, but the new privileged class of talent and intellect. He was indifferent to, or even contemptuous of, the undistinguished many not concerned with art or philosophy or gracious living. From this humanist attitude toward life has come, in part, such a familiar and undemocratic modern attitude as the contempt of artists and intellectuals for the philistines, the Babbitts, the middlebrows. Most modern defenses of an aristocracy—or, since "aristocracy" suggests the old European *noblesse* hardly anyone cares to defend, one might better say, of an elite—have gone back to Renaissance sources for patterns. Nietzsche, following his fellow professor at Basel, Jakob Burckhardt, found in the bright, fierce life of these Renaissance masters of art and man the nearest earthly realization of his master-men, the Supermen.

There is indeed at least one element in the complex of humanist attitudes that has been taken over into democratic tradition—the notion of the career open to talent, to innovating, daring, individual talent. Yet on the whole our modern democrats have not held quite the same notion of talents to be encouraged that the Renaissance held. Obviously the important point about the doctrine of freedom of opportunity is the simple question, Opportunity for what? The eighteenth and the sixteenth centuries, the men of the Enlightenment and the men of the Renaissance, answered this, as we shall see, very differently.

The facts, then, show that the simple view of the Renaissance and Reformation as joint heralds of modern democracy is not accurate. Had modern civilization followed strictly and carefully down the paths blazed for it by humanists or Protestants, we might never have heard the phrase "the century of the common man."

Some of our democratic heritage is very old indeed, as old as the civilization of the Greeks and the Hebrews. Some of it is relatively new, as new as the steam engine. Some of it we owe to the humanists, but not nearly so much as the conventional textbooks of the last few generations usually made out. We must beware of exaggerating the age of our democracy. It is still, in the balance, young, still a growing, striving force in a world long used to other ways of life.

The Range of Humanism

The mere fact of their rebellion against the Catholic Church gave the Protestants at least a common name, no matter how great the differences between an Anglican and an antinomian (from the Greek, *against law*—almost our *anarchist*) or an Anabaptist. There is no such single name for those who in art, letters, and philosophy were in a sense united by the fact that they didn't like medieval art, letters, or philosophy. The best we have is the term *humanists,* a term that has had much wider and much narrower uses than are altogether convenient for the intellectual historian. Especially today, a humanist can be a theologian trying to do without a personal God, an educational reformer who thinks we have too much of natural science and not enough of the humanities, a philosopher who holds that humans are rather more than animals if less than gods, and no doubt much else. Even if we limit ourselves in this chapter to those Renaissance admirers—yes, imitators—of Greece and Rome who are usually classed as humanists, we shall miss much that we ought not to miss.

Let us, then, accept humanism as a kind of cover-all under which may be grouped all men whose world-view is neither primarily theological nor primarily rationalistic. In this use, humanism is not at all necessarily to be taken as a sort of halfway house between the supernatural of religion and the natural of science, though in many cases humanism was just such a halfway house. Humanism tends, in these early modern centuries, to reject medieval habits of mind, medieval ideals, especially as embodied in Scholasticism, but not to accept Protestantism, nor the rationalist view of the universe as a neatly functioning, regular arrangement (almost a machine). The humanist is a great rebel against medieval cosmology, but he has no very clear cosmology of his own. The humanist is a great individualist—he wants to be himself. But he is not very clear about what to make of himself. He is much more in debt to the Middle Ages than he will admit, notably in what he most prides himself on, his learning. And he is not, Leonardo da Vinci and a few others excepted, a scientist. Even Leonardo, perhaps, is better described as an inventor than as a scientist.

We have already seen (p. 257) how far back into the Middle Ages of the old schoolbooks certain of the concrete marks of the Renaissance can be traced. Yet if in the thirteenth century Dante already knows his Latin classics, if Giotto already paints in the round, if Frederick II, *Stupor Mundi,* is already as omnivorously curious about this world of the senses, as headstrong and as heartless as any Renaissance tyrant, it is still true that not until the late fifteenth century is humanism in the full tide of fashion. We must attempt shortly to define, at least in broad terms, what these new things mean as an attitude toward the world. But first we must sample the range of Renaissance humanism.

In many ways the simplest human activity that can be neatly earmarked as "Renaissance" and set off from "medieval" is what we now call scholarship or, in an older term still useful, learning. The humanists proper, in the narrower historical sense of the word, were in fact scholars, though their position in society, at least that of the greater ones like Erasmus, carried a prestige among the ruling classes scholarship does not carry today. (The real analogy today is of course with natural science; Erasmus had in the sixteenth century the kind of prestige Einstein has today.) The humanists had what their medieval predecessors had not, a direct knowledge of Greek; they had access to the originals of most Greek writing that has survived at all. Greek came slowly to the West, by means of hundreds of now forgotten scholars; it did not come suddenly after the fall of Constantinople in 1453 when Byzantine scholars fled from the Turk. Indeed, the medieval scholar after the thirteenth century was by no means as ignorant of Greek as we used to think, and by the late fourteenth century any ambitious, scholarly youth could have access to Greek. The humanists also tried to write the kind of Latin Cicero and his fellows wrote. That is to say, they deliberately abandoned medieval Latin, which was a natural language, limited it is true to an intellectual class, but written and spoken by them with no more than customary respect for tradition. The humanist scholars deliberately revived a dead tongue—which has in a sense been quite dead ever since. They polished and refined the life out of Latin. They had the use of the printing press, and were thus able to communicate more readily with one another than had their medieval predecessors. The humanists were, however, a small privileged group, not interested in a wide audience; some of them damned the printing press as the vulgarization of learning. It is really only in religion that the printing press in these early years touches a democratic audience. How changed in spirit the humanist scholars were from their medieval predecessors we shall try to estimate in the next section. But for purposes of recognition their devotion to the Greeks, their Ciceronian Latin, their contempt for the Schoolmen are ample signs.

In the fine arts, the men of the high Renaissance—the sixteenth century, the *Cinquecento* of the Italians—produced work that looks very different from medieval work. They produced it partly at least in a deliberate imitation of the Romans, whose remains in architecture and sculpture lay all about in the Italy which gave the lead to humanism in art and in letters. But they did not produce it suddenly, and they owed a great deal more than they liked to admit to their medieval predecessors.

In architecture the change is perhaps clearest, the break cleanest. Actually Gothic, soaring Gothic, had never been really popular in Italy. Builders readily took to the round arch, the dome, the classic orders, and to lines that accepted the horizontal as something not to be transcended. They produced indeed a style, a compound of elements each with a classical origin, but which when put together make something new, something original. No Roman, no Greek, had ever built a building quite like St. Peter's in Rome or the Renaissance palaces of Florence. As it travels north, this style gets entangled with local medieval traditions and produces some strange hybrids like the famous French chateau at Chambord, all Renaissance in massive simplicity and horizontality in the lower stories, all Gothic profusion and upward striving in roofs and chimneys. In England, gentlemen's manor houses, though no longer fortified, no longer medieval castles, show Gothic tracery right into the seventeenth century.

In sculpture and painting again, work of the sixteenth century is clearly distinguishable from work of the thirteenth. A painting of Raphael's is not like one of Giotto's, nor is Michelangelo's David—even apart from its heroic size—a statue that would fit into a Gothic cathedral. Yet to the untrained layman trying to use his eyes, Renaissance painting and sculpture look related to medieval painting and sculpture in a way the cathedral of Chartres and St. Peter's at Rome do not look related. If you take as a rough measuring rod what we shall crudely call naturalness, lifelikeness, what a stereoscopic camera sees, then from the thirteenth century on artists are working toward this kind of naturalness, and away from certain conventions that may or may not be "primitive." Those conventions are best identified with Byzantine art, which was stiff, hieratic, flat-surfaced, and made no attempt to anticipate the camera and Technicolor. (We are trying hard to report, and not to judge; but these fields are in the heart of that kind of noncumulative knowledge known as taste, where every word praises or blames; in general today to say that a painting suggests anything photographic is to damn the painting.) That is to say that in painting and in sculpture the medieval thirteenth and the Renaissance sixteenth century join together against the Byzantine, and the Renaissance is clearly the daughter of the Middle Ages, at least in one very central point of technique.

So too even more clearly in imaginative literature the obvious external signs do not so much differentiate the Renaissance from the high Middle Ages as mark a clear continuity of development. The use of the vernacular is certainly no criterion, for the vernaculars are used for poetry and narrative, for literature in contrast to philosophy, even before great medieval writers like Dante and Chaucer use them. No doubt certain forms, especially in poetry, and certain kinds of polished style mark work as that of the humanists. The sonnet, for instance, is a readily recognized form that can at once be ticketed as Renaissance. But the continuity from the thirteenth century on is none the less striking. For a concrete example, take the note of bawdry or obscenity. If you will read in chronological order samples from the *fabliaux,* one of Chaucer's bawdier tales, some Boccaccio, and some Rabelais, you will have gone from the Middle Ages to the high Renaissance, and you will come out in the end with a man always respectfully tagged as a humanist. And yet Rabelais has an exuberance, a small-boyish obscenity, a freshness that has also been tagged Gothic. His vast and miscellaneous erudition may at first sight seem humanist, but it is an erudition piled on with little of the classical sense of discipline.

Rabelais is describing, at great length and with a typical humanist erudition in all fields, a marvelous (and fictitious) plant he calls pata-gruelion, after his hero Pantagruel:

I find that plants are named after several ways. Some have taken the name of him who first found them, knew them, showed them, sowed them, improved them by culture, and appropriated them: as the Mercurialis from Mercury; Panacea from Panace, daughter of Escula-pius; Armois from Artemis, who is Diana; Eupatorium from King Eupator; Telephion from Telephus; Euphorbium from Euphorbus, King Juba's physician; Clymenos from Clymenus; Alcibiadium from Alcibi-ades; Gentian from Gentius, King of Sclavonia. And, formerly, so much was prized this prerogative of giving a name to newly discovered plants, that, just as a controversy arose betwixt Neptune and Pallas, from which of the two the land discovered by both should receive its denomination—though thereafter it was called and had the appellation of Athens, from Athenæ, which is Minerva—just so would Lyncus, King of Scythia, have treacherously slain the young Triptolemus, whom Ceres had sent to show unto mankind the use of corn, previously unknown; to the end that, after his murder, he might impose his own name, and be called, in immortal honour and glory, the inventor of a grain so profitable and necessary to human life. For the wickedness of which treasonable attempt he was by Ceres transformed into an ounce.

Other herbs and plants there are, which retain the names of the countries from whence they were transported: as the Median apples from Media, where they were first found; Punic apples—that is to say, pomegranates—from Punicia; Ligusticum, which we call Lovage, from Liguria, the coast of Genoa; Castanes, Persiques or peach-trees, Sabine, Stæchas from my Iles Hyères; Spica Celtica, and others.

Rabelais's obscenity is often quite as learned, so learned that only a humanist would find it very obscene. He makes long lists, like litanies, of epithets in which only the original object is—or was—unprintable.

This comparative study of obscenity should at least bring home the very great difficulty of pigeonholing works of art (in the widest sense of art, which includes literature) to accord with big generaliza-tions of philosophy or sociology. The note of bawdry may well be peculiarly timeless, and therefore an unfair test. Yet hardly any easily recognized, single, external sign will clearly differentiate medieval art from Renaissance art.

The reader may indeed, if he has been thinking his way through this, have come upon the idea that since the Middle Ages were primarily religious and since the Renaissance meant at least an attempted return to the pagan, the unreligious if not the irreligious, medieval art should be tied to the Church and Renaissance art should enjoy Bohemian freedom. Now this is in part true. By the high Renaissance sculptors and painters are imitating the classical nude as they imitated everything else classic. The artist is beginning to lead something like the kind of life—wild, indecent, improvident, but so interesting—he is still supposed to lead. Benvenuto Cellini's autobiography, which is always appealed to by those who want to simplify the sixteenth century as the Century of the Artist, certainly sets up the myth of the artist as the genius above decency as above dullness. Yet an autobiography of Villon's—did it exist—would perhaps have outdone Cellini's. Of course, you can always maintain that Villon is not really medieval, that he anticipates the Renaissance.

But there is a grave difficulty in accepting the formula: Middle Ages equals religion and inhibition, Renaissance equals paganism and exhibition. All through the high Renaissance the artist is at work for the Church and on religious themes. If you will think of the universally known work of these men, work so famous as to seem to the present-day highbrow almost vulgar—Leonardo's Last Supper, Raphael's Madonnas, Michelangelo's frescoes in the Sistine Chapel, and the like—you will note that they are all religious in theme. Someone may tell you that these works are religious in a purely external way, and that their spirit is worldly, sensuous, pagan, humanistic, and quite the opposite of the medieval. Raphael's madonnas are, they may say, just Italian peasant women, no more spiritual than the winner of an American beauty contest. This contrast between a madonna of Raphael as all flesh and a Gothic sculptured Virgin as all soul is most misleading. Raphael's madonnas are descendants of medieval Virgins and by no means traduce their ancestor, who was very far from being an abstract principle. Indeed, it is chiefly because we exaggerate the asceticism and other-worldliness of the Middle Ages that we find Renaissance art so fresh, so pagan, so human. The

Renaissance artists who gave most of their artistic lives to the task of making Christian beliefs tangible, visible, were carrying on a function they had inherited from the medieval forerunners. Only gradually, and only in comparatively modern times, is art so completely secular that religious art almost disappears. Here again the modern has its firmest and most numerous roots not in the sixteenth, but in the eighteenth century.

The Nature of Humanism

The humanists were, however, conscious rebels, whether their main interest was in scholarship, philosophy, art, or letters. They are very modern in their awareness of being in revolt against their fathers, the men of the Middle Ages. Perhaps the scholars and philosophers, humanists in the narrower sense, were most articulate. Men like Erasmus expressed very freely their contempt for the Schoolmen, wretched slaves of Aristotle, manglers of the noble tongue of Horace and Cicero, idle disputants over the number of angels who could occupy the point of a needle. We still echo their attacks today, though we should have a perspective they did not have. They were, it is true, rebelling against a decayed Scholasticism, not against the mature Scholasticism of the thirteenth century, which they made no real attempt to recover.

Even the artists were in rebellion, consciously striving to put off a tradition they felt to be a burden. Late Gothic was in as obvious a state of decay as was late Scholasticism, and especially north of the Alps those who welcomed the new Italian styles in all the arts did so as rebels against the complexities and fatuousness of late Gothic. Early Renaissance is a simple style, relatively unornamented, consciously avoiding the richness of Gothic, consciously seeking in classical examples simplicity and discipline.

Perhaps at bottom humanists and Protestants were both rebelling because they felt the familiar, but to sensitive men and women never comfortable, gap between the ideal and the real had in late medieval times reached an excessive degree of obviousness. That gap, always pretty plain throughout the Middle Ages, was by the fifteenth century almost too wide for the most ingenious explanations to close. The ideal was still Christian, still an ideal of unity, peace, security, organization, status; the reality was endemic war, divided authority even at the top, even in that papacy which should reflect God's own serene unity, a great scramble for wealth and position, a time of troubles.

So, in a sense like Protestantism, this complex movement in the arts and in philosophy we call humanism is a very self-conscious rebel, a rebel against a way of life it finds corrupt, overelaborated, stale, unlovely, and untrue. The humanists seem to be opening a window, letting in the fresh air, and doing a lot of other pleasant things.

Yet the humanist figures of speech began to wear out for all save the very faithful. Renaissance art soon began to cultivate a lush ornamentation, a fondness for detail, a richness of color that would have satisfied the fifteenth century. Or more accurately, in most of the arts the victorious humanists divided into a lush or exuberant school and an ascetic or spare school. In architecture, for instance, one line of development went through Palladio, a sixteenth-century Italian who loved strict classic simplicity of the schoolmaster's tradition, into the kind of neoclassicism we are familar with in the United States as "colonial"; another line led straight into the baroque and thence, in the eighteenth century, rococo, styles of flowing curves and rich ornamentation. As for writing, the humanists were hardly at any time really simpler than their scholastic opponents, and very soon their scholarship got as pretentious, as heavy, as doctoral as scholarship ever got to be; Plato got rather confusedly substituted for Aristotle as The Philosopher; and even in imaginative writing men got so far away from the ideals of simplicity (which in fact the Renaissance never really did take seriously) that one finds in the sixteenth century two literary movements which cultivated a certain literary preciousness and obscurity more successfully than it has been cultivated until very recently—euphuism in England and gongorism in Spain. Recent popularity among the purest of intellectuals has made us once more familiar with the metaphysical poets of seventeenth-century England, who were certainly not simple, clear, and reasonable. The Renaissance very rapidly created its own gap between the real and the ideal.

For the Renaissance, like the Protestant Reformation, was not really anarchical. It rebelled against one authority, one complex of ideals, habits, institutions in the name of another, and by no means unrelated, complex. Again, as rebels the humanists had to work very hard to discredit an older authority, and in the process they often used libertarian language, at least to the extent of demanding freedom for the new education, freedom from the rules of Scholasticism, freedom for the individual to follow his own bent and not just parrot Aristotle. But even less than the Protestants, some of whom were antinomians, did the humanists really believe in the natural goodness and wisdom of man. Or if you prefer to put it that way, they never really emancipated themselves from the long medieval intellectual tradition of looking for authority, looking for the answer, in the recorded works of famous predecessors. Only, for the Church Fathers, Aristotle, and the medieval doctors, the humanists substituted the body of surviving Greek and Roman writings, literary as well as philosophical, and, where they still were actively interested in religion, the text of the Bible, duly studied in the original Hebrew or Greek. As secondary authorities, they soon built up their own society of mutual admiration and began the modern process embedded in the scholarly footnote. But there is among them the same deference toward authority, the same habit of abstract and indeed deductive thought, the same unwillingness to make experiments, to grub around in an undignified way, that we find in the Schoolmen. They are not really forerunners of free modern scholarly research; they are vainer and more worldly Schoolmen.

The above paragraph is greatly exaggerated, but it is meant to drive home a point. The humanist scholars were not libertarians and democrats in the modern sense. They were a privileged group of learned men, very proud of their scholarly standards, with most of the traditional defects of scholars—vanity, possessiveness, quarrelsomeness, and a great fear of making mistakes. They had a great share of one of the traditional virtues of scholars, a lusty appetite for hard intellectual labor. Of critical acumen, of ability to set and solve problems they surely had no more than scholars must have. They were not the intellectual giants they now appear; they were rather pioneers moving slowly into rough country.

They set a pattern and standards for modern scholarship. In the study of ancient languages they introduced order, accuracy, and tools that we take for granted, like dictionaries arranged alphabetically. They developed analytical and historical standards of criticism. The stock example of the achievements of these scholars is still an excellent one to illustrate their methods at their best. The popes had in the early Middle Ages bolstered the prestige of the Holy See, already firmly based on the Petrine tradition, by the "donation of Constantine." A document purported to come from the emperor Constantine as he left Rome to establish his capital in Constantinople made the pope his successor in Rome and gave to him the direct control of the land around Rome later known as the "States of the Church." This document was shown by one of the earliest of the humanists, Lorenzo Valla, who died in 1457, to be a forgery. Its language simply was not the language that could have been written in the early fourth century A.D. Valla made this evident by methods now familiar to us all; he showed that the document contained *anachronisms,* as if a letter purported to be Abraham Lincoln's should contain a reference to a Buick car.

The formal metaphysical thought of the humanists is not one of their strong points. In these early modern centuries most minds at once systematic and determined to answer the Big Questions were either theologians or rationalists of some sort. Italian humanists like Ficino and Pico della Mirandola were not merely Platonists; they were Neoplatonists, tender-minded believers in this most cerebral and scholarly mysticism. And in general it is true that through most of Europe the humanists welcomed Plato as a relief from Aristotle, as a philosopher closer to the purified but still sacramental Christianity they really wanted. Erasmus, Thomas More, Colet, and other northerners came under the influence of Plato. The thesis that these men simply left one authority, Aristotle, to take refuge in another can no doubt be exaggerated. But they certainly added little to the Platonist tradition, and indeed they are not primarily philosophers.

It is, however, the imaginative writers, the artists, who are near the heart of the humanist attitude toward life. Petrarch, Rabelais, Shakespeare, Cervantes, the painters, sculptors, and musicians whose names we still know—these are the kind of men who sought some way between traditional Christianity as it was handed down by the Middle Ages and the new rationalism that seemed to take all the magic and mystery out of the universe. By the seventeenth century, some of them, like Milton, could invest with awe and mystery the world science was trying to make clear. But few artists could accept the world of Bacon and Descartes. It is from these centuries that the modern distrust of the artist for the scientist dates.

Now, as we have seen, these artists were in more or less conscious rebellion against the medieval Christian tradition. They repudiated one authority, but—and this is most important—they had to seek out, perhaps sometimes to set up, another authority. The scholar's simple acceptance of anything written by an old Greek or Roman was not enough for these men of imagination. Like everyone who touched at all things intellectual, these artists too went back to Greece and Rome. But like the architects, they reworked their materials into something new. Indeed, we may take a lead from architecture, impersonal art though it may seem to be, in the difficult task of sorting these writers out into some order.

One kind of Renaissance architecture—Palladio will do as a name to associate with it—found in its classic models simplicity, regularity, moderation (nothing huge), quiet, graceful decoration (nothing stark). Now one kind of Renaissance artistic and literary return to the ancients found there essentially the same kind of authority; they found the classics were "classical." They found, that is, substantially that ideal of the beautiful and the good which has never yet quite been banished from formal Western education. They found that the Greeks and Romans—the ones that count, the ones we have to read—were gentlemanly, disciplined, moderate in all things, distrustful of the wild, the excited, the unbuttoned, the enthusiastic, free from superstition but by no means irreligious, controlled, mature men of imagination, not narrow rationalists. One could go on at great length, and indeed we shall return to some phases of these ideals. Suffice it here to say that these Renaissance admirers of the classical culture of Greece and Rome found in that culture above all a *discipline*. They did not see what Professor Gilbert Murray, whose opinion we have earlier cited (p. 73), thinks might have been seen there had not generations of men like these humanists pretty well suppressed it— exuberance, color, wildness, the desire of the moth for the star, high adventure, and deep romance.

We shall call this the *spare,* in contrast with the *exuberant* interpretation of the classics. You can find traces of it even in the high Renaissance of the late fifteenth and early sixteenth century, and especially in the more imaginative of the scholar-humanists like Erasmus. There is much of it in Montaigne, though Montaigne always holds himself back from anything like a movement. And this spare classicism did become a movement, a fashion, a way of life. Its great flowering was in the France of the seventeenth century, and the Age of Louis XIV is in many ways a good sampling of the ideal.

Here is a passage from Boileau in which both form and matter illustrate the classical ideal of his age—clarity, sobriety, respect for authority, distrust of the unusual, the eccentric, the departure from the norm:

> When authors have been admired for a great number of centuries and have been scorned only by a few people with eccentric taste (for there will always be found depraved tastes), then not only is there temerity, there is madness in casting doubt on the merit of these writers. From the fact that you do not see the beauties in their writings you must not conclude that those beauties are not there, but that you are blind and that you have no taste. The bulk of mankind in the long run makes no mistake about works of the spirit. There is no longer any question nowadays as to whether Homer, Plato, Cicero, Vergil are remarkable men. It is a matter closed to dispute, for twenty centuries are agreed on it; the question is to find out what it is that has made them admired by so many centuries; and you must find a way to understand this or give up letters, for which you must believe that you have neither taste nor aptitude since you do not feel what all men have felt.

The relation of this spare classicism to Christianity is by no means a simple one. The great writers of the French classical period who are perhaps the best representatives of it are all good Catholics—or at least all practicing Catholics. Indeed it would have been indecent self-assertion for them not to have been Catholics; moreover, they could hardly hope for preferment at the court of Louis XIV had they been heretics or skeptics. But the classicists were often separated by the thinnest of lines from the rationalists, the men who were building up an attack on any form of revealed religion. Obviously the Boileaus, the Bossuets, even the Racines—and more important, the people who were the direct audience of these writers—could not be enthusiasts, mystics, rebels, Protestants, and still maintain the decorum that was part of their ideal. This decorum, and much else prescribed for them, like the famous formal rules of French drama, they would all maintain to be perfectly consonant with deep feeling, with a sense of mystery and the inadequacy of men to run their own lives without the guiding hand of God. They felt they were good Christians.

And so they were, almost all of them. But they were enlightened and conformist Christians, not evangelical ones. Some, like Racine, might in their later years regret their worldly past and turn to a sincere but still conventional piety. On the edge of this world there might be heresies like Jansenism, which has been called the Calvinism of the Roman Catholic Church, and which was indeed an austere and almost classical version of Christianity. Some of the gentler members, like Bishop Fénelon, might go over to a much more modern heresy, the quietism that seems in some ways an anticipation of the sentimental belief in natural goodness of the eighteenth century. But the great bulk of these classical humanists were surely marginal Christians, or at least Christians not much moved toward the imitation of Christ, Christians for whom the Church was above all a discipline for nat- urally unruly men who lacked the sense of these classical humanists, their education, their feeling for what was fit.

It is easy, and tempting, to consider the way of life and ways of thought of the classical humanists as without influence on the forma- tion of the modern mind, especially in the English-speaking world, as something that might move a schoolmaster or two—or a T. S. Eliot—but as not particularly germane to our own thinking and feeling. Yet one distinguished French historian of ideas, Taine, maintained the thesis that what he called the classic spirit (*esprit classique*) with its tendency to regard the universal, the regular, the uniform as a kind of standard, its habit of simplifying, its belief in rules and formulas, helped to produce the state of mind we call the Enlightenment. Certainly rebels like Voltaire had sat at the feet of the great masters of the seventeenth century. We shall have to return later to this problem of the relation of *l'esprit classique* to the Enlightenment. In their own time, the classical humanists believed that they had found a principle of authority, a measure, decency and decorum, something that could stand with the medieval synthesis as a practical ordering of this messy world.

The exuberant humanists we Americans feel more at home with, and we commonly credit them as in very important senses makers of our own way of life. These are the heroes of the Renaissance proper, the men whose doings make good reading, even in textbooks—Cellini, murdering, whoring, sculpturing, posturing, talking with kings and popes; Leonardo da Vinci, painting, building, writing, inventing airplanes and submarines (on paper), engineering. Then there are kings like Francis I of France and Henry VIII of England who not only looked kingly, who not only had the athletic and hunting skills essential to esteemed position in the upper class of Western society right down to the United States of 1950, but who were also learned in the ancient tongues, witty, capable of turning out a poem or an essay, and, of course, great lovers. There are whole families like the Borgias, full of the most fascinating and unconventional people.

Their flavor is really unmistakable. There have been strivers, ardent pursuers of the ultimate, in all ages, and the whole spirit of some ages is sometimes as zestful, as pushing, as that of the Renaissance; late nineteenth-century America was a great age of push, and as we have noted, philosophers of history have labeled our whole Western culture, from the ancient Greeks on, or from the Dark Ages on, as "Faustian," "Nordic," "dynamic," restless, striving. But there is a curious childlike cruelty, abandon, and immediacy of aim in the striving of the high Renaissance. Cellini provides a mine of illustrations. Here is one:

> Having discontinued my connection with that wretch Caterina, and the poor unfortunate young man who had conspired with her to wrong me being gone from Paris, I intended to have my ornament for Fontainebleau, which was of bronze, properly cleaned, and likewise to get the two figures of Victory, which extended from the side angles to the middle circles of the gate, furbished up. For this purpose I took into my house a poor girl about fifteen years of age. She was extremely well-shaped, lively, and of a complexion rather swarthy; and as she was somewhat rustic, spoke little, walked rapidly, and had a sort of wildness in her eyes, I gave her the name of Scozzona; but her name was Gianna. With her assistance, I finished my Fontainebleau and the two Victories intended for ornaments to the gate. By this Gianna I had a daughter, on the seventh of June, at three in the afternoon, in 1544. I gave this child the name of Constantia, and she was held upon the font by Signor Guido Guidi, one of my most intimate friends, physician to the King. He alone stood godfather; for the custom of France is, that there should be but one godfather and two godmothers. One of these was Signora Maddalena, wife to Signor Luigi Alamanni, a gentleman of Florence, and an admirable poet, the other godmother was a French lady of good family, wife of Signor Riccardo del Bene, also a citizen of Florence and an eminent merchant. This was the first child that I ever had, to the best of my remembrance. I assigned the mother such a maintenance as satisfied an aunt of hers, into whose hands I put her; and never had any acquaintance with her afterward.

It is not the sexual irregularity here that is striking, nor Cellini's obvious lack of any sense of sin; it is his apparent self-centered unawareness of others as persons, as objects of concern—it is his childlike innocence.

The exuberant humanists, it might seem, were in fact casting off *all* authority, not merely that of the medieval church; they were humanists in the sense that they believed that man is the measure of all things, and that each man is a measure for himself. The tag word is "individualism"—these men were great individualists as opposed to the timid conformists of the monkish Middle Ages; they were men who dared to be themselves, because they trusted in their own natural powers, in something inside themselves. They were the kind of men we Americans like, men with no stuffiness, men who might almost have come from Texas.

Rabelais again is a case in point. He loves to make fun of the monkish Middle Ages, its superstitions, its pretenses to chastity, its Aristotelian learning. He is going to free men and women from this nonsense. His Abbaye de Thélème is a very lay abbey indeed, open to both sexes, and inscribed on its gate is the pleasant command, *Fay ce que vouldras* (Do what you like).

We must, be it repeated, avoid the excesses of debunking. These men of the Renaissance in its more athletic phase were also makers of the modern world. They helped greatly to destroy the medieval world, especially the political and moral phases of that world. They produced many works of art that are an inescapable part of our inheritance. They had taken on by the nineteenth century the stature of giants, and fulfilled for almost all the great nations of Europe, except for Germany, which had to wait for Goethe, the essential function of culture-heroes. Do not think this unimportant; without Shakespeare, British self-esteem, and even our own, would be not shaken, perhaps, but surely lessened. No one else could take his place.

Yet these men of the Renaissance were by no means working for ends like ours, and were we really to encounter them in the flesh we should hardly feel them kin. It is not merely, as we shall see in the next section, that they had no sympathy with, hardly any idea of, democracy in our modern sense. The difference is deeper, or rather, this fundamental difference ramifies into all fields of life and can be expressed in many different ways. Underlying our modern democratic beliefs there is an optimism, a notion of the possible orderliness and widespread prosperity for all, which the men of the Renaissance did not have. There is today a doctrine of formal progress, of better times that lie ahead in the nature of things. There is a belief in the essential goodness and educability of ordinary human beings. There is a very basic belief that man somehow fits into the universe, that, to put the matter with not wholly deceptive simplicity, men are made to be happy.

Now these are very big and very risky generalizations indeed. It may well be that in the mid-twentieth century the beliefs we have noted above are not really held by most men, that we are coming into a new age and a new faith. But these beliefs are clearly the beliefs of eighteenth- and nineteenth-century democratic optimism. On the Renaissance end of our generalizations, it must be admitted that since these early centuries of the modern era were a seedbed for our own ideas, since above all they were centuries of great intellectual fermentation and experimentation, since there was on the whole great freedom of thought in most of Europe, you can find examples of almost anything you search for in these times. A Jacksonian democrat would find the English Levellers congenial enough. Science, invention, geographical discoveries gave a modern tone to intellectual life. Novelty and excitement were, if not commonplace, at least always available with a little effort. And it was a humanist of these centuries who gave us the word with which we sum up the notion that men might be happy and well adjusted in a perfect society on this earth—*Utopia*.

Yet this last should give us pause. We use the word *Utopia* with a slight twist of scorn. The word carries with it an unmistakable note of the dream, the myth, the unreal. And not unjustly, for Sir Thomas More's *Utopia* is no more modern than Plato's *Republic*. If you have a certain type of mind and training, you will add "and no less modern." Both are the work of metaphysical idealists, tender-minded men who hope that the spirit may somehow transcend the flesh. More's book reflects the early sixteenth-century interest in geographical discovery—Utopia itself is an island that the sailor Ralph Hythloday has visited—and it is much more preoccupied with economic questions than was Plato's *Republic*. But both are authoritarian in spirit, and neither seems aware of change in human relations as a process, let alone an evolution. Perhaps most writers who deliberately set out to invent a Utopia are by temperament authoritarian, even though, like Karl Marx, they put down on paper as an ultimate ideal the withering away of the state or some other distant, anarchical goal.

Sir Thomas More was one of the humanist-scholars, a Catholic who suffered martyrdom at the hands of Henry VIII, and by no means one of the exuberant humanists we are now chiefly concerned with. And it is the exuberant humanists who have given the Renaissance the flavor that now seems so interesting to us—from afar. These active, adventurous, questing, excited men were at heart unsure of themselves and their place in the universe. They tried hard to believe in themselves, but not very successfully. They did not have the dogmatic security the spare classical humanists arrived at. They were always experimenting, always trying something new.

They had, however, certain ends, certain purposes, certain ways they sought to follow. They were contemptuous of their medieval forefathers, not so much because of what they thought was their empty logic-spinning, but also because of what they thought was medieval fear of life—the life of the appetites. The Renaissance as a fashion among fashionable people—and the exuberant humanists were at the height of sixteenth-century fashion—set a great store on being frankly pagan about its enjoyments. These humanists and artists were not going to be like the late medieval decadents, worried and obsessed with sin while they tried to enjoy themselves. Theirs was to be no Dance of Death, but a Dance of Life.

But it was a public dance, and the performers were out to shine. Each dancer was determined to outdo the others in polish, in verve, in endurance. In the groups that set the tone of aristocratic life, competition was as frenzied, as intense, as it has ever been in human society. Within the elite that competition was perhaps even more deadly than the more widespread competition of late nineteenth-century life. The Renaissance was the age of the hero, the hero as artist, the hero as soldier of fortune, the hero as explorer, the hero as scholar, even the hero as poisoner. If you were less than a hero, you were a failure.

The great word—there is a big critical and historical literature upon it—which seems to point up this mad scramble of all the talents is the Italian *virtù*. The word, like our modern *virtue*, comes from the Latin *vir,* man. But Renaissance *virtù* emphasizes "man" in the way our manliness does, and adds a great deal more. Like the ideals

of chivalry from which it in part descends, *virtù* is an upper-class
ideal, to which a gifted person of lesser birth may indeed rise. Again
like that of chivalry, this ideal can be made to emphasize a code of
conduct not unchristian and can quite readily be turned into a rather
overrefined, but decent, code for a gentleman, as in Baldassare Castiglione's *Libro del Cortegiano* (Book of the Courtier). Castiglione writes
like a humanist, with abundant references to classical literature. But
he is almost medieval in his tender-minded belief in the validity of
the ideal; his prince is far nearer the prince of the medieval John of
Salisbury than the prince of his own contemporary, Machiavelli:

> "Since it costs us nothing but words, tell us on your faith every-
> thing that it would occur to your mind to teach your prince."
> My lord Ottaviano replied:
> "Many other things, my Lady, would I teach him, provided I knew
> them; and among others, that he should choose from his subjects a num-
> ber of the noblest and wisest gentlemen, with whom he should consult
> on everything, and that he should give them authority and free leave
> to speak their mind to him about all things without ceremony; and that
> he should preserve such demeanour towards them, that they all might
> perceive that he wished to know the truth about everything and held
> all manner of falsehood in hatred. Besides this council of nobles, I
> should advise that there be chosen from the people other men of lower
> rank, of whom a popular council should be made, to communicate with
> the council of nobles concerning the affairs of the city, both public and
> private. And in this way there would be made of the prince (as of the
> head) and of the nobles and commonalty (as of the members) a single
> united body, the government of which would spring chiefly from the
> prince and yet include the others also; and this state would thus have
> the form of the three good kinds of government, which are Monarchy,
> Optimates, and People.
> "Next I should show him that of the cares which belong to the
> prince, the most important is that of justice; for the maintenance of
> which wise and well-tried men ought to be chosen to office, whose fore-
> sight is true foresight accompanied by goodness, for else it is not fore-
> sight, but cunning; and when this goodness is lacking, the pleaders' skill
> and subtlety always work nothing but ruin and destruction to law and
> justice, and the guilt of all their errors must be laid on him who put
> them in office.
> "I should tell how justice also fosters that piety towards God which

is the duty of all men, and especially of princes, who ought to love Him above every other thing and direct all their actions to Him as to the true end; and as Xenophon said, to honour and love Him always, but much more when they are in prosperity, so that afterwards they may the more reasonably have confidence to ask Him for mercy when they are in some adversity. . . ."

The mixture of Xenophon and the Christian God is by no means uncharacteristic. The whole tone is that of Platonism, now watered down to the uses of an upper class—and its imitators, anxious to learn gentility from the new humanists.

In practice *virtù* can almost mean doing something, doing *anything,* better than anyone else. The skills it honors are the skills of the champion, the record breaker. Perhaps man is by some sort of instinct a record breaker; but a lot depends on what sort of records he tries to break. The Renaissance was as promiscuous in this as in other respects. It is true the Renaissance was not favorable to attempts to break records for asceticism; fasts, hair shirts, and hermits were not its style. But almost anything else would do. Don Juan, with his famous 1003 female conquests in Spain alone, is more in the Renaissance tradition of record breakers.

Don Juan clearly did not have a very good time setting up his record. Even in the earlier Spanish form of the legend, Don Juan is an unhappy man driven to his innumerable love affairs by some demonic push which is not quite what Hollywood and most of us mean by sex. Don Juan is indeed a brother of another figure of legend who by the Renaissance has become a literary figure—Doctor Faustus. Both Faust and Don Juan want something excessive—their very wanting is excessive. Yet they cannot satisfy their unending wants in a way the Christian tradition had long provided in its many variants of mystic other-worldliness. They have to get what they want in the flesh, here and now, like other men. But their wants are not the wants of other men; they would blush to think they had so little distinction of body and spirit as to have their wants requited. They have the restless striving after something infinite that men like Spengler find in northerners, in the Faustian man. But as good children of humanism, they want all this without God, without *theoria, nirvana,* or any other mystic self-annihilation.

In real life, they get this sense of transcending limitations only by trying for the record, only by this conscious pushing to excess the quality we have called exuberance. In the fine arts this striving for the excessive is curbed by the degree of reverence all shared for Greek and Roman work. The Renaissance artist is still so full of problems in working out the natural, realistic representation of things on this earth that he feels no need to be wild, or abstract, or unintelligible. He can do *big* things, as Michelangelo was fond of doing; and admire Michelangelo as you may, you will have to admit that there is in his work—in the David, in God and Adam and Eve of the Sistine Chapel —a sense of strain, an heroic strife to attain the heroic, the overpowering. Indeed, just putting God, a majestic and powerful God, but a God not altogether without *virtù,* on the ceiling of the chapel was the kind of thing that suited the exuberant humanists—and more than one humanistically inclined pope. It is not that the high Middle Ages had had scruples about bringing God too close to men by painting or sculpturing him. In the Last Judgments, which were a favorite subject for the sculptor of the early Middle Ages in particular, God has to appear. But he never looks like the perfect knight. And in the later Middle Ages there is a tendency to confine concrete representation to Jesus, the Virgin, and the saints, as if God were not in fact of our kind.

In writing of all sorts, even in the work of the scholars, this Renaissance quality of striving for the unique, the extreme, the grand, comes out clearly; we have already noted euphuism and gongorism. But in fact there is hardly a writer who does not at some phase in his career work so hard at being himself that he becomes precious, difficult, full of allegory and conceits. Sometimes there is an incredible piling up of details of erudition, of odd lore, of odds and ends of experience of all sorts, as in Rabelais. Later French writers of the spare classical school, shocked by this Rabelaisian fertility and formlessness, called him "Gothic," which he of course is not; he is merely an exuberant humanist, most emancipated, who would have been very uncomfortable *as an intellectual* in the thirteenth century. (He would, of course, not have written in the thirteenth century, but followed his profession of medicine heartily and creditably, with no undue worries about his ignorance.) Sometimes this quality comes out in a prose style that in almost any other period would be found intolerably artificial, like that of Sir Thomas Browne's *Urn Burial*. You may say that this is the dead hand of Latin at its most Ciceronian, periodic, and spiritually periwigged. But it is what these writers thought a suitable style, something they quite deliberately sought for. Sometimes the Renaissance writer just doesn't know how to stop, a failing that again may well be timeless among the literary, but which in those days seems especially common. This is by no means true only of the early exuberant writers, like Rabelais. One finds it in later writers, among them the English poet Spenser, whose unfinished *Faerie Queene* runs on for eighty cantos.

Finally, this quality of excess may well be brought out in the work of a man who lived long after the last of the Renaissance worthies was dead. All the American critics at some time or other had to drag out the epithet "Renaissance" for Thomas Wolfe, the North Carolinian novelist who died in 1938. The critics were well justified; the epithet had to be used. Wolfe's desires were all appetites, and his appetites were all Gargantuan. He tells in *Of Time and the River* how, as a young graduate student at Harvard, he got stack access to the library, even then of some two to three million volumes, and started to read them all, going up and down the rows of stacks, pulling down book after book. In a magnificent moment of concentration, he would register each book somewhere in his mind, and add it to his record. He came far short even of the first million, but this means no more than that the Renaissance can hardly come again. Certainly a dip into Wolfe should make clearer the note we have been attempting to describe.

It must not be thought that these exuberant humanists were all wild men, that none of them ever enjoyed a quiet moment. Some of them tired, if they lived long enough. Some of them won their way through storm and stress to what their world had agreed to call wisdom. Some of them seem always to have had a certain kind of wisdom about human beings. Yet the serenity, the wisdom, the recognizable state of balance that does come out of this Renaissance way of life is very different from that of the medieval Scholastic, very different from that of a spare classicist like Boileau. Shakespeare by his whole career and environment belongs to what we have called the exuberant humanists. He has most of the Renaissance mannerisms, followed most of the Renaissance fashions. He was a wise man, but to judge him from his works—and fortunately, perhaps, that is all we have to judge him from—there is a bitterness in him not found in orthodox Christianity, and not found in the Enlightenment. There is the full Renaissance contempt for the many, for the vulgar; Shakespeare is not in the least a democrat. There is no good evidence that Shakespeare was a Christian. He certainly has no Christian warmth, no Christian feeling for the will of God. Fate, the universe, the scheme of things seem to him not quite meant for man, not even meant to test man. He does not seem to believe in any way of changing this; he is clearly no man for good causes. He ends up extraordinarily close to Montaigne, who never went through as much turbulence and exuberance as did Shakespeare. The world is an interesting place, while you are young a rather exciting place, but not really a very nice place, and certainly not a sensible place.

The humanism of the early modern centuries is not an attitude that can be summed up clearly. As we have noted before, the systematist, the taxonomist, in the natural sciences does not expect his classifications to be like watertight compartments; he knows that in real life his species vary and shade into one another, and he knows that his own work is not perfect. Men who shared some of the humanist ways and beliefs were also in part theists, men in the direct Christian tradition, Sir Thomas More, for instance—he is, in fact, now Saint Thomas More; other humanists come pretty close to the rationalists we shall discuss in Chapter 10, come close to accepting a mechanistic view of the universe. Nevertheless, the humanist attitude is one that can be in part isolated and described. It differs from the historical Western Christianity of its own time in its distrust of

Scholasticism and the whole medieval complex and in its dislike for the more evangelical, Old Testament aspects of Protestantism; it differs from rationalism in that, persuaded though it is of the superiority of the natural to medieval formalism, sacerdotism, and convention, it clings, or seeks to cling, to the notion that man is not wholly a part of nature, that he is not just the cleverest of animals, *but actually not wholly an animal.*

The human being, the full, complex human being, is for the humanist a standard. To oversimplify, his slogan might be: Neither superhuman (theism) nor subhuman (mechanism). Humanism as a system of values, however, we have already noted, has the range, the spectrum, of concrete behavior that any of the other great Western systems of value have had. Man may be the measure of all things, but he is not a neat standard meter or yardstick. He can, for instance, get bestially drunk, or sparkle wittily and benignly on a few glasses of wine, or take a little wine for his stomach's sake, or abstain severely, and try to make others abstain, from all forms of alcoholic drinks. In the last four or five hundred years, the cultivated minority that has liked to call itself humanist has tended quite definitely toward the second of these practices; it has sought a pleasant temperance. But in the lustier days of the Renaissance humanism was not quite so confined. It could be rowdy with Rabelais, gentle with More, academic with Erasmus, frantically active with Cellini, skeptical and tolerant with Montaigne, even, at the court of Lorenzo the Magnificent in Florence, Neoplatonist with some very charming ladies and gentlemen.

The Political Attitudes of Humanism

The two centuries with which we are here concerned are commonly tagged in political history the "period of absolutism." It is a fact that in these centuries the modern territorial state emerged from the medieval state all over the Western world, even where, as in the Germanies, the territorial unit was not our nation-state, but the lands of a prince or a free city, perhaps no greater in area than its predecessor of the Middle Ages. The simplest practical manifestation of this change was the existence in the new territorial unit of a single chain of authority backed by a graded system of law courts and an armed force, police and military, paid, controlled, and administered by those at the top of the chain. Feudal remnants persisted almost everywhere, and this new state had by no means the neat table of organization and chain of command a modern army is supposed to work with. But the difference from the complex medieval nexus of rights and duties, of counterbalancing authorities and limiting custom, was very great. The new state—even if you take Soviet Russia as its ultimate embodiment—has never quite been the ruthlessly efficient, antlike, regimented society its many critics have made it out to be. But historically it originated at least in part from a demand for standardization and efficiency, for some curbing of the human tendency to stray, to be lazy, to be eccentric.

We may once more make use of a simple dualism. If you set up a polar contrast between authority (compulsion) and liberty (spontaneity), then in the balance the new state *in all its forms,* even when those forms are democratic, belongs on the side of authority. There are, of course, great historical and geographical variations, and some states can be put nearer the absolute pole of authoritarianism than others. But all of them have more political control over most individuals than was common in the Middle Ages.

Certainly the theory of the absolute state was put in these years about as nakedly as it has ever been put. (Modern totalitarian theory seems rather reluctant to come out flat-footedly against such nice words as *liberty* and *democracy.*) The English seventeenth-century philosopher Hobbes invented for the new state the term *Leviathan,* which has ever since been a reproach among libertarian writers. Hobbes made use of an old concept of political theory, with a long tradition of respectability from Rome through the Middle Ages, that of the contract. But he twisted this concept, which on the whole had been used on the libertarian side, so that it fits neatly into authoritarian theory. The contract had been supposed to put *limitations* on all parties to it, rulers and ruled alike, but above all to provide a kind of fence within which the individual could be on his own. With Hobbes, the contract is entered into by all individuals in order to avoid the horrible war of each against all that would prevail were man to remain in a "state of nature." (We shall have to return to this notion of a state of nature; for the present we may note that for Hobbes this was a most unpleasant state, so unpleasant that it had perhaps never existed.) These individuals contract among one another to create the sovereign, the authority that prescribes the laws all must obey and that substitutes order for the disorder of the state of nature. *But there is no contract between the individual or any group of individuals and the sovereign.* The sovereign is absolute, and the individual must obey the sovereign absolutely. Hobbes does indeed make one reservation: The sovereign is there to preserve order, to make the individual secure, and if he should fail in this purpose and the state become disorderly and life insecure, then the individual has the right to protect his own life and security as he can. But Hobbes's heart was not in this hypothetical reservation; it was very much in setting up a sovereign above the contract that created him.

The contract theory, as we shall see, was not altogether safe ground for the partisans of absolutism in its characteristic Renaissance form of monarchical absolutism, and indeed became one of the most useful of wedges for the introduction of democratic ideas. But there were whole arsenals of argument and theory available to the monarchical absolutists in the new historical erudition that was available to all educated men. The Bible—especially the Old Testament—Greek and Roman history, patristic literature (at least for the Catholics), and even the first and very uncritical beginnings of fields of knowledge like prehistory and ethnology were all drawn upon for arguments. That these same fields were increasingly drawn upon by opponents of monarchical absolutism in the seventeenth and eighteenth centuries need not surprise us. Common sense has long admitted what only the very tender-minded will deny, that the devil also can quote scripture.

It would be tedious and unprofitable to review a great number of these defenses of absolutism. A perfectly fair example is the patriarchal theory, which among English writers reached its perfection in the book Locke spent so much time tearing apart, Sir Robert Filmer's *Patriarcha*. The patriarchal theory is well worth study as an example of the complex and devious ways of what it is now fashionable to call "rationalization" or something even more scornful. We are obviously not here dealing with scientific theories, with cumulative knowledge. But we are dealing with an essential part of intellectual history, with an essential part of human relations.

The monarchist writer is seeking, in simplest terms, to put into words reasons why individuals should obey the government of the new centralized state, a government at least symbolically headed by a monarch. In the patriarchal theory he makes use of an analogy between the relation of father and son and that of monarch and subject. He is free with metaphors that call the subjects "children," "the flock," and the monarch "father," "shepherd," and the like. Now even to-day and in the United States, where it has been remarked by epigrammatic European travelers that the children often bring up their parents, the feeling that the normal child-parent relationship is one of obedience by the child is still very strong indeed. Its strength has varied in different times and places, but the weight of Western cultural inheritance in its favor is great. It seems to many just one of the facts of life. The Hebrew society in the midst of which the Old Testament was put together was a strongly patriarchal society in which the son was very firmly indeed under the control of the father. You can find suitable texts to emphasize the wickedness, the unnaturalness, of filial disobedience almost anywhere you look in the Old Testament. In Roman society too the *patria potestas,* the power of the father, was in republican days quite absolute, even extending to power over the son's life. Roman law as it filtered down into medieval society continued to carry this firm paternal authority. Christianity had made much use of the paternal power and the sentiments that had grown up around it. The metaphor of the shepherd and his flock was of long standing; the priests of the Church were called "father."

It was easy to extend the metaphor from the Church to the State, the more since the new model modern state in Catholic as well as in Protestant countries took over where it could the spiritual prestige, the human nexus of sentiments, which in the Middle Ages had centered in the Church as an institution. How deliberate this taking over was no one can be sure. Certainly men like Filmer were not of the mental disposition to say to themselves, "The Pope managed to make the idea of his being Holy Father very useful toward strengthening his power   Why can't we strengthen the power of the state if we keep hammering at the idea that our king is the Father of his people?" Quite the contrary, Filmer was certainly as persuaded of the truth of his theories as was Tom Paine of the truth of his quite contrary ones.

But the patriarchal theory is a set of arguments that depend for their persuasive force largely on the sentiments, not on the logical capacity and training, of those who accept them. It is a metaphor and not a theory, and can be made invalid, untrue, for anyone who simply says that he feels that a king is to him in no way a father. Especially if one stays within the terms of humanism or rationalism, one can say that there is only one kind of father-son relation, the kind that we should call biological and that they in those days would call natural. The patriarchal theory, as a justification of unquestioning obedience from subject to monarch (citizen to government), can be still more readily refuted, granted your sentiments flow the right way, by substituting another and contrary metaphor with its own claim to be the right theory. This the Lockeans did when they maintained that the true relation between subject and king was that of agency. The king is not the father of his subjects—he is their agent. He exists to give them good government, and if he fails to do so, they are fully justified in dismissing him as one would dismiss an agent who proved unsatisfactory. To most Americans, this agency theory of government will seem very sensible. But over the long course of Western history, there is no doubt that the patriarchal theory is much more representative of common opinion.

Indeed, the patriarchal theory in one form or another seems immortal in writing on social relations. We all know that, following the lead of Freud, modern psychologists have emphasized the importance of the parent-child relation. The psychologists, too, have to write on political theory, and once more they have recourse to the patriarchal theory. It is true they emphasize the son's ambivalent feeling of dependence on, and desire to revolt from, the father. It is true that they consider themselves scientists, and maintain that they are adding to the sum of cumulative knowledge. But read Mr. Geoffrey Gorer's recent book, *The American People*. Mr. Gorer explains our politics and our culture largely in terms of the father complex and the Oedipus complex, and comes up with a wonderfully Freudian explanation of the young American male's fondness for milk. It is highly likely that in the twenty-third century Mr. Gorer's adaptation of the age-old father analogy will seem at least as silly as Sir Robert Filmer's does now.

There were other arguments in favor of absolute monarchy. One went back to Roman precedent, not of the Republic, but of the later Empire, when the Roman state was itself well streamlined with a bureaucracy and an absolute prince at its head. A favorite tag was *quod principi placuit, legis habet vigorem*—"what has pleased the prince has the force of law." This put the matter with excessive baldness, and was perhaps the most irritating of arguments from the point of view of the republicans.

The consecrated phrase, however, the one that has gone down into history, is the "divine right of kings." The king is, in no blasphemous sense, God on earth; in the language of the theory, he is God's deputy on earth, and to oppose his will is to oppose God's will, which is indeed blasphemy. He is God's anointed—and indeed by medieval precedents European kings received at their coronation ceremony a special anointment with a consecrated oil. Most of the rest of the arsenal of arguments for royal absolutism could, of course, be subsumed under this one.

It is significant that in all these defenses of the new absolutism the basic arguments are all traditional. The notion of contract is merely given a slight twist, and you have Hobbes's Leviathan instead of the Christian feudal state of John of Salisbury. The notion of the spiritual shepherd, the Christian father, is given another twist and you have the father-king who cannot be disobeyed.

Admirers of the Middle Ages are particularly shocked by what they regard as the Renaissance perversion of the medieval doctrine of the divine right of kings. In the medieval doctrine, they maintain—and quite rightly as far as the words go—that the ruler rules by divine right as long as he rules as God wants him to; he rules by divine right not just in the sense of right as possession, an incontrovertible claim, but in the sense of right as morally just. When he rules wickedly and not in accordance with divine right, then he has no right to rule, and his subjects are released from their duty of obedience and justified in revolting. At this point we should inevitably inquire, who judges whether a king is ruling in accordance with God's intentions? Suppose one group in the state says the king does so rule, and another says he doesn't. How do we know which is right? The medieval and indeed the Renaissance mind could answer these questions much more serenely than we can, for they were not yet disturbed by the idea that God's intentions were by no means as clear as scientific truth, which of course could never be found in such problems. The medieval *and the humanist mind* were both firmly in the habit of believing that God's will was as clear as anything on earth.

The argument we nowadays, at least in English-speaking countries, regard as a clincher is never used clearly. This is the argument that the new-style monarchic state is more efficient than the old, that the monarch has to have absolute power in order to sweep up the debris of feudal autonomous areas, in order to rationalize, standardize, so that the new middle-class businessmen can sell in a wider market and with greater security and greater convenience. The justification of an institution by its *utility,* an argument familiar enough to us, does indeed crop up in defense of monarchy, even so far back as Pierre Dubois in the early fourteenth century. But in most of the writers here considered it is mixed with many other arguments. The French *politiques,* writers who in the religious wars of the late sixteenth century put the nation as represented by the Crown ahead of both Catholic and Protestant parties, seem to have some such modern notions as might be labeled nationalistic in the back of their minds. But they do not speak our language.

One of the best of them is Jean Bodin, who is indeed often regarded as rather more than a *politique*. Bodin was a scholar-humanist of wide learning, and with many interests. He has an important place in the history of historical writing as one of the first writers to concern himself with systematic historical methods. In political theory, he is perhaps the most balanced writer on the vexed subject of sovereignty. He is by inclination a moderate and a sensible man. He wrote in the late sixteenth century, after the prestige of Aristotle had rebounded from the first humanist disparagement, and he had the benefit of the abundant common sense evident in Aristotle's politics. Bodin comes out in the end as a defender of the absolutism of the sovereign prince. As the maker of laws, according to Bodin, the sovereign was—because he had to be—above laws. But Bodin hastens to qualify this as a legal principle only; morally, of course, the prince is bound by the law of God and the law of nature, and by the decencies. If he does not so abide he is a tyrant, though apparently still a sovereign. Bodin too brings in the patriarchal argument, reinforced by the Roman *patria potestas,* and the usual arsenal of Biblical quotations.

It would not be fair to say that all the political thought of the humanists and the classicists of the early modern centuries was on the side of absolutism. From the start of the revival of Greek and Roman classics in the Renaissance sense, there is discernible an attitude that can be followed as a clear thread in the Western political tradition right down into the French Revolution, which made Brutus one of its heroes. This is the tradition of *classical republicanism,* with its heroes from Livy, its Roman hatred of kings—and, often, its Roman distrust of *mobile vulgus,* the inconstant common people.

We have again come up against a word that has had a history and therefore can be ambiguous. We Americans are likely to think that "republican" is really just another way of saying "democrat"—and this entirely apart from our liberals' fondness for saying that our two parties, Republican and Democrat with capital letters, are as alike as Tweedledum and Tweedledee. But the *res publica Romana* was no more than the Roman political organization, which was—and remained right through to the founding of the Empire—politically and socially aristocratic. This tradition of aristocratic republicanism, which had little ground to work on in the Middle Ages, began to thrive in the Renaissance. From its very nature it could hardly be a mass belief. It has been a creed above all among artists and intellectuals, especially artists and intellectuals of good birth, an assumption of aristocrats. It is a creed that, with such holders, naturally enough conforms to no simple, common, stereotyped pattern. Classical republicanism is almost always libertarian rather than collectivist, or socialistic; or at any rate, where it emphasizes that the necessary order and discipline of a society involves care for the lower classes, it is the collectivism of *noblesse oblige,* of what nineteenth-century Englishmen called "Tory democracy." Where you do find men working toward some basic and radical reform of society to get rid of poverty through the efforts of the poor, you will find that these men are in these early modern centuries inspired rather by religion than by humanism, and by a violently sectarian kind of religion.

One kind of humanist republicanism is really at heart directed against a specific monarchy. In the late sixteenth century political thought in France was sharpened by the great civil wars of religion, and a body of theory resulted that has on the surface a pretty democratic look. Huguenots like Etienne de la Boétie and François Hotman came out firmly against all theories of monarchical absolutism, and urged instead that ultimate authority lies in the hands of the people The author of the pamphlet *Vindiciae contra Tyrannos*—he was probably du Plessis-Mornay—brought in the contract theory and much scriptural and medieval history to justify actual revolt and even tyrannicide You can extract from this literature something very close to what came to be the conventional eighteenth-century doctrine of the rights of man, the need for constitutional government in the hands of a representative parliamentary body, the supremacy of the law, and so on. Yet the temper of these works is definitely not eighteenth century. They *sound* medieval, if only because of their usual reliance on arguments from precedent, historical or Biblical, and their rather heavy scholarship. These men are by no means rabble rousers. They have not the popular touch, moved though they are by the justice of their cause. One feels that they are inevitably antimonarchical because the French monarchy was against them, but republican also by necessity, since they have no other choice. Some of them set up a principle of "natural leadership." They are a long, long way from Thomas Paine, or even Benjamin Franklin; they are republicans, not democrats.

Yet another pattern is nearer the center of this aristocratic republicanism, nearer in the sense of setting a pattern that survived into the nineteenth century in men like Lord Byron and even into the twentieth in a Wilfred Scawen Blunt or that curious American representative of the type, the late John Jay Chapman. Algernon Sydney, an Englishman of noble family who died on the scaffold in 1683, a martyr to republicanism, is an admirable example. His *Discourses Concerning Government* was not published until 1698, and was much read in the next century. It is full of Roman history, seen in the glow of gentlemanliness that has long accompanied British classicism. It attacks divine right and defends popular sovereignty. It has no radical social doctrines—indeed it talks the language of moderate constitutionalism, and had Sydney lived into the next century he might well have been a good moderate whig with no "republican nonsense." Sydney is against the upstart Stuarts with their doctrines of divine right, and in favor of an English ruling class that will have all the Roman virtues and none of the Roman vices.

Milton himself belongs in this group of aristocratic republicans, as far as his politics goes. He is a humanist by taste and training, and rather on the spare than on the exuberant side. His most famous prose writing is doubtless the *Areopagitica,* one of the classic defenses of liberty of speech and its train of attendant liberties. There is no doubt a timelessness about any eloquent defense of freedom of speech in Western culture, which has hardly ever been absolutist enough not to nourish some spark of this freedom. But it is very doubtful if Milton even in this pamphlet was anticipating laissez-faire notions of the usefulness of individual freedom. At any rate, it is an interesting if very delicate exercise in intellectual history to read together and compare the *Areopagitica* and John Mill's *On Liberty* of 1859.

Milton's rolling classic eloquence may get in the way of an understanding of what he is about; but even when this allowance is made, he seems to be arguing for freedom for the elect, for the humanist, for men like himself, and not, like Mill, for freedom even for the crank, the mistaken, the ignorant—in short, the people.

The aristocratic quality in Milton's political and moral ideas is quite clear in his lesser writings, in the *Eikonoklastes* or the *Ready and Easy Way to Establish a Free Commonwealth*—the latter an unsuccessful attempt to prevent the recall of King Charles II. Of course, Milton hated the sectaries and their uncouth hopes for heaven on earth, and he was disillusioned by the failure of moderate Puritanism to establish a comfortable halfway house between the Anglicans and the millenarian sects. Like many another refined and cultivated defender of individual liberty, Milton in the end proved that it was refinement and cultivation he really meant to defend, and not the liberty of men who were coarse and unthinking. He came in the end so much to distrust common men voting by head, or by pressure groups, that in his plan for a commonwealth he made the legislature a self-perpetuating body with lifetime tenure of office, a kind of House of Lords without peerage.

But the most fully rounded work of this school of humanists with leanings, not precisely toward the Left, but at any rate toward a more popular form of constitutional government, is that of another seventeenth-century Englishman, the *Oceana* of James Harrington. In form this is an imaginary commonwealth, a Utopia, a form perhaps dictated by the need to evade the censorship of the new dictator Cromwell in the year of its publication, 1656. It is a treatise on government, a very thoughtful one in which the importance of the distribution of wealth and the class structure is recognized very specifically. It recommends a constitutional state with proper balance of interests, and including a senate of natural aristocrats and a popular representative body to approve or reject the proposals of the senate. Harrington has many modern ideas, among them the secret ballot and universal compulsory education. Indeed, the *Oceana* might well be classified as the work of a rationalist, and its influence on the next century was great.

But Harrington has the classical style, the classical set of mind, and seems in this book rather to sum up the best thought of the politically moderate humanists than to break any new paths.

Of necessity, the category of humanists cannot be as neat as that of the other two strains in the early modern centuries, the Protestants and the rationalists. In the search for standards, for an authority, which at all times in Western history has been one of the main activities of the intellectual classes (even when they thought they were just casting off *all* authorities), the humanist appeal to something peculiarly *human*—not divine, not animal—has tended in practice to have as its first consequences a bewildering variety of possible standards and authorities. For, in simple language, *human* is a blanket word that can stretch to cover almost anything—including the divine and the animal.

Simply for convenience, and knowing well that our systematic work of classification must be most imperfect, we may separate these humanists of the sixteenth and seventeenth centuries roughly into the groups we christened "exuberant" and "spare." Most of the earliest are in some senses exuberant, even when they are sober scholars; and by the seventeenth century most of the men who are predominantly interested in humanism are of the spare or disciplined sort. Crudely, but at least simply, it may be said that predominantly the earlier men who went back to Greece and Rome found there freedom for the individual to be himself, to follow his own bent even if that bent were a series of contortions; and that the later men, for whom the first had made the way to Greece and Rome easy, indeed a part of ordinary schoolwork, found there discipline, quiet, order, simplicity. The first group tended to believe that the many would let the few be free to cultivate their uniqueness—or they were just not interested in the many; the second, who had known the horrors of the wars of religion, tended to worry a great deal about the masses, and the ways of keeping them in a decent place—they were, in short, monarchists and authoritarians. But neither group was really passionately and actively interested in what we should now call the democratic cause. Even that subbranch of the classical humanists, the aristocratic republicans like Algernon Sydney, were not democrats.

The humanists have left imperishable works of art. They had their part in the destruction of medieval attitudes, and, in a positive way, in the establishment of the modern territorial state with its standardization and its drive toward efficiency. Still, on the whole, we have less of the humanists in us than the textbooks usually tell us. The humanists were by no means the major architects of the modern world, nor the makers of the modern mind. Insofar as these two centuries went to make us what we are, by far the most important makers were the Protestants, the rationalists, and the scientists.

Making the Modern World ~ II

—————————————————————————————PROTESTANTISM

MARTIN LUTHER was an Augustinian monk. There is some appro-
priateness—though, of course, no causal connection—in this faint link
between the two men. For, as we have seen, though St. Augustine's
life work made him one of the pillars of the Catholic Church, there
is in his personality that mystical straining for perfection which has
always presented problems to the less saintly persons who have to run
things on this earth. The Protestant movement is, in one very important sense, simply another manifestation of what we have previously
analyzed as the persistent Christian tension between this world and
the next, the real and the ideal. We moderns hardly need reminding
that Luther, Calvin, and Zwingli headed movements that differed
greatly in aims and organization from medieval attempts to reform
existing religious practices. For one thing, they succeeded in establishing churches, where Wycliffe and Hus failed. Or, from another point
of view, they were not, like the mendicant friars, tamed and absorbed
into the Catholic Church.

We hardly need reminding of the part played by economic institutions, by nationalism, by the personalities of the leaders in dif-
ferentiating the Protestant Revolt from medieval reform movements.
We rather need reminding that, no matter how deep its economic and
political causes, Protestantism won men's hearts and minds by appeals
to Christian tradition. Even formally—and form is by no means

298

unimportant—this is true. The Protestant reformers all insisted that they were not innovating, but were going back to Jesus and the early Church, the *real* Christian Church. It was Rome, they maintained, that had changed, by corrupting it, the *true* Christian tradition. The Protestant reformers believed quite sincerely that theirs was an *imitatio Christi,* an imitation of Christ. They did not think they were changing but restoring, and they would have been astonished and puzzled to be told they were agents of progress.

Theirs was, as a performance visible to a neutral observer, an extremely different imitation from that of St. Francis. If Protestantism is simply one manifestation of the Christian effort to best the old Adam in men, we must remind ourselves that there are many ways in which the old Adam comes out, and many ways of trying to best him. We must ask ourselves what was new in the Protestantism of the early sixteenth century—new even though its makers thought it was old. These elements of novelty will go a long way toward explaining why the Protestant groups became schismatic churches instead of mere heretical groups leading a more or less underground existence, like the Lollards and the Hussites.

But we must first record the fact that the Roman Catholic Church itself was subject in the fourteenth and above all in the fifteenth century to pressures from the time of troubles that then marked a decline of medieval culture. Just as the church buildings took on the flamboyancy of the overripe Gothic, so the life of the Church grew more worldly, more decadent, lost that careful balance of the age of Aquinas. The Schoolmen grew emptily disputatious, the monastic orders grew richer, unpriestly priests grew more numerous, or at least more conspicuous. As a general rule, we may say that no institution is as bad as those who attack it—especially if they attack it successfully—make out. The old regime in France was not nearly as bad as the French Revolutionists made out; George III was by no means the tyrant American Revolutionists painted him. The Church of Pope Alexander VI (Rodrigo Borgia) was by no means as immoral as that scandalous pope, by no means the sink of iniquity it appears in Protestant propaganda. Like our newspapers, history loves the headlines; but the

299

routine and not newsworthy still goes on. Many a quiet fifteenth-century priest or monk led quite as Christian a life as his thirteenth-century predecessors.

Still, there was a real decline in the level, and certainly in the peaks, of Christian life and institutions in the last years of the Middle Ages. Efforts were made to stem this decline. There were the open revolts anticipating that of Luther, notably that of Wycliffe in England and Hus in Bohemia. Many of the ideas, many of the organizing methods used by later Protestants are to be found in these movements, and there is undoubtedly here what the historian rather loosely calls "influence." Did not Luther himself, perhaps reluctantly, acknowledge his debt to Hus?

Second, there was the movement to reform the Church from within by methods we should today call constitutional, the Conciliar Movement of the fifteenth century, which produced many writings held in high esteem by the historian of political thought. These clerical intellectuals of the late Middle Ages, of whom Jean Gerson may stand as a type, were still clearly working within a frame of medieval ideas. You can extract from Gerson something like the standard recipe of a mixed constitution, mingling elements of monarchy, aristocracy, and a polite democracy. This recipe has been attractive to moderate, sensible men from Aristotle to Montesquieu and Victorian Englishmen. Gerson and his fellows have the full academic faith in the quiet "ought," the full medieval belief that God has really ordained the right running of the universe so clearly that no reasonable person can fail to understand it. Since in fact they did meet in councils that came into active conflict with popes, the men of the Conciliar Movement did their bit toward preparing the way for the Reformation. They did not succeed in making the pope subject to a parliament-like group of the clergy, but they did challenge the growing power of the Roman bureaucracy. Their words, their attitudes, however, lacked the bite, the fierceness, the frank appeal to popular passions of Luther's; they lacked the revolutionary intensity of Calvin's; they lacked the touch—so familiar to us today—of the hard-boiled realist Machiavelli. All this is perhaps to say not that

Gerson and his colleagues were medieval rather than modern, but merely that they were examples of that constant Western phenomenon, the moderate idealist and reformer, the man of words, nice words.

Words, however, do things in this world of human relations. They do not do things all by themselves, any more than the gas in an internal combustion engine explodes by itself. We have already (see Chapter I) refused to be drawn deeply into the contemporary form of the futile debate over the priority of the chicken or the egg—that is, the debate over the economic interpretation of history. We need not ask whether Protestant ideas made economic changes or economic changes made Protestant ideas. The reader should be warned, however, that the Protestant Reformation is one of the great battlegrounds of the debate over economic determinism. From the point of view taken in this book, economic changes, changes in the way men of Western society did their daily work, are an important element in the whole social situation in which the Protestant Reformation proved a success. They are, in medical terms worth the reader's trip to the dictionary, part of a *syndrome* of which we do not fully understand the *etiology*. Grave changes like those involved in turning a self-sufficing manorial economy into a money economy based on extensive trade we should expect to be accompanied by, and followed by, grave changes in all human life. We should not expect them necessarily to be accompanied by, or followed by, a Protestant Reformation, as in fact they were. Similar changes in simple non-European economies in recent times—in Japan, for instance—have not been accompanied by a Protestant Reformation but by quite other changes.

The simplest economic explanation of the Protestant Revolution well antedates Marx, and is perhaps most vigorously stated by the English radical William Cobbett, who lived at the turn of the eighteenth into the nineteenth century. The Catholic Church everywhere, so runs this explanation, had over the pious medieval centuries grown enormously wealthy from bequests of rich donors anxious to ensure a place for themselves in heaven. Kings, princes, and their followers, the ruling classes in short, always in need of money, looked enviously at this wealth. They seized upon the abstract ideas of Luther and his co-workers as a means of making the spoliation of the clergy seem respectable in the eyes of the world. They were indebted heavily to the new merchant and banking class, and were able to pay them off in part with lands and other property seized from the Church. Thus was created a new, money-hungry ruling class, out of which came our modern capitalists.

This whole explanation is too neatly tailored to English experience. In Germany, the territorial princes were the chief gainers from the expropriation of the Roman Catholic Church. In France, where the Reformation, though not triumphant, played a very important part, the economic stakes were not nearly so clear. Furthermore, there is no evidence that in most parts of Europe that remained Catholic the ruling classes were less needy or less greedy than in those parts that turned Protestant. The Italian princes needed money as badly as did the German; even the Spanish Crown saw the wealth of the New World sift away and was in chronic financial trouble. Obviously we need a subtler explanation. This the Marxists have provided.

According to the Marxist interpretation, there is first a whole series of material economic changes, adding up to a new trading economy. (Let us, for the moment, not ask what caused these elemental changes.) The people who make this new economy run, or at least who benefit by it, are the money men, the traders, the first of a class destined to fame or power, the *bourgeoisie*. These men cannot get on with the older feudal ruling class, whose habits of mind and body are fixed by their position as landed gentlemen. The older feudal class taxes the trader, scorns him, cheats him, and helps the Church try to enforce those class notions of fair price, those prohibitions of interest in the name of usury, the whole medieval attitude toward business we have earlier analyzed (see p. 205). The new trader wants simply to buy in the cheapest and sell in the dearest markets. He does not want to be father and protector of his workmen; he just wants to be their employer. He is already by 1500 the modern businessman in embryo—a good, big embryo. Naturally he makes use of Protestantism against a Church that tries to enforce economic ways contrary to his interests. Naturally Protestantism is successful in parts of Europe where the new businessmen are most prosperous, a failure where they are least so. Progressive England and Holland go Protestant, for example; backward Spain and Naples stay Catholic.

Another fillip is added to the economic interpretation by the distinguished German sociologist Max Weber. Weber accepts part of the Marxist explanation, in particular its emphasis on the class struggle, and on the adoption of Protestantism by the rising middle classes. But he maintains that the Protestant attitude toward life, Protestant ethical ideals, were not just seized upon by greedy money-makers as an excuse for despoiling the Catholic Church (the Cobbett thesis). He maintains that these Protestant ideas molded the people who adopted them, made them more fit to make money, made them into the middle class we all know. Luther's idea that each man had a vocation from God, that work in that vocation was God's will, helped form this businessman's ethics. But Calvin was the real source of these ethics, and it was in Calvinist countries that the capital which financed the later Industrial Revolution was saved in these early centuries. Calvinism not only preached the dignity of labor. It insisted on labor, since the devil lies in wait for idle hands, and since work is a part of man's debt to an overpowering God. Success in business was a sign of God's favor. Interest, of course, was quite legitimate. So your Calvinist works hard and produces income. But on the side of outgo, Calvinism discouraged luxury, ostentation, sport, decoration of churches—in short, it discouraged spending, except for the necessities of virtuous but solid living. Income is greater than outgo, so your Calvinist saves. This saving is capital, plowed back into the business. So the Calvinist becomes a capitalist, a rich man—and he will go to heaven, too. More than that, he has the pleasing assurance that the heavily indebted nobleman who lorded it over him so unpleasantly the other day will not only die poor, but, since he is not a Calvinist, will go to hell.

We have in the last few sentences somewhat vulgarized Weber's thesis, but in the main lines we have reproduced it clearly enough. Altogether, the arguments for *some* economic interpretation of Protes-

tant origins and growth are pretty convincing. Nevertheless, something else is necessary. Economic symptoms, even with subtly sociological and psychological additions thereto, do not wholly exhaust the
syndrome. Moreover, were Protestantism and Capitalism rigorously
linked together, they would at all times coincide, so that a map of
Europe showing the newer, richer banking and trading centers would
coincide with a map showing the growth of Protestantism. There
has never been such complete coincidence, even after 1800, when
Protestantism and Industrialism *tended* to coincide geographically. In
the early modern period, before the Lutheran outburst, the great
centers of the new economy, Milan, Florence, Augsburg, the Low
Countries, were in regions little affected by pre-Protestant movements.
And after Luther, all through the sixteenth century, northern and
central Italy, the Catholic Netherlands, the Rhineland, and Catholic
northern France continued to be leaders of the new economy. Calvinism certainly helped maintain and strengthen the spirit of capitalism; but the capitalist ethics of Calvinism by no means explains the
success of the Protestant movement. It is but one of the sources of
Protestant success.

Another source is the complex of habits, interests, and sentiments
we call nationalism, one of the most powerful forces in the modern
world. Nationalism is a subject to which we shall return. Here it
will be enough to suggest that the place of nationalism in the
Protestant Reformation may be regarded under two heads—the
nationalism of the ruling groups, and the nationalism of the great
masses.

One can readily be cynical about the motives of makers of
Protestantism like Henry VIII of England. After the fashion of his
newly intellectual times, Henry aspired to be an all-around man,
scholar as well as athlete and statesman. He accordingly composed
(or had a ghost writer compose) a defense of Catholicism against
Luther's recent pamphlet on *The Babylonish Captivity of the Church,*
and was rewarded by the pope with the official title of *Defensor Fidei,*
"Defender of the Faith." He then proceeded to break with the
Roman Catholic Church and set up what became the Church of

England (Protestant Episcopal). In the process of change, as we have indicated, much of the corporate wealth of the Roman Church in England went to endow the new Tudor nobility and gentry, supporters of the Tudor monarchy. Henry himself became the head of the English Church, a pope of sorts in his own right. Similar histories would hold for dozens of German princelets.

Yet we must beware of the narrow economic motivation. These rulers and their followers were not merely lining their pockets; they were also clearing the way for the new bureaucratic state, eliminating clerical privileges, canon law, that whole claim of the Catholic Church to be at a certain point wholly free from lay control. These new Protestant rulers sought to build up churches that would be, so to speak, the moral police force of the state. But if power and wealth were both at stake for these rulers, why not also their conscience? Men like Henry VIII, or the German Philip of Hesse who stood by Luther, were good patriots, who really believed that corrupt Italians were exploiting the souls as well as the bodies of their countrymen. Their patriotism seems so clearly in accord with their worldly interests that we incline to discount it; whereas John Hodge and his German fellow man-in-the-street could satisfy little more than their emotions by railing at the papists, and we therefore somehow feel they were sincere. But surely one can believe, even when one profits?

The common people clearly did satisfy their emotions. Notably in England, Scotland, Holland, and Germany, Protestantism came to identify itself thoroughly with the "in-group" of the territory. From Luther's own pamphlets—especially those written in German—from most of the literature of the conflict, indeed, there sounds the love and praise for Germany, the hatred and contempt for "foreigners"—in this case Italians—that we have heard now for so many generations:

> For Rome is the greatest thief and robber that has ever appeared on earth, or ever will. . . . Poor Germans that we are—we have been deceived! *We were born to be masters,* and we have been compelled to bow the head beneath the yoke of our tyrants. . . . It is time the glorious Teutonic people should cease to be the puppet of the Roman pontiff.

The same note is sounded, perhaps a bit less blatantly, in other Protestant lands. Later, and defensively, certain lands begin to identify patriotism and Catholicism. This is notably true of subject nationalities, like the Irish and the Poles. But the Roman Catholic Church has always maintained an international organization, an organization with many of the attributes of state-power. Protestantism has never achieved such an organization; its international meetings are groups, conferences, leagues, with no shred of what is called "sovereignty" or even authority. Thus Protestantism has been identified with certain given territorial entities, and with no true international entity.

Protestantism, then, found in the sixteenth century many sources of strength that were lacking in earlier movements of reform. Above all, Protestantism in the sixteenth century took on many forms, adapted itself to many different concrete situations in different parts of the West, so that no one formula can explain its success. Some of its doctrines, some of the ways of life it encouraged, were doctrines and ways that made the life of the businessman, the new *bourgeois*, easier. Protestantism owes something to capitalism. Other doctrines made it easier for rulers and their followers to grow in wealth and power. Protestantism owes something to simpler and older economic and political drives. Protestantism came to reinforce the common language, common culture, common *behavior* of the in-groups we call nations, in-groups already clearly marked as such even in the thirteenth century. Protestantism came to an open and successful break with a Roman Catholic Church, which for several centuries had had its own time of troubles, its own conciliar movement, its Babylonian captivity, its discontented intellectuals, its crude careerists, its conspicuously worldly leaders. Luther may have been no stronger than Wycliffe or Hus; his opponents were almost certainly weaker than theirs.

What has become, if we accept this interpretation, of the rightness, the progressiveness, the modernity and democracy of the Protestant movement? Isn't the Protestant Reformation one of the great landmarks in Western history? Above all, did not the Protestants side with individual freedom and democratic self-rule, the Catholics with authority and privilege, and weren't the Protestants therefore modern, the Catholics retarded and medieval?

Now these questions do suggest an element lacking in our previous analysis of the sources of Protestantism. One of the livest and most abundant of those sources was the perennial human capacity for being moved by high ethical ideals. Most Protestant movements did enlist this most human force on their side, along with other forces the realist and the cynic like to focus on. For a period disastrous to the cause of the religious unity of the West, the Roman Catholic Church made no successful, concerted effort to enlist this moral force on its own side; and when, with St. Ignatius Loyola and the Catholic Reformation, the Church did make such an effort, it was too late to preserve Western religious unity.

Since Protestantism was an attack on established institutions, part of its vocabulary was the vocabulary of resistance to authority, part of its appeal was an appeal to the individual, to his rights and his liberty, and against authority. Luther appealed from good works, which are prescribed by authority, to faith, which is locked in the bosom of the individual. There is a certain congruence between the Protestant appeal to the individual (men did not then talk of "individualism") and the nineteenth-century appeal to individualism. Furthermore, as we have noted, Protestantism in its actual working out helped the individual initiative of the capitalist businessman; it helped break down the medieval feudal nexus in politics, and made the way easier for the more streamlined and efficient royal bureaucratic state.

To attempt to understand in concrete territorial cases the reasons for the success or failure of Protestantism (of any and all kinds) against Catholicism is a fascinating exercise in the still immature social sciences. All the variables we have discussed are at work in any one case, and many more. There is clearly no simple litmus-paper test. Blonds did not all turn Protestant, nor brunets all stay Catholic; Northerners did not all accept Protestantism, nor did Southerners all reject it; "Germanic" peoples were not wholly Protestants, nor were

"Latin" peoples wholly Catholic; enterprisers, businessmen, did not all turn Protestant, farmers and peasants did not all stay Catholic.

Yet some variables are more important than others. To this writer, the concrete instances of England, Ireland, France, the Low Countries, and the Germanies indicate that where Protestantism became identified with the dominant in-group feeling (or nationalism) it prevailed, and where it did not, it failed. In France, for instance, Protestantism had great strength in the sixteenth century. Calvin himself was a Frenchman and, despite common American notions about the French national character, Frenchmen make as good Puritans as any others. But the French Crown, the focus of French patriotism, had nothing of importance to gain from a split with Rome; it already possessed great independence. Most Frenchmen never identified Frenchness with Protestantism, as most north Germans identified Protestantism with Germanness. Indeed, toward the end of the civil wars in sixteenth-century France, most middle-of-the-road Frenchmen identified Protestantism with treason to France. Again, Calvinism meant patriotism to the Dutch, and resistance to Calvinism, or loyalty to the Catholic faith, meant patriotism to those unassimilated, indeed rival, southern provinces of the Low Countries which were to become independent modern Belgium. Incidentally, this contrast between Protestant Holland and Catholic Belgium is an interesting one for the simple economic determinist to grapple with, since these small contiguous areas have both been trading and industrial centers for centuries, have both had, in short, very similar economies.

There is a great gap between sixteenth-century Protestantism and the nineteenth-century individualism of the Americans who wrote textbooks equating the two. The men who made Protestantism, especially Luther and Calvin, were not really modern in spirit (the term *modern* is not used in this book in praise or blame, but merely to indicate attributes of Western culture since roughly 1700), and they certainly did not believe in freedom. Protestantism, historically considered, can look quite medieval. Rightly held to be one of the forces that made the modern world, Protestantism turned modern almost in spite of itself and its leaders. Protestantism was in nature and purpose a last medieval, a last great purely Christian, effort to justify in action God's ways to man.

The Nature of Protestantism

There are, in fact, many Protestantisms. The ways of the High-Church Episcopalian have little in common with those of the convinced Unitarian or those of a primitive fundamentalist. We shall shortly attempt some classification of the varieties of Protestantism as they appear in the sixteenth and seventeenth century. Yet some things can be predicated of Protestantism as a whole. Most of these things are negative things, but one very important one is positive.

The Protestant movement displays a special form of the tension, the contradiction we have noted in other forms of Western culture. Protestantism was a revolt against an established authority possessing the external attributes (organization, laws, ritual, tradition) of authority. It asked men to *disbelieve and disobey*. It did indeed, and most earnestly, ask them to believe in better things and obey better men, better laws; its most successful advocates, Luther and Calvin, insisted that what they called on men to believe and obey was the true Christianity of Jesus, and no new thing. But no Protestant of the early years could wholly disavow the fact of his rebellion, a rebellion each individual had to decide to make. Luther, who had the man of action's indifference toward philosophical consistency, an indifference that seems to the logical person almost a kind of stupidity, frankly put the case for revolt in its most risky terms.

Since the papist priest has come as an obstacle between man and God, runs Luther's appeal, let us get rid of anything that might again prove such an obstacle; let every man be his own priest. It is presumptuous to suppose that God the all-powerful and all-knowing would let any such petty human device as the Church interfere with his relations with his own creatures. Moreover, God had made his intentions clear in the Bible, which each man could read for himself without priestly intermediary. With some of the theological implications of this famous Lutheran appeal to the conscience of the individual we shall come in a moment. Politically and morally, the Luther who preached thus was preaching anarchy, was telling each man to listen to something inside himself and disregard all outside himself—law, custom, tradition, the Christian inheritance of the Middle Ages. But really—and some things in this world are disconcertingly simple—Luther was telling the man to listen to what his conscience, heart, Germanness, whole soul prompted, in the firm, naive, and most human belief that this prompting would be wholly consonant with what conscience, heart, Germanness, and whole soul kept hammering into Luther himself. Luther appealed to free men because he believed free men were all Luthers—quieter little Luthers, not indeed so gifted, but still Luthers. When during the Peasants' Revolt he began to discover that free men wanted very different things, wanted social and economic equality, wanted heaven on earth as soon as possible, wanted something more done about the problems of sex than just letting priests marry, wanted a lot he did not want them to want, then Luther willingly supplied some intermediary between God and these benighted men. He provided the Lutheran Church, which has its own laws, dogmas, bishops, priests—and its own practical doctrine of good works. Justification by faith could never, to Luther, justify Anabaptism or antinomianism. The rebel against authority ended by building up his own authority.

Many, perhaps most Protestants of the earlier years would have been outraged or baffled by our last paragraphs. They did not think of their movement as an attempt to free men so that they could somehow spin anew their fate from their own inner resources; they thought of their movement as getting men back under the right authority, the right master, God. The Roman Catholic Church had perverted God's word, but fortunately that word was available, ready for translation into the living languages of Europe. With the Bible available in the vernacular, the priest no longer had the monopoly he had enjoyed when only a Latin version existed. The great reformers, Wycliffe, Hus, Luther, Calvin, all made possible the wide circulation of the Bible in their native tongues. The printing press by the sixteenth century had begun to make something like mass production of Bibles possible. Any reader could now lay his hands on a Bible. The Bible was thus to be the real, the incontrovertible authority, God's words, not man's.

Those who still believe that reading the Bible is a solution for the problem of liberty and authority are a minority we rather patronizingly call fundamentalists. From the point of view we have deliberately assumed in this book, it is clear that the Bible is not what most people mean by an authority. If you get into a dispute about the population of New York City at the last census, you can find an authority in any one of a dozen reference books. If you get into a dispute about the real meaning of the Last Supper, you can nourish your argument from the Bible, but you certainly won't settle it. In oversimple terms, men seem to have found in the Bible what they were looking for. The Protestant appeal to the Bible pushed the search for authority back just one more step; *somebody* had to say what the Bible meant on given points, *somebody* had to do the kind of thing the Fathers, Canon Law, the Roman Church had done long ago. Not the Bible, but the interpreters of the Bible, provided authority. Once more, the nonconformist had to have his own conformity.

Such conformity is the common fate of all revolutionists of this world, if they survive their revolution. In practice it has usually been easy for political revolutionists, even economic revolutionists, to rebuild an authority to take the place of the one they rebelled against; Jacobin France and Bolshevik Russia soon made obedience respectable. But for some reason, perhaps in truth because of the high level of aspiration to eternal truth with which the theologian and philosopher work, the Protestant Revolution has never quite so successfully lived down its revolutionary origins. It has preserved alive, at least in its borders, in its depths, the impossible tension of its birth. It would have men justified only in their faith, it would see none but free men; but it would also have an orderly, a disciplined world. Put from the Catholic point of view, as Bossuet for instance put it, this means that Protestantism is always spawning new sects, protesting against the original protesters, world without end, that Protestantism can have no unity because it has no principle of authority. Put more sympathetically, perhaps, it is that Protestantism is the true heir of the striving for an unearthly perfection on earth, the striving that in medieval Christianity was expressed in mystic flight, in crusades, and in monastic reform, the eternal heresy. Or *was* the true heir, until the Enlightenment brought another, more worldly, promise.

For—and this is a first negative generalization—the major Protestant faiths accepted the old Christian dogma of original sin. Calvin, we know, intensified the gloomier side of the Catholic view of animal man. Extreme Calvinism is most pessimistic about man's ability to lead the good life in this world. Luther's doctrine of justification by faith was by no means an affirmation that men are born good, that they can by following their natural desires find the best guide to life. Even at his most anarchical moments, early in his struggle with Rome, Luther held to the doctrine of man's natural weakness. It is God who gives man faith, who *makes* him and *keeps* him good. On the periphery of Protestantism, among some of the wilder sects, you will find anticipations of the later doctrine of the natural goodness of man. Among the so-called antinomians you will find an open anarchism, the doctrine that no law, no prescription, no ritual should bind the free human spirit in the individual, since all such laws, prescriptions, rituals, are simply fixed formulations that straightjacket the infinitely various human soul. Now antinomianism and later ideas of the natural goodness of man may well be affiliated; but even the antinomians talk the language of Christian theology. This human spirit that cannot rightfully be caged is also the divine spirit, is a personal God at work in this world.

A second negative follows clearly. Protestantism is not, in these centuries, in any far-reaching sense a rationalistic movement. Later rationalists of the eighteenth and nineteenth centuries claimed Protestantism as a parent—or, in a less exacting metaphor, claimed that Protestantism was the thin edge of the wedge that began prying humanity loose from Catholic "superstition." There are difficulties of definition here. If you believe that paring off worship of saints and of the Virgin Mary, reducing ritual, emphasizing the sermon, altering greatly or even abolishing the role of music and the decorative arts, and making corresponding reductions in theology—if this process seems rationalistic, then Protestantism as compared with Catholicism is rationalistic. But many of these changes took place only in the eighteenth and nineteenth centuries, when it was most evident that rationalism had greater influence in Protestant churches than in the Catholic. If you will go to the sixteenth century itself, and read the polemical religious literature of the time, you will hardly feel yourself in a rationalistic environment.

Millions of tourists have seen the dark spot on the walls of the castle of the Wartburg where Luther threw his inkpot at the devil. There is nothing in spirit apocryphal here. Luther believed in the supernatural as firmly as any more loyal Augustinian. Calvin's terrible God was as real as old Jehovah, whom he often recalls. Early Protestantism resisted the new scientific theory about the relations of the earth and sun as did the Catholic Church, and for much the same reasons. Modern American Protestant fundamentalist distrust of geology and biology has sound roots in the sixteenth century. If Protestants (with some exceptions, such as the Anglicans) ceased to believe in saints, they continued to believe in the devil, in witches, and in the whole court of darkness. Indeed, to just the extent that Protestantism meant for the individual a renewing of deep religious emotion, a getting away from the perhaps too comfortable formalism of the Catholic Church of the late Middle Ages, it revived the sense of the miraculous, the irrational.

Thirdly, early Protestantism was not tolerant. The first Protestants neither preached nor practiced religious toleration. Historically, it is true that the practice of religious toleration first developed in Protestant countries, notably in England. The extreme hard-boiled formula, that religious toleration came solely because the many sects were weary of trying to kill—or at least to argue—one another off, that practical and unbelieving politicians achieved adjustments among exhausted sects no longer afire with zeal, that theories and ideals about religious toleration played no part at all in the process—this formula will not do. It is unfair to such genuinely religious groups as the Quakers, for whom toleration was a positive good, as it is to hundreds of writers and workers of all faiths and no faith who came in these strife-ridden centuries to defend religious toleration as in itself a desirable goal. But religious toleration was not the goal of Luther, nor of Calvin, nor of the other more conspicuous and successful fighters for a cause they felt to be above experimentation and above doubt, and hence, of course, above the cowardice or laziness men called toleration. Defenses of religious toleration as in itself morally good did indeed occur even in the early years of the Reformation, but they came from the lesser figures. Among the early humanists there was a disposition toward toleration, toward rationalism, and even toward skepticism. Yet many of the humanists preserved more than a touch of the drive toward perfection that underlay Protestantism. Many of them, like Erasmus himself, had not the courage and drive to work for real toleration.

After these negatives, it is hardly necessary to add that early Protestantism was not, in the conventional modern American sense, democratic. A great deal has been written about the relation between the Protestant movement and the growth of modern Western democracy. Much, of course, depends on the definition of democracy. If you stress the importance of individual freedom in democracy, then clearly neither Luther nor Calvin was a democrat, for neither believed a man should in practice be left free to sin (see p. 323). If you find that in democracy equality rather than individual freedom is the crucial point, then even more clearly the great Protestant groups were not democratic. The tiny group of the Calvinist elect, the saints, the saved, are among the most exclusive of aristocratic groups. Few attitudes are less democratic than that of the English Puritan who, in answer to the suggestion that men who were going to hell anyway might as well enjoy a few pleasures on earth, replied that their behavior stank in the nostrils of the faithful. As for Lutheranism, after the Peasants' Revolt its authoritarian and aristocratic flavor is very clear. It is early the suitable Church for the Prussian Junker. Out of early Protestantism, let us repeat, much that helps make modern democracy was to come, but not intentionally.

There are exceptions to the above statement, as to most big historical generalizations. The seventeenth-century English Revolution—not the "Glorious Revolution" of 1689, but the great Revolution of the 1640's—was one of the main sources of modern democracy. The left-wing movements of that Revolution are bewildering combinations of religious, political, and economic ideas and aspirations. There are chiliastic sects, there are antinomian sects, and there are sects that are more Calvinist than Calvin. There are groups, like the Levellers, that aim at political democracy in very close to our modern sense. Even major groups like the Presbyterians and the Independents (Congregationalists) in their attacks on king and bishops set up parliamentary supremacy, a bill of rights, a constitution, much of the institutional side of democracy. More, there are to be found among many of these groups democratic notions of social equality, democratic distrust of an authority whose decisions are beyond the control of the whole people. The spirit of the leaders who set up the Puritan Commonwealth in Massachusetts Bay, we know well enough today, was *not* democratic. The government founded by Winthrop and his associates was the government of the elect, of the saints. Yet even in Massachusetts, resistance to this oligarchy soon developed. And in Roger Williams you find in full seventeenth century a Protestant leader who is also—indeed, above all—a democrat.

Yet it must be repeated, in the general view the negation holds: the Protestants of the Reformation are not democratic in spirit.

Put all this together—a vivid and extensive supernaturalism, the more vivid perhaps for being focused on the divine trinity and its satanic opponents, or rather, agents; a heightened sense of sin; a renewed drive toward the ideal; a hatred for other religious groups that banished toleration from theory as from practice—and you have a whole that does not much resemble the staid and established American Protestantism of the twentieth century, the Protestantism of Ladies' Aid, Boy Scouts, church suppers, African missions, and all sorts of good causes, from temperance to world government. Early Protestantism is a much more untamed thing, a ferocious, and to the calm rationalist or the innocent idealist, a rather unpleasant thing. For the early Protestant still has the medieval man's sense of the violence and uncertainties of a universe ruled by a terrible, inscrutable God, a God not confined by statistics, science, or common sense. Indeed, to the extent that the Protestant God is a darker and more inscrutable God than the God of the Schoolmen, the Protestant of the sixteenth century lived in a world more violent and more uncertain than the world of the Catholic thirteenth century. Early Protestantism came to bring not peace, but a sword. A sword does bloody and terrible things. Boy Scouts and Ladies' Aids do not use one.

The Protestant Spectrum

We have hitherto sought in the main to make generalizations about Protestantism as a whole. And yet, as even the most kindly Catholic writers enjoy pointing out, the most obvious generalization you can make about Protestantism is that it is *not* a whole. Protestant unity, if it exists, has got to be sought among the abstractions and the generalities of the spirit. In mundane matters of organization, administration, finance, in the outward signs of group existence, there is only the bewildering variety of the sects. That familiar American reference book, the *World Almanac,* notes that "there were in the continental United States in 1947 256 Religious Bodies." Look under "Church of God," for example, and you will find

> Church of God
> Church of God (Anderson, Ind.)
> Church of God, Seventh Day
> The (Original) Church of God
> The Church of God
> The Church of God

The duplication of the last name is no misprint.

The systematist who undertakes to classify the Protestant churches finds no single test at his hand; and indeed the title we have used for this section, "The Protestant Spectrum," if taken literally suggests a regularity of disposition that does not conform to reality. You might classify Protestant groups, at least for a given country, by their social prestige, the wealth of their members, their theological distance from the Roman Catholic Church, their degree of evangelical warmth, their Biblical fundamentalism. We shall here take the two great national—and in their critics' eye, Erastian—churches, the Anglican and the Lutheran, as the Right Wing of Protestantism, the Calvinist sects as the great Center, and the more "radical" sects as the Left Wing. Note that Methodism is an eighteenth-century development that cannot come into our reckoning here.

Erastian was once a fighting word, as certain to warm our forefathers to argument as *socialist* is to stir us. Briefly, it is the doctrine, fathered on the Swiss theologian Erastus (not to be confused with the Dutch humanist Erasmus of Rotterdam) that makes the Church no more than a department of state, the clergy the moral police of the state, the laymen patriots who equate God's word with that of their rulers.

Now a national church, by the very fact that it is limited in its temporal organization to a given nation-state, is inevitably somewhat Erastian. In England, the national church has never had anything like a monopoly in the religious life of the country. It was very early opposed by strong separatist movements, and was split within by groups so "high" as to be nearly Roman Catholic and so "low" as to be nearly Unitarian, with a broad or latitudinarian group in the middle. The Church of England, in short, has been a paradox of churches, a single Church with both aspirations toward catholicity (universality) and a singular variety of minds and dispositions. Even so, the Church of England has seemed Erastian to its enemies, and there is no doubt that over the early centuries it was the reflection of the way of life of the new gentry and the conservative classes generally. The Church of England had for the first few decades of its existence a most stormy history of ups and downs, from which it emerged under Elizabeth as a classic example of English ability to compromise—or, if you prefer, to pretend that certain difficulties do not exist. Even in the first two centuries after Luther, then, the

Church of England is no simple thing, but a sort of microcosm of the Protestant world. Basically a conservative Protestant Church, respectful of civil authority if not slavishly Erastian, theologically and liturgically close to the Roman Catholic Church, lacking the Protestant zeal to clean up this world, the Church of England nevertheless kept under its elastic control—the metaphor here is fairly exact, for the Anglican mind can *stretch*—a whole host of potential rebels who might go over to Rome, or to Geneva, or direct to heaven itself. At various times, these potential rebels have become real rebels, but the Church has stayed on, a puzzle to the logically minded, an offense to the moral perfectionist, a delight to the admirer of the irrational English.

The doctrinal history of the Church of England from the Supremacy Act of 1534, when Henry broke away from Rome, to Elizabeth's Act of Uniformity in 1559 is an extraordinary example of masses of human beings carried through a series of mutually conflicting orthodoxies. The phenomenon is not new or unique in Western history, where in periods of social and intellectual change men have often had to adjust their minds, if not precisely to keep them open. The changes in the official party line of the Communists since 1938 are a classic example familiar to us all. A good party member had in 1940 to believe in Hitler's goodness and in 1941 to believe in his wickedness, and so on through many bewildering turns. But the party is already an elite, a relatively small group even in Russia. These changes in sixteenth-century England were undergone by a whole churchgoing people. The same quiet, ordinary subject of the king had first to accept Henry VIII in place of the pope, the use of English instead of Latin in church services, and a few other changes, of which the most conspicuous must have been the priest's taking a wife. Archbishop Cranmer, the king's right-hand man in these momentous affairs, a priest who had studied abroad and knew his German reformation firsthand, had set the example by marrying. Next, our faithful subject was to learn that Henry thought Cranmer had gone too far. The enemy of Luther, the defender of the faith, was not going to see that faith destroyed. He wanted to have his people Catholics under Henry, not under the pope. So in 1539 Henry in person pushed through Parliament the Six Articles, the "bloody whip with six strings." By the third article "priests, after the order of priesthood received, as afore, may not marry, by the law of God." Auricular confession was restored, and the Roman doctrine of the Eucharist reaffirmed.

But this was only a beginning. On Henry's death his young son Edward VI succeeded. The boy had been brought up in Protestant ways, and under his brief rule our good subject went to a church where the services were very Protestant, and in 1551 subscribed to forty-two articles drawn up by this same Cranmer, compromising with the extremes, but still repudiating much Catholic doctrine. Once more his priest might marry. But Edward died childless in 1553, and was succeeded by his elder sister Mary, who had been brought up a Catholic. Under Mary, the "Bloody Mary" of later English school-books, the whole English nation returned, in form at least, to the Roman Catholic fold. Cranmer was burned at the stake, a martyr to something a little less clear than martyrdom usually deserves. Our good subject went back to his Paternoster and his Ave Maria. But Mary herself died in 1558 after only five years on the throne, and was succeeded by her younger sister Elizabeth, destined to the long life denied her brother and sister, and to an ultimate place in English Protestant hearts.

Elizabeth was a Protestant, and under her the national Church was once more thoroughly reorganized, a new Supremacy Act setting the Crown in place of the pope was passed, an Act of Uniformity prescribing a uniform worship all over the kingdom put through, and another set of articles of faith and doctrine drawn up, the famous thirty-nine articles that are still the charter of the Church of England. Our faithful subject went back to services in English, to a theology that banished the old sacraments and preserved only the apostolic or more English of the saints, became, in fact, an Anglican. His son might live to see Cromwell stable his horses in the church; but at any rate, the crisis with Rome was over.

Now unless our faithful subject was irresponsible to the point of feeble-mindedness, he cannot possibly have believed the quite contradictory things he professed, if he duly conformed, in those twenty-five years of ups and downs. Here is a classical case of a difficulty that will confront us to the end, when we attempt to estimate the importance of ideas in social relations. If our faithful subject took with full seriousness all the ideas he had to accept, he must have gone mad. Perhaps he by temperament preferred one shade or another, but lacked the energy or courage to do anything about it, and so took what came along. If many people behaved this way, it is most important for us to understand this behavior. Perhaps he really didn't care about any of these ideas; perhaps he went to church as some people are said to go to movies, just for the sake of something to do. Naturally he wouldn't care whether Edward, Mary, or Elizabeth were directing. If there are many such people, it is important that we know it. Probably most people took no such simple position, but adjusted their behavior in subtle and complicated ways we cannot yet understand. But one thing is clear from these twenty-five years of English history alone: Masses of men can and do accommodate themselves to changes in abstract ideas, philosophies, theologies, to conflicts among these ideas, in a way that the sincere and single-minded idealist cannot possibly explain except by ceasing to be an idealist about his fellow men.

The Lutheran Church has been the established national church in most of northern Germany and Scandinavia. Especially in Prussia, it has seemed to outsiders to be a stock example of extreme Erastianism, governed through submissive ministers by the rulers of the state, and inculcating that very strong German sense of the propriety of obedience which is not at all a myth of Allied propaganda in two world wars. No more than the Anglican has the Lutheran Church taken to Calvinist austerity. It has always encouraged music, has preserved a dignified ritual and enough of Catholic theology so that the Eucharist remains a miracle, and no mere rationally sentimental recollection of the Last Supper. Luther himself was adamant—he loved being adamant—on this matter. Christ had said "this is my body," and a body is no mere symbol. The Catholic doctrine of transubstantiation he had to repudiate, since it was so central a

Catholic belief; he produced his own doctrine of *consubstantiation,* and defended it with what we shall have to call late scholastic argumentation. Luther's doctrine uses the Latin *con,* "together with," instead of *trans,* "across, through." His thinking is hard to follow: The untrained layman has to understand that the elements are bread and wine *together with* the body and blood of Christ, are *both* natural and miraculous, *really* both, not just apparently. It is in some ways a typical compromiser's doctrine, a rather empty effort to have a cake and eat it. And yet men died for *con* against *trans,* as they had died for *homousion* against *homoiousion* and as they were to die for democracy against totalitarianism.

Calvinism is the center of Protestantism. The way of life that grew out of Calvin's work on earth is still a very great element in Western culture. Unfortunately, there is no royal and easy road to an understanding of Calvinism. It has a founder and a great book, the *Institutes of the Christian Religion,* which Calvin published in 1535, but a mere reading of this book will give you less insight into Calvinism than a mere reading of *Capital* would into Marxism. Calvinism grew from a book and a little theocratic community at Geneva into a world-wide religion through the efforts of thousands of men and women in hundreds of communities. The intellectual historian, try though he will, finds that he cannot encompass a movement that is in some senses identified with all Western history since the sixteenth century.

There is an obvious contrast between the excitable, inconsistent, undisciplined German Luther and the cold, logical, systematic French Calvin. You can expand this contrast into a book, as you could the contrast between the Parthenon at Athens and the cathedral of Chartres. But you must not lose sight of the fact that Calvin too was a rebel, a man who *wanted things different.* For Calvin too the Roman Catholic Church was handling men in the wrong way, was not living up to what God intended when he sent Jesus to earth. For Calvin too a way had to be found back to true Christianity.

He found it, as so many have, in the works of that pillar of orthodoxy, St. Augustine. There is not much use attempting to

321

apply a system of psychological analysis to Calvin, nor to begin, at least, with sociology. It is probably true that Calvinism as it worked out was a most fitting system of beliefs, cosmological, theological, ethical, for a commercial and industrial capitalist middle class. But Calvin did not sit down to work up such a system for a middle class, as in a way Marx sat down to work up such a system for what he called a proletariat. Calvin sat down to put once more before men the true word of God.

Calvin's God had the conventional monotheist's attributes—he was all-powerful, all-knowing, all-good. But he was all these so completely, so inhumanly, that he could not conceivably allow what men vainly call free will. God is not precisely outside space and time, but he is the creator of space and time, and of all that goes on inside them. He has absolute and complete foreknowledge of all he has created. No man has any choice in anything he does. God has determined everything. He planned, or willed, if we can use these limited human words to try to describe the action of a Being so far above us poor worms, Adam's fall and its consequences. Planning the fall of Adam may seem not to accord with the attribute of perfect goodness but again it is highly presumptuous of us to use our wormlike vocabulary to judge the works of God. God can do nothing but good in his own eyes, so the sin of Adam must have been good—for God.

Ever since Adam's sin men have been damned to hell. Damnation is no doubt a sort of punishment for the human presumption in Adam's first disobedience; you will remember that he disobeyed God's clear personal command not to eat the fruit of the tree of knowledge. True, Adam could not help himself, since God had willed Adam's presumption and had moved Adam's teeth as Adam bit the apple, and it might seem that God was being a trifle unfair. . . . Again, from the Calvinist point of view we are obtruding most unfairly into our analysis our petty human rationalist views of justice. God is *above* logic; indeed, God made logic just as he made the apple.

God next sent Jesus to earth to bring to a happy few salvation through election. Once more, it would be too human and wormlike

to say that God relented and decided to give some of Adam's descendants a chance to redeem themselves. Out of the fullness of his
Godliness, God through Jesus has given grace and consequent salvation to a few, a very few. Who these few are in fact is known only
to God. But it is not unlikely that most, perhaps all, of them are
Calvinists—the Calvinists who are the *elect*.

Calvin's is a far more rigid and radical determinism than St.
Augustine's. We have seen that the Bishop of Hippo tried hard to
give men free will and keep determinism for God. Calvin seemed
to feel no need for any such concessions. Yet the logic seems inexorable: If I have no thoughts, no desires of my own, but only those
God has arranged for me, I am surely justified in taking my thoughts
and desires as they come. That state of moral tension which I speak
of as "resisting temptation" is surely unreal? To resist what I want
to do is to resist God. If I want to commit fornication, God wants
me to do so. If I am to be saved, that salvation is wholly through
God's grace, and nothing that delusion I call my conscience may say
has anything to do with the process. Therefore, I might just as well
sin to my heart's content.

The reader need hardly be reminded that such is not the Calvinist
position. At some point the Calvinist slips from under his logic,
and sets up the Christian moral conscience at its most tense. In
fairness to Calvin it should be said that this point is basically the same
one at which all the great Christian thinkers escape from the moral
nihilism that seems to flow from a complete determinism: To say
"I know that, whatever I may do, I do because God wills it" is in
fact to claim that I understand what God wants, that I am God's equal
and not just his helpless agent. To be sure of one's salvation—this
is the great sin of pride, the antipodean opposite of the humility so
central to Christianity. Though they are not humble in the folk-
sense that equates humility with weakness, a disposition to yield,
though indeed they are often decided and commanding men, the
great Christians have had this humility. Even Calvin has it.

I cannot then be *certain* that what I want to do is what a man
chosen by God as one of the elect would want to do; what I want

to do *may* be what a man chosen by God as one of the damned would want to do. Note that we are being very careful of our language. Later and more careless Calvinists might say I cannot be sure that what I want to do is what God wants me to do—but that would imply that I can resist God's will, which would destroy determinism. The point should be clear: I cannot *resist* God's will, but I can never, even if I am of the elect, *fully know* God's will. Indeed, if I think I know God's will it is a sign I am damned. But only very humble Calvinists could be quite consistent here, and *on a general level,* among its ordinary adherents, Calvinism did not precisely breed humility.

The Scotch poet Robert Burns, in his *Holy Willie's Prayer,* has his Calvinist elder begin

> Oh Thou, wha in the heavens dost dwell,
> Wha, as it pleases best thysel'
> Sends ane to heaven, and ten to hell,
>   A' for thy glory,
> And no for ony guid or ill
>   They've done afore thee!

Burns puts the doctrine with satirist's scorn, but it is quite good Calvinist doctrine. A few stanzas later, however, Holy Willie breaks into the spiritual pride outsiders—and not only outsiders—have for three centuries so readily detected in Calvinists:

> Yet I am here, a chosen sample,
> To shew thy grace is great and ample;
> I'm here a pillar in thy temple,
>   Strong as a rock.
> A guide, a buckler, an example,
>   To a' thy flock.

The way is now clear for the ethics of Calvinism, for what the last few generations of intellectuals in America, under the illusion that they were free from it, call Puritanism. I cannot know God's will, according to the Puritan, but he has given me some indications of the way a member of the elect would behave. These indications are chiefly in his own words as recorded in the Bible. The Calvinist, however, though he repudiated the historic Catholic Church, did not wholly repudiate a more general Christian tradition of authority; moreover, the elders, the men in authority in the Calvinist communities, were held to possess rather more reliable premonitions of God's intent than the laymen.

Now the Bible and Christian tradition, reinforced by the minister and elders of the church, made it overwhelmingly clear to a Puritan that if he really wanted to commit fornication this desire was put there by God working through Satan and not (this language is not Calvinistic, but should be clear) by God working directly, on his own. It is the kind of desire that would come to one of those destined for damnation; it is the kind of desire that should give our Puritan grave concern over his future life—perhaps he is not to be saved; it is the kind of desire he had better suppress completely and wholly if he really wants to be saved. If he really is to be saved, he will have the strength to suppress it. God, who for all his inexorable determination apparently listens to prayer, at least to Calvinist prayer, will help the man who asks him for help in avoiding this sin.

We are back in the full tide of Christian piety and Christian morals. Calvinism as a way of life is one of the forms of idealistic or other-worldly Christianity. It has often been reproached for un-Christian exclusiveness, for holding that the elect are no more than a tiny minority. Yet in fact it represents an attempt to extend to life in this world something of the ideals the historic Catholic Church had long given up trying to extend beyond the monastic and the secular clergy. Spiritual pride there certainly was in many a Calvinist, but they were not better Calvinists for that. The Calvinist would not let sinners sin freely, if he could help it, even though in strict logic it might be maintained that God obviously intended the sinner to sin. Where they were in power, the Calvinists censored, forbade, banished, and punished behavior they thought sinful. In this they were clearly in their own minds God's agents, doing God's work. In practice, these firm believers in the inability of human effort to *change* anything were among the most ardent of workers toward getting men to change their behavior. To an amazing extent they succeeded. They helped make the Industrial Revolution and the modern world.

The note of Christianity the Calvinists most clearly emphasized is that of asceticism. But it is easy to misunderstand and caricature Calvinist asceticism. The Calvinist is not the mystic who seeks to annihilate sense awareness, not the mystic who seeks passiveness, the quieting of the will, seclusion from this world. He seeks rather to select among his worldly desires those which will further his salvation, and to curb or suppress those which will not. The Calvinist thought the world a very serious place indeed, in which laughter was somewhat out of order. This world is for most of us, the Calvinist believed, an antechamber to hell and eternal suffering, and if you really feel this you are not likely to be much amused. The Calvinist thought that many pleasures to which the human race is addicted— light music, dancing, gambling, fine clothes, drinking, and playgoing, among others—were the kind of thing Satan liked, the kind of thing, not that God disliked, for he did nothing so human as like or dislike, but that somehow, somehow, derogates from that awful Majesty.

The Calvinist did not hold, as some Christians have held, that sexual intercourse is sinful. He did hold firmly to the notion that it was sinful if indulged in outside a monogamous marriage duly entered into with the sanction of the Church. You will find in Calvinist literature the notion that the purpose God had in mind in providing sexual intercourse was the continuation of the race, and not the sensuous pleasures of the participants. Those pleasures are all the more dangerous since they may lead to extramarital indulgence, which is a very great sin. But there seems to be no reason to believe that the Puritans who produced such large families, notably in New England, did so out of a painful sense of duty. The Puritan was not often addicted to mortifying the flesh in one great form of the ascetic tradition. He liked to eat well, sleep well, live in a comfortable house. Indeed, one of the reproaches certain modern liberal intellectuals have made to our Puritan forefathers is that they neglected the fine arts and the nobler ways of the flesh in favor of stuffy commercial success, earthly comforts of a vulgar sort—in short, that they were ancestors of George Babbitt.

Calvinism also sounds very loudly another Christian note, that of ethical meliorism. The Calvinist had a high moral code, pushed to extremes in certain directions precisely by his serious-mindedness, but still essentially a code in the tradition of all the higher religions. In spite of, or because of, his belief in determinism, he was always trying to live up to his code, and see that other people did so too. Both inward and outward directions of this effort are important.

The Calvinist certainly felt the "civil war in the breast," the struggle between what has become famous as the Puritan conscience and the temptations of this world. This notion of a higher part of human consciousness that can and should censor and suppress the promptings of a lower part has left a firm imprint on the West, an imprint especially strong where Calvinism has set the dominant tone. Neither Rousseau nor Freud seems to have seriously shaken this conception of the role of conscience—not even in themselves.

In its outgoing direction, this ethical meliorism has taken many forms other than that of the outright, police-enforced prohibition the critics of Puritanism single out for condemnation. The method of outright prohibition of dancing, theater, and the like is certainly there, and was resorted to by the early Calvinists the more naturally because, as we shall see, they had no democratic worries about the freedom of the individual. But the Calvinist also believed in persuasion; he made the sermon a central part of his worship. He did not force the note of anti-intellectualism we have found in Christianity—indeed in the long run the influence of Calvinism was to further what we can call rationalism—but in these early years the Calvinist is certainly no rationalist. He believes in hell-fire and in the moral uses of fear of hell-fire; he believes in emotional conversion, and is a good missionary, though not at his best among primitive peoples.

Puritanism, which we Americans commonly use, to the despair of the semanticist, in a very loose way as shorthand for the Calvinist way of life, is one of those great clusters of ideas which cannot in fact be analyzed with chemical exactness. In the scientist's sense of "define" you cannot define Puritanism. We have attempted very cursorily to indicate some of the elements of the Puritan way of life in its first two centuries, but we have barely skimmed the surface. Even so, there remains one major and very difficult problem we cannot neglect, that of the political aspects and results of Calvinism.

In a previous chapter we pointed out that one of the tensions in Christianity is that between its sense of the importance of the individual as an immortal soul, and its need to overcome the individual's ego (selfishness, self-importance) either by submission to God or by melting in with a community, or by both. Something of this same tension exists in modern democracy as a way of life, or ideal, a tension usually expressed as that between liberty and equality. The more individual liberty, the more competition, the more big winners and just plain losers; the more equality, the more security, the more limits on competition, the less individual liberty.

In Calvinism this tension exists in a particularly complex form. Calvin, like Luther, was forced to a certain degree of individualism just because he broke with an established church. He had to sweep away the authority of the Catholic Church in the minds of his followers, and to do that he had to urge them to think for themselves. He and his followers, as Weber, Troeltsch, Tawney, and others have pointed out, did much to encourage the competitive individualism of the businessman. The Puritan's struggle with his conscience was the struggle of an individual keenly aware of his self-sufficiency—or insufficiency. Even the Calvinist's sense of the littleness of man in the face of the awfulness of God was in no very paradoxical sense a heightening of the individual's importance here on earth, for only as an individual, not as one of a mass, could he grow to an awareness of God. Finally, Calvinism had throughout its early years to struggle against constituted authority for the mere right to survive as an active religion. The power it early attained in Geneva and in Boston, the security it attained in later centuries everywhere it survived, it did not have in France, England, and Germany in the first years. It had to defy authority—Calvin himself, so authoritarian in Geneva, could at moments be a libertarian in his advice to followers elsewhere.

Put all this together and you can almost think Calvin anticipated what the social Darwinists of the nineteenth century were to picture as the right state of man, a fine free-for-all of competition in all walks of life, with the devil appropriately taking the hindmost. Such a view would be wrong, and you have only to dip into the practicing Calvinism of sixteenth-century Geneva or of seventeenth-century Boston to see a community in some ways almost Spartan in its discipline and its collectivism. These communities were ruled from above by a minority of the virtuous; they were not in our sense of the word *democracies*. They were not societies in which collectivism was extended to economic goods, though in both societies the poor were a public charge—if only because the morals of the poor usually needed tending to. They were even in a sense societies of status, as anyone who has studied early New England social history knows. For instance, early class lists of Harvard students are arranged in some order of status—social standing—we do not clearly understand. We do know that they are not arranged alphabetically, nor according to excellence in studies, nor even according to the income of their parents.

In the balance, however, Calvinism has swung toward democracy. The decisive influence here has probably been the form of its church government, congregational or presbyterian, in any case one in which all church members in good standing take part in meetings that handle the affairs of the parish, and that are free from authority of bishops or other constituted authority, lay or priestly. In the sixteenth century and in seventeenth-century New England the practice of this government is more clearly an oligarchy of the "saints" than an egalitarian democracy. The fact remains, however, that Calvinist experience, hammered out in years of resistance to established churches, gave training of a sort that perhaps was transferred to democratic government, and in New England, at least, provided some of the machinery of that government. It may even be that the Calvinist habit of appealing to the Bible as the written word of God prepared men to appeal to a written constitution; but this is the kind of generalization one can hardly test.

The Left Wing of the Protestant movement is made up of a great number of struggling sects. Perhaps they are to be classed as on the Left merely because none of them ever became powerful and established groups identified with a great country. Even the Quakers, in many ways the most successful of these sects, and certainly one of the most interesting, have always remained small in numbers. They have for the systematist relatively little in common beyond their scattering, their general opposition to established churches, their small membership, and their great variety. Seventeenth-century England is one of the best places for a modern American to study them, for there is no language difficulty—that is, no such difficulty as with Latin or German, for it must be admitted that the innumerable tracts of English seventeenth-century religious dispute are not written in our present language.

A full list of the sects would be a very long one. There are the Diggers, simple Biblical communists who took to digging up certain commons—the rough equivalent of our public parks—on the ground that God had given the land to all. There are the Fifth Monarchy men, or Millenarians, who held that the fourth monarchy of Biblical revelation was drawing to a close, and that they were destined to usher in the fifth or final monarchy. They were divided into a passive group who believed that God would take care of the work of making his prophecy come true, in good time, and an active group who proposed to get out and help bring the prophecy true by violence if necessary. There were the Levellers, whose name is self-explanatory, but who were rather a political than a religious sect. There were the followers of Ludovic Muggleton, the inspired tailor, who still exist as the Muggletonians, a name difficult to take with high seriousness. There were the Behmenists, the Bidellians, the Coppinists, the Salmonists, the Dippers, the Traskites, the Tyronists, the Philadelphians, the Christadelphians, the many variants of Adventists and Baptists. The prevalence of proper names—the names of the leaders or prophets of the sects—suggests that they represent the ultimate splintering down of Protestantism in search of *some* final authority.

Many of the sects belong clearly on or beyond what has been called the "lunatic fringe." Their study should be of great interest to the sociologist and the psychologist, who will find three hundred years ago symptoms he may otherwise think uniquely modern, and thus not really understand. Their very existence is one of the signs of grave social changes. These extremists confront the historian who attempts to treat human affairs objectively, without wrath or zeal, with a serious problem, for they themselves are full of wrath and zeal. They are immoderates, heaven-stormers, men to whom the qualities the objective historian tries to cultivate in himself are abhorrent. He fancies that he can see clearly how much more satisfactory, how much more decent, more humane, the course of history would have been without these troublemakers, these impossibilists. He can see their unpleasant side—their readiness to persecute (if they attain a position in which they can persecute), their authoritarianism (if they attain a position of authority), their delusions of grandeur, their egocentricity, their inability to appreciate the rich variety of the good lives men may lead.

In his too easy condemnation of these extremists, the man of moderation misses their greatness and fails to understand their usefulness in society. The obvious metaphors are weak; these heaven-stormers are not quite the leaven, not quite the gadflies, not quite the vanguard of society. Sometimes they are, and often they are not, what these metaphors would have them. They are reminders to us all, though we do not often heed them, that men cannot decently do without the prick of the ideal, cannot lapse safely into comfort—not even the comfort of objectivity. Montaigne, who liked extremists as little as any man, could say of the excesses of revolutionaries:

> I see not one action, or three, or a hundred, but a commonly accepted state of mortality so unnatural, especially as regards inhumanity and treachery, which are to me the worst of all sins, that I have not the heart to think of them without horror; and they excite my wonder almost as much as my detestation. *The practice of these egregious villainies has as much the mark of strength and vigor of soul as of error and disorder.*

Some of the wildest of the sects seem almost abstractly chiliastic—that is to say, they promise heaven on earth, but with no concrete touches, or in the misplaced concreteness of a revelationary symbolism taken mostly from the Old Testament and the last book of the New. But many of them, and many of the less crazy ones, are what we have already agreed to call loosely socialistic; they are the kind that appear in histories of socialist thought. Their main emphasis is the solution of the problem of poverty—no more rich, no more poor, just good men sharing as nature and God meant them to share the riches of this world. Many insist they are but going back to the primitive Church, which they found to be communist. They all use the vocabulary of religion, even when they are concerned with economic matters. They are not really very different from their late medieval predecessors. They are hostile to conventional Calvinism—though they may well share some Calvinist theological and ethical ideas—because it is clear already that conventional Calvinism does not believe in sharing the wealth.

We should not be surprised to find that some of the most collectivist of these groups should also be radically individualist, indeed anarchical. We have already noted that human beings can apparently live happily in the midst of various logical contradictions. The socialists of modern times have always had their anarchist wing. At any rate, one of the few valid generalizations that link these early Protestant extremists is the tendency to what was then called antinomianism. The antinomian carried the fundamental Protestant position—justification by faith as opposed to justification by works—to the utmost extreme. To him a law, a custom, any command was in fact a "work," and should therefore be disregarded unless his inner voice told him that what was so prescribed was right—and usually in those excited early days it did not. The inner voice is all that counts. Some of the antinomians actually followed out in practice the logic we have earlier traced as flowing from an absolute determinism; they argued that if their inner voice told them they were saved, then clearly whatever they did was ordained of God, and would not interfere with their salvation. The radicals who in Westphalia in the 1530's enjoyed brief periods of power were accused by their enemies of all sorts of debauches; and though conservatives have always accused radicals of shocking personal, and especially sexual, morals, there seems to be no doubt that some of the antinomians did follow their logic into behavior usually thought well beyond logical justification.

But, as we have already suggested of the proliferation of heresies in the second and third centuries of Christianity, the proliferation of the sects is in some ways a sign of youthful strength in Protestantism, a sign that men take in deadly and fecund seriousness the hope of a much better life here, if only in due and necessary preparation for a perfect life in the hereafter. These sects—and they are really Protestant heresies, offensive though the term may be to conventional Protestants today—have in them a wild energy, even when their goal seems an absurd heaven.

By 1700, Protestantism had settled down. Its rebelliousness had been tamed by success, and even the Calvinists were now established or tolerated almost everywhere. Protestantism had not necessarily become stuffy and self-satisfied; it still had much missionary fervor, especially in work overseas, and it still numbered many zealous Christians. But it had come to a stalemate with its old Catholic enemy. The Catholic Church itself had from the mid-sixteenth century on summoned great sources of spiritual strength, had reformed the abuses of worldliness, indifference, and corruption that had crept into many places in the late medieval Church, and without in any basic way altering its theology and liturgy, had in the Council of Trent knit the fabric of Catholicism firmly together. The revived Church had reconquered spiritually rather than by force much of Germany and of eastern Europe, and after the Thirty Years' War it was clear that Protestantism was not likely to make further large territorial gains in Europe. Protestantism was in the main and in its historic forms no longer a fighting faith. The very sects that split off after 1700— Pietists in Germany and Methodists in England and America—were at bottom what may be not unfairly called *consoling* sects, groups aiming at making the individual happy (in a Christian way, of course) rather than at the conquest of this world and the next. There was much emotion in Pietism and Methodism, much courage and devotion among their leaders, but one misses the stormy idealism, the channeled violence, of earlier Protestantism. The search for perfection on earth was moving elsewhere, into what became the Enlightenment.

Making the Modern World

ONCE MORE we confront a big word—*rationalism*. Like most such words, this one can be defined in a variety of ways. We shall here define it very broadly as a cluster of ideas that add up to the belief that the universe works the way a man's mind works when he thinks logically and objectively, that therefore man can ultimately understand everything in his experience as he understands, for instance, a simple arithmetical or mechanical problem. The same wits that showed him how to make, use, and keep in repair any household contrivance will ultimately, the rationalist hopes, show him all about everything.

The foregoing is a rather informal illustration of rationalism, but it should bring home the extent to which the complete rationalist departs from Christian belief, even from such forms of Christian belief as Scholasticism with its emphasis on the ability of the human mind to understand at least in part God's plan for the universe. There are, of course, all sorts of compromises between rationalism and Christianity, some of which we shall encounter in the Age of the Enlightenment. But the push of rationalist belief is away from Christianity. The rationalist tends to the position that the reasonable is the natural and that *there is no supernatural*. At most there is for him the unknown, which should someday be the known. There is no place in his scheme for a personal God, no room in his mind for the mystic surrender to faith. Violent antithetical dislikes are often useful as bench marks; what the rationalist most dislikes is the mood of the *credo quia impossibile.*

Rationalism tends then to banish God and the supernatural from the universe. It has left only the natural, which the rationalist holds to be ultimately understandable, almost always by what most of us know as the methods of scientific investigation. Historically, the growth of scientific knowledge, the ever more skillful use of scientific methods, is closely tied with the growth of the rationalist attitude toward the universe, with the rationalist cosmology. For most rationalists have indeed a complete world-view, a way of life tied up with their belief in reason. Many practicing scientists have been rationalists; any scientist who holds that we have no other true knowledge except knowledge arrived at by the use of the scientific method is logically either a rationalist or a skeptic. But—and this is a very important point—science and rationalism, though historically intertwined, are not by any means the same thing.

Science, both in the sense of a body of accumulated scientific knowledge and in the sense of a way of going to work on problems (that is, scientific method), is not concerned with metaphysics. *As science* it provides neither a cosmology nor an ontology. Science *as science* makes no attempt to answer—does not even ask—the Big Questions of human destiny, of God's ways to man, of Right and Wrong and Good and Bad. Some scientists as individuals come near not asking any of the Big Questions, come near guiding themselves in daily life by custom and authority, as do most of us most of the time. Some scientists, that is, may be without metaphysical curiosity, or metaphysical anxiety—as may be many of the human race. (This is a point about which even professional psychologists seem to know little—the writer's guess is that very few human beings indeed are altogether free of metaphysical anxiety, or at any rate, metaphysical concern.) As soon as the scientist asks and tries to answer any of the Big Questions, however, he is ceasing to behave as a scientist. He is at the very least doing something *additional;* he is probably doing something *different.*

The point of view that science is in no sense directly normative is, as we noted in Chapter I, rejected by some modern thinkers, and does challenge the long Western tradition that man must use his mind to make sense of his whole experience, his universe. Yet the orthodox tradition within science is that the scientist *as scientist* does not make any value-judgments. The philosophic depths of this question are very great indeed. Here we can but record the orthodox position, and note that there are heretics, heretics that are by no means agreed, save in their opposition to the orthodox. If anything is common to those who oppose the orthodox doctrine of science as non-normative, it is the doctrine that human intelligence can solve problems in morals, aesthetics, even theology, as effectively, as successfully, as it solves problems in natural science. The evidence seems to be against them today, but the case is still open, and the court has not decided. Perhaps there is no court.

The rationalist, on the other hand, has usually a full set of answers for the Big Questions, or at any rate is confident that time and diligence on the part of right-thinking men will produce answers, *correct* answers. Rationalism as it grew up in the sixteenth and seventeenth centuries in the West is in fact a complete metaphysical system; more than that, it served for a minority, and continues so to serve, as a substitute for religion. As such a semireligious system, rationalism is perhaps better given specific labels, such as materialism, positivism, and the like, which indicate more exactly the whole complex of beliefs, habits, and organization involved. Thus, to take a rough parallel, rationalism is the broad general term, like Protestantism; materialism, positivism, atheism, yes, even unitarianism, even deism, are the sect names, like Anabaptist or Quaker.

Natural Science

By 1700 most of what we call the natural sciences—then, with the exception of mathematics, known as "natural philosophy"—had reached a stage that made the great synthesis of Newton possible. In the two previous centuries most of the separate disciplines of science, and in particular physics, astronomy, and physiology, had become mature—although not, of course, finished—sciences. There was once more on earth what there had been in Hellenistic Alexandria two thousand years before, a body of researchers and teachers, laboratories, collections, means of exchange of information and ideas—in short, a social and intellectual environment suitable to the advancement of science. The earlier generation of humanists had been no more favorable to natural science than had their medieval scholastic predecessors, but as the sixteenth century wore on scientists like Galileo flourished in the midst of the artists of the Renaissance; and the seventeenth century is not only the century of genius, of men like Newton, Harvey, Descartes, Pascal, it is also the century of the founding of the great scientific societies, such as the British Royal Society (1660), and the French *Académie des Sciences* (1666), the century when, with hundreds of active workers tied together by societies, their publications, and an extraordinary system of private correspondence, science as a social activity came of age.

Science was not yet, in 1700, the most respectable of intellectual occupations. It had by no means acquired the position of wealth and prestige it has achieved in the twentieth century. Classical or liberal education still gave to natural science only the kind of attention the Middle Ages had given to the *quadrivium;* that is, to mathematics and the better-known applications of mathematics in music and mechanics; experimental science, laboratory science, was not yet quite respectable in ordinary education. But the scientific knowledge of these early modern times did seep down into the minds of the literate public; science was one of the vehicles that helped carry rationalistic notions throughout the Western world.

We cannot answer simply and finally the question, Why did the study of natural science flourish at this particular point in space and time? As in the somewhat analogous question of why the Protestant Reformation of the sixteenth century broke out from the Catholic Church in the West in a way no other heretical movement did, there are certainly many variables involved. One of the major variables, and one our own generation understands so well that it is not here emphasized, is the economic one, the growth of a complex money economy run by capitalist businessmen (entrepreneurs). We see readily enough that these businessmen were eager to innovate, willing to endow research, undeterred by the undignified, ungentlemanly nature of much scientific work, untied to the prejudices of a classical education. We see all this too readily, perhaps, because most of these factors operate far more clearly from the late eighteenth century onward than they do in these early years. As we have pointed out, the scientists learned from the craftsmen and technologists, rather than as today, the technologists from the scientists; the most distinguished scientists were gentlemen, sometimes noblemen, and very rarely indeed businessmen. From the start, science was genuinely international and knew no religious bounds. If Spain produced few scientists, and England and France many, again there is no simple answer why. Still, we must note that wealth and increasingly modern economic organization are related to the flourishing of science. This relation is not the whole story, but it is clearly part of it.

There is no wholly satisfactory formula for relating the rise of natural science to the social environment in which it rose. But with somewhat deceptive simplicity it may be said that almost every cultural change in these centuries had its influence on the growth of science. For science, though it can go on to most abstract concepts, rests on things, on facts, on great numbers of different material objects. Thus any multiplication of its data is in itself of great importance to any natural science. The geographical discoveries of the early modern period, themselves furthered by scientific investigations in astronomy, navigation, and geography, brought before Europeans thousands of new facts, thousands of challenges to the inquiring mind. The medieval discovery of gunpowder began with these centuries to be used for practical purposes of warfare, and its use stimulated efforts to defend against it. Then in turn efforts were made to produce more powerful explosives. Once again, we repeat that this is technology and invention, not science; but this multiplication of "things," this preoccupation with things, this attempt to get more and more complex things, is in itself and in its influence on men's minds one of the indispensable conditions for the growth of science.

Warfare is a good instance. There have been theories—the best known is associated with the German economist Werner Sombart—that the growth of large-scale nationalistic warfare in these centuries was the root cause of everything else we call modern, since the need of the state for money to pay a professional army stimulated efforts to make the state structure more efficient, since the demand for material things to fight with stimulated economic change, and since the demand for more effective weapons of offense and defense stimulated technology and invention. Naturally this thesis of organized warfare as the mother of modern civilization proved extremely offensive to good liberals and democrats, and they proceeded to write books showing that warfare had nothing to do with the rise of modern culture. Actually both extremes are nonsense of the chicken-or-egg-first kind. Warfare, geographical discoveries, inventions, business techniques, fashionable luxuries, discoveries, and many other factors worked together, each influencing the other, and all together providing the material setting for modern science.

The psychological setting is quite as complex as the material, and of course greatly influenced by this multiplication of "things." Some men have always been curious, and a great many have been willing to hunt for new experiences. Some men have been patient and systematic in sorting out details, and a great many have had some share of the collector's instincts in amassing material. In fact, the scholar of the Middle Ages already had most of these traits to a very high degree. What was needed to provide a state of mind suitable for the cultivation of natural science was first, a willingness to turn these gifts for patient, meticulous investigation and collection of facts from the dignified world of philosophical and literary scholarship to the undignified world of smells, weights, measures, chills and fevers, and all the rest so familiar to us now; and second, a willingness to give up a good deal of the very strong medieval respect for the authority of previous writers, especially Aristotle, and adopt the habit of checking up on, subjecting to the test of experimentation or verification even the very nicest explanations of natural phenomena.

It was necessary, then, to make the study of natural science respectable by providing it with a philosophy, not necessarily a meta-physics, but at least a method and an aim. That was achieved in the course of these centuries, and notably by Francis Bacon, to whom we shall come in a moment. But do not be misled by the scientist's often naive notion of his newness and uniqueness. The transition from the scholar, indeed from the Scholastic, to the scientist was no miraculous revolution creating something out of nothing. The modern scientist took over from those scholarly predecessors he now so often looks down on almost all those slowly learned habits of mind and work so necessary to natural science—patience, accuracy, the hard-won accumulation of mathematics and logic, the great community of men and women devoted to the cultivation of the mind.

But before we come to Bacon's attempt to make science philosophically respectable, we must consider another possible factor in the rise of science, one that has perhaps already occurred to the reader. Isn't *freedom* one of the essentials for the cultivation of the sciences? Didn't the scientist have to win his freedom from all sorts of medieval restraints and taboos, just as did the Protestant and the humanist? How about Galileo?

Once more let it be noted that the relation between a flourishing natural science and the degree of individual or group freedom from legal or moral restraints in a given society is by no means clear and simple. It would be pleasant to hold that there is a direct correlation, the more freedom (as we Americans understand freedom) the greater scientific advancement. Now it is clear, of course, that in a society where all novelty is forbidden there can be no science, since science depends on someone's producing something new. But such despotic societies exist only in imagination, at least in the Western world. The actual record shows that science grew up in a Europe for the most part ruled by absolute monarchs, and that it owed much to the patronage of these monarchs and their ministers. Indeed, as science slowly proved itself useful in adding to man's command of his material environment, the possessing classes were persuaded of its value to themselves, and were delighted to endow and protect scientists. After all, the discovery of the law of gravitation did not endanger in any obvious way their interests. Freedom for scientific investigation is by no means the same thing as freedom for artistic, philosophical, political, or moral experimentation. No doubt scientists need some kinds of freedom, but most of all they need freedom from the dead weight of custom and authority *in their own fields*.

When a scientist announces a discovery that upsets widely and deeply held beliefs, it is not surprising that he meets resistance and has to struggle to be heard. The interesting part about the record in Western society is that he does get heard, that the censorship that would shut him up is an ineffective and sloppy censorship, that somehow or other such censorship seems rather a stimulus than a hindrance. Even in the most famous case of scientific martyrdom, that of Galileo, censorship did ultimately no more than dramatize Galileo's work. This Italian scientist himself built on the work of still earlier scientists, going back indeed to the late Middle Ages, but especially on that of the Polish astronomer Copernicus. The issue is familiar to all. Galileo's newly invented telescope enabled him to register additional facts, such as the existence of satellites of Jupiter, suggesting a model for the solar system, and the existence of dark spots on the surface of the sun which by their apparent foreshortening seemed to indicate that the sun was revolving. These and many other observations bolstered up the Copernican (and, as we have seen, Aristarchian) theory that the earth revolves in an orbit around a sun that is also revolving. Christian belief had thoroughly committed itself to the other theory, that the earth is stationary and that the sun revolves around it. Sentiments of great strength held many intelligent men to the belief that our planet, the place of Christ's sacrifice, *must* be the center of all things. The interests against Galileo were in fact a coalition, and by no means a united Catholic Church that simply refused to cultivate astronomy. One of the strongest interests against him was a group of Jesuits whom he had offended by seeming to neglect prior Jesuit investigations. In fact, the coalition against Galileo is a fascinating mixture of old and new, of academic rivalry (no new thing, surely), of vested interests, of plain neophobia, perhaps even of a kind of metaphysical anxiety, for the prospect of an infinity, or at least a plurality, of worlds opened up by the telescope horrified many. Ultimately Galileo was brought to trial before the Inquisition and chose to recant rather than be judged guilty. But nothing could undo and unprint Galileo's writings, and no power in seventeenth-century Europe was strong enough to suppress such ideas as Galileo had set circulating. The triumph of the heliocentric theory was assured.

The man who came closest to systematizing in general terms what this new "natural philosophy" was about was the Englishman Francis Bacon, later Lord Verulam. Bacon has had a bad press. He was not a good man, not a kindly man. He was ambitious for power and wealth; his political career, which culminated in the Lord Chancellorship, was marked by time-serving and lack of scruple; he was finally impeached. Later scientists have rarely been able to pardon him for being such a bad scientist, such a poor practitioner of what he preached. Yet he was a good, if almost posthumous, child of the humanist Renaissance, immensely learned, versatile, energetic, eager to push forward in all directions. His admirers in later generations have even advanced one of the most remarkable ideas in all intellectual history, the notion that Bacon wrote the works commonly attributed to Shakespeare.

Bacon planned, and in part carried out, a great work called the *Instauratio Magna* or *Novum Organum* (1620), one of the last of the great seminal works of our culture to be written in Latin. Many of his ideas, however, come out as well in the English *Advancement of Learning* of 1605. It would be misleading to say that this great opus was planned as a sort of *counter-summa* against Aristotle and the Schoolmen. It was rather an ambitious classification of and program for the new scientific studies by which Bacon hoped that men would secure new mastery over their environment. It is full of attacks on Aristotle and his medieval disciples, on deductive reasoning, full of appeals to go to the evidences of sense perception, to appeal to facts, to employ induction. Here are some of the key passages from the *Instauratio Magna*:

> The subtlety of nature is greater many times over than the subtlety of the senses and understanding; so that all those specious meditations,

speculations, and glosses in which men indulge are quite from the purpose, only there is no one by to observe it.

The syllogism is not applied to the first principles of sciences, and is applied in vain to intermediate axioms; being no match for the subtlety of nature. It commands assent therefore to the proposition, but does not take hold of the thing.

The syllogism consists of propositions, propositions consist of words, words are symbols of notions. Therefore if the notions themselves (which is the root of the matter) are confused and over-hastily abstracted from the facts, there can be no firmness in the superstructure. Our only hope therefore lies in a true induction.

There is no soundness in our notions whether logical or physical. Substance, Quality, Action, Passion, Essence itself, are not sound notions: much less are Heavy, Light, Dense, Rare, Moist, Dry, Generation, Corruption, Attraction, Repulsion, Element, Matter, Form, and the like; but all are fantastical and ill defined.

There are and can be only two ways of searching into and discovering truth. The one flies from the senses and particulars to the most general axioms, and from these principles, the truth of which it takes for settled and immovable, proceeds to judgment and to the discovery of middle axioms. And this way is now in fashion. The other derives axioms from the senses and particulars, rising by a gradual and unbroken ascent, so that it arrives at the most general axioms last of all. This is the true way, but as yet untried.

Historians of philosophy and of science have written a great deal about Bacon's idea of induction. Perhaps he has, from our point of view, a naive notion of induction, a belief that if the scientist will only observe enough facts he will somehow find these facts arranging themselves in an order that will be true knowledge. Certainly in polemic against the Schoolmen he often seems to imply that the process we call thinking has no part in the work of the scientist; but this is surely because he identifies the syllogism, which he scorns, with mental activity pure and simple. A close reading of Bacon should convince a fair critic that, although he by no means understood even as well as we do (and that isn't very well) what goes on in the mind of the great creative scientist, he did not really hold that the scientist merely hunts out and records facts.

Far from it. What has misled critics of Bacon is at bottom what ties him to the Schoolmen he so bitterly fought, and to the generation of Renaissance humanists to which he belongs. Bacon was out after answers to the Big Questions; he thought he had found a way to *certainty,* and therefore to agreement, in those matters men had so long been debating without achieving agreement. As we shall see, the modern scientist does not aim at theories that will be absolutely, unchangingly true. Bacon does so aim. He is by temperament a nominalist in almost the medieval sense; he starts with the reality of the "objects" he apprehends with his senses. But he is hunting for a way to get at the kind of permanent form amid the flux of sense knowledge the medieval realist declares he knows offhand, just by thinking or believing. Bacon, to oversimplify greatly, wants to start with nominalist notions and end up with realist ones.

He will achieve that by a long patient series of observations and recordings in which gradually—to use scholastic terms that would have infuriated Bacon himself—the *substance* emerges out of the *accidents,* the permanent out of the fleeting. Bacon himself, in spite of his dislike for the old terms of philosophy, finds himself forced to use the word *form.* Here is a passage of major importance:

> For since the Form of a thing is the very thing itself, and the thing differs from the form no otherwise than as the apparent differs from the real, or the external from the internal, or the thing in reference to man from the thing in reference to the universe; it necessarily follows that no nature can be taken as the true form, unless it always decrease when the nature in question decreases, and in like manner always increase when the nature in question increases.

To attempt to go much further would be to trespass on the fields of the professional philosopher. It may be that Bacon was no more than foreshadowing in terms like *apparent* and *real* what Locke was to call *secondary* and *primary* qualities—that is, for example, color, a secondary quality about which our sense impressions differ, and mass, a primary quality objectively measurable by scientific methods. Bacon's *forms* are perhaps no more than what later scientists meant by *laws* or *uniformities;* but for Bacon these forms are ultimately knowable, are in fact absolutes.

The role of the separate sciences now begins to be so crowded with names and discoveries that the historian of science needs at least as much space as the conventional historian of politics and war used to take up. We can here but summarize briefly. Mathematics continued the progress it had made since the high Middle Ages and reached a point at which it was able to cope with the new problems the astronomers and physicists were presenting. Decimals, no more than a device, but like zero an indispensable device, were invented by the Fleming Simon Stevin in the late sixteenth century. The Scottish mathematician John Napier invented logarithms at about the same time, and in the next century Descartes, about whom we shall hear more, developed the useful device now known as the Cartesian coordinates from which stemmed those graphs which even the man in the street now understands. Pascal, chiefly known to us as a man of letters, made important advances in geometry and in the theory of probability.

In astronomy there is a famous sequence—Copernicus, Tycho Brahe, Kepler, Galileo—out of which the heliocentric conception of our own solar system emerged clearly, together with the beginnings of knowledge of the great universe outside our planetary system. We have already noted how Galileo's summing up and confirmation of all this brought about his trial—and good publicity for his ideas. Taken together with the work of Kepler, that of Galileo set up the conception of a universe that ran in accordance with mathematical laws, but that definitely *moved,* unlike the fixed and unchanging heavens of Aristotelian tradition. Kepler's first law, for instance, noted that the planets do not move around the sun in perfect circles (if they had moved in Aristotelian tradition, they would, of course, have moved in perfect circles, and no one would have made the fine observations and complicated calculations necessary to prove that they did not so move) but that they do move in ellipses of which the sun is one of the foci. The Greeks knew the ellipse from the study of conic sections, but they had never applied it to an attempt to ascertain any "law of nature."

Kepler was a German Protestant, full of visions and enthusiasms.

He seems to have taken astrology seriously, as did all but the most skeptical, or the most Christian, of his time. In his younger days he worked out an elaborate scheme, the *Mysterium Cosmographicum,* which attempts to discern mathematical relations among the planets and the sun such that they confirm a long-standing and purely abstract sequence of relations worked out long long ago by the Pythagoreans of early Greece—the five perfect or "Platonic" bodies, pyramid, cube, octahedron, dodecahedron, icosahedron. But when Kepler found he had made a mistake in his data—he had wrongly estimated the distance of some of the planets from the sun—he gave up his theory. Perhaps we can get no better capsule summary of the significance of scientific method than this. Kepler was looking for a cosmology, a set of truths about the real nature of the universe, just as Plato or Aquinas had looked; but, since he had been trained as a scientist, a corrected observation—a measurement—made it necessary for him to scrap his system and start all over again. Factual data do not so obviously get in the way of the philosopher.

Physics, and especially two of its branches, mechanics and optics, came fully into its own in these centuries. Here too Galileo is of great importance. His experiment with falling objects from the leaning tower of Pisa is one of the most familiar in the history of science. Aristotle had said that bodies fall with velocities proportional to their weights, a heavy body falling faster than a lighter one. Galileo let two such weights fall from the leaning tower of Pisa, and noted that they did not behave as Aristotle said they should. From these observations by much more elaborate experiments and mathematics he developed our modern notions of acceleration and of compounded motion. Again, the Aristotelian notion is that of something "perfect"— circles instead of ellipses, straightforward motion determined by the nature of what is moving; the modern scientific notion is much more complex, takes more complicated mathematics to express, and must be constantly checked against observation to see if the motions it postulates (or predicts) really do take place.

Another Italian, Torricelli, invented the barometer, a German, Von Guericke, the air pump, and many obscure workers helped in the steady improvement of lenses and other instruments that made more refined measurement and observation possible. Boyle and his helper Hooke studied the air and other gases, and began the century-long process that ended in the discovery of oxygen and the founding of modern chemistry.

All these investigations pointed toward some great underlying mechanical principle in nature, a set of very elaborate rules that could be put only in terms of higher mathematics, but still rules suggesting that all nature was a machine. Inevitably this notion inspired researchers in the field we now call biology, and the great seventeenth-century discovery in physiology is an attempt to follow some of the leads given by physicists. Harvey in 1628 published his demonstration that the human heart is in fact a pump, and that the human blood is driven by the heart along a system of circulation. Borelli showed that the human arm is a lever, and that the muscles do mechanical "work." Finally, the microscope as well as the telescope came into use, and scored its first triumphs in the discovery of microorganisms. The Dutchman Van Leeuwenhoek is perhaps best known among these early microscopists, but as has constantly been true in the growth of science, many lesser and now forgotten workers helped in the patient accumulation of data and in limited interpretations of their meaning.

Someone, finally, comes to bring together all this work into a major scientific generalization, a law or uniformity that—still within the limits of natural science—simplifies and explains, co-ordinates many separate laws or uniformities into one general law that sums up millions of man-hours of investigation. The new law is not (still within the limits of science) a final, unalterable, perfect law. It will almost certainly be modified or even, conceivably, shown to be in some sense wrong, given time and long further investigation. But still it is *relatively* permanent, a plateau, a temporary resting place. Galileo almost made this achievement, and a dozen other major figures such as Kepler made essential contributions to the big generalization. It was Newton, however, who drew everything together into that grand mechanical conception which has been called the "Newtonian world-machine." To Newton we shall return in our chapter on the century that revered him, the eighteenth.

Now any such big generalization as that achieved by Newton seems inevitably to influence human thought in many ways, to have its repercussions in fields outside science, in philosophy, in theology, in morals, even in art and literature. Science, we must repeat, does not *as science* provide a cosmology. But scientific achievements, at least in the modern world, have been translated into metaphysics. The scientists of these two centuries were a most varied lot, with varied religions and varied *Weltanschauungen*. Some could not resist the temptation—indeed they could hardly have thought a temptation was involved—to see God as the master mechanic, or to hold that their mathematics were a clue to all life and death, or to hunt in the laboratory for some kind of absolute truth. Some, indeed, like the pious Robert Boyle, kept their science and their religion pretty well in separate compartments, an achievement many scientists can bring off happily even today.

The increasing body of scientific knowledge was chiefly, however, translated into the attitude toward the universe we have here called rationalism. The scientists of the early modern world had shown how great a degree of orderliness underlay many different physical phenomena, how notions natural enough to common sense, like that of the rising and the setting of the sun, were not accurate descriptions of what really went on. Appearance and reality were in their work sharply contrasted. Indeed, their work suggested that the great order of the universe was not altogether what Aristotle and the Christian Fathers had said it was, that this order could not be apprehended by faith, or by reasoning according to a received word, but could be apprehended by rigorous re-examination of everything in the human cultural tradition—a re-examination to be conducted by that deceptive and well-known faculty, reason.

Philosophy

Francis Bacon might well lead off this section, for he was rather a philosopher than a scientist, and we have already noted that he was searching for absolute truth and an infallible way to arrive at it. But Bacon's position in intellectual history, and perhaps his major influence on Western thought, has been as the enemy of deduction and the champion of induction, and though many of his aphorisms have been of great use to the kind of people we call rationalists, his work has on the whole been that of a prophet of natural science. So too was in his own time at least the work of the man who represents with unusual completeness the full philosophic development of seventeenth-century rationalism, the Frenchman René Descartes, whose name we have noted briefly as a mathematician. Descartes is, like so many of the figures we have glanced at in these years of the Renaissance, a polymath, a man of very wide scholarly and scientific interests.

Though Descartes broke with both medieval Scholasticism and with the vague, watered-down Platonism that was about all the high Renaissance produced in formal philosophy, he talked the language of philosophy, cast his thought, revolutionary though in a sense it undoubtedly was, in what anyone would recognize as a philosophic mold. Like all great philosophers, he was by no means a simple thinker; commentators can still find something in him no one else has quite found—at any rate, doctoral theses can still be written about him. For our purposes, however, he can be simplified. Here, as throughout, we are interested in what ordinary educated men made of the work of a great thinker. Descartes, it must be admitted, can hardly be said to have filtered down to the uneducated, save in the most general and vaguest way as one of the men who prepared for the Enlightenment. He presents to the layman unused to the rigors of formal philosophy the kind of difficulties that most of the great philosophers present. Yet he wrote a clear if dry French, and even in translation his work is as readable as can be expected. The background of his most important philosophic ideas is in the *Discourse of Method* (1637).

Descartes grew up in a learned world full of conflicting groups and ideas, a learned world clearly in transition from persisting Scholasticism to some new synthesis. He early decided that his contemporaries and teachers were in a muddled state of mind about the universe, and that he was born to set it right. He has himself described the steps he went through in his progress from repudiation of all authority to his discovery of what he thought was a solid, absolutely certain, rock-bottom truth on which he could build:

I thought . . . that I ought to reject as absolutely false all opinions in regard to which I could suppose the least ground for doubt, in order to ascertain whether after that there remained aught in my belief that was wholly indubitable. Accordingly, seeing that our senses sometimes deceive us, I was willing to suppose that there existed nothing really such as they presented to us; and because some men err in reasoning, and fall into paralogisms, even on the simplest matters of Geometry, I, convinced that I was as open to error as any other, rejected as false all the reasonings I had hitherto taken for demonstrations; and finally, when I considered that the very same thoughts (presentations) which we experience when awake may also be experienced when we are asleep, while there is at that time not one of them true, I supposed that all the objects (presentations) that had ever entered into my mind when awake, had in them no more truth than the illusions of my dreams. But immediately upon this I observed that, whilst I thus wished to think that all was false, it was absolutely necessary that I, who thus thought, should be somewhat; and as I observed that this truth, *I think, hence I am,* was so certain and of such evidence, that no ground of doubt, however extravagant, could be alleged by the Sceptics capable of shaking it, I concluded that I might, without scruple, accept it as the first principle of the Philosophy of which I was in search.

It should be clear that however brazen Descartes's defiance of tradition, this is the language of high philosophy. A true skeptic, an unpleasant skeptic, might ask, Why not "I sweat, therefore I am"? But from this famous "I think, therefore I am" Descartes went ahead to build a system of philosophy that went right on up to God. It was a somewhat remote and impersonal God—Descartes in his sixth Meditation writes, "I now mean by nature . . . nothing but God himself or the order of created things established by God." We need hardly be surprised that the Catholic Church did not feel that the philosopher had redeemed himself from his early doubt, and that the Church has ever since regarded him as belonging to the ranks of its enemies.

Descartes much more clearly than Bacon put the central position of the rationalist. The world is not the confused and rather messy place it seems to be in our first crude, common-sense reflections. On the other hand, the world is not the world of Christian tradition, with its immanent, interfering God and his unpredictable miracles, with its absurd other-worldliness, with all its irrational clutter of medieval ways. Nor is it the Neoplatonic world of the innocent and youthful Renaissance lovers of life and their disillusioned successors. The world is really a vast number of material particles spinning, combining, forming fascinating patterns of such complexity that we are fooled into all sorts of false common-sense and pre-Cartesian philosophic notions. Yet the particles do in fact obey one set of rules, perform their complicated rondo to one tune, and work harmoniously as worked the geometer's mind of René Descartes. The clue to unraveling the obscurities and confusions of our experience is then mathematics. We should think out all our problems as we think out mathematical problems, being careful of our definitions, taking each step carefully and reasonably, seeking above all for clarity and consistency, but never embroiling ourselves in scholastic complexities, never arguing for the sake of arguing. Descartes is not the worshiper of induction Bacon was, and he has the full rationalist contempt for the raw facts our sense impressions pick up.

As a polymath, he interested himself in many fields, and has for instance a small place in the history of physiology, for he did some study in the working of the nervous system. But here as usual he is the philosopher, not the patient laboratory investigator. He was really looking for the seat of the soul (which he thought was uniquely human, not possessed by other vertebrates). He thought he found the seat of the soul in the pineal body, now considered to be a remnant of a once important sense organ in ancestral forms.

Descartes thought it important to find a place for the soul in the body because his system had involved him in a technical problem of great importance in the future history of formal philosophy. We shall not here do more than call the reader's attention to this problem. He can follow it down through Locke, Berkeley, and Kant right into the nineteenth, and even the twentieth, century. It is not, however, a problem that moved the world, however much it moved philosophers, and is, indeed, a good example of how the historian of philosophy and the historian of ideas at work in the crowd must employ different methods and focus on different topics.

Very briefly, then, Descartes was driven from his initial *cogito ergo sum*—I think, therefore I am—to a psychology and a theory of knowledge in which clear thought is contrasted with a muddy sense world somehow outside thought and yet, if we're not all quite mad, in some relation to thought. The soul guides our thinking—perhaps Descartes meant *does* our thinking—and in some way, probably through the nervous system, tells the body what to do. Other animals Descartes definitely thought were mere machines, responding through something close to what we call conditioned reflexes, to environmental stimuli; but men were not quite machines in this sense. Men ran themselves through their souls, souls that shared the rationality of universal laws, mathematics, and God.

From Descartes on many philosophers tried to remedy this dualism of soul and body, spirit and matter, thinking and perceiving. The matter came closest to popular levels in the next century, as may be seen from Boswell's *Life of Johnson*. An English philosopher, George Berkeley, had solved the problem by deciding that "matter" does not exist, that, in a Latin aphorism much like Descartes's own, *esse est percipi*—to be is to be perceived—and that all reality is an idea in the mind of God. Sam Johnson's common sense was outraged by the proposition that matter does not exist, and according to Boswell he kicked a hitching post on the street-side and announced firmly, "Thus, sir, do I confute him."

But the more absurd reaches of the dilemma come out in the problem of solipsism, which is a problem that could hardly arise except in the Cartesian sequence. My thought processes tell me all I know; these processes depend for information on the sense impressions recorded on the nerve-ends and transmitted to my brain; but I never *really* touch what lies beyond those nerve-ends, those telegraph wires that come into my brain; perhaps all these messages are fakes—perhaps there is nothing there; perhaps I am the only person in the universe, and all the rest is an illusion; I *think*, therefore *I* am—but nothing else need be. This is, of course, a position on the lunatic fringe of philosophy, but the whole problem raised by Cartesian dualism is really insoluble, and there exist philosophers today who would class it almost with Zeno's paradox (see p. 39) as no more than an intellectual puzzle.

It must not be thought that Descartes is the sole philosophical rationalist of these centuries, though he is probably the best example of one. Hobbes, whom we have met as the philosopher of the Leviathan state, was in many ways as complete a rationalist as Descartes. Many historians and philosophers have thought it profitable to contrast with rationalism what they call empiricism. Such a classification actually *accepts* the terminology and point of view of the Cartesian dualism. The rationalists are those who emphasize the mental, rational, or "ideal" side of the polarity of soul and body; the empiricists are those who emphasize the material, bodily, sensation side of the polarity. Both sides, however, both empirical and rationalist philosophers, from Bacon through Descartes and Hobbes to Locke himself, held that the universe made sense because it was reasonable, because it had the kind of underlying pattern we see best in the great mathematical and scientific advances of these two centuries. In other words, one philosopher's spirit did the same kind of work another philosopher's matter did. Of course, there are many and great differences in the world-views of such men as Hobbes and Locke, and many philosophical problems on which they do not agree. Still, rationalism and empiricism in the early modern centuries do have one significant thing in common: They hold that the world makes sense—mathematical sense, at bottom.

In fact rationalism with the seventeenth-century Jewish philosopher Spinoza reached quite as far into the intense inane as ever Plato did. Baruch Spinoza, of a Portuguese Jewish family settled in Holland, lives up completely to popular notions of the disinterested philosopher. He refused to succeed in a world which to sensitive souls measures success so crudely and vulgarly. In a century that rewarded men like Descartes with very great public attention, Spinoza turned away and earned his living grinding lenses in The Hague—a job at which he was very expert. He was banished from the synagogue for his unorthodox ideas. He lived the simplest of lives and wrote, in the fashion of his times, most subtly devised metaphysics. We cannot here attempt a real analysis of this philosopher's philosopher. His best-known work, perhaps, is an ethics, *mathematically demonstrated,* in which he uses the outward forms of mathematical demonstration to arrive at God and perfect goodness. Spinoza is sometimes given the label of "pantheist," but the label is a cold and unfeeling one for so ardent a seeker after a God at once perfect and remote, and yet not quite beyond our imperfect human understanding. Reason leads him to mystic surrender, to the "intellectual love of God":

> And this intellectual love of the mind toward God is the very love of God with which God loves himself, not in so far as he is infinite, but in so far as he can be expressed by the essence of the human mind, considered under the form of eternity; that is, the intellectual love of the mind toward God is a part of the infinite love with which God loves himself. From this we clearly comprehend in what our salvation, or blessedness, or freedom, consists; to wit, in an unchangeable and eternal love toward God, that is, in the love of God toward men. This love or blessedness is in the sacred Scriptures called glory.

It is a shame to dismiss Spinoza thus curtly; he is worth the attention of anyone who wants to penetrate into a temperament intellectuals have always admired, the sweet, unworldly rebel capable of amazing firmness in matters of the mind. For us, however, it must be enough to note that Spinoza in the great century of scientific advance, and working with the concepts of mathematics, arrived at as "other-worldly" a philosophy as ever any medieval thinker did. Many, many roads lead to the no-place of the mystic.

Political Ideas

The political ideas of the early rationalists are for the most part of the kind we discussed in the last chapter. Hobbes, notably, rejected theories like that of the divine right of kings, for the rationalist has to deny the divine in the traditional Christian sense. But he still believed that there was a system of *right* political relations that could be discovered by thinking about certain given propositions concerning human behavior—such as the proposition that all men want security first and the proposition that in a state of nature they do not have security. From this, according to Hobbes, it follows "rationally" that men will get together and make a contract to create a sovereign quite as absolute as any divine one, but the creation of men in nature. Thinkers like Hobbes, Harrington, and Bodin were humanists influenced by the rationalist current of their times, all working in a traditional frame of reference. They prepared the way for the politics of the Enlightenment, the political attitudes we Americans inherit firsthand, but they did not quite reach the full optimism of the eighteenth-century philosophers.

What is new and original in the political thought of these centuries is the work of Machiavelli. Now Machiavelli shares with all those we have called rationalist a complete dismissal of the idea that there is anything supernatural, that there is any kind of God who intervenes in the day-to-day affairs of men. Machiavelli simply pays no attention to the medieval notion that God is behind the moral order. He sets out with Renaissance curiosity to find out how men actually behave. We shall see that he also has really pretty firm notions of how men ought to behave. But there is certainly a basis for Francis Bacon's praise of him: We owe a lot to Machiavelli, said Bacon, for telling us what men do instead of what they ought to do. In other words, some part at least of Machiavelli's work seems to be of the kind the natural scientist does; it is based on observation, on the collection of the facts, as the starting point of all thinking on the subject. Some of his thinking is based on patriotism, on an Italian's hatred for the foreign powers who dominated Italy. He is by no means a modern anti-intellectual. Like Bacon, he carries with him much of the Middle Ages. But, again as with Bacon, and notably in some pages of *The Prince,* he is trying to analyze his data and put them together without concern for morals or metaphysics.

Machiavelli's famous—and to many still infamous—little book *The Prince* was published in 1531, four years after its author's death. With the *Commentary on Livy,* it gives a fair cross-section of Machiavelli's mind and method. In *The Prince* Machiavelli sets out to describe the ways in which an individual ruler (prince) can most readily retain and strengthen his position as ruler. He does not attempt to ascertain what the good or the best prince will do, nor what is the justification for obedience, nor indeed what are the rights and wrongs of politics. He sets himself a technical problem: given certain conditions, what other conditions will maintain, strengthen, or weaken the original conditions. But let him say it:

> We now have left to consider what should be the manners and attitudes of a prince toward his subjects and his friends. As I know that many have written on this subject I feel that I may be held presumptuous in what I have to say, if in my comments I do not follow the lines laid down by others. Since, however, it has been my intention to write something which may be of use to the understanding reader, it has seemed wiser to me to follow the real truth of the matter rather than what we imagine it to be. For imagination has created many principalities and republics that have never been seen or known to have any real existence, for how we live is so different from how we ought to live that he who studies what ought to be done rather than what is done will learn the way to his downfall rather than to his preservation. A man striving in every way to be good will meet his ruin among the great number who are not good. Hence it is necessary for a prince, if he wishes to remain in power, to learn how not to be good and to use his knowledge or refrain from using it as he may need. . . . Further, he should have no concern about incurring the infamy of such vices without which the preservation of his state would be difficult. For, if the matter be well considered, it will be seen that some habits which appear virtuous, if adopted would signify ruin, and others that seem vices lead to security and the well-being of the prince.

Machiavelli then goes on to test in concrete problems the validity of this general thesis. Should a prince be generous or mean? Should he be *thought* to be generous or mean? Is cruelty or clemency the wiser course? Machiavelli answers, as a physician or indeed in low ordinary matters anyone of common sense would answer, that it all depends on the other elements in the situation, on the other *variables* in a human situation too involved to be put into any mathematical equation. But again let us sample Machiavelli:

> Here the question arises; whether it is better to be loved than feared or feared than loved. The answer is that it would be desirable to be both but, since that is difficult, it is much safer to be feared than to be loved, if one must choose. For on men in general this observation may be made: they are ungrateful, fickle, and deceitful, eager to avoid dangers, and avid for gain, and while you are useful to them they are all with you, offering you their blood, their property, their lives, and their sons so long as danger is remote, as we noted above, but when it approaches they turn on you. Any prince, trusting only in their words and having no other preparations made, will fall to his ruin, for friendships that are bought at a price and not by greatness and nobility of soul are paid for indeed, but they are not owned and cannot be called upon in time of need. Men have less hesitation in offending a man who is loved than one who is feared, for love is held by a bond of obligation which, as men are wicked, is broken whenever personal advantage suggests it, but fear is accompanied by the dread of punishment which never relaxes.
>
> Yet a prince should make himself feared in such a way that, if he does not thereby merit love, at least he may escape odium, for being feared and not hated may well go together. And indeed the prince may attain this end if he but respect the property and the women of his subjects and citizens. And if it should become necessary to seek the death of someone, he should find a proper justification and a public cause, and above all he should keep his hands off another's property, for men forget more readily the death of their father than the loss of their patrimony. Besides, pretexts for seizing property are never lacking, and when a prince begins to live by means of rapine he will always find some excuse for plundering others, and conversely pretexts for execution are rarer and are more quickly exhausted.

These passages may seem true or false, or a mixture of both, to a reader of the mid-twentieth century; but they will not seem new. The psychologists have got us used to the notion that men's bad actions should be studied as well as condemned, or even studied rather than condemned. But all this was very new when Machiavelli committed it to print. Though men in the Middle Ages conducted themselves no better than in Machiavelli's description of the constants of human nature, the people who wrote books did not do much more than note the existence of such behavior. Chiefly, they preached against it, they were indignant at its immorality, and, most important of all, they held it to be unnatural behavior for human beings, even though they could hardly help admitting that it existed.

Machiavelli is then original, at least in the context of Western Christian culture, in his realistic political analysis. He is in some senses trying to do what the natural scientists were just beginning to do—observe phenomena carefully and arrange these observations into laws (uniformities, generalizations) that would enable successful prediction of the future phenomena in the given context. But he did not succeed in his field as well as the scientists did in theirs. We may here note three ways in which Machiavelli fails to apply the scientific method to the study of politics (it has not yet been wholly successfully applied, and there are those who do not think it can be at all profitably applied, to the study of politics).

First, even in the brief quotations given, you will have noted an excessively low or pessimistic view of human nature. Men in general, he says, are ungrateful, fickle, and deceitful. Scientifically speaking, it is probably impossible to make any sensible generalization of this sort about human beings; on one view of science, a problem of this sort is meaningless. Most of us do, however, make some sort of judgment, in the balance, about our fellow creatures seen as a whole. But all the way from a trusting love of one's fellows to a passionate contempt for them there are variant attitudes which, though often wise and useful to individuals who take these attitudes, are most certainly not to be classified as scientific judgments. Machiavelli's attitude is far out toward extreme cynicism. It was probably inspired partly as a reaction against the pious commonplaces of Christianity, which, if it accepts the doctrine of original sin, is not in fact cynical about human beings, is indeed much concerned with their possible salvation. Machiavelli seems to want to shock, to seem to be a wise and wicked fellow. He may, of course, be an inverted idealist, a man who is cynical just because he wants so much perfection. There are grave psychological problems here, difficult to solve in the study of living men, almost impossible with figures of the past. Machiavelli does indeed seem the balked intellectual; he is clearly taking a position not that of the vulgar, the average, the conventional intellectual of his day.

Second, Machiavelli's detachment is greatly limited by his warm Italian patriotism. *The Prince* is not in intent an academic or scientific treatise on the art of governing. It is a treatise on the art of governing in Italy in the Cinquecento; and it is a treatise in which the duty—quite as much as the benefits—of uniting Italy and expelling the foreigner are urged upon the prince. Machiavelli's last chapter in *The Prince* is an ardent paean to Italy, and helped redeem Machiavelli's reputation with later generations who found Italian nationalism a noble cause. We need here no more than note that this too is a distortion in Machiavelli's effort to see things as they really were. He wants things so different, he wants Italians so different, that he cannot quite attain detachment.

Finally, though Machiavelli had had a certain experience of international relations and of other government business on an appointive or bureaucratic level, he wrote these most famous works of his in something like academic retirement. Just as he leaned over backward in an effort not to write piously about unreal human beings (as say John of Salisbury must have seemed to him to write) so he leaned over backward in his effort to be no academic intellectual but a man of the world. This last is a disastrous pose, a distortion of the worst sort. Machiavelli tries too hard to be worldly; he has shocked quite unscrupulous but conventional people for several centuries. His very reputation for wickedness—or for counseling wickedness—in itself is proof of his failure. Scientific knowledge does not contain the corrosive acids of Machiavelli's wit.

Yet Machiavelli is rightly regarded as one of the pioneers of the effort to study the behavior of men in society as the scientist studies the behavior of gases or of insects. This effort may be doomed in advance to failure; in another few centuries the "social science" of today may seem one of the blind alleys men have followed. But at present, committed as we are to their pursuit, we must be grateful to Machiavelli. Much of what he said had indeed been said before, much of it in Greek political thought; Aristotle, for example, had observed some of the ways men behaved in political life and had noted them down. There is a whole literature of aphorisms and short essays on human nature, on the quirks and foibles and little and big follies of men. But most of this adds up to common sense or to a sort of equivalent folk-wisdom. It is like the weather-wisdom of the old inhabitant. Science must always attempt to systematize and measure and put into somewhat formidable terms—in the long run most useful—what folk-wisdom puts in hunches. The first meteorologists may be less reliable than the weather-wise old salt. They may seem rather crude and brash and impractical. But in the long run the systematic science wins out.

Machiavelli is the scientist in his initial and very self-conscious stage. He is going to get at what really lies behind all these fine words men write about politics and ethics. He is not going to be content with a few random reflections on these matters. He will study systematically certain problems, not to find what is right, but just to find what is. He does not wholly succeed in keeping an even temper, in being as detached as he should be. Above all, he fails in general—though there are signs that he sees the factor concerned—to realize that men's ethical ideas and ideals, even though they do not stand in a simple causal relation to men's deeds, stand in *some* relation to men's deeds. In other words, Machiavelli makes the mistake still repeated by some of our deliberately hard-boiled writers on politics and morals; he writes off men's professions of good just because they do not wholly live up to them.

Francis Bacon, too, belongs in his own right to the list of those who have attempted to study human behavior as the scientist studies anatomy or physiology. Notably in the first book of his *Instauratio Magna* he outlines a subject that has much concerned social and political psychologists in our own time—the systematic study of the way in which the human mind is influenced in its workings by nonlogical, nonexperimental factors. Again, men have known since our culture began that the "human understanding is no dry light," as Bacon put it. We have long known that the wish is father to the thought, that men entertain prejudices, that our very language is full of ambiguities and double meanings, so that even if the will to be precise and objective is there the way is still hard. But Bacon's analysis of these difficulties under the name of "idols" is still suggestive, still one of the best systematic attempts to classify our rationalizations.

He finds four classes of idols which beset men's minds, the Idols of the Tribe, of the Cave, of the Market-place, and of the Theater. By Idols of the Tribe he means the errors that have their origin in human nature itself, in our sense apparatus and in our minds. The statement "man is the measure of all things" means in fact that even in science our standards tend to vary subjectively. By Idols of the Cave Bacon means something close to the ordinary meaning of prejudice, the errors molded and produced by our own personality, the little cave we have hollowed for ourselves in this harsh world. By the Idols of the Market-place he means what we should call the distortions of propaganda and advertising, the mutual excitation men work upon one another in crowds or in almost any kind of social intercourse, the errors of men gathered together. By Idols of the Theater Bacon means the errors men accumulate when they try to work out systematic interpretations of the universe—these are the errors of philosophers and intellectuals, the errors of system-building in which it is easy to hold that Bacon himself erred. But let him define this last Idol:

> Lastly, there are Idols which have immigrated into men's minds from the various dogmas of philosophies, and also from wrong laws of demonstration. These I call Idols of the Theater; because in my judgment all the received systems are but so many stage-plays, representing worlds of their own creation after an unreal and scenic fashion. Nor is it only of the systems now in vogue, or only of the ancient sects and philosophies, that I speak: for many more plays of the same kind may yet be composed and in like artificial manner set forth; seeing that errors the most widely different have nevertheless causes for the most part alike. Neither again do I mean this only of entire systems, but also of many principles and axioms in science, which by tradition, credulity, and negligence have come to be received.

It goes without saying that the attempt to apply to the study of human relations methods similar in some respects to those of the natural sciences bore no such fruits as did the application of these methods to the natural sciences. Even today, there is no unanimity about the social sciences—though it is definitely fashionable to contrast them unfavorably with the "real" sciences.

Just as Cartesian rationalism or Baconian empiricism did in fact aim at achieving a cosmology, a certainty about all possible relations in the universe, so most of those who broke with medieval notions of political thought were themselves working up a system of politics that seemed to them somehow outside the imperfections of politics as practiced. We shall see in the next chapter that the political and moral thinking of early modern times had by the eighteenth century turned definitely into rationalist channels. But the result was not so much a science of politics as another political ideology, or rather a group of ideologies. All this is not said in complaint. Unless men change their nature radically, political ideologies and metaphysical systems seem essential to human spiritual needs. We are still living in the system of ideas about the Big Questions that was prepared in the early modern centuries and came to fruition in the eighteenth century.

Making the Modern World – A Summary

Between the fifteenth and the eighteenth centuries the modern culture of Western society was formed. By the eighteenth century educated men and women, and we may believe many of the uneducated, had come to hold certain beliefs about themselves, about the universe, about what was worth doing on earth, about what could be done on earth, beliefs that their ancestors of the Middle Ages had not held. They lived in a world that seemed to them new, since their ideas about it were new. They were not, of course, totally new; most of Western society was Christian in 1700, as it had been in 1400. It is a central thesis of this book that much of what the men and women of the eighteenth and later centuries believed was incompatible with some very important parts of traditional Christian belief; or less ponderously, that the Enlightenment *radically altered* Christian belief. Still it is clear that a very great deal of Christianity has remained—and not merely the formal organization of the churches.

Yet one very simple and unambiguous change is there for all to see. In the thirteenth century there was but one organized ecclesiastical body in the West, the Roman Catholic Church; in the eighteenth there were already several hundred sects in the whole of Western society. Even in such countries as France where on the surface the Catholic Church was still supreme, there were several hundred thousand Protestants and an unknown number of deists, atheists, and skeptics, all pretty open about their beliefs or lack of belief, and very few exposed to any serious danger of the medieval punishment of their kind. Voltaire's pamphlets against the executions of Calas and de la Barre by persecuting Catholics must not mislead us; theirs were the *rare* case, at least in the West. The working unity of Christianity had been broken, and already by 1700 there was a body of writings that defended the notion that religious differences *ought* to be tolerated, that Church and State are rightfully separable, that the individual should make up his own mind in matters of religious belief. Indeed, the way was clear for such eighteenth-century ideas as the notion that there is *some* truth in all religions—even in non-Christian religions.

To Americans today such notions are so common that it is difficult to realize how very new they are, how sharply contrasted with what men and women of only a few centuries ago assumed with equal confidence to be true. They are notions that imply a new criterion of truth—metaphysical and theological truth—rather than the abandonment of the search for this sort of truth. In the Middle Ages these truths were held to be revealed, and perfect in their revelation; men might lose sight of them, might even as heirs of Adam's sin go against them; but no one could be *right,* no one could know the truth, and be against them. In the light of these medieval notions, the burning of heretics was understandable. They were rotten fruit, and if left alone they might corrupt the sound fruit; moreover, they were damned, and to cut them off from actual living was doing them no real harm—they had done that to themselves already. In short, if you know you are right, anyone who differs from you must be wrong.

People should be right, and not wrong. You cannot let wrong notions spread without doing very great harm.

Now although the rationalizations or justifications of religious toleration are only beginning to spread and develop in the early eighteenth century, the main lines of defense are clear. Though they vary in detail, they add up to one of three propositions: that there is a new truth, deeper than that of traditional Christianity, which will if tolerated ultimately supplant or thoroughly modify it; that truth is not revealed perfect and complete to men, but must be discovered progressively by trial and error, by investigation, by human effort; or to the proposition, *little held in these early days,* that there is no such thing as truth or certainty in such matters, that all truth is "relative," that neither revelation nor thinking and studying will arrive at absolutes. But all these propositions agree in rejecting at least something in the Christian heritage from the Middle Ages; they all claim to lead to something new and something better.

The change in fundamentals is neatly pointed up at the turn of the seventeenth into the eighteenth century by an apparently insignificant debate among men of letters in France and in England, a debate usually called by its French name *la quérelle des anciens et des modernes*—the quarrel between the ancients and the moderns. One of the memorials of its English phase is Swift's amusing *Battle of the Books.* Briefly, one side maintained that the Greeks and the Romans had achieved a culture in general and in detail unsurpassable; they were the giants who staked out the fields of human culture and set examples we can but imitate from afar. Classical culture was to these people a kind of lay or humanist Eden; it was blasphemy to suppose that the like could ever again appear on earth. The other side maintained that, although the achievements of the Greeks and Romans were very great indeed, they were, so to speak, records that modern Europeans had the chance to break; modern culture could be as good, or better, in every field; there was no use in holding the men of old to be inevitably our superiors, for we could benefit by their works, we could stand on their shoulders and reach all the higher.

The position of the moderns in this quarrel is one of the first forms of the very important doctrine of progress so familiar to all Americans today, the idea that novelty is neither a delusion nor a falling off, but the natural working out of some kind of universal plan. We do not know how this basic, revolutionary change in outlook came about. We do know that it was a very complex and relatively slow process, in which we can discern three main intellectual constituents.

First came a great series of changes in the practices and ideals of Christianity under the name of Protestantism. The Protestant movement had its full share of human heroism and human weakness, of struggle and accident and strange ends. Its narrative history, over which in a book of this sort we have to pass wholly, is a fascinating record. But for the intellectual historian it is probable that the chief importance of Protestantism is as a *dissolvent*—the strongest at work in these years—of medieval authority. The Protestant movement broke through the formal unity Western Christendom had preserved for a millennium and a half, and set up a dozen major and hundreds of minor groups or sects in the position of claiming full religious authority in their fields. Protestantism, by the fact that it split into sects and subsects, prepared the way for religious skepticism. For to a mind at all inclined to doubt, or addicted to logic, the spectacle of a great number of contradictory and antithetical beliefs—each claiming monopoly of truth—could be taken as evidence that there existed no truth to be monopolized. More positively, Protestantism, especially in its Anglican and Lutheran forms, worked as a buttress to strengthen the patriotic sentiments of members of the new territorial national states. God was still—to put it otherwise would have been to leave Christianity wholly behind—a God of all the human race; but in a sense he played favorites, treated the English or the Prussians or the Danes as his preferred children. In the practice and administration of day-to-day religious life these new national churches had no share in an international and cosmopolitan life of the kind the old medieval church had possessed. Calvinist Protestantism in particular encouraged among its faithful a paradoxical mixture of other-worldly longing for union with God, a longing that stands out in all Puritan living, and a very this-worldly respect for the man who worked hard and prospered materially. But the first Protestants made no new universe; they believed in original sin, in the inspiration of the Bible, in an authority not, to be sure, invested in the pope of Rome, but still an authority above the trial-and-error processes of ordinary living. The Protestants believed in an immanent God not at all like the laws of mathematics. They believed in hell-fire and, for the elect, in heavenly bliss.

Humanism, the second force making for change, was much more than the application of some vague Protestant or libertarian spirit to the secular life. It had in common with Protestantism a corrosive effect on what was left of medieval standards. It questioned the authority of immediate custom and of established scholastic philosophy. It was an active rebellion of artists and scholars. Some of its artists mastered their media magnificently (with the help of methods worked out by generations who had been trained in medieval methods) and produced very great art. Many of them were adventurous, free-living, romantic, and exciting people who helped set our modern standards of the artist and writer as necessarily unconventional, impractical, selfish, but rather winning. Its *virtù* was in no clear sense a very Christian ideal, but rather the ideal of an athletic youth. Humanism, like Calvinism, had its own deep-seated paradox. The humanists rebelled against clerical authority and the weight of tradition; they seem at least in their practice to hold the modern notion that men *make* their standards, *make* their truth, and do not merely discover it. Yet as a group they fell into a most pious attitude of respect for the masters of antiquity, whom they set up as authorities quite as absolute as any the Middle Ages worshiped. They had little awareness of the coming spread of ideas and aspirations to the masses; they were a privileged group of educated men, rather inclined to aristocratic and monarchical ideals, in no sense democrats. They did not think the world could be a very much better place, except perhaps for themselves.

Rationalism, the third force, was also an agent of destruction, less obvious and less powerful in the early years of the modern age than

Protestantism or humanism, in the long run more important and more powerful. The rationalist threw overboard far more of traditional Catholic Christianity than did the Protestant or the humanist. He not merely banished the supernatural from his universe; he was prepared to place man himself wholly within the framework of nature or the "material universe." He thought indeed that man had to guide himself by standards of right and wrong. The rationalists of the earlier centuries of our modern era thought these standards were fixed and certain, and that men *found* rather than made them. But where the medieval Christian found these standards in custom, in authority, in what had been so time out of mind, the rationalist sought to find them beneath appearances, custom, and apparent diversities, and to find them by a patient investigation in which the rational mind found the mathematical reality behind the vulgarly varied and colored appearance. Rationalism has none of the obvious paradoxes of Protestantism and humanism—unless, indeed, you are so far a real skeptic as to hold that it is a paradox to try to think any kind of orderly system into human experience of this world. Rationalism even in these years owed much of its slowly growing prestige to the achievements of natural science. Finally, when with Newton science succeeded in attaining to a marvelously complete scheme of the universe, one that could be tested mathematically and that worked in the sense that it enabled successful prediction, the stage was set for the new rationalist worldview, for a cosmology as different from that of St. Augustine or St. Thomas Aquinas as theirs was from that of a Greek of the fifth-century B.C.

II

The Eighteenth Century

WITH THE EIGHTEENTH CENTURY the intellectual historian finds himself faced with a difficulty that faces all historians of the last few centuries: He is overwhelmed with materials. You can make exhaustive lists of medieval thinkers; and a conscientious scholar could master the actual writings of all the Greek and Roman survivors. But with the invention of printing, with the proliferation of writers of all sorts who could be supported by a society with increasing command over its material environment, the mass of writings in all fields is too much for any single scholar, and indeed for any organized company of scholars. Moreover, there seems to be an increasing range of taste and opinion. A process like that which multiplied Protestant sects multiplies opinions of all sorts in all fields of *noncumulative* knowledge; and *cumulative* knowledge continues to pile up in something like geometric progression. Now possibly this range and complexity can be explained by the printing press and good rag paper (unlike our modern newspapers, which will disintegrate into unusable shape in less than half a century, even the periodical and fugitive writings of the eighteenth and early nineteenth centuries have survived in full legibility). The Middle Ages may have been as many-minded as our own. But we have to go by what we have, and what we have is—well, all but a tiny fraction of the over *eight million* books and pamphlets in the Library of Congress were published since 1700.

Our generalizations must, then, be based on but a small sampling of the immense amount of information available. We cannot even pay as much attention to the great seminal minds as we have been able to pay hitherto, for we must concentrate on ideas as they get to work among the nameless many. We can but suggest that the reader go himself to the work of the men and women who put the last touches on our intellectual inheritance, who gave our Western culture its characteristic modern form or, if you are a certain kind of pessimist in these matters, its modern formlessness.

The Agents of Enlightenment

It is most foolhardy to attempt to summarize the Enlightenment in a sentence; and indeed we shall shortly return to the task of shading and filling in. For the present, we may say that the basic idea and the striking novelty of the Enlightenment—the idea that makes it a cosmology—is *the belief that all human beings can attain here on this earth a state of perfection hitherto in the West thought to be possible only for Christians in a state of grace, and for them only after death.* St. Just, the youthful French revolutionary, put it with deceptive simplicity before the Convention: *le bonheur est une idée neuve en Europe*—happiness is a new idea in Europe. Not new in heaven, of course, but new in Europe, pretty new even in America.

This perfectibility of human kind had not been brought about by nearly two thousand years of Christianity, nor by the preceding paganism of other millennia. If it were to be brought about in the eighteenth century, obviously something new—some invention or discovery—had to be made. This something new is best summed up in the work of two late seventeenth-century Englishmen who brought to a focus the preparatory work of the early modern centuries, Newton and Locke. Newton's life work, and especially his perfection of the calculus and his grand mathematical formulation of the relation of the planets and the laws of gravity, seemed to contemporaries to explain all natural phenomena, or at least to show how all such phenomena—

including the behavior of human beings—could be explained. Locke, taking the methods of clear simple reasoning out of the bewildering metaphysics where Descartes had landed them, seemed to make them a nice extension of common sense. He seemed to show men the way Newton's great successes could be applied to the study of human affairs. Together, Newton and Locke set up those great clusters of ideas, Nature and Reason, which were to the Enlightenment what such clusters of ideas as grace, salvation, and predestination were to traditional Christianity.

Nature was to the Enlightenment wholly a benign concept. To the Christian, even to the Thomist Christian, Nature was always somewhat suspect, and certainly always inadequate without the help of the divine. From the time of the Enlightenment on, however, those who used the term Nature to try to influence human beings enjoyed to the full the benefits of the ambiguity we noted earlier in our discussion of the natural law of the Romans (see p. 130). Nature, to the man of the Enlightenment, was the external world he lived in, a world that clearly existed but in which by no means everything that happened was "natural." In fact, to the really ardent eighteenth-century partisan of the Enlightenment almost everything that happens, that exists at the moment, almost everything in the *actual* external world of Nature —or at any rate, of *human* nature as organized in society—was *unnatural*. Class distinctions, the etiquette of society, the privileges of clergy and nobles, the contrast of slum and palace—these did exist, but they were unnatural. Of course our partisan was thinking of *natural* in the sense of "good," or "normal," *unnatural* as "bad" or "abnormal." The point is that the Nature of Newton as filtered down into the educated and half-educated was the orderly, untroubled, beautifully simple working of the universe *properly understood*. Once we understand this Nature in human affairs, all we have to do is to regulate our actions accordingly, and there will be no more unnatural behavior.

We understand the workings of this immanent (but not to the *untrained* obvious or indeed perceptible) Nature by what the Enlightenment loved to call Reason—often, as here, with a capital R. Reason is at its clearest, and indeed first showed itself among men, as mathematics. Reason, argued the agents of Enlightenment, enables us to penetrate from appearances to reality. Without Reason, or even with the faulty kind of Reason that, as common sense, men got along with for so many centuries, we should believe that the sun actually "rises" and "sets"; with Reason, we know the true relation of earth and sun. Similarly, Reason applied to human relations will show us that kings are not fathers of their people, that if meat is good to eat on Thursdays it is good to eat on Fridays, that if pork is nourishing to a Gentile it is nourishing to a Jew. Reason will enable us to find human institutions, human relations that are "natural"; once we find such institutions, we shall conform to them and be happy. Reason will clear up the mess that superstition, revelation, faith (the devils of the rationalists) have piled up here on earth.

With the validity of this leap, or series of leaps, from the law of gravity to human relations we are not at the moment concerned. The point is that the generation that read Newton and Locke made the leap. Neither Newton nor Locke went as far as the men of the next two or three generations who appealed to their authority. Outside his own work as a natural scientist, Newton was no innovator, and indeed is best known in such fields for a most unmodern and unenlightened excursion into Biblical literature. Locke, whose main concern was indeed psychology, ethics, and political theory, was a cautious person, a middle-of-the-roader, for whom the new methods served in part at least to confirm ancient wisdom.

Nor is the first generation to spread the new gospel of Reason radical in a simplifying, extremist fashion. This generation did indeed popularize and make available for ordinary educated men—and very definitely by this time, women—the ideas of the seventeenth century, which Alfred Whitehead has called the "century of genius." They are mostly Frenchmen, and indeed if on the whole England had rather more than her share of the seminal minds that produced the ideas of the Enlightenment, it was above all the French who transmitted these ideas throughout Europe and into Russia, even into the growing outposts of Western society all over the world. The greatest of these Frenchmen is Voltaire, in whose ninety-odd volumes you will find neatly and often wittily expressed the whole stock of ideas with which the Enlightenment started.

Started, not finished. For Voltaire, with Montesquieu, Pope, the English deists, belongs to the first or moderate generation of the Enlightenment. They are still greatly influenced by the current of taste we analyzed in Chapter VIII, the "spare humanists" of the Age of Louis XIV. They still believe in restraint, in decorum, in those "rules of old discovered, not devised" which preserve a social as well as an aesthetic equilibrium. They don't like the stuffy old ways, especially when the stuffiness is applied with compulsion, and in particular they dislike the old churches, Catholic and Anglican. They make fun of what they don't like. The next generation will find the old ways much too objectionable to joke about.

Montesquieu's *Spirit of the Laws* (1748), the great sociological work of the moderate first generation, marks a kind of turning point. Though Voltaire lives until 1778, an object of hero worship in his final years, the new men after 1750 are mostly radicals. Like most radicals, they tend to be one-sided, to push a particular idea into the ground, to be, in short, sectarian. If their main interest is in religion, they go on from a mild deism to outright materialism and atheism. This atheism is not in any sense a form of skepticism, but a positive belief that the universe is a great machine. If they are psychologists, they go on from Locke's innocent distinction between primary and secondary qualities to construct a whole man on the basis of sensations impinging on an automatically recording psyche; that is, they have already the essence of twentieth-century notions of behaviorism, conditioned reflexes, and the like. Helvetius and Holbach are already at the point of view neatly summarized in the title of a book by a lesser colleague, La Mettrie's *L'homme machine,* "Man the Machine." If they are economists, they go on with the French physiocrats to coin one of the great simplicities of our world—and a powerful one—*laissez-faire, laissez-passer*—or to such long-popular slogans as "that government governs best which governs least, and least expensively."

Adam Smith, whose *Wealth of Nations* was first published in 1776, and the Scottish group generally are exceptions to our rule. Smith is a moderate, a man temperamentally of the first generation of the Enlightenment, by no means a doctrinaire believer in absolutely free economic competition; it was his followers who simplified his doctrines into "rugged individualism." Or finally, with Rousseau this second generation could plunge into complete emotional rejection of their social and cultural environment and seek to make it over wholly in accord with the dictates of the Nature that spoke so clearly to simple peasants, primitive savages, children, and literary men like themselves.

By the time a third generation had grown up, the two elements of the later Enlightenment, the rationalist-classical and the sentimental-romantic, had been fully developed. In the critical years before the French Revolution, these two attitudes, these two clusters of ideas, worked together at least to the discredit of the old regime. We shall attempt in a later chapter a more detailed analysis of the importance of the Romantic Movement, which exists quite full-blown in Rousseau. Here we may note that rationalism and romanticism are inseparably woven together in the minds of most eighteenth-century Western men of the Enlightenment. Reason and sentiment not merely agreed to condemn the old ways of nobles, priests, and the unenlightened generally; in many minds, they combined to approve the new, the rule of the *intelligent and kind-hearted* majority of unspoiled men. Indeed, the *natural* man of the simpler followers of the Enlightenment was *both* naturally virtuous and naturally reasonable; his heart and his head were both sound.

It is not here maintained that differences between Rousseau and the rationalists did not exist. They were real, they were picturesquely expressed, and they are worth studying. Romanticism was a *revolt* from rationalism. But it is much more important for us to note that the revolt was the revolt of a child from its parent—a child that greatly resembled the parent. The resemblance lay in a fundamental: both rejected the doctrine of original sin, and both held that man's life on earth can be almost indefinitely improved—that he can lead the good life—if certain environmental changes are made.

A third generation listened to both rationalist and romantic and made the American and the French revolutions, remade Britain without a revolution, and set the foundations for the developed cosmology of the nineteenth century. These men were of varied kinds, by no means in agreement. Indeed, at the height of the French Revolution they set a classic example of quarrels to the death—for power, no doubt, but power embodied in ideas. To seek a least common denominator among John Adams, Sam Adams, Thomas Jefferson, Tom Paine, La Fayette, Danton, Robespierre, Francis Place, Lord Grey, and the other leaders of this movement would be difficult and unprofitable. We shall here attempt only to indicate the broad lines of the attitude toward human relations, toward society in the broadest sense of the word, which might be that of an ordinary, educated, forward-looking young person of the later eighteenth century in the Western world.

He must of necessity be a fictitious person. Even in the cosmopolitan eighteenth century there would be firm national and regional imprints; the young Westernizing Russian aristocrat reading Voltaire in French was not much like the Yankee lad discovering in Locke and the English deists how wrong his Congregational minister was about hell-fire. The young German, especially, was even by 1780 the soulful, deep, questing German never contented with the shallow rationalism of his French neighbors and enemies. He was already on his German way to something more, something greater, something immeasurable, something impossible. We shall, however, have much to do later with nationalism. Here we must attempt frankly a process of simplification and abstraction.

One further word is needed before we attempt to see what the new cosmology was. With the eighteenth century we are in many ways in modern times. Certainly we have no longer any serious question about the *fact* of the spread of ideas in some form among many thousands, indeed millions, who cannot be numbered among the intellectuals, nor among the ruling classes in any restricted sense of the term. There are many and unresolved problems regarding the nature of their spread, indeed there are in essence all the problems that face us today in the study of public opinion. But at least we know there *was* a public opinion, and we have some clues to what it believed.

The newspaper was in its infancy at the beginning of the century, though by the end it had attained something like its modern form, especially in England, the United States, and France. Throughout the century, however, the cheap pamphlet or broadside meant that the printed word could circulate very widely. Books remained relatively expensive, but there were the beginnings of the circulating library in many social clubs and other voluntary groups. Literacy now began to extend to a considerable part of the population in the West. The masses did not yet read, though by the end of the century the skilled workers in the more advanced countries could and did read. Only the rural masses were still completely illiterate, and the French Revolution made a beginning of literacy even for them. The important thing, however, is the existence in all these countries of a strong, literate middle class, numbering all told several millions, and devoted to the ideas of the Enlightenment.

Finally, the eighteenth century saw the ripening of those characteristically modern agents of the spread of ideas for which we really have no good single name—they were voluntary groups organized sometimes for a specific goal, like the later Anti-Saloon League in the United States, sometimes for social ritual and insurance, like the many fraternal societies, sometimes for pure amusement, like the informal conversation groups the French call *salons*. Western society in the eighteenth century had a very rich group life indeed. As the century wore on, especially in France, all these groups, even those that seem as remote from the history of ideas as a *tabagie* (i.e., smoking club, from *tabac,* tobacco) became in fact agents for the spread of the new, and by then actually revolutionary ideas. Of course, these bourgeois flirted, danced, played cards, and indulged in small talk; but they probably mixed in more serious intellectual effort than is usual in such circles. Even their pleasures took on a tinge of what they fashionably called *patriotisme,* which is not what we call patriotism, but rather loyalty toward the Enlightenment. The French have a game of cards, a variant of whist, which they call *le boston,* after the town that stood up so valiantly in the 1770's for the new ideas.

The Faith of the Enlightened

In the widest terms the change in the attitude of Western men toward the universe and everything in it was the change from the Christian supernatural heaven after death to the rationalist natural heaven on this earth, now—or at least very shortly. But the clearest way of realizing the greatness of that change is to start off with a very basic modern doctrine that is unquestionably new—the doctrine of progress. Belief in progress, in spite of the two world wars of our generation and the grave economic crisis of the thirties, is still so much a part of the way young Americans are brought up that very few Americans realize how unprecedented that belief is. Of course, men have long felt that one way of doing something is "better" than another; they have known specific improvements in techniques; above all, they have been aware as members of a group that their particular group was in a flourishing state, or the reverse.

But go over briefly what you have learned of fifth-century Athens. Here were men in the flush of a very great corporate achievement, men who were quite aware of the fact that they were doing many things better than their ancestors had done them. Thucydides almost calls his Peloponnesian War a "bigger and better" war than any that had been fought before. There is in the funeral speech of Pericles a touch of the Chamber of Commerce of today. Yet you can find no clear notion of progress as a part of the cosmos, as a process of development from lower to higher, in these confident years of Athenian culture. And you find even less that resembles the doctrine of progress if you look at other phases of ancient and medieval history.

You find, indeed, several organized schemes of man's destiny. The popular pagan legends of the Mediterranean put the happiest and best age of mankind in the distant past, in a Golden Age, an age of heroes, an age of which the Hebrew version is our familiar

Garden of Eden. Among the intellectuals of the Graeco-Roman world there were various sophisticated ideas about the course of history, and notably a series of cyclical theories. Such for instance is the most widely accepted one of a Golden Age followed by a Silver Age in turn followed by an Iron Age, after which there was to be a catastrophe, a new Golden Age, and then the cycle all over again, world without end. It seems quite likely that some of these ideas are related to Hindu ideas about transmigration of souls, eternal recurrences, and the like, and that they mark an otherwise unrecorded meeting of the East and West. They are, of course, quite unlike our ideas of progress. And notably, they are held by men who think of themselves as living in an Iron Age. They are, in short, for those holding them, like the notions of a past Golden Age, based on a belief in *regression* or decadence, not on a belief in progress.

We have already noted that traditional Christianity did not have a theory of progress in nature on this earth—certainly not in the clear form this theory took in the Enlightenment. We shall return at the end of this chapter to the subtle and difficult problem of the relations between traditional Christian belief and the Enlightenment. We may note here in passing that the relation is a very close one indeed, that in fact the Enlightenment is a child of Christianity—which may explain for our Freudian times why the Enlightenment was so hostile to traditional Christianity. There is even in Christianity a certain emotional basis not at all incongruous with belief in progress. The formal cosmology of traditional Christianity is, however, clearly closer to pagan notions of man's course on earth than to those of the Enlightenment. The best was first—the state of innocence before the Fall; man has *lapsed;* he cannot reconstitute Eden on earth; he can better himself, it is true, but not actually by any *process,* not even by actions that are properly speaking historical, but only by a transcendental miracle, that of salvation through grace; heaven is quite definitely not to be achieved on earth.

We noted in the *quérelle des anciens et des modernes* of the late seventeenth century the beginnings of public debate among intellectuals on these matters. The doctrine, in broad lines much like our own American folk notions of progress, gets itself very quickly accepted in Western culture of the eighteenth century, though by no means unanimously, and by no means without opposition. You can get from Voltaire, for instance, as much evidence for the thesis that he believed in cycles, with 1750 *lower* in a cycle than the Age of Louis XIV, as for the theory that he believed in progress, and in his own Age of Enlightenment. At the very end of the century, however, Condorcet's *Progrès de l'esprit humain* gives a complete, full dress account of the ten stages by which men had lifted themselves from primitive savagery to the brink of perfection on earth. Fifteen hundred years after St. Augustine comes this philosophy of history in which the *civitas Dei* and the *civitas terrena* are melted indistinguishably together.

Condorcet is rather vague about the way in which all this happens, about the moving force that pushes humanity from one stage to a higher one, and in general it can be said that until in the next century Darwinian ideas of organic evolution were drawn upon in the social sciences, there is hardly a satisfactory general theory of progress that attempts to explain why and how detailed progressive changes are made. The favorite explanation among the intellectuals in the eighteenth century was that progress is due to the spread of reason, to the increasing enlightenment (*les lumières*) that enables men to control their environment better.

Here is already seen most clearly the historic association of scientific and technological improvement with the idea of progress in the moral and cultural sense. By the eighteenth century the work of scientists from Copernicus through Newton had produced a very broad set of generalizations about the behavior of the material universe—generalizations by 1750 known to laymen at least as well as we know those of relativity and quantum mechanics. Moreover, it was clear that these Newtonian generalizations were better, truer, than those of his medieval predecessors. Still more, by mid-century there was evident the kind of material progress that is with the unreflective perhaps a much firmer source of belief in progress than is pure science. There were better roads along which coaches traveled each year a bit faster, there were obvious, homely improvements such as water closets, there was even, at the end of the century, the beginning of the conquest of the air. The conquest was an imperfect one in balloons, it is true, but even so, in 1787 a Frenchman achieved a very modern death attempting to cross the English Channel in the air. In short, a very old man in the eighteenth century might look back to his childhood as a time when men had fewer conveniences, a simpler material environment, fewer and less efficient tools and machines, a lower standard of living.

The theory of progress, however much it owes to the growth of cumulative knowledge and to the increasing ability of men to produce material wealth from their natural environment, is a theory of morals and indeed metaphysics. Men are, according to this theory, becoming better, happier, more nearly what the ideals of the best of our cultures have aimed at. If you try to pursue this notion of moral improvement into concrete details, you will come up against something of the same kind of vagueness that has always clung to Christian notions of heaven —in itself, perhaps, some evidence for the idea that the doctrine of progress is no more than a modern eschatology. Progress will lead us —and in the original, eighteenth-century notion of progress, will lead us very quickly, within a human generation or two—to a state in which men will all be happy, in which there will be no evil. This happiness is by no means just physical comfort. It is not inaccurate to say that in the eighteenth century most of those who talked of progress and the perfectibility of man were thinking in terms close to those of Christian, Greek, and later Hebraic ethics, of peace on earth to men of good will, of the absence of all the traditional vices, of the presence of the traditional virtues.

So much for the broad basis of a belief in progress on this earth. This progress was to be brought about by the spread of reason. Reason, to the ordinary man of the Enlightenment we are attempting here to follow, was the great key word to his new universe. It was reason that would lead men to understand nature (his other great key word) and by understanding nature to mold his conduct in accordance with nature, and thus avoid the vain attempts he had made under the mistaken notions of traditional Christianity and its moral and political allies to go contrary to nature. Now reason was not quite something that came suddenly into existence about 1687 (this is the date of the publication of Newton's *Philosophiae Naturalis Principia Mathematica*). It must be admitted that there were intolerant modernists who came very close to holding that everything prior to about 1700 was one huge series of mistakes, the blundering of an awkward man in a darkened room; but our average enlightened intellectual was inclined to credit the old Greeks and Romans with having done good spade work, and to believe that what we call the Renaissance and Reformation had begun once more the development of reason. It was in the Church, and especially in the medieval Catholic Church and its successors, that the enlightened found the source of darkness, the unnatural suppression of nature—in short, the Satan every religion needs. To this matter we shall return, for it is of great importance. For the moment, we can register the fact that the man of the Enlightenment believed that reason was something all men, save a few unfortunate defectives, were capable of following; reason had been suppressed, perhaps even atrophied, by the long rule of traditional Christianity. But now, in the eighteenth century, reason could once more resume its sway, and do for all men what it had done for men like Newton and Locke. Reason could show men how to control their environment and themselves.

For reason could show men how nature worked or would work if men ceased impeding that work by their unnatural institutions and habits. Reason could make them aware of natural laws they had in their ignorance been violating. For instance, they had been trying by tariffs, navigation acts, and all sorts of economic regulations to "protect" the trade of their own country, to secure for their country a larger share of wealth. Once they reasoned on these matters, they would see that if each man pursued his own economic interest (that is, acted naturally) to buy most cheaply and sell most dearly there would be established by the free (natural) play of supply and demand a maximum production of wealth. They would see that tariffs, and indeed all attempts to regulate economic activity by political action, made for *less* production, and could benefit only a very few who thereby got an *unnatural* monopoly.

Or again, men had been trying for generations to drive out or exorcise the demons they believed had somehow got into the insane. They whipped the poor insane people, they tied them down, they went through all sorts of ritual performances to drive out the demons. But reason, working on the problems of religion, could show men that there are no such things as demons; and working on the level of medical and psychological research, it could show that insanity was a natural (if regrettable) disturbance of the mind (and perhaps body), a *disease,* in short, which might be cured or at least alleviated by further use of reason.

Or finally, men and women had for centuries joined monastic orders, taken oaths of chastity, obedience, poverty, and lived out their lives as monks and nuns. Reason would show that, though originally monks had perhaps cleared fields and drained swamps, though still perhaps they occasionally did some useful work, on the whole monasticism meant a great waste of human productive power; even more clearly, reason would show that it was most unnatural for healthy human beings to abstain entirely from sexual intercourse, and that theological justification for such unnatural behavior was as much nonsense as was the idea of demons possessing the insane. When reason got through with monasticism, that institution was seen as a typical example of bad beliefs, bad habits, bad ways of doing things; monasticism would disappear in the new society.

All this added up to the enlightened man into a system that explained the universe. For that system we have already noted the useful term "Newtonian world-machine." It was a machine which, especially as it concerned human relations, the enlightened were only beginning to understand. Thanks to Newton and his predecessors, they understood the solar system, gravity, mass, and in fact in its broad lines all natural science; research was needed only to fill in the details. But as to human relations, though they knew enough to know that their unenlightened predecessors, under the influence of traditional Christianity, had been all wrong about human relations, had indeed built up a system of laws and institutions inadequate at best, vicious at worst, they had as yet not quite attained their Newton. He was, however, just around the corner, this Newton of social science, the man who would sum up our enlightened knowledge into a system of social science men had only to follow to ensure the *real* Golden Age, the *real* Eden—the one that lies ahead, not behind.

Traditional Christianity could no longer provide a cosmology for the enlightened. There was beginning to be enough geology so that the date of creation—4004 B.C. according to Archbishop Ussher—and the story of the flood came to seem more and more unlikely. But there was no need to wait for the growth of geological knowledge. Take the Christian doctrine of the Trinity. Mathematics was against that: In no respectable arithmetical system could three be three and at the same time one. As for miracles, why had they stopped? If you could raise the dead in the first century why not in the eighteenth? And so on, in arguments nowadays familiar enough, but then fresh and daring.

Those whose faith in traditional Christianity was shaken, however, did not at once do away with the idea of God. Most of the enlightened in the first half of the century, including such great figures as Voltaire and Pope, were, at least publicly, deists. Now deism is a fairly definite and concrete belief about the universe, and save in some polemics of the time and since, is not a synonym either of atheism or of skepticism (agnosticism). *Deism* needs to be distinguished from *theism*, which involves a more personal God, a God not necessarily anthropomorphic, but at least in some senses immanent, capable of being prayed to; from *pantheism*, which has God penetrate every particle of the universe; and from *philosophical idealism*, which talks of spirit (*Geist*) rather than God. Actually your deist is very firm about the existence of God, remote and chilly though this God be. The deist's belief is the neatest possible reflection of Newton's orderly universe, spinning around according to law. The deist's God is the person responsible for planning, building, and setting in motion this world-machine: for how can one have a machine without a maker, a result without a cause? In technical terms, the deist proved the existence of his God by two very old arguments, the argument from a First Cause, and the argument from Design. But once this necessary God had got the world-machine to running, he ceased to do anything about it. This clockmaker God had made his clock-universe, wound it up for eternity, and would let it run for eternity, according to the laws Mr. Newton had just made clear. Men in this universe are on their own. God has designed them as part of his machine, and has arranged for them to run on, but with the special gift of getting to know by the use of their reason just how they run. Clearly there is no use praying to this clockmaker God, who could not if he would interfere with his own handiwork. Clearly this God never showed himself to Moses on Sinai, never sent his only begotten son to earth to redeem sinful men—couldn't possibly have such a son.

He seemed, in fact, a by no means necessary God, a sort of do-nothing God. That men should have set up so emotionally unsatisfactory a God at all is an interesting example of the way intellectual changes have to proceed slowly. The jump from a Christian God to no God was simply too great. But deism was one of the unsatisfactory kinds of compromise, as inadequate intellectually as emotionally. Voltaire's own famous epigram about his God—"if God did not exist, he would have to be invented"—betrays a fatal weakness. The radicals of the next generation saw no need to invent him. They were already familiar through mathematics with the concept of infinity. The world-machine had always existed and would always exist, at least as far as mere men could tell. How could anyone possibly know that a God as remote as that of the deists existed? If he was altogether outside the created universe, how could he be inside, even inside our minds as a conception? Clearly he was not necessary. Nature was enough—this great universe we should never have enough time to study in its entirety. Let us stop worrying about God, and make ours a religion of reason, a system of ethics without all the nonsense of theology.

Such at least was the view of the milder rebels, materialists who found God unnecessary. Others went beyond them, and found God a positive evil, especially if he were the God of the Roman Catholic

Church. They proudly called themselves atheists, men without a God. Theirs was no longer a doubt. They knew the Christian God did not exist; they knew the universe was a system of "matter" in motion, which could be fully understood by the use of human reason along lines established by the natural sciences. Their materialism, their atheism was a positive belief, not a form of skepticism; it was a definite form of faith, a kind of religion. This positive belief in a knowable universe ultimately composed of particles of matter has remained ever since an element in Western culture. And yet no one knows at all accurately how many people have accepted, and still accept, some form of this belief.

Deist and atheist both rejected the organized Christianity of their day. The eighteenth was the great century of anticlericalism, the century when all kinds of hostilities and grievances against Catholic and Protestant Christianity could come out in the open, thanks to the "spirit of the age" of the Enlightenment, to cheap printing, to lax censorship, to inefficient police, to the amused approval with which the old ruling classes greeted these attacks on the established religion. What was legal in those two amazingly free countries, England and Holland, was readily bootlegged into France and the Germanies. For the first time since the Roman Empire, Christianity felt itself under heavy attack within its own culture. By the time of the French Revolution, that attack was to attain an extraordinary bitterness, especially in continental countries, and Christians were once more to suffer martyrdom for their faith, this time on the guillotine.

All the faithful of the new religion of reason, deist and complete materialist alike, even though they dismissed the Christian God, had to contend with the problem of evil. It was a very knotty problem for them. They postulated a world-machine, of which man is definitely part, which runs according to the laws of nature. They further postulated a faculty in men, which they called reason, by the exercise of which men could understand these laws of nature, orderly and just laws, and by conforming in their conduct to these laws of nature could live together peaceably and happily. Yet as they looked about this world of the eighteenth century they saw strife and misery everywhere, they saw all sorts of evils. Were these evils in accord with the laws of nature, benign nature? Of course not, they were most unnatural, and the enlightened were naturally at work rooting them out. But how did they get there? How did the unnatural get to be the natural? How did the higher become the lower?

We have encountered this difficulty already in our study of Christianity. But Christianity has at least its Satan, however difficult it may be to reconcile Satan's existence with God's goodness. Those who accepted the cosmology of the Newtonian world-machine had still graver difficulties in introducing, or at any rate in justifying, their obvious desire to change, to improve, something that was already perfect, automatic, determined. In fact, in no monistic naturalism is it easy to slip in the unnatural. Rousseau himself was no admirer of the Newtonian world-machine and of reason. The nature he found at the bottom of all things was the spontaneous, outgoing, loving-kindness of the heart as displayed by simple and uncorrupted persons, such as children, savages, and peasants. Above all, he found this state of nature in the past, before civilization brought corruption. In his *Discourse on the Origin of Inequality* Rousseau attempts to describe the origin of evil. The first man who dared to take from the common ownership a plot of ground, fence it in, and say "this is mine!"—he is the villain responsible for the end of the state of nature. Rousseau does not explain *why* this child of nature acted so unnaturally.

If the enlightened could not solve the problem of the origin of evil, they had very firm ideas about good and evil in their own time. Evil they considered to be a historical growth embodied in customs, laws, institutions—that is to say, in the environment, especially in the social environment, in what man had made of man. The physical environment they realized, especially after Montesquieu's *Spirit of the Laws,* was often harsh and barren, or too easy and luxurious; and they knew that certain diseases were apparently not wholly the result of the social environment. But they hoped they could master the physical environment; indeed they hoped they could master the social environment. The social environment of their own time they thought was almost wholly bad, so bad that perhaps it would have to be destroyed root and branch. They did not, for the most part, believe that this destruction would be violent. They foresaw a French Revolution, but not a Reign of Terror.

They equated evil with the environment, and good with something innate in human beings, with human nature. Man is born good; he is made bad by society. The way to make him good again is to protect this natural goodness from the corruption society brings with it. Or more tangibly, the way to reform individuals is to reform society. Reason can show us how; every law, every custom, every institution must be submitted to the test of its reasonableness. Is a hereditary nobility reasonable? If it is not, we must abolish it; if it is, we must retain it. Hereditary nobility when examined by reason as reason worked in the minds of most enlightened men at least by the 1780's turned out not to be reasonable. One of the first acts of the French National Assembly called to remake France was to abolish nobility.

We have come up against one of the great forms in which ethical and political problems present themselves to modern men, the form we all know as environment vs. heredity. Occasionally someone will announce firmly that he finds war and its attendant sufferings and cruelty a Good Thing, and someone else will complain that our physical comforts are a Bad Thing. But men in Western society are mostly agreed on the broad lines of what they find good and what they find evil. Where they differ is in their explanation of the persistence of evil. The Enlightenment and we ourselves as heirs of the Enlightenment push the emphasis over onto the side of environment; we tend to believe—most of us Americans tend to believe—that if we can only work out the proper "arrangements," laws, institutions, above all education, human beings will get along together in something pretty close to the good life. Christian tradition tends to push the explanation over onto the side of human nature; men are born with something inside them that makes them incline to evil; they are born in sin. It is true that Christianity sees a way out in the possibility of salvation Jesus brought us, but this is not quite environmentalism, not quite faith in the possibility of passing laws and working out educational curricula.

Now it is important to realize that even in its most hopeful early phases modern environmentalism did not usually go to absurd extremes. Only a madman would assert that any infant taken at random from a number of newborn babes could by the manipulation of his environment be made into anything at all—into a heavyweight boxer, a great musician, or a great physicist. Eighteenth-century psychology, taking its cue from Locke, did indeed think of the human mind as a blank receptacle into which experience poured the content of life; but not even the psychology of the *tabula rasa* interpreted human equality as human identity. More characteristic of eighteenth-century environmentalism is a statement by one of its younger sons, the socialist Robert Owen:

> Any general character, from the best to the worst, from the most ignorant to the most enlightened, may be given to any community, even to the world at large, by the application of proper means; which means are to a great extent at the command and under the control of those who have influence in the affairs of men.

Here the key word is "general." Owen does not think he can achieve certain specific results with each individual; he does think he can do so for large groups. After all, is this very far from the notions that lie behind all efforts to influence and condition peoples today?

In fact, a belief in environmentalism is still essential for all who hope to bring about fairly rapid and *extensive* changes in the actual behavior of human beings on earth. There are few today who believe such changes can be accomplished by the intervention of a supernatural power, by religion in the traditional sense. And only the crank could believe that quick results are possible by any eugenical manipulation of the human organism. We cannot *breed* better men and women fast; we shall have to *make* better men and women from our present materials. Let Owen speak again with the optimism of the Enlightenment, undimmed in him by the horrors of the French Revolution and the Napoleonic world wars:

> These plans must be devised to train children from their earliest infancy in good habits of every description (which will of course prevent them from acquiring those of falsehood and deception). They must

afterwards be rationally educated, and their labour be usefully directed. Such habits and education will impress them with an active and ardent desire to promote the happiness of every individual, and that without the *shadow of exception* for sect, or party, or country, or climate. They will also ensure, with the fewest possible exceptions, health, strength, and vigour of body; for the happiness of man can be erected only on the foundations of health of body and peace of mind.

The Program of the Enlightenment

The men of the Enlightenment were not quite as unanimous as they have seemed to be up to this point in our analysis. Indeed, it is just at this point that the great division in their ranks, a division still by no means healed, comes out most clearly. Not all of the enlightened would have agreed that reason was against a hereditary nobility, and certainly not all the enlightened would have wished to do away with all class distinctions. Reason turned out in practice to have different ways for different men.

The great bifurcation in the ranks of the enlightened may be put as that between those who believed that a relatively few wise and gifted men in authority could manipulate the environment so that everybody, manipulators and manipulated alike, would be happy and those who believed that all that was needed was to destroy, cancel out, the existing bad environment, and that then everyone would co-operate spontaneously in creating the perfect environment. The first group, whatever lip service they may have given to the ideals of democracy and freedom for all men, were in fact authoritarians; in the particular background of eighteenth-century thought and institutions, they tended to pin their hopes on wise rulers and trained civil servants, on what historians call the movement for "enlightened despotism." The second group tended to believe that the ordinary man, the common man, the man in the street or the field, was a sound and sensible fellow, as well as the most numerous of mankind; they wanted such men to be free to follow their innate wisdom; they tended to believe in democratic methods, in voting by head, in majority rule; the more extreme of them were philosophical anarchists who believed that any government is bad, that men must abolish all government.

There is a very clear example of the reality of these contrasting positions in the career of one of the most influential of the philosophers of the Enlightenment, Jeremy Bentham. Already as a young man Bentham had worked out the neat, and to many most plausible, formula for his utilitarianism: Everything should be done to secure the greatest happiness of the greatest number. Since he accompanied this formula with a method, satisfactory to himself and his followers, of actually *measuring* happiness, he had what he needed to provide a good environment to take the place of the bad old one. He had the blueprints for a wonderful job of social engineering.

Bentham's first notion was that the ruling classes of Britain, the great lords and merchants he knew so well—he himself was of prosperous merchant stock, and a frequent guest of the intellectual Lord Shelburne—would do his work for him. After all, these gentlemen read and talked and were fully up to what was going on in the enlightened world. But they had certain privileges under the old system—indeed it was clear that the old bad environment seemed to them subjectively rather a good one—and Bentham found he was not able to persuade them to adopt his proposed reforms. So early in the nineteenth century he began to turn toward the people, and before long had become a convinced democrat, holding for universal suffrage, frequent elections to secure rotation in office, and the rest of the machinery of democracy. He now believed that the masses would make the changes the privileged classes could not be persuaded to make. Of course, the masses needed teachers, needed leaders, and these were to be provided by a relatively small group of educated but not aristocratic followers of Bentham, the "philosophic radicals." But these were to be a spearhead for democracy, not a privileged group of wise men monopolizing the work of government.

We wrote a moment ago of a bifurcation in the ranks of the enlightened. Unfortunately for the understanding of these matters, the human mind rarely confronts such a simple choice as that between two tracks. Indeed, the human mind can jump lightly from one path to another, until its course seems a maze. Our distinction between the environmentalists who trust to the manipulation of the environment by the few (*philosophes,* engineers, planners, technocrats, brain trusts) and those who expect the many to provide the necessary changed environment by the democratic process of majority vote— this distinction is worth making, and is one that will give us a first approximation, especially for the eighteenth century. But at least one other simple dual classification, not quite identical with the first, is necessary here. This is the distinction between those who believe that the new environment will exercise over ordinary men a kind of compulsion—one they will get to enjoy but still something in part external that ties them together in a disciplined group—and those who believe that the new environment will in fact hardly involve institutions and laws at all, that men under the new order will spontaneously live up to the Golden Rule. The one point of view is authoritarian; the other libertarian, or anarchical.

In most matters the believers in enlightened despotism took an authoritarian position; for them the *old* authority, the Christian authority, was bad, not the *principle* of authority; authority in the hands of men trained to use enlightened reason was all right—was, in fact, necessary. Yet in economic affairs many of these authoritarians held that businessmen should be quite free to handle their own business, free from the restraints of governmental or guild authority. Actually what they defended even in economics was not freedom for all individuals, but merely freedom for the economic enterpriser, the industrialist. Within the little realm of the factory or other business, there is to be that organization, efficiency, rationalization so consonant with the authoritarian side of the Enlightenment. The same Robert Owen who stated so neatly the theory of environmentalism had himself been part owner and whole manager of a profitable textile mill at New Lanark in Scotland. New Lanark was for those days a model factory, surrounded by really neat company houses, with excellent working conditions, and with Owen's own favorite experimental progressive schools available for the worker's children. But there was no "industrial democracy" at New Lanark. Owen's word was law; Owen manipulated the environment; Owen was the father in a most paternalistic system.

Bentham provides an even neater example of the carefully contrived environment—contrived from above by the wise, fatherly authority. Bentham's basic principles are that men seek pleasure and avoid pain (note the apparent similarity to such concepts of physics as that of gravity), and that since this is a fact we must accept it as a moral good. The secret of government is therefore to devise a system of rewards and punishment such that socially and morally desirable action on the part of the individual results for him always in more pleasure than pain; and that socially and morally undesirable action should always bring him more pain than pleasure. Bentham went into great detail working out his calculus of pleasure and pain, classifying, weighing, and measuring various kinds of pleasures and pains. Of course what he did was to assign values such as a kindly, philosophical, serious-minded English gentleman would esteem. His ethics, like those of most Westerners in revolt against Christianity, turn out to be most Christian. But Bentham would not trust the ordinary institutions of society to measure out pain and pleasure properly. Somehow society was rewarding the actions that did not bring the greatest good to the greatest number, penalizing the actions that would do so if given a chance. But mere freedom wouldn't bring that chance. Men like Bentham would have to sit down and work out new devices, a new society.

Thus reason tells us that crime—say stealing—has to be punished because it brings more pain to the victim and, in the form of fear and anxiety more pain to everybody who knows of the theft (they are afraid it may happen to them) than it does profit to the thief. But reason tells us that notions of sin, damnation, penitence, and the like in relation to the theft are nonsense. We are dealing with a simple matter of bookkeeping. The thief must be caught and so punished that pain brought by the penalty will just barely outweigh in the thief's mind the pleasure (profit) brought by the crime. If the pleasure is greater than a very light penalty, the thief will be tempted to repeat the crime. If the pain is very much greater—if the punishment is extremely heavy as in the then criminal law of England—the thief will feel martyred, or crushed, or rebellious, and will certainly not be reformed. And the whole purpose of the law is by reforming the criminal to prevent repetition of the crime. So the punishment must be made to fit the crime.

Bentham's psychological detail seems to us nowadays rather naive, and the elaborate plans he makes seem quite unworkable. But the reforming spirit we know well. Much of what Bentham and his followers tried to achieve in the reform of institutions has indeed been put on the statute books. No one is now hanged for stealing a sheep. We cannot quite hope for the sweeping results Bentham hoped for, but we continue to use many of his methods; and we continue, good democrats though we may be, to pin much of our hopes on institutional changes planned from above. The New Deal had a good deal of old Bentham in it.

Those on the side of liberty show a clearer split than do the authoritarians. There is throughout the century a current of thought, culminating perhaps in the *Political Justice* (1793) of the English radical William Godwin, which is a kind of lay antinomianism. Godwin held that men did wrong only because they tried to obey, and make others obey, fixed laws; if everybody did freely what he really wanted to do at each moment—and if all had been properly emancipated from prejudices, fanaticism, ignorance—then they would all act reasonably. No reasonable man would injure another, or try to amass more goods than he could use, or be jealous of anyone who did something he could not do. Godwin carried this doctrine of philosophical anarchism so far that he objected to an orchestra conductor's beating the time for the orchestra as a form of unjustified tyranny over the players; the players left to themselves freely would hit a natural rhythm and do better without a leader.

Anarchism even as an ideal has always seemed absurd to most men, yet it must not be dismissed as of no importance. At its extreme it is clearly of the lunatic fringe, but it is an ingredient in many less extreme views. As a goal, and as a kind of half-rejected hope, it has had its part not only in many kinds of socialism, but in our own democracy. As an ideal, it somehow keeps alive in our much-governed world.

There is, however, a better-trodden path that most of those on the side of liberty have taken—a path that has many branches, some of which have a disconcerting way of taking sudden one-hundred-and-eighty-degree turns toward authority. We shall have to examine a little more closely one of the famous documents in the history of pure political philosophy, the *Contrat Social* of Rousseau (1762). This little treatise has been disputed over for generations. Some readers find it basically a document on the side of individual liberty; others find it on the side of authoritarian collectivism, one of the intellectual antecedents of modern totalitarianism.

Rousseau is at bottom grappling with the problem of political obedience. His earlier work, the whole bent of his disposition, lay toward what we have just called anarchism. "Man is born free," he writes in a ringing first sentence, "and everywhere he is in chains." Why? Because, answers Rousseau, he has had to exchange the state of nature for the state of civilization (never mind *why* he had to leave the state of nature—we have noted many times that there is no good logical answer to the problem of evil). In the state of nature man obeyed no one, or if you prefer, obeyed his own whims and desires. Now in the state of civilization he must obey commands he knows do not stem directly from within himself. If, for instance, he is a slave, he has to obey a person like himself, a most degrading and unpleasant experience, indeed an unnatural and inhuman one. Even in existing eighteenth-century societies he has to obey laws he never helped to make, men he never helped select as his rulers. What is the way out?

You may have noted that Rousseau is at once attempting to analyze the psychological factors of obedience and to persuade his readers what kind of obedience is good and what bad. To use an approach he might not have approved, but one suitable to our day, we may say that men do not actually obey even in ordinary political routine unless they have managed to feel that they are not obeying another *human* will, like the slave obeying the master, but are obeying a higher will of some sort of which their own will is a part. This will Rousseau calls the *general will*. To the out-and-out nominalist the general will is, of course, a mere fiction. But no one can have had any sort of emotional participation in any group, from family to college to nation, without catching a glimpse of what Rousseau is groping for. The general will of Rousseau is created by the social contract; the social contract for him follows the Hobbesian pattern in that each member of a society enters into the contract with everyone else; the resultant group, however, does not turn government over to an absolute monarch as Hobbes would have it, but treats any governing authorities as its mere agents, dismissible whenever the general will thinks such dismissal best.

But how does this general will make itself known? After all, an individual's will can be apprehended by watching what he does. But who ever saw the United States, or listened to it? What sense does "the will of the American people" make, for those who won't be fobbed off with idealist metaphysics, but want to see or hear or somehow apprehend? Well, if in a national election one candidate gets 55 per cent of the popular vote and another 45 per cent, can't you say that the elected candidate represents the "will of the American people"? Or if the Congress is duly and freely elected, do not its votes represent the will of the people?

Rousseau would have answered with a firm "No!" to that second question. He believed in direct democracy, as in the old Greek city-state or a small Swiss canton, and thought that a big country like France could not be a real commonwealth with a general will. This denial that a big country can be a true state is a mere twist of Rousseau's mind, an interesting example of an almost Renaissance devotion to classical forms, something always pointed at in comments on Rousseau, but not of great importance. To the first question, granting that he would admit a nation of 150,000,000 could be a nation at all, Rousseau would have had to give an ambiguous answer: Yes, if the candidate who got 55 per cent of the votes *really* embodies the general will of the United States; No, if he does not. Rousseau has often been carelessly interpreted as supporting the theory that the will of the majority is always right. Actually he does no such thing.

We must add one more of Rousseau's terms to "individual will" and "general will"; this is "will of all." When a group makes a decision in any way, voting or applauding or even rattling shields as in Sparta, the general will is present if the decision is *right;* whereas the will of all, the mere mechanical sum of the selfish, unenlightened individual wills, is present if the decision is *wrong.* But who decides what is right and what is wrong? We are at a point we have reached before, a point where many human beings feel hopelessly lost. Clearly there is no litmus-paper test of right and wrong. You can perform no scientific "operational" test to distinguish the general will from the will of all. Rousseau writes as if he held that in a small group, say a New England town meeting, after full and free discussion, a decision by majority vote will in fact reflect the "sense of the meeting," will be the exercise of the general will. But not necessarily. The ultimate test is a transcendental one, a matter of faith.

You may find this confusing and much too philosophical, in a bad sense. But even though you refuse to follow Rousseau into the metaphysics of the general will, you should see that he is groping for a profound psychological truth. He notes that in a free democratic society those who had at first opposed a proposed measure voluntarily accept it when it becomes clear to them that it represents the general will. That is, the 45 per cent accept the wishes of the 55 per cent as *in fact,* for practical purposes, the wishes of the whole 100 per cent. Though this sounds sentimental to many deliberately hard-boiled persons, there is no viable democracy unless something approximating this process goes on. We may not quite accept the election of the man we opposed as the fulfillment of our "individual will"; yet if we refuse to accept that election at all we have become rebels, and if there are a lot of us in the same position we have a Latin-American republic at its caricatural worst, and not a stable democracy. The imaginative acceptance of something like what Rousseau means—part of the time at least—by "general will" seems necessary for the stability of any free society.

Rousseau's great ambiguity, however, lies just a step further on. By signing (even metaphorically, so to speak, by being born into a society) the social contract I give up my natural, simple liberty, and in return get the very great liberty of obeying the general will. If I didn't I should be rebelling against the right, I should actually be a slave of my own selfish will. In such a case to force me to obey is in fact to make me free. Rousseau puts it clearly:

> In order, then, that the social compact may not be but a vain formula, it must contain, though unexpressed, the single undertaking which can alone give force to the whole, namely, that whoever shall refuse to obey the general will must be constrained by the whole body of his fellow citizens to do so: which is no more than to say that it may be necessary to compel a man to be free. . . .

We have come a long way from the libertarian bias with which we started. The argument (or metaphor) is indeed an obvious one, which stands ready for anyone who wants to defend a restriction on individual liberty. Through various intellectuals like Kant and Herder it has passed into ordinary German belief, and has been used in one form or another by German authorities to justify obedience. It has always seemed a little dangerous to Western Europeans and Americans, has seemed to sacrifice the individual too completely to the state. But that Rousseau should have pushed his analysis to the point where he makes his general will sovereign and unimpeachable is an interesting example of where the human mind can go along the track of abstract thought. Rousseau as a person was an eccentric, an individualist, a man whose basic emotional objections to the pressure of organization of any kind on the individual remind one of Thoreau's; and yet here he is, one of the prophets of modern collectivist society.

There lies behind this ambiguity of the *Contrat Social* another of those polar distinctions that we can analyze out of the whole experience of these eighteenth-century people. The ardent young follower of the Enlightenment in the 1780's did not pull his own ideas apart as we are trying to do. He was against the established order, against convention, against what he called error and superstition; he was for nature, reason, liberty, common sense, for all that seemed new and hopeful in this progressive world. But what gave shape to the new, the hopeful better things that were to take the place of the old? The formula we have hitherto encountered is reason, the kind of thinking that Newton did, the kind the *philosophes* were doing. But as the century wears on we begin to encounter new words, or old words with a new emphasis: sensibility, enthusiasm, pity, the heart. With the great vogue of Rousseau after 1760, the heart comes into its own against the head. No longer will reason be the guide, the architect of the new world; sentiment, feeling, will tell us how to work together to build anew. Reason begins to be suspect:

> If abstract reason only rules the mind,
> In sordid selfishness it lives confin'd;
> Moves in one vortex, separate and alone,
> And feels no other interest than its own.

We shall leave until the next chapters a consideration of the Romantic movement which, heralded well back in the eighteenth century by Rousseau and such English writers as Shaftesbury, came to be one of the main elements in the nineteenth-century view of life. For an understanding of the later Enlightenment, it is necessary to note that this turn toward emotion gave to concepts like "nature" a quite different coloring from that of the "nature" of the Newtonian world-machine. Nature was no longer the neat, the orderly, the mathematical; it was what "nature" still suggests to most of us, the external world untouched, or little touched, by men, untrimmed, untamed, wild, spontaneous, and quite unmathematical. Here we are concerned with the political implications of this change of base from classical nature to romantic nature.

You may hold, and be quite justified in holding, that the dichotomy between reason and emotion, between head and heart, is just one of the clichés of bad thinking. Thinking and feeling are not separable acts of human beings; our thoughts and our emotions are fused in our opinions. Nevertheless, simply as a working tool for analysis, the distinction is worth making. Here is a good concrete instance from the late eighteenth century, involving a problem still with us. The professional economists, by this time an established group with a respected, if new, discipline, could "prove" that poor relief and charity that gave the recipients a home and family of their own was bad for everybody, even for the recipients. When Malthus published his *Essay on the Principle of Population* in 1798, the arguments of the economists were rounded out: the more you did to soften the lot of the poor man, the more children he produced, the less there was to go around among workers, and the worse off they all were. The utilitarians took this up, and helped bring in a system of workhouse relief in Britain whereby the poor who had to have relief were segregated by sex in most unattractive poorhouses. The full logic might have led to letting the poor starve if they could not earn a living, but the West has never quite carried out the logic even of its economists.

We need not debate whether the reasoning of the economists in this matter actually is in accord with what "reason" should mean in our tradition. The point is that they claimed they were following reason—and their opponents accepted their claim. Their opponents said something like this: "We can't see what's wrong in your chain of reasoning. Perhaps the race would be better off if the incompetent were weeded out. But we can't take your argument. We're sorry for the poor man. We know you're wrong because we feel you're wrong. Perhaps the poor man is lazy, untrained, awkward, incompetent; but . . ." The defense could go on indefinitely, and even when conducted by the purest partisans of the heart would certainly lapse into arguments, into reasoning; that is, the poor would be defended as having a right to the good life, or as actually being poor because they never had a chance (the environmentalist argument). Or the very modern argument might be brought forth, as it was by Robert Owen, that to raise the standard of living of the poor is to raise the demand for industrial mass production and to make possible steady economic progress. But the basic argument remained: We *feel* that the workhouse treatment is cruel.

Now, once more very roughly, the partisans of the head tended in the later Enlightenment to bolster the side of enlightened despotism, planning, and authority; the partisans of the heart tended to bolster the side of democracy, or at least of self-government by a numerous middle class, "natural" spontaneity, and individual liberty. But, as we noted above in contrasting thinking and feeling, these two are not separate strands, but combine in various strengths in our political attitudes.

The kind of American we call "progressive" or "liberal" has long been torn by the difficulty thus presented. His emotions, backed by the American democratic tradition, are strongly on the side of trusting the people, letting them decide after free discussion, letting them bring out that quality of being right that ordinary men in groups possess. He would like to believe in the people, to trust their judgment. On the other hand, his reason, backed by American intellectual habits, tells him that the man in the street is superstitious, has low tastes, is incapable of objective thinking of any great complexity, is driven by ungenerous and unlovely impulses. Again let us try to be concrete by example: The liberal would like to think that a few wicked Tory politicians, rich men, and misled intellectuals are responsible for Jim Crow in the South, but something keeps telling him that the real enemy of the Negro is the mass of whites, especially the poor whites. From there he may go on to argue that the poor white fears the Negro because of economic institutions. Even so, he is, in dealing with a specific problem, faced with a real question: Do I or don't I trust the wisdom and good will of the common man? He can't be sure. His hesitation has deep historical roots, at least as far back as the Enlightenment.

The Enlightenment and the Christian Tradition

The ideas of the Enlightenment, whether they sprang from the head or the heart, or from both working hard together, were clearly corrosive of existing institutions. If you agree with Bacon's aphorism that "the subtlety of nature is greater many times over than the subtlety of the senses and understanding," you will see that any human attempt to think about social institutions has to *simplify* them. There results a neat pattern, or blueprint, compared with which the reality is always more complex, and therefore to many kinds of thinkers, less perfect. To put it more simply: Almost anybody can think of a better

399

way than the actual one of doing something—running a club, devising an educational curriculum, coaching a football team, administering a government department—and can, as critic, point out the imperfections of what is actually done. Notably, if you hold that all things human should be conducted with the neatness and clarity of the best mathematical reasoning, if you have just steeped yourself in Descartes, Newton, and Locke, you can be a most devastating critic of what goes on—even today. In 1750 you could perhaps find even more inefficiencies, irregularities, irrational survivals of the Middle Ages. Not only would the doctrine of the Trinity seem irrational to you; the fact that the actual size of a bushel measure, the value of a piece of money, would vary from town to town would offend your reforming zeal.

The eighteenth-century thinkers have indeed a somewhat exaggerated reputation as "destructive critics." More especially, they are accused of devotion to abstract thought, at the expense of attention to empirical detail. After the French Revolution had come to shock the civilized world with its violence, it became fashionable in conservative circles, and even in popular circles, to blame the philosophers of the eighteenth century for destroying the old regime with their criticisms and leaving nothing in its place. Into this nothing came the passions and imperfections of the real human beings the eighteenth-century philosophers had neglected in their preoccupation with the rights of abstract man. Edmund Burke led the attack on the philosophers of the Enlightenment, and it was continued by many nineteenth-century writers like Taine, who blamed the French Revolution on the simplifying, abstract *esprit classique*. French popular wit summed it up neatly:

> C'est la faute à Voltaire
> C'est la faute à Rousseau

(It's Voltaire's fault, it's Rousseau's fault!)

We cannot here go into this very vexed question, which has become one of the classical debates over the place of ideas in history, of the relative effectiveness of the kind of thinking the eighteenth-century philosophers did. We are inclined nowadays to doubt whether their writings could ever have weakened a society in other respects strong and well-organized; we tend to see them as *symptoms* of social disintegration rather than primarily as causes. But there can be no doubt that their writing served to focus men's minds and unite them on troubles that might otherwise have given rise to more sporadic and occasional protests. The philosophers of the Enlightenment sharpened men's sense of grievance by referring them constantly to a standard of right and wrong, to a *Weltanschauung* that dignified and intensified these grievances.

What must interest us now is a very big question indeed, a question we cannot fully answer: How is this world-view of the eighteenth-century Enlightenment related to that of traditional Christianity? Again, it would be easy to answer with a sweeping assertion of the identity of the two, or of their polar difference. Such answers have been given. To men like Burke, Joseph de Maistre, to all who focus their attention on the eighteenth-century doctrine of the natural goodness and reasonableness of man as a basic heresy, the Enlightenment seems as anti-Christian at heart as it was on the lips of violent anti-clericals like Holbach and Helvetius; but to men like the Christian socialists of the nineteenth century, to our contemporary American liberal clergymen—John Haynes Holmes, for instance—the Enlightenment is a prolonging, a fulfillment, of what Christianity was meant to be. Here again the truth is complex. The world-attitude of the Enlightenment, of which we Americans are now the chief heirs and representatives, contains both Christian and anti-Christian elements mingled in a whole that, as world-attitudes go, is new.

At this point, a brief word of caution may be necessary. The word *skeptic* is sometimes loosely applied to men like Voltaire, to the writers of the great French Encyclopedia, to the whole attitude we have called the Enlightenment. That is, of course, a misuse of the word. The temper of the eighteenth century is not skeptical. It is anticlerical, positivist, at its extremes materialist. But the *philosophes,* if they disbelieved in traditional Christianity, believed in their own brave new world. Of course, large groups of men, even of intellectuals, are never skeptics. Skepticism is never anything like a mass movement; the Enlightenment was an intellectual mass movement of considerable scope. There is a small trickle of true philosophical skepticism from the Greeks on, though it dries up in the Middle Ages; the trickle flows again with the Renaissance, and produces in Montaigne the most famous and most charming of literary doubters.

In the eighteenth century there was indeed a very well-known professional philosopher, the Scot David Hume, who carried the Cartesian dilemma of thought and matter to a point where skepticism has certainly begun. Hume was one of the most urbane questioners of revelation—his attack on miracles is still one of the great weapons in the armory of the anti-Christian—and of deism or "natural religion." But he had much company in this activity. Where he is more original is in his questioning the truth—in the sense of fixed, absolute, metaphysical certainty—of the generalizations the scientists had arrived at. Reason, as well as our senses, is for Hume subjective, or at least in no finally verifiable way a transcript or report of reality. Hume, like many other doubters of men's mental and moral capacities, found in custom, habit, tradition a firmer ground for life on this earth. He thus ended up in a position singularly at odds with that of his time, a believer in the old instead of the new. Yet he reads like one of the *philosophes;* he has the eighteenth-century touch in style; and his is a singularly dispassionate recognition of the place of passion in human acts. Hume is at bottom not so much the skeptic as the rather tired rationalist.

We need hardly repeat what we have brought up in other connections. The spirit of the Enlightenment is hostile to organized Christian religion. "In every country and in every age, the priest has been hostile to liberty. He is always in alliance with the despot, abetting his abuses in return for protection to his own." Thomas Jefferson is here, of course, using "priest" in a general sense to denote any minister of religion. His statement is by no means extreme, but rather in the center of a spectrum that runs from Voltaire's "Let's eat some Jesuit"—and there are more ferocious extremes than that— to the "natural religion" or deism of professing Catholics like Alexander Pope. The corrosiveness of the Enlightenment is nowhere clearer than in its attacks on Christianity.

Yet before we go on to the key problem of how much Christianity is left in the Enlightenment, how far Christianity survives in this modern faith, we must note that then as now many groups of Christians continued along the old ways, sometimes actively counterattacking in press and pulpit, sometimes quietly living out lives untouched by the new ways. The literature of the eighteenth century in the West is overwhelmingly on the side of the new Enlightenment; the names we remember, from Bayle and Voltaire to Jefferson and Paine, are on the attack. But all through the century little groups like the Bollandist monks went on in their lives of the saints with their pious but critical work as historians; the established churches continued to educate and to carry on their usual services. The masses and a good number of the middle classes and of the aristocracy continued all during these years to observe the ways of traditional Christianity.

In Britain and her American colonies and in Germany, a new form of Protestantism, by no means rationalist in bias, rose in the Methodist and Pietist movements. These movements were evangelical in their desire to bring peace on earth and do God's work; they turned ultimately, as so many Christians have done in modern times, to humanitarian goals; but they retained the essential other-worldliness of Christian tradition, and they were by no means revolutionary in their social and political outlooks. Indeed, we may note here parenthetically, as an example of the kind of hazardous but suggestive generalization one can draw from intellectual history, that historians like Lecky and Halévy have held that the popularity of Methodism among the British lower classes was a stabilizing factor that turned them away from the kind of revolutionary attitude that spread to the masses in France.

We confront, in short, in the eighteenth century as almost always in the Western world that range of opinion, that *multanimity* so characteristic of our culture. That multanimity seems to increase as we approach our own age, for to old ideas organized in old groups come ever newer ones. And so little dies—and what does die takes a very long time to disappear completely. They say there are still Eng lishmen who believe seriously that the rightful heir to the throne of Britain is one of the House of Stuart, driven out in 1688 for good The Enlightenment we are striving to understand is then no totally new belief that supplants a totally old belief. It is rather a series of experiments, hunches, and attitudes old and new, another and very important ingredient in what to the despairing lover of peace and simplicity must seem the stew—the hash—of modern culture.

You can see the subtlety of the problem of how Christian the En lightenment is if you will compare the attitudes toward nature and natural law of St. Thomas Aquinas and Adam Smith. The com parison is well worth making, because at first sight and in accordance with conventional formulas it is so easy to say that Adam Smith as one of the fathers of laissez-faire economics is at the opposite pole from the authoritarian economics of the just price, prohibition of usury, and the rest of the medieval formulas for economic relations. Of course, it would be silly to say that there are no differences between Aquinas and Adam Smith. But Smith is no anarchist, no believer in the natural goodness of man. He makes many qualifications even for the kind of economic liberty for the businessman that is the back bone of his system; he would not let free trade go so far as to leave a country without its own necessary resources in wartime. The kind of economic controls he objects to are those he finds contrary to na ture, and of these by far the worst in his mind, indeed the central vice of the mercantilist system he was attacking, is *monopoly*, the artificial control the capitalist or group of capitalists favored by laws can es tablish over a product which by the natural play of supply and demand would be priced at a level as advantageous to society as possible in this world of sweat and scarcity.

Smith, like Aquinas, believes in a "just price"; and like Aquinas he believes that behind the apparently chaotic processes of individual buying and selling there is a natural order, to which men ought to conform. If they do not conform, it is to both Smith and Aquinas at bottom because some men will perversely attempt to upset the natural order in their own shortsighted interest. But the natural order is there, and it is a permitted Christian hope that men may learn to conform to it. It is true that for Aquinas nature prescribed certain social controls, amounting at times to price fixing, which were repudiated very specifically by Smith. Both doctors believe in a *vis medicatrix naturae,* a healing force in nature; they disagree on the amount of help nature needs, and on the best way of administering that help. They disagree, but not as completely as appears on the surface, on the nature of nature. But for both the great *unnatural* thing is monopoly, through which an individual or group of individuals can control a market in such a way as to benefit personally from an artificial scarcity.

Of formal parallels between traditional Christianity and the Enlightenment there are no end, for both are efforts, shared by many men and women, to give some sort of systematized set of answers to the Big Questions; both are systems of moral values, of ends and means, or, if you prefer, both are religions. These parallels are skillfully brought out in Carl Becker's *Heavenly City of the Eighteenth-Century Philosophers.* Becker's main point is that the faith of the Enlightenment has an eschatology as definite as that of the Christians, a heaven that stands ahead as the goal of our earthly struggle. The heavenly city of the eighteenth century is indeed to be on earth; but the important point is that it lies in the future—the near future, it is true, for men like Condorcet, but still not in the here and now. Men are indeed to enjoy it in the flesh (but remember that the resurrection *in the flesh* and the enjoyment of heaven are parts of Christian doctrine). It is not profitable to try to make out the concrete details of life in the hoped-for heaven. Perhaps the heaven of the Enlightenment is more fleshly, less spiritual than that of the Christians. But the essential part of each is the absence of evil, of frustration; the soul—and body—are happy in both heavens. To many Christians— to the most spiritual Christians—the above is, perhaps, a caricature of their heaven. Theirs is an indescribable ecstasy, and no mere negation. Yet, as with all mystic goals, theirs must seem to an outsider, a man of this world, to be a subduing, a canceling out, of what makes life worth living. And for the run of Christians, surely, heaven is no more than vague happiness, cessation of struggling, of *wanting*.

In both faiths the outcome is determined by a power stronger than any single man. Men can understand and adapt themselves to the designs of this power—indeed they must if they are to attain heaven—but they cannot alter the designs. That is to say, both religions, that of Christianity and that of the Enlightenment, are deterministic. And though both are deterministic, both in practice temper their determinism for the individual with an ethics of struggle for the good and against the bad, an ethics that leaves the individual at least the illusion of personal freedom. The Christian grace is paralleled by the philosophic reason, Christian redemption by philosophic enlightenment. Even in such matters as organization and ritual, the parallel is by no means farfetched. This comes out most clearly in the early years of the French Revolution of 1789, when the Jacobin Clubs that embodied the new faith took to an almost caricatural copying of Christian religious practices: There were republican hymns, processions, love feasts, catechisms, even a "republican sign of the cross." One of the most remarkable examples of the survival of religious forms is found when professed deists indulge in prayer, as they occasionally did. After all, the whole point about the deist's clockmaker God is that he has set the universe in motion according to natural law and has thereupon left it to its own devices. Prayer to such a god would seem peculiarly inefficacious, but in the hearts of patriotic French Jacobins he is readily transformed into an avenging God.

Still, the most striking thing traditional Christianity and this new faith of the Enlightenment have in common is a feeling that man is no misfit in this world, which is a world in some sense designed for man's good living, and that, though something in man—original sin for the Christian, ignorance for the enlightened man of the eighteenth century—keeps him from attaining the good life on earth, he can yet by a serious moral and intellectual effort attune himself to this good element of design in the universe, to God, Providence, or Nature. Both Christianity and the faith of the Enlightenment are intensely active melioristic faiths; both want to clean things up. Both want to clean up pretty much in the same way; both have essential ethical goals, peace, moderate bodily satisfactions, social collaboration and individual freedom, a life quiet but not dull; and both have the similar conceptions of evil, which, since they are both fighting faiths, they probably make more of than they do of good—cruelty, suffering, jealousy, vanity, selfishness, self-indulgence, pride, all the long list we know so well.

Yet we must keep the balance. If the faith of the Enlightenment is a kind of Christianity, a development out of Christianity, it is from the point of view of the historical Christianity of the Middle Ages a heresy, a distortion of Christianity; and from the point of view of Calvinism, a blasphemy. The faith of the Enlightenment has no logical place for a personal God accessible to human prayer, a God not bound by any limitations, by any rules of the kind men discover when they study themselves and their environment. It admits no supernatural above the natural. Partly because of its close alliance with natural science and with abstract thinking generally, the faith of the Enlightenment tends to be more rationalistic than even the most extreme of rationalist Christians, tends to make the mystic self-surrender of Christian experience impossible. Do not mistake here: The difference is not between "emotional" Christianity and "cold" rationalism; very strong emotions indeed have gone into the faith of the Enlightenment, and many rationalists are very feeling people; the difference lies in the *quality* of the emotion, and to a degree, in its *object*. Though the term is somewhat old-fashioned and simple, you can begin to formulate the difference if you think of the Enlightenment as less consonant with the emotions of the *introvert* than Christianity.

Again, it is by no means unimportant that the heaven of the Enlightenment is on earth—in the future, but on earth. The Enlightenment made its own the doctrine of progress, with its corollary doctrine of the perfectibility of man. Now from a sufficiently remote point of view you can maintain that both Christianity and the Enlightenment are much concerned with man's place in history, that both indeed have philosophies of history, and that both provide for a

407

nappy ending. But the doctrine of progress both simplifies and hastens, at least in the form it was held in the eighteenth century, the moral pilgrimage of man; it gives great emphasis to the material aspect of progress; and above all it expects progress to come from the liberation of naturally good and reasonable human beings from the restraints of law, tradition, convention, and authority, from most of what traditional Christianity had been at work building up for seventeen hundred years. It is this doctrine of the natural goodness of man that is, to the traditional Christian, the fundamental heresy of the Enlightenment. Its logical consequence is philosophical anarchy —the abolition of all external restraints on the behavior of the individual. As we have noted, no important eighteenth-century movement really pursued anarchy as a practical goal. But the slant remained in most progressive or democratic thought: The individual is right, the group wrong; freedom is a good in itself, discipline an evil in itself, or at best, unnecessary.

The Enlightenment promised heaven on earth, soon, and by a process that meant for the individual a "natural" release of expansive, appetitive forces within himself, not self-denial and inner discipline. Or at least, this is the easy, optimistic, vulgar side of the Enlightenment, the extreme of the Enlightenment, the immoderate side from which we can learn something of its weaknesses and dangers. Not all the enlightened were so naively optimistic. Still, the Enlightenment clearly did not come to promise blood, toil, sweat, and tears. We shall see what happened to the dream of the Enlightenment under the troubles that followed those hopeful earnests of Utopia, the American and the French revolutions.

12

The Nineteenth Century~I

THE DEVELOPED COSMOLOGY

SUCH WAS THE OPTIMISM of the early days of the French Revolution that many intellectuals thought there would be no more history. For to them history had existed only as a record of struggles, of slow upward progress through suffering. Now the suffering was over, now the goal had been reached, and there would need to be no history, since there would be no struggle and no change. Heaven has no history. At any rate, the past with its horrors had been overcome, and no one need be reminded of it again. Mankind was starting afresh. Condorcet, therefore, felt obliged to apologize for having any recourse to history in his account of human progress.

Everything tells us that we have come to one of the great revolutions of the human race. What is more suitable for enlightening us as to what we should expect from that revolution, for providing us with a sure guide in the midst of these movements, than an account of revolutions which preceded and prepared this one? *The actual state of human enlightenment guarantees to us that this revolution will be a happy one; but is this not on condition that we be able to make use of all our strength?* And in order that the happiness which this revolution promises may be less dearly bought, that it may be extended more rapidly over greater space, that it may be more complete in its results, do we not have to study in the history of the human mind what obstacles we must still fear and what means we have to surmount these obstacles?

The author of that passage died a few months after he had written it, probably a suicide, perhaps from mere exhaustion, in the prison of a suburb of Paris, renamed during the Revolution Bourg-Egalité—Equalityville. A moderate member of the Convention, he was fleeing the wholesale proscriptions the triumphant extremists had directed against their enemies the moderates (see our quotation from Thucydides's account of like events in Corcyra 2,300 years earlier, pp. 91, 92). At the time, the Western world had just begun what was to be a world war of some twenty-five years, war into which even the virtuous and isolated new republic of the United States of America was to be drawn in 1812. The war was the costliest and bloodiest the human race had yet indulged in.

Into the course of the French Revolution—which was in its repercussions Western, not merely French—we cannot enter here. To its makers, as well as to its enemies, it was a proving-ground for the ideas of the Enlightenment. Here the experiment of abolishing the old bad environment and setting up the new good environment was actually made. The experiment produced the Reign of Terror, Napoleon, and a bloody war. Obviously something had gone wrong. Yet the intellectual leaders of mankind by no means drew the simple conclusion that the ideas behind the experiment were wholly wrong. They drew indeed many conclusions, and from these conclusions much of the nineteenth and twentieth centuries is understandable. We shall in the following chapters make a very rough division into those who, though shocked by the Revolution, continued to hold, with the kind of modifications suited to respectable middle-class people, the basic ideas of the Enlightenment; those who attacked these ideas as basically false; and those who attacked these ideas, at least as incorporated in nineteenth-century society, as basically correct, but distorted, or not achieved, or not carried far enough. Putting the matter in terms borrowed from politics, we shall consider the points of view of Center, Right, and Left.

Adjustments and Amendments in the New Cosmology

The firm ground of nineteenth-century common belief in the West remained the doctrine of progress. Indeed, that doctrine in the developed cosmology seemed even firmer than in the eighteenth century. The human race was getting better, growing happier, and there was no limit to this process on earth. With some of the concrete values and standards of this process we shall shortly have to deal. Here we may note that if the tragic events of the wars and revolutions at the end of the eighteenth century suggested that progress was not uninterrupted, not a smooth and regular curve upward, in the comparative quiet from 1815 to 1914 there was plenty of material evidence to confirm the belief in some sort of progress, perhaps irregular and uneven, especially in the field of morals, but still clear progress.

In the first place, science and technology continued an apparently uninterrupted advance. We have reached a stage in the history of science where we need hardly attempt any sort of chronicle. By the end of the eighteenth century Lavoisier's "new chemistry" had become simply modern chemistry, though Lavoisier himself suffered in the French Revolution a fate like Condorcet's. Geology too had come of age, and in 1802, according to the French lexicographer Littré, the word *biology* was first used. Though much had yet to be done in the biological sciences, it is true enough that by 1800 the broad bases had been laid, especially in taxonomic and morphological studies. Just before the middle of the century Auguste Comte made his well-known list of the sciences in the order of their command over their materials, and their "ripeness" or perfection. The older ones were in his eye the more complete, since their materials were easier to master. They run from mathematics and astronomy through physics and chemistry to biology and psychology. The "life sciences" even to Comte were not yet quite what they should be. There is one with which he ends his list, a science not yet born, but conceived, at least in Comte's ambitious mind, and which he christened, in a mixture of Latin and Greek that has always offended the classicists, *sociology*. The science of man was to be the crowning science.

It is more important for our purposes to note that this growth of the sciences was accompanied by a growth of inventions and of the business enterprise necessary to put them to use. Thus was strengthened an attitude Westerners began to hold early in the eighteenth century, a state of mind that welcomed and expected material improvements, faster travel, bigger cities, better plumbing, more varied and more abundant diet. Moreover, these were not just improvements for the privileged few; they were improvements everybody, even the humblest, could hope some day to share. There was a common pride in these achievements, a common expectation that they would go on, measurably, statistically, an attitude we Americans sometimes rather parochially think of as typically American, whereas it is typical of the Western world since the so-called Industrial Revolution. There were go-getters in England as well as in the Middle West. Liverpool in England was to all intents and purposes as new a city as its transatlantic namesake in Ohio. Almost everywhere in the Western world, you could see "things" multiplying around you. Whether or not it is progress, the fact of increasing human ability to produce usable goods was so obvious that no one could fail to see it.

In the second place, one could in the mid-nineteenth century make at least a plausible argument that there was moral and political progress. From 1815 to 1853 there was no important war within Europe and merely routine colonial wars. Slavery had been abolished in English colonies, and was about to be abolished in the United States. The serfs were freed in Russia. All sorts of good causes, from temperance to chastity, seemed to be making progress. Herbert Spencer could hope that women would soon rise above the use of cosmetics. Human life was valued, or at least preserved, in a way it had never been before. Cruel sports, cruel punishments, no longer made public appeal in the West. The kind of human behavior found in the witchcraft scare of the seventeenth century, a scare that took some of its worst forms in new-world Massachusetts, seemed quite impossible anywhere in the Western world in 1850.

The great contribution of the nineteenth century to the doctrine of progress is to be found in the work of the biologists. Darwin reaps—and deserves—most of the fame, but a long line of workers had for several generations been building up the notion of organic evolution. Geological research made it evident that life on this planet had been going on for a very long time, thousands, and then as the evidence came in, millions of years. Fossil remains seemed to show that the more mobile and nervously complicated organisms like the vertebrates came comparatively late, and that the earliest forms of life were, roughly speaking, the simplest. It looked from the record of the rocks as though life were on a sort of ascending scale through time, with man on the top. Thus as early as the late eighteenth century there was in the air—the air the intellectuals breathed—an idea of organic evolution. Progress had gone from the seashell to man. Darwin, like Newton, tied together in a theory that could be communicated to the ordinary educated man a mass of facts and theories derived from detailed studies.

Here is by no means the place to attempt an analysis of Darwin's theories of evolution. To the layman, who does concern us, these theories meant something like this. All living organisms are constantly competing with their own kind and with other kinds of organisms for food and space to survive. In this struggle for existence the individual organisms best adapted to get plenty of food and other good living conditions live on the whole best and longest, get the most sexually attractive and capable mates, and beget fit offspring like themselves. This adaptation is at bottom a matter of luck at birth, for organisms reproduce in quantity, and in that reproduction the offspring vary ever so slightly and apparently quite at random—one is a bit taller, a bit stronger, has a single muscle especially well developed, and so on. These lucky variations tend to be continued in the offspring, however, and thus a line, a species, tends to get established, more successful and better adapted to the struggle for life than the one from which it evolved. The organism *homo sapiens* developed not from apes, but from earlier primates. Man has emerged from the struggle as Evolution's major triumph. This process is going on constantly, though very slowly. Man, with his brain, his upright posture, his hand, is at present apparently the favorite child of Evolution, of this cosmic process, but like other organisms the geological record tells us about, he may well *regress,* may fail as the dinosaurs failed, and be replaced by a fitter organism. Such, briefly, was the popular Darwinism of the Victorians.

413

Darwinian ideas are thus by no means necessarily optimistic. But those who accepted them for the most part found them full of hope. They seemed to make it quite clear that what is called progress is just as real as what is called gravity. They gave the sanction of natural science to moral and political ideas, much as Newton's ideas had done a century and a half earlier. It is true that with the publication of Darwin's *Origin of Species* in 1859 one of the great conflicts between religion and science came to a head. Darwin's work, especially when spread abroad by determined disciples, seemed to many Christians not merely to conflict with a literal interpretation of the Book of Genesis but to deny that man is in any way different from other animals—except that the purely natural development of his central nervous system has enabled him to indulge in symbolic thinking and have moral ideas and "invent" God. The conflict has not yet wholly died out. In our time, and among intellectuals at least, it seems to be taking another form, a struggle whose catchwords are *humanism* or *the humanities* on the one hand, and *science* on the other.

Our chief interest here, however, is not the struggle over man's place in nature as it was fought out in the nineteenth century, nor even in the warfare of science and theology. The influence of Darwin's work spread over into philosophy, economics, and indeed all the nascent social sciences. We shall encounter it again. Here we may note that organic evolution as Darwin and his followers brought it out was a very, very slow process indeed, so that all history from Homer to Tennyson was to time since the first Cambrian fossils as a few minutes to a year. The struggle for existence and indeed the whole armory of Darwinian ideas were far from suggesting a future of peace, co-operation, and absence of frustration and suffering. In short, the implications of Darwinism for morals and politics would seem to be rather against than for the hopeful tradition of the Enlightenment, which emphasized the possibilities of *rapid* change for the better. Yet the results of the whole process seemed most uplifting, and it is probable that Herbert Spencer was merely putting neatly the point of view of the average European and American when he wrote that Nature's discipline is "a little cruel that it may be very kind."

Evolution not only seemed to the believer to provide an explanation of the way progress took place; it made that progress clearly inevitable and good.

Moreover, there were ways of reconciling even the harsher aspects of the Darwinian struggle for life with the humanitarian and pacifist traditions of the Enlightenment. The struggle for existence among lower organisms could be considered as somehow sublimated among human beings. "Nature red in tooth and claw" could, especially for the prosperous city-bred businessman, easily seem to have become peaceful and co-operative in the cultivated fields of Victorian England. Men competed now in productivity and in high conduct, not in the crude struggle of warfare. Still another interpretation, by no means without its dangers for the optimism of the Enlightenment, considered the Darwinian struggle in human life to be a struggle among organized groups, more especially nation-states, and not, or not primarily, among individuals within these states. Within the organization, within this *political organism* as these thinkers liked to call it, there prevailed co-operation, not competition. The competition was between Germany and England, say, not among Germans or Englishmen. Interpretations of this sort, even before Darwinian ideas were developed, were favored by almost all German publicists of the century, from Fichte to Treitschke. Their implications, like the extreme nationalism they are based on, are hostile to the whole eighteenth-century outlook, and are no mere modification of it.

Darwinian evolution was, however, for most educated men of the nineteenth century a clarification and a confirmation of the doctrine of progress, a strengthening of their inheritance from the Enlightenment. But it probably helped, as the century wore on, to add to the hold over their imagination of increasingly powerful ideas of national or racial superiority. The relation between the ideas of nationalism and the ideals of the Enlightenment is a very difficult one to analyze. The Enlightenment held all men to be equal, all differences such as those of color to be merely superficial and of no effect on human capacity for culture and the good life, and was therefore wholly cosmopolitan in its outlook. The nineteenth century fell into the trap of nationalist doctrines, betrayed its intellectual ancestors of the Enlightenment, and allowed the growth of that divisive nationalism from which we still suffer.

Let it clearly be understood that this contrast between cosmopolitanism and nationalism rests on certain general ideas of the eighteenth-century philosophers and certain other contrasting ones of nineteenth-century writers—between Lessing, say, writing his *Nathan the Wise* against race prejudice, and Gobineau, writing his *Essay on the Inequality of Races* in defense of race prejudice. In actual practice there is very little difference in the international relations, the international morality, of the two epochs. Warfare was the final recourse in both centuries, and diplomacy was hardly more virtuous in one than in another. It is not even true that the professions of the nineteenth-century diplomatists were nobler than those of their predecessors.

Nationalism is at bottom no more than the important form the sense of belonging to an in-group has taken in our modern Western culture. That culture has from its beginnings in ancient Greece had a richness of group life, from the family up to so huge and catholic a group as the Church of Rome in the Middle Ages. One of these numerous groups has been consistently based on a territorial political and administrative area, and on the kind of sentiments anchored in the word *motherland* or, more commonly in the West, *fatherland*. It would be extremely useful for a qualified student of history and the social sciences to study as amalgamations of ideas, sentiments, and interests this particular in-group feeling in a series of contrasting areas in space and time—fifth-century Athens, for example, imperial Rome, the France of Saint Joan of Arc, the France of Voltaire, the France of the Third Republic. The researcher would unquestionably find differences, in the intensity and purity of the sentiments of belonging to the national group, in the distribution of these feelings among social classes, in the extent and intensity of hostile feelings toward other national groups (out-groups), and so on.

He would also find similarities. This needs to be said emphatically, for nationalism is no sudden and new thing, a villain or devil that sprang out of the otherwise progressive, democratic, and peaceful culture of the Enlightenment. Nationalism is an age-old way of thinking and feeling focused as the result, in particular, of the formative first three centuries of the modern Western era (1500-1800) on certain territorial units. These units are not absolutely fixed, though most of them have been relatively firm throughout modern times—France, for instance, or to take an "oppressed" nationality, Ireland. No single outward test of nationality exists. Actually language is usually an adequate test, for the policy of those who govern modern nation-states has been to try to bring to the members of a national group the obvious unity a single language affords. In bilingual states like Belgium and Canada there is an evident stress and strain not found in otherwise comparable states like Holland and Australia. Switzerland remains the classic, and almost sole, example of a multilingual state that everyone admits is a true nation, a fatherland for its members.

The nation has been made by a most complex interplay of actual human relations for many years, often for many centuries. Modern liberals are fond of insisting that there is no physical, no physiological basis for nationalism, that no innate "national" characteristics, psychic or somatic, exist except in normal random distribution among the individuals who make up nations like France, Germany, the United States. Frenchmen are not born with innate skill at making love, Englishmen are not born law-abiding and full of political common sense, Germans are not born blonds, nor with an innate feeling for authority. All this may well be true; but education and many more powerful molders of human sentiment and opinion have been at work for many years convincing people that national traits are facts of life. Nationalism may be the product of environment, not heredity, but a cultural environment established by a long historical development may be quite as hard to change as any physical traits.

Nationalism was unquestionably reinforced, in fact was given its characteristic modern form, as a result of the ideas of the Enlightenment and their interaction with the complex of human relations we call the French Revolution. In terms unduly abstract, perhaps, you

417

can say that notions of popular sovereignty, democracy, the general will according to Rousseau, got translated into political reality as a justification for the sovereign nation-state. We have noted already that there is behind the eighteenth-century rationalist language of Rousseau's *Social Contract* a feeling for a group will transcending the nominalist limitations of most eighteenth-century reason, a feeling that the political whole is greater than the sum of its parts, a feeling not unfairly labeled mystical. Specifically focused on a given national group, this mystical feeling clothes the idea of nationality in symbols, ideals, shared by all its members. Nationality is for its real zealots substituted for Christianity and often for all other organized forms of group life. No doubt for the average man nationalism is no more than one of the faiths that live together in actual if illogical partnership in his heart and mind (illogical and in the sense that some of these faiths, say Christianity and national patriotism, may have mutually incompatible ethical ideals). Yet it is hard to exaggerate the extent to which for many modern Western men the worship of the nation-state occupies a major part of their conscious relations with groups outside the family.

Indeed, the religious parallel we drew in the last chapter between traditional Christianity and the "heavenly city of the eighteenth-century philosophers" can be made even more concrete for the religion of the fatherland. Here instead of a vague humanity to be bettered, instead of fairly abstract ideas of "liberty, equality, fraternity," you have a definite territorial unit organized with the full benefit of political power behind it. Citizens can be indoctrinated from the very beginning so that they identify themselves emotionally with the fate of the national group. The ritual surrounding the flag, patriotic hymns, the reverent reading of patriotic texts, the glorification of the national heroes (saints), the insistence on the nation's mission, the nation's basic consonance with the scheme of the universe—all this is so familiar to most of us that unless we are internationalist crusaders in favor of a world-state or some other proposed means for securing universal peace we never even notice it. But if you want to realize how far this nationalist religion has gone even in the United States, where it is not stimulated by any sense of being nationally oppressed, any sense of wanting pieces of land we haven't got, read the fascinating chapter on the cult of Lincoln in Mr. Ralph Gabriel's *Course of American Democratic Thought*. You will find that men have actually prayed to the dead Lincoln.

Nationalism, then, is one of the *working forms* the new doctrines of popular sovereignty, progress, the perfectibility of man took in the world of reality. Nationalism is congruous with many of the elements in modern Western group life. Psychologically, it is congruous with the rise to power of a middle class that lacked the cosmopolitan experience and personal knowledge of other lands of a nobility, a class that found the abstract devotion of the intellectual to all humanity beyond its range, a class for whom the nation stood ready to provide the enduring if vicarious satisfactions of "pooled self-esteem" (this last is the harsh definition the English humanitarian Clutton-Brock gave for patriotism). Nationalism is wholly congruous with the facts of economic organization of the early and middle Industrial Revolution. Indeed nationalism, like all other phases of human relations, has been explained by the fanatics of the economic interpretation of history as wholly the result of the economic organization of the means of production in the early stages of modern industrial capitalism. If you feel the illumination of being right from such statements as that Waterloo was a conflict between British and French capitalism, probably nothing you read here will take away the glow. From our point of view, the profits obtainable through the nation organized as an economic unit—profits furthered by all sorts of acts within the frame of the nation-state, from standardization of weights and measures to protection of the flag in colonial trade—such profits and their implications reinforced what we call nationalism; they do not "explain" it.

Finally, nationalism on the whole got adapted to the generally optimistic cosmology of the eighteenth century as this cosmology filtered down to ordinary educated Westerners of the nineteenth century. This adaptation seems most neatly done, most fitly part of the kindly hopes of the Enlightenment, in the work of the Italian nationalist Mazzini. For Mazzini, the nation was an essential link in a chain that might be described as individual-nation-humanity. If *all* groups that feel themselves nations were free, then there would be no difficulties, certainly no wars, among them. It is only because the Italy of the early nineteenth century was under foreign rule, was cut up into artificial little units, that Italians showed hatred of foreigners. A free Italy would never make war or harbor hatreds. As Mazzini himself put it:

> What is true for one nation is true as between nations. Nations are the individuals of humanity. The internal national organization is the instrument with which the nation accomplishes its mission in the world. Nationalities are sacred, and providentially constituted to represent, within humanity, the division or distribution of labor for the advantage of the peoples, as the division and distribution of labor within the limits of the state should be organized for the greatest benefit of all the citizens. If they do not look to *that* end, they are useless and fall. If they persist in evil, which is egotism, they perish: nor do they rise again unless they make atonement and return to good.

These ideas sound somewhat unreal in our mid-twentieth century, when men of Mazzini's idealist and crusading temperament are rarely nationalist—except, perhaps, in lands still subject to Western imperialist control. But it is one way in which nationalism can be reconciled with liberal cosmopolitan ideals. In an attenuated form, the average Englishman or Frenchman probably made some such adjustment: Men are ultimately to be equals and brothers, and in the meantime the men of our nation can lead the less civilized rest to better things. But nationalism could be readily pushed into an attack on, rather than an amendment to, the ideas of the Enlightenment. The various brands of nationalism that exalted one national group into masters, all others into slaves, or which aimed at peopling the whole earth with one chosen group, the others having been duly killed off, were not consonant with the ideals of the eighteenth century. Of these anti-Enlightenment nationalisms the German variety that culminated in the Nazi faith of only yesterday is merely the best known and the most nearly successful.

Darwinism, we have noted, strengthened in the popular mind a belief in earthly progress, and was readily enough accommodated to the optimistic attitude of the Enlightenment toward human capacities. Nationalism could also be accommodated, at least in theoretical works like those of Mazzini, with the idea of a peaceful world of free men living rationally in mutual toleration—indeed, in mutual love. There is, however, a third great current in nineteenth-century intellectual and emotional life which presents much more difficult problems in relation to the prevailing attitudes of the "Age of Prose and Reason." However, even this current—the great "romantic" movement of revulsion against the culture of the eighteenth century which is one of the characteristic attitudes of the early nineteenth century—is in the broad perspective of Western history not really a sharp break with the Enlightenment, but for the most part, and in its effect on the attitudes of ordinary men and women toward the Big Questions of man's activities on earth, a continuation of the Enlightenment.

First, there is no doubt about the fact that the generation of the early 1800's looked back at its fathers with more than the usual modern Western contempt of one generation for its immediate predecessor. The young man wrapped up in Wordsworth shared all Wordsworth's own contempt for a writer like Pope, who seemed to him shallow, conceited, prosaic, no poet at all. The young Frenchman of 1816, perhaps born in exile, and now an ardent Catholic, felt a strong disgust for his aged grandfather, a Voltairean unrepentant, a hater of priests, a lover of good talk, good food, and bad women. Here indeed the customary order of the generations is reversed, as in a less pronounced way it seems to be in the mid-twentieth century: It is the younger generation that finds the older loose and undisciplined.

Put more abstractly and in the conventional terms of cultural history, to the classicism or neoclassicism of the eighteenth century succeeded the romanticism of the early nineteenth; to the materialism, the nominalism, the atomism of the Enlightenment succeeded the idealism, the emphasis on organic wholeness, of the late nineteenth century; to the deism, ardent atheism, occasional skepticism, and frequent anticlericalism of the eighteenth century succeeded the widespread revival of Christian forms in the nineteenth. In short, the shift to romantic tastes is one of the classic examples of a rapid change in many phases of culture.

Now we do not wish to deny the reality of this change, nor the value of studying it—and it has had a great deal of study, especially from students of literature. The differences between a painting of Watteau's and a painting of Delacroix's, between a poem of Boileau's and a poem of Lamartine's, between a baroque church and a Neo-Gothic church, are real and important. Even more important is the shift in philosophy from the nominalist to the realist position or, if you do not take the toughness too seriously, from the tough-minded philosophy to the tender-minded. We have already encountered this very basic philosophical dichotomy as far back as in Greece. Like most dualisms, it breaks down into a bewildering range of variables under close analysis, yet it has its uses. We must pause a moment to outline the steps from eighteenth-century head-philosophy to nine-teenth-century heart-philosophy.

The temper of eighteenth-century thought in the heavy fields of epistemology can be taken from Bentham, who may be on the extreme side, but is especially clear. For him the objects of sense perception are so real as to be not worth debating about. At the level of human relations, our senses make us aware of the existence of human beings, ourselves and others. That's all there is. Each human being is an individual, a social atom. Any grouping of such individuals is just a group of individuals; terms like "general will," "soul of a nation," and the like are pretentious nonsense. No group can feel or think or do what an individual can do. The whole is hardly even the sum of its parts. The whole (remember medieval nominalism) is in this case a fiction, a convenient fiction, but still a construct of the mind.

The movement away from this position is usually considered as having begun with the German philosopher Kant, whose productive period was the last half of the eighteenth century. Kant is a very difficult professional philosopher, probably for the average cultivated person today still the most typical and most representative of philos-ophers. For what the distinction is worth, he is probably in tempera-ment and influence an idealist, a tender-minded thinker. But like

Adam Smith in another field, he is by no means an extr[e]
as it was the nineteenth-century disciples of Adam Smith [w]
doctrines of economic individualism to an extreme, so it i[s]
ciples of Kant as the early nineteenth-century German Hegel who
are out-and-out idealists. Kant, in spite of his German vagueness
and long-windedness, in spite of being so obviously on the side of
the angels, is quite as obviously a child of the Enlightenment. He
was disturbed by Hume's logical development of the Cartesian dualism
of spirit and matter into skepticism about the conformity of human
reason with an external world. He set out definitely to rescue
philosophical certainty and did so to the satisfaction of many people.
Briefly, he agreed with Hume that receptor experiences (*Sinnlichkeit*)
and understanding (*Verstand*) could give us only contingent, changing, uncertain judgments. But he found in reason (*Vernunft*) the
certainty he was looking for. Reason he saw as of two kinds, *practical
reason,* which tells us infallibly through our moral intuition what is
right and wrong in a given situation, and *pure reason,* which somehow or other makes valid judgments in a way mere ordinary calculating cannot make. Obviously the distinction between *Verstand* and
Vernunft is of a piece with that between *dominium* and *proprietas,*
or that between *substance* and *accidents* (see p. 193)—that is, a distinction made on criteria different from those the scientist uses,
probably different from those common sense uses, and certainly different from those the nominalist uses.

Vernunft had a magnificent career in a line of German philosophers from Kant through Fichte and Schelling to Hegel. We may
here concentrate on Hegel, who is the best known of them, in many
ways a very typical specimen. Hegel's *Vernunft* is a communication
from the world-spirit, from the immanent, almost Spinozist God or
Supreme Reality that rules the world. Now Hegel, as you can judge
from one of his most quoted principles, that the real is rational and the
rational real, was caught in a difficulty other idealists had had before
him. His countryman of the end of the seventeenth century,
Leibnitz, had come to the conclusion, so bitterly attacked by Voltaire
in *Candide,* that this must be the best of all possible worlds. We have

noted that for the theologian who posits a God all-knowing, all-powerful, and all-good, the problem of the origin of evil is rather tough. These philosophers, however, are not really theists, nor even deists, however much they use the word God; they posit a principle, a spirit (nothing the senses of men can get at) which is, so to speak, the power that moves the whole universe, from mice to men. But they run into a difficulty much like that of the theologians; the spirit has to do what it does, and therefore whatever is, is right, or it wouldn't be. This sort of argument is very offensive to many men, and often even annoying to the thinker who makes it.

Hegel was no fatalist, but a patriotic German who wanted some things on earth different—wanted, for instance, French ways disesteemed and German ways esteemed. He got out of his logical difficulties—or thought he did—by having his world-spirit go to work historically, in time, on a plan that was perfect, but not static. The process, which Hegel's part-disciple Karl Marx made even better known, was called the *dialectic*. The spirit sets up a thesis, say Greek liberty. That *thesis* somehow rouses up its exact, polar, antithetical opposite, in this example, Oriental despotism, the *antithesis* of Greek liberty. Thesis and antithesis, embodied in human wills and appetites, fight it out in a gorgeous set of struggles designed by the World-Spirit, and out of these struggles finally comes the *synthesis,* in this example, German *disciplined liberty*. Here is a somewhat unfair specimen of Hegel's ideas and methods—unfair since it deals with concrete facts most of us assume are not really illuminated by the kind of thing Hegel does:

> The typical crystal of the earth is the diamond in which every eye delights, recognizing it as the first-born son [synthesis] of light [thesis] and gravity [antithesis]. Light is abstract, completely free identity— air is the identity of the elementary; the subordinate identity is passivity in respect of light, and this is the transparency of the crystal. Metal, on the other hand, is opaque because in it the individual itself is concentrated into an existence for itself through high specific gravity.

The synthesis is not a compromise between thesis and antithesis, not an averaging out of the difference between them, but a brand-new thing, born of exhilarating struggle. It is true that Hegel seemed to think that the Prussian state of his professorial maturity was the end of the process, the perfect synthesis. But for us the important point to note is that even formal philosophical idealism, which tends to emphasize the static over the dynamic, the unchanging over the changing, seemed in this nineteenth century to have to accommodate itself to strong feeling for time, process, change, progress, evolution.

What is more important for us than the details of these idealistic philosophies is the fact of their success. In Germany they had the dominant position from the start of the century. In England, and especially in academic circles, they gradually overcame the resistance of the strong tradition of British empiricism, and by the end of the century T. H. Green, Bradley, and Bosanquet, idealists all, were certainly the most conspicuous of professional philosophers. In the United States echoes of Josiah Royce's idealism sounded from hundreds of chairs and pulpits. Idealism had even invaded France, that land of simple, prudential logic, where the language couldn't readily distinguish between *Verstand* and *Vernunft*. Naturally, in a century of so much intellectual freedom as the nineteenth, no philosophical school had things all its own way. Various forms of materialism, positivism, pragmatism, and other deliberately tough-minded philosophies flourished, even in Germany. Indeed, the English thinker Herbert Spencer attempted a kind of *summa* of nineteenth-century evolutionary, scientific materialism, and was for several generations a kind of culture-hero for "advanced" people generally.

Now it is clear that the ordinary educated person—and by the late nineteenth century there were millions of them in the Western world—had in the hundred years that followed the American and the French revolutions changed his intellectual garments considerably. We have just emphasized the change in formal academic philosophy, from say Locke or Bentham to Hegel and Bosanquet. You may argue that formal philosophy has never had great influence on even educated laymen; and you can add to that argument the special fact that by the nineteenth century philosophy was getting to be a very specialized and academic subject, cultivated almost wholly by professors, and thus even more cut off from ordinary educated people. But there are all sorts of other tests, art, literature, religion, and in all these the men and women of the nineteenth century tended to look down on their forefathers and mothers of the eighteenth as shallow, prosaic, superficial people who never really felt or thought deeply, who never lived life whole.

Yet these differences pale before the fact that both centuries share the essentials of the modern cosmology; both believe in progress here on earth, both believe that something radical can be done about all sorts of arrangements here that will increase happiness and diminish suffering; both are at bottom optimistic and melioristic. The romantic and idealistic elements in the nineteenth-century revulsion from the eighteenth ought in strict logic, perhaps, to have made optimistic belief in human perfectibility impossible. The revival of emotion, imagination, of a feeling for organic wholes ought to have made laissez-faire individualism, simple, innocent attachment to schemes for reform, very high expectations of radical change in human behavior, much less common. Some did draw some such consequences from the revolt against the age of prose and reason. But the man-in-the-street did not. Nature might for the nineteenth century stand for wild scenery, savage joys, unplanned exuberance, instead of the quiet fields, conventional art, order and uniformity that seemed "natural" to the eighteenth. But Nature was in both centuries a comforting ally of man, just on the point of overcoming once and for all his unnatural enemies. Lewis Morgan, the American anthropologist, sounds in 1877 almost like Condorcet a century earlier:

> Democracy in government, brotherhood in society, equality in rights and privileges, and universal education, foreshadow the next higher plane of society to which experience, intelligence and knowledge are steadily tending.

The Victorian Compromise

There is, of course, a grave difficulty in attempting to outline the world-attitude of the average Westerner of the nineteenth century in the fact that averages don't live. Moreover, the multanimity we know in the twentieth century is also a fact of the nineteenth. Still, the nineteenth is the great century of English power and prestige. The Englishman set the tone even for those "lesser breeds" who hated him. The ordinary Englishman of the middle classes is the most successful, most hopeful, in many ways most representative of *homo sapiens* in the last century. He is the obvious heir of the Enlightenment, but he has experienced to the full the various winds of doctrine hostile to the Enlightenment. He led the fight against the French Revolution. His poets, preachers, artists, all welcomed the new depths of feeling the romantic movement brought. His traditions were definitely not on the perfectionist side, not encouraging to those who hoped very much for rapid, planned change in human behavior. He was the great beneficiary of the Industrial Revolution, a member of the greatest and richest nation-state of a competing world of nation-states. His patriotism need show no touch of the inferiority complex, for the Englishman was on top of the world. What he did to the heritage of the Enlightenment is worth investigating.

The Englishman believed in material progress. Indeed, all over the Western world men now took it for granted that enterprise and invention would produce ever more and more conveniences. Utopias now came fully equipped with gadgets that often enough were ultimately put in production. Thus the American Edward Bellamy, whose *Looking Backward* (1889) is the best known of these mechanical paradises, has his Rip Van Winkle hero marvel at a device whereby a push of a button floods the room with music. The prophets were occasionally wrong, however; in the first flush of enthusiasm over railroads Macaulay predicted that in the twentieth century there would be no more highways or streets, for everything would move on rails. Our Victorian took material prosperity in his stride. He was not ashamed of being comfortable, and was not greatly worried over the aesthetic inadequacies of the products of the machine. He knew that there were artists like Ruskin and Morris who thought that these cheap, machine-made goods were deplorably ugly, but there is no sign that this knowledge lessened his buying.

The Victorian was quite sure he knew why this material prosperity had come to Great Britain. The British people, he believed, were especially gifted with initiative, hard-headedness, inventiveness, and love of hard work; they had, in short, the necessary human qualities to prosper. But they also had, he believed, a set of institutions, social and political ways of doing things, essential to giving these gifts free play. We have come to the great Victorian belief in the economic doctrines of laissez faire. It is not, of course, that businessmen were all economists. But Christians are not all theologians. We have here, in fact, one of the classic instances of popular adoption of doctrines worked out by the intellectuals. Economics is the most developed of the social sciences; it has its own history, which needs for coverage a volume at least as large as this. We have hitherto encountered it but casually; in the nineteenth century, however, notions of how properly to conduct the production and distribution of wealth, not merely common-sense or traditional notions about a given way of making a living, but a fully developed theoretical scheme with political and ethical consequences, come into general circulation. In short, there is in the Victorian cosmology a strong economic component.

The fundamental doctrine is simple. Individuals, or freely associated individuals in joint-stock companies or the like (but not, for the typically nineteenth-century man, in trade unions) should try to make, buy, and sell whatever they wish and in any way they wish. Prices and standards will be set by the free play of this competition in accord with the law of supply and demand (a law your Victorian thought was essentially like the law of gravity). From such competitive processes by a law of nature would come a maximum of goods distributed with a maximum of social justice, each man getting essentially what his talents and his work had earned. Economic activity should go on almost without any participation by governmental authorities. Businessmen do, however, need at least to have some fixed contractual arrangements, and, though their selfish acts are usually excellent in their effects on society, some businessmen do occasionally overreach themselves. Fraud must be combated, and agents of government are needed to enforce contracts. No positive regulation by government, however, such as the establishment of minimum wages, for instance, should be permitted to interfere with the harmony of nature. There is indeed a corollary in classical economics, clear already in the work of Adam Smith: Monopoly, the control of any market by any single business organization, is the greatest of evils. But many of the classical economists and their followers, good children here of the Enlightenment, believed that actually monopolies were the *creation* of governments, the results of licensing, chartering, and so on; they believed that businessmen left to themselves would not voluntarily create monopolies of their own, though Adam Smith, with his usual good sense, could not help noticing that whenever merchants get together they try to combine, to form a monopoly. When it became clear, especially in nineteenth-century America, that monopolies or trusts were being so created, pure laissez-faire economics came to extend its approval of government controls beyond the enforcing of contracts. Monopolies in restraint of trade may be forbidden by law; the state may *enforce competition*.

Such, at least, is the theory of classical economics as it filtered down in relatively simple form to nineteenth-century businessmen. Among some of the intellectuals, at least, the doctrine was met with opposition we shall study in the next chapter. Workingmen did not hesitate to attempt to violate the law of supply and demand for labor by organizing in trade unions from the very first part of the century. Yet some of the attitudes of reliance on self-help and individual initiative, and of distrust of government regulation of economic activities, seeped down into the working classes. Classical laissez faire is still in 1950 the ideal, the credo, of the American business and professional community—though this community has had to adjust its behavior to a real world very far indeed from that of classical economic theory.

Actually the theory of the laissez-faire state is an admirable example of the complex and by no means well-understood problem of the relation between theories about human relations and actual life on this earth. That relation, we have noted already, is not the same as the relation between the law of gravity and the work of the engineer. Indeed, many modern students of human affairs take a position something like that of the French political theorist Georges Sorel, who calls theories of this sort "myths." The believers in such myths are heartened by their belief, and find the myths useful in many ways. But the myths are not analytical generalizations about reality. We must return to this anti-intellectual explanation in a later chapter. It is difficult to reject this explanation altogether, especially in regard to the grand social theories. An American can perhaps best understand the problem from our familiar theory of states' rights. In 1814 at the Hartford Convention it was the New England states that appealed to the theory and threatened secession; only a generation later these same states fought to prevent the Southern states from making good *their* appeal to the same theory; and in general it can be said that the most varied American political groups have from time to time appealed to the theory of states' rights.

Now if the theory of laissez faire is as adaptable as that of states' rights, one would expect that businessmen would be against state intervention and for individual initiative at times when they found such a policy agreeable to their own interests as they saw them, but that they would be willing to accept state intervention in their own interest. And so they have been. Even the British business community, which by the mid-nineteenth century had won the country over to international free trade, accepted without too much ado a whole set of government regulatory acts relating to factories, child labor, chimney sweeps, trade unions, and the like, mostly of Benthamite inspiration. British telegraphs were nationalized almost from the first (1856). In other countries, and notably in Germany and the United States, the business community was never offended in principle and in general (though sometimes in detail) by a form of strict government regulation known as the tariff. In the United States the rugged individualists of the Western states were the loudest howlers for "internal improvements" paid for and put through by the federal government; and in general it can be said to be American experience that though the expected attitude an American must take is to denounce politics, politicians, and government spending, extremely few American communities have refused to let the federal government spend money in the community.

Yet when all these qualifications—and they are important ones—are made, when we recognize that the facts of social life never quite fitted the theories of classical economics, there remains a push of the ideal away from the pole of authority and toward the pole of individual liberty. Laissez faire fits in not as an absolute, but as part of a Victorian way of life that encouraged, especially in business life, men who could try new ways, men who could take risks. Such encouragement meant that some men tried new ways that were not successful; it meant that there were failures as well as successes. It meant indeed that more human beings wanted to improve their lot—their physical welfare, their social standing—than could actually so do. It meant, as we shall see, that some force, some kind of compensatory social belief and practice was needed to compensate for the extreme individualism, what the German idealists scornfully called the "atomism," of much of Western economic and social activity.

Most Americans are familiar with this ethical-economic core of Victorian belief; indeed we have our own pat phrase for it—"rugged individualism." It takes many forms. One is the general distrust of government, of politics and politicians, we have just noted. There are hosts of popular aphorisms—"paddle your own canoe," "God helps those who help themselves," and many others—that point out this distrust of "the government" as one of the persistent ingredients of Western culture, which merely takes on in the nineteenth century a greater emphasis and is spread among all classes.

All over the Western world the nineteenth century sees some degree of belief in individualism, a belief that has one kind of theoretical justification and backing in the doctrine of *natural rights*. This doctrine we have seen is a very old one indeed. In the Middle Ages, for instance, natural rights were possessed by individuals, but not equally, not even absolutely, but rather as a part of the whole complex of custom and tradition in which they were brought up. Rights and reason were wedded in eighteenth-century thought, and by the end of the century the "rights of man" had become a commonplace. The concrete contents of such rights varied with the political thinker who was claiming them, but they did get codified in bills and declarations of rights, especially in the United States and in France. The English-man of Victorian days was likely to feel that he had the rights with-out needing any explicit statement of them.

The essence of this concept of rights is that the individual—any and all individuals—may behave in certain ways even though other and stronger or richer individuals or groups of individuals do not want to let him behave that way. One of the groups that may not interfere with his behaving in certain ways is the powerful group we call the state. Indeed the *state* is the organized group against which the eighteenth- and nineteenth-century form of the doctrine of the rights of man is directed. The rights commonly included freedom of speech, freedom of business enterprise (usually put as "property"), often freedom of association, and, if only in the form of a right to life, at least an implied right to certain minimum standards of living. This conception of individual rights is essentially the modern equiv-alent of the Christian concept of the sacredness of the immortal soul in every man, the humanist conception of the dignity of man. Again, it is an equivalent from which most of the richness and mystery of Christian feeling has been stripped—a bare equivalent. But the common, even vulgar, concept of "rugged individualism" is recogniza-bly in the Western tradition, as totalitarian denial of individual rights is not.

Americans need hardly be reminded that these rights are not in practice absolute and unchanging, that, for instance, the state can take anyone's property by eminent domain—though in our kind of society the state must recompense the owner—that the state and in fact various voluntary societies for guarding our morals can curtail an individual's freedom of speech, that, in short, the little area the indi-vidual can fence off for himself under the protection of this doctrine can sometimes almost vanish. Nor need we be reminded that in the last century or so since mid-Victorian times this little area has been cut down even in the United States. You cannot get a more repre-sentative definition of the areas a good Victorian liberal thought should be sacred to the individual than John Mill's essay *On Liberty* of 1859. Parts of Mill's writings sound today like the writing of a conservative defender of old-fashioned individualism against the New Deal.

But Mill is too much an intellectual. You can see better how the ordinary Victorian felt in a book all the social historians mention, but which no one reads, for it is in no sense a great book. This is *Self-Help,* by Samuel Smiles, published (1860) at almost the same time as Darwin's *Origin of Species* and Mill's *On Liberty.*

> . . . it is every day becoming more clearly understood, that the function of government is negative and restrictive, rather than positive and active; being resolvable principally into protection,—protection of life, liberty, and property. Hence the chief "reforms" of the last fifty years have consisted mainly in abolitions and disenactments. But there is no power of law that can make the idle man industrious, the thriftless provident, or the drunken sober; though every individual can be each and all of these if he will, by the exercise of his own free powers of action and self-denial. Indeed, all experience serves to prove that the worth and strength of a state depend far less upon the form of its institutions than upon the character of its men. For the nation is only the aggregate of individual conditions, and civilization itself is but a question of personal improvement. . . . In the order of nature, the collective character of a nation will as surely find its befitting results in its law and its government, as water finds its own level. The noble people will be nobly ruled, and the ignorant and corrupt ignobly. Indeed, liberty is quite as much a moral as a political growth,—the result of free individual action, energy, and independence. It may be of comparatively little consequence how a man is governed from without, whilst everything depends upon how he governs himself from within. The greatest slave is not he who is ruled by a despot, great though that evil be, but he who is the thrall of his own moral ignorance, selfishness, and vice. There have been, and perhaps there still are, so-called patriots abroad, who hold it to be the greatest stroke for liberty to kill a tyrant, forgetting that the tyrant usually represents only too faithfully the millions of people over whom he reigns. But nations who are enslaved at heart cannot be freed by any mere changes of masters or of institutions; and so long as the fatal delusion prevails, that liberty solely depends upon, and consists in government, so long will such changes, no matter at what cost they be effected, have as little practical and lasting result as the shifting figures in a phantasmagoria. The solid foundations of liberty must rest upon individual character; which is also the only sure guaranty for social

security and national progress. In this consists the real strength of English liberty. Englishmen feel that they are free, not merely because they live under those free institutions which they have so laboriously built up, but because each member of society has to a greater or less extent got the root of the matter within himself; and they continue to hold fast and enjoy their liberty, not by freedom of speech merely, but by their steadfast life and energetic action as free individual men.

There is an extraordinary amount of conventional Victorian belief in those short passages—including the typical nominalist denial that a whole is anything but the sum of its parts. But Smiles puts even more explicitly the factor that balances the apparently anarchic individualism he preaches.

> . . . thus we come to exhibit what has so long been the marvel of foreigners,—a healthy activity of individual freedom, and yet a collective obedience to established authority,—the unfettered energetic action of persons, together with the uniform subjection of all to the national code of Duty.

This balance is of course the famous "Victorian morality," the "middle-class morality" of Shavian wit, the thing the generation of the 1890's rebelled so vigorously against. Probably these rebels, who were also intellectuals offended by Victorian tastes and Victorian successes, are poor reporters of actual Victorian practices. Yet go direct to the Victorian novelists, and especially to Trollope, and you will see that, at least in the middle and the upper classes, the ruling classes, the individual is held to a very strict code of conduct, and above all is trained from childhood on to conformity, to accepting discipline, to the willing merging of himself in a group. This conditioning is achieved by a subtle social training, and of course is to be found in some form or another in all societies. In Victorian society, economic life was supposed to be a scramble. Social life, however, was supposed to be orderly. The emphasis on liberty is balanced by the emphasis on authority.

We need not go into great detail about this code of behavior. It is worth close study in the records of Victorian culture itself, so near to us, so much a part of us, and yet in the mid-twentieth century so far away. Perhaps the modern American finds most remote the social and moral structure of the family—its relatively large size, the great authority of the father, the strict discipline undergone by the children, the subordination of the females to the males, the infrequency—indeed the horror—of divorce. The kindest of Victorian parents would hardly have thought of treating his children with the "permissiveness" that is the fashion in most American families. Samuel Butler's *Way of All Flesh* is the work of a very intellectual rebel and its picture of a Victorian father may well be false as well as exceptional. But Butler's father could hardly have been formed in any other society.

What the family had begun was continued in the boarding schools, the famous "public" schools that correspond to the American private schools, to which at least the boys of the upper and middle classes went. These schools were in some ways Spartan in their taming of the individual, in their molding him to a member of the team, the group. Adolescents are perhaps especially likely to want to conform. The English public schools made their boys into the pattern so familiar in English novels and Hollywood pictures—the Englishman who knows his duty, who doesn't need a policeman because he has his conscience, the Englishman who can do what he likes because he couldn't possibly like to do anything very dangerous to society. There were, of course, always boys who couldn't be so molded. These were the rebels, some of whom drifted off to the far parts of the world, some of whom conformed just sufficiently to be classed as eccentrics, a group the Victorians tolerated on principle, and some of whom, like the poet Shelley at one end of the century and the poet Swinburne at the other, attacked the whole system, root and branch.

For the average Englishman of the ruling classes, then, the wild scramble, the Darwinian struggle for life to which his economic beliefs invited him was balanced by the orderly world of decency and decorum that his education and family background prepared for him. Although there were many, many elements of instability in this Victorian compromise, still for the generation or two that it lasted it provided one of those rare periods of balance in Western history, a period peaceful but not lethargic, a time of change and experimentation that was not, however, a time of troubles, not an age of stomach ulcers and nervous breakdowns.

The compromise was in part a compromise with Christianity. All over the Western world, especially in Catholic countries, the anticlericalism of the Enlightenment lived on, taking firm roots in a Western culture where outward religious conformity had ceased to be prescribed by the law. But after the severe persecutions to which Christians were submitted during the "de-Christianization" movement of the French Revolution, there was a swing of the pendulum back toward Christianity, at least among the intellectual classes, a swing well marked by the French romantic writer Chateaubriand's *Génie du Christianisme* (1802). It would be unfair to say that Chateaubriand was unimpressed with the *truth* of Christianity, but its truth was certainly not what he brought out in his book; what struck him, and what he thought would impress his generation, was the beauty of Christianity, the moving quality of its liturgy, the haunting background of its Gothic past.

It will not do to leave the impression that Chateaubriand is typical of the Christian revival of the nineteenth century. Where that revival was markedly hostile toward the spirit of the age, toward the Victorian compromise we have here been attempting to define, it will be considered in the next chapter. Christian protest against the compromises Christian churches were making with the spirit of the age was firm and loud; no fair student of the nineteenth century will neglect that protest, whether it came from Maistre, from Newman, or from General Booth of the Salvation Army. But there can be no doubt that, especially in Protestant countries—though the Catholic peoples do not altogether escape it—this revival is in fact itself very much a compromise. The basic optimism toward human nature that is the mark of the Enlightenment penetrates nineteenth-century Christianity, along with a willingness to compromise with rationalism as well as with the comforts of the flesh. Were you merely to count Christian heads, were you to measure by the spread of missionary work in all parts of the globe, or by Bibles printed and by Sunday-school attendance, you might well conclude that the nineteenth was the greatest of Christian centuries. For all these indices show an upswing. Of course, the hopeful believer in human perfectibility can maintain that these indices are what count, and that this new synthesis of Christianity and the Enlightenment is a stage in attaining his perfectibility.

From the historian's point of view, the nineteenth century is not marked by any great new Christian sects, none, indeed, as successful as were in the full tide of the age of prose and reason the Methodist and Pietist groups of the eighteenth century. Numerically, two new American groups, the Mormons and the Christian Scientists, were the most striking. But probably the multiplication of religious splinter groups, of heresies against heresies, and in particular of cults variously compounded from Eastern brews, was greater than ever. Unitarian and Universalist groups that explicitly denied the sacramental character of the worship of Jesus, groups that showed a strong rationalist influence, flourished among the prosperous intellectual classes. At the other extreme, on the surface at least, were the High-Church movements in England and America with their appeal to ritual and tradition. Thus the Christian revival, whatever else it was, was not a revival of Christian unity. The nineteenth is as many-minded, as eclectic, a century in religion as in architecture.

But for the average middle-class person we are here concerned with, churchgoing was a necessary thing. The Victorian compromise meant that the leading elements in the community could no longer take the extreme anti-Christian position many of the enlightened had taken in the eighteenth century. Jefferson's hostility to organized religion had begun to be inconvenient to him when he became President in 1800. A Jefferson in the mid-nineteenth century would simply have had to deny himself a political career in most countries had he taken so outspoken a position against organized Christian churches. This does not mean that the Lancashire mill owner as he attended the service of the local Congregational chapel, the coupon-cutting bondholder as he went to his village church, were outright hypocrites. Some such hypocrisy must have existed in a community where so

437

many social and business pressures pushed toward formal religious conformity, but we have every reason to believe that most of these churchgoers were undisturbed by the contrast between their lives and Christian ideals. After all, we have had worldly Christians for a very long time—if not from the start.

What makes these worldly Victorian Christians so conspicuous to us may be no more than the brilliance with which later intellectuals like Bernard Shaw have attacked them. Still, from a mid-twentieth-century point of view they do look too self-righteous, too unaware of the depths of human incapacity for comfortable adjustment to routine, too much at ease in Zion. Perhaps it is just that from our point of view they look too lucky. But their merging of eighteenth-century rationalism and nineteenth-century sentiment didn't quite come off. They seem at least as shallow as the pure rationalists, and much less convinced that God really needs help from us.

The forms of the political and social life of the Western world in the nineteenth century show a very great variation, from the traditional democracy of the United States to the traditional monarchy of Prussia. In a sense, the Western world is like the much smaller world of fifth-century Hellas; it has as national components its equivalents of Sparta, Thebes, Athens; the nation-state is the city-state on a grander scale. Yet in modern Europe even more than in ancient Hellas, one feels that there is a kind of pervading set of general attitudes, never quite the same in different countries, never quite in the same relation with other currents in different countries, but still not by any means a myth. There is a Western culture, a Western consciousness of kind in the nineteenth century. The Marxist does not hesitate to label the whole set of attitudes "middle-class," and if one understands that many of these attitudes were adopted by upper and lower classes as well, there is no harm in using the label.

In politics as in morals and religion there is a nineteenth-century compromise. We have noted that the Enlightenment itself was divided in its political hopes and program, that sometimes even the same man—say Bentham—believed in a benevolent manipulation of the environment by a wise minority and also in the ability of the

438

mass of men to pick their own rulers by universal suffrage. The nineteenth century managed without too much frustration to hold inconclusive views on this difficult question. It believed in liberty for all, but. . . . The favorite way out was to believe in liberty but not in license. The distinction between liberty and license was a moral one: One was free to do right, but to do wrong meant license, and that should be stopped. Thus the politics of the Victorian ties in with his moral code.

Briefly, the Victorian had some such political credo as the following. First, there is the inevitable start in the doctrine of progress, according to which ultimately all men will be free, equals, and brothers, there will be no police and no taxes, work will be pleasant and voluntary and there will be no poor, and no violence in any form —in short, the kind of Utopia we have called "philosophical anarchism." This ideal society, though some way off in time, is certain and will be achieved by education and the gradual extension of democracy. Democracy, though perhaps dangerous even in England in the 1860's, was for the man of the nineteenth century definitely the "wave of the future." The good liberal even in countries by no means in the center of the Victorian compromise, in Germany, in eastern Europe, held the view that the ultimate realization of democratic ideals lay in the course of events. For the present, the best fitted should rule as trustees for the slowly improving masses. The best fitted are not the old aristocracy, whose blood has run thin, but the men of any class who have shown by their success in business or the professions that they can cope with practical problems. The Victorian believed in liberty, but the kind of liberty that means competition; and he believed in equality, but the kind of equality of opportunity that gives all men an equal start in the race, not the kind that would have no race—or at least, no prizes for the winners, and perhaps no winners. He came to be increasingly aware that his society handicapped the child of poor parents, that the equal start was a myth; and he came in general as the century wore on to feel that though the big race of Life was a fine thing, though from it came ever better champions, still the course needed cleaning up, needed first aid stations, needed firm rules against tripping, crowding, and other dirty tricks. He came to believe more and more in state intervention to help the little fellow, to lessen actual economic inequalities, to do the kind of thing we all know as the work of the "welfare state." Still, the typical man of the mid-century was clear that in a choice between liberty and equality, democracy if it were to be healthy should lean toward liberty.

We have been considering what the Victorian thought was right; it is a harder task to describe what he thought was beautiful. We had best attempt here no more than a few generalizations on this phase of Western culture, once more with the warning that there are not only grave differences among social classes and other cultural groupings, but that over all is the great difference of nationality, perhaps plainer in matters aesthetic than elsewhere. Yet there are at least one, and perhaps two, safe generalizations to be made.

First, this is a period of very great—unusually great—variations in standards of taste. You can put it unfavorably as a lack of standards, an anarchy of taste; or favorably as a period when in art and culture as in economic life there was free play of individuality and competition out of which came a rich variety, the best of which was very good indeed. At any rate, you can note the facts of the situation clearly in a matter like architecture. Hitherto in the West a man who set out to build any kind of building, from the humblest up, knew in what style he was going to build, for he would build as people around him had been building. It is true that the style had changed, most conspicuously at the time Gothic gave place to classical, and that there had been a slow variation within these styles. In cities like Paris and London the Middle Ages had left survivors that stood out rather strikingly in the midst of early modern buildings, most of them in, roughly, the style Americans call colonial. But as the nineteenth century wore on what is called eclecticism took complete possession of the builder, public as well as private. There is a short flurry of Neo-Gothic in the early part of the century, but not even Neo-Gothic was a universal fashion.

Ultimately there came the position we Americans still apparently take as natural. A man wants to build a good house; he consults his family and an architect, and the consultation revolves largely about the question of what style—Cape Cod, bungalow, ranch house, English Tudor half timber, French chateau, South African Dutch, adobe, mission, and so on. It is unfair to take the building on American motor roads as typical of anything, but they do put the matter with great force: If you want to build a hot-dog stand there are no limits left— you may build a beaverboard Eskimo igloo, a derby hat, a large lion, an immense hot dog itself. At no other stage in human history has man built in the bewildering variety he has built in since 1800. In no other culture have his cities looked like an architectural hash.

Second, it is probably true that in the nineteenth century there developed, along with this very great variety of tastes, a widespread feeling among cultivated people that they were increasingly being surrounded with ugly things. One assumes that no Athenian found the buildings on the Acropolis ugly, for these buildings have unity of style and are built in a single tradition. You would hardly get anything like unanimity among Americans on the subject of the public buildings of the city of Washington—though Washington has much more consistency in planning than any other great American city. Perhaps we do not have a good enough record of past ages. Certainly the intellectuals in all periods of Western history have complained bitterly enough about the manners, morals, and intelligence of the many; no doubt that Plato found popular tastes as low as he found all other things popular. But one has the impression that the nineteenth century, and we ourselves as its heirs, have added taste to the many other elements that separate social groups, and that more especially set off an intellectual class in partial isolation.

Yet again, there probably is a sort of cross section or least common denominator of taste in the nineteenth century, and again it is the taste of the successful man of affairs—and his wife. The Victorian liked things solid and just a bit showy; he liked abundance, and disliked the spare, the austere. He was a romantic, an escapist, with a great interest in distant and exotic things; but he also prided himself on his hard-headed sense of reality, on his ability to record and

441

report. The literature of the century has almost the full range of the spectrum, from the romantic writhings and ironies of lost souls like Byron and his European disciples to the calm but very decent common sense of Trollope and the crusading "naturalism" of Zola. Everything is there—again as in a hash.

It is, however, a well-blended hash with a flavor of its own. Looking back on that age from ours, one is struck by the fact that in spite of its diversity of tastes, its romantic escapism, its disputes over fundamentals, the nineteenth century does attain a paradoxical kind of unity, and is an age of balance, a "flowering." The man of the nineteenth century had a sense of *belonging* (deeper than mere optimism) that we lack. His universe had not, as ours seems to have, got out of hand for him. He did not need to take refuge in fantastic styles or simple, often inhuman, functionalism, as we have done. He did not need to try to escape from escape.

One hesitates to try to find a symbol of nineteenth-century culture, as one finds the Parthenon a symbol of Periclean Athens, the cathedral of Chartres a symbol for the thirteenth century. A railroad station? A great factory? A bird's-eye view of Manhattan? These are all unfair, for the nineteenth century was not just an age of industry and material achievement. The nineteenth century invested heavily in public buildings of all sorts, but none of them seems a suitable symbol. Perhaps after all, since so much of the effort of the century was spent in making the lives of individuals more comfortable, more happy, more important, we can take as a symbol one of the better residential streets of a great city—London, Manchester, Lyons, Dresden, Baltimore, perhaps one of those streets dedicated to separate private houses, "villas" as they are called in Europe. Here you have comfort, plenty of room, greenery, quiet, neatness—and an anarchy of taste in architecture. If your sympathies are with the radicals, you will think that this street should be balanced with a street from the slums. But do not worry. That slum street was very much in the minds of the dwellers in the villas. They hoped that someday there would be no slums, though they did not think they could do much about it right away. But the slums worried them, even in mid-century. As a master class, the Victorian middle class had too brief and insecure a rule to acquire the serenity of self-confidence the feudal aristocracy had once had.

The slum street would have liked to transmute itself into the street of villas. We have insisted throughout this chapter that there are all sorts of groups besides the Victorian middle class we have chosen as a most typical specimen. And so there are: national groups, confident almost as the British, as for instance the Prussian or the American, or irredentist, complaining, full of martyrdom, like the Irish or the Poles; anticlerical, positivist, ethical-culture groups proudly not going to Christian churches, but very insistent that their ethics were at least as Christian as those of the orthodox; little groups of fanatics, mostly mild ones, devoted to one single crank device or social gadget, but otherwise conformist enough, the single taxers, the theosophists, the vegetarians, the preventers of cruelty to children or animals, the antialcoholics, and so on through the long roster of nineteenth- and twentieth-century "good causes"; and, by no means the least conspicuous, the intellectuals, trying very hard to repudiate or remold the strange, chaotic society in which they found themselves.

What we have called the developed cosmology, then, was the basic belief of most Western educated men and women of the nineteenth century, the standard by which even the uneducated or less educated masses guided their aspirations. This cosmology accepted the belief of the Enlightenment in the progress, in the perfectibility of man here on earth, in the attainment of happiness here on earth. But the nineteenth century took from these beliefs their sharpness and their immediacy, in some ways much as later Christian belief took away from primitive Christianity the frightening, if hopeful, possibilities of an immediate second coming of Christ. The Victorian compromised with the hope and the heroism of the Enlightenment. He was for gradual progress, for a slow, careful process of educating the masses, for a strict moral code enforced by the full social pressure of men in groups, for liberty to experiment but not at the expense of what he felt to be moral absolutes, for the career open to talents yet not closed to inherited wealth and position, for peace on earth but not at the cost of his national honor and dignity—for democracy, even, but not for radical, not for socialist democracy, not for democracy that took literally "liberty, equality, fraternity." Surely, thought the Victorian, one can be a democrat, a liberal, an enlightened, modern person, and yet be prosperous, happy, comfortable even in this world where not all are yet prosperous, happy, and comfortable. The "yet" was a great salve to his conscience. Someday all men would be as well off as he was now; meanwhile, the lucky and the privileged should not jeopardize the possible by trying—or letting others try— to achieve the impossible. In this nineteenth-century world the existence of the rich man, or at any rate of the moderately rich *bourgeois,* should not inspire any silly metaphors about the difficulty of putting a camel through the eye of a needle.

Yet we should not take leave of the confident Victorians, envious as indeed we must be of their self-confidence, without recognizing the fact that we are the heirs of their faith in human beings—a modified faith compared with the wild optimism of the Enlightenment, a faith we have further vastly modified, have perhaps almost abandoned. You can see in John Stuart Mill that faith at its clearest, and in some senses at its best, as it is found among intellectuals. Most of the intellectuals parted company with the Enlightenment as reflected in the Victorian compromise. It is true that a Longfellow, a Tennyson, a Dickens and many another imaginative artist is in some ways in tune with the triumphant middle classes, or at least not diametrically and bitterly opposed to all they stand for. But there are not many *politiques et moralistes* who stick to the colors of the Enlightenment. Of these, Mill is an admirable specimen.

He was the son of James Mill, a self-made Scot who was a favorite disciple of Bentham. John Mill is then a sort of grandchild of Bentham. All his life he maintained that he was true to the Enlightenment—anti-Christian in a theological, but not in an ethical, sense; a firm believer in the power of reason working on common-sense and empirical grounds; a distruster of philosophical idealism, of German idealism especially (Mill once said that he always felt slightly nauseated after trying to read Hegel); a reformer anxious to improve

444

the material condition of the masses; a believer in liberty for all, in toleration of other people's ways even when they conflict with your own; above all, perhaps, a man who felt deeply that there is something profoundly necessary to human life expressed in that formal and all too often empty term, *liberty.* Yet this same Mill had retreated from, had modified in many ways what he had inherited from his spiritual grandfather. Under the influence of romantic poets like Wordsworth and Coleridge he had come, just like the ordinary folk of his generation, to qualify the stark rationalism of the Enlightenment with a feeling for the uncertainties, the emotional responses, the *irrational,* as an enrichment of life, not a delusion; he had even had, under the influence of Carlyle, a brief period when he thought he was attracted to mysticism, but he soon returned to a moderate rationalism; he believed in liberty, yet toward the end of his life he called himself not only a democrat, but in some senses a socialist, for he had come to believe that the government must interfere, not only to enforce contracts, but to make positively better the position of the poor and the handicapped; he was a utilitarian, the heir of the Bentham who had in his *Deontology* decided that the pleasures of belief in God were less than the pains of such belief, and had therefore decided against the utility of religion; and yet toward the end of his life John Mill embraced a sort of modern Manichaeanism of his own, in which a good God and a bad Spirit fought out the uncertain battle and sought to enlist us all. The successor of the school that believed in the perfectibility of man had a great fear of the possible tyranny of the majority, and wrote this revealing aside—"for ordinary human nature is such poor stuff."

Yet Mill stated as clearly as anyone has ever stated the central doctrine of nineteenth-century liberalism:

> . . . the only purpose for which power can be rightfully exercised over any member of a civilized community, against his will, is to prevent harm to others. His own good, either physical or moral, is not a sufficient warrant. He cannot rightfully be compelled to do or forbear because it will be better for him to do so, because it will make him happier, because, in the opinions of others, to do so would be wise, or even

right. These are good reasons for remonstrating with him, or reasoning with him, or persuading him, or entreating him, but not for compelling him, or visiting him with any evil in case he do otherwise. To justify that, the conduct from which it is desired to deter him, must be calculated to produce evil to some one else. The only part of the conduct of any one, for which he is amenable to society, is that which concerns others. In the part which merely concerns himself, his independence is, of right, absolute. Over himself, over his own body and mind, the individual is sovereign.

This will sound to many intellectuals today remote, too simple, perhaps wrongly focused, perhaps wrong-headed. We distrust all kinds of sovereignty today, at least if we have been swept into fashionable currents of philosophical relativism; or if we still trust in absolutes, the absolute sacredness of the individual's sovereignty over himself is not one of the absolutes we hold. Yet some such beliefs as Mill here expresses are surely very widely held here in America in the mid-twentieth century. We still have that sympathy with the human individual trying to define, assert, and make appreciated his uniqueness, which is one of the traditions of the West. We still dislike regimentation, paternalism, deference to authority, even though we want security and are tired of the fine, free Darwinian fight. We still think of *homo sapiens,* not as a member of a society like those of the bees and the ants, but as a free, roving, adventurous animal. In short, we are still living in part on the intellectual and emotional capital of the last century—and, indeed, of the whole tradition of Western ethics and philosophy.

13

The Nineteenth Century ~ II

—————————— ATTACKS FROM RIGHT AND LEFT

THE NINETEENTH CENTURY sees the full development of a change in the sources of livelihood of that very important part of the intellectual classes, the writers; and it sees the final touches in the process of making the characteristic modern group we call the intellectuals. Both these topics must receive attention in any intellectual history of the West.

From the days of the Greeks to early modern times writers of all sorts, poets and storytellers and scholars, had either to have income from their own property, or to be subsidized by rich patrons, like the Roman Maecenas; by the state, as with the Attic dramatists; or by an institution such as a monastic order. With the invention of printing in the fifteenth century there came gradually to be a large enough market for books, so that slowly authors and publishers were able to work out a copyright system, and the writer became a licensed merchant selling his product in collaboration with a publisher who took much of the commercial risk. There came also to be a periodical, and by the eighteenth century a newspaper, press for which the writer worked for pay, sometimes on salary, sometimes at piecework rates. The eighteenth century is here a period of transition. Copyright is imperfect, patrons are still important, and journalism hardly offers prizes even for its most successful practitioners. The English "Grub Street" remains a set phrase for the struggling proletariat of the written word. Yet there grew up notably in England and in France a group of men who lived, however badly, by selling in a true market what they wrote. Sir Walter Scott is perhaps the first man to make a fortune from his pen, which like Mark Twain later he proceeded to lose by unwise investments in the new business of big-scale publishing.

By mid-nineteenth century authors have their full modern status; there are great prizes for those who write best sellers, and there is a livelihood dropping down to meager for the less successful. There is a full-fledged newspaper and periodical business, fed both by salaried reporters and staff men and by free-lance writers. The drama had begun to pay with Shakespeare, who was apparently a first-rate theatrical manager. By Victorian times the royalties from really successful plays had begun to be large. From there the road to Hollywood is clear. There is beginning to be still another opportunity for those who gain a living by putting words together on paper, and that is commercial advertising. But in 1850 advertising was in its infancy, and not altogether a respectable profession.

Learned writing, including pure science, continued to be subsidized, chiefly by institutions. But the institutions that do the subsidizing were already by the nineteenth century secular rather than ecclesiastical institutions, and on the European continent were usually under state control. There developed in the textbook trade a welcome subsidiary source of income for members of the learned world. On the whole, however, the rest of the more purely intellectuals, those who preached and taught, continued to be supported by groups—state, church, college, and the like—on fixed and relatively low stipends. The law remained as it had been for centuries a learned profession as individually competitive as any business. Medicine, hardly a learned profession at all until early modern times, had by the mid-nineteenth century become one of the most esteemed of professions, though like the law it was, in terms of economic livelihood, almost entrepreneurial.

We cannot here go into that relatively neglected and fascinating field, the sociology of professions. We have made the obvious point that by the nineteenth century professional writers were fully in the current of economic competition as sellers of words, and that in a very broad way all those—now much more numerous than ever before, certainly absolutely, and *probably* relatively to the whole population—whose main job was some kind of deliberate thinking and planning, were more and more drawn into the currents of individual economic competition of the nineteenth century. Only preachers and teachers seem an exception, and they were not altogether so. Yet the intellectuals remained intellectuals, proud of it, and even in the more competitive ranges of, say, journalism, always conscious of some separateness of outlook from those who bought and sold material things. Great commercial success, especially in marginal fields like Hollywood, advertising, and publicity, tends in contemporary America to give a bad conscience to the successful writer, and drive him leftward.

From our point of view, the importance of this change in the economic and to a certain extent the social status of intellectuals in the Western world is not that they get thrown into a vulgar commercial whirl, that they lose serenity and detachment. Intellectuals in the West have by no means commonly lived in ivory towers isolated from the dust and heat of the world in any age. What is new in the modern world is the process, clearly complete by the nineteenth century, that made the intellectuals dependent in part for their livelihood on a wide public, and did this notably for writers.

This dependency upon the custom of the many might be expected to have led most successful writers to flatter the public, to accept human relations as they found them—in short, to conform. And of the millions and millions of printed words, no doubt many *were* written merely to amuse or excite the ordinary man, to help him escape, to confirm him in his prejudices, to back up the Victorian compromise. Yet almost all the men we now study as part of our heritage, almost all the great writers, as well as a great number of writers of the forgotten and the incidental, *attacked* things as they were. The editorial writer, like the preacher, has in the modern world to be *against* something. The great writers of the nineteenth century and of the twentieth have belabored the race for its failures. Think of Carlyle, Emerson, Thoreau, Marx, Nietzsche. These, of course, were *politiques et moralistes,* and could hardly be such without finding their fellow creatures wrong, or wicked, or lazy, or stupid. But even the novelists are crusaders—some of them the more obviously crusaders when they avow they are scientific analysts of human behavior. Zola or Dreiser comes to mind at once.

We are, however, edging over into a second point about the role of the intellectuals in the modern Western world, a central problem in a branch of sociology even less advanced than the sociology of the professions—that is, *Wissenssoziologie,* the sociology of knowledge, learning, ideas. We need make only one additional note on the modern position of the writer dependent on the wide popular market for his goods. Very often the most profitable occupation for such a writer is to abuse his customers, to tell them what fools they are, particularly in America, where the boobs of Mr. Mencken's *booboisie* used to read him with pleasure, where thousands of Babbitts bought Mr. Lewis's *Babbitt* to make it a best seller.

We by no means have for the three thousand years of Western history an adequate supply of facts about the attitude of the intellectuals—that is, the "intellectual classes" of Professor Baumer's definition (see p. 8)—toward the accepted cosmology of their societies; and we have not yet worked out any satisfactory interpretation or theory of the social role of the intellectuals. We have scraps of information and beginnings of theories, both of which have from time to time appeared in this book. We can say that as a group, except perhaps in the earliest and most consecrated days of Christianity, the intellectuals have been pretty well aware of their separateness from the bulk of their fellow men, pretty "class-conscious." At all times, even in the Dark Ages when the new ruling class was illiterate, or even in deliberately anti-intellectual Sparta, some members of the intellectual classes have been at the very top level of the social hierarchy. Some—the rural parish priest of the Middle Ages, the schoolteacher in most periods—have been in terms of real wages fairly close to the bottom.

Yet it is very hard indeed to make an effective generalization, even for a given period, to say nothing of the whole course of Western history, concerning the attitude of the intellectual classes toward the established order of their society. Rebels at the very top there have always been, though we know little of them in the Dark Ages. From Plato through the first Christian Fathers to Abelard, Wycliffe, and the innumerable intellectual rebels of today the succession is clear. Yet probably the great bulk of the intellectual classes, the great majority even of those who preach, teach, orate, editorialize, and comment have been conformists, supporters of things as they are, conservatives in the simple sense of the word, that of "keeping intact what we have." Certainly their listeners and readers have been in their conduct conformists and conservatives, or we should not be here to study the intellectual history of the West—there would be no West. It is probable indeed that even in the modern West the many readers of nonconformist writings, of writings attacking the established order, are not influenced at all to rebel themselves. They get a sort of catharsis or relief, much as our ancestors used to get relief through sermons on hell-fire.

At any rate, it is clear that since the beginnings of the Enlightenment, the *creative portion* of the intellectual classes have in general been dissatisfied with the world they saw around them, anxious to reform it, convinced it could be reformed. The eighteenth-century philosophers were agreed among themselves, in spite of certain differences over methods, that the job could be done fairly soon, that society could be made over according to standards (those of Nature and Reason) evident to all, once they were enlightened. These intellectuals of the Enlightened hated the *privileged* unenlightened—the priests, the conventional noblemen, the very few intellectuals who opposed them—but they loved and trusted the *unprivileged* unenlightened, the common people whom they were going to train for life in Utopia.

Now with the nineteenth century the creative intellectuals are still in rebellion, but they are no longer a united band. Some have moved in ideal toward the right, toward the old religion, toward the old, or a rejuvenated, aristocracy, toward some kind of authority, some definite design for making and keeping the many nice and quiet, and perhaps also happy. Some have moved left, toward some form of what now begins to be a word of fright to the conventional man of property—socialism. More important, the creative intellectuals come as the century goes on more and more into conflict with precisely the kind of people the eighteenth-century philosophers had cherished and nursed—the ordinary educated but not intellectual middle-class person. Most of the standards set up in the last chapter as those of the Victorian compromise were very largely repudiated by the nineteenth-century writers we still remember and read. These writers share some of the attitudes of the middle classes, notably a conviction that progress is real and possible; at the very least, they share a sense of history, of process, of flow. But they quite specifically dislike the middle classes, for whom they invent uncomplimentary names like "philistine." Even a writer who glories in the achievements of the middle classes, a writer whom the aesthetes and arty folk generally thought a philistine, the Herbert Spencer who wrote a nineteenth-century *summa,* is no conformist, no contented man, but a strong anticlerical, a man convinced that a lot is wrong with the world. Spencer, in short, protests, complains, bellyaches; he cannot for long describe or analyze without blaming—and very occasionally praising—without displaying annoyance or anxiety; he has, in short, the acid flavor we have come to expect from serious writers. Already in the nineteenth century the creative intellectuals are working up to the state they have reached in contemporary America, where one expects an intellectual to complain as naturally as he breathes, where one expects to open any serious publication and begin to read about what's wrong with our colleges, the crisis in the family, the destruction of our topsoil, the crossroads in international relations, the coming end of our culture. You will even find complaints about the role of the intellectual. Some years ago a distinguished French writer, Julien Benda, wrote a book called *La trahison des clercs,* which can be informally translated "What's Wrong With the Intellectuals."

We are, of course, exaggerating. Science, or cumulative knowledge, cannot in itself praise or blame, hope or fear; and there is a great deal of scientific writing in these times. Some artists may work with intent to please rather than to improve, though probably most art involves a judgment about the universe. Still, by and large it is true that roughly since the French Revolution the more creative and productive of the intellectual classes, and notably the writers, have rejected most of the way of life of the middle classes of the West, have rejected the values current among that class—and it must not be forgotten, the imitators and aspirants to middle-class status who make up the very great bulk of the working classes of this period.

Attacks from the Right

For convenience we shall classify attacks on the conventional ways of nineteenth-century life as from the Right and from the Left. These terms grew up out of French parliamentary practice early in the century, when the conservatives or monarchists took to sitting in a group to the right of the presiding officer, and the constitutionalists and radical reformers grouped themselves on his left. There is a certain symbolic fitness in this, since on the whole the Left wishes to push on to as full a realization as possible of the "principles of 1776 and 1789," the democratic aims of the American and French revolutions, and on the whole the Right wishes a much less democratic society. Of course, the simple linear differences suggested by these terms are inadequate to measure the complexities of opinion even in politics. For one thing, the center from which we measure Left and Right is not a clear fixed point, for there is always that democratic tension between the ideals of liberty and equality we have already noted. The ideal of security adds still another complication. Still, as a rough means of sorting out attacks on the position outlined in the last chapter, the division into Right and Left should be useful, especially if we note that the line is a curved line that can come full circle so that the extremes meet. In the last years of the Third French Republic it is striking to note how often the Monarchists and the Communists, in political terms extreme Right and extreme Left, voted on the same side of a given question. They both hated with virtuous ardor the vulgar conformists who did not want revolutionary change.

What the eighteenth-century *philosophes,* with the sound instinct that makes us recognize our enemies, singled out for their bitterest attacks was the Roman Catholic Church. For if you hold, as the *philosophes* mostly did, the doctrine of the natural goodness and reasonableness of ordinary men, then the polar opposite is the idea of original sin. But a great deal more of the cluster of ideas of the Enlightenment—naturalism with its denial of the supernatural; materialism; belief in assured progress on earth; dislike of tradition, of established hierarchies; belief in liberty or equality, and sometimes in liberty *and* equality—finds in traditional organized Christianity a cluster of antithetical ideas. We have already noted that in some senses the Enlightenment itself is a child of Christianity. We shall see that even the more conservative churches, the Roman Catholic and the Anglican, for instance, have by no means refused to adapt themselves in part to changes since the eighteenth century. It would be very wrong indeed to set up the formula: "Christianity" and the "modern spirit" are mutually exclusive systems of values. In fact, we have noted in the last chapter that conventional, churchgoing Christianity, Catholic as well as Protestant, was one of the elements of the Victorian compromise. Notably in the United States, where all but a crank minority believes in democracy, it follows that Christians have to believe in democracy.

Nevertheless, the established churches have from time to time produced thinkers who have been the most determined and absolute of opponents of democracy. Of these, there is surely no more eloquent, able, and one fears, at bottom unrealistic, thinker than Joseph de Maistre. This Savoyard civil servant exiled by the French Revolution sought to bring his fellows back to what he held to be eternal verities. With a good deal of insight he picked on Francis Bacon as one of the founders of the modern evil, which is precisely the notion that *something new and good is possible*. Few Americans can read a passage like the following without amazement, and usually

indignation; yet it is important that we realize men in o[u]r
culture have held these beliefs:

> The very title of his [Bacon's] main work is a striking error. There
> is no *Novum Organum* or, to speak English, *new instrument,* with
> which we can reach what was inaccessible to our predecessors. Aristotle
> is the true anatomist who, so to speak, took apart under our eyes and
> showed to us the *human instrument.* One can only smile somewhat
> scornfully at a man who promises us a *new man.* Let us leave that ex-
> pression for the Gospel. The human spirit is what it has always been.
> . . . Nobody can find in the human spirit more than is there. To think
> the thing possible is the greatest of errors; it is not knowing how to look
> at one's self. . . . There may be in particular sciences discoveries which
> are true machines very suited to perfect these sciences: thus the differ-
> ential calculus was useful to mathematics as the toothed wheel was to
> watchmaking. But as for rational philosophy, it is clear that there
> cannot be a new instrument just as there are none for mechanical arts
> in general.

Maistre's big work, *Du Pape,* is a defense of papal authority, indeed,
papal infallibility, and in general of an authoritarian system in a world
he felt was falling into an anarchy of belief and practice. "Protestantism, philosophism," he wrote, "and a thousand other sects, more
or less perverse or extravagant, having prodigiously diminished the
truth among men, the human race cannot remain in the condition
in which it now finds itself." Yet he apparently was realistic enough
not to hope for any sudden mending, especially among peoples as far
gone as the Anglo-Saxons. What he did hope was that a nucleus of
wise and disciplined men in countries still Catholic at heart could hold
fast during the storm of materialism, unbelief, and scientific progress
and be there to bring the world to its senses after the inevitable breakdown.

To Maistre a usually rhetorical term of abuse can be almost
literally applied: He was a *reactionary,* a man who held that nothing
new could be good and nothing good could be new, that the Catholic
synthesis of the Middle Ages was valid for all time. Yet even
Maistre could not escape history, and at least in his sharp, clear, epigrammatic style bears the unmistakable mark of the eighteenth cen-

tury. More than that, in his dislike of sentimental enthusiasm, in his scorn for the humanitarians of his day, he shows signs of the slightly cynical Catholic authoritarianism that was to trouble gentler souls within the Church itself. Note the way in which he suggests in the above passage that expressions like "new man" had better be left to the Gospel. Moreover, if you read him carefully enough, Maistre will be found to have some of the notions about the "organic" nature of society, the saving strength of tradition and prejudice, we shall find in Burke; but Maistre's *manner* is even less conciliating than Burke's, and he leaves the impression that his good organic society is rather inconsistently an unchanging society.

Maistre can hardly be to most twentieth-century Americans more than a queer specimen from another world. Unfortunately, most Americans have almost as much difficulty in the sympathetic under-standing of a much profounder critic of democracy, the Irishman Edmund Burke. Now Burke lived in the second half of the eight-eenth century, and his greatest book, the *Reflections on the Revolution in France,* was published in 1790. He is, however, one of the most able thinkers to question the basic beliefs of the Enlightenment, and continued throughout the nineteenth century to be the great source of a certain kind of conservative opposition to the tendencies of the age. Burke was a Protestant, a sincere Anglican who had grown up under English influence and who made his career in the British House of Commons. He supported the cause of the American rebels in speeches that were long read in this country; but from the very start he detected what he thought were disastrous possibilities in the French Revolution, and early made himself a leader in an intellectual crusade against it. This step brought him into violent conflict with the ad-vanced thinkers of the time, and in particular made most Americans of the age of Jefferson regard him as a benighted soul. Tom Paine's *Rights of Man* was a reply to Burke, and to this day most Americans are likely to feel that Paine had the better of the argument. Yet Burke is well worth the attention even of the convinced democrat of the Left, for he seems to many to have made some analyses of human relations that deserve to be considered additions to our slender stock of cumulative knowledge in the social sciences. It is hard to distill this from the mass of his rhetoric; moreover, there remains in Burke a solid core of Christian faith that is clearly not reducible to cumulative knowledge in the scientific sense.

To Burke the French Revolution was predominantly the work of a certain type of idealist educated in the great hopes of the Enlightenment. Burke did not maintain that everything was satisfactory in the France of the old regime, that nothing needed to be done to improve French social and political life. Burke was not that kind of reactionary, though as his polemic continued and the Terror came on in France, he was capable of an occasional passage in which he sounds almost as rigid as Maistre. The base of Burke's criticism of the leaders of the French Revolution is that, instead of going ahead and trying to repair a defective flue, rebuild a wall or so, tighten a roof, they proposed almost literally to tear down the whole building and then put up a brand-new one for which their philosopher teachers had given them the blueprints. But the old building was the only building in existence, and even if men could have agreed to build according to the theorist's blueprint, the building must have taken some time. But they were not in fact so agreed. All that happened was that the old building was pretty well torn down, and the French people left without shelter from the storms. The new one had finally to be pieced together largely with the old materials, for men cannot live in the modern world without shelter. But the philosophers didn't build the new-old building; it had to be built by a more ruthless master builder, a man who could get things done by authoritarian means if necessary —by a Napoleon Bonaparte, in short. It is quite true that Burke, writing in 1789-1790, foresaw and specifically predicted a dictator like Napoleon, who finally did come to power in 1799.

Now the above figure of speech does less than justice to Burke but it may help the reader to follow his analysis. Burke starts with a Christian pessimism about the animal man; indeed, one of his great hatreds was his hatred for the Rousseau who preached the natural goodness of man unsoiled by civilization, the Rousseau whom he called the "insane Socrates of the National Assembly." Ordinary men

457

if left to the promptings of their desires, their passions, will, according to Burke, always *tend* to run amuck, to cheat, seduce, violate, to make beasts of themselves. Yet in daily life most of them do none of these things, and the criminal exceptions can always be coped with in a sound society. Civil society presents the striking spectacle of potentially, "naturally," bad men behaving like good ones, or at least quiet ones. We must conclude that just the opposite of what Rousseau said is true: Man is saved, not ruined, by his membership in society, by his obedience to convention, tradition, prejudices, law, and the like. His social and political environment is the one thing that stands between him and a chaotic mess.

It follows that you must never destroy the great bulk of arrangements, institutions, set ways of managing human relations that we call "civil society." It is true that any bright person with the right aptitudes can devise all sorts of new ways of handling these matters, theoretical improvements that if they would only work might well be real improvements. But Burke holds that you must go cautiously along this road, attempt very few changes at a time, and never attempt to change *all* civil society. The French in 1789 did really attempt such a complete overthrow; they sought to change everything from the system of weights and measures to the election of bishops and the structure of the central government. They turned the job over to theorists instead of sticking by men of practical experience.

What keeps ordinary men on the decent road, however, is in part at least habit, and a kind of emotional identification the individual makes with the society of which he feels himself part. This feeling is not something that can be produced to order; it has to grow, slowly and naturally. Burke would *not* have appreciated the story about the American college campus where a notice was posted, "Beginning tomorrow it will be a tradition that freshmen remove their caps when they pass before the statue of the founder." For Burke, what holds society together is nothing rational in the simple sense of the word, nothing planned, nothing put down on paper as a new constitution. In fact, he would hold the term "new constitution" to be complete nonsense. At most, you can introduce new elements in a constitution, as you might make a graft on a tree, by an organic, not a mechanical process.

Burke does not, of course, use the kind of language we have used above. He uses the terms current in his own age, including the hallowed one of "social contract." But note what a very different emphasis he gives to this notion. We are no longer dealing with Lockian or Benthamite calculation of interests, but with concepts clearly in the medieval Christian tradition.

Society is, indeed, a contract. Subordinate contracts for objects of mere occasional interest may be dissolved at pleasure; but the state ought not to be considered as nothing better than a partnership agreement in a trade of pepper and coffee, calico or tobacco, or some other such low concern, to be taken up for a little temporary interest, and to be dissolved by the fancy of the parties. It is to be looked on with other reverence; because it is not a partnership in things subservient only to the gross animal existence of a temporary and perishable nature. It is a partnership in all science, a partnership in all art, a partnership in every virtue and in all perfection. As the ends of such a partnership cannot be obtained in many generations, it becomes a partnership not only between those who are living, but between those who are living, those who are dead, and those who are to be born. Each contract of each particular state is but a clause in the great primeval contract of eternal society, linking the lower with the higher natures, connecting the visible and invisible world, according to a fixed compact sanctioned by the inviolable oath which holds all physical and all moral natures each in their appointed place.

One more passage may be cited to show how Burke takes still another famous—and explosive—phrase of the Enlightenment, "natural rights," and brings it around to conformity with traditional notions of authority and inequality.

Government is not made in virtue of natural rights, which may and do exist in total independence of it; and exist in much greater clearness, and in a much greater degree of abstract perfection; but their abstract perfection is their practical defect. By having a right to everything they want everything. Government is a contrivance of human wisdom to provide for human *wants*. Men have a right that these wants should be provided for by this wisdom. Among these wants is to be reckoned the want, out of civil society, of a sufficient restraint upon their passions.

Society requires not only that the passions of individuals should be subjected, but that even in the mass and body, as well as in the individuals, the inclinations of men should frequently be thwarted, their will controlled, and their passions brought into subjection. This can only be done *by a power out of themselves,* and not, in the exercise of its function, subject to that will and to those passions which it is its office to bridle and subdue. In this sense the restraints on men, as well as their liberties, are to be reckoned among their rights. But as the liberties and the restrictions vary with times and circumstances, and admit of infinite modifications, they cannot be settled upon any abstract rule; and nothing is so foolish as to discuss them upon that principle.

What happened in France, according to Burke, was that foolish if well-meaning men got a chance in the financial crisis that led to the calling of the States General to try to destroy the old French society, and did succeed in breaking down much too much of it. The average Frenchman, no longer able to rely on the settled ways of old, was thrown off balance, frustrated. He took his frustration out in aggression. The Reign of Terror was the normal result of trying to effect too big changes in society. Burke, had he been alive, would no doubt have argued that the gangster bootlegging era of the 1920's was the normal result of trying by changing the law to make men change very old drinking habits.

Burke was not, however, a reactionary. He did believe in the possibility, indeed in the necessity, of the new, the experimental. He would "reform in order to conserve." His proposed reforms seemed mere stopgaps to impatient radicals like Paine and Owen, and indeed the real reforming temperament must find Burke fundamentally antipathetic. For he is at the very bottom a pessimist. He simply does not believe that all men can be happy here on earth, ever. He puts his objections to the rationalist planning of the eighteenth-century enlightened largely in terms that mark the so-called "romantic revival" —in terms of the organic nature of human groups (as opposed to the mechanical), in terms of tradition, sentiment, even *prejudices,* a word almost equivalent to *sin* to the eighteenth-century philosophers. Yet behind this there lies an older nomenclature for an older set of feelings, essentially those of Augustine and Aquinas.

One more Christian thinker must be noted. Cardinal Newman was an Oxford don who became one of the great figures in the High-Church Anglican revival of the early nineteenth century known as the "Oxford Movement." Newman was a sensitive, imaginative young man who felt acutely the need for certainty and for authority. He could not satisfy himself until, in 1845, he went over to the Roman Catholic Church. Newman, like Maistre and Burke and indeed all the Christian conservatives, found the enemy in the philosophy of the Enlightenment, though by the mid-nineteenth century Newman could use "Liberalism" to designate the cluster of ideas he hated.

By Liberalism I mean false liberty of thought, or the exercise of thought upon matters, in which, from the constitution of the human mind, thought cannot be brought to any successful issue, and therefore is out of place. . . . [Liberalism holds that] no revealed doctrines or precepts may reasonably stand in the way of scientific conclusions. Therefore, e.g. Political Economy may reverse our Lord's declarations about poverty and riches, or a system of Ethics may teach that the highest condition of body is ordinarily essential to the highest state of mind . . . [that] there is a right of Private Judgment: that is, there is no existing authority on earth competent to interfere with the liberty of individuals in reasoning and judging for themselves about the Bible and its contents, as they severally please. Therefore, e.g. religious establishments requiring subscription are Anti-christian. . . . [Liberalism holds that] there is no such thing as a national or state conscience . . . [that] utility and expedience are the measure of political duty . . . [that] the Civil Power may dispose of Church property without sacrilege . . . [that] the people are the legitimate source of power . . . [that] virtue is the child of knowledge, and vice of ignorance. Therefore, e.g. education, periodical literature, railroad travelling, ventilation, drainage, and the arts of life, when fully carried out, serve to make a population moral and happy.

Newman's interest for us, however, lies less in his attacks on liberalism, less even in his profound emotional acceptance of traditional Christianity, than in the rather surprising efforts he clearly made to accommodate his thought to the spirit of the Victorian Age. Do not misunderstand. No one was ever less a time-server than Newman. He almost certainly made no conscious effort to put over a message in terms which might be taken to pervert it. He was simply too intelligent, too aware of what was going on around him, perhaps also a bit too much of a Britisher, to take the neat, dogmatic position Maistre took: i.e., that nothing new is good, indeed nothing new is possible. Newman in his *Essay on the Development of Christian Doctrine* (1845) goes so far as to insist that precisely because Christianity in its traditional sacramental form is true it is bound to change, to grow, to develop. He does indeed guard himself from a completely relativist position: In so far as the Church is a divine institution it is of course perfect, and therefore above change. But in so far as it is a human institution here on earth it *must* change, because that is a rule of life. "In a higher world it is otherwise, but here below to live is to change, and to be perfect is to have changed often."

Not all change is good—indeed, Newman holds that such a belief is one of the great Liberal errors. We must distinguish between development and corruption. For life, which has the promise of development, holds also the threat of corruption. We cannot use any simple scientific test to tell us when a given change is good or bad, a development or a corruption. For that we must rest on what Newman called our illative sense. This notion, developed especially in his *Grammar of Assent* (1870), is one of the earlier anticipations of much of the anti-intellectual doctrine we shall study in the next chapter. Briefly, Newman is seeking for some psychological explanation (justification, if you prefer) of belief that will go beyond the sort of criteria of truth modern man associates with natural science, and perhaps with common sense. It would be unfair to say that Newman's illative sense is basically William James's famous pragmatic "will to believe"; certainly Newman does not say that we should believe what we want to believe. But he does insist that full human life on this earth has to be guided by something more than notions of truth that guide the experimental scientist in his laboratory; that something is a mixture of what we Americans call "hunch" and "know-how," of aesthetic sensitivity, of moral sensitivity, of concrete experience of actual problems. Knowledge we arrive at through the illative sense is to knowledge arrived at by pure logic as a cable of many strands is to a single bar of steel; each is strong, but only one is of a simple, single piece.

462

The illative sense varies in different individuals, and in them is often stronger in, for instance, aesthetic than in moral matters. There can be in such matters no such universal test as logic applied to science affords, no way of proving a truth of morals or aesthetics to a person with an imperfect or an untrained illative sense. But this is not to say that there is no such thing as truth in these matters; on the contrary, the general opinion of mankind over the ages has not been cynical or skeptical in these matters of value-judgment, but has recognized saints, artists, and wise men when it met them. Only if we expect Christian truths as we find them at work among men to be perfect, unchanging, absolute, only, in fact, if we are dogmatic where dogmas do not fit, shall we feel that our judgments of value are inferior in validity to the judgments of fact of the scientist.

Newman's own exercise of the illative sense led him in the direction of conservative politics, toward sustaining the existing system of social and economic relations. But the theoretical scaffolding he drew up is one of the very best for what is sometimes called liberal Catholicism, the conscious adapting of Christian attitudes to a greater degree of democracy, toward a greater acceptance of some of the goals of the Enlightenment.

We have chosen Maistre, Burke, and Newman as examples of thinkers who attack from the point of view of traditional Christian cosmology and psychology the optimistic and rationalistic beliefs of the Enlightenment. It is difficult, of course, to draw the line between men like these and other conservatives whose articulate interests are perhaps secular rather than religious. Inevitably, most conservatives are at least outwardly Christian, since Christianity is the established faith of the West. There are indeed attacks on democracy from the Right, from the new *authoritarian* or *totalitarian* positions that are not really Christian or traditional, and to these we shall shortly come. Their great development was in the twentieth century, though their roots lie in the nineteenth. In the nineteenth century, the most important intellectual opposition still came from thinkers who wanted to go back to something they thought better, and once, at least, actually prevailing here on earth. At bottom, what they opposed to democracy was aristocracy, the rule of the wise and the good, the classical tradition of the Greek or the Roman gentleman as it had been modified by later Christian and feudal practice.

We cannot here attempt a systematic treatment of such thinkers, who differ from men like Burke chiefly in their emphasis. By the nineteenth century, many of them are convinced that some form of popular government is inevitable in the West, and their main concern seems to be that some kinds of excellence (other than the gift of making money or that of swaying crowds) be made available for the coming democratic society.

In a sense, two great political thinkers commonly classified as "liberal," John Mill and Alexis de Tocqueville, really belong in this class. Mill was greatly worried about the danger of the "tyranny of the majority," and was much interested in proportional representation and in other schemes to protect the liberty of minority groups. Tocqueville was a cultivated French nobleman who came to the United States in the early nineteenth century to study our prison systems, and who went back home to write one of the classic accounts of American society, *Democracy in America* (1835-1840). The book is rightly enough considered as one of the kind favorable to us Americans, as in some ways the work of a liberal; but Tocqueville was worried about us, about our preference for equality over liberty, about our distrust of intellectual and spiritual refinement and distinction, about the danger to the future of Western man he sees in our great strength and our great indifference toward, indeed dislike of, the traditional excellences of the classical gentleman. He was a generous aristocrat, puzzled by American hopes for immediate perfection, put off by our frontier egalitarianism, alarmed by our faith that the majority is always right. But he foresaw our coming greatness—foresaw, indeed, in a passage of great insight, our conflict with Russia. He has fears that in our greatness we may put material above spiritual ends, but he does not miss the nobler aspect of the "American dream." Unlike so many European commentators, he never takes a nagging tone of superiority.

A later English writer, Sir Henry Maine, puts very clearly the aristocratic distrust of democracy. In his *Popular Government* (1885) distrust has come very near to fright. Maine was by profession a historian, who had specialized in early legal history, and did much work on the frontiers of anthropology. But his studies had convinced him that the line of evolution of mankind, working through Western man as its highest representative, ran from primitive tying up of the individual in definite obligations never consciously or voluntarily assumed to the modern freedom of the individual to decide for himself what he is to do and be. In Maine's famous phrase, man's progress is "from status to contract." What alarmed him in the 1880's was the evidence from trade-union activities in Britain, social-security legislation in Germany, rising socialist propaganda everywhere, that some men preferred security to liberty, the safety of status to the risks of contractual freedom. Maine is one of the first great writers in the West to make use of some eighteenth-century notions of human freedom as a defense of the *status quo*. Maine is the Tory of the 1880's preaching what the radical of the 1780's had preached. Laissez faire, once a threat to the established mercantilist system, was now threatened by socialism, and had become the conservative doctrine of a capitalist middle class. Actually, there is nothing paradoxical about this. In a changing society, successful changes once made are incorporated in the structure of the society. If the society continues to change, as Western society very definitely has, then those who promote the proposed new changes will find themselves opposing what was once radical. Tom Paine in 1790 wanted a government that would govern very little, cost very little, and that would let nature take its beneficent course; if you want that in 1950, you are an old-guard Republican, not a radical like Tom Paine.

Just as Newman seems a wiser man than Maistre because he sought to understand the facts of social change, so another group of conservatives seems wiser than Maine and the other frightened gentlemen. These are the Tory democrats, seen at their best in the England that gave them the name. It is not exactly that the Tory democrats are more practical men than the plain Tories; indeed, though they have in Benjamin Disraeli a man practical enough to rise to the position of prime minister, they are mostly confirmed idealists, gentle-minded people, often theorists like the poet Coleridge, clergymen like F. D. Maurice. They are often very self-conscious Christians and sometimes accept the label "Christian socialist." They believe with Burke that most men are unable to guide themselves in freedom to a good life, that, in short, men are sheep who need shepherds. The Industrial Revolution and the false ideas of the Enlightenment about human equality had in their opinion resulted in the rise of bad shepherds—factory owners, politicians, agitators, journalists. What the people need is good shepherds who will see that government inspectors keep factories clean and sanitary, that the workers have social security, that all runs well. These good shepherds are the natural leaders of the people, the wellborn, the educated, the classical gentleman again.

The favorite doctrine of the Tory democrats—and the justification for the second part of their name—is that if the people are really given free choice, if the press, schools, and all the organs of public opinion are open to all points of view, then in such free conditions the people actually will of their own accord, by democratic voting, choose the right shepherds, the men who have the gifts and the training to rule wisely. The really wise and good, they argue, are in the nineteenth-century West in danger of letting the struggle go by default. They are staying out of the political battle, leaving it to the demagogues, the socialists, the cranks. If they will only go before the people with the truth, the people will know them for their true leaders.

The Tory democrats objected to the disorder, the vulgar scrambling, the harshness of a money-getting society. Many of them objected also to the ugliness of their times. But those whose chief quarrel with democratic ways as they developed in the nineteenth century was aesthetic are worth a brief word in themselves. They are not very easy to classify according to their acceptance or rejection of the Enlightenment. Some of the really tender-minded, like the Englishman William Morris, called themselves socialists, and argued that the trouble with democracy was that there wasn't enough of it, that it hadn't gone far enough, that it had created around ordinary men and women a new bad environment, that you should change that environment and let the natural goodness and wisdom of the masses come out. But John Ruskin, who called himself a Tory, is perhaps a better example of the type.

For this "Tory" Ruskin was named a college at Oxford founded in the late nineteenth century to allow competent sons of laboring men to study in that university of the ruling classes. For years, Ruskin College was a center of opposition to the actual Tory party. Indeed it is difficult to disentangle and label the variants of political and moral opposition to things-as-they-were in the nineteenth century. Ruskin is here perhaps unfairly grouped with those whose main feeling of opposition to their age centers in matters aesthetic. His focus seems to be a dislike for money-getters, a dislike for those who measured success in terms of material success, or the honors achieved in a vulgarly competitive society. In such moods he sounds like Carlyle, and at times comes, like Carlyle, close to asking for a Leader to get us out of this morass of materialism. You may judge of his aesthetic social criticism by two quotations, "There is no wealth but life" and "Life is the possession of the valuable by the valiant."

The aesthetic critics of nineteenth-century democratic culture were united at least in their belief that it produced "cheap and nasty" things in quantity, that the machine had killed any pleasure in creative work of the kind the old craftsman used to feel, that it had made work an unalleviated burden, that it had poisoned even the leisure of the workingman by leaving him only mass-produced mediocrity even in his amusements. They were not in agreement about the way out, but most of them held that the uncorrupted few, the men like themselves who still knew the beautiful and the good, must somehow take the lead and create here and there little cells of beauty and wisdom. The nineteenth century was the great century of little social experiments, of ideal communities designed to prove that a given social environment will remake fallen men. There was still a good deal of space available in the United States, which is one reason why so many of these communities were founded there. Brook Farm in Massachusetts, the Phalanx in New Jersey, New Harmony in Indiana—the list is long, a fascinating catalogue of human hopes and failures. Morris, who was a gentleman of independent means, founded various shops for handwork, preached faithfully before little groups of converts, and wrote a Utopia called *News from Nowhere* (1891) in which men have got rid of machines and great ugly cities and live once more in a green and pleasant land of arts and crafts.

In this classification of aesthetic opponents of democracy you will no doubt find the greatest concentration of cranks, of men with one-way formulae for heaven on earth, the kind of fanatic who in the sixteenth century went in for the wilder sects. They offend the settled bourgeois sometimes out of all proportion to their importance. It was not Morris or Ruskin, it was not the Utopian socialists of the little communities, but the Marxists who really threatened the comfort of the philistine in his little suburban castle-home. Nevertheless it will not do to dismiss the aesthetic criticism of democracy too lightly. The slums of Manchester or Liverpool, the hot-dog stands, filling stations, motels, and cabin slums that line major American motor highways are surely among the ugliest things man has ever built on this earth. If there really is progress, it has hardly achieved the elimination, or even the lessening, of the ugly. Moreover, these critics, impractical and soft though many of them seem, focused attention on aspects of the very important problem of the incentives and rewards of labor in modern society. Capitalist and socialist thought alike tended, and still tend unduly today, to consider the problem of labor solely in terms of wages and "efficiency" in the technical sense of factory organization. Men like Morris, or the French Utopian socialist Fourier, incompetent though they were in the ways of the world, knew better. They pointed out that the problem of getting people to do the necessary work of the world is a full, complex, human problem, not merely a problem of dollars and cents or of efficient motions. They pointed out that men do not like to be bored, that they like to feel they have made something useful or even beautiful, that they have pride of workmanship, that they enjoy being part of a team.

Morris in *News from Nowhere* has the outsider notice, in the lovely public forest—Kensington Forest—where ugly suburban London used to be, gangs of sturdy young men cheerfully digging ditches,

nd is told by his guide that they enjoy competitive ditch-digging.
When the outsider expresses surprise, his guide remarks that he un-
lerstands that in nineteenth-century Oxford and Cambridge eight-
oared crews went through the hardest physical labor with pleasure.
The sermon may seem rather silly and sentimental; and yet on reflec-
ion you will realize that the amount of "work" expended by a college
crew or a football team would easily build a housing project. There
s no magic that can turn labor into sport, and Morris does not persuade us that there is. But there is a real problem of using the
abundant energies of men in socially effective ways.

You can make a pretty effective argument that the critics of democracy with whom we have so far been engaged in this chapter are
of purely historical and intellectual interest (no slight thing) but that
they have not in fact greatly influenced the world we now live in.
The immediately effective attacks on democracy have indeed been
made from some other base than that of Christianity or the classical
ideal of the beautiful and the good; they have at times appealed to
these and other strains in our Western tradition, but their major appeal, and the one we now classify them under, is that of an exclusive
in-group, national, racial—at any rate, biologically determined. From
these attacks there came in the twentieth century those totalitarian
movements of the Right—Fascism, Nazism, Falangism, and the like—
which were perhaps no more than scotched in the war of 1939.

Now the problem of the intellectual ancestry of Rightist totalitarianism is a fascinating one, and one that has already attracted much
attention. Once more, we must warn the reader that it is absurd to
say that Wagner, for instance, is "responsible for," "to blame for," a
"cause of," the German Nazi movement. The Nazis cannot be explained fully and completely, any more than cancer or polio can be
fully explained. We do know that such movements always have a set
of views about all the questions, big and little, and we can see where
they got some of their answers. That should be enough for all but
the most determined metaphysicians.

We have already noted that the cluster of ideas and sentiments
called nationalism gave trouble to those who wished all men to be

469

brothers. Even within national states greatly influenced by the idea of the Enlightenment, even in the states at the heart of the democratic tradition—the United States, Britain, France, and the smaller countries of western and northern Europe—the demands for national unity, for conformity on the part of each citizen to a national pattern, served to lessen the personal freedom, the range of character and eccentricity within these in-groups. Moreover, most of the great democratic states, including the United States, had in the nineteenth century careers of successful expansion in the course of which they came to hold as possessions lands inhabited by men of different color and different culture. Almost universally among the citizens of these democracies there prevailed in the nineteenth and early twentieth centuries the feeling that theirs were better, higher, ways, and that they ought peacefully if possible, to impose their ways on these darker-skinned peoples. A whole literature of the "white man's burden" arose to justify what its authors for the most part considered the inevitable Westernizing of the rest of the world.

Even in the lands where the democratic tradition was strongest however, there were those who held that these non-Western peoples could not in fact be brought up to Western levels, and that they ought for their own good to be kept in a perpetually inferior status, or even be helped to die out. Americans like Lothrop Stoddard and Madison Grant, Britishers like Benjamin Kidd, were alarmed at the "rising tide of color," and urged that something had to be done to protect the hitherto dominant great races of whites. The Englishman Cecil Rhodes, no theorist but a businessman who made a fortune in South Africa, believed that Anglo-Saxons (or rather, English, Scots, Welshmen, and Americans) had achieved standards of moral and political decency no other peoples seemed able to achieve, and that therefore they should unite, get as much of the earth as possible, and multiply as fast as possible to fill it.

But the clearest line of antidemocratic Rightist totalitarian thought and practice comes out in the German and Italian experience. Their nationalism, their later totalitarianism, does not prove the existence of an innate incapacity for political virtue among Germans or Italians.

Their politics is a complex resultant of many historical factors. There are many variables of historical growth in the past two centuries that help explain the rise of totalitarian societies in the twentieth century in these states. We are here interested in the strands of nineteenth-century thought that helped to make Nazism and Fascism. It is true that in the nineteenth century only a few wise men recognized the direction these antidemocratic forces were taking. The very term *proto-fascist* for any nineteenth-century thinker is an anachronism, and therefore in a sense an injustice. Yet if we remember that human beliefs and institutions do not grow even as inevitably as an acorn into an oak, that no later stage is an inevitable consequence of an earlier, the search for totalitarian origins in the nineteenth century will not mislead us.

One strand is certainly the simple strand of historical nationalism we have already noted as universal in the West. To this must be added, especially for Germany, a very strong strand of "racism," the notion that Germans are biologically a special variety of *homo sapiens* —blond, sturdy, clean-cut, virtuous, the destined master race. To outsiders, this is clearly an example of a social myth; the Germans aren't even in a majority blonds. But we today are pretty well used to myths which, though they do not correspond to scientifically established truth, clearly influence people and get them to work together. The irony has often been pointed out: The first strong modern literary source of these ideas of Germanic caste and color lies in the writings of a nineteenth-century Frenchman, the Comte de Gobineau. Actually there is a long history in the West of prestige attached, if not to actual blondness, at least to lightness of color. Even among the ancient Greeks, legend made such gods as Apollo blond; the whole Hindu caste system depends on *varna,* color; even in the Christian artistic tradition you will note a certain tendency to make the saints rather more blond than the sinners. Scientifically speaking, we do not know whether or not blonds tend to be more virtuous than brunettes; the question is simply meaningless. It is, however, a fact that this and other beliefs of a similar sort entered into the antidemocratic faith of the Nazis. As early as 1842, a German historian could write:

> The Celtic race, as it has developed in Ireland and in France, has always been moved by a bestial instinct, whereas we Germans never act save under the impulsion of thoughts and aspirations which are truly sacred.

The American historian of the revolt of the Netherlands, Motley could contrast Celtic "dissoluteness" and German "chastity."

A third strand, and probably in fact the strongest and most important in Nazism and Fascism alike, is the emphasis on the authority of a ruler and a small group of the party elite around the ruler. This concept too has firm nineteenth-century background, and indeed is in one sense merely a reappearance of very old notions like that of the divine right of kings. Perhaps there is no better nineteenth-century proto-fascist than the once-respected Victorian writer Thomas Carlyle, whose *Heroes and Hero-worship, Shooting Niagara, Nigger Question* are full of the leadership principle, the necessity of the stupid many's subservience to the wise few, the need of permanence, status, subordination in our madly and stupidly competitive society. Carlyle at first was moderate in his demands:

> Aristocracy and Priesthood, a Governing class and a Teaching class; these two, sometimes separate, and endeavouring to harmonize themselves, sometimes conjoined as one, and the King a Pontiff-King:—there did no Society exist without these two vital elements, there will none exist.

But as the nineteenth century wore on with democracy still going forward, especially in his own country, he came to be more and more ferociously authoritarian in his demands, and in the end came to call for a universal drill sergeant, a military dictator, a man of deeds and no words—merely commands.

Toward the end of the century, Germany itself produced one of the most articulate enemies of democracy, one of the real, if no doubt unintended, builders of Nazi ideology. This was Friederich Nietzsche, partly insane and wholly intellectual, at bottom a sensitive moralist who could not bear the ugliness, cant, stuffiness of the rising bourgeois empire of the Hohenzollerns. Nietzsche, with all his subtleties, is a fascinating example of the modern intellectual with his infinite capacity for feeling pain, his impatience of the herd-men around him, his horror at the machine-made ugliness of the middle-class world. No doubt had Nietzsche lived he would have found Hitler, Goering, Goebbels, and the rest most hateful. But the fact remains that he called in his lifetime for the "superman" (Uebermensch), for a transvaluation of values that would once more bring noble violence to play against ignoble bourgeois comfort, that he penned some of the most ferocious attacks on the democratic way of life:

> Democracy has in all ages been the form under which organizing strength has perished. . . . Liberalism, or the transformation of mankind into cattle. . . . Modern democracy is the historic form of the decay of the state. . . . The two opposing parties, the socialist and the national —or whatever they may be called in the different countries of Europe— are worthy of each other; envy and laziness are the motive powers in each of them. . . . The equality of souls before God, this lie, this screen for the *rancunes* of all the baseminded, this anarchist bomb of a concept, which has become the last revolution, the modern idea and principle of the destruction of the whole social order—this is *Christian* dynamite.

In fact, Nietzsche wrote a whole platform for totalitarianism of the Right a generation before it came to power:

> The future of German culture rests with the sons of Prussian officers. . . . Peace and letting other people alone—this is not a policy for which I have any respect whatever. To dominate (*herrschen*) and to help the highest thought to victory—that would be the only thing that could interest me in Germany. . . . The same discipline makes the soldier and the scholar efficient; and, looked at more closely, there is no true scholar who has not the instincts of the true soldier in his veins. . . . Ye shall love peace as a means to new wars—and the short peace more than the long. . . . War and courage have done more things than charity. Not your sympathy but your bravery hath hitherto saved the victims.

In summary, the attacks from the Right on the nineteenth-century way of life—on the "Victorian compromise"—are many, varied, and extremely difficult to range in an order. There is the attack from the vantage of traditional Christianity, an attack that centers on the great doctrine of the Enlightenment, the natural goodness and reasonableness of man; an attack that emphasizes the importance of tradi-

473

tion, "prejudice," and constituted Christian authority in an orderly society; an attack that accuses nineteenth-century society of neglecting in its love of competition and progress the essential fact that man is a political animal. There is the attack from the point of view of the older aristocratic ideals—ideals directly descended from the spare humanism of the classical tradition—an attack that centers on the tendencies of democracies to follow noisy, unsound leaders, to be jealous of aristocratic minorities, if not of all minorities, to tend toward the "tyranny of the majority." There is the attack from the point of view of good taste and culture, the aesthetic taste, which finds the new society devoted to the production of the "cheap and nasty." There are other attacks, notably those that foreshadow totalitarianism, which can be described only in a much more thorough study of the nineteenth century than is here possible. No neat summary of these attacks is adequate. But if you must have a single word, what all these attackers find wrong in their time is its *materialism*.

Attacks from the Left

Very broadly, we may say that nineteenth-century attacks from the Left on what the Victorian compromise had made of the ideals of the Enlightenment bore as their gist the broadening out of political democracy into social and above all economic democracy. The formula is a simplification. Men on the Left had as much trouble with the eternal tension between the ideals of liberty and authority as did men on the Center.

There is in the nineteenth century a certain amount of writing and speaking which urges that the real trouble is that the men and methods of 1776 and 1789 have not really been followed, that we need to get back to the simple rights of man, that the cure for the troubles of democracy is more democracy of the old sort—bills of right, written constitutions, universal suffrage, secret ballot, equal electoral districts, rotation in office, compulsory secular education for all, and so on. This is substantially the position of the people usually called "radicals," like the Chartists in the England of the 1830's and 1840's; they hold that if only political democracy is carried out fully, rights of man and all, there will result from the free interplay of human ambitions something like a rough social and economic equality. No one will be very rich, no one will be very poor, but there will be a healthy variety of reward within a broadly egalitarian society. As the century wears on, the radicals come gradually to feel that this equalizing process needs help from social legislation of the kind familiar enough to Americans under the name of the New Deal. The radicals become collectivists, or at least state interventionists, and to their opponents, socialists.

This process can best be seen in Britain, where by the 1880's the Liberal party has begun to back social legislation, and the Tories have been forced into something like the defense of classical laissez faire. John Mill's later career shows how a Benthamite can be prepared quite readily for a mildly collectivist political position. But an even better index is a man like T. H. Green, an Oxford don much influenced by German idealistic philosophy, who helped to form the young men who in parliament and in the civil service were laying the foundations for the partly socialist Britain we know today. Green's *Principles of Political Obligation* (1888) is an attack on the metaphysics and politics of conventional British radicalism. Green finds that utilitarian nominalist notions do in fact leave the individual a mere social atom, blindly struggling with other atoms, in no sense a true social animal. His own notion of the state and of other social groups emphasizes their emotional hold over the individual, their "reality" in something like the German idealist sense. But Green is no totalitarian; he manages to preserve room for individual rights as well as obligations. His state will be more than an umpire in a fair game; it will help the weaker and less skilled to take better part in the game. But it will not abolish the game entirely in favor of a kind of mass drill.

The main point for us here is that toward the end of the nineteenth century a current of collectivist or interventionist thought and practice set in with varying strength in the different parts of Western society. Of the greater countries, the United States was the last to feel this current. It is still resisted by many solid Americans as the

475

destruction of our traditional liberties, as "socialism," as "un-American." Dispassionate analysis of the problem of state intervention in business and other private affairs of the individual is still difficult for an American.

It is fair to say that the kind of policy advocated by the Fabians and the Labour party in Britain, the Third Force in France, the New Dealers in the United States is not identical with policies of even fairly advanced radicals—say Herbert Spencer—a hundred years ago. There is no great harm in putting it that the difference represents the influence of "socialist" thought on the democratic tradition. But one must be very clear that this Fabian-Third Force-New Deal development differs sharply from what is still the best and most definite sense of the term *socialism*—the very specific religious sect founded by Karl Marx.

The differences between the modified democratic way of life, cosmology, culture, or even religion represented by contemporary Leftist trends in the West and the orthodox Marxist position are very great indeed; here we can but indicate some of the main lines an analysis of these differences should take. But first it must be said that both the Marxist and the non-Marxist Left can fairly claim common origin in the Enlightenment, and that both are in important ways opposed to traditional Christianity. Both reject the doctrine of original sin in favor of a basically optimistic view of human nature, both exclude the supernatural, both focus on the ideal of a happy life on this earth for everyone, both reject the ideal of a stratified society with permanent inequalities of status and great inequalities of income. It is only fair to note that today it is possible for a non-Marxist Leftist to accept some measure of traditional Christian pessimism, and indeed to consider himself a Christian; Marxism, a much more rigid creed, can hardly make any open compromise with Christianity or any theistic religion, but must remain firmly positivist and materialist.

Indeed, this rigidity of doctrine is one of the main differences between the two systems of belief. The democratic Leftist retains at his most collectivist at least a minimum of the old liberal belief that there must be intellectual freedom to entertain new ideas, to experiment, to invent. Even when he is no longer moved by a feeling for "rights" of the individual, he is committed to the notion of progress through variation, and he knows that groups as such do not have new ideas. You can tell much from the tags and clichés that even the intellectuals cannot quite avoid; the democratic Leftist will still hold that the only dogma is that there be no dogmas, or that the only room for intoler· ance is for intolerance of the intolerant.

It is true that a very articulate, if clearly also a minority, group in full nineteenth century claimed its inspiration and origin in the eighteenth-century Enlightenment, and yet came in the end to disparage individual liberty, to use most of the slogans of the totalitarians, order, discipline, faith, solidarity. These are the so-called "positivists." The term positivism is sometimes used loosely, as the equivalent of materialism, to describe a belief that rejects the supernatural and stands on the firm, "positive" ground of science. Historically, however, the term means a follower of the French *politique et moraliste* Auguste Comte, whom we have already met as the maker of a table ranking the natural sciences in the order of their "maturity." But Comte did more than call for a supreme science of sociology. In his later years, especially after the failure of the revolutions of 1848, he sought to establish a kind of church based on a formal belief in progress, natural science, humanity, and a formal and very vehement disbelief in the Christian God. Comte himself was the high priest of this positivist faith, which had its own organized churches, and which spread out into various other groups allied in their faith in man, science, and the future. These religious positivists, not yet quite extinct, must not be confused with the "logical positivists" of our own day, to whom we shall come.

Save, perhaps, for these Comtean positivists and their likes (who are not really democrats) the democratic Leftist retains always, even in his most up-to-date form, something of the old distrust of any system of ideas that tries to sink the individual in the group, that seems to make the individual merely a cell of an all-important whole; he preserves at bottom a genuine respect for a great deal of the apparatus of individual rights which, especially as they apply to property,

477

he is likely to dismiss rather cavalierly in some of his moods; he does not believe in the inevitability of the class struggle and of revolution and hopes that he can attain greater social and economic equality, greater stability in society, better administration both in business and government, by a process of voluntary change effected through legislation put through in the usual democratic way; he is, in modern cant terms, a gradualist and a reformist; he is, especially in recent years, increasingly willing to pay some attention to critics of the basic ideas of the Enlightenment, critics of the sort we have here classed as attackers from the Right, and critics of the kind we shall study in the next chapter as anti-intellectuals; and, having observed the totalitarian societies of the Nazis, the Fascists, and the Russian Communists in our own time, he has come to conclude that uniformity, regimentation, and absolute authority are prices much too great to pay for order and security from the whirl of Western competitive society.

We come at last to Marxist socialism, or communism. From our point of view, Marxism—or Marx-Lenin-Stalinism, to give the canonical succession—is a very rigorous development of, or heresy of, the world-attitude of the Enlightenment. It stands toward the central democratic form of the Enlightenment in some ways as Calvinism stands toward traditional Christianity of the Roman Catholics, or perhaps better, toward the Anglicans who under one formal church organization run the spectrum of belief from unitarianism to high sacramentalism. Marxism is a rigorous, dogmatic, puritanical, determinist, firmly disciplined sect of eighteenth-century optimistic humanitarian materialists.

If you feel that the term "religion" should be limited to systems of belief that maintain the existence of a God, or gods, or spirits, or at any rate something *immaterial, supernatural,* then you have already been thrown off the track by our comparing national patriotism with religion. In this book we have applied terms taken from our Western religious history to any organized and articulate set of beliefs about the Big Questions—right and wrong, human happiness, the order of the universe, and so on—which for the believer did at least two things: gave him intellectual orientation in this world (that is, answered his questions) and gave him emotional participation in a group through ritual and other forms of common action. In such terms Marxism, especially as it has been worked out in Russia, is one of the most active forms of religion in the world today, and one that all educated persons must make some effort to understand.

Marxism clearly fulfills one of the simple requirements of a religion: It has its sacred books, its authoritative scripture—in the orthodox tradition the writings of Marx and Engels with the comments, exegesis, and additions brought by Lenin and, to a much less important extent, Stalin. It has also its heresies, of which the most important goes back to the nineteenth-century "revisionist" movement associated first of all with the name of Eduard Bernstein, and which substituted for the *violent* revolution and subsequent dictatorship of the proletariat of orthodox Marxism the *gradual* achievement of social and economic democracy (equality) by legal political action. Revisionism turned into gradualism, which is substantially the position of present-day *socialists* (in contrast to *communists*). Gradualism was to its defenders not merely a device to quiet some bourgeois fears and gain bourgeois converts; it was also, in the minds of leaders like Kautsky, a necessary historical emendation to meet the failure of Marx's predictions of an inevitable violent uprising of the proletariat in the West. There are many other Marxist splinter-groups or heresies, for which we cannot here find space. The existence of such heresies is not necessarily, however, a sign of weakness of the movement; indeed, if one thinks of the rise of Christianity, it is possible that these heresies are an indication of vitality in Marxism, of a continuing intellectual fermentation that is a sign of life rather than of decay and dispersion.

We must here concentrate on the orthodox form of the doctrine Now Marx's great work is *Das Kapital,* which is in form a treatise on economics. Obviously, however, even *Das Kapital* is no narrowly professional study of economic theory, but a philosophy of history, a system of sociology, and a program for political action. Together with the rest of the accepted canon, it gives a rather more complete and systematic cosmology than any *single* work in the orthodox democratic tradition of the Enlightenment. Marxism is a *tighter, neater* thing than conventional democracy.

Marxism bears the clear stamp of the nineteenth century in which Marx and Engels lived and wrote. It is based on a very explicit conception of change, of growth, of evolution as an ultimate fact of universal validity. (Whether or not Marx thought of this evolutionary process as due to come to an end with the achievement of the classless society is an interesting but not central question to which we shall return.) Now one of the central themes of all Western thought on these high matters has been the reality and importance of change. The Platonic type of mind has tended to try to escape from the flow of life and death of this world as we human animals experience it into another world above time and change; and more than this—worldly philosophers like the rationalists of the early modern centuries sought for categories of logic that would be absolute and changeless. Marxism, at least on the surface, glories in process, change, and tries to find in change itself the answer to the riddle of change.

The specific answer to the riddle Marx got from his master Hegel was the dialectic (see p. 424). But for Hegel the process of thesis-antithesis-synthesis went on under the impulse of what he called spirit, an immaterial something, force, idea, or soul, at any rate nothing human senses, common sense, or natural science could ever get at. Marx proudly claimed that he had taken the pyramid Hegel foolishly tried to poise on its point and placed it squarely and sensibly on its broad base; that is, *he made the idealistic dialectic into the materialistic dialectic.* Change for Marx takes place according to a plan, but not the plan of Hegel's silly world-spirit. Change takes place in matter, in the sense world that surrounds us, of which we too are wholly a part, just like all the other animals. The changes in this material world—it can be called simply our environment—determine our whole lives, our physical well-being, our institutions, our ideas of right and wrong, our cosmology. The key word here is "determine," a favorite with Marx, for whom "dialectical materialism" and "historical determinism" were almost equivalent phrases.

Some of these determining environmental factors are, of course, of the kind men have long recognized—climate, for instance. But Marx focuses on a to him much more fundamental aspect of the environment that he calls the "means of production," the way men make a living. From this fundamental set of material conditions everything else in a man's life, in the life of groups of men, must follow. Nomads driving their herds over the Asiatic steppes eat and drink, raise families, obey laws and customs, follow chieftains, fight, and believe in a certain religion all in accordance with inevitable developments from the means of production of a nomadic pastoral society. Marxist scholars have shown great skill and erudition in the concrete working out of these concepts for various societies.

Marx himself was interested primarily in his own Western society, for which he worked out a complete outline of social change in accordance with his dialectic. His base line is the means of production of a self-sufficient manorial economy in the Middle Ages. The society determined by this manorial economy has a serf class that supports a master class of feudal nobles and their attendant priests, has a fairly rigid graded system of status, and holds the kind of beliefs about God and the universe we have already noted in Chapters 6 and 7. This manorial economy and feudal society is the *thesis*. The principle of change is for Marx something "material," not an idea in anyone's mind—though actually even Marx has to admit that the material change comes about because some men want it, conceive it. The change that began the modern world is in its simplest form money, trade, the beginnings of a capitalist economy. As this change slowly goes on, a new class, a trading or *bourgeois* class is formed. Between the old feudal nobility and the new moneyed middle class there follows an active "class struggle" (another very famous Marxist expression). The new class has its own philosophy, characteristically Protestant after a time, its own views of the goodness of competition, the legitimacy of profit, the need of political democracy to get around royal and noble power, in short a full philosophy of life. This trading economy and bourgeois democratic society is the *antithesis*. The long struggle between thesis and antithesis, after preliminary bourgeois victories in England and Holland, culminated in the American and French revolutions and the full victory of the bourgeoisie in the nineteenth century.

The class struggle was by no means over. The victorious bourgeoisie, amalgamated with the conquered remains of the nobility, formed a synthesis, a new thesis, and struggled with a new antithesis, the *proletariat*. This struggle itself, and the classes that made the struggle, were the material result of another change in the mode of production, the introduction of the factory system and the modern form of industrial and financial capitalism. To the old banking and trading bourgeoisie there is added the industrialist, the factory owner, and a new and more powerful capitalist class arises. The workers are now herded together in factories under the eyes of their oppressors, and held down by the iron laws of capitalist economics to a bare subsistence wage. But at least they can organize, if only in secret, and under Marxist leadership become fully class-conscious. Thesis bourgeoisie and antithesis proletariat are now (Marx first announced the outline of this theory in the *Communist Manifesto* of 1848) fighting the last class struggle. The victory of the proletariat is assured.

Marx assured it by a rather complicated economic analysis that we cannot attempt to follow closely. The upshot of his argument is that by laws of capitalist competition production is bound periodically to result in gluts that bring on business crises in the course of which the weaker firms go to the wall, their members get proletarianized, and the surviving firms get bigger and more powerful. But the working class, though it suffers in each crisis, gets more numerous and more desperate. In a famous phrase, Marx saw the inevitable working of economic law making the poor poorer and the rich richer. At last there will come a supreme crisis, in which the proletariat, fully organized and fully class-conscious, will rise in its might and take over the means of production. Thus will be achieved the dictatorship of the proletariat, in the course of which banks, communications, transport, and factories will be taken from their bourgeois owners and collectivized, put in the hands of the new proletarian government. Then comes the final stage. With the liquidation of the capitalist owners there are no more classes—or rather, there is only one class left, the victorious proletariat. There can thus be no class struggle; and since the whole apparatus of the state has, according to the Marxist analysis, been necessary only in order that the thesis class might hold down the antithesis class in the class struggle, there will be no need for the state with its police, its courts, its armies, and its taxes. The state will wither away and we shall at last have the classless society, the heaven on earth of Marxist eschatology. As a matter of fact, Marx himself did not dwell on the details of his heaven, and even Engels and the later commentators are vague on this point. As good nineteenth-century believers in progress, however, they do not like to think of even heaven as static. Perhaps we may say that the Marxist holds that cruel and inhuman struggles like the class struggle will cease with the classless society, but that progress will go on through decent, painless, gamelike competition.

It is now over a hundred years since the *Communist Manifesto,* and the course of history has not gone as Marx planned. It is true that the capitalist business cycle of prosperity and depression has gone on, and that possibly depressions have grown worse. There has certainly been a tendency toward the concentration of capital in giant industry, but it has not been uniform even in the German, British, and American economies. The formula that the rich are growing richer and the poor are growing poorer has certainly not proved true. Government is intervening to regulate industry even in the United States, and in all industrial countries there has been a tendency to some degree of what is often called "state socialism." And, of course, there was in 1917 in industrially backward Russia—a country Marx himself disliked—the one major revolutionary movement to come to power under Marxist auspices. The Russians have established the dictatorship of the proletariat, but there are as yet not the slightest signs of the withering away of the Russian state. Marx, indeed, supposed that once the revolution was successful in a great nation—he apparently thought it would come first in the most advanced one of his day, Great Britain—it would spread at least to all the rest of Western society, and therefore throughout the world. Faithful Marxists can, of course, point out that until the revolution is world-wide, the state cannot possibly be expected to wither away in beleaguered Russia.

Our concern here is not, however, primarily with the question of how well Marx forecast the future. The movement he founded has come to power in a great state, and his followers, though somewhat split by heresies, are strong in many parts of Western society. Marxism is one of the religions—or if that word is too strong for you, one of the great clusters of guiding principles—that compete today for the loyalties of Western men.

The Marxist God is the omnipotent if impersonal force of dialectical materialism. Like the gods of other advanced religions, dialectical materialism is omnipotent. The Marxists themselves do not hesitate to use the word *determinism,* with all its overtones of St. Augustine and Calvin. For them the overtones are those of science. This system, they insist, is a scientific one, which is why it must be true. Theirs is not, to an outsider, the science of the laboratory and the clinic, but a hypostasized science that does for them what the hypostasized science of Newton did for the eighteenth-century philosophers. That is, it gives them the comforting assurance that they have the key to the universe.

Dialectical materialism, then, will for the Marxist bring about the inevitable world revolution of the proletariat. It will bring that about in spite of anything the capitalists can do; indeed, the more the capitalist, following the course of action dictated to him by the means of production under which he works, behaves like a capitalist, the quicker will come the proletarian victory. The Rockefellers and the Morgans are doing just what dialectical materialism wants them to do. This does not apparently make the Marxist feel any more kindly toward them and their like. Nor does the certainty that the stars in their courses are working for the inevitable triumph of the proletariat make the Marxist a fatalist. We have already seen that for the Calvinist the certainty that God's will must prevail seems to make the believer all the more ready to go out into the world and fight to help God's will to prevail; and we have noted that for the Calvinist there is always the saving uncertainty that the individual human worm, even though he is a good member of the church of Calvin, may not really *know* God's will (see p. 323). For the Marxist there is not even this remnant of Christian humility to provide some logical support for his actual conduct as a fighter for the right as he sees it. The Marxist—and Marx himself—knows absolutely that dialectical materialism will do its work in the foreordained way. But one does not see the convinced Marxist sitting back and letting dialectical materialism do its work without him. On the contrary, he is an ardent propagandist, an ethical meliorist, a man who to judge by his conduct believes that his own efforts can make a difference in human behavior. Once more, we can only note that metaphysical belief in determinism seems for the Marxist as for the Calvinist he so much resembles quite consonant with a psychological belief in free will.

To continue with our religious parallel: The Marxist heaven, as we have already noted, is the classless society, a state men can achieve here on earth, and which has in common with the eschatologies of other advanced religions the concept of a state of things where no human desires will be frustrated. It is true that the Marxist prides himself on his materialism, and believes that in the classless societies all *decent* human appetites will be satisfied; he would deny indignantly that his paradise has anything in common with that mystical and among intellectual Christians predominant concept of heaven as a place in which *all* appetites are overcome, extinguished, spiritually sublimated. Yet the classless society is no gross place, no place for the kind of sensual delights the Marxist associates with the vulgar capitalist ideal. Indeed, there is, in almost the common acceptance of the term, a *puritanical* aspect of Marxism; the Marxist is as scornful as any Calvinist of the merely Epicurean side of life, of vulgar, gross pleasures and even more of their aristocratic refinements. Marx himself is a moralist, as indignant at the crassness and injustices of an industrial society as Carlyle or Ruskin. The Marxist tries hard to save a positive aspect of his heaven, to insist that in the classless society men will compete and make progress as good children of our culture should; but what really strikes one in the Marxist as in other heavens

485

is the ideal of absence of conflict and frustration, of the extinction of desire.

The notion of the revolution and the dictatorship of the proletariat can be taken as roughly a parallel to the Christian notion of a day of judgment. Again there is the obvious difference that the Marxist believes his saving catastrophe will be brought about by "natural" rather than by supernatural forces. For the Marxist the state of grace, the thing that marks off the faithful from the heathen, is simply the ability to see the universe in Marxist terms, "scientific" terms as the Marxist would put it. His Marx is the rationalist Messiah set over against the spiritual—and to the Marxist, of course, false—Messiah, Christ.

Again as in most religious bodies, this awareness of belonging, of *knowing the truth,* of having the inner light, is balanced by performance of certain symbolic acts that bind the believer to the whole body of the faithful. In other words, the Marxist has his works as well as his faith: He reads his Marxist holy books, he goes to meetings, he has his party card and his party duties. He has a clue to everything, an answer to all his questions. There should be nothing surprising to an informed outsider that in Communist Russia there is Marxist music, Marxist history, and even Marxist biology.

It is probably true that there is no clear Marxist equivalent for the kind of religious experience that for the Christian is focused in the word *conscience.* One whole aspect of Christianity, as we have noted in an earlier chapter, centers on the plight of the individual soul of sinful man in its willful struggle with God; Christianity is a highly individualistic faith with a highly individualistic concept of salvation. Marxism is committed to the notion that the true fulfillment of the individual is, not of course in mere ant- or beelike automatic participation in the social whole, but at least in a thorough identification of the individual with the whole collectivity. Marxism is a collectivist faith, and its notion of individual salvation cannot be very closely paralleled in Christianity. Yet the Marxist has a conscience, and however ill the notion fits with dialectic materialism, can suffer the tortures of conscience. This you will see readily enough in the hero of Arthur Koestler's *Darkness at Noon;* and if you take the trouble to look into his career, you will see it in Mr. Koestler himself.

In pure theory—or in Marxist theology at its highest level—Marx and Engels did the great work. Though Soviet practice has canonized Lenin and Stalin as having made essential additions to the main body of Marxist beliefs, to an outsider their importance seems rather as organizers than as thinkers. Marxism has not yet combined the thinker and the doer as successfully as they were combined in St. Paul. Lenin indeed, faced with the fact that the wicked capitalist nations of the West seemed in the early years of the twentieth century to be prospering, that at any rate they were not going on the rocks quite as Marx had predicted, added to the Marxist analysis a corollary to the effect that having reached the limit of exploiting their own citizens English and other Western capitalists had postponed the evil day by colonial imperialism, by exploiting the rest of the world. But this in itself was, according to Lenin, a confirmation of Marx; imperialism was the inevitable overripeness of capitalism, the last stage before the revolution of the proletariat.

Actually Lenin's great service to Marxism came as an organizer of a successful revolution in a backward country. To do this at all, Lenin had to organize a violent revolution—which Marx had always preached, though rather academically—a revolution put through by a minority of disciplined and desperate characters with long years of conspiratorial experience underground, and with no "bourgeois-democratic" scruples about legality, humane decency, honesty, and the like. Marx, for all his testy dislike of mere reformers, had definitely not liked the conspiratorial professional revolutionist. To some of Marx's followers, then, Lenin is not so much the exponent as the betrayer of true Marxism. To the kindly, hopeful, other-worldly Marxists (there are such, illogical though their attitude may seem to an outsider) Lenin's ruthless and quite consciously realistic behavior meant accepting the wicked bourgeois world they wanted to transcend. To them, Lenin, and much worse, Stalin, had simply surrendered to such wicked illusions as common sense, practicality, success.

As for Stalin, only for the orthodox Communists is he a thinker at all. His policy of "socialism in one country" is indeed a practical corollary to Marx of the greatest importance; but it seems to have been forced on Stalin as a policy, not as a theory. He has, of course, proved a successful organizer of Marxist belief in a nation-state with a long history and a profound patriotic tradition. He has helped make the amalgamation of Russian culture, of Russian history in its full sense, and the particular set of ideas about the meaning of the universe and the destiny of man associated with Karl Marx and Friedrich Engels. One last and perhaps most outrageous parallel. Stalin has been in some ways in a position analogous to that of the early Christian organizers when it had become fairly clear that Jesus was not going to return to earth immediately, that the whole elaborate Christian eschatology had to be fitted to a different time-scale, and indeed to a different world. In Stalin's Russia the classless society has had to be postponed; there is frustration, unhappiness, competition, and great economic and social inequality in Russia today. Stalin has had to try to temper the basic optimism of Marx to the facts of life on this earth. Someday we shall know how well he succeeded. At present, from the other side of the iron curtain, we can note chiefly that he seems to be using a very old device indeed, that of emphasizing the persistence and toughness of the satanic foe—the capitalist.

The standard of moral and aesthetic values for the Marxist on this earth is essentially bourgeois, capitalist, with a slightly soured puritanical twist. There are advanced circles in Western countries where Marxism is combined with various kinds of moral and aesthetic rebellion against conventional standards of the eighteenth- and nineteenth-century bourgeoisie—but not in Russia. Marxism is, in fact, one of the most legitimate heirs of the materialist and rationalist cosmology of the eighteenth-century philosophers. Marx himself has a vision of the properly functioning society strangely like that of Adam Smith—an economy, and therefore a society, in which each individual by behaving naturally contributes to the well-being and smooth working of the group. The ideal, the end, of Marxism is the philosophical anarchism among free and equal human beings that is one of the persistent themes of the Enlightenment.

The means, however, is violent revolution and a transitional state of dictatorship in which there will be rigorous use of authority from above, strict discipline among the masses, the whole apparatus of a totalitarian society. Here Marxism breaks sharply with the tradition of the Enlightenment, which, though proud of revolutions like the American and the French, was also a bit ashamed of the tar and feathering and guillotining, and regarded political revolution as at best a necessary evil to be avoided if possible. Now in this world the means affects the end. So far, the Marxist effort to arrive at anarchy by the use of authority has not got beyond a very firm use of authority by a small ruling class. And even were the Russian experiment able to continue in a world not hostile to Russia as a political entity, it seems extremely unlikely that the Marxist heaven on earth would be achieved. Only in an Hegelian world of the pure intellect do you achieve an end by trying to achieve its opposite. In this world, if you set out to build a society in which human beings behave as much like ants as possible you are not likely to get a society in which they behave like lions. The Marxist attempt to solve the eighteenth-century tension between liberty and equality has on the whole been even less successful than the orthodox democratic attempt.

Summary

The study of the nineteenth century has led us, perhaps unduly, into many considerations about the twentieth century. We have followed some phases of Marxism far beyond the century in which the doctrine was born. We may return briefly to summarize the doctrines, the tensions we have studied in the last two chapters.

There is a center—not a dead center—in the nineteenth century, which we have called the Victorian compromise. That compromise sought to retain a moderate political democracy, a moderate nationalism, and great individual economic freedom of enterprise balanced by a strict moral code and conventional, churchgoing Christianity. In a

Western society based on that compromise there was great industrial and scientific advance, great material inequalities and yet for the lower classes a higher standard of living in a material way than ever before, and a lively and varied intellectual and artistic flourishing.

Yet this intellectual and artistic flourishing, if contrasted with that of the thirteenth century, or of fifth-century Athens, lacked unity of style, perhaps unity of purpose. For the nineteenth century was a time of extraordinary diversity of thought, an age of multanimity. Its extremes were great extremes, its tensions clearly marked—tradition against innovation, authority against liberty, faith in God against faith in the machine, loyalty to the nation against loyalty to humanity —the list could be very long indeed. Somehow the nineteenth century managed to keep these warring human aspirations, these basically conflicting ideals of the good life, in uneasy balance. Our century has seen this balance upset. Two great wars and a great depression are the witnesses of this upset. We are now attempting, among ideals quite as conflicting as those of the nineteenth century—they are indeed essentially the same ideals—to establish a balance of our own.

14

The Twentieth Century

THE ANTI-INTELLECTUAL ATTACK

THE EXTREMISTS, at least, of the eighteenth-century Enlightenment believed that human beings were very shortly to begin to live in a perfect society, a society in which what all men consider evil would not exist and only what all men consider good would exist. This attitude is for our analysis a sort of base line. Or rather, the reflection of this attitude in the ordinary Western man's more modest hopes of personal improvement in his own lot, of visible social progress in his own lifetime, should be our base line. Now this general optimism has had to hold out against the mere passage of a hundred and fifty years at the end of which evil seems as lively and as prevalent as ever; and it has had to survive two great crises of world war, with their attendant sufferings from death, disease, scarcity, and all the long catalogue of man's inhumanity to man. The first of these crises, the thirty-year struggle of the wars of the French Revolution and Napoleon, we have seen helped make the revision of earlier optimism we have called the Victorian compromise. The second, the thirty-year struggle we parochially call World Wars I and II, we can already see has brought a second flood of pessimistic feeling and criticism, and is now actively at work in further modification of the heritage of the eighteenth century, the democratic dream. We are still too near the process to see it clearly. Perhaps by 2000 critics will find that there was a characteristic twentieth-century faith, culture, *Weltanschauung*.

But already it is clear that the dream has survived the second crisis; we are in the West still children of the Enlightenment. Do not believe the prophets of doom who tell you otherwise. They may be right: Most of the cluster of ideas and values we call democracy may go down in the years to come. We cannot yet foresee the future in matters of this sort. As for the present, the fact of the survival of the basic optimism of the eighteenth century is evident from any newspaper, any periodical, any lecture platform, especially in the United States. Alterations in this fundamental pattern are still for the common man in the West of much less importance than the pattern itself.

It is true that there have been among intellectuals complex tides of fashion; there have been phases of despair, of cynicism, of earnest pursuit of still greater perfection. Even before the war of 1914 there had been the celebrated decade of the nineties, with its self-conscious wit, its rather energetic effort to seem tired and sophisticated, its discovery that decadence is a possibility of history. But the Western world at the turn of the last century was not merely the world of Oscar Wilde and the *Yellow Book;* it was the world of the Fabians as well, of Teddy Roosevelt and the Progressives, of the revived France of the Dreyfus case, a world still full of hopeful conflict. The war of 1914 brought among many intellectuals the feeling of horror and disgust tempered with hope in a really radical Leftist movement that comes out in the most famous of war novels of the time, Henri Barbusse's *Le feu*. By the nineteen-twenties, we seemed settled down to something like the old life once more. Harding's "normalcy," though the term offended the high-minded, was a faithful reflection of what most people wanted.

There are still other tides of intellectual fashion. One of the most obvious—though its real importance is difficult to judge at this date—is for the ambitious historical systems we must still call philosophies of history. From Spengler of yesterday to Sorokin and Toynbee of today through many less-read prophets, intellectuals in the West have been seeking a sign from the past, a sign of what lies ahead, not just for the few decades an adult can hope to live, but for centuries ahead when no man now alive can ever check up, in the flesh, on these prophets. Most of these writers are prophets of impending doom. The favorite parallel is between the last period of the declining Roman Empire and our own day, but there are at hand for historians like Toynbee many other examples of civilizations that failed to meet a challenge like that of "parochial nationalism" he finds we are facing. These philosophers of history are not, however, altogether without hope for the race. They think that in the form of traditional Western culture our present civilization *may* be doomed, but that a new culture is bound to rise on its ruins. Theirs is a philosophy of cycles that turn out to be spirals, of erratic nonlinear evolution (but still evolution), of darkness to be followed by the Great Dawn. There is a tendency to place us now in some materialist abyss, but about to rise to some spiritual height. Thus Gerald Heard's "superconsciousness," Arnold Toynbee's "etherialization," and Pitirim Sorokin's "ideational" culture all seem to have something in common. All three terms attempt to describe—and invite us into—a state of immaterial bliss.

These twentieth-century philosophers of history may or may not prove to be more accurate in their predictions than was Marx; their methods are not the methods of science, and their work is not a part of cumulative knowledge. For us, the important thing to note is that, like Marx, they use history as a cosmology. This use of history is a development from the modern repudiation of the supernatural, and the modern retention of the desire for omniscience and certitude that the supernatural, perhaps only the supernatural, can supply. The Newtonian world-machine supplied this certitude for the eighteenth century, but failed to account satisfactorily for the obvious facts of organic life, growth, change on this earth. Such an explanation was in the nineteenth century very neatly supplied by Darwinian notions of organic evolution. Now we could not only understand how the planetary system worked; we could understand how men and mice and coral reefs came to grow as they do. The key to knowing what is and what will be is for the historicist a knowledge of what has been. The curve can always be plotted in time past—and then, so to speak, it extrapolates itself into the future. If you know how societies and cultures have evolved—that is, if you know their histories—you know what they are going to be, a knowledge some people find comforting.

Now there are many human beings who seem temperamentally unable to accept this kind of historicism; they must transcend mere experience of space-time, they must find God and truth in pure Being freed of vulgar Becoming. If, however, you accept the general validity of the attitudes and approaches of modern science, you will have to agree that *in its basic assumptions* this historicism is consonant with modern science. None the less the gap between men like Sorokin and Toynbee and the natural scientist is very great indeed, certainly in performance, and probably also in method and aims. In the first place, natural science *as science* simply does not attempt to set up a cosmology. (Scientists are *as full human beings* believers in a whole range of cosmologies; many of them are still innocent "materialists" in the direct tradition of the Enlightenment, others good Christians, even good Catholics, still others, like Eddington and Jeans, inventors of rather weird and unsatisfactory cosmologies of their own which they fondly attach somehow to their science.) In the second place, we do not know at present nearly enough about the history of man in society to be able to make even the kind of generalized long-term predictions the meteorologist can make. Moreover, the variables involved are too numerous for our present comprehension in scientific terms. In short, you cannot really plot the curve in the past as the scientist would plot his curve; you can only guess at it, only sketch it in freehand, very dashingly. Patient generations of labor will be needed before we can get much further. Moreover, the curve does *not* extrapolate itself. For there is, in the third place, always the possibility of new variables, of genuine novelty, of the unforeseeable. We have noted already that Marx, by temperament one of the most absolutist of these philosophers of history, proved on the whole a bad prophet, and notably failed to guess at a number of new factors—including whatever brought about his revolution in Russia instead of in Great Britain. We do not know nearly enough about the disease that kills civilizations (if there is such a disease) to recognize it in ourselves. Skilled historians like Toynbee can certainly point out alarming symptoms, much the same in late Roman culture and in our culture; but we don't really know what the symptoms mean. At any rate, worry over such symptoms as the parallel between our divorces and Roman divorces is rather on the edge of hypochondria.

The determinism that goes with most philosophies of history is in our time balanced by a form of indeterminism that also—such is the preoccupation of our time with *process*—is much concerned with ideas of flow, change, growth. This is the voluntarism that crops up in many otherwise disparate formal philosophies of the last fifty years —in Nietzsche, in the Frenchman Bergson, in the Americans William James and John Dewey. Bergson's philosophy was only day before yesterday the fashion among cultivated Westerners, who found in his *élan vital,* his "creative evolution," and his other phrases a most agreeable philosophy of change and flow. Bergson was in the direct romantic line of protest against something the romantics have always found disagreeable, unacceptable, in the tradition of the Enlightenment. It is difficult to put one's defining finger on that something— it is something the romantics think of as dead, finished, cerebral, stuffy, rote-and-formula, dryasdust, unimaginative. We have somewhat apologetically tried (see p. 398) to sum up the cluster of ideas the romantics hated under "head," what they loved under "heart."

At any rate, most determinisms are matters of the head, most voluntarisms matters of the heart. But Bergson, as a modern and a sophisticate, could not take refuge in a simple reversion to the native, the primitive, in a rejection of the complex inheritance of modern thought. So he tried to keep the best of both worlds, the freshness of emotion and the nice, logical ruts and grooves of thought. Indeed, this effort to give to thought itself—to an activity the nonintellectual usually associates with safety and armchairs—a quality of danger and adventure is one of the central themes of the most distinguished of twentieth-century philosophers, the late Alfred North Whitehead.

The pragmatism of James and Dewey—the most distinguished American contribution to formal philosophic thought—is also in revolt against the certainties and the static quality of systematic thought. James held thought to be an instrument of the will; good thinking was thinking that got you what you wanted. He was not, of course, cynical or anarchistic or logical enough to hold that all wanting was good wanting, at least from the point of view of the individual wanter. For James, the good was what a sensitive, tolerant, kindly but at bottom respectable New England intellectual of his day would find good. He liked the odd and the troubled, and he agreed with John Mill that the good, the useful, the profitably new may come from the most unlikely sources. For James variety, conflict multanimity really are practical; they work—or did in 1900.

Finally, the twentieth century, like other recent centuries, did not fail to find a great natural scientist from whose work philosophers and essayists and men of ideas in general could apparently take the kind of lead the eighteenth century took from Newton. This was the physicist Albert Einstein, whose work as a physicist was beyond the understanding of all but a few fellow scientists. But for the general public Einstein was not merely the tribal magician of our times; he was the man who stood for relativity, for the notion that things look different to observers at different places and different times, that truth depends on the point of view of the seeker for truth, that a man moving at one rate of speed sees everything quite differently from a man moving at another rate, that, in short, there is no absolute Truth, but only relative truths.

Einstein's name also sums up in the public mind the great scientific revolution of the first half of this century. With the more detailed history of modern science we have not concerned ourselves in recent chapters. Everyone knows that the natural sciences have continued in our day their fruitful alliance with technology and business enterprise, that they have continued to be cumulative. The work of physicists and mathematicians like Einstein, Planck, and Bohr, however, bore fruit early in the twentieth century in great new master-theorems about the physical universe, so that it became fashionable among popularizers of science to say that Newtonian physics had been "overthrown." It is fairer to say that relativity, quantum mechanics, the further study of the bewildering, complicated atom (Democritus would never recognize his simple philosophical atom) have made emendations in, additions to, Newtonian physics. The fact that a clear element of unpredictability in the behavior of a single atom is recognized in quantum mechanics does not mean that statistically, in masses of atoms, the old predictability has ceased to exist. Newton's physics, in fact, are still good for a lot of rough work. The real importance of the new physics for us is that they helped put the finishing touch on the destruction of the simple nineteenth-century notions of scientific causation, notions that conceived all relations in the universe on a neat mechanical model, and that were associated with very innocent notions about scientific induction. Modern scientific theories about the methods of science are very subtle and complicated, and have recognized that the creative scientist is in a sense a creative artist, that the report his theorems give of the universe is in part the work of his own mind, and no mere mechanical replica of reality. Even more important, the modern scientist knows, or should know, that his theorems are not absolute truths, not truths in the tradition of religion and of most Western philosophy.

For the moment, however, we need merely to record that from the point of view of the historian of ideas, the persistent elements, especially of the last two or three centuries, seem more conspicuous and more important than the elements of novelty. The atom bomb is in a sense a new thing; it explodes in a new way, and of course with a new force and intensity. But the feeling that the atom bomb may bring about the destruction of humanity, the "end of the world," is new only in its relation to the atom bomb; as a *human feeling,* as a part of human experience even in the relatively limited sphere of Western cultural history, the fear of an end to the world is a recurrent one. At times—in the earliest days of Christianity, and rather less so in the year 1000—it has been epidemic; at all times among cranks and the odder sects it has been endemic. The splitting of the atom has no new horrors for the faithful reader of the Apocalypse.

497

So far, at least, most of what we have attempted to analyze in the last few chapters still exists among us. It would be difficult not to recognize as living in the contemporary world most of the ideas that have come before us in the course of this book. Cumulative knowledge, that of natural science, has continued without serious relapse. Indeed, war stimulates some phases of scientific achievement. The tender-minded who maintain that only the vulgar application to practical matters goes on in wartime, and that the creative work of "pure" science must have peace, may be right. The truth is that among the many things we are ignorant about are the social and cultural conditions necessary to the optimum flourishing of natural science. The fact remains that in the West both pure and applied science have unquestionably added to their cumulative achievement in the course of the war-torn first half of the twentieth century.

As for noncumulative knowledge, our culture is an almost incredible palimpsest in which nothing is ever suddenly or *wholly* blotted out. There are shifts in the proportionate success or fashionableness of different attitudes and ideas, but very few are eliminated. Go over the materials of the last few chapters. Christianity most certainly persists in what to an outsider remains its rich diversity and its basic tension between this world and the next. Our century has seen no new great sect of Christians, and it has seen the kind of frittering away of the faithful into the indifference that each generation of preachers of a certain temperament regards—or feigns for preaching purposes to regard—as new. But it has also seen revivals of spiritual energy in all sorts of sects and in all sorts of places— including perhaps the Soviet Russia that tried so hard to destroy Christianity. There has been an intellectual revival markedly parallel to that of the years after the crisis of the French Revolution. Berdyaev, the Russian exile, was in many ways, at least in his feeling for the sins of the godless generation that brought on the crisis of our time, a kind of modern Joseph de Maistre. Two of the profoundest and most influential of attempts to correct by Christian vision what they regard as the shallow optimism on which our democratic Western cosmology is based have been made by Karl Barth in Germany and

Reinhold Niebuhr in the United States. Roman Catholicism has continued to assert its claim to a greater wisdom than the Enlightenment ever found, and at least an equal concern with the lot of the common man on earth. In Jacques Maritain the Catholics have shown that they can still produce the thoughtful, sensitive, orthodox but undogmatic *politique et moraliste*.

And the anti-Christians persist. The successors of Tom Paine and Herbert Spencer, the piously and dogmatically liberal agnostics, humanists, secularists, positivists, materialists, followers of Ethical Culture and the like, though they begin to look a little old-fashioned and quaint, still exist. They may, like the bustle and the slit skirt, suddenly become fashionable again, though like these feminine fashions of Victorian and Edwardian days, in a somewhat chastened form. Indeed, some were apparent in their new costumes in the mid-century vogue of existentialism, which spread into cultivated circles at the end of the war of 1939-1945. Existentialism centered in France, with its best-known figure the writer Jean Paul Sartre. The existentialists did not believe in God—certainly not in a good God—and they found the world a very unpleasant place in which man is clearly born to trouble from which he can never emerge. The doctrine of progress seemed to these determined pessimists great nonsense. Yet they would keep up the struggle, they would lead a substantially moral life (not a prudishly Victorian moral life, of course, but an artistic moral life), they would, in short, exist since existence is human.

It is easy to see in existentialism merely a symptom of the exhaustion of western Europe at the end of a great war. Yet the prophets of the movement, Nietzsche and Kierkegaard, are men of the nineteenth century. From one point of view, existentialism is the pessimistic and disillusioned inversion of nineteenth-century hopeful materialistic faiths. Existentialism and other defiantly anti-Christian philosophies have not, however, gone very far into our Western society. It seems likely that in the Western world the ordinary educated man—*l'homme moyen intellectuel*—is still, as he was in the nineteenth century, a somewhat inconsistent mixture of Christian conformity and eighteenth-century optimistic naturalism.

The Marxists are far from dead. In Russia their faith has suffered the fate that comes to most reforming faiths when they get themselves established. The process of turning Marxism in Russia from an explosive—or at any rate a stimulant—into a sedative has been going on for several decades. It has gone so far that the good citizen of Soviet Russia is apparently no longer disturbed by the contrast between the old Marxist slogan "from each according to his abilities, to each according to his needs" and the existence within the Soviet Union of the equivalent of our millionaires. Any fair appraisal of just what Marxism means within Russia, and indeed within the states now under Russian influence, is beyond the powers of a Westerner. We have not even the necessary supply of facts, for there is clearly no free interchange of ideas and information between the two great rival systems of power in the world today. Even more important, we have not the necessary conditions for a reasonable degree of detachment. It is clear that Marxism is still in many parts of the world a growing and a fighting faith, one we must not dismiss as simply a perverse and wicked thing, but must consider, at the very least, as a grave symptom of our failure to recover even the degree of social stability the West achieved in the nineteenth century.

As for nationalism, it still seems in mid-twentieth century the strongest single factor in the existing networks of interests, sentiments, and ideas binding men into territorially based political groups. Itself a complex blending of almost everything that goes into Western cultural life, nationalism has been a kind of backlog for all the more abstract political forms we have been dealing with in the last few chapters—for Russian Communism (this despite the theoretical cosmopolitan and antinationalistic principles of original Marxism), for German Nazism, for American democracy. The units that fought the last war were *national* units. Those who hate war and hope to abolish it on this earth are nowadays mostly convinced of the need for a world-state or at least a small number of regional states eliminating the nation-state as we know it. Most of these world federationists are in the habit of speaking lightly of nationalism, as if it were an invention of a few villainous men, something foisted on the common people by their wicked masters, an evil that can be lifted from them by good legislation. The careful reader will here discern in its full innocence the eighteenth-century view of evil as the product of environment, of environment as in modern times readily subject to manipulation by the *good* people instead of by the bad. Only in the past, according to these believers, have the bad people created environment. The world federationist holds that nationalism is not in people's hearts, not in their habits, not in their folkways—at least, not the nationalism that makes an American willing to kill Japanese, and Japanese willing to kill Americans. Now there is not the slightest sign that the world federationist is right. To us, two hundred years after the innocent environmentalism of the eighteenth century, it must seem that, even if nationalism is produced by environment, the product is the result of so many centuries of history, is so firm and solid a product that in any given generation it cannot be greatly altered by new and planned environmental pressures—such as a nice world constitution on paper.

Nationalism is one of the facts of life, one of the observed facts no scientist can neglect. It is not identical in any two nation-states, since it is but one element in the complex of culture. It can be transcended, as in a sense the active minority of world federationists have transcended it—though there is nothing so "nationally" American as the optimism, the faith in the magic of written constitutions, the pious intoxication with high ethical abstractions, displayed by most American proponents of world government. But for most people nationalism is a sentiment deeply rooted in their whole lives. It is most usefully studied by the social psychologist, who is as yet no more than at the beginning of his scientific work of building cumulative knowledge. He can already make tentative statements such as that nationalism is likely to take its most aggressive forms in national groups that feel themselves oppressed, put upon, and treated as inferior; and that it seems least aggressive, most like that agreeable cultural variation of life's flavor Mazzini thought it could be, in small, relatively prosperous, but politically independent groups like the Swiss or the Norwegians or the Australians. Even in Australians, however, fear of the vast masses of Asiatics pressing down upon them may breed in coming years a rather depressing kind of outpost nationalism. But this whole subject of nationalism is one of the most fruitful subjects for the newer approach to the study of human relations we shall discuss in the next section of this chapter.

The nineteenth-century patterns of ideals, altered by our own experience, are, then, still with us. We still have our democratic center, and it is still attacked from Right and Left. One more survival from the nineteenth century must be noted. Our intellectuals are still alienated from ordinary people, still in revolt, still not agreed on what that revolt should lead to. Those who write and paint and act and preach are still a group apart. In America, indeed, there was a brief time during the Great Depression and the war of 1939-1945 when the writers rejoiced that they, like George Babbitt of Zenith, Ohio, believed in democracy, individual initiative, the common man, and the American Way. But this was a brief, if not an altogether illusory, honeymoon. Nowadays the intellectual writers and other artists are once more in revolt, writing nasty things about this world as it is, and about each other. Some of them are Marxists, of all the sects from orthodox Stalinism to the latest variety of Trotskyism; others continue to cultivate the subtler and less vulgar kinds of antidemocratic ideas, from those of the late Irving Babbitt to those of really intellectual fascists like Ezra Pound. And all of them continue to bellyache, so that whether you open the *Partisan Review* or the *Atlantic Monthly* or even the *Reader's Digest* you will not read far before you find an article that could be entitled "What's the Matter with. . . ."

Finally, we may revert to the great variety of architectural styles we took as a symbol of the multanimity of contemporary Western society (see pp. 440 ff.). No one can argue that in the mid-twentieth century we have come back to mankind's earlier habit of building in one style at one given time. It is true there has grown up in the twentieth century a reasonably unified style (in spite of some individual variants), a style called "functional" by many of its practitioners, and known to the layman as "modernistic." This style has its suitable concomitants in interior decoration and in the plastic arts, so that it is possible to build and furnish a house that will belong to the mid-twentieth century and to no other part of space-time. Actually this possibility has merely added another ingredient to the hash. Many people are infuriated by the modernistic style; many more cannot afford it, for it is still the most expensive way to build. The result is that the new Syringa Drive, opened just after the war, has in addition to its Cape Cod cottage, its synthetic Georgian, its California mission, and its seventeenth-century salt box, a modern house straight out of Gropius's Bauhaus. The neighbors are in some doubts as to the propriety of this functional starkness in the midst of their prettiness.

The mid-twentieth-century intellectual is in the West likely to be well aware that the multanimity of the modern world on all questions, big and little, is new, relatively speaking, in the history of mankind, and he is more than a little afraid that we can't take it. He is asking for a new synthesis, a new faith, a common basis of agreement on the Big Questions. But he has not even got the obvious beginnings of a new spiritual synthesis, not even of something very new and modern that can at least be added to the mixture as the modernistic building was added to the others. This is not to say that our time has not its own spirit of the age, its own flavor, its own little touches of style by which it will be known to later historians. It is rather to say that we are so far no more than a variant in a fairly consistent cultural pattern that grew out of the Middle Ages and that became distinct in the seventeenth and eighteenth centuries. Indeed, the newest thing in our intellectual lives is probably nothing aesthetic, in spite of the vogue of modernism, but rather a tendency in the study of men and of human relations that may be the beginnings in fact of what we have long had in a phrase—the social sciences.

Anti-Intellectualism: A Definition

Yet this tendency is in many of its concrete manifestations a very old one—you can find traces of it in the *Politics* of Aristotle—and it may be wrong to consider it an earnest of the beginnings of a formal scientific study of human relations. Perhaps what we here call anti-intellectualism will to the future historian be no more than one of the strands of our twentieth-century culture, part of the spirit of the age, part of the whole of our attitudes toward life and the universe that is so much more than cumulative knowledge, or science. It seems safer here to treat anti-intellectualism, especially in its bearings on the study of men in society, as simply one of the characteristic manifestations of the spirit of our age.

The name is an unfortunate one, especially in its emphasis on negation or opposition, yet there seems at the moment no other that will do as well. For, as should be clear in a moment, any attempt to indicate by a name that this tendency positively values, say, emotion as higher than thinking, the heart as superior to the head, drives, urges, impulses, or, if you wish to be Freudian, the "libido" or the "id" as better than the intellect, would be a bad misrepresentation of its nature. Basically the anti-intellectual, in the sense we here use the term, does not regard the instrument of thought as *bad,* but among most men most of the time as *weak.* The romantic agrees with Thomas Hardy that "thought is a disease of the flesh"; the anti-intellectual notes merely that thought seems often at the mercy of appetites, passions, prejudices, habits, conditioned reflexes, and of a good deal else in human life that is not thinking. There is unfortunately no agreed-upon nomenclature in this matter. In this book we shall use the term *anti-intellectualism* to describe the attempt to arrive rationally at a just appreciation of the actual roles of rationality and of nonrationality in human affairs. The term is widely used, however, to describe something quite different—the *praise* of nonrationality, the exaltation of nonrationality as the really desirable human activity, the denigration of rationality. Such an attitude of dislike for rationality and love for nonrationality we prefer to call *romanticism,* the romanticism of Goethe's "feeling is all." Wordsworth has put this hatred for reasoning very firmly:

> One impulse from a vernal wood
>   May teach you more of man,
> Of moral evil and of good,
>   Than all the sages can.

> Enough of science and of art;
>   Close up these barren leaves;
> Come forth, and bring with you a heart
>   That watches and receives.

The modern lover of the nonrational, like many of the apologists for Nazism, goes far beyond these first romanticists, but the root of the concept is in romanticism. It is most unfortunate that there is such confusion in a very important problem of terminology. We shall, however, attempt to use the term *anti-intellectual* without praise or blame, to describe the attempt to ascertain the place of rationality in actual human behavior.

Now the anti-intellectual tends to distrust a certain kind of abstract, deductive thinking about the Big Questions of the kind we have encountered frequently in this book, and nowhere more clearly, perhaps, than in the quotation from Hegel on p. 424. But the anti-intellectual, though in his opposition to the philosophy of the Enlightenment that universal education would overnight teach everybody to think correctly he often seemed to disparage the instrument of thought, *is in a sense a true heir of the Enlightenment,* is at bottom a believer in the power of thought to make man's life here on earth a better one. Freud himself, whom some tender-minded people quite wrongly regard as the apostle of deep, dark, instinctual self-indulgence, believed as firmly as any eighteenth-century *philosophe* in the power of the truth—scientific truth duly established—to promote good conduct on the part of the individual who had succeeded in learning the truth; but—and this is a difference of major importance—the *philosophe* thought that all that stood between the individual and the learning of truth was a rotten shell of decayed institutions, the Catholic Church and the French monarchy; whereas Freud thought that not only a very strong set of institutions but also a strong set of personal habits and inclinations and a strong set of habits established in early infancy stood between the individual and the learning of the truth. Freud, even before his old age of exile and unhappiness, had no hopes that *many* men could win their way through to this sort of truth in a short time.

The tempered hopes for the slow improvement in human relations—an improvement that even the Leftishly inclined among the
anti-intellectuals put well short of Utopian perfectibility—comes out in
a quotation from Graham Wallas, an English Fabian of the days of
Wells, Shaw, and the Webbs, a Progressive member of the London
County Council, and the author of a book called *Human Nature in
Politics* (London, 1908). Wallas had made a mildly anti-intellectualist
and "realistic" study of British politics in which he pointed out that
voters did not coldly and logically reason things out, did not even
very often exercise intelligent self-interest, but were influenced by
flattery, by appeals to their prejudices, by the good looks of the candidate, and above all by a candidate's paying them attention as persons,
by so small a thing as calling them by name. Wallas was grieved
when some of his fellow workers in the Labour party accused him of
selling out to the enemy by this anti-intellectualism, and he wrote:

> Thought may be late in evolution, it may be deplorably weak in
> driving power, but without its guidance no man or organization can
> find a safe path amid the vast impersonal complexities of the universe
> as we have learned to see it.

The anti-intellectual insists that man is a complex creature whose
behavior must be studied as far as possible without preconceptions
concerning the goodness and badness of that behavior. Just as with
the place of logical thinking in human life, so with the place of good
behavior; the anti-intellectual does not deny the difference between
good and bad, does not hesitate to prefer goodness to badness. What
he does insist is that, to judge by the evidence to be obtained by
observation of what men have done and are doing, there is a great deal
of badness about and—this is the important thing—there seems to be
no direct and simple causal relation between men's moral ideals and
their actions. Therefore the anti-intellectual repeats Bacon's praise of
Machiavelli, himself in many ways an early anti-intellectual: "We
are much beholden to Machiavel and others that wrote what men do,
and not what they ought to do."

To sum up: Most anti-intellectuals accept, by and large, the goals of order, happiness, individual freedom, and all the rest we associate with the Enlightenment, but they hold these goals as only imperfectly and only very slowly attainable on earth; and they believe the best way to attain them is not to preach that they must be attained, *not to pretend they have been attained* (a not uncommon claim among American educators, editors, and preachers with aspirations to mass audiences), but to work patiently at building up a true social science based on the long-tried methods of cumulative knowledge and to hope that this knowledge will be used by men to promote the good rather than the bad. They are in more complete agreement on what is good than youthful cynics, fresh in the discovery that human ideas of the beautiful and the good are not quite the same in New Guinea as in New York, are likely to think. They differ more in their hopes. Pareto, whom we are going to meet shortly, apparently had at his death in 1923 very little hope that men would use better knowledge of social science to promote the good on earth; contemporary American social scientists influenced by anti-intellectualism (though they might not like the label of anti-intellectual), among them Clyde Kluckhohn of Harvard and Alexander Leighton of Cornell, are likely, in the good American tradition, to believe that on the whole the new knowledge will be put to good ends—that social science will be used to promote the good working, the health, of society, just as medical science has been used to promote the health of the body.

Contemporary Anti-Intellectualism

We have already noted how such natural scientists as Newton and Darwin gave leads in the social sciences. In our own times the great leads have come from biology and psychology. Probably the two most commanding figures in this respect of influence on the social studies are Pavlov and Freud, both psychologists trained in physiology and the other biological sciences. Note that we are here considering, not the meaning of their professional studies within their own nowadays very specialized professions, but their influence on the much more general currents of thought among men of various training concerned with human affairs.

Pavlov's is the simpler case. What reached the outside world from the laboratories of this Russian scientist whose independence was respected by both Tsarist and Soviet governments was the well-known phrase "conditioned reflexes." Pavlov's dogs are as familiar as any laboratory animals have ever been. Most of us know how, after being repeatedly fed at a certain signal, such as a bell, they came to water at the mouth in anticipation of food at a mere signal. The natural—that is the untrained—response of watering at the mouth would ordinarily come only when the dog had actual food before him; Pavlov got the same response artificially by a signal that certainly didn't smell or look like food to the dog. The upshot was clear evidence that training (conditioning) could produce automatic responses in the animal that were essentially similar to the kind of automatic responses the animal is born with. Conditioned reflexes like watering at the mouth at a signal were the same as natural reflexes like watering at the mouth when a fine red beefsteak was held before the animal.

What this meant in broad lines for the social scientist is this: In a sense, eighteenth-century notions about the power of environment (training, education) of the kind Robert Owen expressed so clearly (see p. 387) were confirmed, in the sense that environment can be manipulated to give organisms new responses; but—and this is a bitter blow to eighteenth-century optimism—once such training has taken hold the organism has, so to speak, incorporated the results almost as if they had been the product of heredity, not environment, and further change becomes very difficult, in some instances impossible. Pavlov, after having trained some of his dogs, tried mixing his signals, frustrating and confusing the dogs by withholding food at the signal that had always produced food for them, and so on until he succeeded in producing symptoms of a kind close to what in human beings would be neurosis, or even psychosis.

Now the cautious social scientist does not, of course, take over Pavlov's conditioned reflexes and apply them uncritically to all human behavior. He does not assume, for instance, that the Vermonter voting the straight Republican ticket is behaving quite like the dog watering at the mouth as an accustomed bell is rung. Even in Vermont, voting Republican is probably not quite a conditioned reflex. But the cautious social scientist will hold that concepts like that of the conditioned reflexes do throw light on a great deal of habit-determined human conduct. For the anti-intellectual, Pavlov's work was further demonstration that a very great deal of our behavior is not determined—nor even greatly influenced—by what goes on in the cerebral cortex.

Freud is a much more complex figure than Pavlov—indeed one of the most complex figures in the intellectual history of the West. He was a scientist brought up in the simple craftsman's belief in a material universe from which the supernatural was ruled out, and with the scientist's contempt for all metaphysical ideas but the unavowed, positivist metaphysics of conventional modern science. His total work is a bewildering compound of natural science and rather pessimistic —almost Christian—metaphysics. In a book of this scope we cannot properly examine Freud's complexities; moreover, his work, like that of all great system-making thinkers, looks quite different to outsiders and to true believers. He has created a method of dealing with certain kinds of human disability usually thought of as mental—nervous breakdown, neurosis, and the like. This method is called psychoanalysis, and must be distinguished from conventional handling of mental disease, usually by physicians with special training as neurologists, which is called psychiatry. Freudian psychoanalysis, though as a part of medical science it is in 1950 vastly more reputable among conventional physicians than one would have thought possible only a few decades ago, is still mostly heretical, the belief of an ardent sect. This is especially true when the ideas Freud developed in the treatment of mental disease are extended, as Freud himself extended them in later life, to most of the fields of the social sciences. Finally, the study of Freud is made still more difficult by the fact that he was always revising even his very fundamental ideas, so that to take his system as complete at any one time is dangerous.

Freud gave leads to many in the study of human behavior who knew nothing, or very little, about psychoanalysis and its metaphysical superstructure. Our century is indeed a century in which psychology is the fashionable science, and in which the chatter of the educated makes use of psychological terms much as the habitués of the eighteenth-century salons chattered about the laws of physics and astronomy discovered by Newton. Many of these modern smooth coins of conversation were once sharply minted by Freud himself—libido, Oedipus complex, infantile sexuality, sublimation. Perhaps the smoothest coin of all—inferiority complex—was minted by a disciple, Adler, who later quarreled with the master and set up his own psychological shop.

Here, as has been our practice in this book, we are concerned rather with this phase of Freud's ideas as they circulated among the intellectual classes than with their professional significance in psychology and medicine. For this purpose, a very schematic outline of his basic ideas as of about 1920 should suffice. To Freud, what makes people go is a whole set of "drives" he first called *libido* and associated very closely with sexual desires and later called the *id,* and made a little less clearly sexual. The id in the human being is part of the unconscious; it wishes, pushes the individual into action. But the whole behavior of the human being involves two other parts of the human psyche, the *ego* and the *super-ego.* Conventional natural scientists are greatly annoyed by the fact that there is no way of locating the id, the ego, and the super-ego in the human brain or anywhere else in the human anatomy; nobody ever "saw" a part of the id, even under a microscope; actually Freud was not in this respect at least sinning against true science—the test of these concepts is not whether they can be apprehended as a part of human receptor experiences aided by instruments, but whether they work, whether their use enables us to understand human behavior better.

The *ego* is wholly—or almost wholly—part of a man's conscious mental life, but it is not pure logical activity; it is an umpire, or governor, the guardian of the interests of the organism as a whole and the arbitrator of conflicting desires rising out of the id into consciousness. Some of these desires, especially if they seem to the ego of the kind to discredit the person, are suppressed by the ego, but continue hard at work in the unconscious id; some of them are "sublimated," turned from a sexual goal, for instance, into art or poetry or governing men. The *super-ego* involves some of the elements that go into the conditioned reflexes. In the super-ego the notions taught the individual about right and wrong, the "proper" way to behave, the "proper" ideas to hold, come to play on the individual's actions. In part, the super-ego is unconscious, its dictates inculcated from infancy on so that they do not go through the logical process, do not present him with problems of alternative action. The ego is like a somewhat un-Christian individual conscience; the super-ego is like a social or collective conscience working on and in the individual. The ego mediates between the id and the external world of material *reality;* the super-ego mediates between the id and the external world of ideals, of "higher things," which last Freud rather begrudgingly granted a kind of objective reality.

In a healthy individual the id, the ego, and the super-ego cooperate to keep him aware of the realities of his environment and to enable him to adjust his conduct in accord with these realities so that he is on the whole a happy man and a good citizen. In the neurotic individual desires balked by the negative of the ego or the super-ego are thereby driven back into the unconscious, where they continue to live and push on as desires must. They make the stuff of a man's dreams. They crop up in disguised (but not genuinely sublimated) form in all sorts of acts that are clearly not in the line of normal, sensible conduct—in obsessive fears, in withdrawal from ordinary responsibilities, in worrying and fretting, in all the great variety of conduct we nowadays label "neurotic." These balked desires are, be it noted, in the unconscious; the neurotic individual does not really know what he wants.

Freud's basic notions of therapy—and it is these that caused us to classify him as a child of the Enlightenment—can be summed up as an elaborate, difficult (and very expensive) way of teaching the patient to know what he really wants. More particularly, Freud held that the original repression, the original driving back into the id of certain desires, was the source of the evil, the *trauma* or wound inflicted in the individual's psyche. Usually, he thought, this trauma went back to infancy and was tied up with the fact that the infant's very early sexual desires are strongly disapproved in our culture, that both his ego and his super-ego are taught rather harshly that they must not allow such conduct. Even if there were no simple single incident of infancy that seemed the origin of a difficulty in later life, Freud believed that the very early years were always of major importance. But how could these forgotten things be dug up by the individual? Only by a long process of "free association," of letting the individual roam back in memory day after day, with the psychoanalyst at his side noting the tiny clues as they came into the flow of memories, and by aid from dreams, recent and recalled.

We cannot of course attempt a detailed account of Freud's methods of therapy. The point should be clear: Freud held that the individual was a bundle of confused thoughts and desires that could only with the greatest difficulty be brought to make sense; but that when after long investigation the analyst could show the individual just *why* he behaved as he did, then the individual would cease to behave badly, unprofitably for himself and for his fellows. Note particularly that Freud did *not* take the old, innocent, Rousseauistic position that since all the trouble came from the original suppression the way to avoid difficulty is to have everybody from infancy on follow all his desires, let the id dictate all his acts. Freud and the Freudians do indeed tend to be "permissive" in child training, tend to sympathize with the ideal of as much individual freedom in society as can be attained. Freud himself seems never to have liked the contents of most of our super-egos, the "higher things" of Western tradition. But the Freudians do not advocate an orgy of lust, they do not want man to be the slave of his cruder appetites, they are not—for the most part— antinomian cranks. They are trained physicians trying to be true to the standards of an exacting profession, trying to see men as they really are.

Freud's contribution to contemporary anti-intellectualism was very great. His work, taken with that of Pavlov and many other psychologists and physiologists, put great emphasis on the proportion of human actions in which the traditional instrument of thought—

Aristotle's *phronesis,* Christian *ratio,* the reason of Locke and the Encyclopedists, even the illative sense of Newman—had no part, or little part. Action came to the anti-intellectual to be the result of automatic responses, natural or conditioned, of all sorts of unconscious drives and urges, of traditions, social habits, even theological and metaphysical principles made by early training and conditioning part of the individual's way of responding to the need to make a decision. To the anti-intellectual actual ratiocinative thought in an individual is to the rest of his living even less than the small part of the iceberg visible above water is to the whole mass of the iceberg. The *amount* of reasoning in human life, then, and not the *existence* of reasoning, is the point over which the anti-intellectual and those who oppose anti-intellectualism really differ. The tradition of American moral and political thinking is *not* anti-intellectual. The practice of a good deal of American politics, and of much of American life—advertising is a clear example—is anti-intellectual.

The roots and ramifications of this view that the actual, functional, place of the instrument of thought in the sum total of human activity on earth is small—and remember it is not either rejoicing over or bemoaning the smallness of this place—can be traced in many fields of modern thought. Important roots lie in what social thinkers made of Darwin; for it became pretty clear that, if in general one could hold that what gave man such good results in the struggle for life was his brain, in most concrete cases it was by no means the intellectual who did best in the struggle for life.

One of the first, and one of the most interesting of nineteenth-century writers on man as *politique et moraliste* to take up this theme was the Englishman Walter Bagehot, whose *Physics and Politics* (1869) is one of the earliest attempts to follow up Darwinian leads in the study of human affairs. The book should have been entitled *Biology and Politics;* Bagehot was merely using *physics* to stand for *natural science.* Bagehot held that the first stage in building civilization from mere savagery was a state of totalitarian rigidity of law and order—not a personal dictatorship, but the dictatorship of what Bagehot called the "cake of custom." In competition among groups, that group wins, by and large, which has the best discipline, the firmest cake of custom. But in the next stage the inventive mind comes more into play; new ideas are produced that enable one group to cope better than another with the environment; and finally there comes the "government by discussion" that is a mark of the modern age.

All this may sound like the conventional Victorian view of unilinear progress. But Bagehot is careful to insist that even after the breaking of the cake of custom by the new ideas, the successful society will still have a lot of the old nonintellectual traits, or it will go under. Indeed, he found what for his age was a paradoxical, and for us a typical anti-intellectualist, explanation for the success of parliamentary democracy: The great trouble with a civilization made up of *homo sapiens* is that human beings are impatient, unrestrained animals, always wanting to *do something;* the great virtue of government by discussion is that it *postpones* action, takes up time in debate and palaver and so allows time for the healing work of nature. In much the same way, Bagehot decided that the trouble with the French is that they are too intellectual, too interested in ideas to achieve adequate political stability; he found that the English people, on the whole, are able to withstand the temptation to indulge in abstract thinking, that they have the necessary stupidity to make democracy work.

The same Nietzsche who in one mood appealed to the Superman and wrote in pseudo-Biblical prose about the prophet Zarathustra was in another mood an early anti-intellectualist. Nietzsche attempted what he called a "natural history of morals"—that is, a rapid survey of how men actually did behave in relation to how they thought they ought to behave. Like many of the school, he was perhaps too much tempted to paradox by his opposition to the general belief of mankind that their acts follow logically from their beliefs. He was, moreover, unable to carry out his study in a systematic way; all his work is a series of aphorisms, a long and uncommon commonplace book. Nevertheless, Nietzsche hit clearly upon another of the main points the anti-intellectualist makes, a point Machiavelli himself had already made. That is the observation that men often gain ends useful to themselves and to society by acting on erroneous ideas.

The falseness of an opinion is not for us any objection to it: it is here, perhaps, that our new language sounds most strangely. The question is, how far an opinion is life-furthering, life-preserving, species-preserving; perhaps species-rearing; and we are fundamentally inclined to maintain that the falsest opinions (to which synthetic judgments *a priori* belong) are the most indispensable to us; that without a recognition of logical fictions, without a comparison of reality with the purely *imagined* world of the absolute and immutable . . . man could not live—that the renunciation of false opinion would be a renunciation of life, a negation of life. *To recognize untruth as a condition of life:* that is certainly to impugn the traditional ideas of value in a dangerous manner, and a philosophy which ventures to do so, has thereby alone placed itself beyond good and evil.

By the twentieth century some of anti-intellectualism had begun to catch on with the intellectual classes, and in less obvious forms had begun to seep down into popular consciousness. In its origins a good deal of the point of view we here call anti-intellectualism is that of a self-conscious "superior," a man wise enough to know how little wisdom prevails in the world. It is a point of view that turns easily into a kind of snobbery, the feeling that the masses are the herd and we wise few are, or should be, the masters. This runs all through Nietzsche, who is the clearest example of this strain in the attitude of modern anti-intellectualism. Yet there is also a strain, clear ultimately in Freud, that emphasizes the possibility that ordinary men may learn the truth about themselves, a truth far more complex than the eighteenth-century view of man, and that once having learned it they can themselves make the necessary adjustments to this newly seen reality. Once men realize the really grave difficulties of thinking straight, they will, according to this more democratic view, be well on the road to straight thinking.

The most familiar phase of contemporary anti-intellectualism brings out this aspect clearly. From obscure and difficult philosophical writers like Alfred Korzybski through more graceful literary figures like I. A. Richards to frank popularizers like Stuart Chase, the word *semantics* has gone far, especially in the English-speaking countries. Semantics is the science of meaning, the study of the way in which human beings communicate with one another. The semanticist will point out, for example, that three different observers may refer to the actions of a fourth person, the first as "pig-headed," the second as "obstinate," and the third as "firm." The actions are the same; the words the observers use to describe the actions are by no means the same; they indicate certain feelings of the observer, and they communicate these feelings, rather than an objective report. Words are, then, charged with emotional overtones and are not mere signs like the *x* and *y* of algebra. *Pig-headed* carries with it strong disapproval, *obstinate* rather less strong disapproval, and *firm* is slightly approving. *Persevering* would in our culture be still more approving.

Again, there are the great big words that draw into themselves all sorts of confusing human hopes and fears, so that even on close analysis it is very hard—the ardent semantic reformer says impossible —to find for them a concrete meaning. In the language of semantics, terms like *liberty, equality, fraternity* have no *referent;* you cannot perform the operation of producing them to be seen and felt; they are "meaningless." Mr. Stuart Chase suggests in his *Tyranny of Words* that whenever we are tempted to use great big vague phrases like *the democratic way of life* or *Western individualism* we should simply substitute *blah-blah* and let it go at that. Of course at this extreme we have merely come to the current form of the nominalist position. We are ready for the reflection of this anti-intellectualism in formal philosophy.

That reflection takes on a paradoxical form: a philosophy that would eliminate philosophy from our studies. The exponents of this philosophy, the "logical positivists," developed their position, not from the simple belief of some nineteenth-century positivists in the induction and natural science of Herbert Spencer's time, but from syllogistic logics and mathematics *and* the modern conceptions of scientific method. Very briefly, logical positivism asserts that the only valid kind of knowledge is cumulative knowledge, the kind one finds in natural science. For this kind of knowledge there exists a process, the process gradually worked out in Western culture by our scientists, through which one can test the truth of any statement that is claimed to be knowledge. In Bridgman's term, you can perform an operation on the statement—sometimes a long and difficult operation involving laboratory and field research, much mathematics and hard logical thinking—but an operation that will enable you to test the truth or falsity of the statement.

Mostly the logical positivists take their illustrations of the legitimate kind of knowledge from the natural sciences. We may vary their procedure and bring the legitimate and illegitimate kinds of knowledge (as they maintain) to bear on at least the same topic. If you make the statement "All men believe in God," you can test that statement by the methods of the public-opinion pollsters. You can send out men to ask everyone they meet the question, "Do you believe in God?" As soon as one of the interviewed says no, you will have an operational proof that the statement is false. But if you make the statement "All men really believe in God deep down within themselves, no matter what they say," you have gone beyond any pollster's tests, beyond the possibility of the logical positivist's tests. Similarly, you cannot really check up scientifically on the statement "There are no atheists in foxholes." If you say "God exists," you are making the kind of statement the logical positivist says cannot be classified as being within the scope of "knowledge." You are making a metaphysical answer to a metaphysical question; you are doing the same thing men have been doing since the Greeks. You are still getting answers that will by no means be accepted by everyone—and especially not by those with expert training in philosophy. The logical positivist tends to regard all traditional philosophic thinking, the kind involved in fields like metaphysics, ethics, political theory, even most epistemology and of course pure Aristotelian logic, as a complete waste of time; the favorite figure of speech compares the traditional philosopher with the squirrel in his treadmill cage.

The logical positivists are themselves most abstract thinkers, whose positive interest is chiefly the modern extension of the mathematician's way of going at things that is called symbolic logic. Some of the more innocent of them hoped that once they had worked out symbolic logic to perfection all communications in symbolic logic would be perfectly understandable by all human beings, who would thenceforth never quarrel, since they would never suffer from ignorance and misunderstanding. But mostly the logical positivists simply pushed aside these questions of moral and aesthetic standards (value-judgments) as to them "meaningless." They did not really believe that just because no scientific answer to these questions could be found there were in fact as many answers as there were human beings on earth. They were not, in their practice, moral cynics or nihilists. They simply took values as not to be thought about profitably, a point of view annoying to those brought up in prevailing Western traditions, which have tended to hold that some judgments about morals and aesthetics are truer, or at least make more sense, than others.

Yet since from its more innocent to its more sophisticated forms anti-intellectualism emphasizes the immense role of the irrational in men's lives, there is a constant temptation for the anti-intellectualist to see only the clear-cut triumph of the objective thinking we call natural science. Heir to the long Western tradition of tough-mindedness, he is afraid of the kind of thinking Newman defended as the work of the illative sense. He sees that *all* sane men of sufficient education can be convinced of the truth of certain propositions in physics; he sees that *all* sane men of sufficient education simply cannot be convinced of any propositions in English literature—beyond simple statements of fact, such as that William Shakespeare wrote a play called *Romeo and Juliet*. And, at that, there are those who maintain that Francis Bacon wrote that play! Yet, of course, the position that on any statement save simple statements of verifiable fact and statements of scientifically established uniformities one man's opinion is just as good as another's, the position that, as Bentham once declared, "push-pin is as good as poetry," is one that most men—even anti-intellectuals—find displeasing.

One way out for them we have seen already suggested by Machiavelli and Nietzsche: The truth of these value-judgments may not be rationally establishable, but their importance in the social life of a given culture *can* be established. A society that believes in the efficacy of certain religious rites wholly incapable of scientific justification may yet gain strength from such belief. Pareto cites as an example a Greek crew in ancient times sacrificing to Poseidon, god of the sea, before they set sail on a dangerous voyage; we today should be willing to accept regarding Poseidon the logical positivist's verdict that there is no possible proof of his existence; yet, says Pareto, it is clear that if under the influence of the belief that they had put themselves right with Poseidon the crew rowed more heartily, maintained better discipline, stuck together better under pressure of danger, then clearly belief in Poseidon was useful to them, and in a sense, true.

We have come with Pareto to a most representative twentieth-century anti-intellectual, a trained engineer, a mathematician who turned first to economics and then to sociology in an effort to build up a social science that would stand comparison with a natural science. Pareto was an Italian who did most of his creative work in Switzerland; but in his last years he accepted a post under Mussolini, and for this and for many of his doctrines as expressed in his *The Mind and Society* he has been labeled a reactionary, a Rightist, the "Karl Marx of the bourgeoisie." He was—like most articulate anti-intellectuals—a confirmed scholar and intellectual. Emotionally attached to the sort of ideal John Mill brings out in *On Liberty,* Pareto saw his world moving apparently farther and farther from individual liberty and toleration of great variety of human behavior, farther from international peace and free circulation of men and ideas. He was in some senses the disillusioned liberal, trying to explain why liberalism hadn't worked, not rejoicing that it hadn't. Of course, for the traditional reforming liberal all wrapped up in words and faith, the mere admission that liberalism wasn't working, the insistence that the facts of life were not entirely what the liberal thought and hoped they were, was a treason on Pareto's part. Moreover, Pareto is profoundly irritating to many readers because he insists too vehemently that he is in effect the first person to study human relations with the cool detachment of the scientist, keeping his value-judgments outside his work, or actually, insisting that he never makes value-judgments. Of course he comes nowhere near living up to these professions; his likes and dislikes, somewhat different in many ways from those of the reforming liberal, come out on every page. His great hatred is for the people he calls the "virtueists," the crusading reformers who wish by legislation, policing, and perhaps some education to wipe off the face of the earth sexual irregularities, alcoholic drinks, gambling, and the other lesser vices.

Pareto prefaces *The Mind and Society* with a somewhat tedious but by no means superfluous essay on just what the scientific method is. This method he calls the *logico-experimental;* other kinds of conscious human mental activity he calls *non-logico-experimental.* Note that he does not use simply the word *logical;* that is because he holds that logical thinking is merely a set of rules for using the mind in a certain way, a way that can be applied to problems like the existence of the Trinity or the Aristotelian entelechy as well as to problems like that of the chemical composition of a given protein.

Pareto as a sociologist is concerned chiefly with the problem of separating out in human action the rational (logico-experimental) from the nonrational (non-logico-experimental). In our social behavior, he found a part to be the expression of certain sentiments he called "residues," and another part the expression of other sentiments he called "derivations." Note that neither residues nor derivations are for Pareto drives, urges, appetites, libidos, or whatever else the psychologist tries to analyze in human behavior as a sort of underlying animal push to action. Pareto is willing to assume this push, and leave its study to the psychologist; what interests him as sociologist is action that is expressed in words, ritual, symbolism of some kind. Buying wool socks for cold weather is one such action. If they are bought deliberately to get good socks at a price the buyer can afford, this is rational, or logico-experimental action in accord with the doer's interests. If, however, they are bought without regard for price by a sentimental lover of England who buys imported English socks in order to do his bit to help England, then clearly something else, something the economist has to disregard in his price statistics, has come into play. This something else is the substance of Pareto's study.

The part of the action of our Greek sailors sacrificing to Poseidon that explained Poseidon as ruler of the seas, maker and quieter of tempests, is for Pareto a *derivation,* a theory or explanation usually logical in form, but *not logico-experimental,* not capable of verification by the methods of natural science. The derivations are close to what Bacon called the "Idols" and to what we all know nowadays as "rationalizations." Pareto gives them a much more complex and useful classification than did Bacon. Indeed, his is for the purposes of semantics one of the very best analyses of the commonest way the human mind has gone to work in social and ethical theory. He is clear in his own mind that these derivations have very little effect on the general behavior of men in society, very little effect on social change. What we have in this book called cosmologies Pareto would have held were mostly tissues of derivations; he maintained that they have little or no effect on the behavior of those who hold them. Yet in his own emotional life he was clearly unable to treat one cosmology as no better or no worse than another. He hated socialism, and medieval Christianity as well; he was himself a good nineteenth-century bourgeois.

What does move men in society, and keeps them together in society, says Pareto, is the residues. These have extraordinarily little intellectual in them, though they are usually put in logical form. They are expressions of relatively permanent, abiding sentiments in men, expressions that usually have to be separated from the part that is actually a derivation, which latter may change greatly and even quickly. Let us revert to our pagan Greek sailors, and compare them with a group of Christian Greek sailors a few centuries later praying, lighting candles, and making vows to the Virgin Mary just before sailing. The *derivations* are the explanations of what Poseidon and the Virgin respectively do. They vary. The believer in the Virgin thinks his pagan predecessor was dead wrong. The *residues* are the needs to secure divine aid and comfort in a difficult undertaking, and to perform certain ritual acts that give the performer assurance of such aid and comfort. The residues are nearly the same for our two sets of sailors. Both the pagans and the Christians have the same social and psychological needs and satisfy them in much the same ways, though with very different rational (intellectual) explanations of what they are doing.

Pareto's conception of the residues was much more original than that of the derivations, and much more difficult to work out. His actual classification of the residues and the detailed analysis of the way they work in human society are by no means as good as that of his derivations. But two of the major classes of residues he distinguishes stand out, and help form what we must call—non-logico-experimental though it may be—his philosophy of history, his limited but genuine cosmology. These are first the residues of *persistent aggregates,* the sentiments that mark men who like regular ways, solid discipline, tradition and habit, men like the Spartans, the lions; and second there are the residues of the *instinct for combinations,* the sentiments that mark men who like novelty and adventure, who invent new ways of doing things, who like to cut loose from the old, the tried, men not easily shocked, men who hate discipline, men like the Athenians, the foxes. Now men as individuals hold all sorts of logically quite inconsistent mixtures of these two and the other (and to Pareto less important) residues. But in societies of many individual members, men influenced largely by one *or* the other of these major residues tend to predominate, and to characterize that society. Like most philosophers of history, Pareto is far from clear on just how a conservative society where the residues of persistent aggregates predominate changes into another kind of society. But he does have this conception of a pendulum swing, a Yin and Yang—even, though the comparison would have angered Pareto—a struggle of thesis and antithesis.

The nineteenth century in the West was in Pareto's mind a society in which the residues of instinct of combinations played perhaps the maximum part they can in a human society. The nineteenth century was a century of competition among individuals full of new ideas, inventions, enterprises, convinced that the old ways were bad, that novelty was the great thing to strive for at the expense of everything else. It was a society notably out of equilibrium. It had to turn toward the other kind of residues, toward the persistent aggregates, toward a society with more security and less competition, more discipline and less freedom, more uniformity and less variety. It had to go the way we are going in the twentieth century.

Pareto's final general conception is this one of an equilibrium in a society, an equilibrium constantly disturbed at least in Western society, but constantly renewed by a sort of *vis medicatrix naturae* not to be supplanted by any social physician or planner. Pareto does not entirely rule out the possibility that human beings by taking thought may in little ways here and there change social arrangements in such a way that what they plan turns out to be a reality. But the overwhelming emphasis of his work is that in human affairs change in human conduct as a whole must be distinguished from change in human ideas and ideals. Man being what he is, and in our Western culture the residue of instinct of combinations being so widespread, there is bound to be change in many fields of human interest. Fashion and all its commercial dependents can almost be said to be change for change's sake. But for Pareto there was also—and more important for him to point out just because the reformers, the liberals, the virtueists, the optimistic planners would not see it—a level of human conduct where change is very slow indeed, almost as slow as the kind of change the geologist and the evolutionist study.

This level of human conduct where change is very slow indeed is the level of the residues. At most, Pareto held, the skilled political leader can manipulate the derivations in such a way that some residues are made relatively inactive, and others are activated. He cannot possibly produce new residues or destroy old ones. He will get effective governmental inspection of meats, for instance, not just by an appeal to men's sense of civic responsibility, not just by a rational argument of the eighteenth-century sort, but also by propaganda, by literary work like Upton Sinclair's *The Jungle,* making as many people as possible *feel fear* that they will eat uninspected dirty meat and die of food poisoning unless the government does inspect. Obviously, the men who direct American advertising are Paretans without knowing it.

The wise leader according to Pareto will read Bacon's famous aphorism, "nature is not to be commanded save by obeying her" (*natura non vincitur nisi parendo*), as "*human* nature is not to be commanded save by obeying it"—or at least taking it into account! You must not expect human beings to be consistently unselfish, sensible, devoted to the common good, kindly, wise. Above all, you must not expect that any institution, any law, any constitution, any treaty or pact, will make them so. But Pareto goes a bit beyond this position. Planning, except for limited and always very concrete ends, is dangerous. Pareto, starting from mathematics and engineering, and with actual hostility to Christianity, comes on this specific question very close to the Christian Burke. Not only is it very likely that a big, ambitious, legislated change will not achieve the results the planners planned; it is likely to produce unpredictable and perhaps unfortunate results. Pareto would have gloated a bit, one suspects, over the fate of the Eighteenth Amendment, which did not promote temperance in the United States, but helped produce newer and in many ways less desirable habits of drinking—helped, for instance, to make alcoholic beverages a respectable drink for middle-class women. Until we know more of social science, the best thing to do is to trust to what the upstart intellectual arrogantly condemns as the *irrational* side of human nature; we must believe that the ingrained habits of the human race are, even by evolutionary standards, more useful to survival than the impertinent logic of the reformers.

Much of modern anti-intellectualism, unpalatable though it is to optimistic democratic taste, is actually widespread in Western culture today. Even semantics has spread into popular consciousness, to be sure in forms Korzybski would hardly recognize. We have all heard about rationalization, propaganda, the ambiguities and other inadequacies of language; we are all reminded daily that to get ahead in this world you must exercise your skill in handling other people, you must deliberately win friends and influence people by arts other than logic. The experts in propaganda know that one of the factors they must reckon with is public awareness and distrust of propaganda, which the French call expressively—and cynically— *bourrage de crâne,* "brain-stuffing."

We are brought squarely up against the problem of the relation of anti-intellectualism to our democratic tradition, way of life, cosmology. Democracy as it ripened in the eighteenth century held out hope of rapid and thorough social change toward universal happiness on earth to be achieved by educating all men to use their natural reason—or at least by entrusting power to an enlightened group of political planners who could devise and run institutions under which all men would be happy. Anti-intellectualism maintains against these democratic beliefs the belief that men are not and cannot under the best educational system be guided by their reason, that the drives, habits, conditioned reflexes that mostly do guide them cannot be changed rapidly, that, in short, there is something in the nature of man that makes him and will continue to make him behave in the immediate future not very differently from the way he has behaved in the past. These two sets of beliefs, the democratic and the anti-intellectual, seem mutually incompatible. Many of the Leftist and Rightist attacks we discussed in the last chapter seem in comparison relatively close to democracy, mere extensions or modifications of it. But Pareto's position, for instance, seems in some ways as much a polar opposite of democracy as Maistre's, and of as little use to us today.

Yet Graham Wallas, as we noted, was in sympathy with what we call democracy, and went part way with the anti-intellectuals. So good a defender of all sorts of democratic causes as Stuart Chase has been greatly influenced by anti-intellectualism. All but the very softest and most idealistic of social scientists in our culture have had to retreat from eighteenth-century rationalism and learn from the anti-intellectuals. And it is difficult for most of us to read Pareto—and Machiavelli, Bacon, La Rochefoucauld, and the other "realists" about human nature and human affairs—without feeling that much of what they say is quite true.

We are back, of course, to the eternal contrast, the eternal tension, so strong in Western culture, between this world and the next, the real and the ideal, the practical and the desirable. The anti-intellectuals are pulling democracy over toward the first of these pairs. Yet to emphasize the facts of life, the "spotted actuality," is not necessarily to adopt the conclusion that no improvement in actual conditions is possible. Indeed, in Western tradition the realists (in our modern sense, which is confusingly different from the medieval sense of "realism"—see p. 190) have more often been ethical meliorists, even optimists, than cynics. They rarely gloat with pleasure over the bad conditions they insist are there, are real. The real and the ideal are not, we have insisted throughout this book, by nature enemies. They belong together. It is only when they are divorced that each, pursued in neglect of the other, is a danger to society. One of the great questions we now face is whether good democrats can accept the reality the anti-intellectuals have brought to their attention without losing their belief in the possibility of improving that reality.

15

Mid-Twentieth Century

WE HAVE HITHERTO, and quite deliberately, treated the intellectual history of the West with but incidental mention of any other culture. For we have focused on the attitude of Western men and women toward the Big Questions, toward cosmologies. And it is a fact that on the whole the West has not been greatly influenced by the cosmological, nor even by the ethical and aesthetic, ideas of other cultures. There is unquestionably a great deal in the first form of Western culture we have here studied, the Greek, which comes out of the cultures of the Eastern Mediterranean region in the millennia before Homer and the Ionians. But in many ways these early cultures are simply the ancestors of our own Western culture; and at any rate, save for the Hebraic and other Near Eastern elements in Christianity, they had mostly done their work before the rise of the great Greek culture.

A detailed study of Western culture would, of course, have to take into account many kinds of contacts with other cultures, especially in India and China, and note many ways in which our inheritance would be different had these contacts never taken place. There is first the familiar interchange of material goods, the kind that even the prehistorian can trace through archaeological remains. The West has usually been willing enough to accept strange wares, to experiment gingerly with strange foods. Western man is not quite the complete devotee of newness, invention, experiment he seemed to the nine-teenth-century progressive to be: There have been neophobes even in our culture. Nevertheless, any modern Western language bears the traces of these borrowings from all over the globe—*sugar, alcohol, curry, tomato, tobacco, pajama, kowtow, bungalow,* and many more.

Sometimes the borrowings involved inventions and ideas. We have already noted a very typical example of this sort of external influence on Western culture in the sign for zero, Hindu in origin and borrowed through the Arabs. This and many other borrowings are important; without some of them at least we could not have Western culture as it now is. The eighteenth-century intellectuals admired the Chinese very much indeed. In part, as we shall see, they used the wise Confucian Chinese as sticks with which to beat their Christian opponents. But they also brought Chinese art into Western art—Chinese Chippendale, for instance. The vogue of *Chinoiserie* is the beginning of that modern eclecticism out of which may yet come a real style. The French physiocrats were much influenced by the Chinese.

With the discoveries of the fifteenth century and the beginnings of the expansion of Europe the study of non-European lands and peoples of all sorts began to take an important part in Western learning. Yet the growth of most of the formal sciences was very slow in these early centuries. Anthropology is in origin a nineteenth-century science; even comparative linguistics, the serious study of India and of China, are no later than the Enlightenment. Still, by the nineteenth century it is true that the very careful study of all phases of the lives and cultures of peoples outside the Western tradition was a common-place among scholars and students. The popular press, books, and the lecture plaform had spread among many millions of Westerners at least some information about other peoples. This knowledge was by no means broad or deep; and it is probable that few Westerners actually thought they could learn anything from the heathen. Perhaps the typical Britisher or Frenchman was not quite so "culture-bound," not quite so narcissistic in his admiration of the West as he was thought to be by the intellectuals who wanted us to be really cosmopolitan, really human, and absorb the best of the universe. Yet the familiar quotation from Tennyson can stand as a fair sample of the value the nineteenth-century West set upon the East: "Better fifty years of Europe than a cycle of Cathay."

There is another phase of the interrelation of cultures that comes out at its best in the eighteenth-century Enlightenment. This is the use of bits of information—actually more often misinformation— about one culture to further a policy you are pushing in your own culture. In the eighteenth century, the *philosophes* loved to invent wise Persians, Chinese, Hindus, Hurons, and South Sea Islanders who, coming in contact with European ways, brought to the criticism of Europe the wisdom of their own points of view. The trouble is that all these yellow, black, brown, and red men, bringing to bear on European problems their own supposedly native wisdom, turn out to be themselves European *philosophes,* with exactly the same ideas about right and wrong, beautiful and ugly, reason and superstition, nature and convention the other enlightened had. These non-Europeans are no more than fictions, straw men, sticks with which to beat something Western, and no proof at all that we Westerners have really learned at high ethical and metaphysical levels from other peoples. With nineteenth-century improvement in sciences like geography and anthropology, this rather innocent game could not go on in quite the same way. Too much was known about the primitive peoples. It is still played, however, though much more skillfully, as witness Ruth Benedict's quietly co-operative Zuñis in *Patterns of Culture* and Margaret Mead's sexually blissful maidens in *Coming of Age in Samoa.*

We return to our point. For the historian of the clusters of ideas about the Big Questions which have prevailed hitherto in the West, it is hardly necessary to devote much attention to other cultures than the Western. This statement is not provincial or otherwise wicked; it is simply a recognition of a fact. Indeed, the marginal and sectarian nature of influences at this level from outside the West is clear from the fate of the little modern groups that appeal to Eastern wisdom, from Bahaism or Theosophy of Madame Blavatsky's kind on to learned admiration for the wisdom of Confucius or Buddha. These exotic cults are all outside the main current of Western thought and feeling, however intense and real some individual conversions to them may be.

It is quite possible that this spiritual self-sufficiency of the West may be changing, and that in the next century or so there will arise in the West and indeed all over the world a great syncretic religion and philosophy into which will pour the long wisdom of the East. Professor Northrop's recent *Meeting of East and West* is perhaps a prophetic as well as a symptomatic book. There may be One World of the spirit to make possible One World of the flesh. Already it is clear that somehow or other a very large number of Western men and women must learn to understand the cultures of non-Western people, even though understanding prove to be not quite conversion. But we cannot be sure of what lies so far ahead, nor of what will go into the cosmologies of the twenty-first or twenty-second century. Even the most high-minded of cosmopolitans should not shut from his mind the possibility that the rest of the world may in the next few generations be won over at least to Western material wants, that the Ford, air conditioning, and the comic strips may conquer both Confucius and Buddha.

A Summary

What can be said to be really persistent notes or traits or characteristics of Western culture since the ancient Greeks? Obviously, at this high level of abstraction, there is nothing that can satisfy the type of mind that refuses to accept the validity of our analogies with the spectrum or with the normal distribution curve. It is probable that somewhere in these three millennia you can dig up at least one Westerner in almost every possible category of human experience. There is not even agreement on the continuity of Western culture. A man like Spengler holds that what we have treated in this book as a continuous stream is in fact three, none of which communicates in any way with the others—the Apollonian, or Graeco-Roman, the Magian, or Arabic, and the Faustian, or European, each of roughly one thousand years' duration. Even if you find Spengler an oversoulful German, you will recall that there are many, both lovers and haters of the Middle Ages, who regard medieval culture as just about the antithesis (in the common, not the Hegelian, sense) of ours today.

Still, certain big generalizations about the intellectual climate of the West can be made. First of all, we must note that in no other culture have the natural sciences flourished as they have in the West. Increasingly, it is true, men from other cultures have practiced the study of science with great success; science is in many ways the most successful of human efforts to break through the bounds of the modern territorial in-group, or nation-state, more successful in this respect than commerce, more successful than religion. But science in its modern form bears plainly the mark of the West in which it was developed. It could hardly have developed save in the Western atmosphere of tension between the real and the ideal, between this world and the next. Complete absorption of the mind, at least, in another world, complete devotion to inner logic, would have made science impossible; but so too would complete preoccupation with the world as it is, so too would mere unsystematic ingenuity in concrete worldly problems. Science needed not merely an interest in material things; it needed the intellectual apparatus to devise the incredibly complex ordering of things we call science; it needed above all the long training in the use of reason afforded by the Greek and medieval philosophy and theology our innocent logical positivists like to deprecate.

But natural science, as we have insisted, does not in itself provide a cosmology. It has congruence or consonance with modern Western cosmologies; it has not such consonance with others. If, for instance, you are an Eastern mystic for whom the body is a complete illusion, you will no doubt have to feed that illusion with a minimum of food and drink (which is also an illusion) but you will not make yourself an expert on human physiology. You cannot, however, get from science an answer to the question, Is the human body an illusion (which is meaningless in scientific terms), nor even to the question,

Is it better, as most of us do in the West, to consider the human body a real thing or is it better to consider it an illusion (which is also a meaningless question for science). In brief, the pursuit of scientific knowledge may well be a *part* of our Western values; it cannot possibly *make* our Western values.

Let us take a concrete case for illustration. That branch of biology that studies heredity, genetics, though it will if it follows precedent improve its command over its material, is already good enough so that it is possible to learn from the geneticist much about the biological possibilities of eugenics, breeding human beings well. From the social sciences, still in their infancy, and often denied the status of science, it is none the less possible to learn something about how to persuade people to accept the recommendations of the biologist, about the kinds of social groups that would probably be produced if certain types of human being were bred, and about many other pertinent social problems. There is indeed an immense area of ignorance in all these fields, especially where they converge; we do not really know, for instance, what is the relation between human body types and human personality. Still, let us assume we know or can know enough to breed human beings.

What kind shall we breed? Shall we specialize on types—the artist, the football player, the manager, the salesman, a graded series of intelligences from the Alphas or intellectuals to the Epsilons or low-caste workers, as in Aldous Huxley's grim *Brave New World?* Or shall we try to breed the all-around man who can turn his hand and brain to anything? Or, since we are looking well ahead, shall we try to breed the body away, so to speak, or at least to a minimum as in Shaw's *Back to Methuselah* and thus paradoxically rejoin the Platonists? Science cannot answer these questions. The human mind, at least in the old simple sense of the logical, ratiocinative mind, does not in fact answer them. They are answered by what is still best called the human will, by the whole force of the personality. In a democracy they are in fact answered by what there is no harm in calling the general will, by a sort of rough adjustment among competing but not antithetical groups pursuing different but not wholly different ends. In the Western tradition the leaders, the *aristoi,* the elite, the ruling classes do much to shape these ends, and to persuade the masses to accept them. But they do not wholly make these ends, or purposes, or values—at least, not in the traditional attitude of the West.

For the first of the generalizations we can make about the noncumulative body of Western thought is that it displays from the Greeks and the medieval Christians down to the enlightened of yesterday and today a belief that men's sense of values is a groping awareness of the organization of the universe, an organization not evident to unreflective men, not provable by scientific methods, never wholly plain to the best and wisest of men, but an *organization,* not a chaos. Over the ages, the clearest common indication of this feeling is the term *natural law,* which to be sure did not mean exactly the same thing to a Stoic, a Scholastic, or an eighteenth-century philosopher, but did to all three mean a faith in the substance of things hoped for. Or, to put it another way, the very concept of *natural law* means that those who hold it believe that the gap between the real and the ideal, between what we have and what we want, is no abyss, not actually a gap, *but a relation.* It is summed up in the *Epistle to the Hebrews:* "For here have we no continuing city, but we seek one to come."

Second, there is throughout Western intellectual history a feeling for what is commonly called the "dignity of man." The area, the group, to which is applied the irreducible notion that men may not be treated as things, or animals, has varied. For the early Greeks this group was limited in some ways to the in-group of the Hellenes; it was clearly so confined to the in-group among the early Hebrews. Greek Stoics and Hebrew prophets extended this idea to the human race. To the Christian all men are equal in the possession of immortal souls. The basic democratic "liberty, equality, fraternity" is, once more, part of the heavenly city of the eighteenth century; it is in our modern cosmology the direct reflection, the direct successor of the Christian conception of the equality of souls before God. One may add as a footnote that the main Western tradition has very firmly separated man from the rest of nature, to which it refuses to give the special status of sharing in the moral struggle. Animals in the West do not have souls. Pantheism, and most certainly metempsychosis, are not normal Western doctrines. Indeed the Hindu, who finds so much coarse about us, thinks we are most inconsiderate of our fellow animals.

Third, there is a striking continuity of Western ideas of the good life here on earth. Once more, we must use the figure of the spectrum. Central in this spectrum is the way of life that was the ideal of the aristocratic culture of Greece—the ideal of nothing too much, of the Golden Mean. This statement will not be acceptable to those who hold that the central Christian ideal, practically realized in the thirteenth century, is ascetic, other-worldly, ineffable; nor will it be acceptable to those who find the central point of Western culture in some kind of manic drive for the heights—any heights. Since indeed we could make as a fourth generalization that Western culture shows, save perhaps for the interval of the Dark Ages, an amazing variety of views and practices moral and aesthetic, since even at its most stable, Western society has rarely even approximated the Spartan model of uniformity and discipline, it is obvious that both the ascetic and the manic (Faustian?) ways of life are present in our tradition. Nevertheless, as a kind of recurring resolution of the complex tensions between Western striving for the ideal, the unattainable perfection, and Western pleasure and interest in the world at hand, the Golden Mean of the old Greeks keeps its hold—sometimes, as in Aquinas or Chaucer, or even John Mill, in forms Pericles might not have recognized. How far this aristocratic code of conduct can be approximated in the masses of society is one of the most acute of modern problems. The basic belief of the eighteenth-century philosophers who formulated the democratic ideal was that the common man can lead this form of the good life now that the material basis lacking to the Greek masses is potentially available to all.

Beyond these generalizations, which will disappoint the adepts of the philosophy of history, it is hardly safe to go. We cannot pretend to answer the fascinating problem of why our Western society has, at least by our own not wholly subjective standard of evolutionary survival, been the most "successful" of societies so far in human history. The answer will lie in many variables we cannot isolate and therefore cannot assemble into anything like a formula. There probably is not even any central taproot, any determining factor of the sort the Marxist sets up in the mode of production. Of course, the Marxist gives us no really satisfactory account of why the development of Western economic life from the simplicities of the hunt to the complexities of modern industrial life was so different from the development of modes of production elsewhere on this globe. Our generation distrusts simple environmental explanations, such as the favorite one that the soil and climate of the small European peninsula off the great Asiatic land mass were particularly favorable to whatever virtues seem most needed to explain the success of Western society—energy, inventiveness, imagination, love of competition, and so on. Most of us distrust the simple —and even the complex—forms of explanation that assign an innate superiority, god-given or evolution-given, to certain groups or races. We cannot believe that there is really any kind of *homo occidentalis,* Aryan, Nordic, Caucasian, or what you will, with hereditary biological equipment different enough from that of non-Westerners to explain the recent success of ours in competition with other societies. Most of us would also distrust any form of idealistic explanation, any form of explanation that attributed to the *mind* of Western man the shape our culture has taken. Indeed, many readers will probably reject the mildly intellectualist notion just advanced in this book, that in part the growth of cumulative knowledge (which surely is the means by which we Westerners acquired the weapons to defeat the rest of the world and the material abundance to tempt them) is due to the happy balance our major cosmological systems have maintained between this world (experience) and the other (logic, planning, the *esprit de système*).

Yet all these explanations, which we rightly reject when they are claimed to be sole explanations, are probably ingredients in the most unstable compound we call Western culture. Take away any one of them, and any one of many others we have not analyzed, and you do not have the Western culture we know. Take coal and iron away from western Europe, and of course you do not have the Industrial Revolution as we know it; take St. Paul and St. Augustine, Calvin and Karl Marx away, and you do not have our Western view of life.

Our Present Discontents

In the perspective of Western intellectual history, we can see that many of the problems that seem to our alarmists so new, so demanding, so imperative of solution, are in fact very old problems that men and women of Western culture have managed to survive without solving. Notably, those prophets of doom who hold that modern Western man must agree on the Big Questions, that we must somehow escape from our present multanimity into a new Age of Faith, have against them several thousand years of Western history in which men have disagreed over these fundamental questions. But beyond this problem of agreement on the Big Questions there lies a more specific cosmological question that is concretely a problem for our times: Can we continue to hold even those modified eighteenth-century ideas of progress, of the possibility of closing here and now, or very shortly, that gap between "is" and "ought to be" which as historians we have to note Western man has never come very close to closing, and yet has never, for very long, given up trying to close?

There is always the possibility that the next few generations will see almost no change in Western cosmology, that we shall continue on the whole to accept as answers to the Big Questions those we accept now, in all their bewildering and mutually contradictory variety. Such a persistence of existing states of mind is, of course, possible, and to certain temperaments, even probable. We certainly do not know clinically how much variation in attitudes toward fundamental problems of value and conduct a society can stand. Yet it does not seem likely that those prophets who keep talking of crisis, crossroads, and the little time left are *wholly* wrong. Some further emendations in our inheritance from the Enlightenment we shall almost certainly have to make. For the gap between our ideals and our behavior, between the world we think desirable—indeed, morally right, necessary —and the world we have to live in has been since the Enlightenment a gap of very different psychological character from the gap the traditional Christian knew and felt.

The gap between what ought to be and what is probably exists in all men's minds, certainly in all civilized men's minds. But ordinary men and their leaders *must not be constantly, naggingly aware of this gap*. Most of the time, they must—though the outside observer may think their position hypocrisy—somehow persuade themselves that the gap really isn't there. There are many ways of filling it. On one's own private account, there are ritual practices, conviction of belonging to a body of the elect, mystic submission to some greater will, all of which will help close the gap. For those who have to take humanity as a whole into view, there is the more difficult way of the optimistic reformer just about to close the gap with one last law, one last sermon. There is also the Christian attitude toward the gap—that it can never be wholly closed here on earth, but that those who work honestly, justly, considerately toward closing it on earth will find it fully closed in heaven, that those who do not will find it fully closed in hell.

But to many of the heirs of the Enlightenment the gap is still painfully there, yawning as wide as ever. They cannot take the Christian way out, for they cannot believe in any other world than this nowadays rather unpleasant one. They have a firm notion of what is on the other, the ideal side of the gap—peace, plenty, happiness in all its range from lazy comfort to the leap of the heart. They believe we human beings should have what we want, and that we cannot successfully fill in the gap between what we want and what we have with words, ritual, or any other consoling illusion. This last is, from a naturalistic-historical point of view, one reason why the Victorian compromise did not hold, why the lower classes refused to stay put, why socialism preached the need for economic democracy after political democracy had been attained. Men wanted economic equality, not just spiritual equality. No ritual could satisfy the desire of the poor to be materially richer. The material ideals of the eighteenth century are deceptively simple; just because they are so simple and so material it has been very hard to pretend we have attained them when we have not.

Now it may be possible to lessen the gap between the real and the ideal by bringing the ideal a long way back toward reality, by setting small, modest goals all along the line—not temperance but less criminal alcoholism; not perfect sexual life on earth but fewer divorces; not the elimination of "soap operas," but better-balanced radio programs; not complete economic security but less disastrous depressions with less widespread unemployment; not a world government that will forever guarantee peace, but a United Nations that will help us stave off war and perhaps make it less barbarous when it comes. The list could be prolonged indefinitely. The moderate realist asks that democracy give up some of its eighteenth-century optimism about the natural goodness and reasonableness of man, about the magic effect of a readily changeable social and political environment (laws, constitutions, treaties, new educational institutions and curricula), about the nearness of the approaching millennium. He asks that democracy accept some of the pessimism of traditional Christianity as embodied in the doctrine of original sin, some of the tragic sense of human limitations that has inspired great literature, some of the doubts about the universal capacity of all men to think straight that come out of modern psychology, some of the practical, common-sense awareness of the impossibility of perfection that most of us have in those fields of activity where we act under the burden of responsibility.

Western democrats may be able to shake off the burden of excessive optimism about human perfectibility that they have inherited from the Enlightenment, and adapt their ideals to this harsh world. Many of them are increasingly aware that something must be done to close the gap between promise and performance the years have opened up in the Western democracies. They cannot go along with the self-deluded idealists who seem to think that all that is necessary is to reaffirm the promise more firmly than ever. For one thing, they begin to detect a touch of bitterness in the affirmation which shows that even the idealists can look about them. You will find the case for a democracy willing to face the facts of life very cogently put by Mr. A. M. Schlesinger, Jr., in his *The Vital Center*. It is not at all unlikely that in the next few years this point of view will make real gains in the West.

But is such a pessimistic democracy likely or even possible—a democracy that resolutely refuses to promise heaven on earth and still does not return to the older heaven in another world? One very strong element in the democratic cosmology, we have insisted, has been a denial of the supernatural, a denial of an afterlife. We have indeed seen that much of the democratic cosmology has been after a fashion reconciled with formal churchgoing Christianity; but we have also noted that, especially in the liberal Protestant groups, very little indeed of the divine, the miraculous, the transcendental has been left in a formal, rationalistic faith. Finally, of course, there remain in all the Western democracies millions of men and women who range all the way from violent positivists and anticlericals to the completely worldly and indifferent, millions who are simply not Christians. Can these men and women find the spiritual resources needed to face hardship, frustration, struggle, and unhappiness—all the evils they have been taught to believe would be banished shortly from human life?

Though there have persisted through these last three centuries many Christian groups who held to the spirit and the letter of the traditional faith, there have also grown up certain surrogates for the Christian faith that many had lost, or that had been altered into pseudo-Christian optimistic rationalism. These surrogates are democracy, nationalism, socialism, fascism, and their many variant creeds and sects. Most of these surrogates have in common a belief in the fairly rapid perfectibility of men here on earth—provided the proper measures are taken. Most of them deny the existence of any supernatural being capable of interfering in the affairs of this earth, though many do indeed retain the notion of some sort of guiding principle of goodness—a kind of impersonal God—and all believe that the universe can be made a comfortable place for man to live in. Back of them all lies the very general attitude or cosmology of the Enlightenment, which perhaps takes on its most representative form in the kind of liberal, democratic system of values you find in John Mill. But the actual institutional form, the Church for this faith, has been the territorial nation-state, so that in practice democracy and nationalism have been united in complex and varying fashion. Socialism is originally an heretical development of earlier democratic thought—or if you prefer, a deepening of democratic aims—which also, wherever it has been successful, has got itself tied up with the nation-state and with nationalism.

Now we have deliberately used of these impersonal faiths—these formally nontheistic religions in which abstractions like virtue or liberty, groups like the national in-group, are hypostasized—the term *surrogate,* with all its connotations of a somewhat synthetic and not quite adequate *substitute.* The inadequacy of the impersonal faiths in comparison with Christianity is especially evident in relation to the problems of the individual in trouble. These impersonal faiths are weak in their cure of souls. It is true that in their fighting and crusading stages—socialism before it comes to power, for instance—they are able to enlist the full spiritual ardor of many of the faithful, give them a sense of belonging to something very great indeed, melt away their petty selfishnesses in emotional self-surrender. But once they are established, once they are faced with this routine world, these impersonal faiths have little to offer the unhappy, the maladjusted, the suffering.

Nationalism is probably the strongest of these faiths. It bulwarks the weak and the inadequate with their membership in the great whole, their share of the "pooled self-esteem" of patriotism. It has in times of crisis been able to rely on both human patience and human daring. But it does not take the place of a consoling God. Marianne, the symbol of the French Republic, is a heroic figure of the barricades. But it is hard to pray to Marianne, as generations have prayed to the Virgin Mary. Socialism would seem to have even less of the consoling touch. It is no doubt encouraging to the faithful Marxist to know that Dialectical Materialism is hard at work making things better for the oppressed. But the really unhappy need something more human, something more aware of *them,* not as temporary victims of the mode of production, but as important, unique, sovereign human beings deserving the immediate attention of God or his agents.

Moreover, there is another psychological weakness in modern surrogates for older theistic faiths. These new lay religions find it very hard to permit repentance. In the numerous trials for treason (heresy) that have gone on in Soviet Russia, though the accused have usually broken down and made most complete confessions of their errors, they were by no means forgiven and taken back into the fold. The United States government tends apparently in these days to the opinion that "once a Communist, always a Communist," especially in the case of Englishmen and other West Europeans. A French intellectual who admits to having joined the Communist party in the dark days of the thirties but has since declared his repentance is apparently still a Communist to the State Department. But the phenomenon is obvious in any study of modern social and political movements. In the great French Revolution, for instance, it was very difficult, indeed almost impossible, for a man who had voted conspicuously with the Moderates in 1790 to excuse himself in 1793 with the then triumphant Extremists by pleading his error, by claiming that he had repented and seen the light. He commonly ended on the guillotine. It is hard to repent effectively in these impersonal religions.

Yet the forgiving of the repentant sinner has been one of the great strengths of Christianity, one of the ways wise Christian leadership has tempered the wind to the shorn lamb. Now it may be that the rigid attitude toward repentance displayed by the newer impersonal faiths is related to the abstract and perfect ideal—*an ideal improperly separated from the real*—that they hold for human behavior in the Utopia they were designed to achieve on earth. Those who hold these ideals desire so passionately that man be perfect that they cannot forgive him the slightest imperfection. A wholly this-worldly idealist can hardly avoid trying to eliminate those who do not behave according to his ideals. No doubt the riper democracies, like the English, are much less exacting than the Communists, much more willing to put up with human weaknesses. Still, none of them seems to offer to their leaders the chance for effective and not at all shaming compromise that the Christian requirement (note that it *is* a requirement) of forgiveness to the penitent affords; nor do they offer to the faithful the spiritual security, the flexible discipline, that the Christian doctrine of sin and repentance offers.

Finally, these abstract faiths are a grave danger for the modern intellectual, since they make easy, indeed they seem to ennoble, his ready assumption that he knows just what is wrong with the world, and how to right it. These faiths encourage the separation of the ideal from the real, as we have noted, for they oversimplify human nature. But the modern intellectual, already separated from the mass of his fellows by a rift that has surely not narrowed since it developed its modern form early in the nineteenth century, needed rather to be called back to the close and realistic study of the whole range of human behavior than to be allowed to develop in fine moral indignation his notions of "ought to be." Indeed, even when these notions take on the appearance of realism, of hard-boiled acceptance of things-as-they-are, they are a very evident form of that "inverted idealism" some writers have already found in Machiavelli. Balance, a sane resolution of the tension between the ideal and the real, is the heart of the matter. Certainly, the balance can be tipped, as many a modern intellectual like Pareto has tipped it, much too far away from the ideal. But at this moment in history, tipping toward the ideal, the *oversimple* ideal, is a grave danger encountered by the rawness and simplicities of our surrogate faiths. The intellectual can so readily let himself go. In retrospect, this furious urge to the ideal in a man like Carlyle, for instance, is what lays him open to the otherwise unfair charge of being proto-fascist. Carlyle, like Nietzsche, would unquestionably have repudiated the flesh-and-blood Nazis; but Carlyle tossed off in complete irresponsibility so many fine and indignant ideas that many of them proved effective Nazi ideas.

In summary, then, these newer faiths do not have the richness and depth of awareness of what human beings are really like that the older religions have; they are therefore not as able as the older religions to cope with the problem of human relations in a time of troubles. Democracy and socialism have hitherto, in a sense, had relatively comfortable going in a world where most of the material indices really were going up in a steady curve. They have not yet had to face from too many unhappy men and women for whom this is not even remotely heaven on earth the menacing and very natural cry of "put up or shut up." Perhaps they will not. It may be that the great masses in the West can take the attitude, hitherto confined to aristocracies like the Stoic, that this is a tough world in which nobody is always happy, in which everybody has got to keep coping with his troubles, and in which there is no reward beyond the grave. But this seems most unlikely. The mass of mankind, even in the West, have never been able to take the tragic view without the help of a personal religion, a religion hitherto always transcendental, supernatural, otherworldly. Somehow, democracy, if it is not to return wholeheartedly to Christianity (which many today would have it do), must take on the cure of souls.

There is still another, and more definitely intellectual, difficulty in the way of a pessimistic, realistic democracy without belief in the supernatural. This democracy would have to extend to all our activities the tentativeness, the willingness to experiment, the patience, the acceptance of slowness, the recognition of the limits set on human effort by those two words *impossible* and *insoluble* which characterizes the work of the scientist as scientist and which, in part at least, all of us attain in the specific tasks we must fulfill. In such a democracy a very large number of people indeed would have to forgo the delights of certitude, the assurance that comes from knowing in advance that certain absolutes are true, that there is something that never changes, something not part of history but still part of ourselves. But it is clear that we humans cling to certitude; those who lost Christian certitude promptly tried to find scientific certitude, historical certitude, certitude anywhere they could turn it up. And we cling to omniscience as the companion of certitude—an omniscient force, if we cannot have an omniscient God. If a thoroughgoing relativism (not of course nihilism) in values is to be asked of our new citizens of a pessimist democracy—and it would seem that only such a relativism could effectively sustain their pessimism and keep them from hoping at least for some new kind of pie in the sky—then such a democracy will be very difficult indeed to set up in our time. It would ask too much of poor human nature, more actually than optimistic democracy asked, since the average citizen of the old optimistic democracy was allowed his bit of the old consoling religion.

Moreover, we come in the mid-twentieth century to the same difficulty we encountered in ancient Athens: Just what is the relation between the attitudes taken toward the Big Questions by the intellectuals and the whole structure, the whole equilibrium, of a society? The slightest attention to what is going on among Western intellectuals—existentialists in France, followers of Barth and Niebuhr in Germany and America, the bright young Catholic converts in England —makes it plain that the intellectuals are tightening their spiritual belts, getting set for a long spell of hard going, growing very scornful of such cheerful democrats as Benjamin Franklin, or such shallow democrats as Thomas Jefferson. The Enlightenment may well be due for even more bitter attacks than those it received from the romanticists of Wordsworth's day. Yet one finds it very hard to imagine the average American—or indeed the average European—in quite the mood of sensitive, high-minded, world-embracing despair that has come over the vanguard of Western intellectuals. There is a certain coarseness, like that that wells up from the *fabliaux* in the midst of the high-minded thirteenth century, that one suspects will keep the fleshpots boiling for a while even in our tragic world.

It will not do, then, to conclude that our Western culture is about to make some sort of *volte-face* into another Age of Faith. The democratic cosmology is almost certain in the West to receive another revision even more thorough than the revision the nineteenth century gave to its original heritage from the Enlightenment. One cannot be at all sure in 1950 what form that revision will take. A very great deal will depend on the result of the struggle between the United States and Soviet Russia, a struggle in which the whole cosmology is at stake. The very necessities of the struggle may drive the West into a much more regimented society than our tradition holds good. For it is one of the unpleasant facts of human relations—one of the kinds of

544

facts that the new realistic democrats have got to face—that in war, cold or hot, you have to have more authority and less liberty than in quieter times.

Very roughly, and with all sorts of specific twistings and turnings in each that contradict the generalization, it would seem that in the United States and in Russia are temporarily embodied a number of the sets of opposites that in some kind of union have hitherto maintained that tension which is so characteristic of the West. We are not, of course, pure Liberty, and they pure Authority. We do not stand for the individualism of the great cats, nor they for the collectivism of the beehive or anthill. We are not variety, and they are not uniformity. Neither of us lives up to the extremes of our own systems of values. Still, the opposition is there, and is very real. We do, on the whole, stand for the series of values that in this book have been treated as the central values of Western culture—a feeling for the irreducible something in each human being still best suggested by that worn old word *liberty,* a feeling which, though it will pause a little and turn on itself when confronted with the very real problems suggested by such phrases as "force a man to be free" or "you are free when you do right, but a slave when you do wrong" or "liberty, not license," is nevertheless deep down defiantly unconvinced that these paradoxes are necessary. The Western tradition of which we are now the chief defenders is not dogmatically, not even idealistically, but all the more firmly *individualist.*

Our chances of maintaining the traditions of the West, and of preserving them in a form not unfairly described as democratic, are greater than our prophets of doom will admit. For if the anti-intellectualism of the last few decades has been corrosive of the more naive hopes of a heaven on earth through the perfecting of human nature, or simply by the release of human nature from its bad environment, it has given us reason to believe that if our democratic way of life really is anchored in our habits, traditions, sentiments, conditioned reflexes, and super-egos it may well survive even a very harsh reality. What to our grandfathers seemed the strength of democracy, its dependence on the rationality of men, now indeed seems its weakness;

but perhaps after all democracy does not depend on the rationality of men. The democratic West has now withstood two wars in which it was supposed, with its addiction to variety, indiscipline, spiritual mult-animity, and even comfort, to go down before the superior discipline, toughness, and unanimity of its antidemocratic foes. It did not go down, but won through to victory in spite of, or more likely because of, what looked to certain critics like weaknesses.

For what looks in purely intellectual analysis like disintegration, squabbling, rank inability to agree on anything at all may well be no more than disagreement on matters we Westerners have been dis-agreeing on publicly and violently most of the time since Socrates played the gadfly in Athens. If you think of the full logical implica-tions of their creeds, it is really astonishing that Catholics, Protestants, Jews, and Marxist materialists fought side by side in the American forces in the two world wars. You may say that they did not really be-lieve as much in their respective formal faiths as in the United States, but this would be much too logical a position to be true. You may say that they "believed in" religious toleration as a positive good, and that would no doubt be true in part of many of them. But the truest thing you could say would be that they never thought at all about the general problem of religious toleration, that most of them simply ac-cepted the existence of Catholics, Jews, Protestants, and all varieties of materialist as one of the facts of life, one of the things you take, like the weather. A very great deal of the Western way of life is thus embedded somewhere in quite ordinary Americans, not in their cere-bral cortexes, probably, but in a much safer place which the physiolo-gist hasn't quite located—we used to say, in the heart.

We come back, then, to the proposition that for all we yet know in terms of a cumulative social science, the relation between the strength of a given society and the degree of agreement on matters cosmological among its members cannot be determined. There seems to be excellent evidence that very considerable multanimity in mat-ters of theology, metaphysics, art, literature, and even ethics can per-sist if the existence of such disagreement is taken, not as a lofty ideal of toleration, of progress through variation (though for many intellectuals it is just that) but as something given, something normal for human beings. If democracy really means anything so unnatural to Western intellectuals as intellectual agreement, then it is all up with democracy. But the whole course of our intellectual history would indicate that in some perverse, obstinate way Western intellectuals have always thrived on their differences, and that somehow these differences have not really disturbed the nonintellectuals enough to upset the social equilibrium. Even today, there is no good evidence that the intellectual alarums of our age of philosophical worries have really gone beyond that small section of the population that possesses high verbal aptitudes. We are not even quite sure that social psychologists like Erich Fromm are right in declaring that nervous instability, even neurosis, is so far common in all parts of our society as to threaten our traditional democratic way of life. Maybe the flight from freedom has been exaggerated.

But even if these diagnosticians are right, even if ours really is a sick society, it seems unlikely that the earnest intellectuals who urge us to get together and believe something lofty together are on the right track. If we must have a new religion, all Western precedent suggests that the religion will not come from the intellectuals, but from a far humbler source, and that for a while at least it will be very hard on established intellectuals—even on those who prophesied its coming.

There is a further grave intellectual difficulty no thinking democrat can avoid facing. We have granted, in accordance with the current of modern anti-intellectualism, and probably also of common sense, that there is a deep energy and toughness in the human race no intellectual system can contain, that our culture has sources of strength not greatly affected by our philosophy—or lack of one. Yet even Pareto lists as one of his strongest residues the *residue to make derivations*—that is, to make sense. The need for satisfying our desire to understand, to have our experience hold together logically, not to be shockingly, patently, inconsistent, not to be hypocrites in our own or in others' eyes—this is a very strong need among human beings. It is safe to say that no civilization has been led by an intellectual class persuaded that their world of values, their explanation of why they were there, was pretense, hypocrisy, pure fake. In a democracy there cannot be for long an unbelieving intellectual class and a believing nonintellectual class; nor can a skeptical or cynical intellectual class devise a religion for the masses.

Now our intellectual classes are by no means today in such a plight. But many of them are puzzled, and they are likely to be more puzzled until they come more successfully to grips with the problem of modifying our eighteenth-century heritage from the Enlightenment. Let us make a final brief summary of that problem.

The democratic world-view was formulated in the eighteenth century at the end of three centuries of change that had culminated in the great triumph of natural science in the work of Newton and his fellows. Whatever may have been the philosophical and theological opinions of these working scientists as private persons—and to this day many of them are sincere Christians—as scientists they had to make use of an intellectual method of arriving at generalizations, a method that was wholly at the mercy of observed facts. These facts were ultimately, no matter how much more subtle than human senses the instruments by which they were recorded, statements about the world of sense experience, this world—and no other. Briefly, a proposition made in accordance with the methods of natural science has to accord with the facts of this world; it may not transcend them and it may not contradict them.

Now two of the master generalizations of the democratic faith as it emerged in the eighteenth and nineteenth centuries, the doctrine of the natural goodness and reasonableness of men and the doctrine of inevitable unilinear progress toward human perfectibility on earth, either transcend the scientific attitude toward truth or contradict it. You have only to follow down through the ages from Thucydides to Machiavelli to the ablest of modern social scientists to note that the tradition among those who really observe carefully the behavior of human beings is one of conviction that men are born to trouble, and that in recorded time, at least, human nature has not greatly changed. If you study the recorded behavior of *homo sapiens* from the earliest times right down to the mid-twentieth century in the spirit and with the methods of the natural scientist (as far as the inadequacies of the historical record will permit such study) you will be unable to take anything like the attitude of Condorcet, for instance, or even that of Paine and Jefferson. You will be unable to accept as even rough scientific generalizations the concepts of the natural goodness and reasonableness of man and of the increasing perfection, in human terms, of our life on earth.

Democracy, in short, is *in part* a system of judgments inconsistent with what the scientist holds to be true. This inconsistency would not create difficulties—or at least would not create some of the difficulties it now creates—were the democrat able to say that his kingdom is not of this world, able to say that his truth is not the kind that is in the least tested by the scientist, any more than the truth of the Catholic doctrine of the Eucharist is tested by the chemical analysis of the bread and wine. Such a solution of the democrat's intellectual quandary is not a happy one, but is not altogether inconceivable. Democracy may become a genuinely transcendental faith, in which belief is not weakened by lack of correspondence between the propositions it lays down and the facts of life on this earth. There are cynics who say that when an American boasts about the lack of class distinctions in his country he never bothers his mind with the facts, the facts of our class structure, the facts about Negroes, Jews, Mexicans, Nisei. We Americans have no trouble at all in recognizing the fact that the basic principles of that democratic heresy, Marxism, are contradicted by almost every principle of the actual structure of present-day Russian social life; we recognize that Russian "democracy" is defined quite differently from ours. In short, democracy may be able to take its promised heaven out of this world, and put it in the world of ritual performed, of transcendental belief, of vicarious satisfactions of human wants, may keep it an ideal not too much sullied by the contrast with the spotted reality.

Or we may see the working out of a democratic attitude toward the world which accepts the limitations of ordinary human nature, which accepts a pessimistic view of this world, a democracy with no pie in the sky and no really ineffable, no all-satisfying pie in the larder.

549

Its enemies have long said that democracy is a fair-weather thing, that even in its incomplete realization of liberty, equality, fraternity it sets for human nature standards that can be approximated in human conduct only in times of ease and prosperity. In a time of troubles, they say, we shall need discipline, leadership, solidarity not to be achieved by letting men even in theory, even in fantasy, follow their own private wills. Such discipline men do indeed accept in times of crisis, as the Western democracies showed well in this last war. The English took with amazingly little apparent psychic damage the bombing of cities which put all civilians on no mere metaphorical battle line. Even more striking in a way was the spirit with which most Americans went into this last war. To the horror of the tender-minded idealist, they went into it with very little apparent belief that they were going to make a much better world, with very little of the crusading spirit of the war of 1914-1918. They went into it as into a disagreeable but necessary task that they were able to do very well indeed, but which they saw no reason to pretend to enjoy, or to ennoble. *They went into it as realists, not as cynics.*

And here we may well conclude, as far as a book of this sort can conclude. An *idealistic* democracy, a *believing* democracy (in the old transcendental sense of religious belief) is perhaps possible, though such a democracy would find it hard to accommodate its this-worldly and scientific heritage to an other-worldly faith. Its God would at the very least need to make some difficult compromises with the psychiatrist. A *realistic,* pessimistic democracy—a democracy in which ordinary citizens approach morals and politics with the willingness to cope with imperfection that characterizes the good farmer, the good physician, the good holder of the cure of souls, be he priest, clergyman, counselor, or psychiatrist—such a democracy would demand more of its citizens than any human culture has ever demanded. Were its demands met, it might well be the most successful of cultures. Finally, a *cynical* democracy, a democracy whose citizens profess in this world one set of beliefs and live another, is wholly impossible. No such society can long endure anywhere. The tension between the ideal and the real may be resolved in many ways in a healthy society; but it can never be taken as nonexistent.

Suggestions for Further Study

*T*HIS BOOK is not a digest or survey of Western thought. If, as is contended in the introductory chapter, most of the substance of such a survey must deal with noncumulative knowledge, then it is quite impossible for anyone to produce an authoritative survey, digest, or elementary manual of intellectual history, such as a good popularizer of science could produce for such fields of cumulative knowledge as physics or chemistry. An intellectual history is inevitably in part a series of private judgments made by the man who writes it. Unless that man is sure that he knows the right interpretation always—and this writer is not so sure—he will do better to afford his readers constant chances to go through the original stuff of intellectual history, and to make up their own minds on many matters.

This book is, then, a kind of guidebook. Now a good guidebook to a specific region of this earth will give the traveler much necessary information about the ways of getting around, about railways, hotels, currencies, and the like, and it will provide maps of the country. But it will also, even though the author thinks he isn't doing so, give a great deal of information about what the author thinks is worth looking at, or important, or improving. A man who loved and appreciated wine could not possibly write the same guidebook to France that a convinced teetotaler would write—if such a man ever dared write a guidebook to France. A guidebook to any such confused and ill-mapped country as the country of the human mind must, though it should try to give as much reliable information as possible about books and writers, inevitably dwell on what the author thinks worth the reader's attention. Yet always the important point is that the traveler —or reader—should put himself into the direct experience of traveling, or reading.

Original Writing

2, 3. THE GREEKS

Broadly speaking, there are two methods of sampling the materials that make up the record of Western intellectual history. One is to read *whole* works as designed by their authors, the other to read selections, anthologies, specially prepared samples. In the first method the reader covers less ground, but he comes nearer the experience the author meant him to have, comes nearer the original. In the second method the reader can cover a great deal of ground, but he never experiences the work as a whole. He experiences only what the modern anthologist or editor of the collection wants him to. The first method is here recommended, if only because it offers the reader a fuller experience and more real challenge to his mental adaptability. But a few anthologies, "readings," and the like are listed, for they are often useful as auxiliaries.

Americans who like reading have long relied on free public libraries. Nevertheless, there are nowadays a good many inexpensive editions of great and near-great books. Here are a few: The inexpensive, paper-bound Crofts Classics of Appleton-Century-Crofts, Inc., New York, N. Y. Another paper-bound series is the Little Library of Liberal Arts, 153 West 72nd Street, New York, N. Y. The Mentor books, mostly contemporary, but serious and very inexpensive, are issued by the New American Library of World Literature, 245 Fifth Avenue, New York, N. Y. Among bound books in the lower-price range, the student will find a very good choice in the Everyman's Library (N. Y., E. P. Dutton), the Oxford World's Classics (N. Y., Oxford University Press), the new Inner Sanctum Library of Living Literature (N. Y., Simon and Schuster), the Home University Library (N. Y., Oxford University Press), the Viking Portable series (N. Y., Viking Press), the Hafner Library of Classics (N. Y., Hafner), and the Van Nostrand Classics (N. Y., Van Nostrand).

A good book of readings to be used with this book is W. Y. Elliott and N. A. McDonald, *Western Political Heritage* (N. Y., Prentice-Hall, 1949).

Thucydides, *The Peloponnesian War.* A number of inexpensive editions are available. For the general reader, the most useful is that edited by Sir R. W. Livingstone in the World's Classics. This is condensed, but only relatively unimportant narrative sections have been sacrificed.

Sophocles, *Antigone;* Euripides, *Bacchae;* Aristophanes, *Clouds.* These are all available in various translations. There is W. J. Oates and Eugene O'Neill, Jr., *The Complete Greek Drama* (2 vols., N. Y., Random House, 1938). The *Fifteen Greek Plays* published by the Oxford University Press is a bargain, and presents a very good choice of the Greek drama. Unfortunately, it does not include the *Bacchae.*

Plato, *The Apology of Socrates* and *The Republic.* There are many translations of Plato's works available of which the most famous is Jowett's. Random House has a good two-volume edition of this translation of *The Republic,* with an introduction by Raphael Demos. *The Republic* is a relatively long book, but if possible should be read entire. One might read Books V through X, which are the more purely Utopian parts of the work. The parable of the cave (Jowett translates it *den*) occurs at the beginning of Book VII. The parable of the gold, silver, and brass and iron men is in Book III, at the end.

Aristotle, *Politics.* There are many editions and translations, including a very good one by Jowett. It is perhaps less essential that this book be read as a whole than that *The Republic* be so read. Books IV and V, dealing with forms of government and their ways of changing and containing some typical criticism of Plato, make a good unit.

For those who wish to read a bit further, the following are suggested: Homer, *Odyssey,* prose translation of Butcher and Lang; *Hippocratic Writings,* Hippocrates in the Loeb edition, which has Greek on one side, English translation on the other (now published by the Harvard University Press; here a sampling will suffice, notably "Precepts" in vol. I and "The Sacred Disease" in vol. II—the first study of epilepsy, which Hippocrates refuses to blame on the gods); Herodotus, *History of the Persian Wars,* Books VII and VIII; *Lyra Graeca,* in the Loeb edition edited by Edmunds—at least the longer surviving fragments of Sappho in vol. I should be read by anyone who wants to form some notion of what Greek lyric poetry is like (many of the choruses in the plays are supreme examples of lyric poetry); Xenophon, *Memorabilia of Socrates, Anabasis;*

Old Oligarch, *Constitution of Athens* (this work is sometimes catalogued in libraries under Xenophon or Pseudo-Xenophon—it is a brief pamphlet, a kind of "letter to the editor," written by an indignant Athenian Tory); Plutarch, *Parallel Lives,* lives of Lycurgus and of Alcibiades (Plutarch himself belongs, as a "Hellenistic" figure, in Chapter 4, but the two lives above mentioned are those of men who bring out forcibly the differences between Athens and Sparta).

Since classicists have long sought to widen interest in their subject, there have been quite a good many selections and anthologies in translation. The latest of these, and a convenient one, is *The Portable Greek Reader* edited by W. H. Auden (Viking Portable Library, N. Y., 1948). One of the most varied, culled in part from sources difficult of access in English, is the "Library of Greek Thought," new American edition (Boston, Beacon Press, 1950), and especially A. J. Toynbee, *Greek Civilization and Character* and *Greek Historical Thought.*

4. LATER CLASSICAL CULTURE

The Jews. For English-speaking people, the King James version carries an overwhelming weight not merely of religious, but of aesthetic authority. No modern version has really caught on. A briefest sampling of the Old Testament would include the books of Genesis, Exodus, Ruth, Job, Proverbs (sample), Ecclesiastes, and Isaiah. A good edition for general use is E. S. Bates, *The Bible Designed to Be Read as Living Literature* (N. Y., Simon and Schuster, 1936).

Later classical writing. It is hard to choose good representative reading on the *Weltanschauung* of the Hellenistic Greeks and the Romans. The level is high, the mass of materials interesting, but the peaks are not striking, especially if we are seeking *politiques et moralistes* rather than more strictly literary figures. But the following should give an idea of the range of the written word in this period.

The lyric poetry of classical Greece in its full range can be sampled in the *Palatine* or *Greek Anthology,* in the Loeb edition, a collection that gave the word *anthology* to literature. For the Romans, there is a convenient single volume of *Catullus,* translated and edited by F. A. Wright (N. Y., E. P. Dutton, 1926), a volume of the Broadway translations. There are many translations of both Horace and Vergil. A few of Horace's odes and satires and perhaps the so-called minor poems of Vergil (the Bucolics and the Georgics) will do.

For the beginnings of the novel, with its great value for social and intellectual history, there is Longus, *Daphnis and Chloe,* often translated. The novelist George Moore translated it into modern English as *The Pastoral Loves of Daphnis and Chloe* (London, Heinemann, 1927). Most of the cheaper reprints employ older translations; the literary are very fond of Renaissance translation, which is unfortunate for the modern American student, to whom Renaissance English is quite naturally also a foreign language. In Latin there is a fascinating novel, Apuleius, *The Golden Ass,* well translated by W. Adlington in the Loeb edition (London, Heinemann, 1928). To these should be added a sampling of Lucian's very Voltairian tales, essays, dialogues. Lucian is translated by A. M. Harmon in the Loeb edition (4 vols., London, Heinemann, 1919-1925); try "The Dream" and "The Parasite" in volume III, "A True Story" in volume I, a parody on the wilder tales current in his time, "Zeus Catechized" in volume II.

The Greek or Roman educated gentleman—the class that ran the Empire—was, of course, formed intellectually by the culture we have discussed briefly in Chapters 2 and 3. To see more directly what he was like in the early centuries of our era, the following is a representative choice. Polybius, *The Histories,* translated by W. R. Paton (6 vols., N. Y., Putnam's, 1922-1927), is essential to understanding the political traditions of the Romans. This can be supplemented by reading in Livy, well translated in the Loeb edition by B. O. Foster and E. T. Sage, and in Machiavelli's *Discourses on Titus Livius.* Most of Cicero is dull reading indeed. You can see him best in his letters, well presented by A. M. McKinlay, *Letters of a Roman Gentleman* (Boston, Houghton Mifflin, 1926). Caesar's *Gallic War and Civil War,* though spoiled for many of us by memories of high-school Latin, remains an admirable reflection of the Roman man of action. For the average cultivated man, Plutarch does beautifully. There are many translations of his *Parallel Lives,* and the rest of his work, especially the *Moralia,* is interesting. For the higher level of the *moraliste,* there are two contrasting works—Marcus Aurelius, *Meditations,* edited by A. S. L. Farquharson (Oxford, Clarendon Press, 1944), for the Stoic side and Lucretius, *Of the Nature of Things,* translated by William Ellery Leonard (N. Y., Dutton, 1916), for the Epicurean. If you wish to try to read a very different other-worldly philosopher, there is *The Essence of Plotinus,* edited by Grace H. Turnbull (N. Y., Oxford University Press, 1934). Of collections, the handiest is Cyril Bailey, ed., *The Mind of Rome* (Oxford, Clarendon Press, 1926), with translations of representative Latin writings and commentaries on them. Two big collections covering all classical noncumulative thought are W. J. Oates and

C. T. Murphy, *Greek Literature in Translation* (N. Y., Longmans, Green, 1946), and Kevin Guinagh and A. P. Dorjahn, *Latin Literature in Translation* (N. Y., Longmans, Green, 1942).

5. THE DOCTRINE OF CHRISTIANITY

In the New Testament, the minimum might be the Gospels of St. Luke and St. John, I and II Corinthians, Hebrews. But the whole should be read.

The ordinary reader will hardly need to go direct to any of the Fathers before St. Augustine (for whom see reading for Chapter 6). A good sampling, moreover, is in H. S. Bettenson, ed., *Documents of the Christian Church* (N. Y., Oxford University Press, 1947), a convenient and inexpensive anthology useful right through the two millennia of Christianity. A more detailed collection for the early Church is J. C. Ayer, *A Source Book for Ancient Church History* (N. Y., Scribner's, 1913).

6, 7. THE MIDDLE AGES

The *Confessions* of St. Augustine (Loeb, Everyman, and others) are among the few personal documents of the Middle Ages. His *City of God* (Marcus Dods, ed., tr., 2 vols., N. Y., Hafner, 1948) is hard going for all but the really philosophical mind. At least one contemporary life of a saint should be read: Jonas, *Life of St. Columban* (University of Pennsylvania, *Translations and Reprints,* II, 1902, no. 7); Willibald, *The Life of St. Boniface* (G. W. Robinson, tr., Cambridge, Harvard University Press, 1916). For the hermits, there is the delightful series of lives translated by Helen Waddell, *The Desert Fathers* (N. Y., Holt, 1936).

The Scholastics are not to be read lightly. If you wish to attempt Aquinas, a good beginning can be made in Father M. C. d'Arcy's volume of selections in Everyman's Library; or for a wider sampling, Richard McKeon, ed., *Selections from Mediaeval Philosophers* (2 vols., N. Y., Scribner's, 1929-1930). There is Abélard's *Historia Calamitatum* (H. A. Bellows, tr., St. Paul, T. A. Boyd, 1922) and his correspondence with Héloise (C. K. Scott-Moncrieff, N. Y., Knopf, 1926). Two saints of the high Middle Ages can be approached in medieval documents: St. Bernard, *Letters* (F. A. Gasquet, ed., London, J. Hodges, 1904), and *The Little Flowers of St. Francis* (James Rhoades, tr., N. Y., Oxford University Press, 1947).

Sampling will do for the chronicles—though some, like that of Otto of Freising, make good general reading. Gregory of Tours, *History of the Franks* (Ernest Brehaut, tr., N. Y., Columbia University Press, 1916; also O. M. Dalton, tr., 2 vols., Oxford, Clarendon Press, 1927); Matthew of Paris, *English History* (J. A. Giles, tr., 3 vols., London, Bohn, 1852-1854); Otto of Freising, *The Two Cities* (C. C. Mierow, tr., N. Y., Columbia University Press, 1928); Joinville, *Memoirs* (Everyman's, N. Y., Dutton, 1908); Froissart, *Chronicles* (Everyman's, N. Y., Dutton, 1906).

For imaginative literature, a start can be made with the *Song of Roland* (English prose translation by Isabel Butler, Boston, Houghton Mifflin, 1904); *Aucassin and Nicolette* (translated into verse by Andrew Lang, many editions, also in Everyman's in another translation); Chrétien de Troyes, *Arthurian Romances* (Everyman's, N. Y., Dutton, 1935). There is a selection of lays and *fabliaux* (proper ones) otherwise impossible to get at in English in Isabel Butler, *Tales from the Old French* (Boston, Houghton Mifflin, 1910). Dante must be taken seriously or not at all. There is no doubt that the *Inferno* is the best choice. There are many translations into English, none of them supremely great translations. That of C. E. Norton is good (Boston, Houghton Mifflin, 1894). There is a *Viking Portable Dante* edited by Paolo Milano (N. Y., Viking Press, 1947).

Probably the best single piece of medieval writing for the reader who wants to go to the great books for himself is Chaucer's *Canterbury Tales,* many editions. Most editions have glossaries and other helps, so that the Middle English in which they are written is not too difficult. There is a version in modern English published by Simon and Schuster (N. Y., 1948).

There are some excellent collections of medieval writings: the Viking Portable *Mediaeval Reader* (J. B. Ross and M. M. McLaughlin, eds., N. Y., Viking Press, 1949); Lynn Thorndike, *University Records and Life in the Middle Ages* (N. Y., Columbia University Press, 1944); R. L. Poole, *Illustrations of the History of Medieval Thought and Learning* (2d ed., rev., N. Y., Macmillan, 1920); J. H. Robinson, *Readings in European History* (2 vols., Boston, Ginn, 1904-1906). Many of the books of the English historian of the Middle Ages, G. G. Coulton, who loved and hated the period he spent his life studying, are direct compilations from the sources, notably his *Life in the Middle Ages* (2d ed., 4 vols., N. Y., Macmillan, 1928-1930).

8. HUMANISM

Five books will give you a representative acquaintance with the humanists: the artist, Benvenuto Cellini, *Autobiography;* the scholar, Erasmus, *Praise of Folly;* the scholarly man of the world, Thomas More, *Utopia;* the robust scholar and man of letters, Rabelais, *Gargantua and Pantagruel* (Donald Douglas, ed., N. Y., the Modern Library, 1928); the courtier, Baldassare Castiglione, *The Book of the Courtier* (L. E. Opdycke, tr., N. Y., Scribner's, 1903; also in Everyman's Library in translation of 1561). Cellini, More, and Erasmus are available in many English versions; in general, the modern translations are more accurate.

9. PROTESTANTISM

A good selection from the writings of the Protestant reformers would be most useful. The major works of Luther, translated into English, are available under the imprint of F. J. Holman, Philadelphia, 1915-1932; there is a good translation of his *Table Talk* by William Hazlitt in an old, unlovely, but still convenient library of "classics," the Bohn Standard Library, London, H. G. Bohn, 1857 and later; three of his most important pieces of writing—the 95 theses, the *Address to the German Nobility,* and the *Christian Liberty*—are thrown into a strange company with *The Prince* and *Utopia* in volume XXXVI of that curious bookseller's venture, President Eliot's Five-Foot Shelf (Harvard Classics, N. Y., P. F. Collier, 1910 and later). Luther was an admirable pamphleteer, and the pamphlets in the Harvard Classics volume make good reading. Calvin is a much harder man for a modern to follow. There is a good choice of his writings in French, with an introduction by Karl Barth, Calvin, *Textes choisis,* edited by Charles Gagnebin (Paris, Egloff, 1948). The *Institutio Christianae religionis* (for some reason translated nowadays as a plural, "institutes") is available in many English and American editions: the official edition is Calvin, *Institutes of the Christian Religion* (7th American ed., Philadelphia, Presbyterian Board of Christian Education, 1936). There are brief selections from the "sources" in J. H. Robinson, *Readings in European History* (2 vols., Boston, Ginn, 1904-1906), II, Chs. 24-29.

10. RATIONALISM AND SCIENCE

Here is a good cross-section—nothing more—of this important part of the modern Western mind: Francis Bacon, *Philosophical Works* (N. Y., Dutton, 1905). This is the text as established by careful editors like Spedding and Ellis. There is a good edition of the *Great Instauration* (Garden City, Doubleday, Doran, 1937). There are countless editions of the *Essays,* including a most inexpensive one in Crofts Classics. Book I of the *Novum Organum,* plus the *Advancement of Learning,* is a good minimum. Machiavelli, *The Prince,* many editions, an inexpensive one in Crofts Classics. The *Discourses on the First Decade of Titus Livius* is a very useful complement to *The Prince,* and is collected with *The Prince* in the edition of the Modern Library, New York. Montaigne, *Essays,* many editions. There is a good one in the Modern Library. Hobbes, *Leviathan,* in Everyman's Library, also a critical edition, Oxford University Press, 1909. Descartes, *Discourse on Method,* in Everyman's Library, also Chicago, Open Court Publishing Company, 1907.

II. THE EIGHTEENTH CENTURY

Locke is the man who must be read. The *Essay Concerning Human Understanding* and the *Two Treatises of Government* underlie most eighteenth-century thought on man as a social and thinking animal. There are many editions of the *Essay,* including one in Everyman's Library. The two treatises are conveniently put together, with an introduction by Thomas I. Cook, in the Hafner Library of Classics (N. Y., Hafner, 1947).

There is not much use in the layman's going direct to Newton. But anyone interested in the eighteenth century should sample some of the popularizers of Newton. These are usually long out of print, but can often be picked up secondhand. Fontenelle, the ablest of them, at least as a man of letters, can be sampled in modern French editions by those who read French. But there are many copies of his *Conversations on the Plurality of Worlds* in English translation, right up through the early nineteenth century. In English, there is a very capable job of scientific popularization: Colin Maclaurin, *An Account of Sir Isaac Newton's Philosophical Discoveries* (published by Patrick Murdoch, London, 1747).

Much of Voltaire is readily available in English. You can make a very good start with B. R. Redman's *Portable Voltaire* (N. Y., Viking, 1949). The *Candide* is available in Crofts Classics.

Montesquieu has never had a wide modern English-speaking audience. Yet his *Persian Letters* in English translation were reprinted by L. MacVeagh (N. Y., Dial Press, 1929), and they make an excellent specimen of eighteenth-century use of the foreigner as a beating-stick for one's countrymen. The *Spirit of the Laws* was translated and published in Bohn's Standard Library (London, 1902); there is also an edition by Hafner (N. Y., 1949).

Thomas Paine is an admirably representative piece of the eighteenth-century mind. His *Rights of Man* is in Everyman's Library, his *Age of*

559

Reason in the Little Library of Liberal Arts (N. Y., Liberal Arts Press, 1948).

Rousseau is a necessary counterbalance to most of the above. The discourses, the *Social Contract,* and the *Emile* will be an adequate sampling. The psychologist will want to go on to the *Confessions.* All these are easy to come by. The *Emile* was published in Everyman's Library and has been reprinted in part in many series of "educational classics." The political writings are in Everyman's and in Hafner's Library of Classics (N. Y., 1947). The *Confessions* have often been reprinted.

In formal philosophy, Hume's *Enquiry Concerning Human Understanding* was printed by the Open Court Publishing Company (Chicago, 1926). Kant is certainly a hard subject for the layman. There is a good choice of his writings edited by T. M. Greene: *Kant, Selections* (N. Y., Scribner's, 1929).

In general, the German writers of the Enlightenment are not available in English. One should, however, sample them, perhaps most readily in Lessing, whose *Laocoön, Nathan the Wise,* and *Minna von Barnhelm* are available in Everyman's Library.

Bentham is a very important thinker, but not an interesting one to go to directly. Still, if you can struggle through the *Principles of Morals and Legislation* (N. Y., Hafner, 1948; also Oxford University Press), you will have a firm notion of what the utilitarians were like.

There is a good omnibus on the social contract, *Social Contract; Essays by Locke, Hume, and Rousseau,* with an introduction by Sir Ernest Barker (London, Oxford University Press, 1947).

12, 13. THE NINETEENTH CENTURY

Just because the nineteenth century is so near us, we are tempted to make it quantitatively more important than earlier centuries. It does indeed, as was pointed out in the text, have an extraordinary range of opinions and values, and these can by no means be sampled completely by anyone but the specialist. The following, on the same scale as for other periods, should give you an idea of the range of belief in the century.

In the central, progressive, but respectable tradition, J. S. Mill's *Liberty, Utilitarianism,* and *Representative Government* are available in Everyman's, and his *Autobiography*—an important book—is in the World's Classics (Oxford). His French opposite number is Tocqueville, whose *Democracy in America* (Henry Reeve, tr., H. S. Commager, ed., N. Y., Oxford University Press, 1947) should be read. The more radical branching out from the positivist base is best covered in Herbert Spencer, whose long books on "principles" are now almost unreadable, but whose shorter *Social Statics* and *The Man versus the State* are most characteristic. It is worth while to sample this tendency in America in some of the writings of W. G. Sumner, for example, *The Challenge of Facts and Other Essays* (New Haven, Yale University Press, 1914). Walter Bagehot, *Physics and Politics* (new ed., N. Y., Knopf, 1948), is an essential beginning for the study of modern anti-intellectualism. All Bagehot's work, including the literary essays, is delightful reading, the work of a thoughtful Victorian liberal. The novel is of great use in these years, but the trouble is to make any sort of choice. Perhaps one could read a Trollope, say *Phineas Finn,* and a Balzac, say *Eugènie Grandet* or *Père Goriot,* as a fairly central view of the Western bourgeoisie.

For the Right, *Burke's Politics* (R. J. S. Hoffmann and Paul Levack, eds., N. Y., Knopf, 1949) is essential. Little continental work is available in English. Hegel has indeed been translated, and *The Philosophy of History* (J. Sibree, tr., rev. ed., N. Y., Willey Book Company, 1944) will do to introduce German conservative thought. Joseph de Maistre's *Soireés de Saint-Pétersbourg* (6th ed., 2 vols., Lyon, J. B. Pélagaud, 1850) is recommended to all who read French. Newman is well worth reading. The famous *Idea of a University* (several eds., London, Longmans, Green; also D. M. O'Connell, ed., Chicago, Loyola University Press, 1927) is best known, along with his *Apologia pro vita sua* (several eds., London, Longmans, Green, also Everyman); the intellectual historian will find *An Essay on the Development of Christian Doctrine* (new ed., N. Y., Longmans, Green, 1949) and *An Essay in Aid of a Grammar of Assent* (7th ed., London, Longmans, Green, 1888) of great interest.

Carlyle is a noisy attacker, but at this distance no longer a very effective one; still, you may sample him at his proto-fascist clearest in *Shooting Niagara* (London, Chapman and Hall, 1867). For the gentlemanly conservatives Sir Henry Maine's *Popular Government* (London, J. Murray, 1885) will do, and for the lovers of the beautiful and the good, William Morris, *News from Nowhere* (N. Y., Longmans, Green, 1935, first printed in *The Commonweal,* 1890), John Ruskin, *The Crown of Wild Olive* (Everyman's, N. Y., Dutton, 1930), and Matthew Arnold, *Culture and Anarchy* (J. D. Wilson, ed., Cambridge, England, University Press, 1932). T. H. Green's *Lectures on the Principles of Political Obligation* (new ed. with preface by Bernard Bosanquet, London, Longmans, Green, 1931) should round out this reading.

The sources of nationalism are as endless as the social sentiment itself is complex. Those coming new to its study should begin with the critical and descriptive books in the section following. But some of the readable sources are Giuseppe Mazzini, *The Duties of Man* (Everyman's, N. Y., Dutton, 1907); J. G. Fichte, *Addresses to the German Nation* (R. F. Jones and G. H. Turnbull, trs., Chicago, Open Court Publishing Company, 1922); Arthur de Gobineau, *The Inequality of Human Races* (Adrian Collins, tr., N. Y., Putnam's, 1915), Book I only of the French original, *Essai sur l'inégalite des races humaines,* Paris, 1853-1855; Madison Grant, *The Passing of the Great Race* (4th rev. ed., N. Y., Scribner's, 1921).

In the attack from the Left, Marx is central. Everyone should read the *Communist Manifesto* (many editions) which contains a surprising amount of the mature doctrine. Many a sincere student has nodded over *Das Kapital,* which is a difficult and learned work. There are various collections and selections from the canon, notably one edited by Emile Burns, *A Handbook of Marxism* (N. Y., Random House, 1935), which includes something of Marx, Engels, Lenin, and Stalin. Here again the beginner will do well to consult the books suggested in the Critical and Descriptive Writing section for this century.

Of other attacks from the Left, Fourier has left little readable, though he is at bottom a striking and original thinker. There is a Fourier, *Selections,* edited by Charles Gide (Julia Franklin, tr., London, Sonnenschein, 1901). Proudhon is more systematic. Any thorough student of Marx will have to consult him; his *Système des contradictiones économiques* (2 vols., Paris, Guillaumin, 1846) is a good sample. Comte is rather a special case—a man who tried to systematize *and freeze* the Enlightenment at a point of his own choosing. In English translation there is *A General View of Positivism* (new ed., London, Routledge, 1908).

14, 15. THE TWENTIETH CENTURY

We have, in spite of the demand for contemporary history, no real historical perspective. The reader who wants a quick review will find it in Hans Kohn, *The Twentieth Century: a Mid-way Account of the Western World* (N. Y., Macmillan, 1949).

The following should enable the reader to form a clear impression of the accumulated force of anti-intellectualism. The best of democrats owes it to himself to examine this body of writing with as open mind as possible. Some of these writers are out-and-out totalitarians; others regard themselves as democrats willing to face the facts of life. Some of these books are probably masterpieces; most represent current popular writing on man as a political animal. Walter Bagehot, *Physics and Politics* (new ed., Knopf, 1948); Georges Sorel, *Reflections on Violence* (T. E. Hulme, tr., N. Y., Heubsch, 1912); Friederich Nietzsche, *The Genealogy of Morals,* in the Modern Library edition of *The Philosophy of Nietzsche* (N. Y., 1937); Adolf Hitler, *Mein Kampf* (N. Y., Reynal and Hitchcock, 1939); Benito Mussolini, article on fascism from *Encyclopedia Italiana,* translated in A. Zimmern, *Modern Political Doctrines* (N. Y., Oxford University Press, 1939); Graham Wallas, *Human Nature in Politics* (London, A. Constable, 1908); J. H. Robinson, *The Mind in the Making* (N. Y., Harper, 1921); T. W. Arnold, *The Folklore of Capitalism* (New Haven, Yale University Press, 1937); Sigmund Freud, *An Outline of Psychoanalysis* (James Strachey, tr., N. Y., Norton, 1949), the master's last word, and worth careful reading; see also *The Basic Writings of Sigmund Freud* (A. A. Brill, tr., ed., N. Y., Modern Library, 1938). Gaetano Mosca, *The Ruling Class* (N. Y., McGraw-Hill, 1939). Pareto is impossible for the ordinary reader; there are two good summaries, one difficult, L. J. Henderson, *Pareto's General Sociology* (Cambridge, Harvard University Press, 1935), the other more popular in style, G. C. Homans and C. P. Curtis, Jr., *An Introduction to Pareto* (N. Y., Knopf, 1934). Reinhold Niebuhr, *Moral Man and Immoral Society* (N. Y., Scribner's, 1932); same author, *An Interpretation of Christian Ethics* (N. Y., Harper, 1935); Stuart Chase, *The Tyranny of Words* (N. Y., Harcourt, Brace, 1938); James Burnham, *The Managerial Revolution* (N. Y., John Day, 1941); Bergen Evans, *The Natural History of Nonsense* (N. Y., Knopf, 1946); Bertrand de Jouvenel, *On Power* (N. Y., Viking Press, 1949).

Toynbee is a superior sample of the philosophers of history. He can best be approached in the one-volume condensation of the *Study of History* by D. C. Somervell (N. Y., Oxford University Press, 1947). For others, see pp. 161-162 of *Bulletin 54* of the Social Science Research Council.

Here are four very recent attempts by younger men to get themselves—and us—straight about the place of democracy in the mid-twentieth century: F. M. Watkins, *The Political Tradition of the West* (Cambridge, Harvard University Press, 1948); Samuel Beer, *The City of Reason* (Cambridge, Harvard University Press, 1949); A. M. Schlesinger, Jr., *The Vital Center* (Boston, Houghton Mifflin, 1949); H. Stuart Hughes, *An Essay for Our Times* (N. Y., Knopf, 1950).

Finally, here are three books in which practicing social scientists try to get the possibilities of social science straight: Clyde Kluckhohn, *Mirror for Man* (N. Y., Whittlesey House, 1949); A. H. Leighton, *The Governing of Men* (Princeton, Princeton University Press, 1945); and the same author's *Human Relations in a Changing World* (N. Y., E. P. Dutton and Co., 1949).

Critical and Descriptive Writing

I. INTRODUCTION

Like many introductions, this should perhaps be read at the conclusion of the book. The problems here stated in general terms should become more concrete, more clear, in the course of the book. But the reader may even at this stage wish to investigate more thoroughly some of these problems, and see how they have been set by other workers in the field. A good starting point is J. H. Robinson, *Mind in the Making* (N. Y., Harper, 1921), which is a kind of sketch or outline for an intellectual history of the Western world written by one of the first American historians to interest himself in just this kind of history. Two interesting discussions of the problem of delimiting the field of intellectual history—i.e. separating it from the history of philosophy, or of literature, or of political thought—are A. O. Lovejoy, *Great Chain of Being* (Cambridge, Harvard University Press, 1936), Ch. 1, and F. L. Baumer, "Intellectual History and Its Problems," *Journal of Modern History,* XXI (Sept. 1949). An excellent survey, dealing mostly with formal thought, is J. H. Randall, Jr., *Making of the Modern Mind* (rev. ed., Boston, Houghton Mifflin, 1940). An encyclopedic treatment is given by H. E. Barnes, *Intellectual and Cultural History of the Western World* (N. Y., Random House, 1937). Herschel Baker, *The Dignity of Man* (Cambridge, Harvard University Press, 1947), is an admirable intellectual history of the West from the Greeks to the Protestant Reformation.

The vastly bigger subject suggested by the distinction between cumulative and noncumulative knowledge can perhaps hardly be pursued profitably here. The reader who wants a brief introduction to the problem of the relation between scientific thinking and the rest of our conscious mental activities can consult J. B. Conant, *On Understanding Science* (New Haven, Yale University Press, 1947), and I. B. Cohen, *Science, Servant of Man* (Boston, Little, Brown, 1948). There is in *Bulletin 54* of the Social Science Research Council, *Theory and Practice in Historical Study* (N. Y., 1946), an extensive bibliography centered on the problem of methods in the social sciences, or more specifically, on the relations between history and historical writing, social sciences such as sociology, anthropology, economics, and the philosophy of science. All these matters, however, are best considered after the reader has finished this book.

2, 3. THE GREEKS

There is an enormous literature of comment on things Greek, almost all of it favorable. The beginner will find the excellent sketch of Greek history, C. E. Robinson, *A History of Greece* (London, Methuen, 1929), most useful. This can be followed by G. L. Dickinson, *The Greek View of Life* (7th ed., Garden City, Doubleday, Doran, 1928), which is very typical of the point of view of a cultivated modern Englishman brought up on the classics. An excellent American introductory handbook is W. C. Greene, *The Achievement of Greece* (Cambridge, Harvard University Press, 1923). Will Durant's *Life of Greece* (N. Y., Simon and Schuster, 1939), written after the professional scholars had found his *Story of Philosophy* "too popular," is a good, clear, careful introduction to Greek life, with useful bibliographies and footnotes. C. M. Bowra's *Ancient Greek Literature* in the Home University Library (London, 1933) is an excellent brief introduction, now published by the Oxford University Press. One of the most delightful popular books on Greece is Edith Hamilton, *The Greek Way* (N. Y., W. W. Norton, 1930), now, as *The Greek Way to Western Civilization,* available in the inexpensive Mentor books (N. Y., New American Library, 1948). A. E. Zimmern, *The Greek Commonwealth* (5th rev. ed., Oxford, Clarendon Press, 1931), is one of the best analyses of the Greek city-state, written by a rather tender-minded lover of Greece. Another good book on the same subject is Gustave Glotz, *The Greek City* (N. Y., Knopf, 1929). For the heritage of Greece the standard work is R. W. Livingstone, ed., *The Legacy of Greece* (Oxford, Clarendon Press, 1921). The great work of our own contemporary generation of classical scholars is Werner Jaeger, *Paideia* (Gilbert Highet, tr., 2d ed., N. Y., Oxford University Press, 1945-   ). This is an advanced study, and should be read only after some knowledge of the Greeks has been attained. The essential tool for exploration of all ancient history, from the Egyptians to the fall of the Roman Empire, is the *Cambridge Ancient History* (12 vols., Cambridge, England, University Press, 1923-1939).

4. LATER CLASSICAL CULTURE

The literature on the Old Testament and on Jewish history is enormous. A good short background book is J. H. Breasted, *Ancient Times* (Boston, Ginn, 1916), Ch. 7—the student will be tempted to read the whole book for an excellent survey of the ancient Near East. Of older books in English there is G. F. Moore, *The Literature of the Old Testa-*

ment (N. Y., Holt, 1913), and the same author's general survey of religions, *History of Religions* (2 vols., N. Y., Scribner's, 1913-1920). An admirable recent study is Robert Pfeiffer, *Introduction to the Old Testament* (new ed., N. Y., Harper, 1948). On the prophets, there is Edith Hamilton, *The Prophets of Israel* (N. Y., W. W. Norton, 1936). For a general history of the Jews, consult A. L. Sachar, *History of the Jews* (N. Y., Knopf, 1932).

For the later classical culture, much of the writing listed under Chapters 2 and 3 is valid. On science there is Arnold Reymond, *History of the Sciences in Graeco-Roman Antiquity* (N. Y., Dutton, 1927). The best brief historical study of the Hellenistic age is W. W. Tarn, *Hellenistic Civilisation* (London, Arnold, 1927). For the great political problem the Greeks never solved see W. S. Ferguson, *Greek Imperialism* (Boston, Houghton Mifflin, 1913). On literature see F. A. Wright, *A History of Later Greek Literature* (London, Routledge, 1932). A popular survey of the major philosophical clash is R. D. Hicks, *Stoic and Epicurean* (N. Y., Scribner's, 1910).

For Roman history there is a good American textbook, A. E. R. Boak and Richard Hudson, *A History of Rome to 565 A.D.* (3d ed., N. Y., Macmillan, 1945), and an excellent cultural survey, W. C. Greene, *The Achievement of Rome* (Cambridge, Harvard University Press, 1934). The Roman spirit is well brought out in Edith Hamilton, *The Roman Way* (N. Y., W. W. Norton, 1932). On political institutions, there is a modern manual, Leon Homo, *Roman Political Institutions* (N. Y., Knopf, 1930). There is a parallel "legacy" volume from Oxford—*The Legacy of Rome,* edited by Cyril Bailey (Clarendon Press, 1924). There is a pleasant account of Roman literary history, J. W. Mackail, *Latin Literature* (N. Y., Scribner's, 1895). Roman law has not really attracted the popularizers, though it is well handled in the *Legacy of Rome.* A rather dry summary is J. Declareuil, *Rome the Law-giver* (N. Y., Knopf, 1926). On this and many other topics, the student will find leads in the appropriate articles in the *Encyclopaedia of the Social Sciences* edited by E. R. A. Seligman and Alvin Johnson (15 vols., N. Y., Macmillan, 1930-1935). See, for instance, articles on Roman Law, Stoicism, Equality. The introduction to volume I of this encyclopedia is a useful collaborative history of thought about man in society.

5. THE DOCTRINE OF CHRISTIANITY

One trouble with the early history of Christianity is that to understand how differently modern men look at it one would have to read dozens of volumes. A good start is to take two poles: a scholarly Roman Catholic view in Christopher Dawson, *The Making of Europe* (London, Sheed and Ward, 1932); a scholarly anti-Catholic view in Charles Guignebert, *Christianity Past and Present* (N. Y., Macmillan, 1927). On the institutional history, there is a sound, large-scale work, K. S. Latourette, *A History of the Expansion of Christianity* (7 vols., N. Y., Harper, 1938-1945), volumes I and II. On doctrine, there is the great Protestant work of Adolph Harnack, *History of Dogma* (tr. from 3d German ed., 7 vols., London, Williams and Norgate, 1894-1899), and A. C. McGiffert, *A History of Christian Thought* (2 vols., N. Y., Scribner's, 1932-1933).

The confusing struggles of ideas and interests out of which Christianity emerged victorious has a huge bibliography. Here are some basic books: Gibbon, *Decline and Fall* (many editions), Chs. 15 and 16 (this will throw as much light on Gibbon's eighteenth century as on the early Christian centuries); Kirsopp Lake, *Landmarks in the History of Early Christianity* (London, Macmillan, 1920); W. R. Halliday, *The Pagan Background of Early Christianity* (Liverpool, University Press, 1925); Franz Cumont, *The Oriental Religions in Roman Paganism* (Chicago, Open Court Publishing Co., 1911); E. R. Goodenough, *The Church in the Roman Empire* (N. Y., Holt, 1931); Samuel Dill, *Roman Society from Nero to Marcus Aurelius* (London, Macmillan, 1904); E. M. Pickman, *The Mind of Latin Christendom* (London, Oxford University Press, 1937); T. R. Glover, *The Conflict of Religions in the Early Roman Empire* (2d ed., London, Methuen, 1909). Albert Schweitzer's *Quest of the Historical Jesus* (new ed., N. Y., Macmillan, 1948), is of much more interest to the general reader than its title might indicate.

6, 7. THE MIDDLE AGES

For medieval intellectual history there is a great inclusive work, H. O. Taylor, *The Mediaeval Mind* (new ed., Cambridge, Harvard University Press, 1949). Leads from Taylor will take you almost anywhere in these 1000 years.

As stark opposition of love and hate of the Middle Ages, we may put J. J. Walsh, *The Thirteenth, Greatest of Centuries* (Memorial ed., N. Y., Fordham University Press, 1943), against H. E. Barnes, *Intellectual and Cultural History of the Western World* (N. Y., Random House, 1937), Part III, 275-595. Or to oppose more consciously literary figures, Henry Adams, *Mont-Saint-Michel and Chartres* (Boston, Houghton Mifflin, 1905), and G. G. Coulton, *Medieval Panorama* (N. Y., Macmillan, 1938). For the background of political history, there is a good short textbook,

Carl Stephenson, *A Brief Survey of Mediaeval Europe* (N. Y., Harper, 1941).

The following should guide the interested student into most phases of medieval culture: Summerfield Baldwin, *The Organization of Medieval Christianity* (Berkshire studies, N. Y., Holt, 1929); C. G. Crump and E. F. Jacobs, eds., *The Legacy of the Middle Ages* (N. Y., Oxford University Press, 1926); C. H. Haskins, *The Normans in European History* (Boston, Houghton Mifflin, 1915); C. H. Haskins, *The Rise of Universities* (N. Y., P. Smith, 1940); Helen Waddell, *The Wandering Scholars* (Boston, Houghton Mifflin, 1927); G. C. Homans, *English Villagers of the Thirteenth Century* (Cambridge, Harvard University Press, 1941); Johan Huizinga, *The Waning of the Middle Ages* (London, E. Arnold, 1924); Henri Pirenne, *Mediaeval Cities* (Princeton University Press, 1925); Ernst Troeltsch, *The Social Teaching of the Christian Churches* (Olive Wyon, tr., 2 vols., N. Y., Macmillan, 1931); Joseph Turmel (A. Lagarde, *pseud.*), *The Latin Church in the Middle Ages* (N. Y., Scribner's, 1915); Sidney Painter, *French Chivalry* (Baltimore, Johns Hopkins Press, 1940).

8. HUMANISM

Probably the best-known book is Jakob Burckhardt, *The Civilisation of the Renaissance in Italy* (S. G. C. Middlemore, tr., N. Y., Macmillan, 1890), the work of a nineteenth-century German professor who loved the Renaissance for its virility. J. A. Symonds, *The Renaissance in Italy,* is an English classic reprinted as a Modern Library Giant (N. Y., 1935). Still another classic, and a most delightful book, is G. F. Young, *The Medici* (N. Y., Modern Library, 1930). A good textbook, with abundant bibliography, is H. S. Lucas, *The Renaissance and the Reformation* (N. Y., Harper, 1934). On Erasmus there is Preserved Smith, *Erasmus* (N. Y., Harper, 1923). H. O. Taylor's *Thought and Expression in the Sixteenth Century* (2d ed., rev., N. Y., Macmillan, 1930) has never had the success of his book on the medieval mind, but it is full of good material. Finally, there is an admirable summary of the Renaissance in Bernard Groethuysen's article, "Renaissance," in the *Encyclopaedia of the Social Sciences,* XIII.

9. PROTESTANTISM

Preserved Smith, *The Age of the Reformation* (N. Y., Holt, 1920), is an excellent American textbook, covering the ground to include intellectual history. There are no "classics" comparable to the writings of Jakob Burckhardt, J. A. Symonds, and G. F. Young on phases of the Renaissance. The reader will get a summary of interpretations from Preserved Smith, from George Stebbing, *The Story of the Catholic Church* (London, Sands, 1915), from R. H. Tawney, *Religion and the Rise of Capitalism* (London, J. Murray, 1926; also in a cheap edition, the Mentor books), from Max Weber, *The Protestant Ethic and the Spirit of Capitalism* (N. Y., Scribner's, 1930), and from Erich Fromm, *Escape from Freedom* (N. Y., Farrar and Rinehart, 1941).

10. RATIONALISM AND SCIENCE

There is a most compendious intellectual history available for Chapters 8, 9, and 10—Preserved Smith, *A History of Modern Culture* (N. Y., Holt, 1930-1934), I, *The Great Renewal*. From this point on, the reader interested in political theory should work closely with G. H. Sabine, *A History of Political Theory* (N. Y., Holt, 1937). For philosophy, the layman can do much worse than W. J. Durant, *The Story of Philosophy* (N. Y., Simon and Schuster, 1926); for a heavier treatment, there is Harald Höffding, *A History of Modern Philosophy* (B. E. Meyer, tr., 2 vols., London, Macmillan, 1900-1924). There is an admirable new study of the relations between natural science and society, Herbert Butterfield, *The Origins of Science* (London, Bell, 1949). There is a long hostile literature on Machiavelli well summed up by Lord Acton in his introduction to Burd's edition—Acton, *History of Freedom and Other Essays* (London, Macmillan, 1907). For a favorable account see James Burnham, *The Machiavellians* (N. Y., John Day, 1943). There is a good modern analysis of Bacon, F. H. Anderson, *The Philosophy of Francis Bacon* (Chicago, University of Chicago Press, 1948). On the seventeenth century, see G. N. Clark, *The Seventeenth Century* (Oxford, Clarendon Press, 1929), and the earlier chapters of A. N. Whitehead, *Science and the Modern World* (N. Y., Macmillan, 1925). For a rounded treatment of French classical culture, see A. L. Guérard, *The Life and Death of an Ideal* (N. Y., Scribner's, 1928).

11. THE EIGHTEENTH CENTURY

Smith, *History of Modern Culture,* II (*The Enlightenment*), gives the full factual background for the intellectual history of the Enlightenment. The student wishing to have bibliographical guidance can find it in the three eighteenth-century volumes of the *Rise of Modern Europe,* edited by W. L. Langer: Penfield Roberts, *The Quest for Security, 1715-1740* (N. Y., Harper, 1947); W. L. Dorn, *Competition for Empire, 1740-1763* (1940); Leo Gershoy, *From Despotism to Revolution, 1763-1789* (1944).

For the general reader, the following gives an admirable cross-section of critical attitudes toward the Enlightenment. For the "advanced" but still very Victorian point of view, John Morley's three biographies (really essays on the French Enlightenment), *Voltaire* (2d ed., rev., N. Y., D. Appleton, 1872), *Rousseau* (new ed., London, Chapman and Hall, 1878), *Diderot and the Encyclopaedists* (new ed., N. Y., Scribner and Welford, 1878); for another liberal nineteenth-century point of view, Leslie Stephen, *History of English Thought in the Eighteenth Century* (2 vols., N. Y., Putnam's, 1876); for the twentieth-century sympathetic (and innocent) radical treatment, Kingsley Martin, *French Liberal Thought in the Eighteenth Century* (Boston, Little, Brown, 1929); for a broad, detached survey, Ernst Cassirer, *Die Philosophie der Aufklärung* (Tübingen, J. C. B. Mohr, 1932), a book that should be translated into English; for a modern, skeptical but not cynical study, C. L. Becker, *The Heavenly City of the Eighteenth-Century Philosophers* (New Haven, Yale University Press, 1932); and for a Marxist interpretation, H. J. Laski, *The Rise of Liberalism* (N. Y., Harper, 1936).

On the Utilitarians, there is Leslie Stephen, *The English Utilitarians* (3 vols., N. Y., Putnam's, 1900), and an admirable book by Elie Halévy, *The Growth of Philosophic Radicalism* (Mary Morris, tr., London, Faber and Gwyer, 1928). For a nineteenth-century criticism of utilitarian assumptions, see James Fitzjames Stephen, *Liberty, Equality, Fraternity* (N. Y., Holt, 1873).

12, 13. THE NINETEENTH CENTURY

The big book is J. T. Merz, *A History of European Thought in the Nineteenth Century* (4 vols., Edinburgh, W. Blackwood, 1896-1914), which deals mostly with science. F. S. Marvin's *Century of Hope* (Oxford, Clarendon Press, 1919) gives a bird's-eye view of the nineteenth century, but does not quite live up to its title. There are three volumes of collected lectures edited by F. J. C. Hearnshaw—*The Social & Political Ideas of Some Representative Thinkers of the Revolutionary Era* (London, Harrap, 1931), *The Social & Political Ideas of Some Representative Thinkers of the Age of Reaction & Reconstruction* (London, Harrap, 1932), *The Social & Political Ideas of Some Representative Thinkers of the Victorian Age* (London, Harrap, 1933)—which together span the century after a fashion. Like all such work of many hands, they are uneven (Professor Hearnshaw edited many such volumes, beginning with the Middle Ages; they can be found under his name in any good library catalogue; together they make a general study of Western political and social ideas). See also Crane Brinton, *English Political Thought in the Nineteenth Century* (new ed., Cambridge, Harvard University Press, 1949), and Roger Soltau, *French Political Thought in the Nineteenth Century* (New Haven, Yale University Press, 1931).

For the background of modern nationalism, there is C. J. H. Hayes, *The Historical Evolution of Modern Nationalism* (N. Y., R. R. Smith, 1931), and *Essays on Nationalism* (N. Y., Macmillan, 1926); Hans Kohn, *The Idea of Nationalism* (N. Y., Macmillan, 1948); Lord Acton, "Nationality," in *Essays on Freedom and Power* (Boston, Beacon Press, 1948); Peter Viereck, *Metapolitics* (N. Y., Knopf, 1941); Frederick Hertz, *Nationality in History and Politics* (N. Y., Oxford University Press, 1944).

There are many who seek to explain Marxism to the many; these explanations are not by any means in agreement. Do not let this discourage you. Here are a few elementary explanations: Sidney Hook, *Towards the Understanding of Karl Marx* (N. Y., John Day, 1933); M. M. Bober, *Karl Marx's Interpretation of History* (Cambridge, Harvard University Press, 1927); Isaiah Berlin, *Karl Marx, His Life and Environment* (2d ed., N. Y., Oxford University Press, 1948); G. D. H. Cole, *What Marx Really Meant* (N. Y., Knopf, 1934); A. D. Lindsay, *Karl Marx's Capital* (N. Y., Oxford University Press, 1925).

On special phases of nineteenth-century intellectual history there are many books indeed. Long bibliographies are given in J. H. Randall, *The Making of the Modern Mind* (rev. ed., Boston, Houghton Mifflin, 1940), and in H. E. Barnes, *An Intellectual and Cultural History of the Western World* (rev. ed., N. Y., Reynal and Hitchcock, 1941). The following is suggested as a good start: Jacques Barzun, *Darwin, Marx, Wagner* (Boston, Little, Brown, 1941); J. A. Hobson, *Imperialism* (rev. ed., London, G. Allen and Unwin, 1938); Guido de Ruggiero, *The History of European Liberalism* (R. G. Collingwood, tr., London, Oxford University Press, 1927); Ernest Barker, *Political Thought in England from Herbert Spencer to the Present Day* (N. Y., Holt, 1915); Lord Hugh Cecil, *Conservatism* (London, Williams and Norgate, 1912); L. T. Hobhouse, *Liberalism* (N. Y., Holt, 1911); Bertrand Russell, *The Scientific Outlook* (N. Y., Norton, 1931); George Nasmyth, *Social Progress and the Darwinian Theory* (N. Y., Putnam's, 1916); Paul Sabatier, *Modernism* (C. A. Miles, tr., N. Y., Scribner's, 1908); Jacques Maritain, *Freedom in the Modern World* (Richard O'Sullivan, tr., London, Sheed and Ward,

1935); J. M. Robertson, *A History of Free Thought in the Nineteenth Century* (2 vols., N. Y., Putnam's, 1930); Yngve Brilioth, *The Anglican Revival* (N. Y., Longmans, Green, 1925); R. B. Perry, *The Present Conflict of Ideals* (N. Y., Longmans, Green, 1918); A. C. McGiffert, *The Rise of Modern Religious Ideas* (N. Y., Macmillan, 1915); George Brandes, *Main Currents in Nineteenth-Century Literature* (6 vols., London, Heinemann, 1901-1923); V. L. Parrington, *Main Currents in American Thought* (3 vols., N. Y., Harcourt, Brace, 1927-1930); R. H. Gabriel, *The Course of American Democratic Thought* (N. Y., Ronald, 1940).

Essay Topics

*I*T IS ALWAYS EASY to compose little set pieces on almost any phase of history. The following suggestions for essays and discussions are frankly difficult, and are not to be answered out of any single book, not, since they involve much noncumulative knowledge, to be answered in any one way, even by the wisest in the wisdom of this world. They demand some exercise of the imagination, some effort to work out genuine problems. They can and indeed should be treated concretely and with a full respect for facts; they are not invitations to mere windy generalizations.

2, 3. THE GREEKS

1. How would you have voted had you been a juror at the trial of Socrates?

Plato, *Apology;* Xenophon, *Memorabilia;* Aristophanes, *Clouds;* background and facts of the trial in any good modern history of Greece, preferably a full one, for example, *Cambridge Ancient History,* V, or J. B. Bury, *A History of Greece to the Death of Alexander the Great* (London, Macmillan, 1900).

2. Is Plato a conservative or a radical (or neither)?

A minimum reading is the *Republic,* Books V-X. See also Jaeger, *Paideia,* Ch. 9, and Ernest Barker, *Greek Political Theory* (London, Methuen, 1918).

3. Judging from his plays, what sort of political beliefs (or theories, or "platform") had Aristophanes?

All the plays are pertinent here, but especially *Knights, Clouds, Lysistrata.*

4. How adequate do you find the ethical standards of "nothing in excess" or the "Golden Mean"?

Aristotle, *Nicomachaean Ethics, Politics.*

5. How adequate to your own do you find the aesthetic standards of the great culture in Greece?

Here you will do best to look at a good many reproductions of Greek art and go over some of the drama. For a general discussion, see Percy Gardner, *The Principles of Greek Art* (N. Y., Macmillan, 1914).

6. In our modern sense of the word, how far was fifth-century Athens a "democracy"?

This is a tricky subject. You can get the facts of political, social, and economic organization out of Zimmern, *Greek Commonwealth,* and Glotz, *Greek City.* For the spirit, it is best to go direct to Plato, Aristophanes, Thucydides—especially the Funeral Speech of Pericles in Thucydides, *History,* Book II, 34-46, Aristotle, the Old Oligarch.

7. How close a parallel do you find between the problems of inter-national relations among the Greek city-states of the late fifth century B.C. and problems of international relations among nation-states in the twentieth century?

For the Greek side, the basis must be a good history of Greece—*Cambridge Ancient History,* Bury, or C. E. Robinson. But see also Thucydides, Aristophanes (especially *Lysistrata, Peace, Acharnians*).

8. Do you think there was a single Greek religion in the fifth century B.C., or actually various cults, or sects, much as in our contemporary Christianity?

This is a difficult problem. G. L. Dickinson, *The Greek View of Life* (7th ed., Garden City, Doubleday, Page, 1925), Ch. 1. Jane E. Harrison, *Themis* (Cambridge, University Press, 1912); Gilbert Murray, *Five Stages of Greek Religion* (2d ed., N. Y., Columbia University Press, 1925); L.

R. Farnell, *Greek Hero Cults and Ideas of Immortality* (Oxford, Clarendon Press, 1921).

9. How useful—if at all—do you think the study of ancient Greece is for twentieth-century Americans?

Here all your reading will have to be brought into play.

4. LATER CLASSICAL CULTURE

1. Suppose you were an intelligent Martian, and could read only the Old Testament. What idea would you have of human nature?

This is a broad but not a vague question. Read at least the books of Genesis, Job, Proverbs, Ecclesiastes, and Isaiah, and try to work it out.

2. What do you make of the Book of Job?

There are hundreds of commentaries. Avoid them all, read Job carefully, and try to put what the book is about in your own words.

3. What do you think Western civilization owes the ancient Hebrews?

There is a "legacy" book, *The Legacy of Israel,* edited by E. R. Bevan and Charles Singer (Oxford, Clarendon Press, 1927), on the whole not quite up to *The Legacy of Greece* and *The Legacy of Rome,* but useful here. See also Pfeiffer, *Introduction to the Old Testament,* J. M. P. Smith, *The Moral Life of the Hebrews* (Chicago, University of Chicago Press, 1923), and Sachar, *History of the Jews.*

4. What are some notes or characteristics of a declining culture as seen in Graeco-Roman culture after 300 B.C.?

Do not try to do a complete survey, but choose concrete examples. Much of the verse, tales, and novels suggested above are good material. You will find plenty of suggestions in A. J. Toynbee, *A Study of History* (6 vols., London, Oxford University Press, 1934-1939), especially volumes V and VI, "The Disintegration of Civilisations"; these are summarized in the one-volume version of Toynbee edited by D. C. Somervell (N. Y., Oxford University Press, 1947).

5. Take any one later writer—Theocritus, Menander (from the fragments, plus the Latin adaptors, Terence and Plautus), Plutarch, Lucian, Longus—and see if you find elements of decadence in him.

This is a more specific variant on 4.

6. To judge the Stoics by Marcus Aurelius and the Epicureans by Lucretius, how far do they differ as moralists?

Background in E. V. Arnold, *Roman Stoicism* (Cambridge, England, University Press, 1911), and W. L. Courtney, "Epicurus," in Evelyn Abbott, ed., *Hellenica* (London, Rivingtons, 1880).

7. What abiding traits of the politician do you find in Cicero?

His letters should be your chief source, but a sampling of the orations will help—say the famous one on Catiline. The letters are translated and commented on in McKinlay's *Letters of a Roman Gentleman*.

8. Write a character sketch of Plutarch; or an essay on Graeco-Roman culture as reflected in Plutarch.

Plutarch is one of the few people of antiquity one can see in the round—as a person, as a man of ideas. He can easily be read in English, from the old-fashioned five-volume edition of W. W. Goodwin (6th ed., Boston, Little, Brown, 1898) to a good *Select Essays* of T. G. Tucker (2 vols., Oxford, Clarendon Press, 1913-1918). There are many translations of the *Parallel Lives*.

9. On the strength of this brief acquaintance, which do you prefer as human beings, the Greeks of their great age (fifth century) or the Romans of theirs (100 B.C.-180 A.D.)?

A difficult subject. All your reading should be grist to your mill. Do not be afraid of saying the wrong thing. These people should be at least partly alive for you, and must in some way affect you. You can, of course, feel "a plague o' both your houses."

10. In your opinion, is the Roman drama justly considered of far lower quality than that of the Greeks?

Take either comedy or tragedy, not both. All the complete dramatic works that have been preserved may be found in Oates and O'Neill, *The Complete Greek Drama* (N. Y., Random House, 1938) and Duckworth, *The Complete Roman Drama* (N. Y., Random House, 1942).

5. THE DOCTRINE OF CHRISTIANITY

1. What is *your* idea of the personality of Jesus?

This is not worth doing except freshly, from the Gospels themselves, and without worry over the fact that generations have gone over the same ground.

2. What is your idea of the personality of St. Paul?

The Acts of the Apostles, the Pauline Epistles.

3. Why was a heresy heretical?

This can be approached in two ways: (1) take a single heresy, say the Arian, and try and decide why it was rejected by the Catholic Church; (2) try the much harder task of seeing what (if anything) the heresies have in common against the Catholic position. McGiffert, *History of Christian Thought,* Harnack, *History of Dogma,* M. L. Cozens, *A Handbook of Heresies* (N. Y., Sheed and Ward, 1947).

4. Why do you think Christianity won out over competing religions of the Roman Empire?

An old question (like that of the reasons for the fall of Rome) but still fresh, if you will look at it freshly. Most of the books cited above, especially Gibbon, Glover, Halliday, Cumont, Dill. See also A. D. Nock, *Conversion* (London, Oxford University Press, 1933).

5. How far does an economic explanation account for the rise of Christianity?

Try—if only to refute him—Karl Kautsky, *Foundations of Christianity* (N. Y., International Publishers, 1925).

6. How much "escapism" is there in early Christianity?

A difficult subject to treat fairly. The anti-Christian can always have a cheap field day on this. Most of the general books above help. For monasticism, see Adolf Harnack, *Monasticism* (N. Y., Putnam's, 1910); C. G. Herbermann and others, eds., *Catholic Encyclopedia* (15 vols., N. Y., Robert Appleton, 1907-1912), article on monasticism; Helen Waddell, *The Desert Fathers* (N. Y., Holt, 1936).

6, 7. THE MIDDLE AGES

1. Could you be sent back by time-machine, would you feel more at home in fifth-century Athens or in thirteenth-century western Europe?

Accumulation from study of Greece; Baldwin, *Medieval Christianity;* Coulton, *Life in the Middle Ages,* sampling; Crump and Jacobs, eds., *Legacy of the Middle Ages;* W. S. Davis, *Life on a Mediaeval Barony* (N. Y., Harper, 1923); Taylor, *Mediaeval Mind.*

2. Comment: "The gap between theory and practice is often wide in human affairs; it was at about its widest in the much-admired 13th century."

Adams, *Mont-Saint-Michel and Chartres;* Coulton, *Life in the Middle Ages;* Maurice de Wulf, *Philosophy and Civilisation in the Middle Ages* (Princeton University Press, 1922); F. J. C. Hearnshaw, ed., *Mediaeval Contributions to Modern Civilisation* (London, G. G. Harrap, 1921); Bede Jarrett, *Social Theories of the Middle Ages* (Boston, Little, Brown, 1926); Taylor, *Mediaeval Mind.*

3. Does medieval social theory show any fundamental changes from the position taken by the Fathers?

Troeltsch, *Social Teaching of the Christian Churches,* I.

4. How far do you think it justifiable to call the thirteenth century an "Age of Rationalism"?

A. N. Whitehead, *Science and the Modern World* (N. Y., Macmillan, 1925), Ch. 1; C. L. Becker, *The Heavenly City of the Eighteenth-Century Philosophers* (New Haven, Yale University Press, 1935), Ch. 1; Etienne Gilson, *The Spirit of Mediaeval Philosophy* (A. H. C. Downes, tr., N. Y., Scribner's, 1936); Etienne Gilson, *Reason and Revelation in the Middle Ages* (N. Y., Scribner's, 1938); Taylor, *Mediaeval Mind,* II.

5. Were Abélard's troubles caused by his excessive rationalism or were they due to the characteristics of his personality?

Helen Waddell, *Peter Abélard; a Novel* (N. Y., Holt, 1933); Joseph McCabe, *Peter Abélard* (N. Y., Putnam's, 1901); *Letters of Abélard and Héloise* (Scott-Moncrieff, tr.); *Historia Calamitatum* (Bellows, tr.); F. A. Gasquet's introduction to *Some Letters of Saint Bernard* (S. J. Eales, tr., London, J. Hodges, 1904).

6. Do you think the Church was justified in using the Inquisition?

A. S. Turberville, *Mediaeval Heresy & the Inquisition* (N. Y., Dutton, 1921); H. C. Lea, *A History of the Inquisition of the Middle Ages* (N. Y., Harper, 1887); Elphège Vacandard, *The Inquisition* (tr. from 2d ed. by B. L. Conway, N. Y., Longmans, Green, 1908); G. G. Coulton, *Inquisition and Liberty* (London, Heinemann, 1938).

7. Was medieval asceticism morbid?

Johannes Jorgensen, *Saint Catherine of Siena* (Ingeborg Lund, tr., London, Longmans, Green, 1938); William James, *The Varieties of Religious Experience* (N. Y., Longmans, Green, 1902), Chs. 1, 6, 7, 16, 17; Taylor, *Mediaeval Mind,* Ch. 20; Troeltsch, *Social Teachings of the Christian Churches,* I, Ch. 2; Heinrich Suso, *The Life of Blessed Henry Suso by Himself* (T. F. Knox, tr., London, Burns, Lambert, and Oates, 1865); *The Book of Margery Kempe, 1436,* a modern version by W. Butler-Bowden (London, J. Cape, 1936).

8. How far is the claim justified that a "Christian Democracy" existed in the Middle Ages?

G. K. Chesterton, *Chaucer* (London, Faber and Faber, 1932), Ch. 2; Christopher Dawson, *Mediaeval Religion* (N. Y., Sheed and Ward, 1934), Part III; G. G. Coulton, *The Medieval Village* (Cambridge, England, University Press, 1925), Chs. 8, 9, 18, 20; Geoffrey Chaucer, "The Canterbury Tales," F. N. Robinson, ed., *Poetical Works* (Boston, Houghton Mifflin, 1933); William Langland, *The Vision of Piers Plowman* (H. W. Wells, tr., N. Y., Sheed and Ward, 1935).

9. Do medieval heresies represent only the "lunatic fringe" of Christian culture?

D. L. Douie, *The Nature and Effect of the Heresy of Fraticelli* (Manchester, University Press, 1932); J. W. Thompson and E. N. Johnson, *An Introduction to Medieval Europe* (N. Y., W. W. Norton, 1937); Turberville, *Mediaeval Heresy & the Inquisition;* Emile Gebhart, *Mystics*

& *Heretics in Italy at the End of the Middle Ages* (E. M. Hulme, tr., London, G. Allen and Unwin, 1922); Evelyn Underhill, *Jacopone da Todi* (N. Y., Dutton, 1919); D. S. Muzzey, *The Spiritual Franciscans* (Prize Essays of the American Historical Association, 1905; N. Y., 1907); Henry Bett, *Joachim of Flora* (London, Methuen, 1931); G. M. Trevelyan, *England in the Age of Wycliffe* (3d ed., N. Y., Longmans, Green, 1900); H. B. Workman, *John Wyclif* (2 vols., Oxford, Clarendon Press, 1926); James Gairdner, *Lollardy and the Reformation in England* (4 vols., London, Macmillan, 1908-1913).

10. Give a critical appraisal of medieval education at the university level.

Hastings Rashdall, *The Universities of Europe in the Middle Ages* (new ed., F. M. Powicke and A. B. Emden, eds., 3 vols., Oxford, Clarendon Press, 1936).

8. HUMANISM

1. How would *you* define the term *Renaissance?*

B. Groethuysen, "Renaissance," *Encyclopaedia of the Social Sciences,* XIII; E. F. Jacob and A. S. Turberville, "Changing Views of the Renaissance," *History,* XVI (Oct. 1931); J. H. Randall, *Making of the Modern Mind* (Boston, Houghton Mifflin, 1940), Part I; almost any reading on the period will give you materials.

2. Comment: "Leonardo da Vinci's career is an example of a typical Renaissance weakness—dispersal of energies over too many fields of human activity."

R. A. Taylor, *Leonardo the Florentine* (N. Y., Harper, 1927); Edward McCurdy, *The Mind of Leonardo da Vinci* (N. Y., Dodd, Mead, 1928).

3. What do you find "modern" in any *one* of the following: Erasmus, Rabelais, More?

For Erasmus, Smith, *Erasmus,* and Johan Huizinga, *Erasmus* (N. Y., Scribner's, 1924); for Rabelais, A. J. Nock and C. R. Wilson, *Francis Rabelais* (N. Y., Harper, 1929); for More, W. H. Hutton, *Sir Thomas More* (London, Methuen, 1895).

4. Satire as a weapon of the humanists: its origins, its purposes.

Samples are Sebastian Brant, *The Ship of Fools* (E. H. Zeydel, ed., N. Y., Columbia University Press, 1944); *Epistolae Obscurorum Virorum,* Latin text with English rendering by F. G. Stokes (New Haven, Yale University Press, 1925); Erasmus, *Praise of Folly,* many editions.

5. Do you agree that the humanists of the Renaissance had little effect on the development of democracy?

9. PROTESTANTISM

1. What seems to you a most satisfactory explanation for the success of the Protestant Reformation?

All the books listed under Critical and Descriptive Writing, Ch. 9, p. 568 are germane.

2. Can you separate out "modern" and "medieval" elements in Luther's *Weltanschauung?*

For more material than listed above, see Preserved Smith, *The Life and Letters of Martin Luther* (Boston, Houghton Mifflin, 1914), and Abram Lipsky, *Martin Luther, Germany's Angry Man* (N. Y., Stokes, 1933).

3. Write a good critical review of Max Weber, *The Protestant Ethic and the Spirit of Capitalism.* (Note that "critical," contrary to some American popular usage of the word, does not mean "damning.")

4. The relations between Protestantism and politics: a case history for a given country (England, Scotland, Holland, Germany, France).

The best way is to go to good political histories and work the problem out for yourself. There are good historical bibliographies in *A Guide to Historical Literature* (N. Y., Macmillan, 1931).

5. Do you hold the proliferation of Protestant sects to be a sign of strength or of weakness?

This really needs careful sociological research. But you can at least set the problem up clearly in a country like seventeenth-century England. See Eduard Bernstein, *Cromwell and Communism* (London, G. Allen and Unwin, 1930); L. F. Brown, *The Political Activities of the Baptists and Fifth Monarchy Men in England during the Interregnum* (Washington, American Historical Association, 1912); G. P. Gooch, *English Democratic Ideas in the Seventeenth Century* (2d ed. with notes and appendices by H. J. Laski, Cambridge, England, University Press, 1927); H. J. C. Grierson, *Cross Currents in English Literature of the Seventeenth Century* (London, Chatto and Windus, 1929); T. C. Pease, *The Leveller Movement* (Washington, American Historical Association, 1916).

10. RATIONALISM AND SCIENCE

1. Try to draw concrete examples of Bacon's Idols from your own experience of the world.

The *idola* are in *Novum Organum*, Book I.

2. Do you think Machiavelli's *Prince* deserves to be called scientific or objective?

3. Do you accept as valid the distinction made in the text between science and rationalism?

This requires a good deal of knowledge perhaps not now available to you. But try to think it out without reference to later work on scientific method.

4. To which of the currents of thought and feeling studied in the last three chapters under the names humanism, protestantism, and rationalism do you think modern democracy owes most?

5. What do you find Descartes and Bacon to have in common? And in what are they most strongly opposed?

Descartes, *Discourse on Method,* and Bacon, *Advancement of Learning,* carefully read, should form an adequate basis.

II. THE EIGHTEENTH CENTURY

1. Examine closely how any eighteenth-century writer uses certain of the great clusters of ideas—i.e., *nature* (and *natural*), *reason, rights, social contract*.

Almost any writer will do. Voltaire will turn out to be more complex, perhaps, and contradictory, than you had anticipated. Rousseau, Diderot, Locke himself are by no means simple, clear-cut propagandists. You will find these ideas at their simplest if you take the propagandists rather than the thinkers—i.e., Paine, Condorcet, the lesser encyclopedists. A. O. Lovejoy's *Essays in the History of Ideas* (Baltimore, Johns Hopkins Press, 1948) will help you with the technique of this kind of essay.

2. Try to define a given eighteenth-century writer's view of "human nature."

Rousseau, so commonly labeled as believing in the "natural goodness of man"—see notably Irving Babbitt, *Rousseau and Romanticism* (Boston, Houghton Mifflin, 1919)—is a *locus classicus* worth re-examining. Godwin, Paine, Bentham—almost any of the enlightened—are worth this sort of study.

3. How far do you think American political ideals (or "way of life") are products of the Enlightenment?

A big but useful study. Start with Carl Becker's *Declaration of Independence* (N. Y., Harcourt, Brace, 1922; reprinted with an introduction by the author, N. Y., Knopf, 1942) and Ralph Gabriel's *Course of American Democratic Thought* (N. Y., Ronald, 1940).

4. To what degree would you call Jefferson a Child of the Enlightenment?

A more modest and concrete introduction to the problem of essay 3 above. The literature on Jefferson is enormous. Go straight to his own works, especially to the *Notes on Virginia* and to his letters. Reread the preamble to the Declaration of Independence.

5. What is your opinion of the relation of the Enlightenment to traditional Christianity?

6. What do you find still valid in the world-view of the Enlightenment?

12, 13. THE NINETEENTH CENTURY

The student will find the nineteenth and twentieth centuries full of problems that should have the easy fascination of contemporaneousness. Suggestions are hardly necessary; here are a few.

1. Attempt a definition of "romanticism."

Irving Babbitt, *Rousseau and Romanticism* (Boston, Houghton Mifflin, 1919); Crane Brinton, *The Political Ideas of the English Romanticists* (London, Oxford University Press, 1926); article on "Romanticism" by G. A. Borgese, *Encyclopaedia of the Social Sciences*, XIII.

2. What does any *one* writer of the period mean by *liberty* (or *democracy, progress, development*)?

J. S. Mill, Carlyle, Renan, Tocqueville, and many others will do. It would be interesting to take a lesser light—a politician who is recorded at least in parliamentary proceedings, a journalist, a preacher.

3. Do you agree with the statement in the text that nineteenth-century intellectuals are overwhelmingly *against* existing middle-class standards?

Survey briefly, through secondary works if necessary, the field of writers, and try and list them as accepting or not accepting their surroundings. This type of essay can be greatly developed.

4. Do you accept the classification of Marxism as a religion?

See the references to Marxist literature listed under Original Writing and Critical and Descriptive Writing. Use your own judgment on this problem.

5. What elements in nineteenth-century nationalism do you think are *new*?

See the references to nationalism and its literature listed under Original Writing and Critical and Descriptive Writing.

INDEX

INDEX

Encyclopedists, 513

Engels, Friederich, 479, 480, 483, 487, 488

English Villagers of the Twelfth Century, 240

Enlightenment, the Age of, 258, 259, 261, 275, 284, 312, 333, 334, 349, 355, 362, 369-408, 410, 414-417, 419, 421, 423, 427, 429, 436, 437, 438, 443, 445, 451, 454-459, 461, 463, 466, 470, 473, 474, 476, 477, 478, 480, 489, 490, 492, 494, 495, 505, 507, 511, 528, 529, 536-539, 548

Epicureans, 120, 121, 485

Epimenides of Crete, 40

Episcopalian religion, 164, 305, 309

Epistle to the Hebrews, 533

Erasmus, 163, 260, 263, 268, 271, 272, 285

Erastianism, 317, 318, 320

Erastosthenes, 110, 112

Essay on the Development of Christianity, 462

Essay on the Inequality of Races, 416

Essay on the Principle of Population, 398

Ethical culture, 499

Eubulides of Megara, 40

Eucharist, 147, 148, 150, 155, 164, 171, 193, 194, 319, 350, 549

Euclid, 110

Euphuism, 269

Euripides, 83, 85

Europa, 41

Evolution, 413, 415

Existentialism, 499

Extremists, 541

F

Fabians, 476, 492, 506

Fabliaux, 234, 235, 265

Faerie Queene, 283

Falangism, 469

Fascism, 469, 471, 472, 478, 539

Fathers, the Church, 158, 163, 184, 194, 197, 200, 270, 311, 348, 451

"Faustian" man, 275, 281, 531

Faustus, Doctor, 281

Fénelon, Bishop, 274

Fichte, Johann Gottlieb, 415, 423

Ficino, Marsilio, 271

Filmer, Sir Robert, 288, 289, 290

Fourier, François, 468

Fourteen Points, 6

Francis I, 275

Franciscan movement, 236, 239

Franklin, Benjamin, 52, 294

Free association, 512

Free will, 322

Frederick II, 191, 262

French Revolution, the, 292, 373, 374, 375, 384, 386, 387, 400, 406, 408, 410, 411, 417, 425, 427, 436, 453, 454, 456, 457, 482, 489, 491, 498, 541

Freud, Sigmund, 289, 327, 505, 507, 509-515

Freudian analysis, 143, 167, 230, 377, 504, 512

Fromm, Erich, 547

Functionalism, 442, 502

Fundamentalists, 311, 313, 317

G

Gabriel, Ralph, 419

Gainsborough, Lord, 55

Galen, 216

Galilee, 140, 161, 162

Galileo, 16, 337, 340, 341, 342, 345, 346, 347

Gallup polls, 8, 223

Gandhi, Mohandas K., 23

Genetic sciences, 19

Génie du Christianisme, 436

Gentiles, 141, 143

George III, 299

Gerard of Cremona, 189

Germanic barbarians, 123

Gerson, Jean, 300, 301

Gettysburg Address, 137

Giotto, Florent., 262, 264

Gladstone, William, 163

Gnostics, 152, 154, 237

Gobineau, Comte de, 416, 471

Godwin, William, 392

Goebbels, Joseph, 473

Goering, Herman, 473

Goethe, Johann Wolfgang, 242, 277, 504

Golden Mean, the, 58, 60, 62, 65, 73, 84, 93

INDEX

INDEX

Nationalism, 304, 374, 415, 416, 417, 418, 419, 420, 421, 469, 471, 489, 500, 501, 502, 539, 540

Naturalism, 442, 454, 499

Natural law, 130, 133, 208, 212

Nature, 370, 373, 379, 383, 384, 385, 404, 405, 406, 523, 524, 525

Nazism, 420, 469, 471, 472, 500, 505, 542

Neoclassicism, 269, 421

Neo-Gothic style, 422, 440

Neoplatonists, 119, 185, 191, 271, 351

Neo-Scholastics, 250

Neo-Thomism, Catholic, 52

Neurosis, 508, 547

New Deal, the, 392, 433, 475, 476

New Harmony, 467

New Lanark, 390

Newman, Cardinal, 436, 460, 462, 463, 465, 513, 518

News from Nowhere, 468

New Testament, 101, 136, 138, 145

Newton, Sir Isaac, 14, 217, 285, 336, 337, 348, 369-371, 380-383, 397, 400, 413, 484, 493, 496, 507, 510, 548

Newtonian physics, 13, 367, 381, 385, 397, 497

Nibelungenlied, 97

Nicomachean Ethics, 43, 58

Niebuhr, Reinhold, 499

Nietzsche, Friedrich, 25, 97, 261, 450, 473, 495, 499, 514, 515, 518, 542

Nigger Question, 472

Nihilists, 518

Nirvana, 51, 282

Nominalism, 421

Noncumulative knowledge, 13, 15, 219, 265, 368, 498, 551

Normative judgments, 27, 335

Norse mythology, 30

Northrop, Professor, 530

Not Paul But Jesus, 140

O

Oceana, 295

Ockham, William of, 192

Odyssey, The, 97

Oedipus complex, 510

Offenbach, Jacques, 27, 28

Of Time and the River, 283

Oklahoma!, 72

"Old Oligarch," 70

Old Testament, 36, 101, 102, 136, 155, 198, 285, 287, 288, 332

Oligarchy, 54

Olympic games, 59

Olympus, 75

One World, 530

On Liberty, 294, 432, 519

Optimists, 526

Original sin, 312, 358, 373, 406, 454

Origin of Species, 414, 433

Orpheus, 81

Orphism, 82, 84

Owen, Robert, 387, 390, 398, 460, 508

Oxford Movement, 461

Oxford University, 467, 469, 475

P

Paine, Tom, 191, 235, 289, 294, 374, 403, 456, 460, 465, 499, 549

Palatine Anthology, 116

Palestine, 36, 99, 107

Palladio, 269, 272

Palmyra, 88

Pandora's box, 76

Du Pape, 455

Paradiso, 246

Pareto, Vilfredo, 507; 519, 520, 521, 522, 523, 524, 525, 542, 547

Parmenides, 39, 43

Parthenon, 60, 61, 64, 76, 115, 321, 442

Parthians, 123

Partisan Review, 502

Pascal, 163, 337, 345

Paternalism, 446

Patriarcha, 288

Patriarchs, 151

Patriotism, 478, 540

Patterns of Culture, 529

Pavlov, Ivan, 508, 509, 512

Peasants' War, 236, 237, 238, 259, 260, 310, 314

Pelagius, 186

Peloponnesian War, 38, 87, 88, 89, 91, 376

Pentateuch, the, 101

Pericles, 56, 57, 61, 66, 67, 68, 69, 72, 73, 79, 87, 125, 376

Peripatetics, 120

Persian Empire, 98, 99

593